A New Dictionary of Chemistry

A New Dictionary of Chemistry

EDITED BY

L. MACKENZIE MIALL M.A. F.R.I.C.

and

D. W. A. SHARP M.A. PH.D. A.R.I.C. F.R.S.E.

with the assistance of many expert chemists

JOHN WILEY & SONS INC

New York N.Y.

Published throughout the world except the United States
by Longmans, Green & Co Ltd

Fourth Edition © Longmans Green & Co. Ltd., 1961, 1968

First published . . *1940*
Second Edition . . *1949*
Third Edition . . *1961*
Fourth Edition . . *1968*

Library of Congress Catalog Card Number 68–18625

PRINTED IN GREAT BRITAIN BY
SPOTTISWOODE, BALLANTYNE & CO. LTD.
LONDON AND COLCHESTER

Preface to the Fourth Edition

In the fourth edition of this Dictionary we have tried to keep to the same principles that were adopted in the previous editions. It is our aim to provide an explanation of the terms used in the various branches of chemistry together with brief accounts of what we consider are important substances, chemical operations, and chemists themselves. It is not intended for the specialist, and certainly is not intended to compete with the larger chemical reference works such as, Beilstein, Gmelin, Landold Börnstein, the 'Dictionary of Organic Compounds', or for quantitative data the 'Handbook of Chemistry and Physics' (The Chemical Rubber Co.) All of these compilations contain much more information than can possibly be summarized in a volume of the present size. This Dictionary is intended for the chemist who wishes to know something of the words and names in use in another branch of chemistry and particularly for non-chemists who may need to know something about chemistry. It is hoped that it contains information which will be of use to those in professions such as law, medicine, journalism, engineering, management, and teaching who need to use or refer to chemical terms.

Once again it is interesting to refer to the phenomenal growth of the subject over the past eight years. The time gap between editions has had to be reduced and it is sobering to realize that the major developments of the past ten years have been made not only on the fringes of the subject but also in the production and characterization of simple but nevertheless vitally important compounds.

We have endeavoured to keep the Dictionary approximately the same size as previous editions and our authors have had to be fairly ruthless in deleting terms that have become obsolete or have lost their previous importance. It is, of course, still a matter of personal opinion as to what should be included and what excluded and certainly we could not hope to include all of the terms which would be required by all general users. As before we have not been able to follow a completely consistent policy in trade names but, whenever possible, we have not used them. Since, however, some substances are better known by trade names than by trivial names we have had to include some but, whenever possible, it has been stated that they are trade names.

The list of contributors is on page vii and we are deeply indebted to these authors, for it is they who have prepared this new edition. Very many others have helped by answering specific queries or by pointing out errors or omissions and these also we thank. We hope that there are not too many errors in the present volume; we would be very grateful if readers who come across omissions and errors would point them out to us.

Department of Chemistry,   D. W. A. SHARP
University of Glasgow,
Glasgow, W.2.

Kingston Court,   L. M. MIALL
Kingston,
Canterbury,
Kent.

CONTRIBUTORS TO FOURTH EDITION

W. H. BENNETT, M.Sc., F.R.I.C., Directorate of Overseas Geological Surveys (Minerals)

T. J. BRADLEY, B.Sc., University of Strathclyde (Pharmaceuticals)

C. J. W. BROOKS, B.Sc., Ph.D., A.R.C.S., The University, Glasgow (Biochemistry)

L. R. COX, B.Sc., A.M.I.Chem.E., University of Strathclyde (Chemical Engineering and Applied Chemistry)

R. A. JEFFREYS, M.Sc., Ph.D., F.R.I.C., A.K.C., Kodak Ltd. (Photographic Chemicals)

F. JORDINSON, M.Sc., F.R.I.C., F.S.D.C. (Dyestuffs)

G. R. KNOX, B.Sc., Ph.D., University of Strathclyde (Organic Chemistry)

A. MCAULEY, B.Sc., Ph.D., A.R.I.C., University of Strathclyde (Physical Chemistry)

J. M. MCLEOD, B.Sc., Ph.D., A.R.C.S.T., F.I.M., University of Strathclyde (Metallurgy)

L. M. MIALL, M.A., F.R.I.C. (Biographies)

A. PHILLIPS, B.Sc., A.R.I.C., Borough Polytechnic (Rubber Chemicals)

D. J. POLTON, M.Sc., Shell Research Limited (Agricultural Chemistry)

J. E. PROCTOR, M.Sc., F.R.I.C., A.P.I., Borough Polytechnic (Plastics)

D. W. A. SHARP, M.A., Ph.D., A.R.I.C., F.R.S.E., University of Glasgow (Inorganic Chemistry)

T. W. WIGHT, B.Sc., Ph.D., A.R.I.C., Naval Ordnance Inspection Laboratory (Explosives)

L. A. WILLIAMS, B.Sc., Ph.D., F.R.I.C., Kodak Ltd. (Photographic Chemicals)

CONTRIBUTORS TO PREVIOUS EDITIONS

E. F. ARMSTRONG	L. M. MIALL
W. H. BENNETT	S. MIALL
J. O'M. BOCKRIS	K. G. A. PANKHURST
T. T. COCKING	T. G. PEARSON
F. G. CROSSE	A. T. PICTON
E. G. CUTBUSH	E. M. POPE
C. E. DENT	A. R. POWELL
P. H. ELWORTHY	J. E. PROCTOR
H. J. EMELÉUS	H. C. RAMPTON
G. H. FORD	C. A. ROBB
W. FRANCIS	E. R. ROBERTS
E. FYLEMAN	A. B. SEARLE
F. J. GARRICK	D. W. A. SHARP
J. HARLEY-MASON	K. J. SINCLAIR
J. F. HERRINGHSAW	K. STEWART
S. IGNATOWICZ	R. G. STITCHBURY
A. REES JONES	R. B. STRATHDEE
L. A. JORDAN	A. G. K. THOMSON
F. JORDINSON	E. TOMALIN
A. KING	E. VERNON
J. A. KITCHENER	E. S. WAIGHT
H. LANGWELL	V. J. WARD
J. MAITLAND-EDWARDS	A. J. E. WELCH
S. MATTANA	A. F. WELLS
P. MAYNARD	T. W. WIGHT

ABBREVIATIONS

The abbreviations and symbols used in this dictionary are largely those recommended by the Symbols Committee of the Royal Society and published in 1951 under the title 'Symbols, Signs and Abbreviations recommended for British Scientific Publications.' The report can be obtained from the Chemical Society, Burlington House, London, W.1, for 9d. a copy. The report recommends the specific letters to represent the various quantities or properties, and the typographic conventions for the different kinds of symbol.

Abbreviations and symbols used in this book include:

Å	Ångstrom unit (see article)
At.no.	Atomic number
At.wt.	Atomic weight
b.p.	Boiling point
Btu	British thermal unit
°C	Degree Centigrade
c	Velocity of light
d	Relative density
D-, DL-	See article 'Optical activity'
E	Energy
°F	Degree Fahrenheit
G	Gibbs function (see article 'Gibbs free energy')
g	gramme
h	Planck's constant (see article)
L-	See article 'Optical activity'
M (in formulae)	Any metal
ml	Millilitre
mol.wt.	Molecular weight
m.p.	Melting point
N	Avogadro's number (see article)
N	Normal solution (see article)
n (with subscript)	Refractive index
P	Pressure
pH	See article 'Hydrogen ion concentration'
R	Gas constant
rH	See article 'rH'
S	Entropy
sp.gr.	Specific gravity
T	Absolute temperature
X (in formulae)	Any non-metal (usually a halogen)
$[\alpha]$	Specific rotation. See Rotatory power, specific
γ	Surface tension
μ	Micron
ν	Frequency
(+)- and (−)-	See article 'Optical activity'.

Throughout the dictionary all temperatures are expressed in degrees Centigrade unless otherwise stated. Abbreviations for journals are those of Chemical Abstracts.

A

Abegg, Richard (1869-1910). Born at Danzig, Abegg was educated at the Universities of Tübingen, Kiel, Berlin, Leipzig, and Stockholm. In 1894 he became assistant to Nernst at Göttingen, and later professor of physical chemistry. In 1901 Abegg was appointed extraordinary professor at Breslau, and in 1909 professor of chemistry at Breslau Technical High School. Apart from his researches upon organic and physical problems, his name will live on account of his 'Handbuch der anorganische Chemie.'

Abietic acid, $C_{20}H_{30}O_2$. A crystalline diterpenoid acid obtained from pine rosin by acid treatment, which causes isomerization of primary resin acids (palustric, laevopimaric, neoabietic) to abietic acid, m.p. 172°-175°, $[\alpha]_D$ −116° (ethanol). The commercial product may be glassy and of low m.p. It is used extensively in the manufacture of plastics, paints, varnishes, paper sizes and detergents.

Abrin. A toxic substance, causing agglutination of the red blood corpuscles, found in the seeds of *Abrus precatorius*, an Indian shrub. It is a mixture of two proteins.

Absolute temperature. A temperature on the 'absolute' or Kelvin scale usually denoted by T; the zero of this scale is the temperature at which a perfect gas would occupy zero volume if it could be cooled indefinitely without liquefaction or solidification. The absolute zero being −273·16°, and one degree on the absolute scale being equivalent to one Centigrade degree, an absolute temperature = the corresponding Centigrade temperature + 273·16°.

Absorptiometer. Two types of apparatus are called by this name. One is an instrument for determining the absorption of light by a liquid, the other for determining the solubility of a gas in a liquid.

Absorption. See Gas absorption.

Absorption bands. See Absorption of light.

Absorption coefficient of a gas. The volume of gas measured at 0° and 760 mm pressure which will dissolve in 1 ml of a liquid. The absorption coefficients in water at 0° for several common

gases are as follows: nitrogen, 0·024; oxygen, 0·049; ethylene, 0·25; carbon dioxide, 1·713; hydrogen sulphide, 4·68; sulphur dioxide, 79·8; hydrogen chloride, 506; ammonia, 1300.

Absorption coefficient of light. See Lambert's law and Beer's law.

Absorption column. Absorption tower. The plant most widely used for gas absorption consists of a long column or tower, usually circular in cross-section but sometimes square, down which the liquid is passed while the gas is passed upwards. There are several types of column, but the two most important are the *plate* or *tray column* (*q.v.*) and the *packed column* (*q.v.*). In all cases the object is to provide the maximum gas-liquid interfacial area and the minimum resistance to gas flow.

These columns are also called *scrubbers*, especially when the object is to remove impurities.

Absorption of light. When light is incident on the surface of a transparent substance, part of the light is reflected, and the rest is transmitted unchanged. If, however, the light falls on a surface of lampblack, it is neither reflected nor transmitted, but absorbed. Since this surface absorbs light of all wave-lengths, the process is called general absorption. A layer of chlorine, on the other hand, appears green in daylight, because it has absorbed all the radiations corresponding with the remainder of the spectrum. This kind of absorption is termed *selective*. If the spectrum of the transmitted light is examined, i.e. the absorption spectrum is obtained, certain regions will be found absent, and appear black. These regions correspond with the light absorbed by the chlorine, and are termed *absorption bands*. If the absorbing medium is a gas in the atomic state, the spectrum of the transmitted light shows dark lines, instead of bands. These *absorption lines* correspond with the light absorbed by the atoms.

The absorption of light is the converse of the emission of light. Whereas a molecule emits a band spectrum (*q.v.*), an atom emits a line spectrum (*q.v.*). Emission of light corresponds with the return of the atom or molecule from a state of higher to one of lower energy, while the absorption of light corresponds with the raising of the atom or molecule from a state of lower to one of higher energy. The energy thus absorbed may be utilized in inducing chemical reactions.

The relationships between the intensity of the incident light, the thickness, concentration, and the intensity of the transmitted light are embodied in Beer's law (*q.v.*) and Lambert's law (*q.v.*).

Absorption tower. See Absorption column.

1

ABS plastics. A group of plastics materials based on blended copolymers of styrene-acrylonitrile (70:30) and butadiene-acrylonitrile (65:35) and on graft interpolymers of styrene and acrylonitrile with polybutadiene. Such plastics, although more expensive than for instance polystyrene, are very tough and of pleasing appearance although generally opaque.

Abyssinian gold. A yellow alloy of 90·7% copper and 8·3% zinc plated with gold on one side and rolled into sheets.

Acacia. See Gum Acacia.

Accelerators. Substances so called because they accelerate desired cross-linking reactions in polymers. In particular they assist the vulcanization (*q.v.*) of rubber, in some cases conferring on it increased resistance to wear. Many types of organic compounds can be used and are classed as ranging from slow to fast accelerators. Of these for example, diphenylguanidine (*q.v.*) is medium fast, the thiazoles, e.g. mercapto-benzthiazole (*q.v.*), are fast, and the thiuram (*q.v.*) disulphides, e.g. the tetramethyl derivatives, are ultra fast. The term is also used for those substances which act as catalysts by increasing the rate at which thermosetting resins cure or harden.

Acceptor. A substance which, while normally not oxidized by oxygen or reduced by hydrogen, can be thus oxidized or reduced in presence of a substance which is itself undergoing oxidation or reduction.

In connexion with molecular structure, an atom, molecule or ion, that has a deficit of one or more pairs of electrons, which can be supplied by a second atom with formation of a co-ordinate link (*q.v.*), is also called an 'acceptor.' Lewis (1923) using valence bond theory proposed a system of Lewis acids and bases, the acid being a substance, an acceptor, which can accept a pair of electrons from a donor molecule, the base.

Acenaphthene, $C_{12}H_{10}$. Colourless needles, m.p. 95°, b.p. 278°. Soluble in hot alcohol. When passed through a red-hot tube acenaphthylene is obtained. Oxidation with acid dichromate gives naphthalic acid. Characteristic picrate, m.p. 161°.

It occurs in the anthracene fraction of coal tar, from which it is readily separated. Can be obtained synthetically by the action of alcoholic potash on α-bromoethylnaphthalene.

It is of increasing importance as a dyestuff intermediate, being much used as a source of nitro- and amino-derivatives.

Acenaphthenequinone, $C_{12}H_6O_2$. Yellow needles, m.p. 261°, very sparingly soluble in water; 100 g of glacial acetic acid at 15° dissolve 0·15 g. It is condensed with thioindoxyl and its derivatives to bright scarlet and red vat dyes of the type

These are known as Ciba Scarlet G, Ciba Red R, etc.

Acenaphthylene, $C_{12}H_8$. Crystallizes in yellow plates from alcohol, m.p. 92°-93°, b.p. 265°-275°, with decomposition. Soluble in alcohol and ether, insoluble in water, d_4^{16} 0·899. It is derived from acenaphthene by catalytic dehydrogenation and polymerizes to give plastic products.

Acetal, $CH_3 \cdot CH(OC_2H_5)_2$. A pleasant-smelling liquid, b.p. 104°-105°, soluble to some extent in water and miscible in all proportions with alcohol and ether. It may be prepared by mixing acetaldehyde and ethyl alcohol in the presence of a catalyst, such as HCl, or by passing acetylene into alcohol in the presence of a catalyst. It is used in the preparation of derivatives, some of which are useful solvents.

Acetaldehyde, Ethanal, $CH_3 \cdot CHO$, is a colourless liquid with a characteristic odour, d 0·8009, b.p. 20·8°. Miscible with water, alcohol, and ether; insoluble in concentrated calcium chloride solutions. Manufactured by (a) vapour phase oxidation or dehydrogenation of ethyl alcohol over a catalyst; (b) vapour phase oxidation of butane (with formaldehyde and methanol as by-products); (c) direct oxidation of ethylene over a cupric chloride/palladium chloride catalyst. Prepared on the small scale by the oxidation of alcohol with potassium dichromate and sulphuric acid, or by warming paraldehyde with 20% sulphuric acid. Compounds are formed with many metallic salts; the crystalline sodium or potassium bisulphite compounds may be used to isolate and purify acetaldehyde. It is oxidized to acetic acid and reduced to alcohol. Polymerization readily occurs to give paraldehyde or metaldehyde: when heated with alkalis, a brown resin is formed. Aldol is formed by the interaction of two molecules of acetaldehyde. Acetaldehyde is used almost exclusively as a chemical intermediate, three compounds, acetic acid, acetic anhydride and *n*-butyl alcohol accounting for the bulk of its consumption. Other industrial chemicals made from it include 2-ethylhexyl alcohol, pentaerythritol, and chloral.

Acetal resin. See Polyformaldehyde.

Acetals are compounds of the general formula shown, and are derived from an aldehyde or ketone, and an alcohol using an acid catalyst. Ethylene glycol or 1,3-dihydroxypropane are frequently used to give 5- or 6-member cyclic products.

$$R^3 \diagdown C \diagup OR^1$$
$$R^4 \diagup \diagdown OR^2$$

Acetamide, $CH_3CO \cdot NH_2$. Crystallizes in long white needles which absorb water and finally liquefy. The crude substance has a strong odour of mice; m.p. 82°, b.p. 222°. Readily soluble in water and alcohol; sparingly soluble in ether. It may be prepared by the dry distillation of ammonium acetate or by the action of ammonia on ethyl acetate. Somewhat unstable salt-like compounds are formed with Na, K, Mg, Zn, Ca and Hg halides, and also with mineral acids.

Acetanilide, C_8H_9NO. White crystals, m.p. 114°, b.p. 304°. Very sparingly soluble in cold, more so in hot water, readily soluble in alcohol, ether, and chloroform.

$NH \cdot CO \cdot CH_3$

Acetanilide is manufactured by reacting aniline with excess acetic acid or acetic anhydride. It has been used medicinally, as an antipyretic and analgesic, but its chief use is in the manufacture of dye intermediates such as *p*-nitroacetanilide, *p*-nitroaniline and *p*-phenylenediamine. It is also used in the manufacture of rubber, and as a peroxide stabilizer.

Acetanilide is hydrolysed by dilute acids and alkalis at 100° to aniline. It chlorinates more slowly than aniline to *o*- and *p*-chloroacetanilides.

Acetates. Salts or esters of acetic acid.

Acetic acid, Glacial acetic acid, CH_3COOH, is a colourless liquid with a pungent, irritating odour, m.p. 16·6°, b.p. 118·8°, $n_D^{20} = 1·0492$. Miscible with water, alcohol and ether in all proportions. Not affected by oxidizing agents such as nitric and chromic acids.

Acetic acid is manufactured by the liquid-phase oxidation of acetaldehyde at 60° by oxygen or air under pressure in the presence of manganous acetate, the latter preventing the formation of peracetic acid. Another important route is the liquid-phase oxidation of butane by air at 50 atm. and 150°-250° in the presence of a metal acetate. Some acetic acid is produced by the catalytic oxidation of ethyl alcohol. Fermentation processes are used only for the production of vinegar.

Acetic acid will attack most metals and can form acidic, basic and normal salts. It can, however, be handled in aluminium, copper, monel or stainless steel equipment, the choice of material depending on the particular conditions encountered.

About half the acetic acid produced is used as acetic anhydride for the manufacture of cellulose acetate. Large quantities are also used for the manufacture of vinyl acetate and various solvents. Because a number of manufacturing processes yield large amounts of dilute acid its recovery is a problem of considerable importance. Simple rectification is expensive and hence various other processes such as azeotropic and extractive distillation and liquid-liquid extraction are used.

Acetic anhydride is a colourless liquid with a pungent odour, d^{20} 1·082, b.p. 139·5°. Soluble in cold water to the extent of 12%; hydrolysed to acetic acid by boiling water; miscible with ether and benzene. Manufactured by bubbling air through a mixture of acetaldehyde and acetic acid in the presence of a catalyst; or by reacting keten, derived by the cracking of acetic acid or acetone, with acetic acid. It reacts with compounds containing an —OH, —SH, or —NH group to give acetyl derivatives which are useful for characterization. Largely used for the production of cellulose acetate, also used for the manufacture of vinyl acetate and aspirin.

$CH_3CO \diagdown O$
$CH_3CO \diagup$

Acetic ester, Acetic ether, $C_4H_8O_2$, $CH_3COOC_2H_5$. See Ethyl acetate.

Acetin, Triacetin. See Acetins.

Acetins are acetates of glycerol. There are five possible acetates, two mono-, two di-, and one tri-acetate. Only four of these have been prepared in the pure state; the commercial acetins are mixtures of the various acetates and form colourless or slightly brown syrupy liquids. *Monoacetin,* d^{15} 1·221, b.p. 130°-132°/2-3 mm, contains chiefly the 1-acetate

$$CH_2OH \cdot CHOH \cdot CH_2OOC \cdot CH_3.$$

It is very soluble in water, and is not thrown out of concentrated solutions by sodium chloride; soluble in chloroform, but not very soluble in ether. Prepared by heating molecular proportions of glycerol and acetic acid with sulphuric acid, or by heating triacetin with glycerol. Used as a solvent for the dyes

3

employed in printing paper bags. *Diacetin*, d^{15} 1·18, b.p. 259° is chiefly the 1:3-diacetate $CH_2COOCH_2CHOH \cdot CH_2OOC \cdot CH_3$. Soluble in water and alcohol, but not in ether or benzene if water is present. Obtained as a by-product in the manufacture of triacetin. Used as plasticizer for cellulose acetate lacquers and as a solvent for basic dyes. *Triacetin*, d^{15} 1·16-1·17, b.p. 260°, is about 90% glycerol triacetate and 10% diacetate. Slightly soluble in water; soluble in ether. Prepared by heating glycerol with a large excess of acetic acid and extracting the triacetin from aqueous solution with ether. Used as a plasticizer for lacquers and as a solvent for certain gums and resins.

Acetoacetanilide, $C_{10}H_{11}NO_2$, m.p. 85°. Prepared by the action of acetoacetic ester on

aniline. Used for the preparation of pigment dyestuffs by coupling with diazotized bases.

Acetoacetic acid, Acetonemonocarboxylic acid, $C_4H_6O_3$, $CH_3CO \cdot CH_2COOH$. A colourless and strongly acid syrup. It is unstable, and decomposes into acetone and carbon dioxide below 100°. Prepared from acetoacetic ester. It occurs in traces in normal urine, but is characteristically present in increased amount in the urine of diabetic patients. Aqueous solutions of the acid give a distinctive violet colour with ferric chloride.

Acetoacetic ester, Ethyl acetoacetate,

$$CH_3COCH_2COOC_2H_5,$$
$$CH_3C(OH):CHCOOC_2H_5.$$

A colourless, mobile liquid with a pleasant odour, d^{20} 1·0256, b.p. 181°-182°, 80°/20 mm. Slightly soluble in water; miscible with alcohol, ether, benzene. Prepared by the action of sodium or sodium ethoxide on acetic ester, or of ethanol on diketen. It is the classical example of *keto-enol tautomerism*, and normal preparations of the ester contain 92·6% keto form and 7·4% enol form. The proportion of the two forms is altered by change of temperature or by solution in solvents. Separation of the keto and enol forms has been effected by distillation from quartz or Pyrex apparatus: the pure components revert to the original equilibrium mixture on standing. Metallic derivatives are formed with sodium and other metals; these are of the type $CH_3C(ONa):CHCOOC_2H_5$; they react with alkyl halides to give alkyl acetoacetates $CH_3CO \cdot CHR \cdot COOC_2H_5$. These also form sodium derivatives, reacting with alkyl halides in a similar manner to give di-alkyl esters.

Acetoacetic ester and the alkyl derivatives react with strong alkalis to give acetic and alkyl acetic acids respectively. Dilute alkalis or acids react to give ketones. With many nitrogen compounds it reacts to form nitrogen-containing rings: thus urea gives methyl uracil; hydrazines give methyl pyrazolones; aniline gives methyl quinoline. Prolonged boiling causes decomposition with loss of alcohol and formation of dehydracetic acid. It is a valuable means of synthesizing a wide variety of compounds and is used in the manufacture of phenazone. Detected by the violet colour given with ferric chloride.

Acetogenins. A term proposed to denote natural organic compounds shown or assumed to be derived biogenetically from the self-condensation of acetate units. See Polyketides.

Acetoin, Acetyl methyl carbinol, $C_4H_8O_2$, $CH_3CH(OH)COCH_3$, is a colourless liquid, m.p. 15°, b.p. 148°. Miscible with water and alcohol; insoluble in ether. Produced from propylene and butylene glycols by the action of acetic acid bacteria, and from acetaldehyde by yeast. Prepared by the reduction of diacetyl. Forms a crystalline compound with sodium bisulphite. Reduces Fehling's solution. When distilled, it forms diacetyl.

Acetol, Hydroxyacetone, Pyroracemic alcohol, Pyruvic alcohol, $C_3H_6O_2$, $CH_3CO \cdot CH_2OH$, is a colourless liquid with a pleasant odour, d^{20} 1·082, b.p. 145°-146°, 54°/18 mm. Miscible with water, alcohol, and ether. Prepared by the action of chloroacetone on potassium acetate: also formed by the action of certain *acetobacter* on α-propylene glycol. Tends to polymerize; methyl alcohol has a stabilizing effect. It has an acid reaction and reduces potassium permanganate and ammoniacal silver nitrate in the cold. Detected by the formation of the fluorescent hydroxymethylquinoline when treated with *o*-aminobenzaldehyde.

Acetolysis is the name given to the process of removing acetyl groups from an organic compound. It is usually carried out by heating the acetyl compound with aqueous or alcoholic alkalis, whereby the acetyl groups are removed as acetic acid.

Acetomenaphthone,   **1,4-diacetoxy-2-methyl-naphthalene**, $C_{15}H_{14}O_4$. A white powder, m.p.

112°-115°, almost insoluble in water, soluble in hot alcohol. Prepared by reducing menaphthone with zinc and acetic acid in the presence of acetic anhydride. It has the same action as menaphthone (*q.v.*), but can be taken by mouth.

Acetone, Dimethyl ketone, C_3H_6O, CH_3COCH_3, is a colourless, volatile liquid with a pleasant, ethereal odour: it is highly inflammable, $d°$ 0·8186, b.p. 56·2°. Miscible with water, alcohol, and ether; sparingly soluble in solutions of calcium chloride. It is largely manufactured by the dehydrogenation of isopropyl alcohol over a copper catalyst at 500° and 4 atm. Considerable quantities are also produced in the manufacture of other chemicals, notably glycerin, hydrogen peroxide and phenol. It occurs in significant amounts in blood and urine in certain pathological conditions. Crystalline compounds are formed with sodium and potassium bisulphites; compounds are also formed with mercuric sulphate and oxide. Ammonia reacts with boiling acetone to give diacetonamine. Sodium hydroxide causes condensation to diacetone alcohol; under more vigorous conditions mesityl oxide and phorone are produced. These are also formed, together with mesitylene, by the action of small amounts of mineral acids. Reduction of acetone gives isopropyl alcohol and pinacol. Crystalline derivatives are formed with hydroxylamine, phenyl hydrazine, and semicarbazide. It is detected by the formation of iodoform when treated with iodine and sodium hydroxide. Sodium nitroprusside and ammonia give a red colour with acetone, which changes to violet on addition of acetic acid. Acetone is used as a solvent and for the manufacture of methyl methacrylate, methyl isobutyl ketone, methyl isobutyl carbinol and various other chemicals.

Acetone alcohol. See Acetol.

Acetone bodies. The acetone bodies, acetone, $CH_3 \cdot CO \cdot CH_3$, acetoacetic acid, $CH_3 \cdot CO \cdot CH_2 \cdot COOH$, and β-hydroxybutyric acid, $CH_3 \cdot CHOH \cdot CH_2 \cdot COOH$, are excreted in the urine in severe cases of diabetes. They are formed by the incomplete breakdown of fatty acids and of amino-acids with an even number of carbon atoms (ketogenic amino-acids) in all cases of carbohydrate shortage. The presence of the acetone bodies is the most serious aspect of diabetes, as they are strong acids and seriously upset the neutrality regulation of the body. Their neutral sodium salts are also toxic. This con-condition, known as ketosis, if untreated, leads to coma and eventually death.

Acetone dicarboxylic acid, β-**Ketoglutaric acid,** $C_5H_6O_5$; $CO \cdot (CH_2COOH)_2$, crystallizes in colourless needles, m.p. 135° (decomp.). Soluble in water and alcohol; insoluble in benzene and chloroform. Prepared by the action of sulphuric acid on citric acid. Readily decomposed by boiling water, acids, or alkalis to

acetone and carbon dioxide. Gives a violet colour with ferric chloride and a white precipitate with mercuric sulphate. The acid or its diethyl ester reacts with sodium in a manner similar to acetoacetic ester. The ester is used in organic syntheses.

Acetone monocarboxylic acid. See Acetoacetic acid.

Acetonitrile, methyl cyanide, CH_3CN, a poisonous liquid, b.p. 82°, n_D^{15} 1·3460, miscible with water and many organic solvents except saturated petroleum fractions. Prepared from acetylene and ammonia or by dehydration of acetamide. Widely used for dissolving inorganic and organic compounds, especially when a non-aqueous polar solvent of high dielectric constant is required, e.g. for ionic reactions.

Acetonyl. The name given to the group $CH_3COCH_2—$.

Acetonylacetone, 2,5 Hexanedione, $C_6H_{10}O_2$, $CH_3COCH_2CH_2COCH_3$, is a colourless liquid which becomes yellow on standing, d^{20} 0·970, b.p. 191°. Miscible with water, alcohol, and ether. It is obtained by boiling 2,5-dimethylfuran with dilute sulphuric acid. It readily condenses with a variety of substances to give derivatives of furan, thiophen, and pyrrole, and is a solvent for cellulose acetate.

Acetophenone, C_8H_8O. Colourless plates, m.p. 19·7°, b.p. 202°, sp.gr. 1·024 at 25°. Odour resembling bitter almonds. Insoluble in water, miscible in all proportions with alcohol, ether, and benzene.

It occurs in coal tar. Prepared by the action of acetyl chloride upon benzene in the presence of aluminium chloride.

It has typical ketonic properties, forming a characteristic oxime, m.p. 60°, and phenylhydrazone, m.p. 105°. It is oxidized by potassium permanganate to phenylglyoxylic acid.

It is used as a solvent for cellulose ethers.

Acetoxy. The name given to the group $CH_3COO—$.

Acetylacetonates. Metal derivatives of acetylacetone. They generally contain the grouping

shown with some degree of aromatic character in the ring. The ring carbons may be substituted. In some acetylacetonates (e.g. Pt derivatives) the metal is bonded to the central carbon atom.

Acetylacetone. $C_5H_8O_2$, $CH_3COCH_2COCH_3$. A diketone with enolic properties. It forms stable complexes with many metals, e.g. ferric acetylacetonate, $FeAc_3$

$$(Ac=CH_3COCHCOCH_3);$$

these complexes are soluble in organic solvents and are often appreciably volatile.

Acetylation is the name given to any process for introducing acetyl groups into an organic compound containing —OH, —NH_2 or —SH groups. It is carried out by heating the compound with acetic anhydride or acetyl chloride usually in presence of an inert solvent such as benzene or acetic acid. In many cases, zinc chloride or pyridine is used to hasten the reaction.

Acetyl chloride, CH_3COCl. A colourless liquid with a pungent odour; it fumes in moist air, producing acetic and hydrochloric acids. $d°$ 1·130, b.p. 55°. Soluble in ether and benzene, but reacts with water and other hydroxyl containing compounds. Prepared by the distillation of a mixture of acetic acid and phosphorus trichloride or oxychloride. It is used to prepare acetyl derivatives of hydroxy- and amino-compounds.

Acetylcholine. $C_7H_{17}NO_3$.

$$[Me_3N(CH_2)_2OOCCH_3]OH$$

Available as the chloride, a white hygroscopic crystalline powder, soluble in water and alcohol, insoluble in ether. Easily hydrolysed by hot water or alkali to choline and acetic acid. Acetylcholine occurs in the animal body, in ergot, and in various plants. It is liberated in small quantities in the body on stimulating the parasympathetic nerves, and causes dilatation of the arteries and a rapid fall in blood pressure at a dilution of one part in ten millions. It is destroyed in the body by the action of cholinesterase.

Acetyl-coenzyme A. A reactive thioester of fundamental importance in metabolism and biosynthesis. The acetyl group is bound to the thiol group of coenzyme A (q.v.), and its high reactivity is reflected in the term 'active acetate.' Acetyl-coenzyme A is the principal substrate of the Krebs cycle (q.v.) It also acts as an acetylating agent, e.g. in the formation of acetylcholine. It has a central role in three major biosynthetic pathways: (i) formation of fatty acids from acetyl-coenzyme A and malonyl-coenzyme A (itself arising by carboxylation of acetyl-coenzyme A); (ii) synthesis of the polyketides via acetoacetyl-coenzyme A; (iii) synthesis of the terpenoids and steroids via mevalonic acid.

Acetylene, C_2H_2, (H—C≡C—H), is a colourless gas which when pure has a pleasant smell. The b.p. is $-84°$ and the m.p. $-82°$, and it is therefore possible to solidify it under atmospheric pressure with liquid nitrogen, or liquify it below its critical temperature of 36·5° by using a higher pressure. It is soluble in water, liquid ammonia and many organic solvents.

Acetylene is an endothermic compound

$$2C+H_2 \rightarrow C_2H_2 \; \varDelta H=+54 \text{ Kcal}$$

and consequently much energy is released when the molecule breaks down. This property is utilized in the oxy-acetylene flame, used for the welding and cutting of metals. The compound has very wide explosive limits in air (2·3% and 80% acetylene by volume) and apart from this the liquid, and also the gas if the pressure exceeds 2 atm., are explosive even in the absence of air. Consequently acetylene can be dangerous to handle. For storage and transportation steel cylinders containing acetone and a porous material such as diatomaceous earth are used. At 15° acetone will dissolve 25 times its own volume of acetylene at a pressure of 1 atm., or 300 times its own volume at a pressure of 12 atm.

Acetylene, discovered by E. Davy in 1836 and studied by Berthelot in 1862, is now one of the most important organic chemicals. The original method for the manufacture of acetylene, the action of water on calcium carbide, is still of very great importance, but newer methods using hydrocarbons are rapidly coming to the fore. They include the pyrolysis of the lower paraffins in the presence of steam, the partial oxidation of natural gas (methane) and the cracking of hydrocarbons in an electric arc.

Acetylene is the starting point for the manufacture of a wide range of chemicals, amongst which the most important are acrylonitrile, vinyl chloride and vinyl acetate. Others include acetaldehyde, acetic acid, tri- and perchloroethylene, neoprene and polyvinyl alcohol. Processes such as vinylation, ethinylation, carbonylation, oligomerization and Reppe processes offer the possibility of producing various newer organic chemicals cheaply.

Like all terminal alkynes, the acetylenic hydrogen atoms are acidic in the sense that they are removed by suitable strong bases such as sodamide or a Grignard reagent to give RC≡CNa or RC≡C MgX. (For acetylene R=H, although a second mole of base will also replace this hydrogen atom.) Many metals will give salts (see Acetylides) which may be used for purification purposes, e.g. silver acetylide, AgC≡CH, a white shock-sensitive solid, insoluble in water, regenerates acetylene on treatment with mineral acids.

Acetylene dicarboxylic acid, $HO_2CC≡CCO_2H$. See Dimethylacetylenedicarboxylate.

Acetylene dichloride. See Dichloroethylenes.

Acetylene tetrachloride, *sym*-**Tetrachloroethane,** $HCCl_2CHCl_2$, is a colourless liquid with a chloroform-like odour, d^{20} 1·600, b.p. 146°. Insoluble in water; miscible with benzene; it is volatile in steam. Manufactured by passing chlorine and acetylene separately into a solution of antimony pentachloride in acetylene tetrachloride; ferric chloride and aluminium chloride are also used. It is an excellent solvent for fats, oils, resins, cellulose acetate, sulphur and phosphorus. It is non-inflammable, but its vapour is toxic, causing jaundice and a fatty degeneration of the organs. In the presence of moisture, metals are slowly attacked and dichloroethylene is formed. Reacts with dilute alkalis to give trichloroethylene; more concentrated alkalis form the spontaneously explosive mono- and di-chloroacetylenes. Used chiefly in the manufacture of trichloroethylene.

Acetylides. Carbides (*q.v.*) which have the carbon atoms in pairs forming the C_2^{2-} anion. Formed by the elements in Groups I, II, III, and some transition elements. On hydrolysis these compounds yield acetylene. Most of the heavy metal acetylides are explosive. Many complex acetylide ions of the type $[M(C{\equiv}CR)_n]^{x-}$ are formed by the transition elements. These complexes are formed particularly easily in solution in liquid ammonia.

Acetyl methyl carbinol. See Acetoin.

Acetyl radical. The radical $CH_3CO\cdot$ which occurs in the free state during the photolysis of acetone. It is dissociated above 60° into CO and CH_3. Acetyl derivatives contain this group.

Acetyl value. The acetyl value of a fat is the number of milligrammes of potassium hydroxide required to neutralize the acetic acid liberated when one gramme of acetylated fat is saponified. It is a measure of the number of free hydroxyl groups in the fat.

Acheson, Edward Goodrich (1856-1931). Born at Washington, U.S.A., Acheson was compelled at an early age to seek employment. Mechanically minded and interested in electricity, he was engaged by Thomas Edison, and worked for him in Italy, Belgium, and Holland. Returning to the United States he was the pioneer in the development of the electric furnace for such products as carborundum and graphite. The lubricants oildag and aquadag are also the results of his researches. He was awarded the Perkin Medal of the Society of Chemical Industry in 1910.

Achroodextrins. See Dextrins.

Acid. An acid on the aqueous system is defined as a substance which is capable of forming hydrogen ions when dissolved in water. Most inorganic acids may be regarded as a compound of an acidic oxide and water; where the oxide concerned is that of a metal, that oxide may exhibit amphoteric character, that is act sometimes as an acid and sometimes as a base. Aqueous solutions of acids have a sharp taste, turn litmus red, liberate carbon dioxide from a metallic carbonate and give reactions characteristic of the anion present.

Since free protons cannot exist, acidic properties can only be shown when the solvent can act as a proton acceptor, i.e. as a base. Thus aqueous solutions of acids contain the hydroxonium ion, H_3O^+, and, since ammonia can also solvate a proton to give the ammonium ion, NH_4^+, substances which dissolve in ammonia to give the ammonium ion, e.g. NH_4Cl, are acids in that system.

Liquid water is ionized

$$2H_2O \rightleftharpoons H_3O^+ + OH^-,$$

this ionization being the reverse of the neutralization reaction in water; substances giving hydroxyl ions are bases in water. Liquid ammonia is also ionized,

$$2NH_3 \rightleftharpoons NH_4^+ + NH_2^-,$$

and amides are bases in this system. This concept has been extended to solvents which are ionized and yet do not contain hydrogen: a substance giving the appropriate positive ion is an acid in that system. Thus bromine trifluoride ionizes,

$$2BrF_3 \rightleftharpoons BrF_2^+ + BrF_4^-,$$

and a substance giving the BrF_2^+ ion in solution, e.g. $BrF_3\cdot SbF_5$, is an acid in the system.

Typical organic acids contain the —COOH group, but many other acid groupings, e.g. the sulphonic —SO_3H, give acidic properties to organic compounds. Phenols have acidic properties and are classified with enols as pseudo-acids.

The term acid has been further extended by Lewis to include substances which are electron deficient. Thus $AlCl_3$ (being electron deficient) can accept electrons from a chloride ion and is a Lewis acid.

The 'strength' of an acid is measured by the value of its dissociation constant, 'strong' acids, e.g. HCl, HNO_3, being substantially fully ionized in solution and 'weak' acids predominately un-ionized.

Acid dyes are the sodium salts of the sulphonic acids or phenolic groupings of dyestuffs. They are substantive to wool, upon which they fix themselves from a bath acidified with dilute sulphuric or acetic acid. They do not form lakes with tannin. They have little affinity for cotton.

Some acid dyes are applied most successfully from a neutral or very slightly acid dyebath, i.e. at pH 6-7. This group is characterized by much higher wet fastness than the typical 'level-dyeing acid dye' (which requires sulphuric acid in the dyebath), and is used in the dyeing of silk and some synthetic fibres.

Acid egg. This is essentially a non-mechanical pump for the handling of highly corrosive liquids. It consists of a vessel of corrosion-resistant material into which the liquid is admitted. The inlet valve is then closed and the liquid forced out into the delivery line by compressed air.

Acid exchange resins. See Ion exchange.

Acid (steel or process). Used with reference to the nature of the slag in steel production.

Acid tar. A tarry residue produced in the wet refining of petroleum fractions with sulphuric acid.

Acid value. A measure of the free acid content of a substance. It is the number of milligrams of potassium hydroxide required to neutralize one gram of the substance, using phenolphthalein as an indicator. The term is used for fats, oils, resins, plasticizers, and solvents.

Acitrizoic acid, $C_9H_6I_3O_3$, is a white powder, slightly soluble in water and in the alkali hydr-

oxides. It contains 68% iodine. Solutions of the sodium salt and the sodium salt of diatrizoic acid,   3,5-diacetamido-2,4,6-tri-iodobenzoic acid are used as X-ray contrast media. They are injected intravenously and used to outline the renal system.

Aconite, monkshood, or wolfbane, is the dried root of *Aconitum napellus*. It contains the intensely poisonous alkaloid aconitine to which it owes its medicinal properties.

Aconitic acid, $C_6H_6O_6$. The most easily obtained form is the *trans* acid, this crystallizes in colourless leaflets, m.p. 194°, with decomposition.

Soluble in water, sparingly soluble in ether. It can be prepared by dehydrating citric acid with 50% sulphuric acid. It is present in cane molasses.

The *cis* form has m.p. 125° and is converted into the *trans* form on heating.

Aconitine, an intensely poisonous alkaloid obtained from *Aconitum napellus*, forms colourless hexagonal crystals, m.p. 197°. Very slightly

soluble in water, soluble in 40 parts of alcohol; $[\alpha]_D + 14·6°$. It is related to delphinine.

Aconitine: $R_1 = OH$, $R_2 = OH$, $R_3 = C_2H_5$.

Delphinine: $R_1 = H$, $R_2 = H$, $R_3 = CH_3$.

Acridine, $C_{13}H_9N$. Crystallizes in colourless needles, m.p. 111°. It is soluble in alcohol and

sparingly soluble in hot water. It occurs in the high-boiling fraction of coal tar.

Acriflavine is a mixture of 2,8-diamino-10-methylacridinium chloride hydrochloride, and 2,8-diaminoacridine dihydrochloride. It may be prepared by partially quarternizing diacetyl-diaminoacridine and hydrolysing the product with hydrochloric acid. It is a red crystalline powder, soluble in water and alcohol, but insoluble in chloroform. It is used for the same purposes as proflavine (*q.v.*).

Acrilan. A brand name for a synthetic fibre, based on a copolymer of acrylonitrile with minor proportions of other unspecified vinyl monomers. See also Orlon.

Acrolein, Acraldehyde, Vinyl aldehyde, C_3H_4O, $CH_2:CH·CHO$. A colourless, volatile liquid, with characteristic odour. The vapour is poisonous, and intensely irritating to eyes and nose; d^{20} 0·8427, b.p. 53°. Soluble in water and alcohol. It is prepared by the distillation of a mixture of glycerin, potassium sulphate, and potassium bisulphate. It is manufactured by direct oxidation of propylene or cross-condensation of acetaldehyde with formaldehyde.

When exposed to sunlight, it is converted to a white insoluble resin, disacryl. Oxidized by air to acrylic acid; small amounts of hydroquinone will inhibit this. Bromine forms a dibromide which is converted by barium hydroxide into DL-fructose. The acrid odour of burning fats is due to traces of acrolein. It is used in the production of methionine.

Acrylic acid, Vinylformic acid, $C_3H_4O_2$,

$CH_2:CH\cdot COOH$, is a colourless liquid having an odour resembling that of acetic acid, d^{16} 1·062, m.p. 13°, b.p. 141°. It is miscible with water. Prepared by oxidizing acrolein with moist silver oxide, or treating β-hydroxypropionitrile with sulphuric acid. Slowly converted to a resin at ordinary temperatures. Important glass-like resins are now manufactured from ethyl acrylate and methyl acrylate.

Acrylic resins. The two important polymers included within this group are polymethyl acrylate and polymethyl methacrylate.

Polymethyl acrylate, manufactured from the liquid monomer by emulsion polymerization, is a tough rubbery material. It is used, usually as manufactured in emulsion form, for certain textile and leather finishes, lacquers, emulsion paints, pressure sensitive adhesives, and safety-glass interlayers.

Polymethyl methacrylate is formed as a hard clear thermoplastic resin by the polymerization of methyl methacrylate in the presence of peroxide catalysts. Mass polymerization of the monomer in closed plate-glass cells gives rise to sheets of Perspex (a brand name), a thermoplastic well known for its high optical clarity and ease of fabrication by hot forming, cementing, and machining. The polymer when produced by emulsion or pearl polymerization is compounded to give materials for injection moulding and extrusion. The extensive use of certain acrylic resins, especially polymethyl methacrylate, in dental and general surgical prosthetics is now well established.

Acrylonitrile. Vinyl cyanide, $CH_2:CH\cdot CN$, is a volatile liquid, b.p. 78°, d^{20} 0·8060. It is manufactured by the catalytic dehydration of ethylene cyanhydrin, by the addition of hydrogen cyanide to acetylene in the presence of cuprous chloride, or the reaction of propylene, ammonia, and air in the presence of a molydenum-based catalyst. It is miscible with alcohol and most organic solvents.

Acrylonitrile is very active, both in polymerization and in undergoing ready addition to compounds containing active hydrogen (e.g. the process of cyanoethylation). Polymers and copolymers of acrylonitrile are industrially important as synthetic fibres (see Orlon), nitrile rubbers, and as components in several thermoplastic compositions. It is an effective fumigant against stored grain insects.

ACTH. See Corticotrophin.

Actin. See Actomyosin.

Actinides. The elements actinium, thorium, protactinium, uranium, neptunium, plutonium, americium, curium, berkelium, californium, einsteinium, fermium, mendelevium, nobelium, and lawrencium are collectively known as actinides. Those with atomic numbers 93 and above are artificial and are produced by irradiation of uranium or other artificial elements with neutrons, alpha particles, or carbon or nitrogen ions. In the actinide elements the 5f shell is being filled and they are thus analogous to the rare-earth elements. There is less shielding of the 5f electrons and valencies greater than three are common, particularly among lighter members of the series. See 'The Chemistry of the Actinide Elements', by J. J. Katz and G. T. Seaborg.

Actiniohaematin. A respiratory catalyst of the same type as helicorubin which occurs in certain *actiniae*. It contains haem, but has a different protein constituent from that of haemoglobin.

Actinium, Ac. At.no. 89, At.wt. 227, m.p. 1190°, b.p. 3300°. Actinium has a face-centred cubic structure, $a=5·311$ Å. It occurs naturally as a minor constituent in uranium ores but in view of the long and tedious methods required for separation it is best obtained by irradiation of radium with neutrons. Actinium is separated from other elements by ion-exchange or solvent extraction. Even the most stable isotope is extremely radioactive, the metal glowing blue in the dark. Actinium metal has been prepared by reduction of actinium fluoride with lithium vapour at 1200°. It is silvery white in colour and is highly reactive.

Actinium compounds. Because of its intense radioactivity very few actinium compounds have been isolated. In its compounds the element is tripositive, forming very similar compounds to lanthanum (*q.v.*). Actinium salts are colourless.

Actinometer. A device which determines the intensity of a beam of radiation. A light-sensitive chemical reaction may be employed as when a solution of uranyl oxalate is used to determine the intensity of ultra-violet light since the rate of decomposition of the oxalate has been standardized by physical methods. Another type of actinometer involves measurement of the e.m.f. generated by a thermocouple with its hot junction embedded in a blackened surface and its cold junction irradiated by the light of unknown intensity.

Actinon, See Radon.

Activated adsorption. There are two types of adsorption; in one the association between the two phases is physical and in the other chemical. The first is the more common and, since van der Waals' forces are involved, is known as *van der Waals' adsorption*, (see Adsorption, physical). The second type involves chemical forces and is characterized by a high activation energy and so is sometimes called activated adsorption. Since chemical forces are involved, this type of adsorption is frequently irreversible, giving rise to *chemisorption* (q.v.).

Activated molecule. Molecules will only react on collision when they possess more than a certain minimum amount of energy. A molecule which has acquired more energy than the average amount possessed by other molecules, and is therefore in a more reactive condition, is said to be activated. Molecules are activated when they absorb a quantum of light, or after coming in contact with a hot surface.

Activation energy. The average energy possessed by molecules is usually insufficient for them to undergo reaction. The excess energy above this energy needed by molecules for reaction is termed the activation energy. In a reaction, molecules possessing this energy will pass through an intermediate state in forming an 'activated complex' before proceeding to the products. Many chemical and physical properties (e.g. diffusion, electrolytic conduction, viscous flow, etc.) seem to require activation and so pass through this transition state. Activation energy may be derived from the increase in reaction rates with temperature according to the Arrhenius equation.

Activator. A substance having little effect itself but when mixed with accelerators (q.v.) increases the rate of vulcanization (q.v.) of natural rubber. An example is zinc oxide which reacts with fatty acids present in or added to rubber (the resulting product acts as an activator).

Active carbon. Carbon is an excellent adsorbent for the removal of small traces of impurities from a gas or liquid, because it has a very high internal surface area and hence good adsorptive properties. It is also highly specific in action, adsorbing one material and excluding another. This enables carbon to be used in the fractionation of the noble gases and also explains its efficient action in gas masks. Another feature of adsorption by carbon is that the bulk of the adsorption takes place at low relative pressures.

The charcoal produced by the carbonization of wood, coal, or other carbon forming materials, such as scrap rubber, although possessing a large surface area, is not a very good adsorbent, as its surface is covered by chemically held hydrogen or hydrocarbon groups. These latter are tenaciously held but can be removed by oxidation at high temperatures, treatment with chlorine, etc., and it is found that the hydrogen content is roughly in inverse proportion to the adsorption capacity.

In order to activate carbon, it is treated at a high temperature with steam, air, or carbon dioxide. These reagents have the effect of removing hydrogen from the surface of the carbon and also of increasing the specific surface by oxidation of the carbon itself, capillaries being opened up and made available for access to foreign molecules. Activation can also be made to take place by means of solid agents such as phosphoric acid or zinc chloride, most of which are dehydrating agents. The surface of carbon is normally covered with a film of chemically held oxygen. See Adsorption.

Active centres. Theories of heterogeneous catalysis generally agree in postulating adsorption of the reactants on the catalyst by either physical or chemical forces. It is found that, in many cases, the addition of catalyst poisons inhibits the reaction by adsorption of the foreign substance on the catalyst, and that the amount of material required to inhibit reaction is very much less than that required to form a unimolecular layer on the surface. The conclusion is that a small number of active centres on the surface are responsible for the catalysis, the remainder acting merely as an inert carrier. These active centres are presumed to be atoms on surface irregularities, and are not firmly bound to the mass material. Thermochemical data confirm the existence of active centres and indicate, in the case of carbon for example, that the small proportion of active surface atoms are in a condition half way between those in a normal lattice and the vaporized solid. The idea of active centres has been extended to enzymes and bacterial action. See Adsorption, Catalysis, Surface compounds.

Active earths. See Bleaching earths.

Active mass. An old term used to express the influence of concentration of a substance on the position of equilibrium in a reversible chemical reaction (see Mass action, Law of). It means loosely the effective concentration of the substance, and is represented exactly by the thermodynamic *activity* (q.v.) which is now the preferred term.

Active nitrogen. See Nitrogen.

Active transport. A term referring to the biological transport of substances, usually against a concentration gradient, other than by osmosis or diffusion. It is a process requiring energy, which is normally supplied by ATP. Active transport is essential to many physiological processes. The species transported include ions such as Na^+, K^+, Ca^{2+}; I^- (in the thyroid); H^+ (in gastric juice formation); and organic materials such as glucose (transport into cells) and amino-acids (reabsorption by kidney tubules).

Activity. A thermodynamic quantity measuring the effective concentration or intensity of a particular substance in a given chemical system.

The *absolute activity* a^0 of a substance is defined by the equation $\mu = RT \ln a^0$ where μ is the chemical potential (*q.v.*) of the substance, R is the gas constant, and T the absolute temperature. The *relative activity*, a, is defined by

$$\mu = \mu^0 + RT \ln a$$

where μ^0 is the chemical potential of the substance in a certain reference state, the activity in which is taken as unity. Frequently, the reference state is chosen to be the pure substance at temp. T and 1 atm pressure; for dilute, ideal solutions the activity is directly proportional to the concentration, while for ideal gases it is proportional to the partial pressure of the gas.

Activity coefficient (*f or γ*). A dimensionless factor by which the concentration (*c*) of a substance must be multiplied to give an exact measure of its thermodynamic *activity* (*q.v.*) in a chemical system, i.e. $a = fc$. It is a measure of non-ideality of the solution, being unity for an ideal mixture and greater or less than unity for non-ideal mixtures. Different activity coefficients are obtained according to the concentration scale employed. The activity coefficient of an *electrolyte* is considered to be the geometric mean of the single ion activity coefficients, the latter being hypothetical quantities which cannot be determined separately.

Actomyosin is the most important protein of muscle. It is made up of two proteins, actin and myosin. Actomyosin is insoluble in water, and gives extremely viscous solutions with neutral salts. It is present in living muscle as a practically insoluble gel. It has a curled chain like α-keratin, which can be converted to a straight chain by stretching in steam. This change is responsible for the contraction of muscle. Actomyosin also acts as the enzyme that catalyses the decomposition of adenosine triphosphate, thus liberating the energy required for muscular contraction.

Acyclic. See Aliphatic.

Acyl. The general name for organic acid groups, which are the residues of carboxylic acids after removal of the —OH group, e.g. acetyl chloride, $CH_3CO \cdot Cl$, is the acyl chloride formed from acetic acid, $CH_3CO \cdot OH$. The names of the individual acyl groups are formed by replacing the *-ic* of the acid by *-yl*.

Acyloin condensation. The preparation of an acyloin, very often a cyclic acyloin, by condensing two molecules of ester on a metallic sodium surface.

Acyloins are $\alpha\beta$-ketoalcohols of the type $R \cdot CO \cdot CHR' \cdot OH$. See Acetoin, Benzoin.

Adamantane, $C_{10}H_{16}$, is a colourless hydrocarbon, m.p. 269°, but subliming readily at room temperature and atmospheric pressure. It occurs

to a very small extent (0·0004%) in certain petroleum fractions, together with alkylated

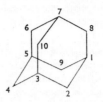

adamantanes. It possesses a unique rigid ring system composed of three fused chair cyclohexane rings, having the same configuration as the diamond lattice. Synthesized by a Lewis-acid catalysed rearrangement of tetrahydro-dicyclopentadiene. 1-Substituted derivatives are available by direct substitution, e.g. by Br_2. 1-Adamantanamine hydrochloride has been found to be a potent antiviral agent.

Addition reactions in organic chemistry cover those reactions where an unsaturated system (C=C, C≡C, C=O, etc.) is saturated or part saturated by addition of a molecule across the multiple bond. Examples include the reaction of bromine with ethylene to give 1,2-dibromo-ethane, hydrogen cyanide addition to an aldehyde giving a cyanhydrin, the Diels-Alder reaction, and addition polymerization. Examples from inorganic chemistry include the reaction of BF_3 with nucleophiles, e.g. ammonia, ether, and various reactions of complexes where the co-ordination number of the metal atom is effectively increased.

Additive volumes, Law of. The volume occupied by a mixture of gases is equal to the sum of the volumes which would be occupied by the constituents under the same conditions of temperature and pressure.

Adduct. A compound formed by direct combination, generally in simple molecular proportions, of two or more different compounds or elements.

Adenase. The enzyme responsible for deaminating adenine to hypoxanthine.

Adenine, 6-Aminopurine, $C_5H_5N_5$. Adenine crystallizes in long rhombic needles with three molecules of water which it loses at 110°. If carefully heated it sublimes at 220°, more rapidly heated it melts at 360°-365°, with decomposition. It is almost insoluble in cold water, and more soluble (1 part in 40) in hot water. It is sparingly soluble in alcohol. Adenine is a constituent of the nucleic acid portion of nucleoproteins, and, combined as adenosine pyrophosphate, it plays an important part in many metabolic processes.

Adenosine. See Nucleosides.

Adenosine diphosphate (ADP). ADP is adenosine 5′-diphosphate, the natural precursor of ATP, and the by-product of phosphorylation effected by ATP.

Adenosine monophosphate (AMP). Normally refers to adenosine 5′-phosphate (muscle adenylic acid), an important structural component of nucleic acids (*q.v.*) and of several coenzymes, e.g. nicotinamide adenine dinucleotide (NAD), flavin adenine dinucleotide (FAD) and coenzyme A. Adenosine 2′-phosphate (adenylic acid a) and 3′-phosphate (adenylic acid b) also occur in nucleic acid hydrolysates. Further phosphorylation of adenosine 5′-phosphate affords the 5′-pyrophosphate (adenosine diphosphate, ADP) and 5′-triphosphate (adenosine triphosphate, ATP) (*q.v.*).

Adenosine triphosphate (ATP). ATP is the most important of the so-called 'high-energy compounds', a group of naturally-occurring organic phosphates characterized by high free energies of hydrolysis, and playing a fundamental role in biosynthesis. Phosphorylation of ADP to yield ATP occurs (i) during photosynthesis, (ii) during fermentation, (iii) during respiration (see Oxidative phosphorylation). ATP is the primary source of energy in the metabolism of plant, animal and bacterial cells. Energy may be conveyed to other molecules (a) through

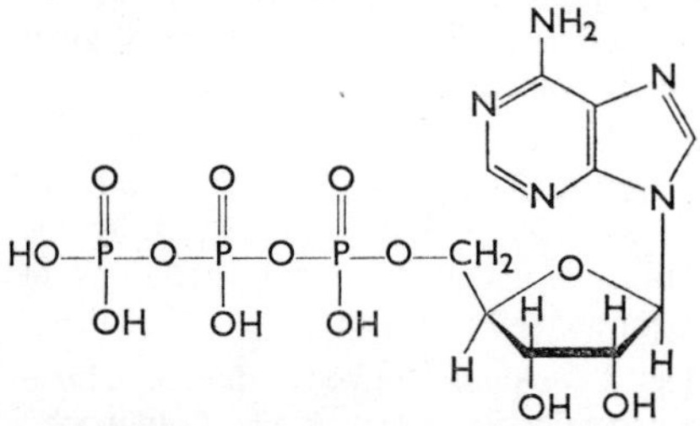

transfer of the AMP moiety with concomitant release of pyrophosphate; enzymic hydrolysis of the latter to phosphate prevents the reversal of the transfer; (b) through transfer of the terminal phosphate group and release of ADP.

Adenylic acid. See Adenosine monophosphate.

Adhesive. Any material which will wet two surfaces which have to be joined and can be solidified so as to form a joint.

Adiabatic change. An adiabatic change is one in which heat is neither added to, nor allowed to escape from, the system during the change.

Adipic acid, $C_6H_{10}O_4$, HOOC·$[CH_2]_4$·COOH, crystallizes in colourless plates, m.p. 153°. It is slightly soluble in water, but readily forms heavily supersaturated solutions; soluble in alcohol and ether. Present in beet-juice;

manufactured by the air or nitric acid oxidation of cyclohexanol, the latter being obtained by the air oxidation of cyclohexane. Distillation of its calcium salt gives cyclopentanone. It forms long chain polymers with diamines and is very largely used in the manufacture of nylon. It is also used for the manufacture of plasticizers and certain vinyl and urethane plastics.

Admiralty brass. See Brass.

Adonitol, $C_5H_{12}O_5$, is the carbohydrate alcohol

$$HOCH_2 \cdot [CH(OH)]_3 \cdot CH_2OH$$

corresponding to the pentose sugar ribose. It is found in *Adonis vernalis*, crystallizes in prisms, m.p. 102°, is optically inactive and has a sweet taste.

ADP. See Adenosine diphosphate.

Adrenaline, Epinephrine, $C_9H_{13}NO_3$. Colourless crystals, m.p. 212°. Insoluble in water and most

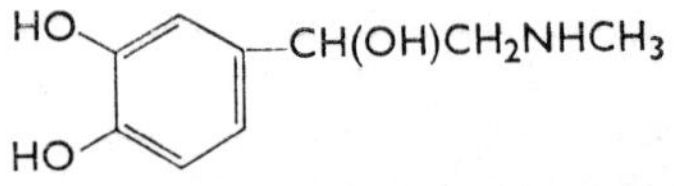

organic solvents, soluble in mineral acids; $[\alpha]_D - 53°$ in hydrochloric acid. It is the chief active principle of the suprarenal medulla, from which it may be obtained. Alternatively it may be synthesized by treating catechol with chloroacetyl chloride, treating the product with methylamine, reducing, and resolving with (+)-tartaric acid.

Intravenous injection causes a rise in blood pressure, inhibits peristaltic movements, and liberates glucose from the liver: because of this last action it is useful in treating insulin overdosage. Its effects are similar, but not identical, to those of stimulating the sympathetic nerves, and it is now known that noradrenaline (*q.v.*) and not adrenaline is liberated at sympathetic nerve endings. It is used as its acid tartrate in the treatment of allergic reactions and circulatory collapse.

Adsorbate. The material which is adsorbed on an adsorbent surface.

Adsorbent. A body on which adsorption takes place.

Adsorption. The abnormal condition of the atoms on the surface of a solid or liquid makes them tend to take up foreign atoms from their surroundings in order to reduce the surface energy. This is manifest by liquids as lowering of surface tension and by solids as adsorption. Adsorption, which is thus the local concentration of a substance at an interface, takes place at all surfaces, but its magnitude only becomes sufficiently great to be easily noticeable in very porous solids of large specific surface, such as charcoal and silica gel, which are able, by adsorption, to lower the pressure of a gas or concentration of a solution with which they are placed in contact.

It is now generally believed that adsorption normally takes place by the formation of a unimolecular layer on the surface, but in some cases multiple layers are undoubtedly formed. The forces which bind the adsorbed layer to the surface may be physical or chemical in nature; also a physically held material may gradually undergo chemical reaction with the surface. Furthermore, physical adsorption may be followed by a gradual diffusion of the adsorbed molecules from the surface into the interior of the solid.

Adsorption is of direct technical application in the purifying of materials, drying of gases, production of high vacua, etc. Adsorption phenomena are the basis of all colloidal and emulsification behaviour as well as of catalysis. References: Brunaer, 'Physical Adsorption of Gases'; N. K. Adam, 'Chemistry and Physics of Surfaces.' See also Activated adsorption, Chemisorption, Capillary condensation.

Adsorption, industrial. Adsorption is of considerable industrial importance, being employed for such purposes as the refining of lubricating oil and the purification and drying of gases. Adsorption operations may be carried out by one of three principle methods: In *batchwise operation* the adsorbent is mixed with the liquid to be treated and afterwards removed by settling or filtration. In *fixed bed operations* the liquid or gas is passed through a bed of the material which is periodically regenerated. In *continuous countercurrent operations* the adsorbent and the fluid are both in motion and flow countercurrent to each other, the adsorbent being continuously regenerated in another part of the equipment. See also Adsorption and Adsorption, physical.

Adsorption, physical. Many adsorption processes (e.g. of benzene vapour by charcoal) are rapid, reversible and not chemically specific. Adsorbability in such systems runs parallel with condensibility of the vapour to the liquid state and is clearly a physical process. The forces attracting the gas molecules to the surface of the solid are similar in nature to those responsible for cohesion in the liquid state, namely, the van der Waals' forces (*q.v.*).

Adsorption theory (of catalysis). See Catalysis.

Aerosol, Aerogel. The type of dispersion in which a finely divided solid is suspended in a gas is common, and is exemplified by smoke. When the dispersion medium is air and the particles are of colloidal dimensions, the system is termed an aerosol. Aerosols can often be formed by the rapid condensation of a vapour such as that of a metal oxide. Nickel aerosols have been made by vaporization of the metal in the arc or by heating nickel carbonyl vapour. By condensation of such sols, nickel aerogels are formed.

Cosmic dust and the stable dust sometimes formed by volcanic eruption are naturally occurring aerogels.

Aerosol sprays consist of a material dissolved or suspended in a liquid which when pressure is released volatalises to produce a fine spray. The spray carries the active material. Used in hair lacquers, paints, etc.; the propellant must be inert and non-inflammable. Chlorofluorocarbons are used extensively.

Aerosol is also a trade name for certain wetting agents, most of which are esters of sodium sulphosuccinic acid. Aerosol OT Dry is the dioctyl ester and is a very powerful wetting agent.

Aerosporin. See Polymyxin.

Aesculin, $C_{15}H_{16}O_9$, the best known of the coumarin glycosides (*q.v.*), has m.p. 205°. It consists of glucose attached at position 6 to 6,7-dihydroxycoumarin. It is found in horsechestnut bark and leaves.

Aetiophyllin. See Chlorophyll.

Aetioporphyrin. See Porphyrins.

Affinity, chemical. The chemical affinity of one substance for another is a measure of the tendency of the two substances to enter into chemical combination. The concept of affinity dates from the early days of chemistry. The term 'affinity of a chemical reaction' is now used to denote the change of free energy in the system when the reaction takes place; this is a true measure of the tendency to react.

Agalite. A term used in the paper industry to indicate ground talc used to give body and gloss to paper.

Agar, or agar-agar, consists of a mixture of two polysaccharides, agarose and agaropectin. Agarose, the main constituent, is a well-defined neutral polysaccharide containing 3,6-anhydro-L-galactose and D-galactose as the repetitive unit. Agaropectin, the other polysaccharide component, contains the carboxyl and sulphate groups of native agar. Agarose can be freed from agaropectin by precipitating the latter from solution with cetylpyridinium chloride.

Agar occurs as a cell-wall constituent of the red marine algae *Rhodophyceae*, from which it is extracted by hot water, and marketed as a dry powder, flakes, or strips. It is produced chiefly in Japan. It dissolves in hot water and sets on cooling to a jelly at a concentration as low as 0·5%. Its chief uses are as a solid medium for cultivating micro-organisms, as a thickener in the food industries, and as a laxative.

Agate. A form of silica similar to chalcedony with coloured bands of purple or brown. Used as a gemstone, for making pestles and mortars, and as a bearing surface in scientific instruments.

Age hardening. See Precipitation hardening.

Ageing, in the rubber industry, means the deterioration or perishing of vulcanized rubber, indicated by hardening, cracking, and loss of tensile strength and elasticity. Changes in colour, external aspect, and in physical, mechanical, and chemical properties occur, according to the quality of the rubber and the duration of ageing. Ageing is due to oxidation with air or ozone under the influence of heat and light. Ageing is mitigated by the use of good quality materials, careful control of vulcanizing conditions, storing away from sunlight, and the use of anti-oxidants (*q.v.*). Even minute traces of the salts of some metals, particularly copper and manganese, greatly accelerate the ageing of rubber. Many plastic materials also age.

Aggregate. Pieces of material which are, or can be, united by a cementitious substance or bond, to form a solid mass. In concrete the aggregate consists of crushed stone, slag, or clinker and sand, united by Portland or other cement. In bricks and other ceramic materials, particles of non-plastic materials form the aggregate; they are united by plastic clay when in the green or unfired state and later (in the burned state) by a crude glass which fuses and, on cooling, solidifies and forms the bond. In silica bricks, the silica is the aggregate and the bond is a crude glass formed by the combination of added lime and some of the silica. The sizes, shapes, and mechanical properties of the pieces forming an aggregate have a great influence on the properties of the bonded product.

Agitation. The process of producing motion in a system by means of a mechanical agent with the object of producing mixing. The term is usually applied to the mixing of two liquids or the mixing of a solid with a much larger quantity of liquid, or to the stirring of a liquid to maintain the mass uniform in some respect, e.g. temperature.

Agitators. The stirring elements, e.g. paddles, propellers, turbines, etc., used for producing agitation in a liquid.

Aglucone, Aglycone. The term collectively used for the non-sugar portion of a glucoside (glycoside) which is split off from the sugar on hydrolysis by means of acids or enzymes.

Agricola, George, was born at Glauchau, Saxony, in 1494; he studied medicine and

metallurgy, and his book, 'De Re Metallica,' gives a useful account of metallurgy as it was then. He died at Chemnitz in 1555.

Air. Normal dry air has the following composition by volume:

Nitrogen	.	.	78·08%
Oxygen	.	.	20·94%
Argon	.	.	0·9325%
Carbon dioxide	.	.	0·03%
Neon	.	.	0·0018%
Helium	.	.	0·0005%
Krypton	.	.	0·0001%
Xenon	.	.	0·000009%
Radon	.	.	6×10^{-18}%

The content of water vapour varies between wide limits according to atmospheric conditions. The physical constants of dry air are as follows: d 1·2928 g per litre at 0° and 760 mm pressure; specific heats 0·2396 at constant pressure, 0·1707 at constant volume (ratio, 1·403); coefficient of thermal expansion 0·0003665 per degree between −30° and 200°; gas constant R, $2·1529 \times 10^3$ (pressure in mm, volume in c.c. per g). Air can be liquefied by strong cooling under high pressure, the process being facilitated by the cooling effect produced by rapid expansion of air into a partial vacuum; the liquid is pale blue, owing to the presence of liquid oxygen; its b.p. at atmospheric pressure varies from −192°, when freshly prepared, to −185°, when the more volatile constituent, nitrogen, has boiled off; d=approx. 0·9.

Liquid oxygen or liquid air should never be used in the preparation of low temperature baths with organic liquids since extremely explosive mixtures are very liable to be formed.

Air classifiers. These are devices for producing a classification according to particle size of the dust suspended in a stream of air. There are a number of different types, but in all of them the particles are removed from the air stream by some type of centrifugal action, and one of the primary objects is to achieve a high air throughput and separation efficiency using a relatively small plant. Air classifiers are commonly used with grinding equipment such as ball mills, where they separate solids from the air stream used to remove the ground product from the mill. They are sometimes known as air separators.

Air conveying. A method of conveying particulate solids by using a stream of air or inert gas to carry the particles along. In conventional air conveying systems, such as are extensively used for the handling of grain, the material is blown along by the air, a low material/air ratio being employed. In fluidizing systems there is a high material/air ratio, and the air being intimately mixed with the solid, the mixture assumes fluid properties, e.g. it will flow down a gradient under the action of gravity. These systems are now widely used for moving powders and granular materials.

Air-cooled heat exchangers. Although water is normally used for the cooling of hot fluids in the chemical and process industries, air cooling may be preferable where cooling water is scarce or expensive. Air-cooled heat exchangers consist of a bank of tubes through which the fluid to be cooled is passed, air being blown over them by means of a fan. The tubes are finned to increase the area for heat transfer.

Air filters. These are filters designed to remove atmospheric dust from an air stream. In general they consist of a space packed with a filtering medium, such as hair or glass fibre, through which the air is passed. The medium may either be dry with relatively small pores (*dry filter*), or it may have rather larger pores and be wetted with a viscous liquid to which the dust particles will stick (*viscous filter*).

Air filters differ from other gas filtration equipment in the quantity of solid they have to deal with, and in the fact that the dust is not recovered.

Air gas. See Producer gas.

Air hardening. A method of hardening steel by allowing it to cool naturally in air, or with an air blast (air quenching). It is applicable only to certain alloy steels, in which the critical cooling rate is less than the normal rate of cooling in air.

Air-lift agitator. This is a plant for the leaching of fine solids. It consists of a cylindrical tank in which is mounted a slowly rotating central shaft carrying sludge rakes at the bottom and a distributing launder above the surface of the liquid. The shaft is hollow and serves as an air lift, compressed air being fed to the base of the shaft by a pipe running down inside it. The sludge collecting at the bottom of the tank is swept to the centre by the rakes, elevated in the air lift and discharged on to the rotating launder, whence it is distributed over the surface of the liquid.

Air-lift pump. A method of lifting corrosive liquids in which the liquid to be lifted flows through a U-shaped tube with one limb much longer than the other. Near the base of the long limb compressed air is delivered at a pressure slightly greater than that of the liquid at this point. The air-liquid mixture rises up the limb and is delivered into a suitable receiver in which the air is released.

Air quenching. See Air hardening.

Air separators. See Air classifiers.

Air tinting. Production of oxidation figures on a polished steel surface (which may first be treated with acid) by heating in air in order to show up the structure (heat or temper tinting).

Akins classifier. A type of mechanical classifier in which the solids that have settled out are removed by means of one or more screw conveyors situated at the bottom of the tank.

Alabamine. The name originally suggested for element no. 85, astatine (*q.v.*).

Alabaster. A fine-grained form of the mineral gypsum, $CaSO_4, 2H_2O$, resembling marble in appearance, and sometimes containing handsome veining and mottling. Occurs with gypsum. Sp.gr. 2·30-2·33. Hardness, 2. Alabaster is soft and easy to carve and polish, and may be artificially coloured; it is therefore much used for ornamental purposes. The term alabaster has been applied to a form of calcite (*q.v.*), which is harder, and, unlike true alabaster, cannot be scratched with the finger-nail.

α-Alanine, α-Aminopropionic acid, $C_3H_7NO_2$. $CH_3 \cdot CH(NH_2)COOH$. Crystallizes in rhombic prisms, m.p. 297°, with effervescence. Soluble in 4 to 5 parts of water, insoluble in alcohol. The naturally occurring substance is dextrorotatory $[\alpha]_D^{20} + 2·7°$. It is one of the amino-acids obtained by the hydrolysis of proteins.

β - Alanine,   β - Aminopropionic   acid, $H_2N \cdot CH_2 \cdot CH_2 \cdot COOH$, has m.p. 200°. Is soluble in water, sparingly soluble in alcohol. It can be prepared by heating acrylic acid under pressure with ammonia and by other means. It is of interest as forming part of the molecule of pantothenic acid and is a step in the manufacture of the vitamin both in the laboratory and the living organism.

Albertus Magnus (1193-1280). Albert von Bollstädt or Albertus Magnus, Doctor Universalis, was born at Lauingen in Schwabia. In 1223 he joined the Dominican order, and after several years spent in travel and in teaching, he returned to Cologne with Thomas Aquinas to organize the Studium generale. Later he became Bishop of Ratisbon (1260) and Lector at Cologne (1262). Teacher, preacher, writer, and philosopher, Albertus possessed a great love of experimental science.

Albuminoids. See Scleroproteins.

Albumins. A widely distributed class of proteins, soluble in water and coagulated by heating. They can be distinguished from the rather similar globulins in that they are not precipitated by half saturation with ammonium sulphate. Typical albumins are ovalbumin from eggs and lactalbumin from milk.

Alcian Blue, Ingrain Blue. The dyestuff, Alcian Blue 8GS, was introduced in 1947 by Imperial

Chemical Industries, Ltd. It is a soluble phthalocyanine derivative, made by the chloromethylation of Monastral Fast Blue and the interaction of the product to give an 'ionium' salt of copper methyl phthalocyanine. The dye can be impregnated into the fibre and made insoluble by subsequent treatment.

Alclad. An American trade name for a composite material consisting of duralumin coated with a layer of aluminium of high purity in order to combine mechanical strength with resistance to corrosion. It is one of the standard structural materials for aircraft frames.

Alcohol, Ethyl alcohol, Ethanol, Spirits of wine, C_2H_6O, CH_3CH_2OH, is a colourless liquid with a pleasant odour, d^{15} 0·7936, b.p. 78·32°. Miscible with water with evolution of heat and contraction in volume; pure alcohol absorbs water vapour. Many gases are more soluble in it than in water. Some inorganic salts and many organic compounds are soluble in alcohol. Although the name 'alcohol' seems to be of Arabic origin, it was probably discovered first in Italy during the 13th-15th centuries. It occurs only rarely in nature, except as a result of the fermentation of sugary plant juices by yeasts, and, less often, by certain bacteria and moulds. Alcohol was formerly manufactured almost exclusively by the fermentation of materials containing starch and sugars, but this method is now relatively unimportant. Most is at present made by the catalytic hydration of ethylene, or by the hydrolysis of the mono- and di-ethyl sulphates formed by absorbing ethylene in 90% sulphuric acid. The ethylene is obtained from refinery gases or other petroleum fractions by cracking. Because alcohol forms an azeotrope with water it is not possible to obtain a product containing more than 95·6% alcohol by weight by straightforward fractionation of an aqueous solution. For the manufacture of 100% alcohol azeotropic distillation (*q.v.*) is employed. Alcohol is oxidized to acetaldehyde or acetic acid; with nitric acid a variety of products, including glycollic and oxalic acids are formed. Ethoxides are formed by the action of sodium, calcium, aluminium, and some other metals on alcohol. It reacts with acids to give esters. With sulphuric acid it yields ether, ethylene or ethyl hydrogen sulphate. Bleaching powder converts it to chloroform, while chlorine gives chloral. Ethanol is chiefly used as a starting point for the manufacture of other chemicals, principally acetaldehyde.

Alcoholates. See Alkoxides.

Alcoholometry is the name given to any process for determining the amount of ethyl alcohol in a liquor. In the case of simple mixtures of alcohol and water, a determination of specific gravity at a standard temperature and reference to standard tables will give the percentage of alcohol. For revenue purposes in Great Britain, the Sikes's hydrometer has been adopted as the legal instrument for measuring specific gravities. The original Sikes's instrument could not be used on liquors containing more than 92·5% alcohol by weight: recent production of absolute alcohol on a commerical scale has led to the introduction of a modified hydrometer known as Sikes's B, which can be used over the range 92·5%-100% alcohol by weight. For liquors other than simple alcohol-water mixtures, more complicated methods involving analysis by chemical or physical methods have to be used.

Alcohols are organic compounds containing one or more hydroxyl groups attached directly to carbon atoms. Benzene derivatives having hydroxyl groups joined directly to the carbon atoms of the ring are called phenols and have properties different from those of typical alcohols. Compounds with one —OH group are called monohydric alcohols; those with more than one are di-, tri-, or poly-hydric alcohols. Dihydric alcohols are known as glycols; the most important trihydric alcohol is glycerol; tetra-, penta-, and hexa-hydric alcohols are generally derived from sugars. Monohydric alcohols are given systematic names as derivatives of methyl alcohol, which, for this purpose, is called carbinol. It is more usual to employ names ending in -ol derived from the names of the corresponding paraffin hydrocarbons, e.g. ethanol for ethyl alcohol, isopropanol for isopropyl alcohol. The monohydric alcohols form a series whose lower members are odorous liquids and higher members white, odourless solids. They react with metals such as sodium, calcium, and aluminium to give alkoxides, and with acids to give esters. Sulphuric acid and other agents remove water to form olefins. Primary alcohols on oxidation give aldehydes; secondary alcohols give ketones while tertiary alcohols break down to give compounds containing fewer carbon atoms than the original alcohol.

Alcoholysis is the name given to any reaction in which an alcohol plays a part similar to that of water in hydrolysis. It is essentially a process of exchange, and is most frequently applied to the reaction between an alcohol and an ester whereby the alcohol replaces the alcohol of the ester. Thus mannitol hexacetate and ethyl alcohol give ethyl acetate and mannitol. Such reactions usually proceed more rapidly in presence of small amounts of a sodium alkoxide. In many cases the reaction is reversible and will not go to completion unless a large excess of the first alcohol is present or the other alcohol is removed as fast as it is formed.

Alcosol, Alcogel. These are specific names for colloidal systems in which the dispersion medium is alcohol. Those substances which are able to crystallize out with alcohol of crystallization can generally be made to form alcogels.

Aldehydes are organic compounds containing the group $-C\underset{H}{\overset{\nearrow O}{}}$ joined directly on to another carbon atom: formaldehyde, HCHO, is included in the class, but some of its properties are not those of a typical aldehyde. They are usually colourless liquids (aliphatic) or solids (higher aromatic) with characteristic odours and are oxidized to acids and reduced to primary alcohols. A number of preparations are available: oxidation of a primary alcohol or treatment of a Grignard reagent with ethyl orthoformate are general methods. More modern methods include the selective reduction of carboxylic acid derivatives (e.g. amides, nitriles, acid chlorides) by complex metal hydrides. Aromatic aldehydes may be prepared by heating aromatic hydrocarbons with carbon monoxide, hydrogen chloride, anhydrous aluminium chloride and cuprous chloride (Gattermann-Koch synthesis). The treatment of alkaline solutions of phenols with chloroform (Riemer-Tiemann reaction) has also allowed the synthesis of phenolic aldehydes via a dichlorocarbene (see carbene) intermediate.

Most aliphatic and aromatic aldehydes give compounds with alkali bisulphites and form cyanhydrins, aldoximes (*q.v.*), semicarbazones, and phenylhydrazones. Aldehydes, unlike ketones, restore the pink colour to Schiff's reagent, and reduce ammoniacal silver nitrate and Fehling's solution. They also form acetals with alcohols. Aliphatic aldehydes form aldehyde ammonias, and some undergo the aldol condensation. Aromatic aldehydes form unsaturated acids when heated with the sodium salt of a fatty acid and its anhydride (Perkin reaction). They form Schiff's bases with primary amines and react with phenols and dimethyl-aniline to give triphenylmethane derivatives. All aromatic aldehydes and some aliphatic aldehydes undergo the Cannizzaro reaction.

Aldehyde hardeners. Many aldehydes and acetals are effective cross-linking agents for gelatin. Thus, glyoxal, its polymers and its cyclic hemi-acetal, 2,3-dihydroxydioxan, are powerful hardeners for use in photography. Other useful aldehydes include succinaldehyde, mucochloric acid and the products of periodate oxidation of polysaccharides. The latter polymers, for example oxystarch, can be used

in multilayer materials where differential hardening of layers is required.

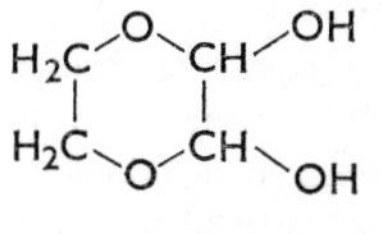

2,3-dihydroxydioxan 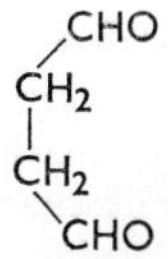   succinaldehyde

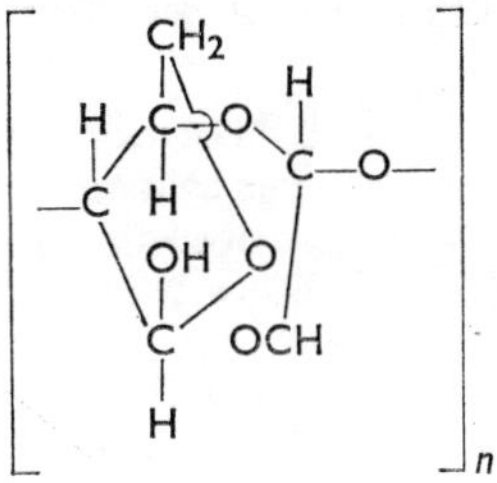

oxystarch

Alder, Kurt (1902-1958). Trained at Berlin and Kiel Universities, Alder became professor at Cologne in 1934, a director of research in the Bayer dye works in 1936, and Rector of the Chemical Institute at Cologne in 1940. He shared the Nobel Prize for Chemistry for 1950 with Otto Diels, under whom he had been a student, for their development of the diene synthesis.

Aldol, Acetaldol, β-Hydroxybutaldehyde, $C_4H_8O_2$, $CH_3CHOHCH_2CHO$, is a colourless oily liquid, d^{16} 1·1094, b.p. 83°/20 mm. Miscible with water. Manufactured by treating acetaldehyde with alkali carbonates, lime, borates, and other alkaline condensing agents. Distillation at atmospheric pressure causes some decomposition to crotonaldehyde. Traces of mineral acid aid the reaction. Aldol slowly changes to a solid, paraldol, m.p. 82°. Reduction with hydrogen under pressure gives 1,3-butylene glycol. It reduces ammoniacal silver nitrate. Used to prepare crotonaldehyde and butylene glycol.

Aldol condensation. A reaction between two molecules of an aliphatic aldehyde whereby a β-hydroxyaldehyde is formed. The simplest case is that of acetaldehyde which gives aldol, $CH_3CHOHCH_2CHO$. The reaction is carried out at a low temperature in presence of a catalyst, usually potassium cyanide, sodium acetate, or dilute sodium hydroxide. Only those aldehydes containing the $-CH_2 \cdot CHO$ grouping can react in this way: other aldehydes undergo the Cannizzaro reaction. The β-hydroxyaldehydes readily lose water to give unsaturated aldehydes. Aliphatic ketones react in a similar manner with aliphatic ketones or aldehydes and with some aromatic aldehydes to give β-hydroxyketones, which also readily lose water, giving unsaturated ketones.

Aldonic acid. An acid derived from an aldose by oxidation of the aldehyde group to a carboxyl group, e.g. gluconic acid.

Aldose. An aldose is a sugar containing a potential aldehyde (CHO) group. The group may be obscured by its inclusion in a ring system, but is obvious if the structure of the sugar is expressed by the old straight chain formula. Aldoses are called aldopentoses, aldohexoses, etc., according to the number of carbon atoms they contain.

Aldosterone, $C_{21}H_{28}O_5$. The most active known steroid hormone secreted by the adrenal cortex, first detected (as 'electrocortin') by Simpson and Tait (1952). The main activity of aldosterone is 'mineralocorticoid', i.e. controlling the balance of electrolytes in the body. An effective dose in Addison's disease is about 0·1 mg per day. The structure has been confirmed by a number of syntheses.

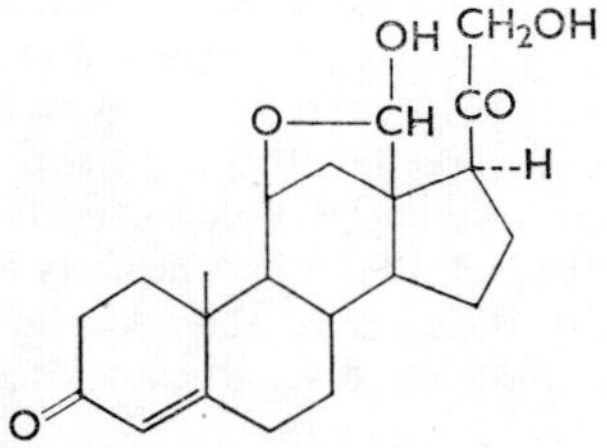

Aldosterone

Aldoximes are compounds formed by the action of hydroxylamine on aldehydes. They contain the group —CH=NOH. They are also formed by the oxidation of primary amines by permono-sulphuric acid. The aliphatic aldoximes are colourless liquids or low-melting solids, some of which are soluble in water. Aromatic aldoximes are crystalline solids, e.g. benzaldoximes. All aldoximes are capable of existing in two stereo-isomeric forms known as the *syn-* and the *anti-* modifications, but in practice only the *anti-* form

anti-aldoxime   syn-aldoxime

is isolated from most aliphatic aldehydes. Aromatic aldehydes yield *syn*-aldoximes which may frequently be isomerized by hydrogen chloride to the *anti*-aldoximes. The *syn*-aldoximes yield acetyl derivatives with acetyl chloride but the *anti*- forms are dehydrated to the corresponding nitriles R—CN. Dilute mineral acids may regenerate the aldehyde and hydroxylamine hydrochloride.

Aldrin is the common name for the insecticidal product containing not less than 95% w/w of 1,2,3,4,10,10-hexachloro-1,4,4a,5,8,8a-hexa-hydro-*exo*-1,4-*endo*-5,8-dimethanonaphthalene.

The pure substance has a m.p. of 104°-105°. Aldrin is obtained from the Diels-Alder

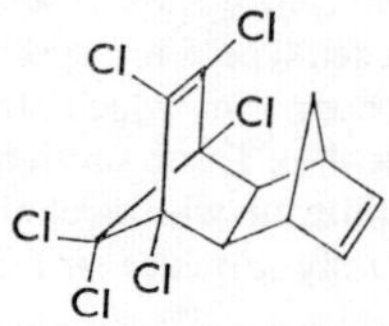

addition product of cyclopentadiene and vinyl chloride by dehydrochlorination followed by condensation with hexachlorocyclopentadiene. It is insoluble in water and soluble in most organic solvents.

Aldrin is insecticidally active as a contact and stomach poison against a wide range of soil pests. Aldrin is available in the technical form and also formulated as wettable powders, dust concentrates, emulsifiable concentrates, and granules. It is non-phytotoxic and does not cause taint.

In common with other chlorinated hydro-carbons, aldrin is toxic to humans and animals. It can be absorbed by ingestion, inhalation and through the skin and is stored in the body, particularly in the fat. It should therefore be handled with care at all times. In recent years chlorinated insecticides such as aldrin have become less used.

The epoxy derivative of aldrin is dieldrin (*q.v.*).

Algaroth. See Antimony oxychlorides.

Alginic acid. A polymer of D-mannuronic acid, with the formula:

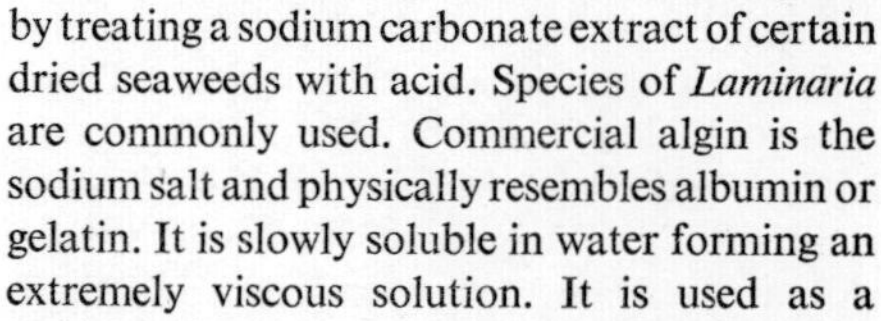

It is obtained as a highly gelatinous precipitate by treating a sodium carbonate extract of certain dried seaweeds with acid. Species of *Laminaria* are commonly used. Commercial algin is the sodium salt and physically resembles albumin or gelatin. It is slowly soluble in water forming an extremely viscous solution. It is used as a stabilizer for ice cream and other food products and pharmaceutical preparations, as a dressing in the textile industry, and for preventing incrustation in boilers. Calcium alginate can be spun into a thread suitable for rayon. Ammonium alginate is also used commercially.

Alicyclic. Alicyclic compounds are cyclic carbon compounds which do not possess a benzene ring with its system of conjugated double bonds. They are cyclic compounds with aliphatic characteristics. For examples cyclopropane, cyclohexane.

Aliphatic. An adjective used in organic chemistry to denote that the compound in question has its carbon atoms in chains and not in closed rings. It was originally used to describe the fats and fatty acids, which are typical of this structure.

Alitizing. Method of producing a protective film on iron, steel, copper, or brass by slowly heating the metal in a mixture of powdered aluminium, alumina, and ammonium chloride (the proportions and temperature varying according to the metal under treatment) in an inert gas. The coating is said to prevent oxidation below 1000°, and to give improved resistance at higher temperatures.

Alizarin, Mordant Red 11, $C_{14}H_8O_4$. Orange-red

needles are formed by sublimation, m.p. 290°. Insoluble in cold water, readily soluble in alcohol and ether, dissolves with a purple-red colour in alkaline solutions, from which it is precipitated as red to violet 'lakes' on the addition of heavy metal salts.

Occurs as a glucoside in madder. Produced synthetically by fusing anthraquinone-β-sulphonic acid with caustic soda and a little potassium chlorate.

It is always used in the form of a paste with water. It is an example of a polygenetic mordant dyestuff since the material to be dyed must first be impregnated with a metallic hydroxide and the shade produced varies with the nature of the hydroxide. The impregnation may be effected by soaking the material in the metal acetate and then precipitating the hydroxide in the fibre by steaming. Aluminium hydroxide gives a bright red lake, chromium hydroxide a different shade of red, and ferric hydroxide a violet lake. The dyeing is carried out in boiling aqueous solution.

Alizarin yellow GG, Mordant Yellow 1, is a

dyestuff belonging to the group of oxyazo dyes, and is prepared from diazotized *m*-nitraniline and salicylic acid. It is used in dyeing either on a chrome mordant or by simple bath or after chrome methods.

Alkali. A hydroxide of one of the alkali metals lithium, sodium, potassium, rubidium, and caesium. In a wider sense the word is used to include such substances as calcium oxide or hydroxide, sodium carbonate, and ammonium carbonate. Since all these substances, in solution in water, increase the hydroxyl ion concentration, the term alkali is synonymous with the term base so long as it refers to aqueous solutions only. An alkaline aqueous solution is one with pH greater than 7.

Alkali metals. The metals Li, Na, K, Rb, Cs and Fr. All are very electropositive with an s^1 outer electron shell.

Alkaline earths. In the past the name 'earth' was given to non-metallic substances, insoluble in water, and unchanged by fire. Lime, magnesia, baryta, and strontia were found to have an alkaline reaction, and hence were called alkaline earths. The name 'alkaline earth metals' is now given to the bipositive elements of group 2 of the periodic table—magnesium, calcium, strontium, barium, and radium.

Alkaloid reagents. A generic name for a number of reagents, most of which are acids with complex negative ions, which give precipitates with alkaloids. The alkaloid reagents include chloroplatinic, phosphotungstic, phosphomolybdic, ferrocyanic, tannic, picric, and sulphosalicylic acids, and potassium iodomercurate (II). They also precipitate proteins.

Alkaloids are organic substances existing in combination with organic acids in great variety in many plants, and to which many drugs owe their medicinal properties. Many of them are very poisonous, and even in minute doses produce characteristic physiological effects. They vary considerably in their chemical properties and constitutions; the majority of them are crystalline and non-volatile, and contain carbon, hydrogen, oxygen, and nitrogen, but a few are devoid of oxygen, and are volatile liquids. All alkaloids have basic characteristics, and combine with acids to form crystalline salts, which are usually water-soluble. The majority of alkaloids are only very sparingly soluble in water, but are usually readily soluble in organic solvents such as alcohol, chloroform, and ether.

In the commercial extraction of alkaloids from the drugs in which they exist, the powdered drug, or an alcoholic extract of it, is treated with an alkali such as ammonia or lime to liberate the alkaloid from its combinations, and the alkaloid is then extracted by means of an organic solvent. The crude material thus obtained is freed from impurities by various methods, and finally purified by crystallization either of the base itself or of its water-soluble salts.

They occur chiefly in flowering plants, especially in the *Ranunculaceae, Papaveraceae,* and *Solanaceae,* but are widespread throughout the botanical kingdom. They often occur not as single alkaloids but as a mixture with rather similar alkaloids. The biogenesis of many alkaloids has been elucidated by feeding selected plants with radioactive chemicals, isolating the alkaloid, and chemically degrading it to determine the location of the radioactive site(s). It is known that they can be formed from various amino-acids combining with formate or methionine, or acetate, or mevalonate, or various higher transformation products of these including shikimic acid and terpenes. Many alkaloids are derivatives of pyridine, quinoline, isoquinoline, or pyrimidine. If solids they are crystalline: they are optically active and most of them are dextrorotatory. They include a number of important drugs, e.g. morphine, narcotine, theobromine, caffeine, nicotine, atropine, cocaine, hyoscyamine, quinine, cinchonine, strychnine, brucine, and pilocarpine. Their part in the physiology of plants is not known.

A minor chemical use for many of the commoner alkaloids is the resolution of racemic compounds (often acids) into their optically active enantiomorphs.

Alkanals are aldehydes derived by replacing two hydrogen atoms of the terminal methyl group of an alkane by an oxygen atom.

Alkanes. See Paraffins.

Alkanolamines, Alkylolamines, are hydroxyamines produced by the reaction of an alkene oxide with aqueous ammonia at 50°-60°. They are hygroscopic solids of low m.p., and usually occur as rather viscous, colourless liquids of ammoniacal odour. They are used as accelerators in rubber manufacture, as catalysts in certain polymerization reactions, and as absorbents for acidic gases such as carbon dioxide and hydrogen sulphide. They form soaps with fatty acids; these are almost neutral in reaction and are used as detergents and emulsifying agents. See Ethanolamines.

Alkanols are alcohols, derived by replacing a hydrogen atom of an alkane by a hydroxyl group.

Alkathene. A trade name for plastics based largely on polyethylene (*q.v.*).

Alkenes. See Olefins.

Alkoxides are compounds formed by the action of certain metals upon alcohols. They may be regarded as hydroxides in which the hydrogen atoms are replaced by alkyl groups. The alkoxides of the transition metals may have to be prepared by indirect methods. Many are of great interest because of their volatility. Alkoxides are used as reagents in chemical reactions and as catalysts.

Alkyd resins. The original materials, also known as glyptal resins, were introduced in 1914. They were produced by the condensation of glycerol and phthalic anhydride. Although such thermosetting resins were used initially as binders in certain plastics moulding compositions, they were slow curing, and consequently are now little used. Alkyd resins are most widely used in the paint industry, both directly and modified by the inclusion of drying oil fatty acids in the resin condensate. Paints based on styrenated alkyd resins are also in common use. Quick curing polyester moulding materials are now available based on unsaturated polyester resins (*q.v.*). These compositions are widely known as alkyd moulding materials.

Alkyl. The residue left when a hydrogen atom is removed from an aliphatic hydrocarbon is called an alkyl radical, as, for example methyl, CH_3—; ethyl, C_2H_5—, etc. Some of these true radicals are formed when certain organo-metallic compounds, e.g. lead tetraethyl, are decomposed by heat under reduced pressure. They may also be produced by thermal degradation of alkanes, as is performed in certain petrochemical processes, and by expulsion of carbon monoxide from acyl radicals produced by photochemically cleaving ketones. Depending upon the concentration of radicals produced and their environment, they may either combine with another radical, eliminate an atom or group as a radical leaving an alkene, or abstract an atom from another molecule to produce a new radical. See Triphenylmethyl.

Alkylation. The production of branched chain hydrocarbons by reacting alkenes with isoparaffins or aromatics; e.g. the production of high anti-knock fuels or synthetic detergents intermediates.

Alkylenes. See Olefins.

Alkylolamines. See Alkanolamines.

Alkyne. A systematic name corresponding to the trivial name acetylene. Thus methylacetylene CH_3—$C\equiv C$—H is properly called propyne, dimethylacetylene CH_3—$C\equiv C$—CH_3, is called but-2-yne, etc. In general, such names correspond to the systematic name for the saturated hydrocarbon, and the alkene.

Allantoin, Glyoxyldiureide, $C_4H_6N_4O_3$.

Crystallizes in prisms, m.p. 235°-236°. Sparingly soluble in cold water, soluble in hot water and alcohol. Allantoin is the end product of purine metabolism, and is excreted in the urine of most mammals, exceptions being man, the anthropoid apes, and the Dalmatian dog.

Allene, 1,2-Propadiene, $CH_2{=}C{=}CH_2$, is a colourless gas prepared by the electrolysis of potassium itaconate, or by the action of zinc and alcohol on 1,3-dibromopropane. It is easily isomerized to propyne (methylacetylene), and is produced as a mixture with this substance from some reactions.

Allenes are 1,2 dienes having the $\diagup C{=}C{=}C\diagdown$ skeleton and general formula C_nH_{2n-2}. They are derivatives of allene (*q.v.*) and are isomeric with alkynes. They undergo typical reactions of alkenes with, e.g., hydrogen, hydrogen halides, halogens, etc., but have not been extensively investigated, probably because pure allenes are not easily prepared and are not stable indefinitely. They are not as stable as alkenes with conjugated, or isolated, double bonds. The action of base is usually sufficient to encourage isomerization to an alkyne. Allenes are usually colourless liquids with garlic-like odours but the higher members are solids. They are prepared by removal of bromine and hydrogen bromide from 1,2-dibromopropane derivatives, usually by zinc and alcohol. Unlike terminal acetylenes they do not form salts with metals.

Allethrin, $C_{19}H_{26}O_3$, 2-allyl-4-hydroxy-3-methyl-2-cyclopenten-1-one crysanthemum monocarboxylate was developed as a result of research to elucidate the structure of natural pyrethrin. It has the formula:

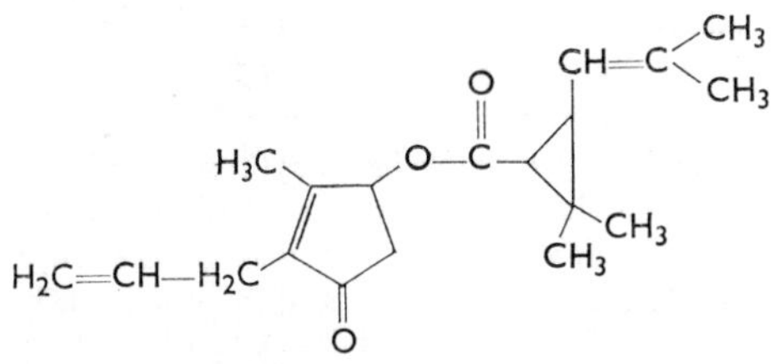

and is a mixture of 4 racemic or 8 optical isomers. Technical allethrin is a viscous liquid of density 1·005, soluble in alcohol, kerosine, and carbon tetrachloride, but not in water. It is formulated in the same way as natural pyrethrin, and has similar toxicity to many insects, notably the house-fly. Piperonyl butoxide has been used as a synergist. Large scale production followed closely after the synthesis in the laboratory and replaced much of the natural product.

Allo-. The prefix allo- before the name of an organic compound indicates that two compounds have the same empirical formula. With sterols and related substances the prefix allo- should indicate that rings A and B are in the trans position to each other, but allocholesterol is an exception. Allomucic acid is an optical isomer of mucic acid.

Allobarbitone, $C_{10}H_{12}N_2O_3$, is diallylbarbituric

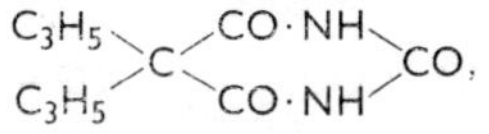

acid, a white crystalline powder, m.p. 172°-174°. Sparingly soluble in cold water; soluble in alcohol, ether, and alkaline solutions. It has hypnotic properties similar to barbitone but its action is less prolonged. For manufacture, see Barbiturates.

Allophanic acid, Carbamylcarbamic acid, $C_2H_4N_2O_3$, $NH_2CONHCOOH$, is not known in the free state as it breaks down immediately to urea and carbon dioxide. The ammonium, barium, calcium, and sodium salts are known and are prepared by treating ethyl allophanate with the appropriate hydroxide. The esters with alcohols and phenols are crystalline solids, sparingly soluble in water and alcohol. They are formed by passing cyanic acid into alcohols or a solution of an alcohol or phenol in benzene. The amide of allophanic acid is known as biuret. Alcohols are sometimes isolated from mixtures and identified by means of their allophanates.

Allose. See Hexose.

Allotelluric acid, H_2TeO_4. See Telluric acid.

Allotropy. Many elements can exist in more than one physical form, e.g. oxygen and ozone; ortho- and para-hydrogen; rhombic sulphur and monoclinic sulphur. Such elements are said to show *allotropy*, and the various different forms are termed *allotropes*. The allotropes of an element consist of the atoms of the element linked together to form different molecules, or different crystals. They have, therefore, different energy contents, which are exhibited in their different chemical and physical properties. Compounds also exist in different physical forms, but the term allotropy is not generally used to cover this phenomenon.

Alloxan, Mesoxalylurea, $C_4H_2N_2O_4$. Crystal-

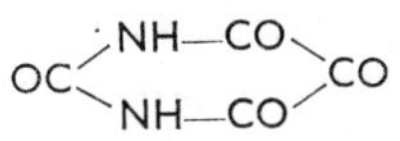

lizes as the tetrahydrate in rhombic prisms with the structure:

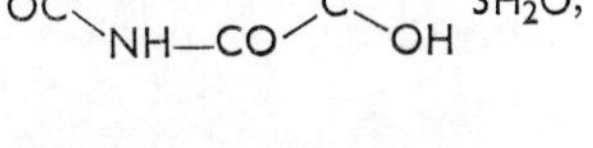

21

losing three of the water molecules with efflorescence, and the fourth at 150°. Decomposes at 170°. Soluble in water and alcohol. It is prepared by the careful oxidation of uric acid or xanthine, or more readily by treating alloxantin with strong nitric acid.

Alloxantin, $C_8H_6N_4O_8$. Crystallizes in prisms

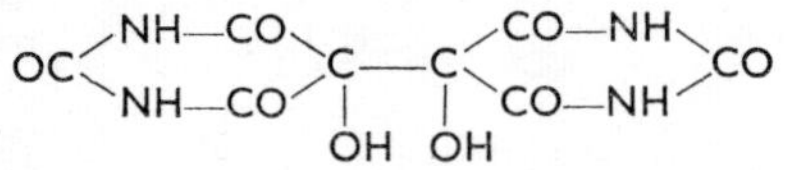

with two molecules of water, decomposing at 253°-255°. Sparingly soluble in water. It is found among the products of hydrolysis of the glycoside convicin from soya-beans or vetches and in small amounts in beets. It can be prepared by oxidizing uric acid or reducing alloxan. It has a toxic effect, particularly on cold-blooded animals.

Alloy. An intimate association of two or more metals, or of a metal and one or more non-metallic elements (gaseous, liquid, or solid), the complex possessing in a marked degree all or most of those characteristics commonly described as metallic. Pure metals are too soft and possess insufficient strength for most engineering purposes. Alloying is one of the common methods of increasing strength and hardness. Where the properties of the alloy are markedly affected by the presence of mechanically admixed inclusions of a non-metallic nature, such inclusions are not to be considered as integral parts of the alloy (e.g. the silicate or slag inclusions in wrought iron). Where a non-metallic component exists in the free form as an inclusion by virtue of the physical conditions imposed upon the alloy during freezing and where, by appropriate adjustment of composition or of physical conditions, such an inclusion can become intimately associated with the alloy, then such a component must be considered as a definite alloying component (e.g. graphite in cast iron). Whether an alloy consists of a homogeneous solid solution or of one or more disperse phases embedded in a matrix constituting the bulk of the alloy, statistically uniform distribution of the components is presupposed.

Alloy cast irons. See Cast irons.

Alloy elements. Elements added to give special properties to alloys, such as resistance to corrosion, heat, creep, etc. (e.g. the addition of chromium, tungsten, molybdenum, vanadium, etc., to ferrous alloys).

Alloy steels. See Steel.

D-**Allulose,** also called D-psicose, a ketohexose which has been isolated as its phenylosazone from distillery slops.

The free sugar has been obtained as a syrup $[\alpha]_D^{20} + 2\cdot9°$.

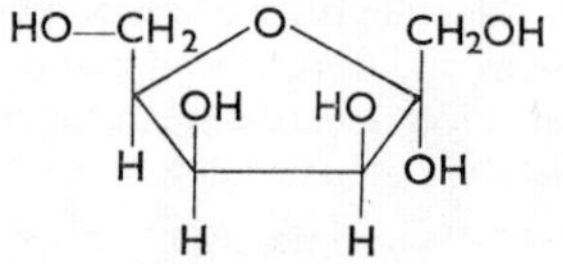

Allyl. The name given to the group $CH_2:CHCH_2—$.

Allyl alcohol, Propenol, C_3H_6O. A colourless
$$CH_2:CHCH_2OH$$
liquid with a pungent odour, d_4^{20} $0\cdot8520$, b.p. 96·9°. Miscible with water and alcohol. Prepared by heating glycerol with oxalic acid, or by reduction of acrolein. Manufacture: (a) direct chlorination of propylene at 500° followed by hydrolysis of the allyl chloride formed; (b) reaction of acrolein and isopropanol (both derived from propylene) at 400° in the presence of a catalyst. It combines quantitatively with bromine, and may be estimated by this means. Forms insoluble compounds with mercury salts, and is oxidized to glycerol by potassium permanganate. Silver oxide produces acrolein and acrylic acid.

Allyl derivatives of metals. The allyl group can bond to transition metals in two ways. There can be a σ bond between the allyl group and the metal or the double bond can also be further bonded to the metal to give a π-allyl derivative.

Allylene. See Propyne.

Allylic rearrangement. The migration of a double bond in a three carbon system from carbon atoms one and two to carbon atoms two and three. The substituent simultaneously migrates from carbon atom three to carbon atom one.

$$\overset{1}{C}=\overset{2}{C}-\overset{3}{C}-X \rightleftharpoons X-\overset{1}{C}-\overset{2}{C}=\overset{3}{C}$$

The simplest example involves the hydrolysis of crotyl chloride to give crotyl alcohol and α-methylallyl alcohol. An intermediate allyl (crotyl, etc.) carbonium ion is involved, which can react with a nucleophile at either end of the delocalized system.

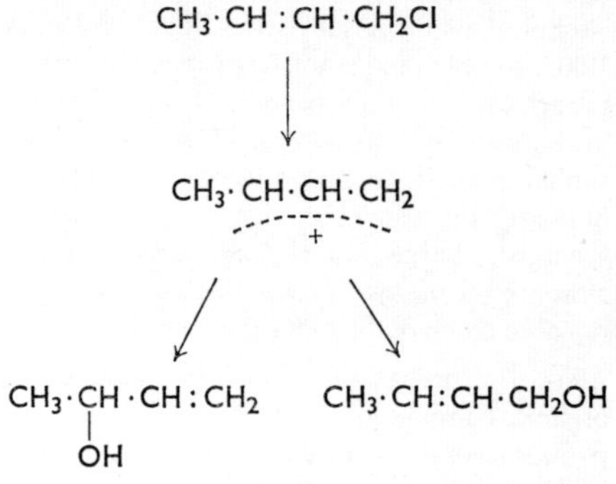

$$CH_3 \cdot CH : CH \cdot CH_2Cl$$

$$CH_3 \cdot CH \cdot CH \cdot CH_2$$

$$CH_3 \cdot CH \cdot CH : CH_2 \qquad CH_3 \cdot CH : CH \cdot CH_2OH$$
$$\;\;\;\;|$$
$$\;\;\;OH$$

Allyl isothiocyanate, Mustard oil, C_4H_5NS, $CH_2{=}CHCH_2NCS$, is a colourless liquid with an intensely pungent odour, d^{15} $1{\cdot}0155$, b.p. $151°$. Sparingly soluble in water; soluble in alcohol and ether. Forms the chief constituent of the oil derived from black mustard. Manufactured by treating a solution of allyl iodide in alcohol with potassium thiocyanate. Reacts with ammonia to give allyl thiourea. It is a strong vesicant and is used, suitably diluted, as a counter-irritant and rubefacient.

Allyl sulphide, Oil of garlic, $C_6H_{10}S$, $(CH_2{:}CHCH_2)_2S$, is a colourless liquid with a pronounced garlic-like odour, b.p. $138{\cdot}6°$. Slightly soluble in water. It occurs in garlic, and is prepared by the action of potassium sulphide on mustard oil at $100°$. Crystalline compounds are formed with platinum and mercuric chlorides and with silver nitrate.

Allylthiourea, Thiosinamine, Rhodallin, $C_4H_8N_2S$, $CH_2{:}CHCH_2NHCSNH_2$, is a colourless crystalline solid with a faint garlic-like odour, m.p. $74°$. Soluble in water and alcohol; insoluble in benzene. Manufactured by treating allyl isothiocyanate with a solution of ammonia in alcohol. It has been given by injection in the treatment of conditions associated with the formation of excessive fibrous tissue. Toxic side reactions may occur.

Allylthiourea is a chemical sensitizer for photographic silver halide emulsions. The addition of minute quantities of the compound to an emulsion increases the sensitivity to light of the final coated product. This occurs by way of a complex formed between the thiourea and silver halide, which decomposes to produce silver sulphide specks (sensitivity specks) on the grain surface. The quantity of allylthiourea added is critical. Excess above the optimum amount causes emulsion fog.

Alnico alloys. Brand names for a series of carbon-free aluminium-nickel-cobalt alloys, with up to 15% Al, 20% Ni, 25% Co, some titanium and the rest iron. They are used for permanent magnets.

Aloin is a mixture of the crystalline principles from aloes, which is the dried juice from the leaves of various species of aloes. It is a yellowish powder, with a characteristic faint sour odour, and is administered with other drugs in pill or tablet form as an aperient or purgative. Aloin is a mixture, of which barbaloin is the most important constituent, of compounds of sugars and hydroxyanthraquinone derivatives.

Alpha particle, α-ray. A He^{2+} ion, i.e. a helium nucleus with no planetary electrons. α-Particles are emitted with high velocity, of the order of 2×10^9 cm per second, by radium and other radioactive substances; they can travel for distances of several centimetres in air and other gases at normal pressures, causing these gases temporarily to become feeble conductors of electricity ('ionization'). Collision of α-particles with zinc sulphide or other substances causes flashes of light, which enable individual particles to be counted (Crookes's 'spinthariscope'). For the detection and estimation of alpha particles, see Counters.

α-Particles may be used, either with or without acceleration, as bombarding agents in nuclear disintegration reactions.

The energy, and thus the range, of α-particles, is characteristic of the source of emission.

Altrose. See Hexose.

Alum, Potash alum. Alum, or potash alum, $KAl(SO_4)_2 \cdot 12H_2O$, is a substance which crystallizes in large colourless octahedra ($a = 12{\cdot}1$ Å, 4 mols. in unit cell). Its solubility in water at $10°$ is $8{\cdot}49$ parts per 100 parts of water. Its crystals on exposure to the air become white, owing to the production of a basic salt. The alum undergoes complete dehydration at $240°$. When heated at a dull red heat, a porous friable mass is formed, which is known as *burnt alum*. A mineral approximating in composition to potash alum occurs in nature. An allied mineral, alunite (*q.v.*) may be used as a source of alum. Other common starting materials for the manufacture of alum are aluminium schists and shales, which contain aluminium silicate and iron pyrites. The latter furnishes the sulphuric acid required, potassium sulphate or chloride being derived from an independent source. Alum is used in the dyeing industries for the production of mordants and pigments, in dressing leather, sizing paper, in water-proofing fabrics, in fireproofing, in gelatin hardening and medicinally as a styptic and astringent.

Alumaloyd. Aluminium-coated sheets which can be worked without injury to the coating.

Alumetizing. Method of producing a protective coating on metal which is sprayed with aluminium, coated to prevent oxidation and provide a flux, and then subjected to heat.

Alumina. See Aluminium oxide.

Alumina gel. A colloidal (gel) form of aluminium hydroxide prepared by precipitation from a solution of aluminium chloride by ammonia, washing and partially dehydrating by heat. No change of structure occurs on heating below $800°$, but above that temperature inversion to α-alumina (corundum) occurs. The principal uses of alumina gel are for drying gases and for removing moisture or any other substances adsorbed by the gel. Medicinally it has useful antacid properties. It is more stable than silica gel and removes water more rapidly.

Aluminates. A large group of compounds which formally contain aluminium in anionic complexes. True anionic complexes containing $[Al(OH)_4]^-$, $[Al(OH)_4(H_2O)_2]^-$, or similar anions may be prepared by adding excess alkali or alkaline earth hydroxide to freshly prepared aluminium hydroxide and solid aluminates may be derived from these solutions by precipitation. Aluminates formed in the absence of water by fusing together a metal oxide and aluminium oxide are mixed metal oxides (*q.v.*) and contain Al^{3+} ions surrounded tetrahedrally or octahedrally by oxygen atoms. Sodium aluminate is prepared commercially by dissolving bauxite in sodium hydroxide solution; it is used as a mordant, in the manufacture of bricks, for sizing paper, and in water softening. Barium aluminate is an efficient but costly water-softening agent. Calcium aluminates enter into the composition of Portland cements.

Aluminised high explosives. Two kinds of aluminised high explosive, torpex and minol, were introduced in Britain during the 1939-45 war. Torpex consists of a mixture of TNT/cyclonite/aluminium, the proportions of which can be varied according to the requirements of the user. Minol consists of a mixture of ammonium nitrate/TNT/aluminium, usually in the proportion 42/38/20.

The presence of the aluminium not only increases the power of these explosives but brings about an economy in the use of cyclonite (*q.v.*). During the war this was of particular importance since cyclonite was relatively scarce. Torpex is used mainly in torpedoes and depth charges, and minol, although not normally used in peace-time owing to the hygroscopic nature of ammonium nitrate, was used in considerable amounts for underwater mines during the war when long storage was not needed. Many varieties of torpex now exist, the composition being adjusted to give more or less shock in relation to bubble energy as the occasion demands.

The German Navy used a mixture of hexanitrodiphenylamine (HND), TNT and aluminium for warheads in the early part of the war. HND is, however, very toxic and was not used in Britain.

Aluminium. Al. At.no. 13, At.wt. 26·97. A bluish-white metal of high tensile strength, capable of taking a high polish, and notable for its lightness. Sp.gr. 2·703, m.p. 659·7°, b.p. 2460°. Occurs naturally in silicate rocks, in clays, as hydrated aluminium oxide (e.g. in bauxite, $Al_2O_3,2H_2O$) and as cryolite, Na_3AlF_6. Aluminium forms 7·3% of the earth's crust. Manufactured by electrolysis of purified bauxite, dissolved in molten cryolite, using carbon electrodes; the product is 99% pure, the chief impurities being iron or silicon. Powdered aluminium combines vigorously with the oxygen in certain metallic oxides, the reaction usually being started by heating at one point by burning magnesium and barium peroxide (Thermit process). The pure metal is almost unattacked by pure water, but traces of impurities in the metal may set up electrochemical corrosion, whilst salt or sea-water rapidly corrodes the metal. Very pure aluminium may be prepared by the electrolysis of the compound $NaF \cdot 2Al(C_2H_5)_3$.

Mineral acids dissolve it, forming aluminium salts, in which the metal is tripositive. Alkalis also dissolve aluminium, forming aluminates containing $[Al(OH)_n]^{3-n}$ anions. The metal is too soft to have many applications but its alloys are important for their light weight and strength, and so are much used in the engineering and aircraft industries. The pure metal is used in overhead electric cables; small quantities are used as a deoxidant in steelmaking.

Aluminium acetate, $Al(OOCCH_3)_3$. Prepared by dissolving aluminium hydroxide in acetic acid, or by adding lead or barium acetate to a solution of aluminium sulphate. Usually occurs in the solid state as a basic salt, of which several are known (e.g. $Al(OH)(C_2H_3O_2)_2$;

$$Al_2O(C_2H_3O_2)_4).$$

Soluble in water, the solution is extensively hydrolysed and contains various complex aluminium-hydroxy species and may even contain colloidal aluminium hydroxide. Much used in dyeing as a mordant, particularly mixed with aluminium sulphate (giving 'red liquor'), or aluminium nitrate. Also used in sizing paper, hardening cardboard, proofing paper and fabrics, in tanning, and in pharmacy as an antiseptic and astringent.

Aluminium alkoxides, $Al(OCR)_3$. See Aluminium butoxide, ethoxide, isopropoxide.

Aluminium alkyls. Organic compounds of aluminium with the general formula $Al(C_nH_{2n+1})_3$. They are used in the Ziegler process for the manufacture of high density Polythene. Long chain hydrocarbons—e.g. for use in the preparation of detergents and fats—are produced by the action of olefins on aluminium alkyls. Aluminium alkyls are produced by direct reaction of aluminium or an aluminium alloy with an alkyl halide.

Aluminium alloys are important for their combination of light weight, strength and generally good corrosion resistance. The high strength Duralumin and 'Y' type alloys are as strong as mild steel having a tensile strength of almost 30 t.s.i. These alloys contain up to 4% copper with smaller quantities of manganese, magnesium, silicon, iron and nickel. The high strength is obtained by the partial precipitation of $CuAl_2$ and Mg_2Si on ageing. Such high strength alloys are difficult to form or shape. For easy hot extrusion the less strong alloy containing about 1% magnesium and silicon is often used. (Tensile strength 20 t.s.i.). For cold forming, alloys are solid solution hardened by 1% manganese or 2% magnesium, while for best corrosion resistance, particularly to salt water, 4%-8% magnesium is added. For high strength castings, the precipitation hardening alloy containing nickel is used; the 10% silicon eutectic alloy is a much superior alloy as far as casting properties are concerned but is less ductile and not very strong (12 t.s.i.). This latter alloy must be modified by the addition of 0·05% sodium to avoid the formation of a coarse structure. A less common alloy containing 7% zinc has a tensile strength of 40 t.s.i.

Aluminium bromide, $AlBr_3$. The anhydrous salt forms white hexagonal crystals, m.p. 97·1°-97·5°, b.p. 255°, prepared by the action of liquid bromine on aluminium, or by passing bromine vapour over a heated mixture of alumina and charcoal. It is very hygroscopic and readily soluble in water, bromine, and many organic solvents. Hydrates with 1, 3, 6 and 15 H_2O are known, and a number of amines have been described. In the solid and liquid states aluminium bromide exists as Al_2Br_6; the vapour is Al_2Br_6 at 440°, and dissociates to $AlBr_3$ molecules at higher temperatures. The bromide can be used in a similar way to aluminium chloride in the Friedel-Crafts reaction.

Aluminium bronze. See bronze.

Aluminium t-butoxide, $Al(OC(CH_3)_3)_3$. Has very similar properties to aluminium isopropoxide (q.v.). In addition it is used, in conjunction with a large excess of acetone, in the oxidation of secondary alcohols to ketones (Oppenauer oxidation).

Aluminium carbide, Al_4C_3. Transparent hexagonal yellow crystals, black powder, or a fused mass, density 2·36, m.p. > 2200°; prepared by strongly heating aluminium or alumina with carbon, or by heating aluminium in a stream of carbon monoxide. Attacked by dilute acids or alkalis, or slowly by water, giving methane. Aluminium carbide reduces metallic oxides to the metals, or alloys of the metals with aluminium, on heating. The use has been proposed of the carbide as a refractory material, and as a starting-point for the manufacture of aluminium.

Aluminium chloride, $AlCl_3$. Colourless or yellowish hexagonal crystals, density 2·44, sublimes at 180°, m.p. 192·6° at 1715 mm. Soluble in water (31·36 g per 100 g solution at 20°) and some organic solvents. Prepared by passing hydrogen chloride or chlorine over heated aluminium, or chlorine over heated alumina and carbon. Manufactured by passing chlorine through molten aluminium or a mixture of coal or coke and alumina. Anhydrous aluminium chloride acts as an electron acceptor in such complexes as $M^+[AlCl_4]^-$; $AlCl_3 \cdot H_2S$; $AlCl_3 \cdot NOCl$; and $AlCl_3$-amines; the hydrate $AlCl_3$, $6H_2O$ is precipitated from aqueous solution by HCl gas, although hydrolysis occurs in water. In the solid and liquid states the chloride exists as Al_2Cl_6 molecules. The principal industrial use is as a catalyst, particularly in the manufacture of ethyl benzenes and anthraquinone. In the laboratory it is used as a catalyst in numerous organic reactions (e.g. Friedel-Crafts reaction).

Aluminium ethoxide, Aluminium ethylate, $(CH_3CH_2O)_3Al$, is a white solid, m.p. 139°, b.p. 320°. Has very similar properties to aluminium isopropoxide (q.v.).

Aluminium fluoride, AlF_3. A colourless substance forming hexagonal crystals; density 3·07, which sublime without melting at 1257°; prepared by the action of hydrofluoric acid on $Al(OH)_3$ or by heating $(NH_4)_3AlF_6$ at 600°. Aluminium fluoride is an inert compound, insoluble in most solvents (0·559 g per 100 ml of saturated aqueous solution at 25°), and unattacked by acids and alkalis. A number of hydrates and ammines are known. Many complex fluorides formed by combination with fluorides of other elements are known; cryolite, Na_3AlF_6, occurs naturally in Greenland as a white mineral with a characteristic lustre; density 2·95-3·0, hardness 3; the compound may also be prepared by adding sodium aluminate to a solution of sodium fluoride and bicarbonate. Cryolite is used in the manufacture of aluminium, and in making enamels and white glass.

Aluminium hydride, $(AlH_3)_x$. A white polymeric substance prepared by the action of lithium hydride on aluminium chloride. When freshly prepared it is soluble in ether, but, on standing, further polymerization occurs and a solid is precipitated. Aluminium hydride reacts with lithium hydride to form the important compound lithium aluminium hydride (q.v.).

Aluminium hydroxide, $Al(OH)_3$ or $AlO \cdot OH$. Generally occurs as a white or yellowish gelatinous mass; crystalline forms, particularly some of natural occurrence commonly regarded as a hydrated alumina, such as bauxite, diaspore and hydrargillite (cf. aluminium oxide), are known. The *orthohydroxide*, $Al(OH)_3$, is precipitated from solutions of aluminium salts by ammonia, and occurs in several forms according to the conditions; the *metahydroxide*, $AlO \cdot OH$, is formed by heating the *ortho* form or by precipitating with ammonia from boiling solutions. The gelatinous 'gels' of aluminium hydroxide partially dried at 200°-500°, are valuable drying agents, catalysts, and adsorbents ('alumina gel'). Sols of aluminium hydroxide, in which the particles are positively charged, are formed by dialysis of aqueous solutions of the acetate, chloride, or nitrate; the sols are thixotropic in the presence of traces of an electrolyte. Chemically the hydroxide behaves as an amphoteric hydroxide, dissolving readily in acids to form the corresponding aluminium salts, and in alkalis to give solutions of aluminates. See Diaspore, Böhmite, Gibbsite, Bayerite.

Aluminium iodide, AlI_3. Colourless or pale yellow crystals; density 3·98, m.p. 179·5°, b.p. 381°. Very soluble in water, carbon disulphide, alcohol, and liquid ammonia; also soluble in benzene and pyridine. Prepared by the action of aluminium on iodine, as the solid, vapour, or in solution in carbon disulphide. Strongly hygroscopic. Forms addition compounds, double salts, and ammines in a similar way to aluminium chloride, which it also resembles in existing as Al_2I_6 in the solid and liquid states; the vapour is 24% dissociated to AlI_3 at the b.p., the vapour burning in air if ignited.

Aluminium isopropoxide, Aluminium isopropylate, is a white, crystalline solid, m.p. 125°, b.p.

$$\left(H{-}\underset{\underset{CH_3}{|}}{\overset{\overset{CH_3}{|}}{C}}{-}O \right)_3 Al$$

242°/10 mm. Soluble in isopropyl alcohol and benzene; decomposed by water. Prepared by heating aluminium powder with dry isopropyl alcohol containing a small amount of mercuric chloride and iodine. Used in the production of esters from aldehydes by the Cannizzaro reaction, and in the reduction of aldehydes and ketones, this reagent being specific for a $C{=}O$ group, and not reducing double bonds. The aluminium isopropoxide-titanium tetrachloride complex is very important in the polymerization of ethylene.

Aluminium nitrate, $Al(NO_3)_3$. White crystals, occurring as various hydrates, of which $Al(NO_3)_3, 9H_2O$ is the most common. This hydrate melts at 73·5°, and is readily soluble in water and alcohol. Manufactured by dissolving hydrated alumina in nitric acid, or by mixing solutions of aluminium sulphate and calcium or lead nitrate, when calcium or lead sulphate is precipitated and a solution of the nitrate remains. The aqueous solution, unless it contains excess acid, deposits aluminium hydroxide, slowly in the cold but rapidly on heating. Aluminium nitrate is used as a mordant in dyeing with alizarin red, and in the manufacture of gas mantles.

Aluminium nitride, AlN. White powder consisting of hexagonal crystals; density 3·05-3·25; sublimes at 1900°, melting at about 2200°; hardness 9. Prepared by the action of nitrogen or ammonia on aluminium at high temperatures. It has the wurzite structure. Aluminium nitride is comparatively inert; it reacts slowly with aqueous alkalis, or rapidly with fused alkalis, giving an aluminate and ammonia; water decomposes it, forming aluminium hydroxide and ammonia, but the action is slow, as a protective layer of hydroxide forms on the nitride.

Aluminium, organic derivatives. See Aluminium alkyls.

Aluminium oxide (alumina), Al_2O_3. Alumina is of wide occurrence in nature as corundum, Al_2O_3 (which, when coloured by traces of other metallic oxides, forms a variety of natural gems, e.g. ruby and sapphire); diaspore, Al_2O_3, H_2O; bauxite, $Al_2O_3, 2H_2O$ (the principal commercial source of aluminium); and gibbsite, $Al_2O_3, 3H_2O$. It may be prepared in the laboratory by heating aluminium hydroxide or practically any compound of aluminium in air; the hydroxide and ammonium alum give the purest products. At least three forms of anhydrous alumina (α, γ, and γ'-Al_2O_3) are known; the chief naturally occurring form is α-Al_2O_3, density 3·99, m.p. 2041°, b.p. 2980°, hardness 9. Alumina is practically insoluble in water (1×10^{-5} mol. per litre at 20°), and its solubility in acids and alkalis depends upon its previous heat treatment; strongly ignited, it is scarcely attacked even by concentrated reagents. The oxide is used in the preparation of most aluminium compounds. Corundum, a crystalline form of aluminium oxide, is widely used as an abrasive; emery is a form of it, It may be prepared artificially by fusing alumina in an electric furnace and allowing it to crystallize. Artificial gems are prepared as single crystals of alumina by dropping the very pure finely divided powder through an oxy-hydrogen flame on to a vertical rod of refractory material. The alumina is fused in the flame and grows to a large crystal.

Aluminium solder. See Tin alloys.

Aluminium sulphate, $Al_2(SO_4)_3$. Occurs as white crystals or powder, consisting of the anhydrous salt (*d.* 2·7) or the hydrate

$$Al_2(SO_4)_3, 18H_2O$$

(*d.* 1·6). Readily soluble in water, 38·3 g $Al_2(SO_4)_3$, $18H_2O$ in 100 g water at 25°. Occurs naturally in considerable quantities in alumstone (alunite) and feather alum. Prepared by dissolving aluminium or aluminium hydroxide in sulphuric acid; manufactured by digesting bauxite in 80% sulphuric acid at 110°, the resulting solution being purified, concentrated and allowed to solidify. Aluminium sulphate decomposes into alumina and sulphur dioxide and trioxide at 605°. It readily forms double salts, among which alum (*q.v.*) is an article of commerce. $Al_2(SO_4)_3$, $18H_2O$ forms the anhydrous salt on heating to 250°. Hydrates are also known with 27, 16, 10, and 6 molecules of water. The sulphate is commercially the most important compound of aluminium; two applications, paper sizing and water treatment, consume over 90% of production.

Aluminium sulphide, Al_2S_3. Yellowish amorphous or crystalline solid, density 2·02. Sublimes in a vacuum at high temperature. Prepared pure by direct combination of the elements. Aluminium sulphide reacts with water to form hydrogen sulphide and alumina. The action of H_2S on the trisulphide gives the monosulphide Al_2S.

Aluminoferric is crude aluminium sulphate containing also iron sulphate. It is used for removing suspended matter from boiler feed water, and in sewage treatment to coagulate sludge.

Aluminon, Ammonium aurinetricarboxylate,

$C_{22}H_{23}N_3O_9$. An organic reagent used for the detection and estimation of aluminium. It is a brownish-red powder, soluble in water, and gives a red lake with aluminium which can be estimated colorimetrically. It can also be used for detecting scandium and indium.

Aluminosilicates. Extensive groups of silicate minerals in which tetrahedral $[AlO_4]$ groups replace $[SiO_4]$ groups with the creation of an additional negative charge per unit of replacement. Important minerals of this type are feldspars, micas, zeolites, and some clay minerals.

Aluminous cement. A hydraulic cement closely resembling Portland cement, but composed chiefly of calcium aluminate. It is made by heating a mixture of chalk or limestone and bauxite in a blast-furnace or in an electric furnace until the mixture fuses and can be cast into blocks which are afterwards ground to a fine powder. It is often known as *ciment fondu.* The chief advantages over Portland cement are: (1) rapid hardening so that roads or articles made with aluminous cement can be used sooner than if Portland cement had been employed; (2) better thermal stability, enabling products to be used at relatively high temperatures, e.g. for flue pipes, furnace linings, etc.; (3) better resistance to corrosive solutions.

Alums. A group of crystalline double sulphates of general formulae $M^I M^{III}(SO_4)_2 \cdot 12H_2O$ in which M^I may be Tl, Cs, Rb, K, Na, NH_4, or NH_3OH and M^{III} may be Ti, V, Cr, Mn, Fe, Co, Ga, In, Rh, Ir, and Al. The sulphate group may be replaced by selenate, fluoroberyllate, or chlorozincate, The crystals are made up of $[M^I(H_2O)_6]^+$ and $[M^{III}(H_2O)_6]^{3-}$ cations and SO_4^{2-} anions and in solution the alums behave chemically as mixtures of the two constituent sulphates. $KAl(SO_4)_2 \cdot 12H_2O$ is normally known as potassium alum (*q.v.*) and the sodium and ammonium derivatives of aluminium sulphates are also commercial materials. These latter derivatives are prepared in the same manner as potassium alum.

Alumstone. See Alunite.

Alundum, an artificial form of corundum, made by fusing calcined bauxite in an electric furnace, and allowing the molten product to cool rather rapidly. There are two varieties: (1) white crystalline alundum containing 1% of impurities, with m.p. of 2050°-2100°; and (ii) a reddish-brown product containing 7-10% of impurities; m.p. 2000°-2050°, sp.gr. 3·9. Hardness 9-10. Thermal conductivity almost three times that of fireclay.

Alundum is used for highly refractory bricks, crucibles, refractory cement, and muffles; also for small laboratory apparatus used at high temperatures (combustion tubes, pyrometer tubes, etc.).

Alunite (or alumstone). A mineral consisting of a hydrated basic sulphate of potassium and aluminium, $KAl_3(SO_4)_2(OH)_6$; the potassium may be partially replaced by sodium. Occurs, usually in volcanic rocks, as white, grey or pinkish masses resembling limestone or marble. Sp.gr. 2·58-2·75. Used commercially as a source of potash alum and of potassium sulphate.

Amalgam. See Mercury amalgams.

Amalgamation. The process of forming an amalgam.

Amandin. A protein, belonging to the globulin

class, found in the kernels of plums and peaches and of the almond.

Amanitins. A group of very toxic cyclic peptides found in the mushroom *Amanita phalloides*: they are more poisonous than the phalloidins (*q.v.*) but slower in action—accounting for the delayed fatal effects of ingesting the fungus. The constitution of the amanitins has been established by Th. Wieland.

Amaranth, Acid Red 27; Food Red 9. A red

dyestuff, prepared by coupling diazotized naphthionic acid with 2-naphthol-3,6-disulphonic acid. The commercial substance is impure and usually contains sodium chloride. It is a reddish-brown powder, soluble in water to give a magenta coloured solution; sparingly soluble in alcohol. It is one of the colouring matters permitted for use in foods and drugs.

The very similar dyestuff, Bordeaux B, Acid Red 17, has one less sulphonate group (that marked *).

Amatol. An explosive consisting of a mixture in various proportions of ammonium nitrate (*q.v.*) and TNT (*q.v.*). It was introduced during the First World War to economize in TNT, and amatol may contain as much as 80% of ammonium nitrate with only 20% of TNT. Amatol is less violent than TNT, so that blast and disruptive effects are less, but it may have a greater cratering effect. Its chief disadvantage lies in the hygroscopic nature of ammonium nitrate and it should not, therefore, be employed where long storage is envisaged.

Amber. A hard, honey-coloured, fossil resin, of considerable beauty when polished; found in sedimentary deposits of the Tertiary era. Origin uncertain, but considered by some authorities to be derived from an extinct, but unidentified, conifer, *Pinus succinifer*. Believed by Kirchner to have been formed from an early form of swamp cypress because of the large number of trapped insects, pieces of coral and plants, often found embalmed in the amber. Believed by Nilsson to have been formed by the flow of resins of the Kauri pine type during extensive forest fires. The masses of cooled resin were then transported by tidal waves and deposited with marine deposits in locations far removed from the sites of the original forests.

When heated to 300° is partially decomposed into the pale yellow 'oil of amber', leaving a black residue called 'amber colophony.' Succinic acid is also evolved. This is not a product of the destructive distillation of modern plant resins, hence the name *Pinus succinifer* for the supposed conifer producing the resin.

Amber mica. See Mica.

Ambident anions. Anions which are capable of reaction at two different sites, e.g. silver nitrite and alkyl halides give products of O-alkylation (nitrites R—O—N=O) and N-alkylation (nitroalkanes R—NO$_2$).

Amblygonite is an ore containing lithium; it normally has the formula AlPO$_4$, LiF and contains about 10% of lithium oxide, but part of the lithium may be replaced by sodium and part of the fluorine by hydroxyl. Amblygonite crystallizes in the triclinic system and in appearance resembles feldspar, from which it is distinguished by a higher sp.gr. (3·01-3·09); hardness, 6.

American filter. The trade name of a well-known type of rotary vacuum disc filter (*q.v.*).

Americium, Am. At.no. 95, At.wt. 243, m.p. 995°, estimated b.p. 2600°. α-Americium, stable up to 75°, is hexagonal, $a=3·642$, $c=11·76$ Å, d 13·67, other phases have not yet been characterized. The two most stable isotopes of americium are ^{241}Am and ^{243}Am; both are obtained by multiple neutron irradiation of ^{239}Pu.

$$^{239}\text{Pu}(n,\gamma)\,^{240}\text{Pu}(n,\gamma)\,^{241}\text{Pu}\xrightarrow{\beta}\,^{241}\text{Am}(n,\gamma)\rightarrow$$

$$^{242}\text{Am}\xrightarrow[\text{capture}]{\text{electron}}\,^{242}\text{Pu}\,(n,\gamma)\,^{243}\text{Pu}\xrightarrow{\beta}\,^{243}\text{Am}.$$

Purification of americium may be effected by chemical methods or by ion-exchange or solvent extraction procedures. Metallic americium has been obtained by reduction of americium trifluoride with barium at about 1200°, it is more silvery in appearance than neptunium or plutonium and is very malleable and ductile; it is known that the metal is highly reactive but little else is known of its chemical properties; ^{241}Am is extremely hazardous to health, but has been recommended as a source of heat in satellites.

Americium compounds. Although americium is intensely radioactive, experiments have been carried out with macro quantities of its compounds. Americium shows considerable chemical resemblances to uranium, but the higher oxidation states are much less stable. *Americium oxides*, of composition between Am$_2$O$_3$, reddish-brown, and AmO$_2$, black, are known. The highest *americium halide* is AmF_4, obtained by the action of fluorine on americium compounds; tripositive americium halides are similar to the corresponding uranium compounds. By the use of very strong oxidizing agents, alkali americium (V) carbonates, $MAmO_2CO_3$, and *sodium americyl* (VI) *acetate* are obtained. Colours of americium compounds are: Am^{3+}, pink; AmO_2^+, yellow; AmO_2^{2+}, brown.

Amethocaine, $C_{15}H_{24}N_2O_2$. Its hydrochloride is

$$H_3C \diagdown N \cdot CH_2 \cdot CH_2 \cdot O \cdot OC \bigcirc NH \cdot [CH_2]_3 \cdot CH_3$$
$$H_3C \diagup$$

a white crystalline powder, m.p. 147°-150°, soluble in water and alcohol. It is prepared from β-dimethylaminoethanol and *p-n*-butylaminobenzoic acid, and is used as a local anaesthetic.

Amethyst. See Quartz.

Amicron. A term given by Zsigmondy to describe particles too small to be visible even in the ultramicroscope. Amicrons are therefore smaller than 10 mμ, and are either small colloidal particles, molecules or ions. See Micron; Submicron.

Amides are organic compounds derived from ammonia by substitution of one or more of its hydrogen atoms by organic acid groups. The primary, secondary, and tertiary amides represent the substitution of one, two, and three hydrogen atoms respectively:

$R \cdot CONH_2$	$(R \cdot CO)_2NH$	$(R \cdot CO)_3 N$
primary amide	secondary amide	tertiary amide

The amides are crystalline solids soluble in alcohol and ether; some are also soluble in water. Primary amides are prepared by the action of ammonia or amines on acid chlorides, anhydrides, or esters. Some amides are prepared by distillation of the ammonium salt of the appropriate acid. Secondary and tertiary amides are formed by treating nitriles or primary amides with organic acids or their anhydrides. Primary amides react with nitrous acid to give carboxylic acids: in many cases, heating with mineral acids or alkalis has the same effect. Primary amides are weakly basic, and form unstable compounds with mineral acids; compounds are formed with metals such as sodium, potassium, and mercury. Hypochlorites and hypobromites react to give chlor- or brom-amides; these give amines when treated with alkali. Amides, particularly dimethylacetamide and dimethylformamide are good solvents for conducting replacement reactions involving ionic reagents (e.g. replacement of a chlorine atom by fluorine using KF).

Inorganic amides contain the ion NH_2^-. They are formed by the action of ammonia on metals or by the ammonolysis of nitrides. The heavy metal amides are prepared by metathetical reactions in liquid ammonia, e.g. $Cd(SCN)_2 + 2KNH_2 \rightarrow Cd(NH_2)_2 + 2KSCN$. The alkali amides are stable, crystalline salts; the heavy metal amides are often explosive. The amides are the bases of the ammonia system.

Amido-. See Amino-.

Amidol. See Aminophenol developers.

Amidopyrine, $C_{13}H_{17}O$. Colourless crystals,

$$(CH_3)_2N-C-----N-CH_3$$
$$CH_3-C \diagdown_C \diagup N-C_6H_5$$
$$\|$$
$$O$$

m.p. 107°-108°. Soluble in 18 parts of water and in 2 parts of alcohol. Prepared from phenazone. It is an analgesic and antipyretic, but its continuous use may lead to agranulocytosis, and it is regarded as a somewhat dangerous drug.

Aminacrine, 5-aminoacridine, $C_{13}H_{10}N_2$.

Yellow needles, m.p. 234°-235°. Its hydrochloride, which has one molecule of water of crystallization, is used for the treatment of infected wounds, and is effective against Gram-positive and Gram-negative organisms. It is soluble in 200 parts of water, and in alcohol.

Prepared by treating N-phenylanthranilic acid with phosphorus oxychloride, and treating the product with ammonium carbonate in phenol.

Amines are organic compounds containing nitrogen. They may be regarded as derived from ammonia by replacement of one or more of its hydrogen atoms by hydrocarbon groups. Replacement of one, two, and three hydrogen atoms results in primary, secondary, and tertiary amines respectively. Compounds in which the nitrogen forms part of a ring are usually known as heterocyclic bases. Aliphatic, aromatic, and mixed aliphatic-aromatic amines are known. Primary amines are obtained by the action of ammonia on alcohols or chloro-derivatives of hydrocarbons. The ammonia may be replaced by primary and secondary amines to give secondary and tertiary amines. Some aldehydes react with ammonia and hydrogen under pressure in presence of nickel catalysts to give amines. Primary amines are also obtained by reduction of nitro-compounds, nitriles, ketoximes, and amides, or by treating amides with sodium hypobromite. Secondary amines are obtained by reducing Schiff's bases. A general reaction for the preparation of amines is that between potassium phthalimide and a halogen compound, with subsequent hydrolysis of the product. The aliphatic amines are strong bases; the lower members are soluble in water and are stronger bases than ammonia; they have ammoniacal or fishy odours. The higher members are odourless solids. Aromatic amines are not such strong bases. They are not generally soluble in water, and have characteristic odours. All types form crystalline salts with acids and adducts with mercuric and stannic chlorides. The picrates and picrolonates are crystalline, rather insoluble salts used for the separation and identification of amines. With nitrous acid, primary aliphatic amines give alcohols. Aromatic amines give diazonium salts in the cold, but these decompose to phenols if the reaction is carried out at higher temperatures. Secondary amines of all types give nitrosamines. Schiff's bases, or azomethines, are formed by the action of aldehydes on primary or secondary amines. All types except tertiary amines give acetyl compounds with acetyl chloride or acetic anhydride. These are usually crystalline, sparingly soluble solids. These amines also yield sulphonamides with aromatic sulphochlorides. Primary amines react with chloroform and potassium hydroxide to give isocyanides, or carbylamines. Primary and secondary amines yield derivatives of thiocarbamic acid with alcoholic carbon disulphide, while aromatic amines give substituted thioureas. The aromatic amines are of great importance as dyestuff intermediates.

Amino-. A prefix used in organic chemistry to denote that a compound contains an amino group ($-NH_2$) joined directly to a carbon atom. Formerly the prefix amido was also used but this is now usually restricted to compounds containing the amide group ($-CO \cdot NH_2$).

Aminoacetal, $C_6H_{15}NO_2$,

$$H_2N . CH_2 . CH(OC_2H_5)_2.$$

A colourless oily liquid with an ammoniacal odour, b.p. 172°-174°. Miscible with water and alcohol; insoluble in concentrated solutions of sodium hydroxide. Prepared by the action of ammonia on chloroacetal. Hydrochloric acid converts it to aminoacetaldehyde. Condensation with aromatic aldehydes gives isoquinoline derivatives.

Aminoacetic acid. See Glycine.

Amino-acids. A large class of organic compounds containing both the carboxyl, COOH,

and the amino, NH_2, group, for example glycine, $H_2N \cdot CH_2 \cdot COOH$. Their chief importance lies in the fact that many proteins are built up entirely of amino-acid groupings, all the amino-acids in proteins being α-amino-acids, with the amino group attached to the same carbon atom as the carboxyl group and with the same L-configuration of asymmetric groups about the α-carbon atom. The following 23 amino-acids are found in very variable proportions as constituents of most proteins:

Ala	Alanine
Arg	Arginine
Asp(NH₂) or Asn	Asparagine
Asp	Aspartic acid
CySH	Cysteine
CyS	Cystine (half)
Glu	Glutamic acid
Glu(NH₂) or Gln	Glutamine
Gly	Glycine
His	Histidine
HyLys	Hydroxylysine
Hypro	Hydroxyproline
Ileu	Isoleucine
Leu	Leucine
Lys	Lysine
Met	Methionine
Phe	Phenylalanine
Pro	Proline
Ser	Serine
Thr	Threonine
Try	Tryptophan
Tyr	Tyrosine
Val	Valine

In representations of peptides the shortened form is used and the amino-acid first listed has the free amino group.

Certain other amino-acids occur in a few proteins, and others, not necessarily α- or L-amino-acids, are found naturally in the free state or as constituents of peptides.

The amino-acids are colourless, crystalline substances which melt with decomposition. They are mostly soluble in water and insoluble in alcohol.

As constituents of proteins the amino-acids are important constituents of the food of animals. Certain amino-acids can be made in the body from ammonia and non-nitrogenous sources; others can be made from other amino-acids, e.g. tyrosine from phenylalanine and cystine from methionine, but many are essential ingredients of the diet. The list of essential amino-acids depends partly on the species; for the rat, Rose and his co-workers have shown the following to be needed for maximum growth: lysine, tryptophan, histidine, phenylalanine, threonine, leucine, isoleucine, methionine, valine and arginine. The chick needs, in addition, glycine and glutamic acid. It has been shown that man can remain in nitrogen equilibrium on the same ten amino-acids as the rat, but can dispense with histidine and arginine.

α-Aminoanthraquinone, $C_{14}H_9NO_2$. Forms red prisms with a metallic reflex, m.p. 252°. It is most conveniently crystallized from xylene.

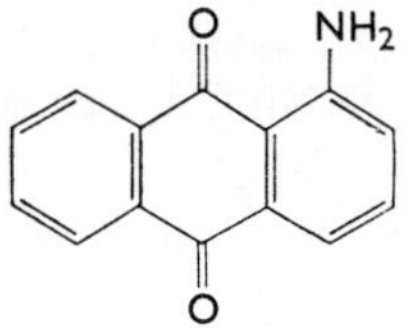

It is a typical aromatic amine.

It is best prepared by the prolonged action of concentrated ammonia solution at a high temperature upon anthraquinone-α-sulphonic acid in the presence of barium chloride. It can also be prepared by reduction of the corresponding nitro compound or by amination of the chloroanthraquinone.

It is used in the dispersed form as a dye for acetate silk, though it has no affinity for other fibres. It is also used as a starting point for alkyl- or acyl-aminoanthraquinones which are used either as vat dyes or, after sulphonation, as acid wool dyes.

β-Aminoanthraquinone, $C_{14}H_9NO_2$. Forms

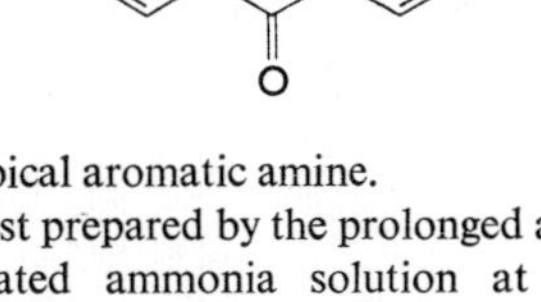

orange-red needles, m.p. 302°. It is insoluble in water, but soluble in chlorobenzene and nitrobenzene. It is a typical aromatic amine.

It is best prepared by the prolonged action of ammonia at 200° on anthraquinone-β-sulphonic acid in the presence of manganese dioxide or a barium salt. It can also be prepared by amination of β-chloroanthraquinone.

It is used in the dispersed form as a dye for acetate silk. It has no affinity for cellulose fibres. Its chief outlet is as an intermediate in the preparation of flavanthrene and indanthrene. Flavanthrene is obtained by heating β-aminoanthraquinone with antimony pentachloride in nitrobenzene solution; indanthrene is obtained by fusion with caustic potash.

Aminoazobenzene, $C_{12}H_{11}N_3$. Crystallizes in

brownish-yellow needles, m.p. 127°. The hydrochloride forms steel-blue needles.

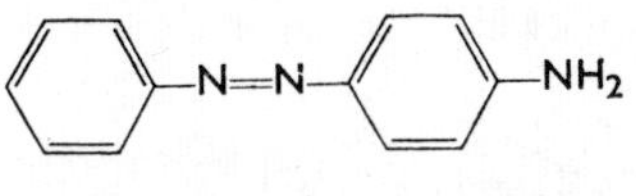

It is prepared by an intramolecular transformation of diazoaminobenzene in the presence of aniline hydrochloride, or in one stage by diazotizing a solution of aniline and aniline hydrochloride with an insufficient amount of nitrous acid.

It is used as a first component in the preparation of azo-dyes. It is also used for the preparation of induline, which is an azine derivative obtained by heating aminoazobenzene with aniline hydrochloride.

Aminoazo-dyes. See Azo-dyes.

o-Aminobenzoic acid. See Anthranilic acid.

p-Aminobenzoic acid, $C_7H_7NO_2$. Yellowish red crystals, m.p. 186°-187°, soluble in water and alcohol. p-Aminobenzoic acid is an essential metabolite for certain bacterial cells and is regarded as a member of the vitamin B group. Sulphonamides, having a similar structure, are believed to act physiologically by competing with p-aminobenzoic acid for a place in the structure of some important substance, possibly folic acid.

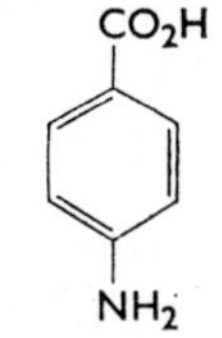

p-Aminodiphenylamine, $C_{12}H_{12}N_2$. M.p. 75°.

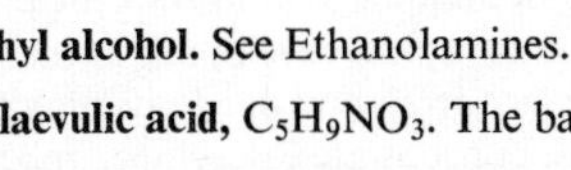

When oxidized in acid solution with ferric chloride or hydrogen peroxide a green dye, emeraldine, is produced.

Prepared by the reduction of p-nitrosodiphenylamine with ammonium sulphide.

Aminoethyl alcohol. See Ethanolamines.

δ-Aminolaevulic acid, $C_5H_9NO_3$. The basic unit

$$H_2N \cdot CH_2CO \cdot CH_2CH_2CO_2H$$

in the biogenesis of porphyrins (q.v.), which furnishes all the carbon and nitrogen atoms in the haem of haemoglobin, myoglobin, cytochromes, catalase and peroxidase, as well as in the dihydroporphyrin ring of chlorophyll. It is also incorporated into the corrin ring of vitamin B_{12}. δ-Aminolaevulic acid is formed from succinyl-coenzyme A and glycine, and affords by enzymic self-condensation the pyrrole derivative porphobilinogen (q.v.). Four molecules of porphobilinogen then condense to give the characteristic porphyrin skeleton.

Aminomethylation. See Mannich reaction.

Aminonaphthols, $C_{10}H_9NO$. These are compounds in which the naphthalene molecule is

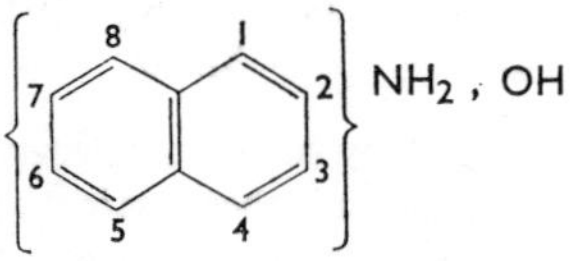

NH$_2$, OH

substituted by an amino and by a hydroxy group. A great many of such compounds exist in which the entering groups are in different positions. Usually prepared by reduction of the nitronaphthols. The sulphonated aminonaphthols are valuable dyestuffs' intermediates.

o-Aminophenol, C_6H_7NO. Crystallizes in colourless scales, m.p. 174°. The crystals darken on exposure to air. Slightly soluble in water, more so in alcohol. It forms a hydrochloride which is readily soluble in water and alcohol.

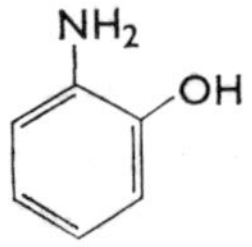

Is is prepared by reduction of o-nitrophenol with sodium sulphide, and is used as a hair and fur dye.

p-Aminophenol, C_6H_7NO. Colourless leaflets, m.p. 184°. Slightly soluble in water, soluble in alcohol. Oxidizes quickly in air. Very soluble in acid and alkaline solutions.

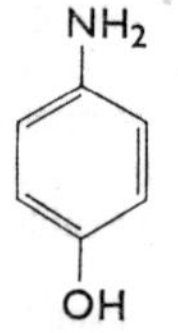

Prepared by reduction of p-nitrophenol with iron and hydrochloric acid, or of p-nitrosophenol with sodium sulphide. Can be diazotized and used as a first component in azo-dyes. Chief outlet is for sulphur dyes in which it is fused with sodium polysulphides.

Aminophenol developers

(1) p-*Aminophenol* (*Rodinol*) C_6H_7NO. The free base is readily oxidized and it forms a hydrochloride which is soluble in cold water. The use of alkaline solutions of the compound as a photographic developing agent has been known since 1891, and due to its high solubility in alkali, concentrated developer mixtures can be formulated.

(2) p-*Methylaminophenol* *hemisulphate.* (*Metol*) $C_7H_9NO . \frac{1}{2}H_2SO_4$. Metol is a colourless crystalline compound, m.p. 250°-260° (decomp.) It is soluble in water. Alkaline solutions of the base are widely used in photographic developers particularly in formulations with hydroquinone with which it exhibits superadditive properties. (See Superadditive developers).

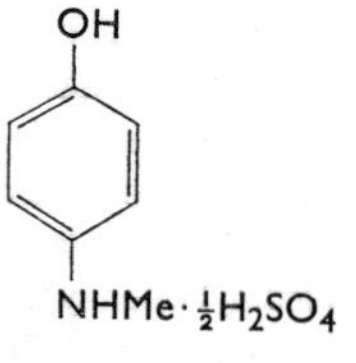

(3) p-*Hydroxyphenylglycine* (*Glycin*). This compound is insoluble in water and the common organic solvents, but is readily soluble in sodium carbonate solution to give solutions which exhibit reducing properties. These solutions function as developers for exposed silver halide grains, and because of the slowness of aerial oxidation the agent is suitable for continuous processing baths.

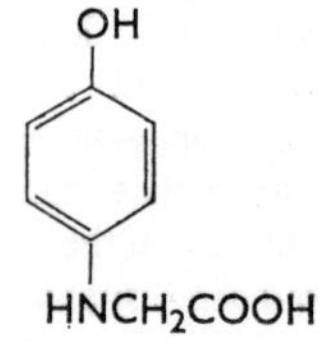

(4) 2,4-*Diaminophenol dihydrochloride* (*Amidol*) $C_6H_8N_2O . 2HCl$. Amidol forms grey to colourless crystals and melts at 168°-170°. It is readily soluble in water to give solutions which exhibit reducing properties and which can be used as photographic developers, either under acidic or basic conditions. Its use is not as widespread as that of hydroquinone

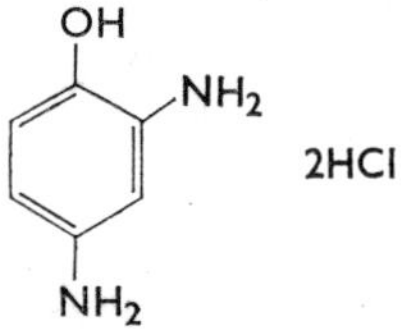

Aminophylline. Theophylline with ethylenediamine. White or yellowish-white granules, soluble in 5 parts of water to give an alkaline solution; insoluble in alcohol.

It is prepared by dissolving theophylline in ethylenediamine hydrate and evaporating to dryness. It contains 75-82% of theophylline, and 12-14% of ethylenediamine. It has a similar action as a diuretic to theophylline, but it is more soluble, and is mainly used in asthma and cardiac or renal oedema.

Amino-plastics. A group of plastics materials made from resins derived from amino compounds such as urea, thiourea, melamine and aniline by reaction with formaldehyde.

Ammines. These are compounds, formed by the addition of ammonia to a metallic compound, in which the nitrogen atoms are linked directly to a metal by co-ordinate bonds. See Cobalt ammines, Nickel ammines.

Ammonal. Explosive of varying composition, consisting of a mixture of ammonium nitrate, trinitrotoluene, aluminium powder, and charcoal.

Ammonia, NH_3. A colourless gas with a characteristic pungent odour, readily liquefied by cooling or compression, the liquid being colourless, b.p. $-33.4°$, forming a white solid, m.p. $-77.7°$, on further cooling. Critical temperature, 132.9°; critical pressure, 112.3 atm. Ammonia

32

is very soluble in water, the saturated solution at 15° containing 36·9% of NH_3, and having a density of 0·875; the gas is also soluble in alcohol. All the gas is expelled from these solutions on boiling. The aqueous solution is alkaline and contains ammonia hydrates; any ammonium hydroxide that is formed is completely dissociated. Two hydrates $NH_3 \cdot H_2O$ and $2NH_3 \cdot H_2O$ are known. Gaseous ammonia was first prepared by Priestley (1774) although an aqueous solution was known previously (Kunkel) and it occurs naturally in the *soffioni* of Tuscany. It is manufactured by reacting together a mixture of nitrogen and hydrogen in stoicheiometric proportions at a pressure of 300 atm. or more and a temperature of 500° in the presence of an iron catalyst; the gases leaving the reactor are cooled to below atmospheric temperature when the ammonia condenses out (Haber process). It is also obtained as a crude aqueous solution as a by-product in the manufacture of coal gas. In the laboratory ammonia is prepared by heating an ammonium salt with slaked lime, the gas being dried by passing over quicklime. Ammonia does not burn readily in air, but ignites, giving a yellowish-brown flame, in an atmosphere of oxygen; a mixture of ammonia and oxygen in certain proportions may be exploded with an electric spark; such mixtures also react readily on passing over a heated platinum catalyst, nitric oxide being formed. Ammonia is also oxidized to nitrogen by passing over many heated metallic oxides. Passed over heated sodium or potassium, *sodamide*, $NaNH_2$, and *potassamide*, KNH_2, are produced. Ammonia joins additively with many compounds, forming amines. Liquid ammonia is an excellent solvent for certain substances, which ionize in the solutions, and give ionic reactions similar to those occurring in aqueous solution. Ammonia gas may be detected by its alkaline reaction in presence of moisture, its odour, and by the blackening of moist mercurous nitrate paper. Traces of dissolved ammonia may be detected and estimated by the use of Nessler's reagent (*q.v.*). The principal commercial use for ammonia is in the manufacture of ammonium sulphate and other fertilizers, but it is also used for the manufacture of nitric acid (*q.v.*) and as a refrigerant. Ammonia is marketed as the liquid, compressed in cylinders ('anhydrous ammonia'), or as aqueous solutions of different strengths. The saturated solution is known commercially as '880 ammonia,' its density being approximately 0·880.

Ammoniacal liquor. An aqueous liquid containing admixed tarry matter and organic compounds, which is obtained by condensation from the gas issuing from the retorts in coal gas manufacture. The liquor contains free ammonia, and various ammonium salts, some of which (e.g. the carbonates and sulphides) are decomposed on boiling, evolving ammonia, and some of which are only decomposed by boiling with lime. The ammonia is recovered in 'ammonia stills,' in which the ammoniacal liquor is treated with steam and lime; the ammonia evolved is passed through 60% sulphuric acid, with which it combines, forming ammonium sulphate. Alternatively, the ammonia is purified from traces of tarry matter and hydrogen sulphide, and dissolved in water to a 25% solution, which is an article of commerce.

Ammonium. The name applied to the unipositive ion NH_4^+, which forms a group of compounds similar to those of the alkali metals. Free ammonium has not yet been isolated. Electrolysis of an aqueous ammonium chloride solution with a mercury cathode causes the mercury to swell into a pasty mass which is unstable at ordinary temperatures, hydrogen and ammonia being evolved in the proportions required by the equation $2NH_4 = 2NH_3 + H_2$; the pasty mass, 'ammonium amalgam,' may contain ammonium. Ammonium salts are formed by the action of ammonia on acids, e.g. $NH_3 + HCl = NH_4Cl$.

Ammonium acetate, CH_3COONH_4. White hygroscopic crystals, very soluble in water. It decomposes on heating.

Ammonium bicarbonate. See Ammonium hydrogen carbonate.

Ammonium bromide, NH_4Br. A colourless crystalline solid with a strongly saline taste, which slowly turns yellow on exposure to air owing to liberation of free bromine. It is readily soluble in water (74 g per 100 g water at 20°). The salt sublimes on heating, the vapour being dissociated into hydrogen bromide and ammonia. It is commonly prepared by the action of hydrogen bromide on ammonia, in the gaseous state or in solution. Additive compounds of the bromide with bromine (e.g. NH_4Br_3), and with ammonia (e.g. NH_4Br, $3NH_3$) have been described. It possesses the general sedative properties of the bromides, but it is absorbed rather more readily than the alkali bromides, and it has less depressing action.

Ammonium carbonate, $(NH_4)_2CO_3$. The white solid known commercially as 'ammonium carbonate' is a double salt of ammonium hydrogen carbonate and ammonium carbamate, having the formula NH_4HCO_3, NH_2COONH_4; this is manufactured by heating a mixture of chalk and ammonium chloride or sulphate, the 'carbonate' subliming on to the walls of cooled chambers. The salt has a strong odour of ammonia, and on exposure to moist air decomposes, leaving solid ammonium hydrogen carbonate. It is used in baking powders and smelling salts, and in dyeing and wool-scouring. It has a stimulating action on the stomach, and is used in the preparation of *sal volatile*. It is also a valuable expectorant. The true ammonium carbonate, $(NH_4)_2CO_3$, is formed on treating the commercial salt with ammonia, and crystallizes as plates or prisms which are very soluble in water, and readily decompose into ammonia, carbon dioxide, and water on heating.

Ammonium chloride, NH_4Cl ('sal ammoniac'). A white crystalline solid, often possessing a fibrous structure, and having a characteristic saline taste. It is readily soluble in water (at 20°, 37·2 g, and at 100°, 77·3 g per 100 g water); a solution in contact with excess of the solid salt boils at 115·6°. Ammonium chloride is manufactured by treating the waste liquor from the Solvay process (see Sodium carbonate) with ammonia and carbon dioxide, when the calcium chloride reacts to give ammonium chloride and calcium carbonate; alternatively, the liquor remaining after the sodium bicarbonate has been filtered off contains sodium chloride and ammonium chloride and these may be separated by crystallization. Another important method is the reaction of ammonium sulphate and sodium chloride at 100°, the sodium sulphate crystallizes out preferentially. Ammonium chloride dissociates into ammonia and hydrogen chloride on heating. The salt is chiefly used in the manufacture of dry cells, but is also important as a mordant in the dyeing and printing of cloth and as a soldering and galvanizing flux. It is not, in general, suitable as a fertilizer, owing to its chlorine content.

Ammonium chlorostannate, $(NH_4)_2SnCl_6$, 'pink salt', is precipitated from very concentrated solutions of chlorostannic acid with ammonium chloride. It is used as a mordant in dyeing.

Ammonium chromate, $(NH_4)_2CrO_4$. A golden-yellow solid prepared by neutralizing chromic acid with ammonia and crystallizing the solution. The salt is soluble in water. On warming it decomposes into the dichromate, ammonia, and water. A very large number of double salts derived from ammonium chromate (e.g. $NH_4NaCrO_4, 2H_2O$), have been prepared.

Ammonium dichromate, $(NH_4)_2Cr_2O_7$. A red crystalline solid, prepared by mixing a chromic acid solution with half the quantity of ammonia solution required for complete neutralization, and crystallizing. The salt is very soluble in water. On heating it decomposes into nitrogen,

water, and chromium (III) oxide, although the latter rarely has the stoicheiometric composition Cr_2O_3.

Ammonium fluoride, NH_4F. A deliquescent solid, forming colourless hexagonal laminar crystals possessing a strong saline taste, prepared from gaseous ammonia and hydrogen fluoride. The salt dissolves in its own weight of water at 0°; it is extensively hydrolysed in the solution, which must be kept in Polythene bottles. Ammonium fluoride is a stable sublimable substance but is partially hydrolysed by moisture. It is used as a disinfectant and preservative. Ammonium fluoride adds hydrogen fluoride to form ammonium hydrogen difluoride, NH_4HF_2.

Ammonium hydrogen carbonate (Ammonium bicarbonate), NH_4HCO_3. A white crystalline solid, moderately soluble in water (21 g per 100 g water at 20°); formed by the decay of nitrogenous material, and occurring in guano. Manufactured by the action of carbon dioxide and steam on ammonium carbonate solution, or by the interaction of ammonia, carbon dioxide, and water vapour at ordinary temperatures. The salt is also formed by the slow decomposition of ammonium carbonate, or the commercial 'carbonate,' at normal temperatures. It is used as a substitute for the sodium salt in baking powders. It is more stable in the dry state than is ammonium carbonate, while its medicinal properties are the same. It is therefore used instead of the carbonate in the preparation of capsules and compressed tablets.

Ammonium hydroxide, NH_4OH. The base of ammonium salts. In aqueous solution ammonium hydroxide is largely present as hydrated ammonia. Is only a very weak base in aqueous solution.

Ammonium iodide, NH_4I. A salt, forming colourless deliquescent cubic crystals, prepared by addition of alcohol to a concentrated solution of potassium iodide and ammonium sulphate, when potassium sulphate separates, leaving a solution from which ammonium iodide may be crystallized. Solubility in water, 167 g per 100 g of water at 15°. The salt sublimes on heating, partial decomposition occurring in presence of air. In concentrated aqueous solution it combines with iodine, forming ammonium tri-iodide, NH_4I_3; additive compounds with ammonia (e.g. $NH_4I, 3NH_3$ and $NH_4I, 4NH_3$) are known. Ammonium iodide is used in the photographic industry.

Ammonium molybdates. Prepared by the action of ammonia on solutions of molybdic acid. The commercial salt, prepared by dissolving molybdenum trioxide in ammonia and crystallizing the solution, is ammonium paramolybdate, $(NH_4)_6Mo_7O_{24}$, $4H_2O$, and forms large colourless or bluish crystals, soluble in water. This salt dissolves in ammonia, giving a solution of the normal molybdate, $(NH_4)_2MoO_4$, from which the crystalline salt may be precipitated by addition of alcohol; the solid evolves ammonia on exposure to air and is decomposed by water. Many other ammonium molybdates and heteromolybdates are known.

Ammonium nitrate, NH_4NO_3. Occurs in the form of colourless crystals, d 1·72; m.p. 169°-170°; very soluble in water (871 g per 100 g water at 100°); manufactured by direct combination of synthetic ammonia and nitric acid. Ammonium nitrate is manufactured on a vast scale for use as a fertilizer. Large quantities, though only a small fraction of total production, are also used in explosives. Although ammonium nitrate can be detonated by the use of a sufficiently powerful priming explosive, it is too insensitive to be used alone as an explosive and is mixed with other materials, as in amatol (*q.v.*). On gentle heating decomposes to nitrous oxide.

Ammonium nitrite, NH_4NO_2. A yellowish solid forming feathery, deliquescent needle crystals. Occurs as a product of the oxidation of ammonia, especially in the presence of catalysts; conveniently prepared by the action of barium nitrite on ammonium sulphate in aqueous solution; the precipitated barium sulphate is filtered off, a solution of ammonium nitrite remaining. The salt decomposes at 60°-70°, sometimes explosively, into nitrogen and water.

Ammonium oxalate, $(NH_4)_2C_2O_4$, H_2O. Colourless rhombic prisms, soluble in cold water up to 4%. It occurs in guano. The acid salt, $C_2O_4HNH_4$, H_2O, is less soluble, and with oxalic acid gives triclinic crystals of ammonium quadroxalate, $C_2O_4HNH_4 \cdot C_2O_4H_2$, $2H_2O$.

Ammonium peroxides. Dry ammonia reacts with a 98% ethereal solution of hydrogen peroxide at $-10°$, a crystalline precipitate of $(NH_4)_2O_2$, H_2O_2, m.p. 14°, being formed. Further treatment with ammonia converts this to an oily substance, $(NH_4)_2O_2$. The latter readily decomposes, evolving ammonia and reforming $(NH_4)_2O_2$, H_2O_2.

Ammonium persulphate, $(NH_4)_2S_2O_8$. A colourless solid, soluble in water (58 g per 100 g water at 0°). Prepared by electrolysis of a cooled saturated solution of ammonium sulphate in dilute sulphuric acid, using a high current density at the anode; the persulphate is formed in solution, or crystallizes round the anode, the anode liquid usually being isolated with a suitable diaphragm. In absence of moisture and light the salt is stable. It is a powerful oxidizing agent; on warming with nitric acid, oxygen containing a large percentage of ozone is evolved. An ammoniacal solution of ammonium persulphate is used to strip brass plating from iron.

Ammonium phosphates. Three crystalline ammonium phosphates are known, the *monoammonium*, *diammonium*, and *triammonium* salts, $NH_4H_2PO_4$, $(NH_4)_2HPO_4$, and $(NH_4)_3PO_4$, respectively. These are all soluble in water, the diammonium salt having the highest solubility at 25°. All are manufactured by the action of ammonia on phosphoric acid under controlled conditions. The salts are important fertilizers. The monobasic salt, $NH_4H_2PO_4$, and the dibasic salt, $(NH_4)_2HPO_4$, are both used in medicine to a small extent for their saline action. They have a diuretic effect and, like most ammonium salts, render the urine more acid. All these phosphates lose ammonia on heating.

Ammonium phosphomolybdate,

$$(NH_4)_3PO_4(Mo_{12}O_{36}) \ xH_2O.$$

The bright yellow precipitate formed by interaction of a phosphate, ammonium molybdate, and nitric acid in solution. It is used as a test for phosphates.

Ammonium sulphate, $(NH_4)_2SO_4$. A colourless crystalline solid, readily soluble in water (at 20° 75·4 g, and at 100° 103·3 g per 100 g water). On careful heating ammonium sulphate gives ammonium hydrogen sulphate, NH_4HSO_4; on stronger heating this gives nitrogen, ammonia, sulphur dioxide, and water. Most ammonium sulphate is now produced from synthetic ammonia. This may be reacted directly with sulphuric acid, or gypsum or anhydrite may be used. In the latter process ammonia and carbon dioxide are passed into a suspension of calcium sulphate in water, resulting in the formation of ammonium sulphate and calcium carbonate. The latter is filtered off and the solution concentrated, when the ammonium sulphate crystallizes out. Coal gas is still a valuable source of ammonia for the production of this salt. Commercially, ammonium sulphate is at the present time the most important ammonium salt, being produced in enormous quantities throughout the world for use as a fertilizer. However, this use is not likely to increase, since other fertilizers with higher nitrogen contents are tending to replace it.

Ammonium sulphides. Colourless crystals of normal ammonium sulphide, $(NH_4)_2S$, are formed from ammonia and hydrogen sulphide at $-18°$. This compound gives an alkaline reaction, and is stable only at low temperatures, decomposing into ammonium hydrogen sulphide and ammonia on warming. White crystals of ammonium hydrogen sulphide, NH_4HS, which sublime at $32°$, are formed on mixing ammonia and hydrogen sulphide in ethyl acetate solution. The salt is soluble in water, undergoing hydrolysis, and readily oxidizing on exposure of the alkaline solution to air or oxygen, giving a yellow solution containing polysulphides with ammonium sulphite and thiosulphate. Various polysulphides, e.g. $(NH_4)_2S_4$, $(NH_4)_2S_5$, $(NH_4)_2S_7$, have been described as yellow, orange, or red crystalline solids, but their individuality is doubtful. A solution of the hydrosulphide prepared by passing hydrogen sulphide through strong aqueous ammonia is used in qualitative analysis; 'yellow ammonium sulphide,' which finds a similar use, is formed from the hydrosulphide solution by oxidation, or by digesting it with sulphur.

Ammonium thiocyanate, NH_4NCS. A colourless solid, m.p. about $150°$. Soluble in water (162 g in 100 g water at $20°$). Manufactured by heating carbon disulphide with an alcoholic ammonia solution, or from hydrocyanic acid and a yellow ammonium sulphide solution. The salt is readily transformed into the isomeric thiourea, $SC(NH_2)_2$, on warming. Ammonium thiocyanate is used as a test for iron; it gives a characteristic blood-red coloration with solutions of ferric salts. It is also used in explosives manufacture, and in photography.

Ammonium vanadate, NH_4VO_3, is precipitated from a solution of a vanadate by ammonium chloride solution, or may be obtained by dissolving vanadium pentoxide in excess aqueous ammonia solution followed by precipitation with alcohol. Ammonium vanadate is sparingly soluble in water (5·18 g per 1000 g of water at $15°$). When heated at $135°-210°$ the salt loses ammonia and forms an ammonium trivanadate; at higher temperatures more ammonia is lost and there is some reduction of the vanadium.

Amorphous. A term applied to solids denoting absence of crystalline form and of an ordered arrangement of the molecules in a space-lattice or three-dimensional geometrical pattern. Such solids show no 'cleavage planes,' i.e. directions in which fracture is comparatively easy, and give an irregular or 'conchoidal,' fracture, like glass. Many substances once thought to be amorphous have been shown by X-ray analysis to consist of minute crystals. Others are probably supercooled liquids. See Devitrification.

Amosite. A variety of asbestos (q.v.).

AMP. See Adenosine monophosphate.

Ampère, André Marie (1775-1836). Born at Polemieux, near Lyons, Ampère was appointed in 1801 professor of physics and chemistry at Bourg, and in 1809 he became professor of mathematics at the École Polytechnique in Paris. His fame rests on his establishment of the relationship between electricity and magnetism and his development of the science of electromagnetism.

Amperometric titration. A method of analysis in which current flowing through a cell by means of a pair of electrodes is plotted against added titrant. There are generally sharp breaks in the curves at the end points.

Amphetamine (trade name Benzedrine), **β-aminopropylbenzene,** $C_9H_{13}N$. A colourless

liquid, which distils with some decomposition at $200°$. Slightly soluble in water, more soluble in alcohol, readily soluble in acids. It is prepared by the reduction of phenylacetone oxime. It is a vasoconstrictor, resembling adrenaline in its properties, and when inhaled relieves hay-fever and catarrh. Its sulphate, which is readily soluble, when taken by mouth has a stimulating effect, causing an increase in mental activity and a feeling of well-being. The dextrorotatory isomer ($[\alpha]_D + 19\cdot5°$) reduces the appetite and is taken in slimming treatments.

Amphiprotic. A term used to describe solvents such as water and alcohols which are both protogenic (i.e. acidic) and protophilic (i.e. basic).

Amphoteric electrolyte, ampholyte. This term refers to substances which behave both as acids and as bases.

Amphoteric oxide or **hydroxide.** An oxide or hydroxide which can be acidic or basic in function, i.e. can combine with either an acid or a base to form a salt. Zinc oxide dissolves in acids to form zinc salts (basic function), and also in alkalis to form *zincates* (e.g. $Na_2Zn(OH)_4$) (acidic function); it is thus amphoteric. Aluminium hydroxide (q.v.) is an amphoteric hydroxide.

Ampicillin. See Penicillin.

Amydricaine hydrochloride. $C_{16}H_{26}N_2O_2 \cdot HCl$.

M.p. about 170° (decomp.). White hygroscopic crystalline powder, bitter taste. Soluble 1 in 1 of water, 1 in 4 of alcohol, soluble in chloroform, insoluble in ether. Aqueous solutions are used for local anaesthesia: 2-4% in ophthalmology, 5-10% in rhinolaryngology, 1-4% in urology.

Amygdalin, $C_{20}H_{27}NO_{11}$, is a cyanophoric glycoside found in the kernels of most fruits belonging to the *Rosaceae*, particularly in bitter almonds. It is one of the oldest and best-known of the glycosides and is gentiobiose mandelonitrile,

$$C_6H_5CH(CN) \cdot O \cdot C_6H_{10}O_4 \cdot O \cdot C_6H_{11}O_5.$$

Emulsin hydrolyses it to benzaldehyde, hydrogen cyanide, and glucose, hence the smell and taste when a bitter almond is masticated. Yeast splits off one molecule of glucose, leaving mandelonitrile-β-glucoside. Gentiobiose has been obtained directly from amygdalin by catalytic hydrogenation in presence of palladium. It has m.p. 215°, $[\alpha]_D$ −40°. It is widely used as a flavouring material in the form of essence of bitter almonds.

Amyl, iso. The group $(CH_3)_2CHCH_2CH_2—$.

Amyl, normal, *n*-Amyl. The group
$$CH_3 \cdot CH_2 \cdot CH_2 \cdot CH_2 \cdot CH_2—.$$

Amyl, secondary. The group

$$\begin{array}{c} CH_3CH_2CH_2 \\ \end{array} \hspace{-1em} \diagdown CH— \\ CH_3 \diagup$$

Amyl, tertiary. The group

$$\begin{array}{c} CH_3 \diagdown \\ CH_3CH_2—C— \\ CH_3 \diagup \end{array}$$

Amyl acetate, $C_7H_{14}O_2$, is a colourless, volatile liquid with a strong pear-like odour, d^{15} 0·8762, b.p. 138·5°. Very slightly soluble in water; miscible with alcohol and ether. Manufactured by heating amyl alcohol with potassium acetate and sulphuric acid or by heating amyl alcohol with acetic ester in the presence of a little sulphuric acid. Commercial amyl acetate is usually a mixture of isoamyl acetate,

$$(CH_3)_2CHCH_2CH_2OOCCH_3,$$

with varying amounts of secondary amyl acetate, $CH_3CH_2CH(CH_3)CH_2OOCCH_3$. It is used as a solvent for cellulose acetate lacquers and paints: an alcoholic solution is used for flavouring purposes as 'essence of Jargonelle pears.'

Amyl alcohols, $C_5H_{12}O$. Eight alcohols of this formula are possible. The amyl alcohol of commerce is obtained by distillation of fusel oil and is a mixture of isoamyl alcohol with from 13 to 60% secondary amyl alcohol; it has b.p. 128°-132°. It is used in the preparation of amyl acetate, amyl nitrite, and amylene. The most important of the amyl alcohols are: (1) *isoamyl alcohol, isobutyl carbinol,* $(CH_3)_2CHCH_2CH_2OH$, a colourless liquid with an unpleasant odour; inhalation of its vapour causes violent coughing, $d°$ 8·823, b.p. 131·4°. Soluble in water to 3·4%; water is soluble in the alcohol to 2%. Obtained from fusel oil or by treating monochlorisopentane with sodium hydroxide. Oxidized by chromic acid to isovaleric acid; (2) *active amyl alcohol, sec. butyl carbinol,* $CH_3CH_2CH(CH_3)CH_2OH$, b.p. 128°, $[\alpha]_D^{20}$ −5·90°; (3) *normal amyl alcohol,* $CH_3CH_2CH_2CH_2CH_2OH$, b.p. 137°, obtained by treating *n*-chloropentane with sodium hydroxide; (4) *amylene hydrate, tert. amyl alcohol,* $CH_3CH_2C \cdot (CH_3)_2OH$, is a colourless liquid with a penetrating camphor-like odour, $d°$ 0·844, b.p. 102°. Prepared from β-isoamylene by passing this into sulphuric acid and then diluting with water. Complex mixtures of various amyl alcohols are manufactured from chloropentanes derived from petroleum.

Amylase, diastase. Amylases are widely present in animal and plant tissues serving to break down starches and glycogen to the maltose stage. In malting, diastase is of prime importance; in the saliva the enzyme acts to hydrolyse starchy foods. There are two types of amylase. α-Amylases, from pancreas, salivary glands, malt, and other sources, split starch or glycogen into dextrins, and slowly split the dextrins to maltose; they act on the branched chain amylopectin molecules. β-Amylase, obtained most readily from grains, splits amylose directly to maltose, but cannot act on branched chains. The two amylases act most rapidly when present together. They differ from phosphorylases in that they use only water to hydrolyse their substrates. Both types of amylase have been obtained crystalline.

Amylene hydrate. See Amyl alcohols.

Amyl ether. A colourless liquid with a pleasant odour, d^{15} 0·7807, b.p. 172·5°-173°. It is almost insoluble in water, but miscible with alcohol or ether. Manufactured by heating amyl alcohol with sulphuric acid. The commercial amyl ether is a mixture of isoamyl ether, $[(CH_3)_2CHCH_2CH_2]_2O$, with varying amounts

$$\begin{array}{c} CH_3 \\ | \\ (CH_3CH_2CH—CH_2)_2O \end{array}$$

of secondary amyl ether. It is used as a solvent for fats and essential oils and also for a variety of chemical reactions requiring a high boiling ether type solvent.

Amyl nitrite, $C_5H_{11}ONO$. A greenish-yellow liquid with a sweetish odour; inhalation of its vapour causes headache, d^{18} 0·870-0·880, b.p. 97°-99°. Insoluble in water, miscible with alcohol. Prepared by adding sulphuric acid to a cooled mixture of amyl alcohol and sodium nitrite. Commercial amyl nitrite is a mixture of isoamyl nitrite with varying amounts of secondary amyl nitrite. It is unstable and rapidly decomposed by light; it should be kept in dark bottles. Used to prepare certain nitroso and diazonium compounds.

On inhalation it causes rapid but transitory reduction of the blood pressure through dilation of the surface blood vessels. It is of great value in attacks of angina pectoris.

Amylobarbitone, $C_{11}H_{18}N_2O_3$. **5-Ethyl-5-iso-amylbarbituric acid.** It is a white crystalline powder, soluble in 1500 parts of water or 5 parts of alcohol; m.p. 155°-158°. It is made by

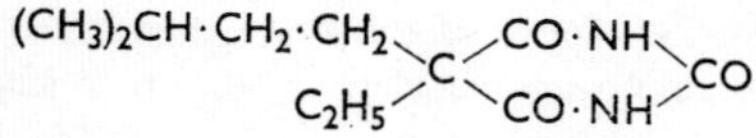

$$(CH_3)_2CH \cdot CH_2 \cdot CH_2 \diagdown \quad \diagup CO \cdot NH \diagdown$$
$$C \qquad \qquad CO$$
$$C_2H_5 \diagup \quad \diagdown CO \cdot NH \diagup$$

condensing ethyl ethylisopentyl malonate with urea. It is an intermediate acting barbiturate, used as a hypnotic and sedative.

Amylocaine hydrochloride, $C_{14}H_{21}NO_2 \cdot HCl$.

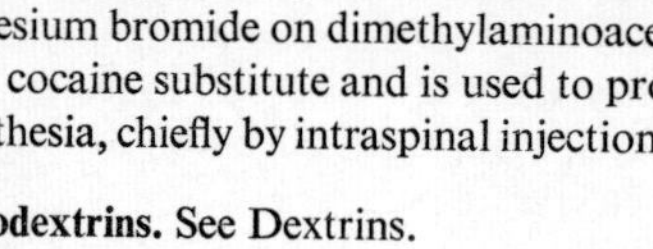

$$(CH_3)_2N \cdot CH_2 \diagdown$$
$$C_2H_5 - C \cdot OOC \cdot C_6H_5, HCl,$$
$$CH_3 \diagup$$

A colourless crystalline powder with a bitter taste, m.p. 177°-179°, soluble in water and alcohol. Prepared by the action of ethyl magnesium bromide on dimethylaminoacetone. It is a cocaine substitute and is used to produce anaesthesia, chiefly by intraspinal injection.

Amylodextrins. See Dextrins.

Amylopectin. See Starch.

Amylo process. A process for the production of alcohol from corn and other sources of starch by the joint action of yeast and a diastase secreting fungus. The fungi used were formerly varieties of *Amylomyces*, but now varieties of *Mucor* and *Rhizopus* are used. The fungus converts the starch to sugar, and yeast converts the sugar to alcohol.

Amylose. See Starch.

Amyrin. The amyrins are pentacyclic triterpenoid compounds, $C_{30}H_{50}O$.

β-Amyrin, m.p. 199·5°-200°, $[\alpha]_D$ +99·8° in benzene, has the structure

β-Amyrin

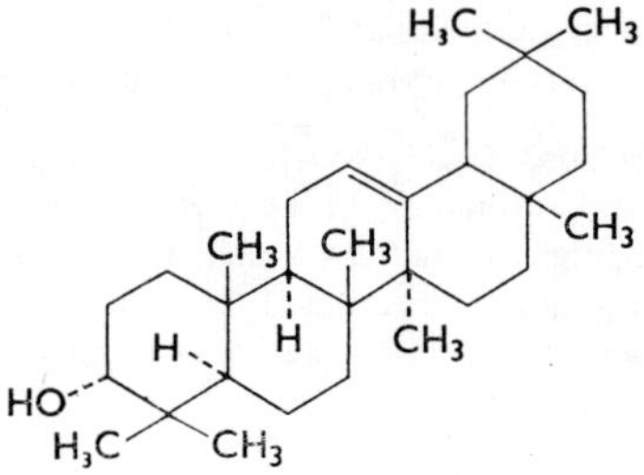

α-Amyrin

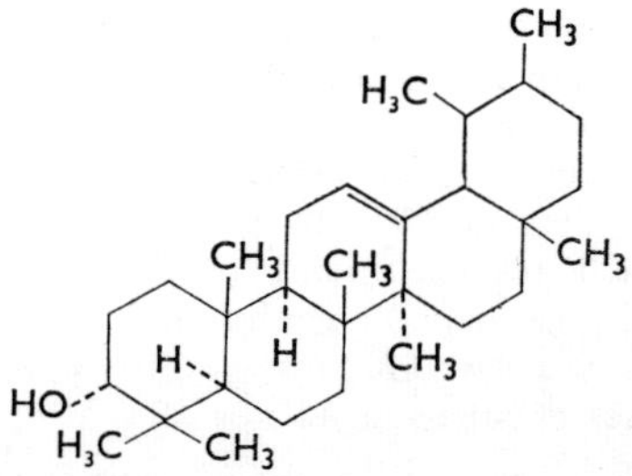

α-Amyrin, m.p. 186°, $[\alpha]_D$ + 88° in benzene, differs in structure only in the position of one methyl group. See 'Elsevier's Encyclopaedia of Organic Chemistry,' Vol. 14, 1940 and 1952.

Amytal. A trade name for amylobarbitone.

Anabasine, neonicotine, $C_{10}H_{14}N_2$, is a naturally occurring liquid alkaloid, m.p. 9°. It is soluble in water, alcohols and ether. It can be distinguished from nicotine as it gives no turbidity with an ethereal solution of iodine. It is very poisonous and can be used as an insecticide.

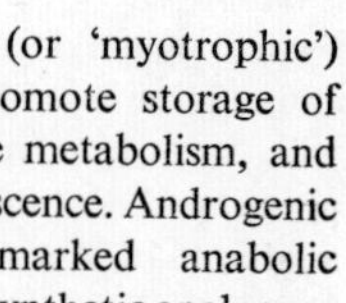

Anabolic agents. Anabolic (or 'myotrophic') agents are drugs which promote storage of protein and stimulate tissue metabolism, and which are of value in convalescence. Androgenic steroid hormones have marked anabolic properties, and a number of synthetic analogues with favourable ratios of anabolic to androgenic activity are in therapeutic use.

Anabolism. See Metabolism.

Analcite. See Zeolites.

Analysis. The identification of a substance or of the components in a mixture of substances is termed qualitative analysis. Analysis of inorganic substances is carried out by various physical methods; e.g. metals are analysed by spark spectra, mixtures may be analysed by ultra-violet or infra-red spectroscopy, or by identification of X-ray powder patterns. Mixtures were formerly analysed by separations based on the different solubilities of various salts of cations, the anions most commonly used being chloride, sulphide, hydroxide, and carbonate. However this method is now used only in academic teaching, and modern chemical analysis is carried out using various organic reagents which are more or less specific for a given metal (see Aluminon, Cupferron, Magneson). Organic qualitative analysis is carried out by identification of the type of compound by physical methods or by specific reactions followed by complete identification by preparation of derivatives or by physical methods. The physical methods most used are ultra-violet, infra-red, or nuclear magnetic resonance spectroscopy, mass spectrometry, or molecular weight determination. Chromatography is much used.

Quantitative analysis is the estimation of the amount of element or group present in a mixture or compound. This is done by various methods, in volumetric analysis a titration, in gravimetric analysis a precipitation followed by a weighing, in colorimetric analysis the estimation of a coloured complex. Other quantitative methods include infra-red spectroscopy, estimation of the opalescence of a precipitate (turbidimetry, nephelometry, and fluorimetry), estimation of optical rotation, electrolytic decomposition, potentiometric, conductiometric and amperometric titrations, and polarography. Using the appropriate methods analysis can be carried out on almost any quantity of material. Organic quantitative analysis is generally carried out by physical methods or by conversion to known derivatives which can be estimated by weighing or by titration.

Anatase, octahedrite. A mineral occurring as steel-blue or yellow isolated crystals in schistose rocks (e.g. in the Alps), or as minute crystals in sedimentary rocks; it consists of titanium dioxide, TiO_2. See also Rutile.

Andalusite, Al_2O_3, SiO_2. An aluminium silicate occurring in some metamorphosed clays as pink or reddish orthorhombic crystals with a vitreous lustre. Sp.gr. 3·1-3·3. Hardness 7-8. Refractive index maximum 1·643, minimum 1·632. It is trimorphous with kyanite and sillimanite (q.v.). The structural difference between these forms lies in the environment of one of the aluminium atoms but the general nature of the three structures is similar, all being orthosilicates. Almost insoluble in hydrofluoric acid. On heating, it shows a very slight exothermal reaction at 940°. At higher temperatures

it changes, first into kyanite and then into mullite and cristobalite. *Uses*—as a refractory material in the manufacture of electrical porcelain (sparking plugs), firebricks, and for the tamped linings of metallurgical furnaces.

Andreasen pipette. An apparatus widely used for obtaining the size distribution in a powder. A suspension of the powder is made and allowed to settle. At various time-intervals small but definite columns of suspension are withdrawn from a fixed level in the suspension by means of a pipette, and evaporated to dryness to obtain the solid/liquid ratio. Application of Stokes's law then allows calculation of the size distribution.

Andrews, Thomas (1813-1885). Born in Belfast, Andrews studied chemistry at Glasgow and Paris before graduating in medicine at Edinburgh University. After a period in medical practice in Belfast, he was appointed, in 1845, professor of chemistry in Queen's College, an appointment which he held until his retirement in 1879. An able experimenter, he is best known for his work on the continuity of the gaseous and liquid states.

Andrews titration. An important titration for the estimation of reducing agents. The reducing agent is dissolved in concentrated hydrochloric acid and titrated with potassium iodate solution. A drop of carbon tetrachloride is added to the solution and the end point is indicated by the disappearance of the iodine colour from this layer. The reducing agent is oxidized and the iodate reduced to ICl.

Androsterone, $C_{19}H_{30}O_2$.

Systematic name 3α-hydroxy-5α-androstan-17-one; a typical urinary ketosteroid arising by metabolic reduction of testosterone. M.p. 182°-183°, $[\alpha]_D + 94°$ in ethanol. Androsterone has androgenic activity but is less potent than testosterone.

Anemometers. Strictly, an anemometer is any instrument for measuring the flow of a gas, but the term is normally reserved for the instruments described below.

The *vane anemometer* consists of a delicate windmill mounted on jewelled bearings and attached to a revolution counter. When placed in a stream of gas the rate of revolution of the windmill gives a measure of the gas velocity. In the *hot wire anemometer* the rate of heat loss from an electrically heated wire is measured, while in the *Thomas meter* the temperature rise of a gas stream due to the addition of a small quantity of heat is measured.

Anethole, $C_{10}H_{12}O$. White leaflets, with a strong smell and sweet taste, m.p. 22°, b.p. 235°, d^{25} 0·983-0·987, n_D^{20} 1·5271, very slightly soluble in water, soluble in alcohol and organic solvents. It is the chief constituent of anise and fennel oils and other essential oils, from which it is manufactured. It can also be prepared from anisole. It is widely used for flavouring pharmaceuticals and dentifrices, and in perfumery.

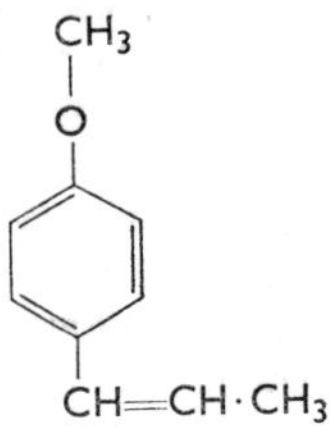

Aneurine. See Thiamine.

Angelic acid, $C_5H_8O_2$, crystallizes in colourless

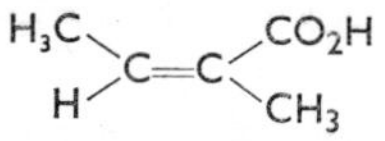

prisms, m.p. 45°-46°, b.p. 185°. Moderately soluble in water; volatile in steam. It occurs free in the roots of *Angelica archangelica*. When heated alone or with acids or alkalis it is converted to tiglic acid.

Angiotensins. Linear polypeptides, isolated from mammalian blood after incubation with renin (*q.v.*), which give rise to strong vasoconstriction, and may be concerned in the disease of arterial hypertension. Angiotensins occur in two forms (I) a relatively inactive decapeptide, and (II) (arising from I by the action of plasma enzymes) an octapeptide which is a potent vasoconstrictor. Both forms have been synthesized.

Asp.Arg.Val.Tyr.Val.His.Pro.Phe.His.Leu.
——Bovine Angiotensin II————|
|——Bovine Angiotensin I————

Angle of contact. A liquid will either rise in a

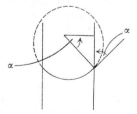

glass capillary tube (e.g. water) or be depressed (e.g. mercury) depending on the relative strengths of the intermolecular forces in the different phases—in particular on the cohesive forces within the liquid and the adhesive forces

between the solid and the liquid. When water rises in a capillary tube the angle which the liquid surface makes with the tube walls is less than 90° and a concave meniscus results. Water is then said to 'wet' the glass surface. In the figure the angle α between the liquid surface and the solid is the angle of contact. If α is less than 90° a concave meniscus results and if α is greater than 90° the meniscus is convex. When $\alpha = 90°$ a plane meniscus is given. The angle of contact of water on pure paraffin wax is about 110°.

Anglesite. A mineral forming brilliant colourless orthorhombic crystals, and consisting of lead sulphate, $PbSO_4$. It occurs in association with galena, PbS, from which it has been formed by oxidation.

Ångstrom unit, Å. A unit of length, equivalent to 10^{-8} (1/100,000,000) cm. Commonly used as a unit of wave-length of light, and of dimensions of molecules.

Anharmonicity. Harmonic vibrations are characterized by a restoring force which is proportional to the displacement (i.e. Hooke's law is obeyed). Vibrations of atomic nuclei within molecules are harmonic only for very small amplitudes. Band spectra show that for larger amplitudes, especially those approaching the dissociation point of the bond, atomic vibrations are markedly anharmonic. The anharmonicity constant is the proportionality coefficient for deviations from harmonic character.

Anhydride. A substance formed by elimination of one or more molecules of water from one or more molecules of an acid, or (less frequently) a base. Thus phthalic acid on heating gives pthalic anhydride. Similarly, sulphur trioxide

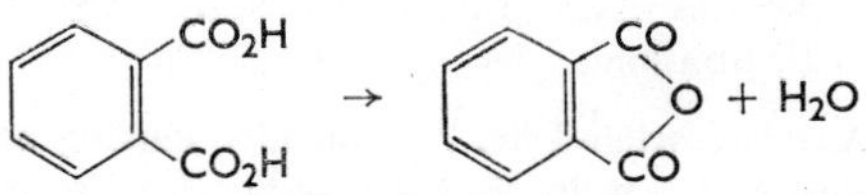

SO_3, is the anhydride of sulphuric acid, H_2SO_4, while ammonia NH_3, is the anhydride of the base NH_4OH.

Anhydrite. A mineral consisting of anhydrous calcium sulphate, $CaSO_4$, associated in nature with gypsum and rock-salt. It resembles marble in appearance, and may be white, grey, reddish, or bluish in colour. Orthorhombic, sp.gr. 2·9-3·0, hardness, 3-3½. Converted by water into gypsum, $CaSO_4,2H_2O$, with an increase in volume of about 60%. Aqueous calcium sulphate solutions containing large quantities of other salts deposit anhydrite or gypsum on evaporation according to the temperature and concentration. Anhydrite is used in the manufacture of ammonium sulphate and sulphuric acid.

Anhydro. A prefix for an organic compound indicating that one or more molecules of hydrogen have been removed.

Anhydrone. See Magnesium perchlorate.

Anilides. A name applied to the acyl derivatives of aniline of which acetanilide and acetoacetanilide are the commonest examples.

Aniline, C_6H_7N. Colourless oily liquid, turning brown on oxidation, m.p. $-6\cdot2°$, b.p. $184°$, d^{15}, $1\cdot027$, n_D^{20} $1\cdot585$. Insoluble in water, soluble in alcohol, ether, benzene, or dilute aqueous mineral acids. Easily volatile in steam. Characteristic smell. It is manufactured from nitrobenzene by vapour phase hydrogenation in the presence of a copper catalyst, or by reduction with iron and water containing a trace of hydrochloric acid. The main use for aniline is in the manufacture of antioxidants and vulcanization accelerators for the rubber industry, but it is also employed for the manufacture of dyes and pharmaceuticals.

On acetylation it gives acetanilide, m.p. $114°$. Nitrated with some decomposition to a mixture of o- and p-nitranilines. It is basic and gives water-soluble salts with the mineral acids. Heating aniline sulphate at $190°$ gives sulphanilic acid. When heated with alkyl chlorides or aliphatic alcohols mono- and di-alkyl derivatives are obtained, e.g. dimethylaniline. Treatment with trichlorethylene gives phenylglycine. With glycerol and sulphuric acid (Skraup's reaction) quinoline is obtained, while quinaldine can be prepared by the reaction between aniline, paraldehyde, and hydrochloric acid.

With sodium nitrite in dilute mineral acid solution at $0°$ aniline gives benzene diazonium chloride, which loses nitrogen on warming and give phenol.

The diazonium group may also be replaced by halogeno- or cyano-groups by double decomposition with cuprous halide or cyanide (Sandmeyer reaction); it can be coupled with phenols and amines to give coloured azo-compounds.

Aniline is readily halogenated, treatment with bromine water giving an instant precipitate of 2,4,6-tribromoaniline.

Oxidation with chromic acid gives p-benzoquinone.

Aniline black, Oxidation Base 1. $(C_6H_5N)_x$. An insoluble black pigment obtained by the oxidation of aniline in acid solution. On reduction it gives di-p-diaminodiphenylamine.

Owing to its insolubility it is dyed by direct oxidation of the fibre impregnated with aniline. Although at one time aniline black was an extremely important fast black for cotton dyeing its use is gradually declining.

Aniline point. The aniline point of an oil is its lowest temperature of miscibility with an equal volume of aniline.

Anils, *N*-Phenylimides. See Schiff's bases.

Anion. A negatively charged atom or group of atoms. Anions are present both in the solid state, e.g. Cl^- ions in $NaCl$, and in solutions of ionized salts. In the electrolysis of solutions anions travel to the anode where they are discharged.

Anisaldehyde, $C_8H_8O_2$. A colourless liquid, b.p. $248°$, sp.gr. $1\cdot123$ at $15°$. It occurs in aniseed and is used in synthetic perfumery under the name 'aubepine' or artificial hawthorn.

o-**Anisidine,** C_7H_9NO. A colourless oil, m.p. $2\cdot5°$, b.p. $225°$, sp.gr. $1\cdot0978$ at $15°$.

Acetyl derivative, m.p. $87°$-$88°$.

It is prepared by the reduction of *o*-nitroanisole with iron and hydrochloric acid. It is used as a first component in making azo dyestuffs.

Anisole, C_7H_8O. Colourless liquid, m.p. $-37\cdot5°$, b.p. $155°$. Miscible with alcohol and ether, insoluble in water, $[n]_D^{22}$ $1\cdot515$.

Prepared by the action of dimethyl sulphate on a solution of phenol in excess of alkali.

Anisotropic. A substance is anisotropic when any of its physical properties (e.g. thermal or electrical conductivity, refractive index) are different in different directions. Crystals, other than those belonging to the cubic system, are anisotropic. Certain substances (e.g. p-azoxyanisole) melt to form a cloudy anisotropic liquid ('liquid crystals'), which again 'melts' at a higher temperature to a normal (isotropic) liquid.

Annealing. Heating a metal to a high temperature, keeping it at this high temperature for a specified time, and then cooling slowly in the furnace, the object being to relieve stresses that may have been set up in the metal by previous treatment. The annealing of steel is extensively practised, the temperature employed being either $50°$ above the upper critical or $100°$ below the lower critical temperature.

Treatment by annealing to relieve stresses is

also necessary in the manufacture of glass and ceramic products.

Annulenes. Simple conjugated cyclic poly-alkenes: a prefix [*n*] is added to indicate the number of carbon atoms in the cycle. Thus [18]-annulene is a reasonably stable brown-red

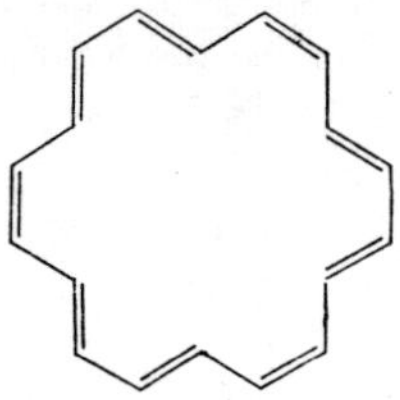

crystalline solid, which has *cis* and *trans* double bonds. A number of annulenes have been synthesized.

Anode. The electrode which carries the positive charge is termed the anode, and it is on this electrode that the negative ions, such as chlorine, are liberated during electrolysis.

Anodic oxidation. Oxidation in solution by means of an electric current. Typical examples are: the oxidation of Mn(II) to Mn(IV) in the preparation of K_2MnF_6; the oxidation of SO_4^{2-} to $S_2O_8^{2-}$.

Anodizing. The anodic oxidation of metal sections with the object of giving protection against corrosion. It is most commonly used for aluminium sheet. A porous oxide coating is formed when the sheet metal is made the anode of a sulphuric–chromic bath. After washing, the sheets may be coloured by dyes which are readily adsorbed in the pores. The pores are finally sealed by dipping in hot water.

Anomers. This is a specific term used to describe carbohydrate stereoisomers differing only in

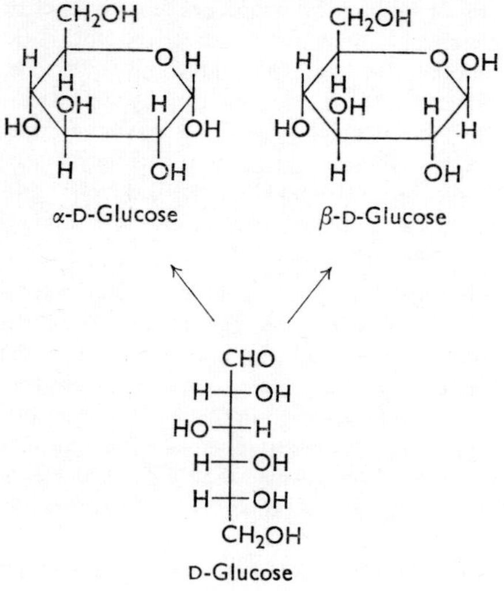

α-D-Glucose   β-D-Glucose

D-Glucose

configuration at the hemiacetal carbon atom, i.e. the carbonyl carbon atom in the open chain projection. These stereoisomers are referred to as the α and β anomers and for D-glucose, for example, both forms are known.

Anorthic system. See Triclinic system.

Anorthite, one of the feldspar minerals, with a composition corresponding to

$$CaO, Al_2O_3, 2SiO_2.$$

Crystals are triclinic, but many partial forms are known and twins are common, sp.gr. 2·73-2·76, hardness 6, m.p. 1310°. Colourless or white (very rarely pink). It is used as a flux for making glazes more fusible, and as a source of lime, alumina, and silica in glazes.

Anserine, β-**Alanylmethylhistidine,** $C_{10}H_{16}N_4O_3$. A dipeptide, crystallizing in colourless needles, m.p. 238°-239°, soluble in water, sparingly sol-

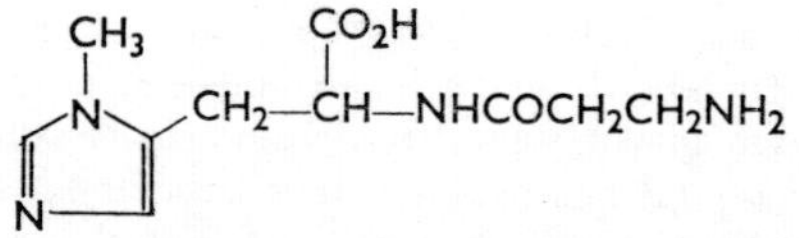

uble in alcohol, $[\alpha]_D^{16} + 11\cdot26°$. It is a constituent of the muscles of birds and fishes, and of the muscles of certain mammals, in which it is found in company with carnosine. Its function is unknown.

Antabuse. A trade name for disulfiram, tetraethylthiouram disulphide, $C_{10}H_{20}N_2S_4$.

$$(C_2H_5)_2:N\cdot CS\cdot S\cdot S\cdot SC\cdot N:(C_2H_5)_2$$

It is a white powder, insoluble in water, soluble in alcohol. The drug is used in treating chronic alcoholism as it interferes with the normal metabolism of alcohol, causing increased production of acetaldehyde, which causes nausea, vomiting, and unpleasant systemic effects. The treatment is only of use when the patient is willing to co-operate.

Anthocyanidins are the coloured aglycones (sugar-free compounds) obtained by hydrolysis of the glycoside-containing anthocyanins.

Anthocyanins. The universal soluble red, violet, and blue pigments of flowers, fruits, and leaves are all glycosides which on hydrolysis yield one or more sugars and an anthocyanidin of which there are three fundamental types: pelargonidin (1), cyanidin (2), and delphinidin (3). These differ in containing 1, 2, or 3 hydroxyls respectively in the side ring. Other anthocyanidins are methyl ethers of these; thus peonidin is the methyl ether of cyanidin, and petunidin, malvidin, and hirsutidin are mono-, di-, and tri-ethers of delphinidin.

42

The effect of pH on the colour of the antho-cyanin, cyanin, is shown:

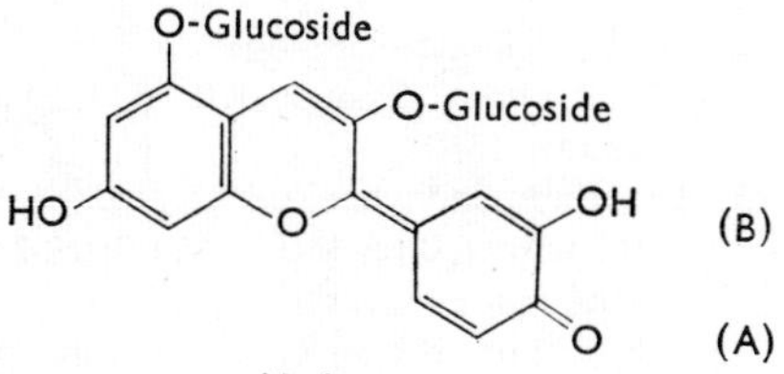

Violet

Acid solution. Protonation at (A) gives Cyanin Cation (Red)

Alkaline solution. Deprotonation at (B) gives Cyanin Anion (Blue)

Many anthocyanins have been synthesized by unambiguous methods. The natural antho-cyanins may be divided into 3-mono-gluco-sides or galactosides, 3-rhamnoglycosides, 3-biosides, 3,5-diglycosides, and acetylated anthocyanins; of these the diglycosides are the most widely distributed. They exhibit amphoteric character forming salts with both acids and bases, a fact made use of in their isolation. The main factors affecting flower colours are the nature and concentration of the anthocyanins, their state of aggregation in solution which is affected by the pH, and the presence or absence of co-pigments.

Anthracene, $C_{14}H_{10}$. Colourless plates with slight blue fluorescence. Insoluble in water,

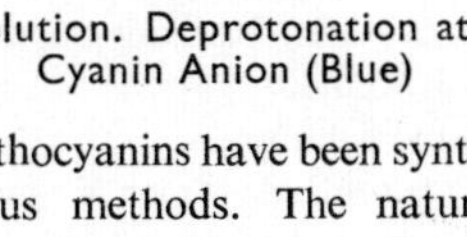

slightly soluble in cold ether, naphtha, and toluene, fairly soluble (12%) in boiling toluene; m.p. 217°, b.p. 354°-355°.

It is present in coal tar to about $\frac{1}{2}$%, from which it is separated by fractional distillation. Can be chlorinated and sulphonated in the usual manner, and nitrated by a mixture of nitric acid, acetic acid, and acetic anhydride. Treatment with sulphuric and nitric acids gives anthraquinone derivatives.

Of little use commercially except as a route to anthraquinone. For this purpose it is oxidized with acid potassium dichromate solution, or better, by a catalytic air oxidation at 180°-280°, using vanadates or other metal oxide catalysts.

Anthracite. A hard coal which usually has a brilliant lustre and a conchoidal fracture; it is relatively difficult to ignite, but burns at a high temperature and with little or no flame. Anthracite probably represents the most ad-vanced stage of coal formation and has more carbon and less hydrogen than all lower rank

coals; the calorific value (about 15,600 Btu. per lb. on the 'pure coal' basis) is high. Extensive anthracite beds occur in the South Wales coalfields.

Anthraflavone, G. This is an anthraquinone vat

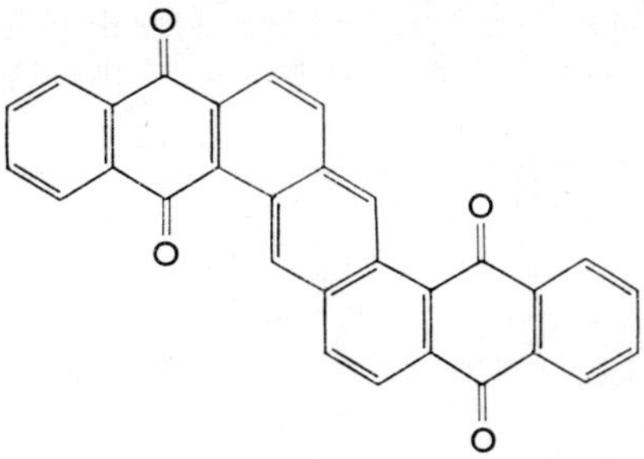

dyestuff which dyes cotton a yellow shade. It was also used in a mixture with indanthren to give a green dyestuff, but is no longer manu-factured commercially.

Anthrahydroquinone. See Oxanthrol.

Anthranilic acid, $C_7H_7NO_2$. Colourless leaflets, m.p. 144·6°. Soluble in water, alcohol, and ether to give a solution having a blue fluorescence. It is both acidic and basic.

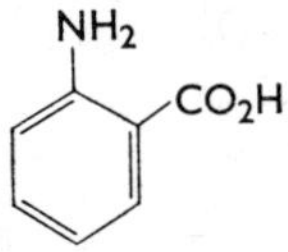

It is prepared by the action of sodium hydroxide and sodium hypochlorite on phthalimide (Hofmann reac-tion). When heated with soda lime it gives aniline.

It is an important dyestuffs intermediate. It condenses with chloroacetic acid to give phenylglycine-o-carboxylic acid for the synthesis of indigo. It can be diazotized and used as a first component in azo-dyes; it condenses also with chloroanthraquinones to give intermediates for anthraquinone dyes.

Decomposition of its internal salt (a zwitter-ion) in, e.g., ether, provides a convenient source of benzyne for organic synthesis.

Anthranol, $C_{14}H_{10}O$. It crystallizes in golden

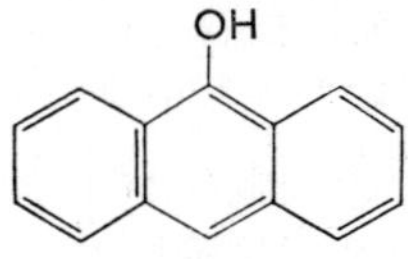

brown needles which sinter at 120° and melt to a clear liquid at 152°. It is easily soluble in caustic alkalis to a deep yellow solution. It couples easily with diazonium salts, and is rapidly oxidized by bromine or ferric chloride to dihydrodianthrone.

It is prepared by acidifying an alkali solution of anthrone or by reduction of anthraquinone with aluminium powder and concentrated sulphuric acid.

Anthranol is isomeric with anthrone, and behaves in its reactions as a typical hydroxylic compound. The equilibrium mixture between the two compounds consists mainly of the keto form; anthranol is largely converted into anthrone on heating.

It is used in the preparation of benzanthrone by heating with glycerol and sulphuric acid (Skraup's reaction).

Anthraquinone, $C_{14}H_8O_2$.

Colourless needles or prisms which can be purified by sublimation or steam distillation. M.p. 284·6°, b.p. 379°-381°. It is insoluble in water, but soluble in ether, acetone and alcohol to varying degrees. It is also soluble in hot conc. sulphuric acid and may be recovered unchanged on dilution. It is manufactured by condensing benzene with phthalic anhydride in the presence of aluminium chloride to give o-benzoyl benzoic acid; this is then converted to anthraquinone by heating with concentrated sulphuric acid at 120°-150°. Another method is the condensation of 1,4-naphthoquinone with butadiene, the former being obtained by the vapour phase oxidation of naphthalene.

Anthraquinone is a very stable compound which probably more closely resembles diketones than quinones: it yields a monoxide with difficulty.

Reduction of anthraquinone with alkaline hydrosulphite yields an alkali soluble anthrahydroquinone which is tautomeric with ex-anthranol also called 'vat' or 'leuco-compound'. More vigorous reduction yields anthrone (q.v.) and finally anthracene.

It has been used as a bird repellant and is the parent compound of the anthraquinone vat dyes in which the dyeing is carried out by immersion in the reduced vat solution followed by air oxidation to the original insoluble compound.

Anthraquinone can be brominated, chlorinated directly to the tetra-chloro (1, 4, 5, 8-) stage, nitrated easily in the 1-position, but gives the 1,5- and 1,8-dinitro-derivatives on prolonged nitration: the nitro groups in these compounds are easily displaced by neutral solutions of alkali sulphites yielding the corresponding sulphonic acids.

Anthraquinone dyes. The very large number of vat dyes based on anthraquinone can be subdivided into several groups, chiefly

(1) Acylamino anthraquinones
    Indanthren Yellow 5 GK (C.I. Vat Yellow 26)
(2) Anthraquinone—acridones
    Indanthren Orange RR (C.I. Vat Orange 13)
(3) Dianthraquinonylamines
    Indanthren Grey K (C.I. Vat Black 28)
(4) Anthraquinone—carbazols
    Indanthren Brown R (C.I. Vat Brown 3)
(5) Anthraquinone—acridines
    Indanthren Red RK (q.v.)
(6) Indanthrones (q.v.)
    Indanthren Brilliant Scarlet RK (C.I. Vat Red 40)
(7) Polycylic quinones
    Caledon Jade Green X (q.v.)

Among other anthraquinone vat dyes are a number which contain free amino groups, the introduction of which has a bathochromic effect on the hue, e.g. Indanthren Turquoise Blue GK. (C.I. Vat Blue 32).

Anthraquinone glycosides. These are present in madder, the ground root of *Rubia tinctorum*; they are yellow or red colouring matters used with mordants and are of great importance as dyestuffs (alizarin). The best-known is ruberythric acid (q.v.). Several are primeverosides, others contain glucose; frangulin has rhamnose as its sugar. They have been found in a limited number of plants and are regarded as the end products of a general type of metabolism leading to aromatic compounds.

Anthraquinone sulphonic acids. Direct sulphonation of anthraquinone is most conveniently carried out with 20% to 30% oleum. In this way only the β-position is substituted, the 2-monosulphonic acid and the 2,6- and 2,7-disulphonic acids being obtained. If the sulphonation is carried out in the presence of a little mercury the α-position is exclusively occupied, the 1-mono- and 1,5- and 1,8-disulphonic acids being obtained.

Anthraquinone sulphonic acids are very important, as nearly all anthraquinone derivatives are obtained from them.

Anthraquinone-α-sulphonic acid forms colourless leaflets, m.p. 214°, soluble in water. The potassium salt is only sparingly soluble in water. It is used in the preparation of α-aminoanthraquinone.

Anthraquinone-β-sulphonic acid forms white leaflets soluble in water and alcohol. The sodium salt, commonly called 'silver salt,' is sparingly soluble in cold water. It is used for the preparation of alizarin and β-aminoanthraquinone and to prepare Fieser's solution (q.v.).

Anthrarufin, $C_{14}H_8O_4$. Crystallizes in yellow

needles, m.p. 280°. It is insoluble in water, sparingly soluble in alcohol and ether, moderately soluble in benzene. It dissolves in caustic alkalis to a red solution.

It is prepared from anthraquinone-1, 5-disulphonic acid by heating at a high temperature with calcium hydroxide solution.

It is used for the preparation of Alizarin Saphirol R, which is an acid wool dye, probably diamidoanthrarufin disulphonic acid.

Anthraxylon. A macroscopic constituent of coal. As defined by R. Thiessen, it is formed from the woody parts of trees and still shows the cellular structure of the original wood when viewed in thin section under the microscope. Anthraxylon can be correlated with vitrain (*q.v.*) in general and with vitrinite in particular, as defined by European workers in coal technology.

Anthrone, $C_{14}H_{10}O$. It forms colourless needles,

m.p. 154°. It is insoluble in cold aqueous alkalis, but on boiling it dissolves as the alkali metal salt of anthranol. It is not affected by ferric chloride or bromine (compare anthranol) in hydroxylic solvents.

It is prepared by reduction of anthraquinone with tin and hydrochloric acid in glacial acetic acid solution or by prolonged treatment with sodium hydrosulphite.

It forms an interesting example of isomerism, since on heating it is partly converted into the enolic compound anthranol, a definite equilibrium concentration being reached. When it is treated with caustic soda, however, the equilibrium is disturbed by the removal of the enol as sodium salt and all the anthrone is therefore converted into anthranol. Anthrone does not couple with diazonium salts or show any of the reactions typical of a phenolic compound.

It is used for the preparation of benzanthrone by heating with glycerol and sulphuric acid (Skraup's reaction).

Antibiotics. A widely used term, including (and confusing) a range of biological effects. Antibiotics have been defined by Oxford (*Ann. Rev. Biochem.*, 1945, **14**, 749) as 'soluble organic substances, produced by micro-organisms from normal constituents of a medium, which have been found to be markedly inhibitory to the growth or activity of a second micro-organism when dissolved, at a concentration of 50 p.p.m. or less, in a medium otherwise suitable for the normal growth or activity of this second micro-organism.' A recent definition (Welsch, in 'Comparative Biochemistry', Vol. VII, Academic Press, 1964) is 'chemical substances possessing antimicrobial properties that are produced by higher plants or animals as well as by micro-organisms.'

As implied by the latter definition, antibiotics have been isolated from numerous sources, but principally from bacteria (e.g. bacitracin, polymyxin, gramicidin, subtilin), actinomycetes (e.g. tetracycline, streptomycin, chloramphenicol) and fungi (e.g. gliotoxin, patulin, penicillins, cephalosporins). Bacterial antibiotics are mostly polypeptides. Fungal antibiotics are biosynthesized chiefly from acetate or, in certain cases, propionate units (see Erythromycin).

Many antibiotics are unsuitable for therapeutic use, frequently because of their general toxicity, or as a result of other drawbacks such as instability, inadequate solubility or malabsorption. The antibiotics which are used clinically, especially the penicillins, have revolutionized the treatment of bacterial diseases.

Antibodies. When the serum of an immunized animal has added to it the bacteria or other substances to which it is immune, substances present in the serum will dissolve, agglutinate, or precipitate the added substances. The substances present in the serum are called antibodies and the added substances antigens. Antibodies are probably colloidal and have been proved to be proteins.

Antibonding orbitals. See Molecular orbitals.

Antibronzing agent. Photographic images obtained from fine grain silver halide emulsions are prone to a degradation in colour if subjected, while wet, to heat, e.g. hot glazing. This bronzing, or plumming as it is sometimes called, is due to a fall in the reflection density of the silver and can be prevented by incorporating antibronzing agents, usually heterocyclic mercaptans, into the emulsion during manufacture. Similar results are obtained by the addition of salts such as potassium iodide or sodium selenite to the fixing solutions.

Anti-cathode. See X-ray tube.

Antiferromagnetism. Magnetic behaviour in which the magnetic susceptibility drops with decreasing temperature. There is generally a characteristic temperature, the Néel point, above which the magnetic behaviour is normal.

Anti-foaming agents. Substances which prevent the formation of foams. They are strongly adsorbed by the liquid medium but they do not have the electrical or mechanical properties required to form a foam. Examples of anti-foaming agents are polyamides which are used in boiler feed water and octanol used in electroplating baths and in paper making. Low concentrations of silicones also find quite general use. Some organic lubricants foam strongly unless fluorinated hydrocarbons are present. In this case, these materials are strongly adsorbed at the liquid/air interface and act by displacing the monolayers of the foam stabilizers. See Foams.

Antifoggant. The formation of fog in photographic materials during storage can be prevented by the addition to the emulsion during manufacture of certain organic or inorganic compounds (e.g. 5-nitrobenzimidazole, potassium bromide) which arrest further ripening of the emulsions. These agents, known as antifoggants, are adsorbed to the surface of the halide grains and, in contrast to stabilizers, cause some loss in sensitivity of the emulsion. Antifoggants are also added to developer solutions to prevent the appearance of fog during development. See also Emulsion stabilizers.

Anti-friction metal. See Tin alloys.

Antigens. Antigens are macromolecular substances which, when injected into the blood of an animal, stimulate the production of antibodies (*q.v.*). Examples are bacteria and viruses (living and dead); many proteins; and certain polysaccharides and nucleic acids. See also Haptens.

Antihistamines. Histamine, when released in the tissues, causes allergic reactions such as urticaria, serum sickness, asthma, and hay-fever. The antihistamine drugs antagonize the action of histamine, but they do not remove the cause of the histamine release. Most antihistamines have unpleasant side effects, including sedation, dizziness, lassitude, muscular weakness, and gastro-intestinal disturbances.

Antihormones. Substances antagonizing the effects of natural hormones. Examples are anti-oestrogens and anti-androgens, of interest in connexion with the control of fertility; and antithyroid substances (*q.v.*). In certain instances, the natural hormones occur in mutually antagonistic pairs (e.g. insulin and glucagon).

Antihypo. Potassium percarbonate solution used to remove any residual 'hypo' (sodium thiosulphate) from photographic negatives or prints after fixation.

Anti-isomorphism. If in the crystals of two compounds the relative positions of the various atoms are the same but with the cations in one occupying the positions of the anions in the other, then the two crystals are said to be anti-isomorphous. The structures of ThO_2 and Li_2O afford a simple example. Both have the fluorite type of structure (see Fluorspar) but in the former the thorium ions occupy the calcium positions of that structure whereas in the latter the oxygen ions occupy those positions.

Anti-knock dopes. Substances such as lead tetra-ethyl which, when added to a gasoline, have the effect of raising the octane number. Lead tetra-ethyl is usually added in quantities of the order of 0·05%, together with ethylene dibromide and ethylene dichloride to assist in the elimination of the lead from the combustion space.

Anti-knock value. See Octane number.

Antimonic acids and antimonates. A number of white solid substances, which have been regarded as antimonic acids, have been prepared by the hydrolysis of antimony pentachloride, the action of nitric acid on antimonates, and by other special methods. These compounds have the composition Sb_2O_5, nH_2O, n varying usually from one to six; they are probably not definite compounds, but antimony pentoxide gels. A number of definite antimonates of the types M^ISbO_3, $M^{III}SbO_4$, and $M_2^{II}Sb_2O_7$ are formed by fusion of the mixed oxides, but these are as mixed oxides. The ion $[Sb(OH)_6]^-$ is apparently present in a solution of an antimonate; the potassium salt is soluble in water but the sodium salt precipitates and is used as a reagent for sodium.

Antimonious acids and the antimonites. The free acid is not known, but gels of hydrated antimony (III) oxide exist. Antimonites, salts derived from the hypothetical acid $HSbO_2$, are formed by the action of alkalis on antimony trioxide. A number of more complex compounds containing antimony trioxide are known.

Antimony, Sb. At.no. 51, At.wt. 121·76. Normally occurs as a metallic substance of a white or bluish-white colour, which on polishing resembles silver in appearance; antimony precipitated by reducing agents from solutions of its salts forms a black powder. The crystals are rhombohedral, $a = 4·51$ Å, $\alpha = 57° 6'$, isomorphous with arsenic and bismuth. The structure is a double-layer structure, each antimony atom having three close neighbours (at 2·89 Å) and three at a greater distance (3·35 Å) in the next layer. Sp.gr. 6·7, m.p. 630·5°, b.p. 1380°. Hardness, 3-3·05. The element, and particularly its sulphide, stibnite, were known in 3000 B.C. or even before, stibnite occasionally being used as an eyebrow pigment. Antimony occurs in nature chiefly as stibnite, Sb_2S_3, smaller quantities occurring in the native state or as senarmontite, Sb_2O_3. The element is extracted from stibnite by heating with iron, or with sodium carbonate and carbon; oxide ores are treated by the latter process. The crude antimony is purified by fusing with sodium carbonate and a little potassium nitrate. A number of allotropic forms of the element have been described. 'Yellow' antimony is prepared by the action of oxygen on antimony hydride at $-90°$; on warming it is converted to 'grey' antimony, an ill-defined form which may not be a true allotrope.

Ordinary antimony does not tarnish in air, and is unattacked by water or dilute acids; at a red heat it decomposes steam. Concentrated nitric acid converts antimony to antimonic acid. The sulphate, $Sb_2(SO_4)_3$, is formed by dissolving the element in concentrated sulphuric acid. Aqua regia gives a solution containing $SbCl_6^-$ ions. Antimony burns on heating in air, white fumes of the tri- and tetroxides being produced. Halogens react very vigorously, giving the penta- or trihalides. Sulphur reacts on warming, giving the sulphide, Sb_2S_3. Antimony gives two series of compounds, with oxidation states of 3 and 5. Salts of antimony are, in general, readily hydrolysed by water, giving insoluble basic salts. The principal use of antimony is in the fabrication of alloys, such as type metals, Britannia metal, pewter, and certain bearing metals; some antimony compounds are used as pigments.

Antimony provides the wear resistance in some bearing alloys and in type metal.

Antimony bromides. *Antimony tribromide*, $SbBr_3$. White deliquescent needle crystals, m.p. 96·6°, b.p. 280°. Prepared by the action of bromine, preferably dissolved in carbon disulphide, on antimony, or by distilling a mixture of antimony sulphate and potassium bromide. The tribromide is analogous in properties to the trichloride.

Antimony tetra- and pentabromides. These compounds cannot be isolated. Salts M_2SbBr_6 are known but they contain equal numbers of antimony (III) and (V) atoms. Hexabromoantimonates (V), $MSbBr_6$, are also known.

Antimony chlorides. *Antimony trichloride*, $SbCl_3$ ('Butter of Antimony'). A colourless crystalline solid, m.p. 73·4°, b.p. 220°, generally prepared by dissolving antimony trisulphide in hydrochloric acid, and concentrating and distilling the solution. Decomposed by water to basic chlorides, but soluble in hydrochloric

acid, giving a clear solution. The solid trichloride is very hygroscopic. Antimony trichloride acts as a Lewis acid and forms adducts with many inorganic and organic compounds.

Antimony tetrachloride, $SbCl_4$. This compound does not exist. Salts M_2SbCl_6 are known but these compounds contain equal numbers of Sb (III) and Sb (V) atoms.

Antimony pentachloride, $SbCl_5$. Normally occurs as a heavy yellow liquid, fuming in moist air, m.p. 3°, b.p. 140°; prepared by the action of excess chlorine on antimony, or of chlorine on antimony trichloride; excess chlorine (which deepens the colour of the pentachloride) is removed by a stream of dry carbon dioxide. The pentachloride is slightly dissociated to the trichloride and chlorine at the normal boiling-point, but may be volatilized unchanged at low pressures. Hot water hydrolyses antimony pentachloride to antimonic acid. Complex chlorides, $MSbCl_6$ are known as fairly stable salts.

Antimony fluorides. *Antimony pentafluoride*, SbF_5. A colourless oily liquid, m.p. 8·3°, b.p. 151°, prepared by the direct action of fluorine on antimony, or by treating antimony pentachloride with anhydrous hydrogen fluoride. Very deliquescent, readily absorbing water and forming a hydrate, $SbF_5, 2H_2O$. Hexafluoroantimonates, $MSbF_6$, are stable salts prepared by the action of bromine trifluoride.

Antimony trifluoride, SbF_3. Colourless needle crystals, m.p. 292°, formed on dissolving antimony trioxide in hydrofluoric acid and evaporating, or by distilling antimony with mercuric fluoride. Readily soluble in water (385 g per 100 g water at 0°). The crystals can be sublimed. It is widely used as a fluorinating agent.

Antimony hydride, Stibine, SbH_3. A colourless gas with a characteristic unpleasant odour, b.p. $-17°$, m.p. $-88°$. It is prepared, mixed with hydrogen, by adding a solution of an antimony salt to zinc and dilute hydrochloric acid, or in a purer state by the action of hydrochloric acid on a magnesium-antimony alloy containing 33% of antimony. The gas is fairly stable at ordinary temperatures when dry, but readily decomposes into hydrogen and antimony on warming, and burns in air, forming water and antimony. On passing the gas into silver nitrate solution, silver antimonide, $SbAg_3$, is formed; this is rapidly decomposed, giving a black precipitate containing silver, antimony, and antimony trioxide.

Antimony iodide. *Antimony tri-iodide*, SbI_3. Occurs in red hexagonal, yellow orthorhombic, or greenish-yellow monoclinic crystals, m.p. 167°, b.p. 401°; prepared by adding powdered antimony to a solution of iodine in carbon disulphide, and evaporating the solution. Antimony tri-iodide vapour is orange-red in colour. The compound readily forms complex salts with metallic iodides.

Antimony oxides. *Antimony trioxide*, Sb_2O_3. Occurs naturally as the minerals senarmontite (cubic crystals) and valentinite (rhombic crystals), having a red, grey, or brown colour. The pure trioxide forms a white powder; it is dimorphic, the lattice containing discrete Sb_4O_6 molecules below 570° and being polymeric above this temperature. Antimony trioxide is also formed on passing steam over red-hot antimony. It turns yellow on heating, and on cooling may retain a pale buff colour, m.p. 656°. The trioxide volatilizes at 1425°, the vapour having the composition Sb_4O_6. On heating in air at 900°, the tetroxide, Sb_2O_4, is formed. Hydrogen reduces antimony trioxide to antimony at a red heat. It is almost insoluble in water, but soluble in dilute hydrochloric acid and in concentrated acids giving derivatives of tripositive antimony (e.g. $SbCl_3$, $Sb_2(SO_4)_3$, $Sb(NO_3)_3$); it is also soluble in solutions of many organic acids, and in alkalis (giving in the latter case solutions of antimonites). Commercial antimony trioxide generally contains other oxides; it is used as an opacifier in paints.

Antimony trioxide is largely used as a pigment, especially in France; it is non-poisonous, very soft in texture, and durable. For this purpose stibnite, Sb_2S_3, is roasted in air by itself or mixed with iron and the oxide is sublimed.

Antimony tetroxide, Sb_2O_4. A white or yellowish-white powder prepared by heating the trioxide or pentoxide in air, preferably at about 900°. Antimony tetroxide contains equal numbers of Sb (III) and Sb (V) atoms. A mixture of the tetroxide with antimony sulphide, known as 'glass of antimony' is prepared by roasting stibnite; this substance is used for tinting glass yellow. The oxide is reduced by hydrogen to antimony at a red heat. Salts (e.g. $K_2Sb_4O_9$) are formed on fusing antimony tetroxide with alkalis.

Antimony pentoxide, Sb_2O_5. A yellow powder obtained by repeatedly treating powdered antimony with concentrated nitric acid, and gently heating the product. The pentoxide prepared in this way always contains some lower oxide. On heating this crude oxide with potassium nitrate a potassium antimonate may be extracted into boiling water which gives a hydrated antimony pentoxide on acidification; this gives the pure pentoxide on gentle heating. On heating in air above 350°-400°, antimony pentoxide decomposes, giving the tetroxide. It is insoluble in water, but soluble in hot concentrated hydrochloric acid. It is only sparingly soluble in alkali solutions, but is attacked by fused alkalis giving antimonates.

Antimony oxybromides and oxyiodides. The compounds $Sb_4O_5Br_2$, SbOI, and $Sb_4O_5I_2$, analogous in preparation and properties to the corresponding oxychlorides, are known.

Antimony oxychlorides. Numerous substances formed by the action of water or dilute hydrochloric acid on antimony trichloride, and supposed to be definite compounds, have been described; two of these, SbOCl and $Sb_4O_5Cl_2$, are of consistent occurrence. They are white amorphous or crystalline powders, formed by the action of water on the trichloride in the cold, using suitable proportions of the reacting substances. Both these oxychlorides are hydrolysed by hot water, or by sodium carbonate solution, to antimony trioxide. 'Powder of Algaroth' probably consists of a mixture of the oxychlorides in indefinite proportions.

Antimony potassium tartrate. See Potassium antimonyl tartrate.

Antimony sodium tartrate. See Sodium antimonyl tartrate.

Antimony sulphates. Normal antimony sulphate, $Sb_2(SO_4)_3$, is prepared as colourless hygroscopic crystals by heating antimony trioxide with concentrated sulphuric acid and cooling the solution; it is readily decomposed to basic sulphates by water. A number of acid sulphates of antimony have been prepared by dissolving the trioxide in fuming sulphuric acid.

Antimony sulphides. *Antimony trisulphide*, Sb_2S_3. Commonly occurs in two forms; that occurring in nature as stibnite is black in colour. By precipitating a solution of an antimony salt in hydrochloric acid with hydrogen sulphide an orange-red form is produced; this is converted to the black form by heating to 200° in an atmosphere of carbon dioxide. It burns in oxygen, giving a mixture of antimony tri- and tetroxides. On fusion with alkali, a mixture of antimonite and thioantimonite is formed; thioantimonites are also formed by the action of solutions of metallic sulphides on antimony trisulphide. They often have complex formulae, but simpler compounds (e.g. Na_3SbS_3, $Na_2Sb_4S_7$, $NaSbS_2$) have been described; the alkali metal thioantimonites are yellow to reddish-brown in colour, and are soluble in water. Antimony trisulphide is used in pyrotechny.

Antimony pentasulphide, Sb_2S_5. Usually occurs as a reddish-brown or brown powder; the commercial article contains free sulphur, and is generally prepared by the action of dilute acid on a solution of an alkali thioantimonate. A purer product is obtained by passing hydrogen sulphide through a solution of antimony pentachloride in hydrochloric acid. The penta-sulphide readily loses sulphur on gentle heating, forming the trisulphide, Sb_2S_3. It is dissolved by solutions of alkalis, giving a mixture of anti-monate and thioantimonate. Thioantimonates are also formed by the action of alkali sulphides on the pentasulphide, or by boiling the tri-sulphide with sulphur and alkali solution. Sodium thioantimonate, or *Schlippe's Salt*, Na_3SbS_4, $9H_2O$, a pale yellow crystalline solid, is prepared by the latter method.

Antimonyl salts. Salts containing the SbO grouping. These compounds are formed by partial hydrolysis of Sb (III) derivatives. A chloride, SbOCl, a sulphate $(SbO)_2SO_4$, and a nitrate $(SbO)NO_3$, are known.

Antioxidants are substances that slow the oxidation rate in autoxidizable substances. They are added for the protection of foods, particularly fats; for stopping the ageing or deterioration of rubber and many plastics; for inhibiting gum formation in cracked petroleum; and for preserving many other products. Many antioxidants are substituted phenols, aromatic amines, or sulphur compounds. Certain seques-tering agents act as antioxidants by inactivating metals that may catalyse oxidation. Many organic raw materials contain natural anti-oxidants. The ultra-violet rays of sunlight are responsible for activating rubbers etc. to oxidation by air. Hence ultra-violet absorbers are added if exposed to sunlight.

Antiparticle. In nuclear chemistry it has been shown that some of the elementary particles should have antiparticles, i.e. there should exist, for example, a particle identical to the electron but carrying a positive charge. Such a particle, the positron, was discovered in cloud chamber experiments in 1932. The antiproton, which has the mass of a proton but is negatively charged, was discovered in 1959.

Antithyroid substances. Substances which inter-fere with production of thyroxine by the thyroid gland. They include anions such as nitrate or thiocyanate, which inhibit the active transport of iodide ion needed for iodination; certain sulphur compounds, e.g. thiouracil, which inhibit the incorporation of iodine; and compounds such as resorcinol, which compete with tyrosine for the available iodine. Anti-thyroid compounds are used in the treatment of diseases due to hyperactivity of the gland.

Antitoxins. Antitoxins are antibodies formed in blood to which bacterial toxins have been introduced. A given antitoxin will only neutralize its own toxin, with which it apparently combines in a quantitative manner. All anti-toxins so far obtained contain proteins.

Antrycide. The trade name for quinapyramine chloride or sulphate.

Antu, 1-naphthylthiourea, $C_{11}H_{10}N_2S$. A white

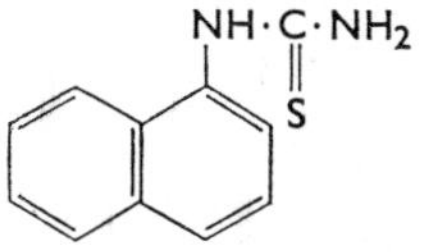

solid. m.p. 198°, practically insoluble in water, soluble in hot alcohol. It is prepared by reacting α-naphthylamine with ammonium thiocyanate. It is a rat poison, the lethal dose is 6-8 mg/kg; baits containing 1% antu are effective. The symptoms are massive pulmonary oedema and pleural effusions. Antu has largely been superseded by warfarin.

Apatite, $Ca_5F(PO_4)_3$, mineral 'phosphate of lime.' Crystals are hexagonal, isomorphous with vanadinite and pyromorphite. There are two molecules in the unit cell. The PO_4 groups are tetrahedral. The cryptocrystalline form is phosphorite or phosphate rock. It is used in the manufacture of phosphorus and its com-pounds, including superphosphates.

A.P.I. gravity. A scale introduced by the American Petroleum Institute to express the specific gravity of oils.

$$°API = \frac{141 \cdot 5}{Sp.gr.@ \, 60° \, F} - 131 \cdot 5.$$

Apiin, $C_{26}H_{18}O_{14}$, is the glycoside present in the leaves and seeds of parsley. The sugar is apiose (*q.v.*), and the aglucone is apigenin (5,7,4'-trihydroxyflavone), the point of attach-ment of the sugar being through the 7-hydroxyl group. It has m.p. 228°, $[\alpha]_D - 130°$.

Apiose, $C_5H_{10}O_5$. A branched-chain sugar

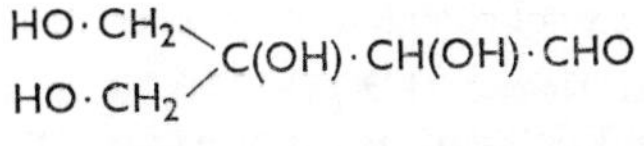

found in parsley where it is a constituent of a glycoside apiin. It is known as a syrup which is optically inactive.

Apo. A prefix indicating a derived compound; thus apomorphine is derived from morphine.

Apocodeine, $C_{18}H_{19}NO_2$. Prepared by the

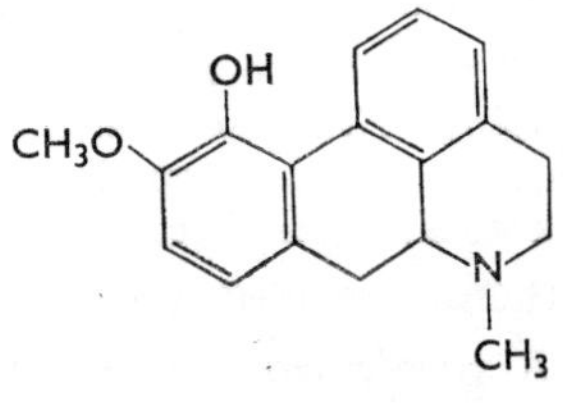

action of zinc chloride on codeine. Its hydrochloride is a grey hygroscopic powder, soluble in water, less soluble in alcohol, and is used medicinally as an expectorant and sedative, particularly for the relief of bronchitis. Injected hypodermically it is a purgative.

Apomorphine, $C_{17}H_{17}NO_2$. White crystals when

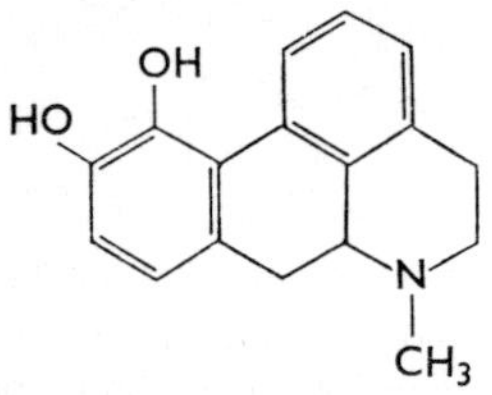

pure, slightly soluble in water, soluble in alcohol and ether. Its hydrochloride, which exists as grey crystals slightly soluble in water and alcohol, is prepared by heating morphine with hydrochloric acid under pressure. It is a very useful emetic and hypnotic when administered hypodermically and in smaller doses taken orally is an expectorant.

Apron conveyor. A common type of conveyor for handling solids. It consists of a number of overlapping pans mounted between two chains, the whole forming a continuous moving trough.

Aquamarine. A coloured beryl (q.v.).

Aqua regia. A mixture of concentrated nitric acid with three to four times its volume of concentrated hydrochloric acid, so called because it will dissolve 'noble' metals, such as platinum and gold. Its strong oxidizing action is due to nitrosyl chloride (NOCl) and chlorine produced by interaction of the two acids.

Aquation. The process of replacement of other ligands by water, e.g.

$$(Co(NH_3)_4(H_2O)(NO_3))^{2+} \rightarrow$$
$$(Co(NH_3)_4(H_2O)_2)^{3+}.$$

The process of complexing by water molecules.

Aquinas, Thomas (1225(?)-1274). Born at the castle of Roccasecca in the province of Naples, Aquinas was educated at the Abbey of Monte Cassino and the University of Naples. In spite of the condemnations of many of his doctrines, Thomas was canonized in 1323 by Pope John XXII. Teacher, philosopher, and theologian, he introduced the term 'amalgam' for solutions of metals in mercury.

Aquo ions. A metal ion co-ordinated by water, e.g. $(Co(H_2O)_6)^{2+}$. The normal state of metal ions in aqueous solution. Aquo ions can lose protons and thus act as acids, e.g.

$$(Fe(H_2O)_6)^{3+} \rightarrow (Fe(H_2O)_5(OH))^{2+}.$$

Araban. A generic term to describe poly-

saccharides present in wood cellulose and associated with pectin giving L-arabinose on hydrolysis. See the review by W. J. Polglase in 'Advances in Carbohydrate Chemistry,' Vol. 10, 1955.

L-Arabinose, $C_5H_{10}O_5$. The pentose sugar of

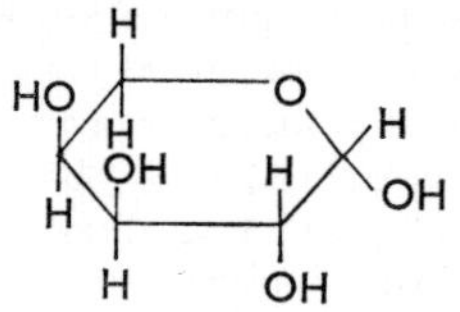

the hemicelluloses, gums, and mucilages, and of some glycosides, in particular the vicianosides. It crystallizes in the β-pyranose form, m.p. 160°, $[\alpha]_D$ +175° (initial), +105° (final, in 1·0% solution).

D-Arabinose is found in the glycoside barbaloin and in the polysaccharides of the tubercle bacillus.

Arachidic acid, *n*-**Eicosanic acid,** $C_{20}H_{40}O_2$, $CH_3 \cdot [CH_2]_{18} \cdot COOH$. Crystallizes in plates, m.p. 75°, soluble in ether, chloroform, or hot alcohol. A fatty acid occurring as glycerides in peanut and other vegetable oils.

Arachidonic acid, $C_{20}H_{36}O_2$. *Cis,cis,cis,cis*-5,8,11,14-eicosatetraenoic acid. The principal

$$CH_3[CH_2]_4[CH\!=\!CHCH_2]_4CH_2CH_2CO_2H$$

fatty acid of the adrenal gland, is present also as an important constituent of brain and liver lipids. Arachidonic acid is an 'essential fatty acid' (q.v.) in animal metabolism and is a biological precursor of prostaglandin E_2 (q.v.). Several syntheses, some of productive value, have been achieved.

Aragonite, $CaCO_3$. An orthorhombic crystalline form of calcium carbonate, the structure of which may be regarded as derived from that of nickel arsenide (q.v.) by replacing nickel by calcium and arsenic by carbonate groups (compare the structural relationship of calcite to sodium chloride). As in calcite each CO_3 group is surrounded by six Ca atoms which are arranged in the structure in approximately the positions of hexagonal close-packing. Sp.gr. 2·94-3·0. Hardness 3-4. On heating to 1000° it dissociates into lime (CaO) and carbon dioxide. Compare Calcite.

Arbutin. A typical phenolic glycoside, hydroquinone-β-D-glucopyranoside,

$$C_6H_{11}O_5\!-\!O\!-\!C_6H_4OH.$$

It is a colourless, crystalline, bitter substance obtained from the leaves of the bearberry, and of most *Ericacae*. Since hydroquinone is a powerful antiseptic, arbutin has pharmacological value; it also has diuretic action. The commercial product has 40% of methyl-arbutin. It has m.p. 195°, $[\alpha]_D^{20}$ $-64\cdot7°$.

Arc spectrum. The nature of the spectrum emitted by a substance depends, to some extent, on the violence of the process employed to excite the emission. Generally the disturbances suffered in a flame or in an electric arc are mild compared with those in an electric spark, so that fresh lines, or lines enhanced in intensity, appear in the spectrum excited in the spark. The spectrum produced in the arc is called the *arc spectrum*; the enhanced and fresh lines in the second case constitute the *spark spectrum*.

Arctons. See Freons.

Arecoline, $C_8H_{13}NO_2$. An alkaloid obtained from the seeds of the betel nut, *areca catechu*. It is an oil, b.p. 209°, soluble in water, alcohol, and ether. Its hydrobromide, which has m.p. 170°-171° and is soluble in water, is used in veterinary practice as a cathartic and anthelmintic.

Arene-metal complexes. Complexes in which an aromatic system is bonded to a metal through its π electrons.

Argentite, Ag_2S. An important ore of silver in Nevada and Mexico. It crystallizes in the cubic system. Hardness $2\frac{1}{2}$.

Argentous and **Argentic.** Compounds of silver (I) and silver (II).

Arginase. The enzyme which decomposes arginine into ornithine and urea. It therefore takes part in the production of urea from carbon dioxide and ammonia in the liver. The cycle is as follows: in the first stage ornithine (α,δ-diaminovaleric acid) is converted into citrulline and this into arginine; in the final stage urea is split off by the enzyme and ornithine reproduced to take part in a new cycle. It is abundant in mammal's liver but absent from that of birds. It has been obtained crystalline and has mol.wt. about 140,000.

Arginine, α-**Amino-**δ-**guanidino-n-valeric acid,**

$$H_2NC\cdot NH\cdot[CH_2]_3\cdot CH\cdot COOH$$
$$\underset{NH}{\|} \qquad\qquad \underset{NH_2}{|}$$

$C_6H_{14}N_4O_2$. Crystallizes in plates or prisms, m.p. 207°, with decomposition. Soluble in water, sparingly soluble in alcohol. The naturally occurring substance is dextrorotatory, $[\alpha]_D^{20}$ $+11\cdot37°$. Arginine is one of the essential amino-acids and one of the most widely distributed products of protein hydrolysis. It is obtained in particularly high concentration from proteins belonging to the protamine and histone classes. It plays an important rôle in the production of urea as an excretory product.

Argol. Crude potassium bitartrate, as obtained from the lees of wine.

Argon. Ar. At.no. 18, At.wt. 39·944, m.p. $-189\cdot4°$, b.p. $-185\cdot86°$. Argon was the first rare gas to be discovered (by Lord Rayleigh in 1893); it was found, mixed with the other noble gases, after removal of the major constituents of air by chemical means. Argon is now made commercially by the fractionation of liquid air. It is the most abundant of the rare gases, constituting 0·941% by volume of carbon dioxide-free air. The solubility in water is about 2·5 times that of nitrogen, the absorption coefficient at 0° is 0·0561; at high pressures hydrates are formed. The gas is apparently inert chemically but a clathrate compound is formed with quinol. In an electrical discharge argon gives a colour which varies from lilac to blue, according to the discharge conditions. Argon discharge tubes have a low luminous efficiency, and are not extensively used for commercial purposes. The gas may be used in conjunction with mercury to give blue and green effects. It is widely used in gas-filled electric lamp bulbs.

Arndt-Eistert synthesis. A procedure for converting a carboxylic acid to its next higher homologue, or to a derivative of a homologous acid, e.g. ester or amide. The synthesis involves treating the carboxylic acid chloride with ethereal diazomethane, and decomposing the intermediate diazoketone with a silver salt.

$$RCO_2H \rightarrow RCOCl \xrightarrow{CH_2N_2} RCOCH_2N_2$$
$$\xrightarrow{Ag^+} RCH_2CO_2H$$

Armstrong, Henry Edward (1848-1937). Born in Lewisham, Armstrong was educated at Colfe's Grammar School and the Royal College of Science, London, where he was a pupil of Frankland. In 1868 he proceeded to Leipzig to work under Kolbe. After a period of research and teaching at St. Bartholomew's Hospital Medical School he was appointed the first professor of chemistry at the London Institution. In 1879 he was appointed professor at what became the Finsbury Technical College. In 1884 he became professor at the Central Technical College, now part of the University of London. Elected F.R.S. in 1876, he was awarded the Davy Medal of the Royal Society in 1911. His original work includes investigations on the terpenes and on compounds of the naphthalene series. He was the author of many books on the principles and teaching of chemistry and a great advocate of the teaching of science in schools. See *J. Chem. Soc.*, 1940, 1418.

Aromadendrene, $C_{15}H_{24}$, is the principal sesquiterpene found in eucalyptus oils, b.p.

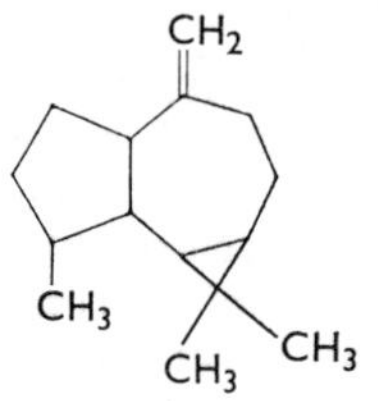

121°/10 mm, d_4^{20} 0·9116, n_D^{20} 1·4978, $[\alpha]_{577}^{20}$ −6·1°; it yields no crystalline derivatives but the derived ketone is a crystalline solid, m.p. 80°-81°. The 5:7 ring junction is probably trans.

Aromatic. The term aromatic was introduced when it was found convenient to divide all organic compounds into two broad classes, namely, aliphatic (fatty) and aromatic (fragrant), but this classification now has little significance. In a general sense the adjective is used to describe the property (aromaticity) which allows benzene to undergo electrophilic substitution reactions, and to account for its stability. Other compounds containing a benzene skeleton are said to be aromatic, whilst non-benzenoid compounds such as ferrocene and many heterocyclic compounds also undergo electrophilic substitution and are termed aromatic using this criterion only. Other definitions of aromaticity include a molecular orbital description which connects aromatic stability with the number of π electrons $(4n+2)$ associated with a planar cyclic conjugated system of double and single bonds, e.g. azulene 10 π electrons, $n=2$: tropylium cation 6 π electrons, $n=1$. For a definition based upon the n.m.r. spectrum of a potentially aromatic system see '*Annual Reports*', The Chemical Society, 1962, p. 307.

Arrester. An apparatus for removing suspended solids or liquids from a gas stream. Frequently consists of a chamber fitted with baffle plates on which the gas stream is forced to impinge.

Arrhenius, Svante August (1859-1927). Educated at the Universities of Uppsala and Stockholm, Arrhenius later studied under Ostwald (Riga), Kohlrausch (Würzburg), Boltzmann (Graz), and van't Hoff (Amsterdam). After a period as assistant to Ostwald, he returned to Stockholm in 1891 as professor of physics at the Technical High School; later he became Director of the Nobel Institute for Physical Chemistry. He was awarded the Nobel Prize for Chemistry in 1903. His main work dealt with the electrical conductivity of solutions. See *Chem. Soc. Mem. Lecture, Trans.*, 1928, 1380; *Chem. and Ind.*, 1959, 245.

Arrhenius equation. The rate of a chemical reaction increases with rise of temperature and can be represented quantitatively by the Arrhenius equation

$$k = A \exp (E_A/RT)$$

where k is the velocity constant and A and E_A are constants for a given reaction (R is the gas const.). Arrhenius (1889) interpreted this law by the hypothesis that E_A is an 'energy of activation' which the reactants must acquire (from thermal energy or by photochemical excitation) before they are capable of reacting. A is a collision frequency factor which is (comparatively) insensitive to temperature. The activation theory is widely accepted and applies also to many other rate processes such as diffusion, electrolytic conduction, viscous flow, etc., all of which obey the Arrhenius equation.

Arsenic, As. At.no. 33, At.wt. 74·91. The normal form of arsenic, γ-arsenic, grey or metallic arsenic, is a grey crystalline solid possessing a metallic lustre. The crystals are rhombohedral, $a=4·159$ Å, $\alpha=53°$ 49', d, 5·7, m.p. 814° in a sealed tube. In the lattice each arsenic atom has three near neighbours and three other neighbours at a much greater distance. Sublimes without fusion at 610°. Insoluble in carbon disulphide. Certain compounds of arsenic were known to the ancients, but arsenic itself was not known until about the fifth century A.D. or later; Brandt, in 1733, recognized 'white arsenic' as the calx, or oxide, of the element, and prepared the latter from white arsenic (arsenic trioxide) by reduction with oil. In nature, arsenic occurs native to some extent, and as an impurity in numerous sulphide ores such as copper and iron pyrites. Other typical sources of arsenic are the minerals orpiment, As_2S_3; realgar, As_2S_2; arsenolite, As_2O_3; mispickel, FeAsS; nickel glance, NiAsS; cobalt bloom, $Co_3(AsO_4)_2$, $8H_2O$. In the roasting of these ores in a current of air, fumes of impure arsenic trioxide are evolved; these are collected in flues, and the product purified by sublimation. The purified oxide is marketed as 'white arsenic'; this forms the primary source of the arsenic compounds of commerce. Arsenic may be prepared by reducing arsenic trioxide with charcoal or the sulphide ores with iron. A number of other allotropic forms have been prepared; α-arsenic, or 'yellow' arsenic, forms light yellow regular crystals, soluble in carbon disulphide, and in this and other respects closely resembles yellow phosphorus. It is prepared by rapid condensation of arsenic vapour, and is very unstable; γ-arsenic is rapidly formed on exposure to light; β-arsenic, or 'black' arsenic, is an apparently amorphous form, insoluble in carbon disulphide; it is formed by rapidly heating γ-arsenic in a glass tube in a current of hydrogen when a black shining deposit of β-arsenic appears in the cooler portions of the tube. β-Arsenic is converted to the stable γ-form by heating to 360°; arsenic gives a colourless vapour containing both As_4 and As_2 molecules; arsenic exists as As_4 molecules in carbon disulphide solution. The γ-form is moderately reactive chemically; it tarnishes in moist air, and burns in air at 400°, giving white fumes of the trioxide; the powder takes fire in chlorine, arsenic trichloride being formed. Concentrated nitric acid oxidizes arsenic to arsenic acid, H_3AsO_4; hot concentrated sulphuric acid is reduced to sulphur dioxide, an unstable sulphate possibly being formed. Aqueous alkali solutions are without action, but fused alkalis react, giving an arsenite and hydrogen, with some arsenate and arsenide at high temperatures. Elementary arsenic is used in the manufacture of lead shot, addition of 0·3-1% to the lead making the metal harder and more readily fusible. Arsenic compounds in quantity are highly poisonous, but some are used in small amounts in medicine. Detection and determination of arsenic are of toxicological importance, the Marsh or Gutzeit tests often being employed.

Arsenic acids and **Arsenates.** A solid arsenic acid, $H_3AsO_4 \cdot \frac{1}{2}H_2O$, is formed by boiling arsenic trioxide with concentrated nitric acid. Condensed arsenates are much less stable than condensed phosphates but can be prepared by heating the acid orthoarsenates (e.g. $Na_4As_2O_7$ and $NaAsO_3$ are formed on heating Na_2HAsO_4 and NaH_2AsO_4 respectively).

The sodium salt, Na_2HAsO_4, $12H_2O$, is used commercially in calico-printing. Solutions of arsenates give a white crystalline precipitate, $MgNH_4AsO_4$, $6H_2O$, with magnesia mixture and ammonia; this precipitate gives magnesium pyroarsenate, $Mg_2As_2O_7$, on heating.

Arsenic bromide, *Arsenic tribromide,* $AsBr_3$. A white crystalline solid, sp.gr. 3·66, m.p. 31°, b.p. 220°, prepared by the action of bromine on arsenic, or on arsenic trioxide in presence of sulphur. In general properties it resembles the trichloride. The tribromide is the only bromine compound of arsenic known.

Arsenic chloride, *Arsenic trichloride,* $AsCl_3$. A colourless oily liquid, sp.gr. 2·2, b.p. 130·2°, m.p. −16°. Conveniently prepared by distilling a mixture of arsenic trioxide, sodium chloride, and concentrated sulphuric acid; also formed when arsenic burns in chlorine gas, or on heating arsenic trioxide in chlorine. The liquid fumes in damp air, and is readily hydrolysed by water, giving first a hydroxychloride, $AsCl(OH)_2$, and then arsenic trioxide or arsenious acid. At high temperatures the trichloride is reduced by many metals to arsenic or a metallic arsenide. Ammonia gas is readily absorbed by the liquid, addition compounds such as $AsCl_3, 4NH_3$ being formed; arsine reacts, giving arsenic and hydrogen chloride. A number of adducts with metallic and non-metallic chlorides are also known (e.g. $AsCl_3$; PCl_5; $Ni(AsCl_3)_4$). Arsenic trichloride is the most important halide of arsenic; it is chiefly used in the preparation of organic arsenic compounds.

Arsenic fluorides. *Arsenic trifluoride,* AsF_3. A colourless fuming liquid, sp.gr. 2·66, b.p. 57°, m.p. −6·0°. Prepared by distilling arsenious oxide and calcium fluoride with concentrated sulphuric acid. Readily hydrolysed by water to arsenic trioxide and hydrofluoric acid. Used as a fluorinating agent.

Arsenic pentafluoride, AsF_5. A colourless gas, b.p. −53·2°, m.p. −79·8°, prepared by the action of fluorine on arsenic, or, more easily, by gently warming a mixture of arsenic trifluoride, antimony pentafluoride, and bromine. Arsenic pentafluoride is highly reactive; it fumes strongly in moist air, and is rapidly hydrolysed by water, giving hydrofluoric and arsenic acids. Arsenic pentafluoride forms complex salts, $MAsF_6$; upon hydrolysis unstable products such as $MAsF_4(OH)_2$ may be identified. Complex fluorides may be prepared by the use of hydrofluoric acid or bromine trifluoride.

Arsenic hydrides. *Arsine,* AsH_3, is a colourless gas possessing a characteristic garlic odour; b.p. −55°, m.p. −113·5°. It is prepared in small quantity by the action of zinc and dilute acid on a soluble arsenic compound, when the hydrogen evolved contains a small proportion of arsine; this reaction is used in the Marsh and Gutzeit tests for arsenic (*q.v.*). Good yields of arsine are obtained by reduction of arsenic trichloride with lithium aluminium hydride. Arsine is highly poisonous. It is a comparatively unstable compound, depositing free arsenic on exposure to light and moisture. It decomposes into arsenic and hydrogen at 230°. The gas is a strong reducing agent.

Diarsine, As_2H_4, has been prepared by passing arsine diluted with hydrogen through an electrical discharge.

Arsenic iodide, AsI_3, Red hexagonal crystals, sp.gr. 4·39, m.p. 146°, b.p. 394°-414°. Prepared by the action of arsenic on a solution of iodine in carbon disulphide, or by adding potassium iodide solution to a hot solution of arsenic trioxide in hydrochloric acid. Slightly soluble in water, giving a yellow solution with an acid reaction; the tri-iodide is much less easily hydrolysed than the trichloride or tribromide.

Arsenic oxides. *Arsenious oxide,* As_4O_6, ('white

arsenic'). There are several forms of arsenious oxide. The monoclinic form is stable from $-30°$ to the melting point, $315°$. The structure of the molecules is similar to that of P_4O_6. Arsenic trioxide is obtained commercially as a by-product in the treatment of certain sulphide ores containing arsenic (cf. Arsenic), and forms the principal commercial source of arsenic and its compounds. It is formed when arsenic burns in air or oxygen. The trioxide is readily oxidized (e.g. by chlorine, hydrogen peroxide, or nitric acid) to the pentoxide, As_2O_5, or to an arsenate if alkali is present; it reduces Fehling's solution, red cuprous oxide being precipitated. It is also readily reduced to arsenic by heating with carbon or potassium cyanide. Arsenic trioxide is soluble in hydrochloric acid, and on boiling the solution arsenic trichloride distils in the steam; fuming sulphuric acid gives a series of unstable sulphates. The trioxide dissolves in alkalis giving arsenites. Arsenic trioxide is used as a vermin and weed killer, in taxidermy, and in the manufacture of glass. Smaller amounts are used medicinally.

Arsenic pentoxide, As_2O_5. A white deliquescent amorphous solid, generally prepared by boiling arsenic trioxide with concentrated nitric acid, evaporating, and heating the residue to $200°$. Loses oxygen at a red heat, forming the trioxide. The pentoxide is soluble in water, but the solid dissolves very slowly; the aqueous solution contains arsenic acids. Arsenates are formed with alkalis.

Arsenic sulphides. *Realgar*, As_4S_4. An orange-red crystalline solid which occurs naturally. Manufactured by heating sulphur with an excess of arsenic or arsenic trioxide. Realgar has a structure containing cyclic As_4S_4 molecules with alternating As and S atoms. Insoluble in water and dilute acids; decomposed on heating with alkalis or alkali sulphides. Used in the tanning industry as a depilatory for certain leathers, and in pyrotechny (see Indian fire).

Arsenic trisulphide, As_2S_3. A lemon-yellow powder, sp.gr. 3·46, b.p. $700°$, which can be sublimed in a vacuum at $230°$. Occurs naturally as orpiment. Prepared by heating together the calculated quantities of arsenic and sulphur, or by passing hydrogen sulphide through a solution of arsenic trioxide in dilute hydrochloric acid. A colloidal solution of arsenic trisulphide is readily prepared by passing hydrogen sulphide through a solution of arsenic trioxide in distilled water. The trisulphide burns on heating in air, giving the trioxide and sulphur dioxide. It is oxidized by nitric acid, but, unlike antimony trisulphide, is insoluble in concentrated hydrochloric acid. Alkalis convert arsenic trisulphide into an arsenite and a thioarsenite

(e.g. K_3AsS_3). Thioarsenites, which form colourless crystals or white amorphous powders, are also prepared by dissolving the trisulphide in alkali sulphide solutions. The thioarsenious acids, H_3AsS_3, $H_4As_2S_5$, and $HAsS_2$, with which these salts correspond, are unknown in the free state.

Arsenic trisulphide is readily soluble in yellow ammonium sulphide. It has a structure containing discrete As_4S_6 units.

Arsenic pentasulphide, As_2S_5. A bright yellow powder, conveniently prepared by passing hydrogen sulphide through a solution of arsenic acid, or an arsenate, containing an excess of ammonia; after the hydrogen sulphide treatment the pentasulphide is precipitated on acidifying the solution. Arsenic pentasulphide is insoluble in water or organic solvents; it dissolves in alkali solutions, giving *thioarsenates* (e.g. K_3AsS_4), and compounds containing both oxygen and sulphur (e.g. Na_3AsO_3S, K_3AsOS_3). The alkali thioarsenates are colourless crystalline solids, soluble in water, prepared by dissolving arsenic pentasulphide in an alkali sulphide solution or arsenic trisulphide in an alkali polysulphide solution. The corresponding acids have not been isolated.

Arsenious acids and arsenites. An aqueous solution of arsenious oxide probably contains ortho- or meta-arsenious acid, H_3AsO_3 or $HAsO_2$. The oxide also dissolves in sodium bicarbonate or alkali solutions, giving alkali orthoarsenites, e.g. Na_3AsO_3, a white powder soluble in water. Salts corresponding to the acids H_3AsO_3, $HAsO_2$, and $H_4As_2O_5$ (pyro-arsenious acid) are known. Certain copper arsenites (see Emerald Green, Scheele's Green) are of some importance. Solutions of arsenites give with silver nitrate solution a yellow precipitate of silver arsenite, Ag_3AsO_3, soluble in acetic acid.

Arsenopyrite. See Mispickel.

Arsenuretted hydrogen. See Arsenic hydrides.

Arsine. See Arsenic hydrides.

Aryl. When a hydrogen atom is removed from a hydrocarbon of the benzene series, the residue is called an aryl group.

Arynes. The transient intermediates, not capable of isolation, having essentially two hydrogen atoms removed from adjacent non-ring junction carbon atoms of the corresponding aromatic compounds. Examples are known from benzene, naphthalene, pyridine and coumarone type compounds. The existence of arynes is inferred from the identity of products resulting from the trapping of such species in Diels-

Alder reactions, and from the isomer orientation of elimination-addition reaction products of haloaromatic compounds. For example, hydrolysis of p-chlorotoluene with alkali at 340° results in a mixture of *meta-* and *para-*cresol. See Benzyne.

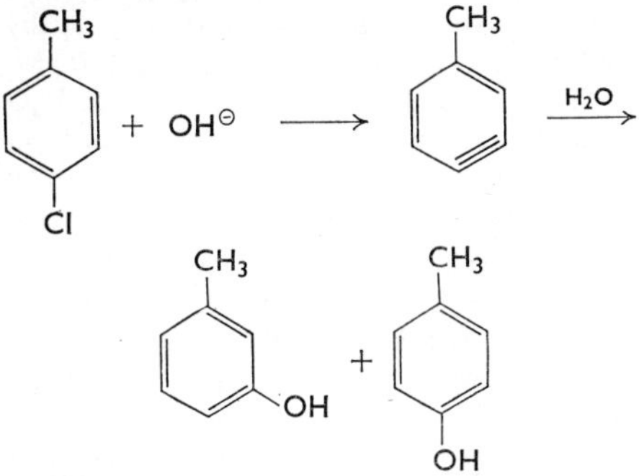

Asarinin. See Sesamin.

Asbestine. A fibrous variety of talc, mixed with tremolite asbestos, which is obtained from deposits in New York State. It consists of approximately 85% hydrated magnesium silicate, 10% calcium silicate, and 2·4% calcium carbonate. It is used as a rubber filler and as a suspending agent in certain paints.

Asbestos. The fibrous varieties of a number of silicate minerals. All have special uses but the most important varieties are chrysotile, a crystalline variety of serpentine approximating to $(OH)_4Mg_3Si_2O_5$, crocidolite, or blue asbestos, approximately

20 mm, on heating in xylene solution to 130°-150°.

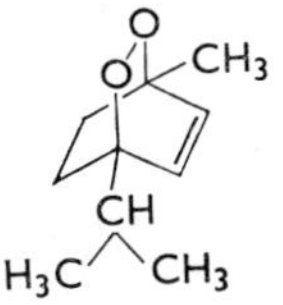

Ascorbic acid, Vitamin C, $C_6H_8O_6$. The enolic form of 3-oxo-L-gulofuranolactone. It may be prepared by synthesis from glucose, or extracted from natural sources, such as rose hips, black currants, or the juice of citrus fruits. It is a colourless crystalline solid, m.p. 190°-192°, $[\alpha]_D$ +22°, soluble in water, less soluble in alcohol. Crystalline ascorbic acid is stable, but it is sensitive to oxidation in solution.

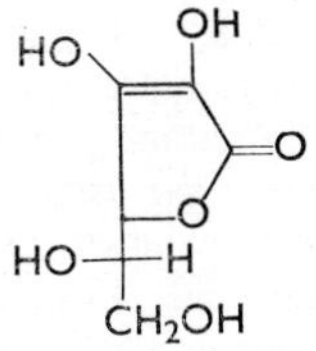

It is essential for the formation of collagen and intercellular material, for the development of cartilage, bone and teeth, and for the healing of wounds. The daily adult requirement is about 20 mg. It is used in the treatment of scurvy, which may occur in undernourished or bottle-fed infants.

Ascorbic acid has also found use as a photographic developing agent, particularly in alkaline solutions.

Asparaginase. The enzyme which converts asparagine into aspartic acid and ammonia. It is fairly widely distributed.

Asparagine, Aminosuccinamic acid, $C_4H_8N_2O_3$,

$$CH_2 \cdot CO \cdot NH_2$$
$$\mid$$
$$H_2N \cdot CH \cdot COOH$$

$(Na_{1\cdot38}K_{0\cdot13}Ca_{0\cdot17}Mg_{0\cdot25})$ $(Mg_{2\cdot81}Fe^{III}_{1\cdot66}Fe^{II}_{0\cdot48}Al_{0\cdot8})$ $(Si_{7\cdot94}Al_{0\cdot06})O_{22}(OH)_2$.

and amosite, resembling crocidolite in composition but with less iron and sodium and possessing a greater fibre length. Asbestos fibres can be spun and woven into textiles and used for heat and electrical insulation and fireproof fabrics. Short fibre asbestos is used as a binder in asbestos-cement building materials. Prolonged inhalation of certain asbestos fibres can cause cancer.

Ascaridole, $C_{10}H_{16}O_2$. A constituent of chenopodium oil, which explodes violently on heating to 130°-150°. It is separated from the parent oil by fractional distillation at reduced pressure and synthesized by the photochemical oxidation of α-terpinene. It has the constants: b.p. 96°-97°/8 mm, d^{20}_{20} 0·9985, n^{20}_D 1·4769, $[\alpha]_D$ +0·7°. No crystalline derivatives are known. It is decomposed explosively by mineral acids. It forms the isomer, ascaridole glycol anhydride, b.p. 122°-125°/

Crystallizes in rhombic prisms with one molecule of water, which it loses at 100°, m.p. 234°-235°. Soluble in water. Hydrolyses slowly with boiling water, and more rapidly with acids or alkalis, to aspartic acid. The most commonly occurring form is laevorotatory. L-Asparagine can be prepared from lupin seedlings, and DL-asparagine is synthesized from ammonia and maleic anhydride. L-Asparagine is very widely distributed in plants, being found in all the *Leguminosae* and *Gramineae*, and in many other seeds, roots, and buds. Its exact function is not known with certainty, but it very probably plays a part in the synthesis of proteins, and it has been suggested that it is the chief form in which nitrogen is transported in the plant.

Asparagosin $(C_6H_{10}O_5)_x$. The fructosan of the asparagus. It has $[\alpha]_D$ −32·6° and is made up of ten hexose units. Hydrolysis of methyl asparagosin yields tetra-, tri-, and dimethyl fructose in the ratio 1:8:1.

Aspartase is an enzyme which acts (a) to

3   55

produce L-aspartic acid from fumaric acid, and (b) to remove NH_3 from L-aspartic acid.

Aspartic acid, Aminosuccinic acid. $C_4H_7NO_4$. Crystallizes in prisms. M.p. 271°. Sparingly soluble in cold water, more soluble in hot. The naturally occurring substance is L-aspartic acid. It is dextrorotatory in cold water

$$CH_2 \cdot COOH$$
$$|$$
$$CH \cdot COOH$$
$$|$$
$$NH_2$$

and acid solutions and laevorotatory in hot water and alkaline solutions. It is one of the acidic amino-acids obtained by the hydrolysis of proteins.

Asphalt. Natural or mechanical mixtures in which asphaltic bitumen is associated with inert mineral matter.

Asphalt emulsions. In order to avoid the necessity of heating the asphaltic binder in the preparation of road carpets, an emulsion of asphaltic bitumen in water in the presence of a suitable emulsifying agent may be used. The emulsion has a viscosity only a little higher than that of water, may be applied cold, and is broken down by soluble salts present in the mineral aggregate. Special types of these preparations have been developed for use in soil stabilization.

Asphaltic bitumen. Described in British Standard Specifications as 'naturally occurring bitumen, or bitumen prepared from natural hydrocarbons by distillation or oxidation or cracking; solid or viscous, containing a low percentage of volatile products; possessing characteristic agglomeration properties, and substantially soluble in carbon disulphide.'

Asphaltic residue. The residue obtained from certain types of crude oil after the removal by distillation of the gasoline, kerosine, gas oil, and light lubricating oil fractions. By further distillation under vacuum or by propane de-asphalting this residue may be worked up to asphaltic bitumen.

Asphodelin, $(C_6H_{10}O_5)_x$. Asphodel tubers contain a fructosan, $[\alpha]_D$ $-31°$, made up of 7 hexose units. Hydrolysis of methyl asphodelin yields tetra-, tri-, and dimethyl fructose in the ratio $1:5:1$.

Aspirin, acetylsalicylic acid, $C_9H_8O_4$. Colourless

crystals, m.p. 135°-138°. Soluble in 300 parts of water, and in 5 parts of alcohol. Manufactured by the action of acetic anhydride on salicylic acid. It is widely used in tablet form as an analgesic and antipyretic.

Associated liquids. Liquids which are composed wholly or in part of loosely combined aggregates of two or more molecules instead of, in the case of normal or unassociated liquids, single molecules. Water and ethyl alcohol are examples of associated liquids. Association in a liquid may be detected by several methods based on surface tension determinations (e.g. by applying the Ramsay and Shields' equation), or by deviations from Trouton's Rule (*q.v.*); it is also indicated by a high b.p. (e.g. compare H_2O with H_2S). Association in liquids arises from bonding between adjacent molecules, notably by hydrogen bonds in water and other hydroxylic compounds.

Association. A term applied generally to the combination of the molecules of one substance with another to form more complex molecules. A substance showing this effect is said to be associated. The phenomenon is encountered in solutions, in pure liquids, and in vapours, and may be determined by the ordinary methods of molecular weight determination, since the associated molecules behave as units of increased molecular weight.

Astacene, $C_{40}H_{48}O_4$. The characteristic pigment obtained from Crustacea in which it is present in the form of its derivative astaxanthin, $C_{40}H_{52}O_4$, combined with protein. These have the normal carotenoid structure with the rings:

Astacene   Astaxanthin

and their mirror images in each case. Astacene crystallizes in bluish-red needles from pyridine, m.p. 243°, soluble in benzene and chloroform, sparingly soluble in alcohol. Astaxanthin crystallizes in lustrous plates, m.p. 216°, readily soluble in pyridine.

Astatine. At.no. 85. Isotopes of astatine of mass numbers from 200 to 219 are known but the important species are ^{211}At and ^{210}At, obtained by the action of alpha particles on bismuth. Very little is known of the chemistry of the element but from tracer studies the At^-, At^+ (solvate)$_2$, and AtO_3^- species are known and are similar to the corresponding iodine compounds. See A. H. W. Aten, jun., *Adv. Inorg. Radiochem.*, 1964, **6**, 207.

Astaxanthin. See Astacene.

A.S.T.M. distillation test. A test designed by the American Society for Testing Materials to determine the boiling range and to give a measure of the volatility of petroleum products.

Astbury, William Thomas (1898-1961). Born near Stoke-on-Trent, Astbury read physics, chemistry and mineralogy at Cambridge. From 1921 to 1928 he was assistant to Sir William Bragg at University College, London, and the Royal Institution, before becoming lecturer and later reader in textile physics at Leeds University, where in 1945 a chair of biomolecular structure was established for him. He is distinguished for his work on the structure of keratin and other proteins by X-ray crystallography. He was the first to indicate the importance of chain folding in fibrous and globular proteins. See *Nature, Lond.*, 1961, **191**, 331.

Aston, Francis William (1877-1945), was born in Birmingham and educated at Malvern and Mason College. He became chemist in a brewery at Wolverhampton and in 1901 went to the Cavendish Laboratory, Cambridge, where he carried out very accurate determinations of the masses of isotopes. He received the Nobel Prize for chemistry in 1922. See *J. Chem. Soc.*, 1948, 1468.

Aston dark space. See under Glow discharge.

Asymmetric induction is a term applied to the selective synthesis of one diastereomeric form of a compound, resulting from the influence of an existing optically active centre adjacent to the developing asymmetric carbon atom. This usually arises because, for steric reasons, the incoming atom or group does not have equal access to both sides of the molecule.

Asymmetry. Literally, the property of lacking symmetry. In its chemical sense the term is applied to asymmetry of molecular or of crystal structure, which is associated with the occurrence of optical activity. Asymmetry in molecular structure is illustrated by the case of lactic acid, which has the structure shown below. In this, the central carbon atom is said

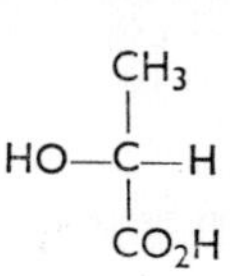

$$\begin{array}{c} CH_3 \\ | \\ HO-C-H \\ | \\ CO_2H \end{array}$$

to be asymmetric, there being no symmetry whatever in the nature of the four groups arranged around it. In certain crystals, e.g. in quartz, there is asymmetry in the crystal structure, and this, as in the case of lactic acid, leads to rotation of the plane of polarization of polarized light, i.e. to optical activity (*q.v.*).

Molecular asymmetry is possible in compounds which have no asymmetric carbon atoms, and yet are not superimposable upon their mirror image structures i.e., those structures having the same relationship to each other as a right hand to a left hand. An allene of the type XYC=C=CXY is asymmetric and may exist in two optically active forms (a) and (b) due to restricted rotation about the C=C=C bonds.

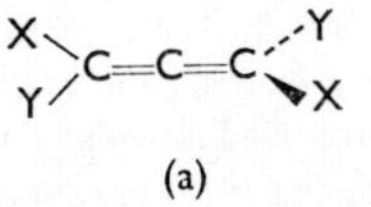

(a) 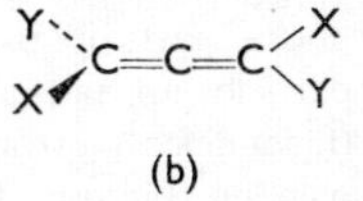   (b)

Restricted rotation about single bonds caused by bulky substituents allows the existence of enantiomers of the diphenyl derivatives (c) and (d).

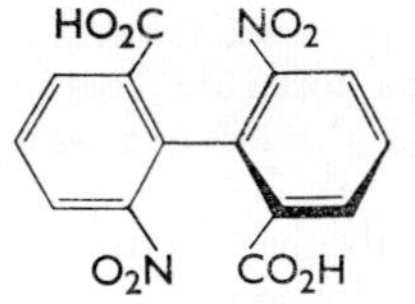

(c) 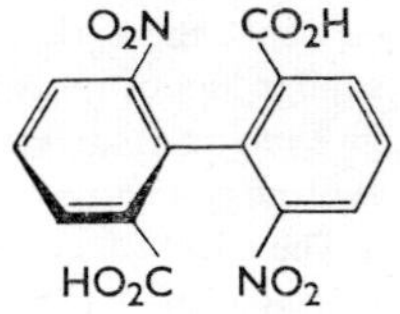   (d)

Atactic polymer. In crystalline polymers it may be considered that the carbon atoms in any chain all lie in the same plane. When there is a regular arrangement of the substituted groups in the system the structure may be either isotactic or syntactic. If, however, there is no stereospecificity of the substituents with respect to the carbon atoms then the polymer is said to be atactic.

Atmolysis. Process of separation of two gases based upon Graham's Law of Diffusion.

Atmosphere, Composition of. See Air.

Atom. The smallest portion of an element which can enter into chemical change, and cannot be further subdivided without destroying its identity. The fundamental properties of an atom are its mass and nuclear charge; the first is measured as its atomic weight and the second is represented by its atomic number. The modern view of the atom is of a positively charged nucleus which is surrounded by an electron 'cloud'. By far the greatest part of the atomic mass is concentrated in the nucleus. The electrons surrounding the nucleus are in discrete energy levels and are equal in number to the nuclear charge. The arrangement of the electrons around the nucleus is dependent on four 'quantum numbers'. These numbers determine the shape of the orbitals and no two electrons may have the same value of all four quantum numbers. The outermost electrons in an atom determine its chemical behaviour and bonds with other species may be formed either by 'sharing' of electrons with an adjacent atom, or by loss or gain of one or more electrons giving an ion, which can interact electrostatically with ions of opposite charge. See Covalent bond, Co-ordinate bond, Electrovalent bond.

Atomic energy. Mass and energy are equivalent, the relationship between them being $E = mc^2$ (E, energy in ergs: m, mass in grams; c, velocity of light $= 3 \times 10^{10}$ cm/sec). In the building up of nuclei, part of the mass of the constituent particles appears as binding energy; the ratio (mass defect): (atomic number) is known as the packing fraction. The elements of low atomic numbers and those of very high atomic number have a negative packing fraction; those of intermediate atomic number have a positive packing fraction and are more stable. If heavy nuclei are split to form nuclei of the more stable elements there is a loss of mass; there is a similar loss of mass if light nuclei are fused to give intermediate elements. This loss in mass is evolved as energy.

The effect of a slow or 'thermal' neutron on a nucleus of ^{235}U is to split it into one or more neutrons and into large fragments of approximately equal mass. There is a liberation of energy equal to the loss in total mass. If the neutrons produced effect further fissions, a 'chain-reaction' of successive fissions may be set up. ^{232}U, ^{233}U, ^{235}U, ^{239}Pu, ^{241}Am, and ^{242}Am undergo fission with thermal neutrons; of these isotopes ^{235}U and ^{239}Pu are the most important as they are most readily obtainable. Other heavy nuclei require fast neutrons to induce fission; such neutrons are much more difficult to control into a self-sustaining 'chain-reaction.'

The rapid fission of a mass of ^{235}U or another heavy nucleus is the principle of the atomic bomb, the energy liberated being the destructive power. For useful energy the reaction has to be moderated; this is done in a reactor where moderators such as water, heavy water, graphite, beryllium, etc., reduce the number of neutrons and slow those present to the most useful energies. The heat produced in a reactor is removed by normal heat-exchange methods. The neutrons in a reactor may be used for the formation of new isotopes, e.g. the transuranic elements, further fissile materials (^{239}Pu from ^{238}U), or of the radioactive isotopes used as tracers. The engineering difficulties in building a reactor are high, owing to the destructive effect of neutrons on normal structural materials and of the necessity to use materials which will absorb as few neutrons as possible. Further difficulties arise from the separation and disposal of the often intensely active fission products.

If light nuclei can be induced to fuse together to produce heavier nuclei, energy will again be liberated. Such fusion can take place only when the nuclei have high thermal energies (temperatures 10^8 °C), Temperatures of this order occur in the centre of stars, where it is considered that atomic fusions are the major source of energy,

and in an atomic bomb. The high temperatures produced in an atomic explosion are used to effect the fusion of very light nuclei (^{1}H, ^{2}H, ^{3}H) in a hydrogen bomb. The practical difficulties in creating a fusion process in a controlled manner are even greater than those of deriving energy from an atomic fission and it is not yet possible to get useful energy from a fusion process.

Atomic heat. The atomic heat of an element is the product of its atomic weight and specific heat. It is the heat capacity, water being taken as unity, of one gram-atom of the element. See Dulong and Petit's Law.

Atomic number. The atomic number of an element is the number of unit positive charges carried by the nucleus of its atom; it is the physical property which uniquely determines the position of the element in the Periodic table (q.v.). If the elements are arranged in order of increasing chemical atomic weight, this is also the order of increasing atomic number (from H, At.no. 1, to element At.no 104), except in the case of four pairs of adjacent elements (Ar, K; Co, Ni; Te, I; Th, Pa), which are anomalous. The atomic number of an element may be directly deduced from its X-ray spectrum.

Atomic orbitals. The energy levels in an atom may be described by the four *quantum numbers*. In wave mechanics, the energy of a particular system may be described by the Schrödinger equation and the wave function Ψ_{nlm} may be used to represent a solution of the wave equation in terms of these three numbers. Wave functions may be used to describe electron distribution and are thus sometimes referred to as atomic orbitals.

The wave function Ψ_{100} ($n=1$, $l=0$, $m=0$) can be shown to correspond to a spherical electronic distribution around the nucleus and is an example of an *s* orbital. Solutions of other wave functions may be described in terms of *p* and *d* orbitals.

Atomic polarization. See Polarization.

Atomic radii. Half the closest distance of approach of atoms in crystals of the elements. The atomic radius of an element is not, however, a constant, for it depends on the nature of the interatomic forces holding the atoms together and also on the number of neighbours around each atom. Thus in the two forms of crystalline carbon the C–C distances are 1·54 Å (in diamond) and 1·42 Å (in graphite). When plotted against the atomic numbers the atomic radii deduced from the crystal structures of the elements show a well-marked periodicity. See Covalent radius.

Atomic spectrum. See Line spectrum.

Atomic theory. The corpuscular theory of matter had been known since early times, but it was first stated in a form which lent itself to experimental investigation by John Dalton in 1807. His views may be summarized as follows: (i) The matter of which elements consist is made up of particles or atoms. (ii) All atoms of the same element are identical in weight, size, and shape, but differ in weight, size, and shape from those of other elements. (iii) Atoms are indivisible; they cannot be broken into smaller parts. (iv) Compound atoms (i.e. molecules) consist of the atoms of elements combined in simple proportions.

Dalton's theory is now held to be correct in broad outline. The discovery of isotopes, however, has led to a modification of the second postulate, for it is now realized that the atom of an element is characterized by the positive charge on the nucleus rather than by the mass of the atom, hence an element may consist of atoms of different weights, provided that the total positive charge on the nuclei of the different atoms is identical. The charge on the nucleus governs the number of electrons around it, and it is the number and arrangement of these electrons which are responsible for the chemical properties of the atom, and the nature of an element is judged by its chemical properties.

The third postulate has also suffered some amendment since it is now possible to break atoms into smaller parts (see Radioactivity), whilst as an amendment to the last postulate it has been found that many compounds do not contain an exact simple proportion of atoms.

Atomic weights. The atomic weight of an element was formerly defined as the ratio of the weight of one atom of the element to that of one atom of hydrogen. Later the atomic weight of an element was defined as the ratio between the weight of one atom of the element and 1/16th of the weight of the atom of oxygen. Another scale, used mainly by physicists, defined the standard as the mass of the oxygen isotope ^{16}O. Atomic weights are now defined as 1/12th part by weight of the dominant natural isotope of carbon, ^{12}C. An atomic weight is a ratio and is not to be confused with the actual mass of an atom.

The atomic weights of the elements, together with their symbols and atomic numbers, are given in the table on page 60. For the artificial elements the atomic weight is that of the most stable or readily available isotope.

ATP. See Adenosine triphosphate.

Atrolactic acid, α-hydroxy-α-phenyl-propionic acid, $C_9H_{10}O_3$. Exists as a colourless racemate, m.p. 94·5°, soluble in water and many polar organic solvents. Prepared from acetophenone cyanhydrin; the amide, atrolactamide, has been used as an anticonvulsant.

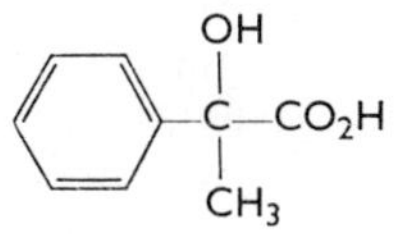

Atropine, (±)-**hyoscyamine,** $C_{17}H_{23}NO_3$.

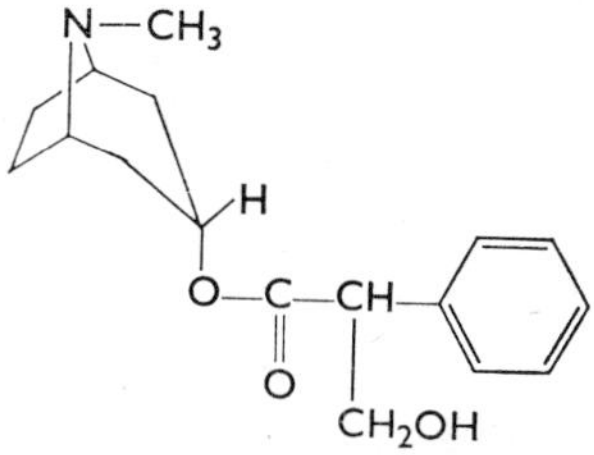

Colourless crystals, m.p. 114°-116°, soluble in 300 parts of water and in 3 parts of alcohol. Prepared by racemization of hyoscyamine. It and its salts are used to dilate the pupil of the eye. Given internally they reduce the secretion of saliva and relieve spasmodic pains.

Attapulgite. See Fuller's earth.

Attrition mill. See Disc grinder.

Aucubin, $C_{15}H_{24}O_9$. The characteristic glycoside of the common spotted laurel. When the plant is injured the glucoside is hydrolysed and blackening is caused by oxidation of the aglucone. Aucubin is prepared from the ripe berries of *Aucuba japonica*, and is present in many other plants which blacken in a similar manner. The structure is probably

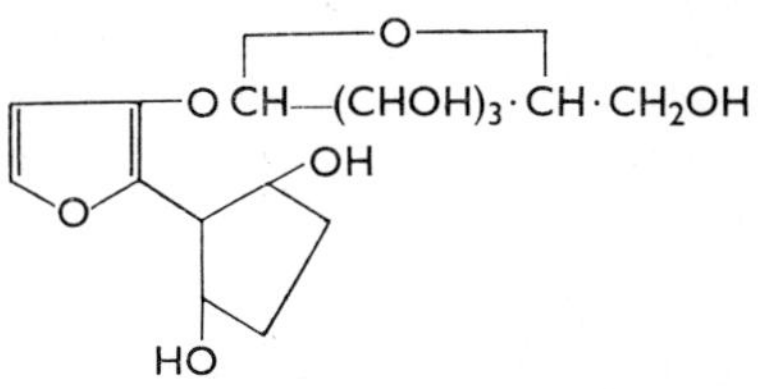

It is obtained as colourless crystals, m.p. 181°, $[\alpha]_D^{21} -171°$.

Aufbau principle. The building up of electronic configuration by placing electrons in orbitals in order of energy.

Augite. A mineral of the pyroxene group of variable composition occurring as brown to green monoclinic crystals, sp.gr. 3·2-3·5, hardness 5-6, refractive index max. 1·723, min. 1·698. Present in many basic igneous rocks and some metamorphic rocks.

(Ca, Mg, Fe^{II}, Fe^{III}, Al) (Si, Al) O_3

ATOMIC WEIGHTS

	Symbol.	At.no.	At.wt.		Symbol.	At.no.	At.wt.
Actinium . .	Ac	89	227	Mercury . .	Hg	80	200·61
Aluminium .	Al	13	26·97	Molybdenum .	Mo	42	95·95
Americium .	Am	95	243	Neodymium.	Nd	60	144·27
Antimony .	Sb	51	121·76	Neon . .	Ne	10	20·183
Argon . .	Ar	18	39·944	Neptunium .	Np	93	237
Arsenic . .	As	33	74·91	Nickel . .	Ni	28	58·69
Astatine . .	At	85	210	Niobium .	Nb	41	92·91
Barium . .	Ba	56	137·36	Nitrogen . .	N	7	14·008
Berkelium .	Bk	97	247	Osmium . .	Os	76	190·2
Beryllium .	Be	4	9·013	Oxygen . .	O	8	16·00
Bismuth .	Bi	83	209·00	Palladium .	Pd	46	106·7
Boron . . .	B	5	10·82	Phosphorus .	P	15	30·979
Bromine .	Br	35	79·916	Platinum .	Pt	78	195·23
Cadmium .	Cd	48	112·41	Plutonium .	Pu	94	242
Caesium .	Cs	55	132·91	Polonium .	Po	84	210
Calcium .	Ca	20	40·08	Potassium .	K	19	39·100
Californium .	Cf	98	249	Praseodymium .	Pr	59	140·92
Carbon . .	C	6	12·010	Promethium .	Pm	61	145
Cerium . .	Ce	58	140·13	Protactinium .	Pa	91	231
Chlorine .	Cl	17	35·457	Radium . .	Ra	88	226·05
Chromium .	Cr	24	52·01	Radon . .	Rn	86	222
Cobalt . .	Co	27	58·94	Rhenium .	Re	75	186·31
Copper . .	Cu	29	63·542	Rhodium .	Rh	45	102·91
Curium . .	Cm	96	244	Rubidium .	Rb	37	85·48
Dysprosium .	Dy	66	159·2	Ruthenium .	Ru	44	101·7
Einsteinium .	Es	99	254	Samarium .	Sm	62	150·43
Erbium . .	Er	68	167·2	Scandium .	Sc	21	44·96
Europium .	Eu	63	152·0	Selenium .	Se	34	78·96
Fermium .	Fm	100	254	Silicon . .	Si	14	28·09
Fluorine .	F	9	19·00	Silver . .	Ag	47	107·880
Gadolinium .	Gd	64	156·9	Sodium . .	Na	11	22·997
Gallium .	Ga	31	69·72	Strontium .	Sr	38	87·63
Germanium .	Ge	32	72·60	Sulphur . .	S	16	32·066
Gold . . .	Au	79	197·2	Tantalum .	Ta	73	180·88
Hafnium .	Hf	72	178·6	Technetium .	Tc	43	98·91
Helium . .	He	2	4·003	Tellurium .	Te	52	127·61
Holmium .	Ho	67	164·94	Terbium .	Tb	65	159·2
Hydrogen .	H	1	1·0080	Thallium .	Tl	81	204·39
Indium . .	In	49	114·76	Thorium .	Th	90	232·12
Iodine. . .	I	53	126·91	Thulium .	Tm	69	169·4
Iridium . .	Ir	77	193·1	Tin . . .	Sn	50	118·70
Iron . . .	Fe	26	55·85	Titanium .	Ti	22	47·90
Krypton .	Kr	36	83·80	Tungsten .	W	74	183·92
Lanthanum .	La	57	138·92	Uranium . .	U	92	238·07
Lead . . .	Pb	82	207·21	Vanadium .	V	23	50·95
Lithium . .	Li	3	6·940	Xenon. . .	Xe	54	131·3
Lutetium .	Lu	71	175·0	Ytterbium .	Yb	70	173·04
Magnesium .	Mg	12	24·32	Yttrium . .	Y	39	88·92
Manganese .	Mn	25	54·93	Zinc . . .	Zn	30	65·77
Mendelevium	Mv	101	256	Zirconium .	Zr	40	91·22

Auramine, Basic Yellow 2. Crystallizes in

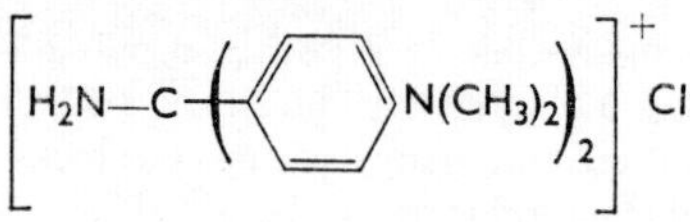

$$\left[H_2N-C \left(\underset{2}{\bigcirc} \right) N(CH_3)_2 \right]^+ Cl^-$$

yellow scales from water, m.p. 267°. It is sparingly soluble in cold water, more soluble in alcohol. The free base crystallizes from alcohol in colourless plates, m.p. 136°.

It is prepared by condensing dimethylaniline, formaldehyde, and zinc chloride together to give a diphenylmethane derivative, which is melted with sulphur and ammonium chloride at 140°-175° in a stream of ammonia. The sulphur behaves as an oxidizing agent.

It is used as a dye for animal fibres or cotton mordanted with tannin. It gives very bright yellow shades. It is also used as an antiseptic.

Aureoline, cobalt yellow. Potassium cobaltinitrite. When used for painting procelain it produces a brilliant blue on baking.

Aureomycin is a trade name for chlortetracycline. See Tetracyclines.

Auric and aurous. Gold (III) and gold (I) compounds respectively.

Aurine, rosolic acid. The prototype of the

aurine dyestuffs, which are derivatives of tri-*p*-hydroxytriphenylmethane. It is a yellow dyestuff, and is manufactured by the action of sulphuric acid on a mixture of oxalic acid and phenol. It is no longer used for dyeing textiles, but its lakes are used for staining paper, and it is also used as an indicator in alkalimetry.

Austempering. A heat treatment process used for alloy steels whereby the component is quenched to a temperature above the transition point and held at this temperature till the austenite transforms isothermally to bainite, a product similar to tempered martensite. This eliminates the dangers of cracking and distortion which occur due to the expansion when a steel is quenched to martensite. See also Martempering.

Austenite. The name given to the solid solution of carbon in gamma iron, but also applied to solid solutions of other alloying elements in the gamma (face-centred cubic) form of iron. It exists normally at elevated temperatures, but the range over which it is stable is altered by alloying elements.

Austenitic steels. See Steel.

Auto-catalysis. In some reactions one of the products catalyses the further decomposition of the reactants. This phenomenon is known as auto-catalysis.

Autolysis. A term meaning self-destruction applied to the disintegrative changes that occur in living systems after death other than those due to external agents such as bacteria. These changes are due to the action of the cellular enzymes on the cell itself, an action that either does not occur in the living cell, or is compensated by other mechanisms, tending to build up the cell structure.

Autoxidation. An oxidation reaction which proceeds only when another oxidation reaction is occurring simultaneously in the same system. Such reactions are normally confined to solutions. An example is the oxidation of oil of turpentine by atmospheric oxygen. When this reaction is taking place, it is possible to obtain simultaneous oxidation of potassium iodide to iodine, or of arsenious acid to arsenic acid. The turpentine is called the *autoxidator*, and the iodide, arsenious acid, etc., the acceptor.

Auxins. The auxins are plant hormones which promote the apical growth of plant shoots and have a number of other effects on the growth of plants, including yeasts and fungi. The substances originally called 'auxin a' and 'auxin b' are not now regarded as auxins. The identification of what was once called 'heteroauxin' with 3-indolylacetic acid (*q.v.*) was an important landmark. It was the basis of the commercial manufacture of selective weedkillers and other synthetic growth regulators. Synthetic auxins widely used in weed control include 2,4-dichlorophenoxyacetic acid (2,4-D), 2-methyl-4-chlorophenoxyacetic acid (MCPA) and 2,4,5-trichlorophenoxyacetic acid (2,4,5-T).

Many derivatives of 3-indolylacetic acid are active in promoting plant growth, and it is probable that the action is associated with the structure and not with any particular substance. Auxin activity is measured by determining the deflection produced when the substance is applied asymmetrically to decapitated *Avena* seedlings.

Auxochrome. In Witt's theory of colour (1876) a group modifying the colour due to the chromophore, e.g. $-NH_2$, $-OMe$. In more modern terms an auxochrome is a group containing lone pairs of electrons.

Aviation spirit (aviation gasoline). Fuels for piston-engined aircraft consisting of specially blended mixtures of high anti-knock value, high stability and low freezing point. Boiling range approximately 35°-150°, about 70% distilling below 100°.

Avogadro, Amedeo (1776-1856). Professor of physics at Turin. He explained certain chemical facts by assuming that equal volumes of gases, whether elementary or compound, under the same conditions contain the same number of molecules. The law is not strictly true, except at very low pressures, or for perfect gases but is the basis of most simple calculations on gases.

Avogadro's number. The number of molecules in one mole of any pure substance. $6 \cdot 023 \times 10^{23}$ denoted N. It has been determined by many methods, including measurements of Brownian movement, radiant heat, electronic charge, and the counting of α-particles.

Axes of symmetry. See Symmetry elements.

Axial. See Conformation.

Axial ratios. The ratios of the cell dimensions (a, b, and c) in the crystal referred to b as unity. In the triclinic, monoclinic, and orthorhombic systems, in which the axes are all unequal, the axial ratios are therefore quoted in the form $a/b:1:c/b$. In the hexagonal and tetragonal systems there are two equal axes ($a=b$) and only $c:a$ is required. Finally in the rhombohedral and cubic systems the three axes are of equal length. See Crystal structure and Crystal systems.

Axis of symmetry. See Crystal symmetry.

Azafrin, $C_{27}H_{38}O_4$. The pigment of Azafranillo

trated by a process for separating an azeotropic mixture of ethanol and water using benzene.

The complete plant consists of three fractionating columns, to be referred to as A, B and C, with two of them, A and B, sharing a common condenser. The ethanol-water azeotrope is fed to column A, whose reflux consists largely· of benzene. From the bottom of the column is obtained pure ethanol, while the ternary azeotrope forms the overhead vapour. This vapour is mixed with the benzene-ethanol-water vapour stream from column B and passes into a common condenser. The condensate stream separates into two layers, the upper consisting almost entirely of ethanol and benzene, which is returned as reflux to column A, the lower mainly ethanol and water. This lower layer forms the feed to column B, which removes the benzene and some of the ethanol to give an overhead vapour consisting of a ternary mixture, and a bottoms product consisting of a dilute solution of ethanol in water. The latter is treated in column C, which returns the overhead ethanol-water azeotrope

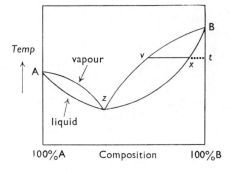

root, a South American plant. It is used in Paraguay for colouring fats. It crystallizes in orange-red needles or prisms, m.p. 212°-214°, soluble in chloroform, alcohol, benzene, and alkali, sparingly soluble in ether, insoluble in water. $[\alpha]_{Cd}^{20} -75°$.

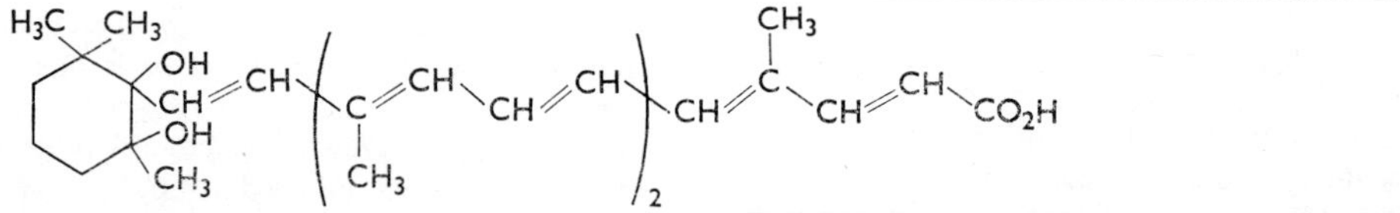

Azaserine, O-Diazoacetyl-L-serine, $C_5H_7N_3O_4$.

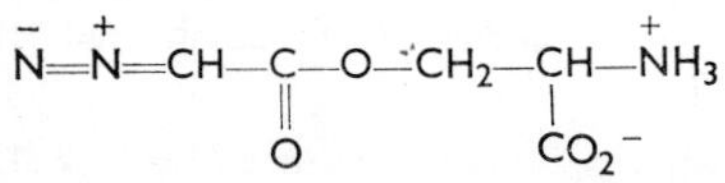

Greenish-yellow crystals. An antibiotic produced by *Streptomyces* spp. Used in treatment of acute leukaemia.

Azelaic acid, Lepargylic acid, $C_9H_{16}O_4$, $HOOC \cdot [CH_2]_7COOH$. Crystallizes in colourless plates, m.p. 106°. Slightly soluble in water and ether; readily soluble in alcohol. Made by the oxidation of oleic acid with ozone. Distillation of its salts gives cyclic ketones.

Azeotropic distillation. If two substances have similar boiling points or form an azeotrope, separation by fractional distillation is either very difficult or impossible. The method of azeotropic distillation consists of adding a third substance which forms azeotropic mixtures with the other two; these azeotropes are then further treated to obtain pure compounds. The method is illus-

to column A and gives water as the bottoms product. Thus pure ethanol is taken from the bottom of column A, water is rejected from the bottom of column C, while the benzene merely circulates around the system.

Azeotropic mixtures. Mixtures of liquids when distilled may reach a stage at which the composition of the liquid is the same as that of the vapour.

Many liquid mixtures exhibit a minimum boiling point (e.g. methyl alcohol and chloroform; *n*-propyl alcohol and water) whilst others show a maximum b.p. (e.g. hydrochloric acid and water) when vapour pressures are plotted as a function of change in composition of the mixture. An example of a system (A + B) where a minimum is seen is shown in the figure. The upper curve represents the composition of the vapour phase whilst the lower that of the liquid. When the liquid of composition x boils at temperature t it is seen that the composition of the vapour (v) differs in that it is richer in constituent A than the liquid, and an increase in the b.p. would result in pure B being given.

At z in the curve, however (the minimum of vapour pressure), the solution and vapour are in equilibrium and the liquid at this point will distil without any change in composition. The mixture at z is thus said to be an azeotropic or constant boiling mixture. It should be noted, however, that the composition of the azeotropic mixture does vary with pressure.

Azide. A salt of hydrazoic acid, HN_3. This acid ionizes to give the N_3^- ion, and will dissolve certain metals (e.g. Fe, Zn, Cu, and Al) with formation of the metallic azides. The azides of the heavy metals (e.g. lead azide, $Pb(N_3)_2$) are dangerously explosive. Sodium azide, NaN_3, is a relatively stable compound. It is prepared by the action of nitrous oxide on sodamide, $NaNH_2$, heated to 190°. Azides of the alkali and alkaline earth metals lose nitrogen when heated to 100°-350°, leaving the free metal. X-ray data indicate that the azide group is linear.

Azidocarbondisulphide, $(SCSN_3)_2$. A pseudo-halogen prepared by the oxidation of an azidodithiocarbonate $MSCSN_3$. Metal azido-dithiocarbonates are formed by interaction of carbon disulphide and a metal azide. Azido-carbondisulphide is a white, shock-sensitive, crystalline solid, slightly soluble in water.

Azidodithiocarbonates. Compounds containing the $(SCSN_3)^-$ ion.

Azimuthal quantum number. See Electronic configuration.

Azines. See Indulines.

Azobenzene, $C_{12}H_{10}N_2$. Orange-red crystals, m.p. 68°, b.p. 295°. Insoluble in water, soluble in alcohol and ether. Reduces to aniline and also hydrazobenzene which can revert to benzidine under the reaction conditions. Substitution in the 4-position occurs on sulphonation with fuming sulphuric acid, on nitration and on

(a)

(b)

bromination. It is prepared by the partial reduction of nitrobenzene.

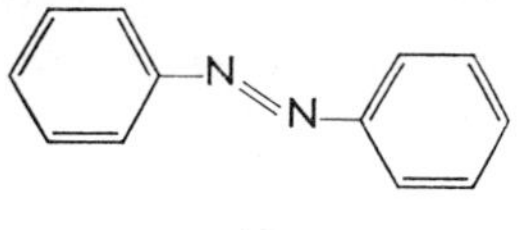

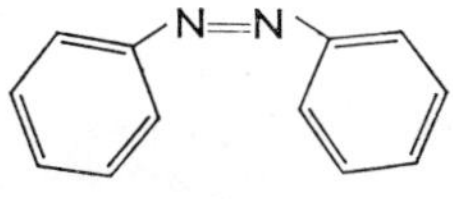

It is the simplest compound containing the chromophoric —N=N— grouping, but is of no practical importance since it lacks affinity for fibres. Normally it exists in the most stable *trans* form (a), but may be converted to a less stable, bright red *cis* form (b), m.p. 71·5 by ultra-violet irradiation. *Cis* to *trans* isomerization occurs rapidly on heating.

Azo-compounds. A large group of compounds which contain the —N=N— chromophore attached to two aromatic nuclei and which absorb light in the visible range of the spectrum. If the aromatic nuclei contain amino, hydroxyl, sulphonic acid or other salt-forming groups the compound will have some affinity for animal or vegetable fibres and will thus be a dyestuff.

Azo-compounds can be obtained by reduction of nitro-compounds (see Azobenzene), or by oxidation of hydrazo-compounds. They are usually prepared, however, by reacting a phenol or amine with a diazonium salt. The coupling usually takes place in the position para to the hydroxyl or amino group, but if this position is occupied it goes to the ortho position, e.g.

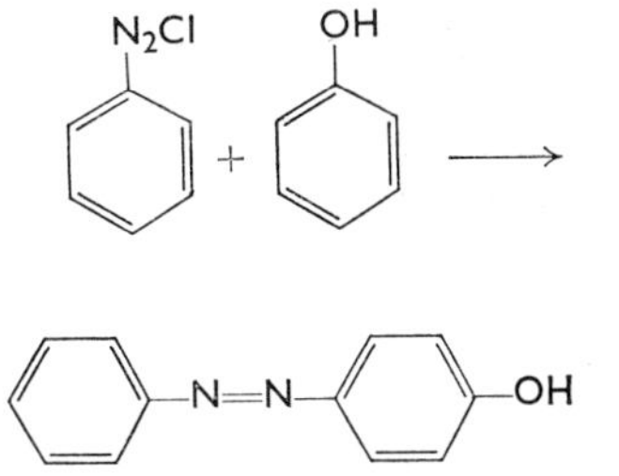

Benzeneazophenol

The azo-compounds are usually very stable, and can be directly chlorinated, nitrated, and sulphonated. On vigorous reduction the molecule splits at the azo group to give two molecules of primary amines, e.g.

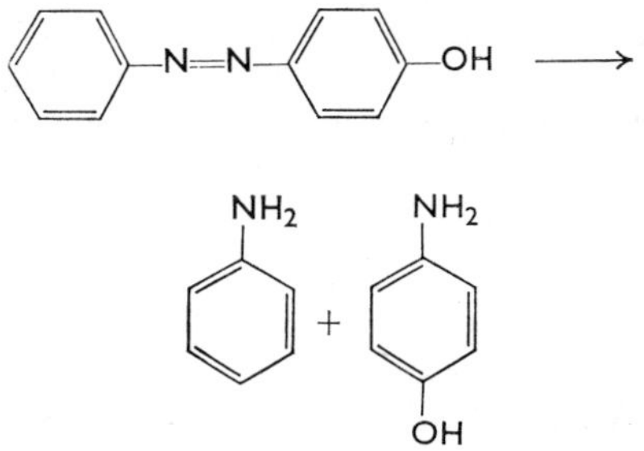

Azo-dyes. The azo-dyestuffs, possessing the the chromophoric group —N=N—, are the most important class of colouring matters.

The azo-compounds are almost invariably prepared by the interaction of a diazo-salt (first component) with an aromatic hydroxy-compound or amine (second component). If the second component is a phenol (naphthol) the aqueous solution of the salt (hydrochloride) of the primary amine is diazotised. The solution of this diazonium salt is then 'coupled' with the phenol by allowing the solution of the former to run gradually into an alkaline solution of the latter.

The dyestuff settles down as a sparingly soluble alkali-compound, or it remains in solution and can be recovered as a salt by precipitation with sodium chloride, or in the free state by the addition of acid. If the second component is an amine the combination of the diazo-salt with the dissolved amine is brought about in neutral or faintly acid solution.

When the second component contains both a hydroxyl and an amino group coupling occurs according to the medium (in acid or in alkali) in the positions indicated by the arrows:

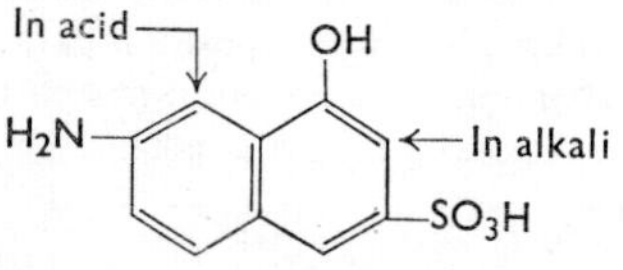

Coupling of dihydroxy-compounds is often carried out in weak acid solution in order to avoid the formation of a diazo-compound. The formation of azo-compounds is usually quantitative. The stability of the diazo-salts varies considerably.

The majority of the azo-dyestuffs used technically are sodium salts of sulphonic acids and are soluble in water. They are used as acid dyes, dyeing animal fibres (wool). Their affinity for cotton is low, but increases with the number of auxochromes and particularly with the number of azo groups. Certain groups (symmetrical tetrazotized diamines or 'J-acid,' or various heterocyclic groups, etc.) cause an enormous increase in the affinity of the dye for cotton (direct or substantive cotton dye).

Colours containing phenol, salicylic acid, or α-naphthol groups are not fast to alkali; alkylation of the phenolic group increases the fastness; α-naphthol dyes with an ortho-azo group are fast to alkali. By increasing the number of azo groups in acid wool dyes the fastness to washing rises. The azo-dyes are not very fast to light, the more complex the dyes, the less the fastness. Pyrazolone and nitro- or sulphonic groups are beneficial. The tetrazo colours used as direct cotton dyes are generally inferior to the simple monoazo colours.

The azo-dyestuffs can be divided into four chief classes:

(1) Monoazo dyestuffs.
  (a) Amino azo compounds (Chrysoidine, Aminoazobenzene, etc.).
  (b) Oxyazo-compounds (Ponceaux Fast Red A, etc.).

(2) Disazo dyestuffs.
  (a) Primary (Naphtol Blue Black, Resorcin Brown, etc.).
  (b) Secondary (Biebrich Scarlet, Diamond Black F, etc.).
  (c) Dyes from tetrazo salts with two similar or different molecules of an amine or phenol.

(3) Dyes from trisazo-dyestuffs (Diamine Green G, and B, Congo Brown, etc.).

(4) Tetrakisazo-dyestuffs (Benzo Brown G, etc.).

Azoic dyes. The name given to dyes—formerly known as insoluble azo or ice colours—which are produced within the fibre by impregnating the material with a naphthol, followed by passage through a solution of a diazotized base (Fast Colour base) or Fast Colour salt (*q.v.*). The earliest naphthols were α or β naphthol and one of the first important insoluble azo colours was Para Red when the components were β naphthol and diazotized *p*-nitraniline.

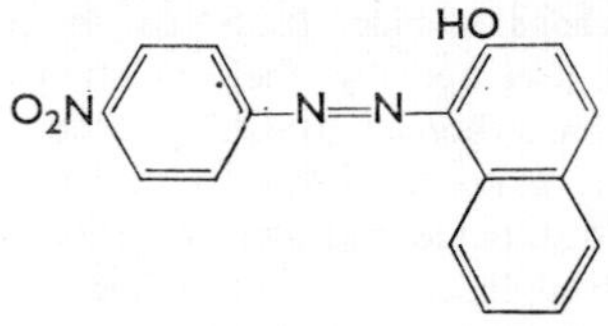

Paranitraniline Red (Para Red)

In 1912, Naphtol AS, Azoic Coupling Component 2 (anilide of β-hydroxynaphthoic acid) was introduced and this soon replaced

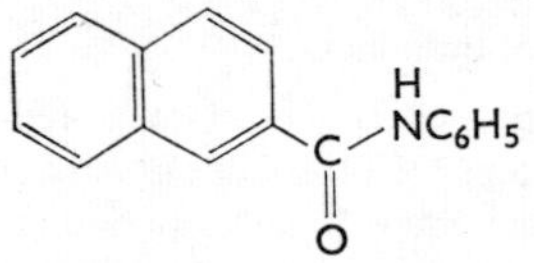

β-naphthol, giving shades of greatly improved fastness, arising from the greatly improved substantivity of the new product for vegetable fibres.

Continuous progress has been made since 1920 with the marketing of further naphthols

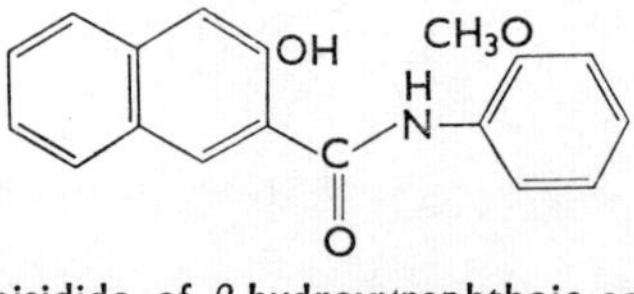

o-anisidide of β-hydroxynaphthoic acid
Naphtol AS.OL or Brenthol FR(I.C.I.)
Azoic Coupling Component 20

which are arylides of sundry o-hydroxy carboxylic acids.

Similarly a wide range of approximately 50 bases (or Fast Colour salts) is now available, so that there exists a very large number of potential azoic combinations, and the shades range through all the colours of the spectrum.

m-nitro-o-toluidine (Fast Red RL base, C.I. Azoic Diazo Component 34

Selected combinations often have characteristic brilliancy of shade along with extremely high fastness to light and to many important wet treatments. The azoic range is particularly strong in reds (ranging from scarlets to bluish reds) and altogether the azoic dyes represent one of the most important classes of dyes for dyeing and printing of cellulose fibres. By suitably modifying the method of application, azoic dyeings can be successfully produced on silk, acetate rayon, nylon and other fibres.

Recent developments include the production of bright green shades in which the azoic range was deficient for many years. For this, new bases are combined with existing naphtols, or various bases are used along with new naphtols, e.g. Naphtol AS.FG.GR (C.I. Azoic Coupling Component 108). For duller shades of green, e.g. olive green, Hoechst have introduced the Variogen Bases (and Salts) (C.I. Azoic Diazo Components 135-138), also Fast Green Salt GT (C.I. Azoic Diazo Component 134), to be coupled with suitable coupling components, e.g. Naphtol AS.BG (C.I. Azoic Coupling Component 19).

Also in line with improvements in other classes of dyes, new products are being developed for producing azoic dyeings on various synthetic fibres, e.g. Intramin dyes for polyester fibres.

Azoimides, Azimino compounds. A type of compound obtained on treating an o-arylenediamine with nitrous acid. In this case it is impossible to obtain normal diazo compounds, e.g. o-phenylenediamine gives azoiminobenzene,

Azolitmin. See Litmus.

Azomethines. See Schiff's bases.

Azophenols. These are compounds obtained by coupling a diazo salt with a phenol, e.g. benzene-

diazonium chloride and phenol give p-hydroxyazobenzene, orange yellow needles, m.p. 148°.

Azorubrum. See Amaranth. A synonym for Bordeaux B.

Azulene, $C_{10}H_8$. A blue-violet crystalline solid with a naphthalene-like smell, m.p. 98·5°-99°.

The generic term 'azulene' was first applied in 1864 to the blue oils obtained by distillation, oxidation, or acid-treatment of many essential oils. These blue colours are usually due to the presence of either guaiazulene or vetivazulene. The structures of these compounds were elucidated by St. Pfau and Plattner, who also synthesized the parent hydrocarbon in 1936 by dehydrogenation of a cyclopentanocycloheptanol over a palladium catalyst at 300°-350°. A better method involves the condensation of cyclopentadiene with glutacondialdehyde anil.

Azulene is an aromatic compound and undergoes substitution reactions in the 1-position. At 270° it is transformed into naphthalene. It dissolves in concentrated acids, from which it may be recovered by dilution with water. It forms a trinitrobenzene adduct, m.p. 166·5°-167·5°.

Azurin. A soluble blue protein (containing copper) of molecular weight about 15,000, isolated from species of *Bordetella* and other Gram-negative bacteria.

Azurite is a native azure blue basic carbonate of copper, $Cu_3(CO_3)_2(OH)_2$. An artificial form is known as *Blue Verditer* or *Blue Ashes* and is used as an artist's colour.

B

Babbitt metal. See Tin alloys.

Bacillus thuringiensis Berliner. A microbial insecticide which affects only certain insects and is harmless to bees and mammals. Preparations containing *B. thuringiensis* have been used for controlling lepidopterous larvae.

Bacitracin. A polypeptide antibiotic produced by a strain of *B. subtilis*. Commercial bacitracin is a mixture of about ten polypeptides: the structure of the major component, bacitracin A, has been established.

$$CH_3CH_2CH-CH-CH \begin{matrix} S-CH_2 \\ | \quad\quad | \\ \end{matrix}$$

CH₃CH₂CH—CH—CH / S—CH₂ / O / CH₃ NH₂ / N—CH—C—L-Leu / D-Asp(NH₂)   D-Glu / D-Phe—L-His—L-Asp / L-Ileu—D-Orn—L-Lys————L-Ileu

Bacitracin is chiefly active against Gram-positive organisms, e.g. streptococci, staphylococci, gonococci, and meningococci. It is used against organisms resistant to penicillin, especially for skin and eye infections. Prolonged internal administration may cause damage to the kidneys.

Back bonding. Overlap of a filled d orbital of a metal with a vacant d or π orbital of a ligand. This process normally relieves the build-up of negative charge on the metal but may only involve electron transfer from the ligand to the metal. It is very important in complexes of metals in low oxidation states, e.g. carbonyls.

Bacon, Roger (1214?-1294?). Bacon was born near Ilchester, Somerset, and studied theology and science at Oxford and Paris. Though believing in the philosopher's stone and other alchemical doctrines, he laid stress on the value of experimental research, and his name is associated with the early history of gunpowder, which he described in a letter to the Archbishop of Paris, 1265. His enlightened views brought him into sharp conflict with the Franciscan Order to which he belonged.

Bacteriophage. A virus which can infect bacteria.

Baddeleyite. A mineral consisting essentially of zirconia (ZrO_2) with variable amounts of impurities, mainly iron and silica. The only commercial deposits are in the Caldas region, Brazil. The crystals are monoclinic, sp.gr. 5·7, hardness 6-7, possessing a high refractive index. It is used in the manufacture of zirconia refractories and in ceramics.

Baekeland, Leo Hendrik (1863-1944). Born and educated in Ghent, Belgium, Baekeland went to the United States in 1889, where he founded a company for the manufacture of photographic paper and materials. In 1906 he undertook a new line of research which culminated in the production of 'Bakelite,' a phenolic condensation product with which his name is associated.

Baeyer, Johann Friedrich Wilhelm Adolf von (1835-1917). Born in Berlin, von Baeyer studied chemistry under Bunsen and Kekulé. In 1860 he returned to Berlin, where he taught organic chemistry at the Technical Institute. In 1872 he was appointed professor of chemistry at Stras-

burg, and in 1875 at Munich. A brilliant chemist whose work lay chiefly in the field of synthetic chemistry, he was awarded the Nobel Prize for chemistry in 1905. See *Nature*, 1917, **100**, 188.

Baffle chamber. See Impingement separators.

Bag filter. This type of filter is employed where it is desirable to remove suspended solids from air or a gas almost completely. It consists essentially of a casing in which are suspended a number of cylindrical fabric bags. Air is passed outwards through these bags, any dust collecting on the inner surface. By means of a suitable mechanism the air supply is periodically cut off and the bags tapped or shaken to remove the collected solids. The air may be passed through this system either by blowing or by keeping the space around the filter bags at a reduced pressure, according to the conditions under which it is to be used.

Baiacalin, $C_{21}H_{18}O_{11}$. One of the two known glycosides of glucuronic acid. The aglucone is 5,6,7-trihydroxy flavone. It has m.p. 223°, $[\alpha]_D^{18} -145°$. It is present in the roots of *Scutellaria baicalensis*, the leaves of which plant contain 4′-hydroxybaicalin, known as scutellarin.

Bakelite. A brand name for phenol-formaldehyde plastics and resins.

Bakelite A (or resol) is the thermoplastic, soluble stage of a one-stage phenol-formaldehyde resin which is fluid when hot. Bakelite B (or resitol) is the thermoplastic insoluble stage of a one-stage phenol-formaldehyde resin which is a gel when hot. Bakelite C (or resit) is the fully thermoset, insoluble one-stage phenol-formaldehyde resin.

Baking powders. Any powders used in baking as substitutes for yeast, and depending for their action on the slow evolution of carbon dioxide. They consist of various acid substances with the addition of sodium bicarbonate, or ammonium carbonate or sodium bicarbonate alone. Acids used are cream of tartar, calcium hydrogen phosphate, or sodium hydrogen pyrophosphate. Inert matter such as flour or starch is often added.

BAL (**British Anti-Lewisite**), **dimercaprol, dithioglycerol,** $C_3H_8OS_2$. Usually obtained as an oil, m.p. 77°, b.p. 95°/1·0 mm, by the treatment of 2,3-dibromopropanol with an alcoholic solution of sodium hydrosulphide. Developed as an

CH₂SH
|
CHSH
|
CH₂OH

antidote to poisoning by organic arsenicals by external application, it has since been found to be of use in poisoning by other heavy metals, for instance mercury, copper, zinc and cadmium. It acts by forming a chelate with the metal and so removing it from the system. It is used in oily injection by the intramuscular route.

Balard, Antoine Jérome (1802-1876). Professor of chemistry at the Sorbonne, Paris, and afterwards at the Collège de France; he discovered the element bromine in 1826.

Balata. See Gutta-percha.

Ball mill. In its simplest form the ball mill consists of a horizontal cylinder with length approximately equal to diameter, which is slowly rotated about its axis. Inside the mill, in addition to the material to be ground, is a quantity of steel or flint balls. The crushing, shearing action produced by the motion of these balls causes size reduction. The feed is normally introduced through a hollow trunnion at one end and taken off through a similar one at the other.

Wear on the balls and the periodic addition of new ones results in a size distribution. The *Hardinge mill* has the discharge end in the shape of a truncated cone tapering towards the outlet. Smaller balls tend to congregate towards the outlet and act on the fine material. This mill gives a finer and more uniform product than the ordinary ball mill.

Other modifications of the ball mill include the *tube mill*, which is like an elongated ball mill, and the *rod mill*, which instead of balls contains steel rods. Ball mills which are vibrated instead of rotated have come into use in recent years.

The ball mill is widely used in the chemical and process industries for fine grinding, being versatile, cheap and economical in power.

Balmer series. In 1885 Balmer observed that the wave-lengths (or frequencies) of certain lines in the spectrum of hydrogen were simply related to each other, and could be expressed by a general formula. The group of lines is termed the Balmer Series. Other series were later discovered in the spectrum of hydrogen by Lyman, Paschen, Brackett, and Pfund.

All these series may be expressed by the equation

$$\nu = 109678 \cdot 8/n^2 - 109678 \cdot 8/m^2,$$

wherein ν is the wave-number, and n and m are integers which can only have certain definite values for each series. Thus, in the Lyman series, $n=1$, whilst each line is expressed by letting $m=2$, 3, 4, etc. In the Balmer Series, $n=2$; in the Paschen Series, $n=3$; in the Brackett Series, $n=4$; and in the Pfund Series, $n=5$.

Balsam of Peru. Black oily liquid obtained from the trunk of *Myroxylon Pereirae*, a tree growing in Central America. It has an aromatic odour, and consists of resinous matter and a balsamic ester known as 'cinnamein', consisting chiefly of benzyl benzoate and cinnamate. It is used externally as an antiseptic and parasiticide in skin diseases, usually in the form of an ointment or diluted with castor oil.

Balsam of Tolu is obtained from the trunk of *Myroxylon balsamum*, a tree growing in Colombia. It is a brown resinous solid with an aromatic odour, and contains up to 50% balsamic acids. It is used in the form of Syrup of Tolu to flavour cough mixtures.

Bancroft, Wilder Dwight (1867-1953). Born at Middletown, U.S.A., Bancroft studied at Harvard, Strasburg, Leipzig, and Berlin. In 1895 he was appointed assistant professor of physical chemistry at Cornell University, and was professor from 1903 to 1937. He founded the *Journal of Physical Chemistry* in 1896 and edited it until 1932. See *J. Chem. Soc.*, 1953, 2506.

Band spectrum. The absorption of energy by a molecule may lead to the transition of an electron from an orbital of lower to one of higher energy (see Line spectrum), but in addition, there may be an increase in the energy of rotation of the molecule as a whole, and in the energy of vibration of the constituent atoms relative to each other. The simultaneous occurrence of these changes multiplies considerably the number of possible energy changes. The resulting spectrum is correspondingly complicated, and consists of numerous very closely spaced lines. In general, the frequency of a line is determined by the algebraic sum of the energy changes involved. An electronic transition is associated with so much more energy than vibrational and rotational changes, that it determines the general position of the line in the spectrum. The spectrum thus consists of well-defined groups or *bands*, of closely packed lines. Such a spectrum, characteristic of a molecule, is termed a *band spectrum*.

Band theory of metals. See Brillouin zones.

Banting, Frederick Grant (1891-1941). Born at Alliston, Ontario, Banting was educated at the Public and High Schools there, and graduated in medicine at Toronto University. After holding various junior appointments, he became professor of medical research at Toronto in 1923. His name is coupled with the brilliant work on insulin. His honours included M.C. (1915), the Nobel Prize (1923), K.B.E. (1934), and F.R.S. (1935).

Barbaloin, $C_{21}H_{22}O_9$. Barbaloin is unusual in

that the glucose residue is attached to the aglycone by a carbon-carbon linkage instead of the normal carbon-oxygen linkage. Treatment with acid gives D-arabinose and aloe-emodin anthrone. It is the active principle of aloes, from which it is obtained by extraction with hot water. It crystallizes in yellow needles, m.p. 147°, $[\alpha]_D - 8 \cdot 3°$ in alcohol.

Barbier-Wieland degradation. A method for the

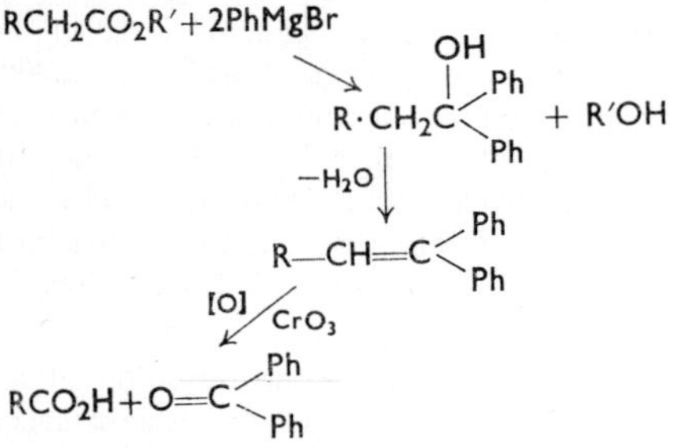

$$RCH_2CO_2R' + 2PhMgBr$$

stepwise degradation of aliphatic acids when one carbon atom is eliminated in each step. Opposite in objective to the Arndt-Eistert synthesis; especially useful for degrading side chains of steroid and other terpenoid molecules.

Barbitone, Diethylmalonylurea, $C_8H_{12}N_2O_3$. White crystals, m.p. 191°. Almost insoluble in cold water; soluble in alcohol, ether, and alkalis. It is taken in tablet form for insomnia, but it does not relieve pain. The sodium salt known as

'soluble barbitone' is readily soluble in water and is used when the drug is given in solution.

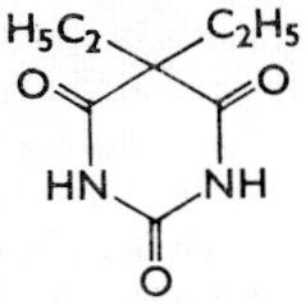

Barbiturates, Barbituric acids. An important group of hypnotic and sedative drugs derived from barbituric acid by replacement of the hydrogen atoms on C_5 by alkyl or aryl groups. They are colourless, crystalline solids, having a slightly bitter taste. Sparingly soluble in cold water; soluble in alcohol and chloroform. They form soluble sodium salts. Manufactured by heating the appropriate dialkylmalonic ester with urea and sodium ethoxide. They are generally divided into three groups: long acting, e.g. barbitone, medium acting, e.g. allobarbitone, and short acting, e.g. pentobarbitone.

Barbituric acid, Malonylurea, $C_4H_4N_2O_3$. Crystallizes as the dihydrate in colourless prisms, m.p. 253°. Soluble in hot water. Prepared by heating malonic ester with urea and sodium ethoxide, or by heating alloxantin with sulphuric acid. It is a dibasic acid. Decomposed

to malonic acid and urea by boiling alkalis. Forms violuric acid when treated with sodium nitrite. Reacts with nitric acid, bromine, and acyl halides.

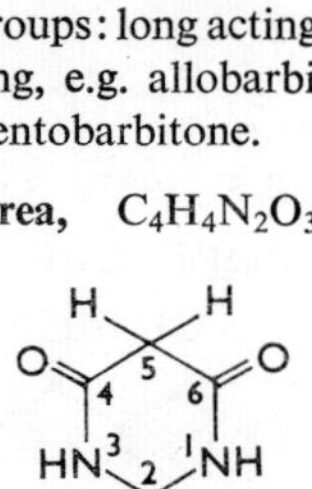

Barger, George (1878-1939). Barger received his early education in Holland before proceeding to University College, London, and King's College, Cambridge. After a period as research chemist, he was, in 1909, appointed head of the Chemical Department, Goldsmiths' College. In 1913 he was appointed professor of chemistry, Royal Holloway College, University of London, in 1919 professor of chemistry in relation to medicine at the University of Edinburgh, and in 1937 to a similar appointment at Glasgow. His research work covers a wide field; with Harington he synthesized thyroxin. He was elected F.R.S. in 1919.

Barium, Ba. At.no. 56, At.wt. 137·36, m.p. 710°, b.p. 1560°, d 3·59.

Occurs chiefly as the sulphate, heavy spar or barytes, $BaSO_4$, and to some extent as the carbonate, witherite, or as alstonite, a mixed carbonate of calcium and barium.

The metal is now generally obtained by the electrolysis of the fused chloride, using a cooled cathode which is withdrawn slowly as the deposit of metal 'grows.' The metal may be readily distilled in vacuum, is silver-white in colour, soft, and oxidizes spontaneously in air. It is used as a getter for oxygen, and as an alloy constituent in bearing metals. Metallic barium has a body-centred cubic structure, $a = 5 \cdot 01$ Å.

Barium carbonate, $BaCO_3$. A white crystalline solid, d 4·29. It occurs native, particularly in England, as the mineral witherite, but is produced by treating a solution of barium sulphide with carbon dioxide or sodium carbonate. It is the most important of the barium salts, since besides being the starting point for the manufacture of other barium compounds, it is widely used as a flux in ceramics and as an ingredient in optical glasses and fine glassware. It is also employed for removing sulphate and various metal ions from solutions, and as a carbon carrier in case-hardening baths.

Barium chloride, $BaCl_2$. This is prepared by dissolving the native carbonates in hydrochloric acid, removing the iron by precipitation as ferric hydroxide, and evaporating the filtered liquid, when crystals of $BaCl_2.2H_2O$ separate. It is used for the preparation of metallic barium by the electrolytic method. It has m.p. 962°, b.p. 1560°, solubility 37·2 g in 100 g water at 25°.

Barium chromate, $BaCrO_4$. A yellow solid, precipitated by the addition of a soluble chromate to a solution of a barium salt. Its solubility in water at 18° is 0·0038 g per litre. It is insoluble in acetic acid but soluble in mineral acids. It is used as a pigment.

Barium dithionate, BaS_2O_6. A white crystalline solid, the most stable salt of dithionic acid.

Barium halides, BaX_2. These are very similar to the calcium halides. Barium fluoride, precipitated from barium nitrate by potassium fluoride solution, is only slightly soluble in water, m.p. 1285°, b.p. 2137°. Barium bromide, m.p. 847°, forms a di- and mono-hydrate. Barium iodide, m.p. 740°, forms a hexa-, di-, and mono-hydrate. Both the bromide and iodide are very soluble in water.

Barium hydride, BaH_2. Formed by heating barium amalgam in hydrogen at 1400°. It melts at 1200° and can be distilled in hydrogen at 1400°. With water it gives hydrogen and the hydroxide.

Barium hydroxide, Baryta, $Ba(OH)_2$. A white solid which is formed by acting on barium monoxide with water, or by the action of sodium hydroxide on soluble barium salts. It forms hydrates with 8 and 1 molecules of water of crystallization. The octahydrate is sparingly soluble in water (3·74 parts per 100 at 20°), and its solutions have a strongly alkaline reaction and are used in volumetric analysis.

Barium nitrate, $Ba(NO_3)_2$. A colourless crystalline solid, m.p. 595°, formed by dissolving barium oxide in nitric acid and crystallizing, or by double decomposition. The salt crystallizes from hot solutions in the anhydrous form. The solubility of the anhydrous salt in water is 4·8% at 0° and 40·1% at 180°.

Barium oxides. *Barium oxide*, BaO, is obtained as a white powder, by ignition of the nitrate or carbonate. It has the sodium chloride lattice.

Barium peroxide, BaO_2, is obtained by heating BaO in dry oxygen at about 550°; on strongly heating to 800° all the oxygen is evolved and BaO remains. This equilibrium was formerly a method for the commercial preparation of oxygen by the Brin process. Barium peroxide is used as a bleaching agent and in the production of hydrogen peroxide.

Barium sulphate, $BaSO_4$. Occurs naturally and is readily precipitated by the addition of sulphuric acid to barium chloride. It is a white, very insoluble (2·4 mg/litre) heavy powder. The reaction is used for the estimation of barium or the sulphate anion. In hot concentrated acid a soluble acid sulphate, $Ba(HSO_4)_2$, is formed and in quantitative estimations the precipitate should not be washed with strong acid.

The mineral is of great importance as the principal raw material for the manufacture of other barium compounds. Purified it is also used as a cheap pigment, or filler for paper or rubber, while barium sulphate co-precipitated with zinc sulphide forms the pigment lithopone.

Barium sulphide, BaS. A white powder, crystallized in cubes or octahedra, which is formed by reduction of barium sulphate with carbon. Barium sulphide is of commercial importance as the intermediate by which the other barium compounds are manufactured from the naturally-occurring sulphate. As prepared, it contains heavy metals as impurities, and these render the sulphide strongly phosphorescent. The colour of the phosphorescence depends on the temperature.

Barker, George Frederic (1835-1910). Barker was born at Charlestown, Massachusetts, and educated at Yale. After holding professorships at Wheaton College (1861), the Albany Medical College (1862-1863), and Pittsburg (1864-1869), he was appointed professor of chemistry and toxicology at Yale Medical School, and in 1872 became professor of physics at the University of Pennsylvania, retiring as emeritus-professor in 1900. He was President of the American Chemical Society in 1891, and wrote the first American textbook to give a systematic presentation of modern chemistry.

Barn. The unit of cross-section which is used in nuclear chemistry to describe reaction yields. If a stream of particles of a given energy strikes a target each bombarding particle will cause a reaction in the solid if the distance between the nuclear centres is greater than a certain minimum distance, l (l will include a probability factor for the interaction being effective). Considering 1cm^2 of target material, containing N nuclei per cm^3, the probability of interaction is $N\sigma$, where $\sigma = \pi l^2$, and is the cross-sectional area per nucleus. Nuclear diameters are of the order of 10^{-12} cm, so that σ is approximately 10^{-24} cm^2. The unit of area 10^{-24} cm^2 is called the barn.

Other interaction processes using the concept of cross-section include ionization and scattering.

Barometric condenser. This is a plant for condensing steam at pressures below atmospheric. It consists of a vessel situated at the top of a vertical tube called a *barometric leg*. Steam passing into the vessel is condensed by direct contact with a spray of cold water and discharges by gravity through the leg. The water in the leg acts as a seal which enables the vacuum to be maintained.

Barometric condensers are cheap and economical to operate. They are commonly used in conjunction with evaporators.

Bart's reaction. The formation of an aryl

arsonic acid by the action of an alkaline solution of sodium arsenite on a diazonium salt, e.g.

$$p.NO_2C_6H_4N_2Cl + Na_3AsO_3 \rightarrow$$
$$p.NO_2C_6H_4AsO(ONa)_2 + NaCl + N_2$$

The reaction is best carried out in dilute aqueous solution with warming and stirring until evolution of nitrogen ceases. The yield is rarely above 40 to 50%. In a few cases, e.g. 2,4-dinitroaniline, the reaction proceeds best in strongly acid solution.

Barytes, Heavy Spar. A common mineral consisting of barium sulphate, $BaSO_4$; it often forms well-developed crystals, which are ortho-rhombic and have sp.gr. 4·5, hardness 2·5-3·5. Pure specimens of barytes are colourless or white, but brownish or bluish tints may be introduced by impurities. The mineral is used as a source of barium compounds; when finely ground it is used as a pigment and in oil-well drilling muds.

Base. On the simplest view a base is a substance which in aqueous solution reacts with an acid to form a salt and water only, i.e. is a substance which furnishes hydroxyl ions. A more modern definition (Lowry, Brønsted), which also applies to non-aqueous solutions, states that a base is a substance with a tendency to gain protons. By this definition, OH^- and the anions of weak acids, e.g. CH_3COO^-, are bases in aqueous solution.

For ionized solvents which do not contain protons a base is a substance which reacts with the acid of that system to give a salt and the solvent. Thus the base $KBrF_4$ reacts with the acid BrF_2SbF_6 to give the salt $KSbF_6$ and BrF_3 in bromine trifluoride. A Lewis base is any molecule with 'excess' electrons. Thus ammonia, with a lone pair of electrons, is a Lewis base.

As an adjective applied to metals base represents the opposite of noble, i.e. a base metal would be attacked by mineral acids.

Base exchange. An old term, still used in connexion with soils, zeolites, clays, etc., meaning their capacity to exchange some or all of their monopositive or dipositive cations (e.g. Na^+, K^+, Ca^{++}) for an equivalent quantity of other cations without undergoing change of structure. The effect was discovered in 1845 by Spence who found that a solution of ammonium sulphate, when passed through a column of soil, was transformed into calcium sulphate. This is an example of the more general process of ion exchange (*q.v.*).

Base-pairing. A term used with reference to a nucleic acid double helical structure, to indicate the specific hydrogen-bonded association of pairs of complementary purine and pyrimidine bases, viz. adenine with thymine or uracil, and guanine with cytosine.

Basic or **cationic dyes.** These dyes are salts of various colour bases and were the first synthetic dyes to be manufactured. When marketed in the form of hydrochlorides they are moderately soluble in water and have direct affinity for protein fibres, e.g. wool and silk, arising from the presence of amino or substituted amino groups. If the base is combined with certain organic acids, e.g. stearic or oleic, the corresponding salts are readily soluble in many organic solvents and are used in printing inks, typewriter ribbons, also inks for stamping pads and for ball-point pens. Also by reacting basic dyes with phosphotungstomolybdic acid, insoluble colour lakes are produced possessing high fastness together with brilliant shades. These are extremely important in the modern wallpaper and paint industries. For example, C.I. Pigment Blue 7 is the phosphotungsto-molybdic lake of Victoria Pure Blue (C.I. Basic Blue 7).

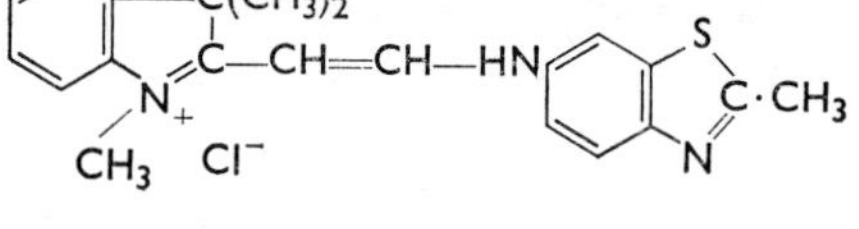

Although the number of basic dyes is small compared with other classes of dyes, many different chemical types are represented, even among the older dyes, e.g. azo, triphenyl-methane, acridine, azine, thiazine, oxazine and thiazole. For very many years these basic dyes played an important part in dyeing wool and silk despite their low fastness to light and indifferent fastness to washing, rubbing and other agencies, as they yielded shades of great brilliancy. In addition they were widely used in dyeing and printing of cotton and other cellulosic fibres, in spite of requiring a mordant (usually a natural or synthetic tannin) and often a fixing agent, before the dye could be successfully applied. These difficulties in application, and inferior fastness properties, have led to their replacement on natural fibres by other types of dyes. This decline in importance of basic dyes is, however, being rapidly offset by the introduction of new or modified basic dyes which are proving very successful for dyeing some synthetic fibres, chiefly polyacrylics. No mordant is required and the dyeings have the brightness usually associated with basic dyes, together with much higher fastness to light and washing than was given by the older basic dyes. Some of these new basic dyes are quaternary ammonium salts whilst others belong to the anthraquinone, cyanine or methine class; e.g. C.I. Basic Yellow 12 is the methine dye with the structure shown at the bottom of the previous column, (Astrazon Yellow 5G).

A recent development is to produce basic dyes where the electro positive nitrogen atom is separated from the chromophore. The improved fastness to light of these dyes is attributed to this arrangement, shown in C.I. Basic Red 18 (monoazo dye).

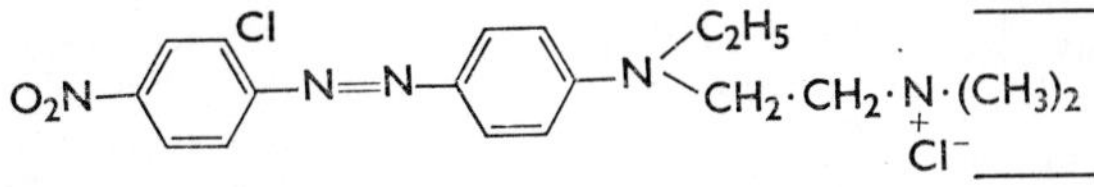

$$O_2N\!-\!\langle \rangle\!-\!N\!=\!N\!-\!\langle \rangle\!-\!N\!\!\begin{array}{c} C_2H_5 \\ CH_2\cdot CH_2\cdot \underset{+}{N}\cdot(CH_3)_2 \\ Cl^- \end{array}$$

Basic slag. See Slag.

Bastnaesite. A fluoro-carbonate of the cerium group of the rare earths. Extensive deposits, which are worked on a commercial scale, occur at Mountain Pass, California.

Bathochromic shift. A shift in absorption of light to longer wavelengths, i.e. to lower energy; the reverse is hypsochromic.

Batyl alcohol, $C_{21}H_{44}O_3$. Glyceryl-1-stearyl ether, m.p. 70°-71°. A constituent of shark and other fish-liver oils, also isolated from the non-saponifiable matter of yellow bone marrow, and of egg yolk. Batyl alcohol is present in athero-sclerotic aortal tissue. It shows erythropoietic properties and improves the survival of irradiated mice.

Baum washer. A type of jig (q.v.).

Baumé, Antoine (1728-1804). Born at Senlis, Baumé went to Paris, where he became a master apothecary in 1752. He published several works on chemistry, was professor of chemistry at the Collège de Pharmacie and a member of the Académie des Sciences, but is to-day chiefly remembered as the inventor of the Baumé hydrometer.

Baumé. See Hydrometer.

Bauxite. The principal ore of aluminium. It is a mixture of minerals formed by the weathering of aluminium-bearing rocks and contains hydrated alumina in variable amounts as

$$Al_2O_3\cdot 3H_2O$$

(named either gibbsite or hydrargillite) and $Al_2O_3\cdot H_2O$ (existing in two forms, böhmite and diaspore). It occurs extensively in France, Hungary, Jamaica, Guyana, Surinam, and the U.S.A. Sp.gr. 2·5-2·9, hardness 1-3. Bauxite is readily attacked by acids but after calcination above 900° it forms alumina and becomes almost insoluble. It is used in the manufacture of aluminous refractories, as a source of aluminium and as a catalyst in refining petroleum. See 'Bauxite, Alumina and Aluminium', S. Bracewell, H.M.S.O., 1962.

Bayerite, α-$Al_2O_3\cdot 3H_2O$. A form of aluminium hydroxide formed by the slow hydrolysis of an aluminate solution.

Bayer's acid. See Crocein acid.

Bearing metal. Most bearings have a thin lining of a bearing alloy. These alloys have the following properties; low coefficient of friction, good wear and shock resistance, good retention of the lubricant, good heat conductivity and good corrosion resistance. They should be softer than the shaft and have a lower m.p., so that in the event of failure only the bearing will need replacement. Tin base Babbit metals are the most common type, suitable for medium loading at high speeds as in internal combustion engines. Highly turned engines require an alloy with better fatigue strength such as the 70% copper 30% lead alloy or the aluminium alloys containing 6-25% tin. Gun metal (90/10 bronze) is used for slow-moving and reciprocating bearings where the lubricating conditions are poor.

Becher, Johann Joachim, (1635-1682). Born at Spires, he published his 'Œdipum Chemicum' in 1663, and became a teacher of medicine at Mainz. He suggested the existence of an inflammable principle almost universally present; this was afterwards developed into the phlogiston theory.

Beckmann, Ernst (1853-1923). Originally an apothecary, Beckmann took up the study of chemistry in 1875, when he went to Leipzig to work under Kolbe. Later he studied under Wislicenus and Ostwald. In 1897 he was appointed professor of applied chemistry and Director of the Laboratory for Applied Chemistry at the University of Leipzig. He is remembered by the Beckmann rearrangement, an apparatus for the determination of the elevation of the boiling-point, and a thermometer.

Beckmann rearrangement. Under the influence of certain reagents, ketoximes are converted to amides by a process of intramolecular rearrangement. The reaction was discovered by Beckmann, who found that benzophenone oxime was changed to benzoylaniline when treated in ice-cold solution in ether with phosphorus

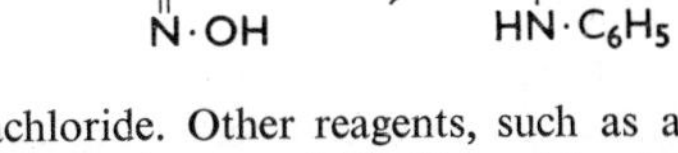

$$\underset{N\cdot OH}{\overset{C_6H_5\!-\!C\!-\!C_6H_5}{\|}} \rightarrow \underset{HN\cdot C_6H_5}{\overset{O\!=\!C\cdot C_6H_5}{|}}$$

pentachloride. Other reagents, such as acetyl chloride, antimony trichloride, sulphuric acid, or hydrochloric acid in acetic acid may produce the same effect, but in certain cases they give other products. With the oximes of cyclic ketones, the rearrangement involves an enlargement of the ring by the inclusion of the nitrogen atom. The rearrangement has been used to determine the structure of the isomeric ketoximes, since the different isomers were found to give different products when rearranged. The steric course of the rearrangement involves retention of configuration in the migrating group and inversion of configuration at the migration terminus; in other words the migration is intramolecular and attack on the nitrogen atom occurs on the side opposite to that from which the oxygen group leaves.

Beckmann thermometer. A very sensitive mercury thermometer, used in determining molecular weight by the freezing-point or boiling-point methods. It has a small temperature range, but can be used for different ranges by transferring mercury to the capillary from a bulb used as a reservoir.

Becquerel, Antoine Henri (1852-1908). Born in Paris, Becquerel was educated at the École Polytechnique; later he entered the Corps des Ponts et Chaussées and studied as an engineer. In 1875 he was appointed demonstrator at the Polytechnique, where he became professor in 1895. He discovered the emission of rays by uranium, and carried out important researches on rotatory magnetic polarization, phosphorescence and radioactivity. In 1889 he was admitted into the Academy of Sciences. See *Chem. Soc. Mem. Lect.*, 1912.

Beer's law. This law states that the proportion of light absorbed depends on the thickness (d) of the absorbing layer, and on the *molecular concentration* (c) of the absorbing substance in the layer. It is an extension of Lambert's law (*q.v.*), and may be written in the form

$$I = I_0 e^{-Kcd},$$

where I_0 is the intensity of the incident radiation, and I that of the transmitted radiation; and K is a constant, the *molecular absorption coefficient*, which is characteristic of the absorbing substance for light of a given frequency. The *molecular extinction coefficient*, α_m, is the thickness in centimetres of a layer of a molar solution which reduces the intensity of light passing through it to one-tenth of its original value. It is easily shown that $\alpha_m = 0.4343\ K$. The law does not hold for substances whose absorption spectra and the species present are affected by concentration.

Beguin, Jean. A native of Lorraine, born about the middle of the sixteenth century, author of a once well-known text-book of early chemistry, the 'Tyrocinium Chymicum,' first published in 1610; many subsequent editions of it were published. He died in 1618 or 1619. See article by Patterson, *Annals of Science*, July, 1937.

Béhal, Auguste (1859-1941). Béhal was born at Lens and educated in Paris at the Sorbonne and the École Supérieure de Pharmacie, where he became professor of toxicology, He later became professor of organic chemistry both at the École de Pharmacie and in the University of Paris, and also chief pharmacist at the Hôpital de la Maternité, Paris. He was President of the Académie de Médecine in 1924-1925, and for 1939 was elected to the Presidency both of the Académie des Sciences and the Institut de France. His papers dealt chiefly with camphor and menthol derivatives. See *J. Chem. Soc.*, 1946, 1092.

Behenic acid, *n*-**Docosanic acid,** $C_{22}H_{44}O_2$, $CH_3 \cdot [CH_2]_{20} \cdot COOH$. Crystallizes in needles, m.p. 80°, sparingly soluble in alcohol and ether. A fatty acid occurring in oil of ben.

Beilby, Sir George Thomas (1850-1924). Born in Edinburgh, Beilby was educated at the University there. In 1869 he became associated with the Oakbank Oil Company, and later was appointed a director of the Cassel Cyanide Company, the Castner-Kellner Alkali Co., and many other important undertakings. He invented a new process for the synthesis of alkali cyanide and many of his researches were directed towards a more economical use of fuel. He was elected F.R.S. in 1906 and knighted in 1916. See *J. Chem. Soc.*, 1925, 955.

Beilby layer. When a metal is polished the crystalline surface is converted into a thin amorphous skin known as the Beilby layer.

Beilby's process. See Potassium cyanide.

Beilstein, Friedrich Konrad (1838-1906). Born of German parents at St. Petersburg, Beilstein studied chemistry under Bunsen (Heidelberg), Liebig (Munich), Wöhler (Göttingen), and Wurtz (Paris). In 1866 he succeeded Mendeléeff at the Imperial Technological Institute at his native city. He ultimately gave up all research for the production of his famous 'Handbuch', the first edition (two volumes) of which appeared during the years 1880-1882. The present or fourth edition was begun in 1918 and, with two supplements, comprises over eighty volumes.

Beilstein's test. A method for detecting the presence of halogen in an organic compound. A piece of copper gauze is heated in an oxidizing flame until the flame is no longer tinged green; the compound is placed on the gauze, which is reheated. If halogen is present the flame is tinged bright green.

Belladonna, Deadly Nightshade. The dried root is used for the preparation of the liquid extract from which a plaster, liniment, ointment, and suppository are made, while the leaves and flowering tops are used for making the dry extract, the green extract, and the tincture. Essentially the root preparations are for external purposes and the leaf preparations for internal use. Belladonna owes its medicinal activity largely to the alkaloid hyoscyamine which is present in all parts of the plant. It is used internally as an antispasmodic and to check excessive secretion. Externally, it relieves the pain of lumbago and neuralgia.

Bell metal. Composition 80% copper and 20% tin. It is hard and brittle, and extremely sonorous.

Belt conveyer. A machine for conveying articles or particulate solids, consisting of an endless belt running on rollers.

Bemegride, β-ethyl- β-methylglutarimide. A white flaky or crystalline powder, m.p. 126°-128°. Sparingly soluble in water. Soluble in alcohol, in acetone, in chloroform, and in solutions of alkali hydroxides.

It is used in the treatment of barbiturate poisoning, by intravenous injection of 50 mg every 10 minutes, up to a total dose not exceeding 1 g.

Bence-Jones proteins. Proteins derived from γ-globulin and found in the urine in certain diseases of the bone marrow. When isolated from single individuals, Bence-Jones proteins are obtainable in homogeneous form, and have been studied in detail in relation to the structure of (inhomogeneous) γ-globulin.

Bendrofluazide. A white crystalline powder,

m.p. about 225° with decomposition. Prepared by the action of chlorosulphonic acid on 3-trifluoromethylaniline and the treatment of the resulting 4,6-disulphonyl chloride with ammonia and then with phenylacetaldehyde.

It is insoluble in water and in chloroform, soluble in alcohol and in acetone, sparingly soluble in ether.

It is a diuretic used against oedema and hypertension.

Bengal fire. See Indian fire.

Bentonite. A clay-like material consisting largely of montmorillonite (q.v.) first found at Fort Benton, Wyoming. Two types are found, one swelling considerably in water, displaying thixotropy and other colloidal properties and finding application as an emulsifying agent for bitumen and as a suspending agent. The other type is non-swelling but has absorptive properties which are enhanced by chemical activation.

Benzal chloride, $C_7H_6Cl_2$. It is a colourless strongly refracting liquid, b.p. 206°, sp.gr. 1·256 at 14°. Insoluble in water, miscible with organic solvents.

It is prepared by the direct chlorination of toluene in the absence of metallic catalysts. The chlorination is measured by the increase in weight of the mixture.

It is much used for the preparation of benzaldehyde. For this purpose it is usually heated with slaked lime and water under pressure.

Benzaldehyde, C_7H_6O. Colourless refractive liquid with almond-like odour. Soluble in alcohol and ether, insoluble in water, volatile in steam; m.p. −13·5°, b.p. 179°-180°, d^{14} 1·057.

It occurs in nature as part of the glucoside, amygdalin, in which it was discovered in 1803. It is manufactured from toluene, either by vapour phase air oxidation over a catalyst, or by chlorination to benzal chloride followed by hydrolysis with boiling water.

It is readily oxidized by air to benzoic acid. With aqueous caustic potash gives benzyl alcohol and benzoic acid. Gives addition products with hydrogen cyanide and sodium bisulphite.

Its chief importance is as a source of cinnamic acid by condensation with sodium acetate and acetic anhydride and as a source of triphenylmethane dyestuffs by condensation with pyrogallol, dimethylaniline, etc. It is also used in the manufacture of perfumes.

Benzaldoxime, C_7H_7NO. There are two stereoisomers. The β-isomer cyclizes to a benzisoxazole and has the anti-configuration shown.

The α-isomer is stable and is prepared by the action of hydroxylamine on benzaldehyde; it has m.p. 34°. The β-isomer is obtained by irradiating a benzene solution of α-isomer, or by saturating an ethereal solution with hydrogen chloride; it has m.p. 127°.

73

BENZALKONIUM

BENZENE

Benzalkonium chloride. A mixture of alkylbenzyldimethylammonium chlorides. The aqueous solution contains 50% w/v calculated as $C_{22}H_{40}ClN$. It is a clear, colourless or pale yellow syrupy liquid, miscible with water, with alcohol and with acetone. It is used as an antiseptic detergent.

Benzamide, C_7H_7NO. Crystallizes in colourless plates from water, m.p. 130°, b.p. 288°. Soluble in alcohol, ether, hot water, and hot benzene. Dehydrated by phosphorus pentoxide to benzonitrile, hydrolysed to benzoic acid by dilute acids or alkalis.

CONH₂

Forms metallic salts, e.g. silver benzamide, $C_6H_5 \cdot CONHAg$.

Prepared by the action of ammonia on benzoyl chloride or benzoic ester, or by partial hydrolysis of benzonitrile.

Benzamine hydrochloride, Betacaine hydrochloride, β-Eucaine hydrochloride,

$$C_{15}H_{21}NO_2, HCl$$

A white crystalline powder, m.p. 274°, with

H₃C CH₃
H₂N⁺ —OOCC₆H₅
Cl⁻

decomposition. Soluble in 30 parts of water and 35 parts of alcohol. It acts as a local anaesthetic, but is little used as it is inferior to cocaine and is intensely irritating when injected. Benzamine lactate is more soluble and hence preferable for certain purposes.

Benzanthrone, $C_{17}H_{10}O$. Crystallizes in pale

O

yellow needles, m.p. 170°. It is soluble in alcohol and other organic solvents. It gives an orangered solution in sulphuric acid. It is prepared by heating anthrone or anthranol with glycerol and sulphuric acid for a few hours at 120°.

It is a valuable dyestuffs intermediate. When fused with caustic potash, two molecules of benzanthrone combine at the positions marked * above to give a dibenzanthrone. This is in itself a vat dye, Indanthrene Dark Blue BO, Vat Blue 20, which is also used as an intermediate for the preparation of the valuable Caledon Jade Green.

Benzedrine. A trade name for a brand of amphetamine.

Benzene, C_6H_6. The benzene molecule contains

six carbon atoms arranged in the form of a regular hexagon; the carbon to carbon bond length is 1·39 Å. The six π-electrons, or aromatic sextet, represented by the double bonds, are not localized but are distributed uniformly around the ring. A thin, colourless, highly refractive liquid. Characteristic smell. Highly inflammable, burning with a smoky yellow flame. A good solvent for fats and lower molecular weight aromatic compounds. Miscible with alcohol, ether, acetone, and acetic acid.

M.p. 5·49°, b.p. 80·2°, d^{15} 0·884, n_D^{15} 1·5044. Shows strong absorption bands in the ultraviolet. Water dissolves 0·082% of benzene at 22°, benzene dissolves 0·054% of water at 15°. The vapour is toxic when inhaled over long periods.

Benzene was first isolated by Faraday in 1825 from the liquid condensed by compressing oil gas. It is the lightest fraction obtained from the distillation of the coal-tar hydrocarbons, but although this source is still of commercial importance, most benzene is now manufactured from suitable petroleum fractions by dehydrogenation and dealkylation processes. Its principal industrial use is as a starting point for other chemicals, particularly styrene, phenol and nylon precursors.

Structurally benzene is the simplest compound typifying the aromatic character (*q.v.*). It can undergo addition reactions and add on up to six halogen atoms, but the most widely used reactions are those of substitution.

It is readily sulphonated and nitrated by heating with sulphuric acid, or a mixture of sulphuric and nitric acids respectively, a maximum of three substituting groups being symmetrically introduced in the 1,3,5 (meta) positions. Direct halogenation can also be brought about, and the halogen atoms tend to be orientated in positions ortho or para to one another.

It is identified by conversion into a solid dinitro derivative, and by physical properties. Forms π-bonded complexes with metals.

Benzene-*m*-disulphonic acid, $C_6H_6O_6S_2$. This exists in very deliquescent crystals, $+2\frac{1}{2}H_2O$. It is prepared by sulphonation of benzene at 225°. It gives resorcinol on fusion with caustic potash.

SO₃H SO₃H

Benzene hexachloride. See BHC.

Benzenesulphonic acid, $C_6H_6O_3S$. Large colourless plates with $1\frac{1}{2}H_2O$ (from water), m.p. 43°-44°. Anhydrous acid, m.p. 65°-66°. Deliquescent, very soluble in water and alcohol, sparingly soluble in benzene.

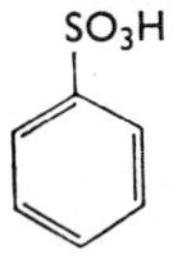

Prepared by the sulphonation of benzene in the liquid state or by passing benzene vapour into concentrated sulphuric acid at 150°-180°.

Forms water-soluble alkali and alkaline earth metal salts. With phosphorus pentachloride forms benzenesulphonyl chloride; with potassium cyanide gives benzonitrile. Chief use is in preparation of phenol by fusion with caustic soda or potash. Further sulphonation at 250° gives benzene-*m*-disulphonic acid.

Benzfuran (Coumarone) ring system. The system

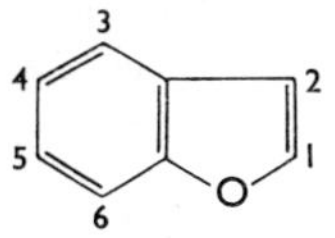

numbered as shown.

Benzidine, $C_{12}H_{12}N_2$. Leaflets from water, m.p.

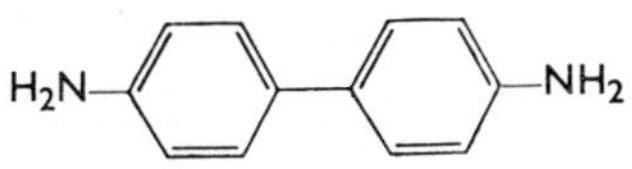

127·5°, b.p. 400°-401°. Slightly soluble (1%) in hot water, less so in cold, readily soluble in alcohol. Dibasic, forms readily soluble salts with mineral acids. Readily diazotizes.

Prepared by treating hydrazobenzene with hydrochloric acid, intramolecular rearrangement taking place.

Valuable dyestuffs intermediate. Both amino groups can be diazotized to give a tetrazocompound which readily couples with two molecules of amines or phenols. The azo-compounds thus produced have good affinity for cotton.

Benzidine conversion. The name given to the intramolecular rearrangement which occurs when the hydrazobenzenes are heated in acid

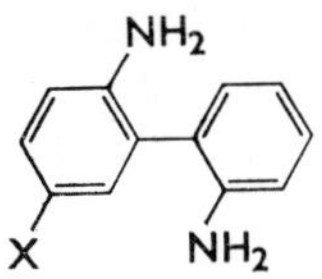

o-Benzidine   o-Semidine

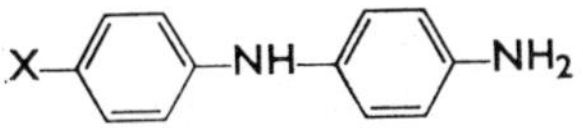

p-Semidine

solution. If both *para* positions in the hydrazobenzene are free a benzidine is produced; if one or both para positions are occupied by other groups then either an *ortho* benzidine or *ortho* or *para* semidines are formed.

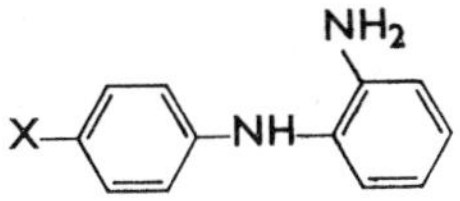

Benzil, $C_{14}H_{10}O_2$. Forms yellow, six-sided

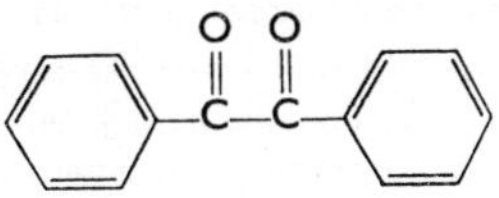

prisms, m.p. 95°, b.p. 346°-348°, with slight decomposition. It is insoluble in water, easily soluble in alcohol and ether. It is prepared by the oxidation of benzoin with nitric acid. It is reduced to benzoin by acid reducing agents and to hydrobenzoin by sodium amalgam. It is nitrated by boiling with fuming nitric acid. It forms three distinct isomeric dioximes (RH). The α-(*anti*)form, m.p. 238° (decomp.), produces a nickel derivative NiR_3. The β-(*syn*)form, m.p. 207° (decomp.), does not produce a nickel derivative, but the γ-(*amphi*)form, m.p. 164°-165° yields NiR. By heating in alcohol the α- and γ-forms are transformed into the β-form. The stereochemistry of the free oximes is shown:

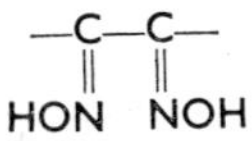

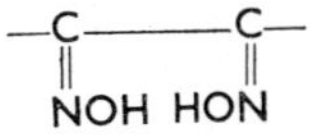

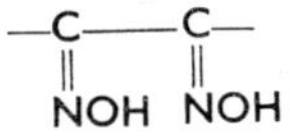

Benzoates. Salts or esters of benzoic acid.

Benzocaine, ethyl *p*-aminobenzoate, $C_9H_{11}NO_2$. White crystals almost insoluble in water, soluble in 8 parts of alcohol. m.p. 90°-91°. Prepared from *p*-nitrotoluene by way of *p*-aminobenzoic acid. It is used as a local anaesthetic on mucous surfaces, injected for pruritis, and taken internally to relieve gastric pain.

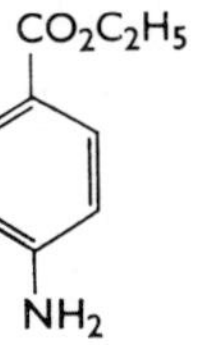

Benzoic acid, $C_7H_6O_2$. Colourless lustrous leaflets, m.p. 122°, b.p. 249°. Readily volatile at 100°; best purified by sublimation. Sparingly soluble in cold, fairly soluble in hot water. Soluble in alcohol and ether

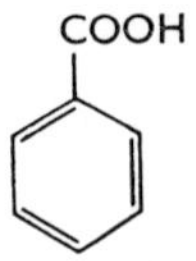

It was first described in 1608 when it was sublimed out of gum benzoin. It also occurs in many other natural resins. Benzoic acid is manufactured by the air oxidation of toluene in

BENZOIN

the liquid phase at 150° and 4-6 atm. in the presence of a cobalt catalyst; by the partial decarboxylation of phthalic anhydride in either the liquid or vapour phase in the presence of water; by the hydrolysis of benzotrichloride (from the chlorination of benzene) in the presence of zinc chloride at 110°.

It gives benzene when heated with soda lime. It is very stable towards oxidizing agents.

Much of the benzoic acid produced is converted to sodium benzoate, which is used as a food preservative (as is the acid) and a corrosion inhibitor. Other important uses of the acid are in the manufacture of alkyd resins, plasticizers, caprolactam, dyestuffs and pharmaceuticals.

Benzoin, $C_{14}H_{12}O_2$. It can be resolved into

optically active isomers. The $(\pm)$-compound has m.p. 137°, and the active forms have m.p. 131°-132° and $[\alpha]_D^{12}$ $\pm117\cdot5°$-120·5° in acetone. Slightly soluble in boiling water, soluble in hot alcohol.

It is usually prepared by the action of sodium cyanide on benzaldehyde in dilute alcohol. It is oxidised by nitric acid to benzil, and reduced by sodium amalgam to hydrobenzoin

$$C_6H_5CHOHCHOHC_6H_5;$$

by tin amalgam and hydrochloric acid to desoxybenzoin, $C_6H_5CH_2COC_6H_5$; and by zinc amalgam to stilbene $C_6H_5CH{=}CHC_6H_5$. It gives an oxime, phenylhydrazone and acetyl compound with the usual reagents. The oxime exists in two stereoisomeric forms known as the α- and β- forms. The α-oxime is used under the name 'cupron' for the estimation of copper and molybdenum.

The name is also given to a balsamic resin obtained from *Styrax Benzoin*, which consists of white tears embedded in a brown resinous matrix. It contains benzoic and cinnamic acids and esters, and is used almost entirely for the preparation of friar's balsam or compound tincture of benzoin, which contains the alcohol-soluble constituents of benzoin, balsam of Tolu, styrax, and aloes. Benzoin is carminative and mildly expectorant, and the compound tincture is applied undiluted for dressing small wounds, and is also given for sore throats.

Benzole. A mixture of predominately aromatic hydrocarbons produced by the carbonization of coal, obtained from coal gas by adsorption or from coal tar by distillation. After refining and redistillation this is classified in Britain according to purity as 'Motor Benzole,' 'Industrial

Benzole,' '90's Benzole,' 'Pure Benzole,' and 'Nitration Grade.' Recognized specifications for these grades are issued by the National Benzole Association.

Benzonitrile, C_7H_5N. Colourless refractive liquid, b.p. 191°. Slightly soluble in water, miscible with alcohol and ether in all proportions.

Prepared by the dehydration of benzamide. Hydrolysed by dilute acids and alkalis to benzoic acid.

Benzophenone, $C_{13}H_{10}O$. Colourless rhombic

prisms, m.p. 49°, b.p. 306°. Characteristic smell. Insoluble in water, soluble in alcohol and ether. It also exists in a metastable modification, m.p. 26°. It is prepared by the action of benzoyl chloride upon benzene in the presence of aluminium chloride or by the oxidation of diphenylmethane. It is much used in perfumery.

Benzopurpurin. A direct cotton dyestuff derived from *o*-tolidine. In Benzopurpurin B (C.I. Direct Red 21) tolidine is tetrazotized and coupled with two molecules of β-naphthylamine sulphonic acid; in the 4B (C.I. Direct Red 2) it is coupled with two molecules of naphthionic acid. The 10B (C.I. Direct Red 7) is derived from dianisidine and naphthionic acid.

Benzo(a)pyrene, 1,2-benzpyrene, $C_{20}H_{12}$. Pale

yellow crystals, m.p. 179°. A constituent of coal tar with strong carcinogenic properties.

Benzoquinone, $C_6H_4O_2$. Yellow monoclinic prisms, m.p. 115·7°, readily sublimes, volatile in steam, penetrating odour. Soluble in alcohol, ether, benzene, and hot water, less in cold water. Electrolytic reduction gives quinhydrone, reduction with hydrogen sulphide gives hydroquinone. Gives mono- and di-oximes. Vigorous oxidation gives maleic and oxalic acids. It is prepared by the oxidation of aniline with chromic acid.

Used as a source of hydroquinone and of some sulphur dyes.

Benzotrichloride, $C_7H_5Cl_3$. It is a colourless liquid, b.p. 213°-214°, sp.gr. 1·380 at 14°. Insoluble in water, miscible with organic solvents.

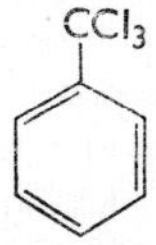

It is prepared by chlorinating toluene until no more chlorine is taken up, though care has to be taken to avoid undue nuclear chlorination. When heated with water at 100°, or with milk of lime, benzoic acid is obtained.

Benzoyl. The name given to the group

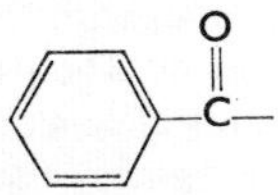

Benzoyl chloride, C_7H_5ClO. It is a colourless lachrymatory liquid, b.p. 198°, sp.gr. 1·212 at 20°. It has a pungent smell, and is slowly hydrolysed by cold water to give benzoic acid. With alcohols benzoic esters are obtained. It is prepared by heating benzoic acid with phosphorus pentachloride or thionyl chloride. It is much used as a benzoylating agent in organic chemistry. In the Schotten-Baumann method the calculated quantities of benzoyl chloride, phenol, and caustic alkali are shaken in a stoppered bottle until no more benzoyl chloride remains. The benzoyl derivative has then separated from the solution, and can be filtered off. It is also used on the large scale for benzoylating aminoanthraquinones and other compounds.

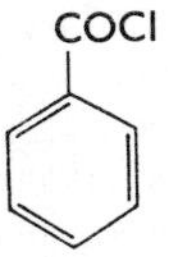

Benzyl. The name given to the group

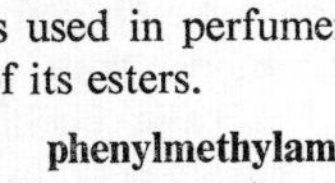

Benzyl alcohol, C_7H_8O. Colourless liquid, b.p. 205·3°. Soluble in alcohol, ether, and acetone. Oxidizes to benzaldehyde and benzoic acid. Prepared by the hydrolysis of benzyl chloride. It is used in perfumery in the form of its esters.

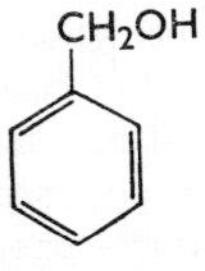

Benzylamine, phenylmethylamine, α-amino-toluene, C_7H_9N. A colourless liquid, b.p. 185°, which, like many amines, becomes dark coloured on exposure to air. It is soluble in water and organic solvents. It behaves as a typical primary amine.

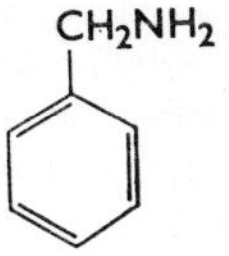

Benzyl benzoate, $C_{14}H_{12}O_2$, White crystals, melting at 20° to a colourless oily liquid, which readily supercools. Insoluble in water. It is used medicinally in capsules, in alcohol solution, or as an emulsion, to decrease the contractions of

unstriped muscle in colic, diarrhoea, dysentery, whooping cough and asthma and as an external application for the treatment of scabies.

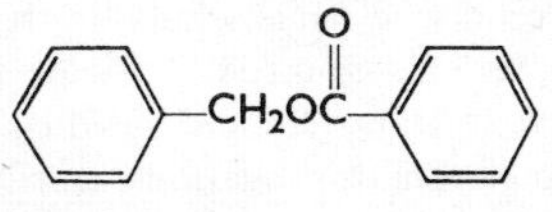

Benzyl chloride, C_7H_7Cl. It is a colourless liquid with a characteristic odour, b.p. 179°, sp.gr. 1·104 at 15°. Insoluble in water, miscible with organic solvents. It is slowly hydrolysed by boiling water, yielding benzyl alcohol.

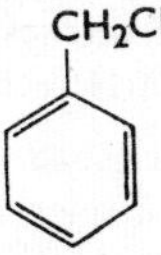

It is prepared by the direct chlorination of toluene in the presence of a little phosphorus pentachloride. It is purified by fractionation from the unchanged toluene and the higher chlorinated products. It is used for benzylating amines and for preparing benzyl alcohol.

Benzyne, C_6H_4. The commonest aryne, or dehydroaromatic compound. It is a highly reactive intermediate with an estimated lifetime of 10^{-5}-10^{-4} seconds in the vapour state, and cannot be isolated. Its existence has been largely inferred from experiments where it has been trapped in Diels-Alder type reactions (see Triptycene) and from mechanistic considerations. A variety of methods are available for its production, including the decomposition of benzenediazonium-2-carboxylate and the base induced elimination of hydrogen halide from halobenzenes, e.g. phenyllithium and fluorobenzene The reactivity of benzyne must result from the formal incorporation of a triple bond in a six-membered ring: other evidence suggests that benzyne is better represented by a dipolar structure. See Arynes.

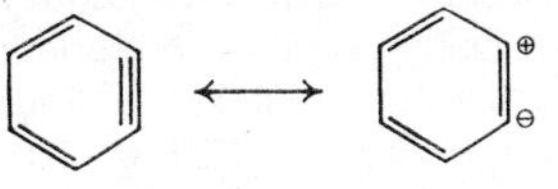

Berberine, $C_{20}H_{19}NO_5$. An alkaloid obtained

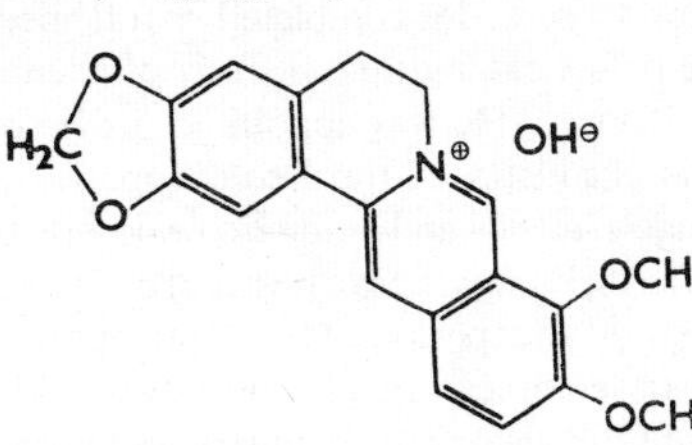

from *Hydrastis canadensis, Berberis vulgaris,* and other plants. It crystallizes from water in yellow needles with six molecules of water. Soluble in water and alcohol. Optically inactive. It is relatively inactive physiologically, but toxic in large doses.

Bergius, Friedrich (1884-1949). Born at Goldschmieden, near Breslau, Bergius studied at the Universities of Breslau, Leipzig, and Berlin, and at the Technische Hochschüle in Karlsruhe and Hanover. He founded a private research laboratory in Hanover, and devoted himself entirely to private investigations, chiefly on the influence of high pressure on chemical reactions. The 'Berginization' of coal is a result of his researches. He shared a Nobel prize in 1931 with Carl Bosch. See *Chem. & Eng. News*, 1949, 1073.

Bergman, Tobern Olof (1735-1784). Born at Katrineberg, Sweden, Bergman was educated at the University of Uppsala. In 1767 he was appointed professor of chemistry and mineralogy. He performed many researches in mineralogical chemistry and greatly extended and improved the methods of qualitative and quantitative analysis.

Berkeley, Randal Thomas Mowbray Rawdon, 8th Earl of Berkeley (1865-1942). Berkeley succeeded to the title in 1888. As a scientist he carried out numerous researches. With E. G. J. Hartley he showed that in concentrated solutions the simple laws of osmotic pressure, announced by van't Hoff, are no longer applicable. He was elected a Fellow of the Royal Society. See *J. Chem. Soc.*, 1943, 503.

Berkelium, Bk. At.no. 97. Various isotopes of berkelium of masses from 243 to 250 have been obtained by alpha or neutron bombardment of americium and other heavy isotopes. Heavier isotopes of masses 251-255 have been found in the debris of a thermonuclear explosion. The most stable isotope is ^{247}Bk, half-life 7000 years, but so far only minute traces of this isotope have been prepared. Berkelium has been separated by ion exchange procedures. No solid berkelium compounds have been isolated but from tracer studies it is known that the $+3$ and $+4$ states exist in solution.

Berthelot, Marcelin Pierre Eugène (1827-1907). Berthelot was born in the heart of old Paris. A brilliant scholar, he completed a full medical course before taking up the study of chemistry under Pelouze. He was appointed professor of organic chemistry at the École Supérieure de Pharmacie in 1859 and at the École de France in 1865. Berthelot was the greatest and most prolific chemist of the period. His contributions to chemistry embrace organic and physical chemistry and the history of chemistry and alchemy. See *Chem. Soc. Mem. Lectures*, Vol. 2, 167.

Berthollet, Claude Louis, (1748-1822). Born in Savoy, Berthollet later became physician to the Duke of Orleans. He studied chemistry, and became director of the factory of the Gobelins. He was in substantial agreement with the views of Lavoisier, but doubted whether chemical combination always took place in fixed and definite proportions. He discovered the bleaching power of chlorine and prepared potassium chlorate. He was an intimate friend of Napoleon, and accompanied him to Egypt.

Beryl, $Be_3Al_2Si_6O_{18}$. Crystals are hexagonal, blue, yellow, green, or white. The unit cell has planes parallel to the base at heights 0 and $\frac{1}{2}$. Hexagonal rings, formed of six silicon-oxygen tetrahedra, lie with the Si and shared O atoms on the reflection planes with the remaining O atoms above and below. The Al and Be atoms lie in sheets at heights of $3c/4$ and $c/4$ half-way between the reflection planes. Each Al atom is in six-fold co-ordination and each Be atom in four-fold. Sp.gr. 2·7, hardness 7·5-8. Transparent forms of beryl are rare; when coloured green by chromium oxide they are known as emerald, and when blue-green as aquamarine. Beryl is also used for the extraction of beryllium and the manufacture of beryllia refractories.

Beryllates. Solutions of beryllium salts are extensively hydrolysed but anionic beryllate species do not seem to be present. The solutions contain oxygen and hydroxyl bridged cationic species.

Beryllia. Beryllium oxide.

Beryllium (Glucinium), Be. At.wt. 9·013, At.no. 4. Hard white metal, d 1·86, m.p. 1280°, b.p. 2487°. Crystal structure, hexagonal close-packed, $a=2·267, c=3·594$ Å.

The chief source of beryllium is beryl, although it is a constituent of a number of other minerals (gadolinite, chrysoberyl, etc.).

The free metal was first obtained by reduction of the chloride or fluoride with an alkali metal, lithium, sodium, or potassium. In the technical production an electrolytic method is employed. The Siemens-Halske process uses a fused mixture of basic beryllium fluoride, $5BeF_2$, $2BeO$, and barium fluoride, BaF_2, as electrolyte. This is contained in an Acheson graphite crucible, which serves as anode, with a cathode of wrought iron. The basic beryllium fluoride is obtained directly from beryl by heating with an equal weight of sodium fluorosilicate at 650°-700°. The Beryllium Corporation of America uses a fused mixture of sodium and beryllium chlorides as electrolyte in an iron crucible.

A number of light alloys containing beryllium are known, but their use is limited, owing to their high cost. Beryllium metal offers wide possibilities for use in atomic reactors. Beryllium compounds are used in Lindemann Glass and in 'daylight' lighting. Beryllium compounds are toxic and beryllium-containing materials can cause serious respiratory conditions and also dermatitis.

Beryllium acetate, $Be_4O(C_2H_3O_2)_6$. Obtained by evaporating beryllium hydroxide with acetic acid. Is soluble in chloroform. The four Be atoms are arranged at the corners of a regular tetrahedron, with the oxygen at the centre and the six acetate groups occupying the edges. A normal acetate, $Be(C_2H_3O_2)_2$, may be prepared from beryllium chloride and the anhydrous acid.

Beryllium bromide, $BeBr_2$, has very similar properties to the chloride. It has m.p. 488° and sublimes below this temperature.

Beryllium bronze. See Bronze.

Beryllium carbonate. Basic carbonates of beryllium of indefinite composition are precipitated on boiling solutions of beryllium hydroxide in alkali carbonate solutions. A salt having the approximate composition $BeCO_3,3Be(OH)_2$, is obtained on keeping the precipitate from beryllium hydroxide and ammonium carbonate solution over sulphuric acid in a desiccator. A normal carbonate, $BeCO_3 \cdot 4H_2O$ has been prepared under an atmosphere of carbon dioxide. Various basic double carbonates of beryllium and alkali metals (or ammonium) have been described.

Beryllium chloride, $BeCl_2$. Obtained by passing chlorine over a heated mixture of the oxide with carbon. It forms white crystals, m.p. 405°, b.p. 488°, which sublime readily, and fume in moist air. Above 630° the vapour density corresponds to the formula $BeCl_2$. Is very readily hydrolysed to the hydroxide. A hydrate, $BeCl_2 \cdot 4H_2O$, is formed from aqueous solution. The anhydrous salt is a very good catalyst, similar in properties to aluminium chloride.

Beryllium fluoride, BeF_2. A colourless solid, m.p. 542°, b.p. 1096°, best prepared by heating ammonium fluoroberyllate, $(NH_4)_2BeF_4$. It is very soluble in water and the solution is hydrolysed on evaporation.

Beryllium hydroxide, $Be(OH)_2$. Precipitated from beryllium solutions by alkali, but the hydroxide is readily soluble in excess of the reagent. An insoluble form crystallizes out of such solutions on standing.

Beryllium iodide, BeI_2. Prepared by the action of hydrogen iodide on beryllium carbide at 700°, m.p. 480°, b.p. 488°. It is violently hydrolysed by water.

Beryllium nitrate, $Be(NO_3)_2,4H_2O$. Obtained as deliquescent crystals by evaporating a solution of basic beryllium carbonate in nitric acid to a syrup and adding concentrated nitric acid. The salt readily loses nitric acid on exposure to air, and its aqueous solutions are strongly acid owing to hydrolysis. Beryllium nitrate is soluble in alcohol and acetone. Small quantities of the salt are frequently added to solutions used in impregnating incandescent gas mantles.

Beryllium oxide, BeO. The hydroxide or carbonate on ignition gives the oxide, beryllia, BeO. This is a white powder, m.p. 2450°, used to some extent in the manufacture of gas mantles, accompanying the thoria to the extent of 2 to 5 parts per 1000. It is said to increase the mechanical strength of the mantle. It is as hard as corundum.

Beryllium sulphate, $BeSO_4,4H_2O$, is obtained as fine tetragonal crystals on evaporation of a solution of beryllium oxide in moderately concentrated sulphuric acid. The anhydrous salt is prepared from the oxide and concentrated sulphuric acid; it is stable up to about 530°, and dissolves with some difficulty in water. A dihydrate is formed by heating the tetrahydrate to 89°. The tetrahydrate is soluble in its own weight of water, giving a strongly acid solution with a sweet taste. Double sulphates of beryllium (e.g. $K_2SO_4,BeSO_4,2H_2O$) are known.

Berzelius, Jöns Jakob (1779-1848). Born in East Gothland, Sweden, Berzelius studied chemistry and electricity at Uppsala, and became President of the Swedish Academy of Sciences, in 1810. He was created a baron in 1835. He was a skilful and conscientious analyst and discovered cerium, selenium, and thorium. He isolated silicon, zirconium, and tantalum, and studied the phenomenon which he called *catalysis*. He wrote important books on mineralogy and chemistry, and had a great reputation as a teacher; among his pupils were Mitscherlich, Wöhler, Gmelin, and Mosander.

Bessemer, Sir Henry (1813-1898). The son of an artist, Bessemer was born at Charlton in Hertfordshire. Of artistic and inventive mind, his success commenced with his discovery of a means of manufacturing 'gold' paint from Dutch metal. His name is associated with the Bessemer Converter used in the manufacture of steel from cast iron. He erected steelworks in Sheffield to develop the process. Elected F.R.S. in 1879, Bessemer was knighted in the same year. See *Nature*, 1898, **57**, 487.

Bessemer process. A method of manufacture of steel from pig iron by oxidation of the impurities (C, Si, P, Mn) by blowing air through the molten metal. The operation is carried out in a converter, which is a pear shaped vessel lined with refractory material. Two processes are worked: (1) Acid process—for pig irons low in sulphur and phosphorus and containing about $2\frac{1}{2}\%$ silicon, the oxidation of which generates the heat required to keep the charge molten. The silicon oxidizes first and forms a slag and is followed by oxidation of the carbon. Blowing is discontinued when oxidation of carbon is complete, indicated by drop of flame at converter mouth. This is followed by recarburization to desired carbon content by addition of ferro-manganese. (2) Basic process—suitable for irons rich in phosphorus and low silicon content. Operation of process is similar to the acid process but oxidation of phosphorus follows the oxidation of carbon. Basic refractories are required as highly basic slags are formed which must be removed before recarburizing.

The steels produced by these processes are usually plain carbon steels of low carbon content.

Besszonoff's reagent. A complex phospho-tungstic-phosphomolybdic acid obtained by heating a solution of sodium tungstate with phosphomolybdic and phosphoric acids. It crystallizes from water in colourless crystals having the composition $(17WO_3)(MoO_3) (P_2O_5, H_2O)$, $21H_2O$. When dissolved in water, it gives a deep blue colour with ascorbic acid. This reaction has been used to estimate or detect ascorbic acid in fruit juices and plant extracts; it is, however, not a specific test for ascorbic acid.

Betacaine. See Benzamine hydrochloride.

Betaine, Trimethylglycine, $C_5H_{11}NO_2$. Crystallizes in deliquescent prisms or leaflets, with one

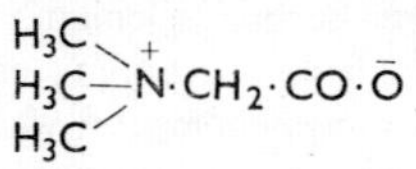

$$H_3C \diagdown +$$
$$H_3C-N\cdot CH_2\cdot CO\cdot \bar{O}$$
$$H_3C \diagup$$

molecule of water, which it loses when heated to 100°, m.p. 293°. Soluble in water and alcohol. It is a very feeble base. It occurs in beets and mangolds and many other plants, and can conveniently be prepared from beet molasses. It has little, if any, physiological activity.

Betaines. A group of feebly basic substances, resembling betaine, which occur chiefly in plants. They are intramolecular salts of, particularly, quaternary ammonium compounds. They include stachydrine, trigonelline, and carnitine.

Betamethasone, 9α-fluoro-16β-methylpredniso-

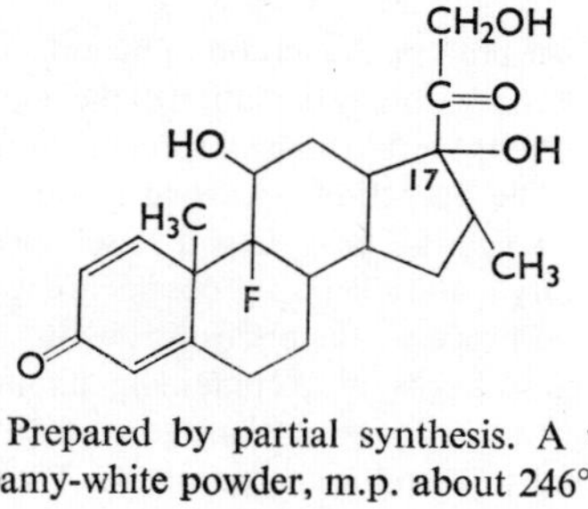

lone. Prepared by partial synthesis. A white to creamy-white powder, m.p. about 246° with

decomposition. It is almost insoluble in water and in chloroform, slightly soluble in alcohol $[\alpha]_D$ +115° to +121° (0·5% w/v in dioxan). It is a corticosteroid used systematically as the disodium phosphate salt, and widely used topically as the 17− valerate.

Beta particle or **beta ray.** An electron (*q.v.*). Beta particles are emitted during many radioactive disintegrations; as normally produced they have a very high velocity comparable sometimes to that of light. They have a long path in air at normal pressure; their path may be deflected by both electrostatic and magnetic fields. They may be detected by counters.

Betatron. The betatron is an apparatus for accelerating electrons. The principle of it is that an electric force is produced round the axis of a fluctuating magnetic field. Energies of the order of 2000 million electron volts have been obtained in a betatron but much energy is lost in the form of radiation.

Bevan, Edward John (1856-1921). Bevan was born at Birkenhead. At the age of 17 he entered the laboratory of the Runcorn Soap and Alkali Co., but was advised to undertake a systematic chemical training at Owens College. There he became associated with C. F. Cross, and together they proceeded to carry out research on the cellulose industry. By converting cellulose into viscose they made possible the artificial silk industry. They established a firm of consulting chemists, and in 1892 Bevan was appointed Public Analyst under the Middlesex County Council. See *J. Chem. Soc.* 1921, 2121.

BHC, Benzene hexachloride, $C_6H_6Cl_6$. A chlorinated hydrocarbon insecticide which exists in several isomeric forms. Crude BHC contains at least 5 isomers, which have widely differing melting points and other physical properties. It is active against several insects, the most active isomer being gamma-BHC, which is also known as lindane.

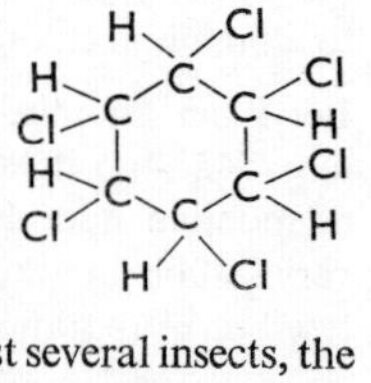

BHC is manufactured by chlorination of benzene in the presence of ultra-violet light. The gamma-isomer is obtained from the crude mixture by selective crystallization, and forms colourless crystals, m.p. 113°. It is insoluble in water and soluble in most organic solvents. Both crude BHC and the gamma-isomer are non-phytotoxic. The latter, however, is toxic to mammals, whereas the other isomers are of low toxicity. Thus crude BHC is safer to handle than the refined gamma-isomer.

Biacetyl. See Diacetyl.

Bidrin, $C_8H_{16}NO_5P$. The trade name for 3-(dimethoxyphosphinyloxy) - *N,N* - dimethyl - *cis* - crotonamide, a compound of high insecticidal

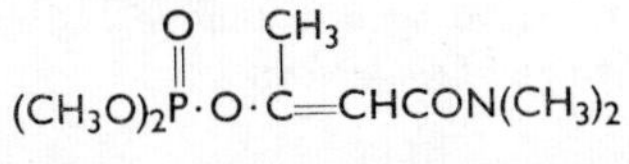

$$(CH_3O)_2 \overset{\overset{O}{\|}}{P} \cdot O \cdot \overset{\overset{CH_3}{|}}{C} = CHCON(CH_3)_2$$

activity against a very wide range of species. It is a liquid, b.p. 400°/760 mm, soluble in water but rapidly hydrolysed in solution. Of particular importance in cotton protection but also in other crops. It is made from dimethylaceto-acetamide by chlorination and reaction with trimethyl phosphite.

Bicarbonates. Another name for acid carbon-ates. See Carbonic acid.

Bile acids. See Cholic acid.

Bile pigments. The chief pigments of the bile are bilirubin, $C_{33}H_{36}N_4O_6$, and its oxidized form biliverdin. Bilirubin has the structure:

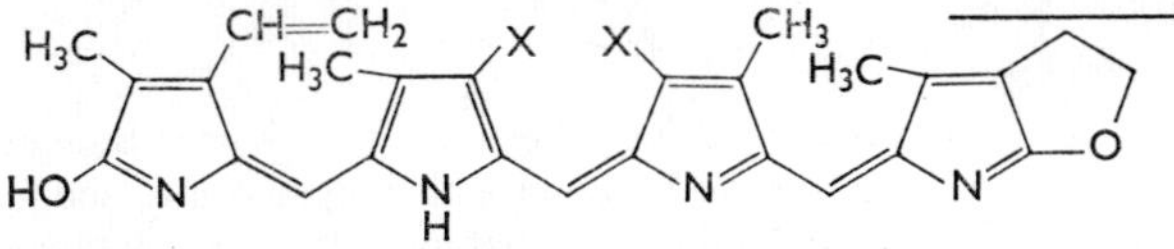

$$X = CH_2CH_2CO_2H$$

It forms brown crystals, insoluble in water, sparingly soluble in alcohol and ether, soluble in alkalis. The bile pigments are breakdown products of haemoglobin. They can be detected by Gmelin's reaction; on treatment with strong nitric acid the colours change from green to blue, violet, red, and yellow. See 'The Bile Pigments' by C. H. Gray.

Bile salts. These are the sodium salts of glyco-cholic and taurocholic acids, which are present in the bile of animals. They have a very low surface tension, and so act as stabilizers for the emulsion formed by the fat particles in the intestine, thus rendering further chemical action on the fats easier. They also serve to hold in solution the otherwise insoluble fatty acids. They can be detected by Pettenkofer's reaction, a brilliant purple colour being given by the addition of sucrose and sulphuric acid.

Bilirubin. See Bile pigments.

Biliverdin. See Bile pigments.

Billet. A standard steel section produced by hot-rolling steel blooms in a billet mill. The cross-section is usually round or square.

Bimolecular reaction. A chemical reaction in which the molecular mechanism consists of reaction between pairs of molecules, e.g. $2HI \rightarrow H_2 + I_2$. The great majority of reactions are bimolecular or proceed by two or more consecutive bimolecular steps.

Bingham, Eugene Cook (1878-1945). Born at

W. Cornwall, Vermont, Bingham studied at Middlebury College, the Johns Hopkins University, Leipzig, Berlin, and Cambridge. After being professor of chemistry at Richmond College from 1906 to 1915, and assistant physicist at the U.S. Bureau of Standards, 1915-1916, he was appointed professor of chemistry at Lafayette College, Easton, Pennsylvania. His researches dealt with viscosity and plastic flow.

Biogenic amines. An important group of natur-ally occurring amines derived by enzymic decarboxylation of the natural amino-acids. Many of the biogenic amines have powerful physiological effects (e.g. histamine, serotonin, tyramine); others are constituents of larger biological units (e.g. ethanolamine in phospha-tides; β-mercaptoethylamine in coenzyme A). Biogenic amines derived from aromatic amino-acids, and their synthetic analogues (e.g. amphetamine) are of pharmacological value.

Bioluminescence. The phenomenon of light emission by plant or animal organisms, fre-quently due to reaction of oxygen with an oxidizable substrate (luciferin, *q.v.*) catalysed by an enzyme (a luciferase).

Bios. The name originally given to a substance of vitamin nature necessary for the proper growth of certain highly cultivated yeasts. The original bios has been shown to contain biotin, panto-thenic acid, thiamine, and *i*-inositol.

Biose. A carbohydrate with two carbon atoms.

$$\overset{\textstyle CH_2OH}{\underset{\textstyle CHO}{|}}$$

The only biose is glycollic aldehyde.

Biosynthesis. A term describing the processes by which living organisms build up the manifold substances required for growth and reproduc-tion—ultimately from carbon dioxide, water, light energy, and inorganic materials. The expression is frequently used to describe the biological synthesis of particular natural pro-ducts. The term biogenesis is not quite synony-mous, since it may also be used to refer to non-synthetic biological transformations.

Biot, Jean Baptiste (1774-1862). Born and educated in Paris, Biot was appointed professor of physics at the College de France. In 1804 he was associated with Gay-Lussac in the first balloon ascent for scientific investigations. Two years later he undertook some geodetic measurements with Arago. His work on the polarization of light earned him the Rumford Medal of the Royal Society in 1840.

Biotin. This is one of the vitamin-B factors. It is necessary for the growth of certain micro-organisms and prevents an eczema-like dermatitis in rats caused by feeding raw egg white. The active factor in egg white is a protein-carbohydrate complex called avidin, which reacts with and inactivates biotin. Biotin is needed in very small quantities; it can be detected by a yeast growth method at a concentration as low as one part in 10^{10}. Biotin is present in yeast, egg yolk, liver and other usual sources of the vitamin-B_2 complex. The biotins from egg yolk and liver are different substances.

β-*Biotin* (from liver) is 2-keto-3,4-imidazolido-2-tetrahydrothiophen-*n*-valeric acid, $C_{10}H_{16}N_2O_3S$. It crystallizes in long colourless

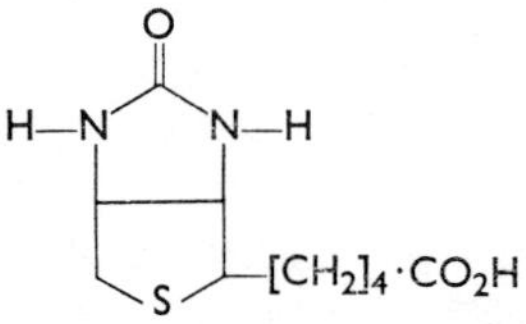

needles, m.p. 230°-231°, $[\alpha]_D^{25}$ +91·7° (in 0·1 M NaOH). It has been synthesized and is available commercially.

α-*Biotin* (from egg yolk) is believed to have a similar structure to β-biotin, but with the side-chain

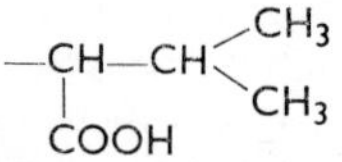

Biotin can be estimated by microbiological assay techniques. It is a constituent of certain co-enzymes concerned with decarboxylation and deamination.

Biotite, Black mica. Is ideally

K(Mg, Fe)$_3$(AlSi$_3$)O$_{10}$(OH, F)$_2$.

It occurs extensively in many rocks, especially granite, but is of no economic importance.

Biphenyl. See Diphenyl.

Birkeland, Kristian (1867-1917). Professor of physics in the University of Christiania, Birkeland, in 1903, developed with Eyde the process for the production of nitric acid by the fixation of atmospheric nitrogen.

Birlane, $C_{12}H_{14}Cl_3O_4P$. The trade name for 2-chloro-1-(2,4-dichlorophenyl)vinyl ethyl phosphate. Both *cis*- and *trans*-forms have insecticidal activity. Birlane is a liquid, b.p. 168°/0·5 mm, sparingly soluble in water, in which it

decomposes slowly. It may be made from tetrachloroacetophenone and triethyl phosphite. It is mainly active against *Diptera* and certain *Coleoptera* and *Lepidoptera*.

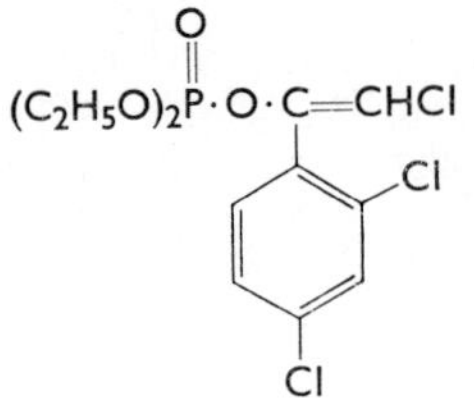

Bisabolene, $C_{15}H_{24}$. One of the most widely

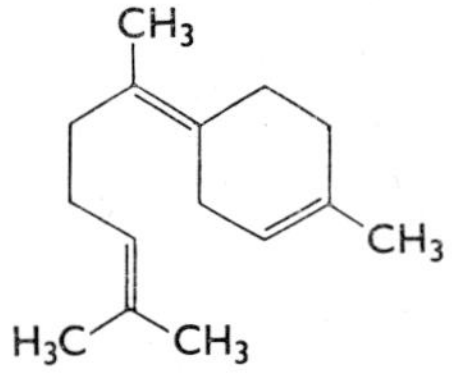

distributed sesquiterpenes. It is found in Bisabol myrrh, in bergamot and opopanax oils, and in many other essential oils. It is a colourless viscous oil and has b.p. 133°-134°/12 mm, d_4^{21} 0·8717, n_D^1 1·4923. It forms a trihydrochloride of m.p. 79°-80°, from which it can be liberated by sodium acetate in acetic acid solution. It can be prepared by acid dehydration of farnesol.

Bisacodyl (trade name Dulcolux) $C_{22}H_{19}NO_4$.

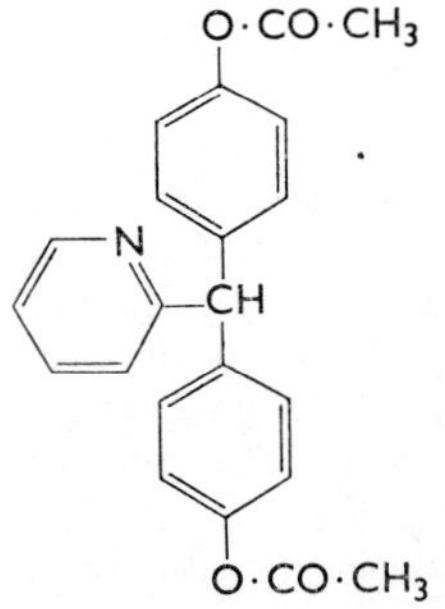

A white or almost white crystalline powder, m.p. 133°-135°. It is almost insoluble in water, sparingly soluble in alcohol and in ether. It is soluble in chloroform. It is extensively used as a contact laxative.

Bismarck brown, Basic Brown 1. Basic azo-dyestuff; dyes wool a reddish-brown shade. It has no affinity for cotton unless mordanted with tannin. It was discovered in 1864, and is one of the oldest azo-dyestuffs.

It is prepared by the action of nitrous acid upon *m*-phenylenediamine. The tetrazo compound first produced combines with two molecules of excess diamine to give Bismarck brown.

Bismuth. At.wt. 209·00, At.no. 83. A brittle,

reddish-white metal, d 9·8, m.p. 271·3°, b.p. 1420°. The crystals belong to the rhombohedral system, $a = 4·736$ Å. $\alpha = 57°$ 14′, and are isomorphous with those of arsenic and antimony, having a polymeric structure with each bismuth atom bonded to three neighbours.

The metal has been known from antiquity and often confused with tin and lead. It occurs native with arsenic and tellurium, as the oxide Bi_2O_3 in bismuthite or bismuth ochre, the sulphide Bi_2S_3 in bismuth glance, and in many copper, tin, and lead ores. The ore is first concentrated by washing and picking, roasted in a tubular furnace to the oxide, which is reduced by coal or coke. The metal is separated and to some extent purified by liquation. Another source of bismuth is in the anode slimes from copper refining. Pure bismuth is obtained by electrolysing a solution of $BiCl_3$ in HCl with graphite or pure bismuth cathodes and crude bismuth anodes.

Bismuth is fairly basic in character forming stable salts. It burns in air with a bluish-white flame to the yellow trioxide Bi_2O_3, which has no acidic properties. Bismuth is unattacked by dilute, slightly attacked by strong acids, but is soluble in the presence of oxidizing agents. Finely divided bismuth obtained by the reduction of bismuth chloride with hypophosphorous acid is used in the treatment of syphilis. It is administered by intramuscular injection in the form of a suspension in a sterile solution of dextrose. The metal is used extensively in the form of its alloys. The metal can be used in atomic piles as a liquid refrigerant.

Bismuth alloys. Alloys of bismuth with lead, tin, and cadmium are of special interest; they melt at low temperatures, in many cases below 100°. These alloys give well-defined castings, and with sufficient bismuth present expand on cooling. Some of these alloys are:

Name		Bi	Pb	Sn	Cd	m.p.
Newton's	.	50	31·25	18·75	—	98°
Rose's	.	50	28	22	—	100°
D'Arcet's	.	50	25	25	—	97°
Lichtenberg's		50	30	20	—	98°
Wood's	.	50	25	12·5	12·5	71°
Lipowitz's	.	50	27	13	10	71°

These are used for fire protective devices, fuses, solders, etc. The alloys of bismuth with lead and antimony are used for stereotype plates.

Bismuthates, $MBiO_3$. Very impure bismuthates are obtained by oxidizing an alkaline suspension of Bi_2O_3 with chlorine. They possibly contain some free Bi_2O_5. Bismuthates are very strong oxidizing agents and, for example, may be used to oxidize manganese (II) to permanganate (VII).

Bismuth carbonate. The basic carbonate $2(BiO)_2CO_3$, H_2O is obtained as a white powder by precipitation of a solution of bismuth nitrate with ammonium carbonate. It is tasteless and insoluble in water and neutral organic solvents. On drying at 100° it loses a molecule of water, with the formation of $(BiO)_2CO_3$; on further heating the oxide is produced. It is given internally for the relief of indigestion.

Bismuth chloride, $BiCl_3$. M.p. 232°, b.p. 447°. A soft white crystalline material obtained by passing excess chlorine over bismuth. The vapour density corresponds to $BiCl_3$. By dissolving bismuth in aqua regia and evaporating, crystals of $BiCl_3$, H_2O are formed. Solutions of the chloride in concentrated hydrochloric acid deposit crystals of chlorobismuthous acid, H_2BiCl_5. Salts of this acid and of $HBiCl_4$ and HBi_2Cl_7 are known. Aqueous solutions are readily hydrolysed with the precipitation of white bismuthyl chloride, BiOCl.

Bismuth fluorides. *Bismuth pentafluoride,* BiF_5, is obtained by the action of oxygen-free fluorine on bismuth trifluoride at 550°. Impure hexafluorobismuthates, $MBiF_6$, are obtained by reaction with alkali fluorides in bromine trifluoride.

Bismuth trifluoride, BiF_3, is a white non-volatile powder precipitated from a bismuth solution by addition of hydrofluoric acid. It is the most salt-like of the bismuth halides.

Bismuthine, BiH_3. An unstable gas prepared by dissolving an alloy of magnesium and bismuth or a finely divided magnesium–bismuth mixture in dilute acid. The gas decomposes into its elements rapidly even at room temperature. Bismuthine is exceedingly toxic.

Bismuth iodide, BiI_3, m.p. 408°. A black powder formed by adding bismuth oxide, Bi_2O_3, to a solution of iodine in stannous chloride saturated with hydrochloric acid; or by heating a mixture of the elements. It sublimes readily, giving greyish-black tablet-shaped crystals which are stable in air. It is slowly attacked by cold water, more readily on boiling, with the formation of red bismuthyl iodide BiOI. The tri-iodide dissolves in hydriodic acid, giving iodobismuthous acid, $HBiI_4$, $4H_2O$, of which salts such as $KBiI_4$ have been prepared.

Bismuth nitrates. Bismuth dissolves in warm 20% nitric acid, and the solution after evaporation gives crystals of $Bi(NO_3)_3$, $5H_2O$. This is the most important salt of bismuth. It is very easily hydrolysed, the solution in dilute nitric acid giving on dilution a white basic nitrate, $Bi(OH)_2(NO_3)$, and this on washing with water is finally converted into the hydroxide $Bi(OH)_3$. The hydrate $Bi(NO_3)_3$, $1·5H_2O$ is also known.

Bismuth oxides. *Bismuth trioxide,* Bi_2O_3, m.p. 820°. The hydroxide, $Bi(OH)_3$, precipitated by caustic alkali from a bismuth nitrate solution, on drying at 100° gives BiO(OH) and, on ignition, yellow bismuth trioxide, Bi_2O_3. This is also obtained directly by ignition of the basic carbonate or nitrate.

Bismuth trioxide is used to produce an iridescent white glaze on porcelain, and, when mixed with other oxides, in the preparation of stained glass.

Bismuth pentoxide, Bi_2O_5, may be prepared in an impure form by the action of oxidizing agents such as potassium chlorate on Bi_2O_3 under alkaline conditions.

Bismuth sodium tartrate. There are two compounds with this name, both being soluble in water. (1) The acid compound contains an excess of tartaric acid, and is used for the preparation of bismuth mixtures containing pepsin such as are used for acute dyspepsia. (2) The neutral compound is used for the preparation of solutions for intramuscular injection in the treatment of syphilis.

Bismuth sulphates. By dissolving the metal in hot concentrated sulphuric acid, a white bismuth sulphate, $Bi_2(SO_4)_3$, is obtained. On the addition of water a basic sulphate, $Bi_2(OH)_4SO_4$, is formed, and, on heating, this forms yellow bismuthyl sulphate, $(BiO)_2SO_4$. With potassium sulphate a double salt, $KBi(SO_4)_2$, is formed.

Bismuth sulphide, Bi_2S_3. Precipitated from solutions of bismuth salts by hydrogen sulphide as a brownish-black substance, or obtained crystalline by fusing bismuth with sulphur. The compound is insoluble in alkali, but dissolves in nitric or hot concentrated hydrochloric acids. It is soluble in very concentrated potassium sulphide and fine crystals of $KBiS_2$, with a metallic lustre, are formed. On diluting the solution Bi_2S_3 is reprecipitated.

Bismuthyl compounds. Compounds containing the BiO grouping. Prepared by hydrolysis of normal bismuth salts. The bismuth cation is probably normally polymeric. In neutral solutions of the perchlorate the $(Bi_6O_6)^{6+}$ ion is present as a hydrate and other species have been identified.

The solvents commonly used are: (1) pyridine and chloroform, giving three fractions; (2) benzene under pressure, which after treatment with other solvents gives four fractions; (3) amino compounds and other specific solvents, which resolve coals in a similar manner to pyridine; (4) tetralin and other hydrogen donating solvents, which can convert coals quantitatively into liquid products.

Bituminous coal. Under this heading comes a large variety of coals varying in content from about 80 to 92% carbon and from 4·5 to 5·8% hydrogen, with a volatile matter of from 15 to 40%, all on the 'pure coal' basis. Within this range are found the coking coals, used for foundry coke or blast furnace coke, and the more volatile coals for gas works' practice and for producers. Nearly all the domestic uses for coal are satisfied by this range of bituminous coals.

Bituminous mastic. A mixture of asphaltic bitumen with inert fillers.

Bituminous plastics. Compositions based on bitumen, coal tar pitches, and petroleum still-residues which are used as thermoplastic moulding materials and as flooring compositions.

Biuret, Ureidoformamide, $C_2H_5N_3O_2$.

$$NH_2 \cdot CO \cdot NH \cdot CO \cdot NH_2$$

Crystallizes in needles with one molecule of water, m.p. 193°, with decomposition. Formed by the action of heat on urea.

Biuret reaction. Substances containing two —CO—NH— groups attached to one another. to the same nitrogen atom, or to the same carbon atom, give a violet or pink colour when treated with sodium hydroxide and copper sulphate. The reaction therefore serves as a test for biuret, oxamide, peptides, and proteins.

Bivariant system. A system with two degrees of freedom. See Phase rule.

Bixin, $C_{25}H_{30}O_4$. Crystallizes in violet-red needles, m.p. 198°. Autoxidizable in solution. It

Bistre. Highly purified Vandyke brown pigment.
Bitumen. 'Mixtures of hydrocarbons of natural or pyrogenous origin or combinations of both, which can be liquid, semi-solid, or solid and are largely soluble in carbon disulphide'.

In coal technology the term is sometimes applied to the extractable constituents of coal.

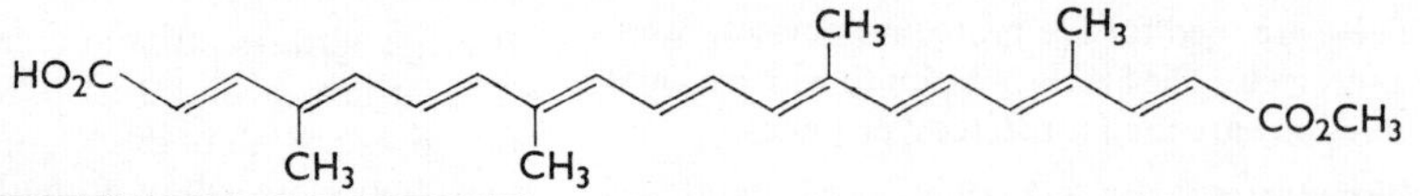

is the principal pigment of annatto, the colouring matter of the shrub, *Bixa orellana*, which was once used for dyeing, and is still used for colouring foodstuffs and in the manufacture of varnishes. Several geometrical isomers and derivatives of bixin are known. The naturally occurring *cis* form is unstable and changes to the stable *trans* form, orange to purple plates, decomp. 217°.

Bjerrum, Niels Janniksen (1879-1958). Born in Copenhagen, and trained at the University there, Bjerrum became professor of chemistry at the Royal Danish Veterinary and Agricultural College in 1914. He worked on many branches of electrochemistry, including hydrogen ion concentration, and his work strongly influenced the modern theory of electrolytes. See *Nature*, 1959, **183**, 290.

Black, Joseph, (1728-1799). Born in Bordeaux, Black studied at the University of Glasgow. In 1755 he wrote a paper called 'Experiments upon Magnesia Alba, Quicklime, and Other Alkaline Substances'. In this he proved that magnesia was an earth similar to, but different from lime, and that both magnesia and lime would combine with carbonic acid gas to form carbonates. He played an important part in the discovery of latent and specific heats. He became professor of chemistry at the University of Glasgow, and in 1776 became professor at the University of Edinburgh.

Blackheart iron. See Cast irons.

Black lead. The commercial name for powdered graphite used for blackening and polishing purposes. See Graphite.

Blake crusher. A well-known type of jaw crusher (*q.v.*).

Blanc fixe. This fine white pigment, used extensively for the coating of paper to produce a good printing surface, is essentially precipitated barium sulphate. It should be quite free from iron and is remarkable for its low adsorptive powers.

Blanc's rule. This rule states that all dicarboxylic acids, with the exception of oxalic and malonic acids, up to and including 1:5 acids, give anhydrides when treated with acetic anhydride and subsequently distilled; 1:6 and higher acids lose carbon dioxide to give ketones. Thus glutaric acid gives glutaric anhydride, adipic acid gives cyclopentanone. Some exceptions to this rule, presumably due to steric hindrance, have been found.

Blasting gelatin. A very powerful form of dynamite introduced by Nobel and consisting of nitroglycerin with about 7% of collodion cotton (nitrocellulose) dissolved in it to form a yellowish translucent elastic solid. It has the advantage that it is unaffected by water, and its elasticity makes it less sensitive to shock and friction, etc., than nitroglycerin and ordinary dynamites (*q.v.*).

Bleach bath. A bleach bath is used to convert developed silver in a photographic material into silver halide. In the case of a black-and-white material this may be an intermediate step to a sulphide toning; the bleach bath is followed by a sulphiding bath. In colour materials the bleach bath converts unwanted silver into silver halide prior to its removal in a fixing bath. A common bleach bath contains potassium ferricyanide and potassium bromide and the bleaching reaction is represented by the equation

$$[Fe(CN)_6]^{3-} + Ag + Br^- \rightarrow [Fe(CN)_6]^{4-} + AgBr$$

Bleaching earths. There are two types (a) *Fuller's earth* (*q.v.*) possessing absorptive properties in the natural state, and (b) *Activated earths*, in which the absorptive powers which are low in the raw state are enhanced by heat or chemical treatment (usually a mild acid leach). Non-gelling bentonites (*q.v.*) and some clays with a high content of gibbsite respond to activation in this way giving a product which often has greater bleaching powers than natural fuller's earth.

Bleaching powder. This is also called chloride of lime, and is manufactured by the direct union of chlorine gas and slaked lime. It is a mixture, the overall formula approximating to $CaCl(OCl)$, but the following phases have been shown to be present to a greater or lesser degree

    (i) $Ca(OCl)_2 \cdot 3H_2O$
    (ii) $3Ca(OCl)_2 \cdot 2Ca(OH)_2 \cdot 2H_2O$
    (iii) $Ca(OCl)_2 \cdot 2Ca(OH)_2$
    (iv) $CaCl_2 \cdot 6H_2O$
    (v) $CaCl_2 \cdot Ca(OH)_2 \cdot H_2O$
    (vi) $CaCl_2 \cdot Ca(OH)_2 \cdot 12H_2O$.

The major proportion is of phases (ii), (iii), and (v).

On treatment with dilute acid it readily yields chlorine, and is sold on the basis of 'available chlorine' (about 35%). It is used in bleaching and as a decontaminating agent for dimefox (*q.v.*).

Blende, or **Sphalerite,** ZnS. Cubic, often in dodecahedra {110} with faces of {311}. Hardness 3½. Black or dark brown crystals, sometimes green or yellow. It is usually contaminated by iron, to which the colour is due. For the crystal structure see Zinc blende.

Blood group substances. Mucopolysaccharides of molecular weight near 250,000 present in red blood cells (erythrocytes). They react specifically with isoagglutinins (*q.v.*) causing haemolysis (rupture of the cells) when blood of an incompatible blood group is transfused. Three well-known blood groups, A, B and O, with many other groups and sub-groups, are distinguishable. The characteristics of blood groups are genetically determined. See 'Blood Group

Substances', E. A. Kabat, Academic Press, 1956.

Bloom. A steel section produced after the first stages of reduction of an ingot in a hot-rolling (or blooming) mill.

Blooming. A whitish cloudy appearance sometimes seen on the surface of vulcanized rubber goods, and caused by the separation of minute crystals of sulphur.

Blowing agent. Chemicals used for making foam and sponge rubber and plastics. They include sodium carbonate, ammonium carbonate, diazoaminobenzene, and other azo and nitroso compounds marketed under trade names. Usually between 5 and 10% is added to the rubber formulation.

Blown asphaltic bitumen. By a suitable oxidation process it is possible to convert a proportion of the heavy distillates removed from asphaltic residues in the preparation of steam-refined bitumens into asphaltic substances. The process consists in blowing air through the heated base material; hydrogen is split off with the formation of water, and condensation of the oxidized molecules to asphaltic substances occurs.

Blue print paper. Paper impregnated with a solution of ferricyanide and ferric citrate in the dark. When exposed to light, ferric iron is reduced by the citrate and prussian blue is formed. The paper is fixed by washing with water.

Blue vitriol. See copper sulphate.

Blue water gas. Straight coal gas is usually diluted with blue or un-enriched water gas to a declared calorific value. In its manufacture coke is alternately air-blasted to incandescence and then steamed for the production of the water gas. A five-minute cycle is common practice.

An average analysis of a good B.W.G. would be—

Carbon monoxide	.	.	42·3%
Hydrogen .	.	.	49·3%
Methane .	.	.	0·3%
Carbon dioxide .	.	.	3·9%
Nitrogen .	.	.	4·2%

with a gross calorific value of 295 Btu/ft³.

Boat form. See Conformation.

Bodenstein, Ernst August Max (1871-1942). Born at Magdeburg, Bodenstein was educated at Heidelberg, Wiesbaden, Charlottenburg, and Göttingen. After lecturing at Heidelberg and Leipzig, where he became extraordinary professor in 1904, he went in 1906 to Berlin, and in 1908 was appointed professor at the Technische Hochschule, Hanover. In 1923 he became ordinary professor in Berlin University and Director of the Physikalisch-Chemisches Institut, retiring as professor-emeritus in 1936. His chief researches dealt with equilibria, reaction kinetics, and photochemistry.

Body-centred cubic lattice. A modification of the cubic lattice having, in addition to an atom at each corner of the cube, a further atom in the body of the cube, equidistant from its corners. In this arrangement each atom or ion has eight similar equidistant neighbours. The following metals crystallize with the body-centred cubic structure: the alkali metals (Li, Na, K, Rb, Cs), Ba, β-Zr, V, Nb, Ta, α-Cr, Mo, α-W, and α-Fe.

Boerhaave, Hermann, was born near Leyden in 1668; he studied at the University of Harderwyk, and became professor of medicine in the University of Leyden. He had a great reputation as a teacher, spoke several languages, and published, in 1732, the 'Elementa Chemica,' the most complete chemical treatise of its time. He died in 1738.

Bogert Marston Taylor (1868-1954). Born at Flushing, New York, Bogert was educated at the Flushing Institute, and subsequently at Columbia University, where he became professor of organic chemistry in 1904. He worked on the synthesis of organic compounds; in particular of the quinazolines and thiazoles. He was President of the American Chemical Society in 1907-1908, and was awarded the Nichols medal (1906) and the Priestley Medal (1938). See *J. Chem. Soc.*, 1954, 4709.

Böhmite, γ-$Al_2O_3 \cdot H_2O$. Hydrated aluminium oxide; precipitated from boiling aluminium salt solutions by ammonia. It is stable in steam at 400° but on heating in air gives aluminium oxide.

Bohr magneton. The unit of magnetic moment for atoms, ions, and molecules. The theoretical values of magnetic moments for unpaired electrons, taking spin only into account are: $1 = 1 \cdot 73$ B.M., $2 = 2 \cdot 83$, $3 = 3 \cdot 87$, $4 = 4 \cdot 90$, $5 = 5 \cdot 92$, $6 = 6 \cdot 93$, $7 = 7 \cdot 94$.

Bohr, Niels (1885-1962). Born at Copenhagen, Bohr was educated at his local university before proceeding to Cambridge to work under Sir J. J. Thomson. Later he joined Rutherford at Manchester. In 1916 he was appointed professor of theoretical physics in the University of Copenhagen, and later head of a newly established institute for theoretical physics. Bohr, in the theory which bears his name, showed how the quantum theory could be applied to the problem of atomic structure. He was awarded the Nobel Prize for Physics in 1922. See *Proc. Chem. Soc.*, 1964, 351.

Boiling-point. The boiling-point of a liquid is that temperature at which the vapour pressure of the liquid is identical with the atmospheric pressure.

Boiling-point diagram. A graph showing equilibrium compositions of liquid and vapour plotted against temperature for a two-component system at any given pressure.

Boiling-point, Elevation of. The increase in boiling-point of a solution, compared with that of the pure solvent, due to the dissolved substance. The elevation of boiling-point is proportional to the weight of a particular solute. Molecular proportions of different solutes produce the same elevation. The following values represent the elevation of boiling-point produced in different solvents by dissolving 1 g molecule of any solute in 100 g of solvent. This is known as the molecular elevation of boiling-point.

Solvent	Molecular Elevation
Water	5·2°
Chloroform	38·8°
Ether	21·1°
Acetone	17·2°
Benzene	25·7°
Alcohol	11·5°

Boisbaudran, Paul Émile Lecoq de (1838-1912). Born in Cognac, a descendant of an ancient Protestant family, Boisbaudran, after his early education, joined his father and brothers in the wine trade. His interest in physics and chemistry was encouraged by his family, and ultimately he devoted his life to scientific investigation. He discovered the elements gallium, samarium, and dysprosium, and ranks with Bunsen, Kirchhoff, and Crookes as one of the founders of the science of spectroscopy. See *Nature*, 1912, **90**, 255.

Boltzmann constant, k. A fundamental constant, important in statistical mechanics, equal to the gas constant, R, divided by Avogadro's number, N. $k = 1·381 \times 10^{-16}$ erg degree^{-1} molecule^{-1}.

Bomb calorimeter. An instrument for determining heat of combustion or the calorific value of foodstuffs and fuels. The combustion is carried out under a pressure of oxygen and the sample is ignited electrically.

A great deal of very precise thermochemical data on the formation of organic compounds has been obtained using this method.

Bond. It is often convenient to imagine that the atoms in the molecule of a compound are attached to each other by bonds, by means of which their positions in space are fixed. The nature of the valency bond is discussed under Valency, Theory of (*q.v.*).

Bond energy. The energy required to break a particular bond. Bond energies of multiple bonds are generally larger than those of single bonds.

Bonderizing. See Phosphate coatings.

Bonding orbitals. See Molecular orbitals.

Bone, William Arthur (1871-1938). Born at Stockton-on-Tees, Bone was educated at Leys School, Cambridge, before graduating in chemistry at Victoria University, Manchester. Later he studied under Meyer at Heidelberg. After holding several junior posts he was appointed professor of applied chemistry at Leeds (1905) and professor of chemical technology, Imperial College of Science and Technology (1912). His researches were mainly on combustion and fuels. He was elected F.R.S. in 1905. See *J. Chem. Soc.*, 1946, 1165.

Bone and Wheeler gas analysis apparatus. The gas is measured at constant volume by means of the pressure which it exerts, and the apparatus consists of a U-tube, one limb of which has volume marks, and the other is calibrated in mm to measure the pressure corresponding to that exerted by the gas when expanded to the same constant volume mark in the first limb. The U-tube is surrounded by a water jacket.

Connected to the millimetre-calibrated limb are an explosion chamber and an absorption vessel which is open under mercury and into which the absorbing reagents are placed in turn. The gas is then forced backwards and forwards into this vessel and the diminution in pressure recorded after each absorption.

Bone ash. A white or creamy powder obtained by calcining bones. It consists essentially of tricalcium phosphate with some calcium carbonate. It is a characteristic constituent of English china ware, known as bone china.

Cupels for assaying gold and silver are made of bone ash.

Bone black, or animal charcoal, is the residue remaining after the destructive distillation of degreased bones in iron retorts. The volatile products are gases, a watery liquid containing ammonia and nitrogenous organic bases, and bone oil or Dippel's oil containing pyridine. The black residue, bone black, contains about 10% amorphous carbon, disseminated through a very porous substrate of calcium phosphate (80%), and carbonate, etc. Treatment with mineral acid dissolves away the salts and leaves a charcoal known as Ivory Black, much used in sugar refining as a decolourizing agent.

Bone china. The chief English china-ware; a soft porcelain which is made almost exclusively in Great Britain. It is made of a mixture of china clay, ball clay, flint, Cornish stone, and bone ash in various proportions. In many of its properties it resembles true porcelain, but is less refractory and not quite so hard. It permits special styles of decoration which are inapplicable to hard porcelain.

Booth, James Curtis (1810-1888). Booth was born at Philadelphia, and after graduating at the University of Pennsylvania, studied in Germany in the laboratories of Wöhler and Magnus. His laboratory in Philadelphia was the first established in America for the teaching of analytical chemistry. He assisted in the first geological survey of Pennsylvania, was State Geologist of Delaware (1837-1838), and established a reputation in the field of mineral analysis. From 1849 until his death he was Melter and Refiner of the U.S. Mint. He was President of the American Chemical Society, 1883-1885, and has been termed 'the first American industrial chemist.'

Boranes. See Boron hydrides.

Borates. Salts of boric acid (q.v.). Generally occur as hydrates. Contain BO_3 and BO_4 groups which may be arranged in polyanions by sharing of oxygen atoms. Cyclic polymers, e.g. the $B_3O_6^{3-}$ ion in $K_3B_3O_6$, are particularly well known.

Borax, $Na_2B_4O_7 \cdot 10H_2O$. Known from fairly early times. Sodium borate occurs naturally in California as the minerals kernite $(Na_2B_4O_7 \cdot 4H_2O)$ and tincal $(Na_2B_4O_7 \cdot 10H_2O)$ and in the brines of Searles Lake. Various other minerals containing boron occur throughout the world, particularly in the U.S.A., which supplies most of the world's demands. These include ulexite $(NaCaB_5O_9 \cdot 8H_2O)$ and colemanite $(Ca_2B_6O_{11} \cdot 5H_2O)$. Where sodium borate occurs by itself or in solution it may be obtained by crystallization; where calcium is present this must be precipitated by treatment with sodium carbonate.

Borax and boric acid are the source of all other boron compounds. The borates are chiefly used in the manufacture of hard and optical glasses and vitreous enamels. Other uses are in detergents, herbicides and fertilizers, welding fluxes, corrosion inhibitors and fire-retarding chemicals, etc. Used as a standard in titrimetry. Owing to hydrolysis in solution with the formation of boric acid it is used as an antiseptic. It is used medicinally as a mild alkaline antiseptic, and as a cleansing skin lotion. It has a sedative action on the skin and relieves the itching of pruritis.

Borazines. Substituted borazoles.

Borazole, $B_3N_3H_6$. A cyclic compound prepared by heating a mixture of diborane and ammonia to 200° or by heating lithium borohydride with

ammonium chloride at 200°. Borazole is isoelectronic with benzene and, in many of its physical properties (m.p. $-58°$, b.p. 53°), shows

resemblances to the latter compound. It is stable to oxidation but is slowly hydrolysed by water. Substituted borazoles may be prepared by use of alkylboranes or alkylamines.

Bordeaux mixture. A mixture of copper sulphate and lime made up in water as a fungicide for spraying on crops, especially vines. It can vary in composition; a common mixture with 8 lb of copper sulphate and 10 lb of slaked lime in 100 gallons of water is called 8:10:100 Bordeaux. See E. Somers, *J. Sci. Food Agric.*, 1959, **10**, 68.

Boric acid, H_3BO_3. A white crystalline solid, with a characteristic greasy feel; the crystal contains planar $B(OH)_3$ units linked in layers by hydrogen bonding. It is obtained by treating borax or colemanite with a mineral acid. The acid is volatile in steam. Its solubility in water is 1·95 g per 100 ml at 0° and 16·82 g per 100 ml at 80°. It is a very weak acid. It may be titrated with alkali, using phenolphthalein as indicator, if glycerol is added. On heating at 100° H_3BO_3 (orthoboric acid) loses water and forms HBO_2 (metaboric acid). Further dehydration yields $H_2B_4O_7$ (pyroboric acid). Ordinary borax is a salt of the last-named acid. Most metallic borates are insoluble in water.

Boric acid is mildly bacteriostatic, inhibiting the growth of some bacteria. It is used as an ointment for wounds, and in aqueous solution as an eye lotion, mouth wash, and skin lotion. It is also a purgative.

Borides. Metallic borides are formed by most metals. The formulae of most frequent occurrence are MB_2 and MB_6. They are generally prepared by fusion of the metal and boron, but nickel boride, Ni_2B, is precipitated from aqueous solution by a hypoborate.

Borine derivatives. Derivatives of the unknown compound borine, BH_3. Prepared from boron hydrides (e.g. diborane). They afford evidence for the transitory existence of borine. The simplest compounds are borine carbonyl BH_3CO (b.p. $-64°$), prepared from diborane and carbon monoxide at 100° followed by rapid cooling, and borine ammonia, BH_3NH_3, prepared by treating ammonium chloride with lithium borohydride.

Borneol, $C_{10}H_{18}O$. The secondary alcohol related to the ketone camphor. Borneol or camphol is known as Borneo camphor when obtained as a (+) form from the oil from *Drybalanops aromatica*, but the (−) form is called Ngai camphor and occurs in the oil from *Blumea balsamifera*. The racemic form occurs in several other oils.

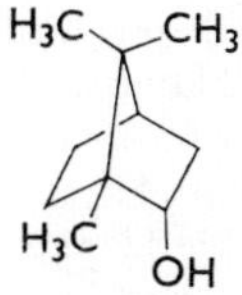

Borneol and isoborneol (*q.v.*) are respectively the *endo* and *exo* forms of the alcohol. Borneol can be prepared by reduction of camphor; inactive borneol is also obtained by the acid hydration of pinene or camphene, for example by heating turpentine oil with acetic acid at 100°. Borneol has a smell like camphor, but sharper. The m.p. of the optically active forms is 208·5°, but the racemic form has m.p. 210·5°. The optical rotation of borneol in toluene solution is $[\alpha]_D \pm 37·92°$. On oxidation camphor is produced, whilst dehydration yields camphene. It may be identified by its *p*-nitrobenzoate, m.p. 137°.

Bornesitol, $C_7H_{14}O_6$, is the monomethyl ether of *i*-inositol (*q.v.*). It is present in Borneo rubber, and has m.p. 199°, $[\alpha]_D +31·6°$. It is isomeric with sequoyitol.

Born-Haber cycle. A thermodynamic cycle which is used to calculate the lattice energies of solids. Considering sodium chloride as an example:

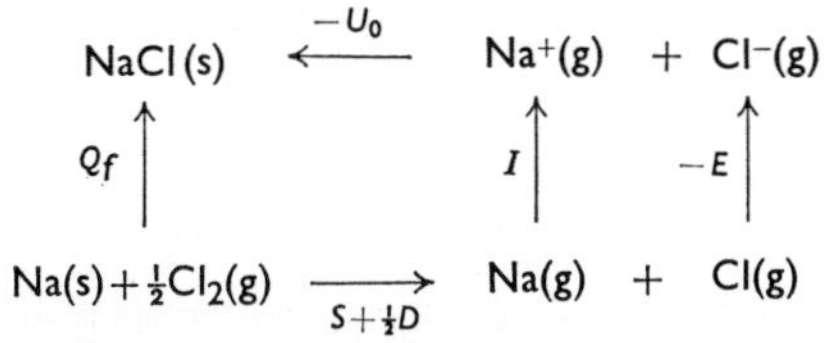

$$NaCl(s) \xleftarrow{\;-U_0\;} Na^+(g) \;+\; Cl^-(g)$$

with vertical arrows: Q_f (up, left), I (up), $-E$ (up, right)

$$Na(s)+\tfrac{1}{2}Cl_2(g) \xrightarrow{\;S+\frac{1}{2}D\;} Na(g) \;+\; Cl(g)$$

S = Heat of sublimation of sodium.
D = Energy of dissociation of chlorine molecule into atoms.
I = Ionization potential of sodium.
E = Electron affinity of chlorine.
U_0 = Lattice energy of the sodium chloride
Q_f = Heat of formation of sodium chloride

In the first part of the cycle (bottom left-hand corner) energy $(S+\tfrac{1}{2}D)$ is required to yield each mole of gaseous sodium and chlorine atoms. The ionization potential energy (I) is needed to give sodium ions and when the chloride ions are formed energy is released corresponding to the electron affinity (E). The ions now come together to form a mole of sodium chloride crystal with the release of energy U_0. By the first law of thermodynamics, the net energy change is the heat of formation of sodium chloride, i.e.,

$$Q_f = S+\tfrac{1}{2}D+I-E-U_0.$$

All the terms in the equation except U_0 may be derived experimentally so that U_0 can be calculated.

The lattice energies of ionic crystals may be calculated by an empirical formula of Kapustinskii which has general application both for simple structures and for those where there is a decrease in symmetry:

$$U_0 = \frac{287\cdot2\nu z_1 z_2}{(r_c+r_a)}\left[1-\frac{0\cdot345}{(r_c+r_a)}\right]\text{Kcal/mole}$$

where ν is the number of ions in the chemical molecule, z_1 and z_2 are the ionic charges and r_c and r_a are the radii of the cation and anion respectively. Since the Kapustinskii formula ignores contributions from zero-point energy and permanent multipole interactions, values obtained are low compared with those derived from the Born-Haber cycle (e.g. lattice energies in Kcal/mole).

Born-Haber		Kapustinskii	
NaCl	183·8	NaCl	179·9
KCl	166·8	KCl	162·7
RbCl	162·0	RbCl	160·7

Extended equations may be used to yield more precise values but these are generally restricted to salts the crystal structures of which are exactly known.

See T. C. Waddington, 'Advances in Inorganic Chemistry and Radiochemistry', Vol. 1, (1959) Academic Press, New York, p. 157.

Bornite. An important copper ore, dark bronze in colour, tarnishing to purple or deep reddish. Often occurs intermingled with chalcopyrite. Its composition is uncertain, probably Cu_5FeS_4.

Bornyl and isobornyl chlorides, $C_{10}H_{17}Cl$.

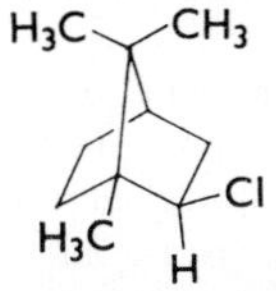

Isobornyl chloride (exo)

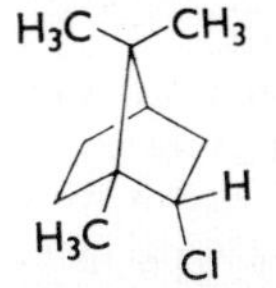

Bornyl chloride (endo)

Bornyl chloride, also known as 'artificial camphor', is formed by the action of hydrogen chloride on α-pinene, and is also formed, together with its stereoisomer, isobornyl chloride, by the action of phosphorus pentachloride on borneol. Bornyl chloride is easily tautomerized to isobornyl chloride. By the elimination of hydrogen chloride it forms camphene. Bornyl chloride crystallizes in leaflets of m.p. 132°, b.p. 207°-208°, $[\alpha]_D \pm 33·4°$ (in alcohol). Isobornyl chloride has m.p. 147°; $[\alpha]_D \pm 30·35°$. It can also be produced from camphene by the action of alcoholic hydro-chloric acid, (+)-camphene yielding (−)-iso-bornyl chloride and vice versa.

Bornylene, $C_{10}H_{16}$. A dicyclic terpene which does not occur naturally, but is obtained from bornyl iodide by interaction with strong alcoholic potash, or by distil-ling methylbornyl xanthate. It is a very volatile crystalline solid of m.p. 113°, b.p. 146°, $[\alpha]_D$ −21·69°, as prepared from (+)-camphor.

Borohydrides, $M(BH_4)_n$. Made by the action of a hydride on a boric acid ester or diborane or by metathesis (e.g. $AlCl_3 + NaBH_4 \rightarrow Al(BH_4)_3$). In addition to species containing the BH_4^- ion, mixed borohydride ions (e.g. $BH(OCH_3)_3^-$), are known. The alkali metal compounds are ionic and are quite stable, even in aqueous solution. Sodium borohydride is an extremely important reducing agent, reducing –COOH groups to $–CH_2OH$. It is a rather milder reduc-ing agent than lithium aluminium hydride. Borohydrides of metals such as Be and Al are covalent and spontaneously inflammable.

Boron, B. At.wt. 10·82, At.no. 5. Obtained in several forms. Amorphous boron is impure. Where structures of the crystalline forms are known there are B_{12} units in the lattice, m.p. 2000°, b.p. about 3900°. The element oxidizes only slowly in air.

Boron occurs in borax and the minerals used in the preparation of borax. The element is obtained by fusion of the oxide with magnesium or potassium, or potassium fluoroborate, KBF_4, with potassium. These methods yield the amorphous boron. Pure boron is obtained by striking a high tension arc in boron bromide vapour; this gives the very hard, black, fused variety.

Boron is essentially a non-metal, giving rise to only very few basic compounds. The element itself is only very slightly attacked even by strong acids. Ignition in air gives a mixture of the oxide and nitride BN. It also forms a carbide of hardness similar to that of silicon carbide.

Boron bromides. *Boron tribromide,* BBr_3, is prepared by passing bromine over boron. It has m.p. −46°, b.p. 91°, and has very similar pro-perties to boron chloride but is a stronger Lewis acid.

Diboron tetrabromide, B_2Br_4, is also known.

Boron chlorides. *Boron trichloride,* BCl_3. Colour-less mobile liquid, m.p. −107°, b.p. 12·5°. Obtained directly from the elements or by heating boron trioxide with phosphorus penta-chloride in a sealed tube. The product may be purified by distillation *in vacuo.* It is extremely readily hydrolysed by water to boric acid. Tetrachloroborates containing the BCl_4^- ion are prepared by addition of BCl_3 to metal chlorides.

Diboron tetrachloride, B_2Cl_4, m.p. −93°, b.p. 55°, is obtained by passing boron tri-chloride vapour through a glow discharge or by interaction of boron monoxide with BCl_3. Decomposes above 0° to *tetraboron tetrachlor-ide,* B_4Cl_4, and other non-volatile chlorides.

Boron fluorides. *Boron trifluoride,* BF_3. Colour-less gas, m.p. −127°, b.p. −101°. Obtained by the spontaneous combustion of boron in fluorine, by heating a mixture of calcium fluoride, boron trioxide, and sulphuric acid or by heating a diazonium tetrafluoroborate. It is formed when any boron compound is mixed with calcium fluoride and concentrated sul-phuric acid; since the gas imparts a characteristic green colour to the flame, this reaction forms a delicate test for the presence of boron. The gas fumes strongly in moist air and reacts with water to give boric acid and fluoroboric acid, HBF_4. Salts of this latter acid are known, and show similarities with perchlorates ($HClO_4$). Boron trifluoride is a good electron acceptor and forms complexes with donors such as ammonia and its derivatives. Boron trifluoride is a very efficient Friedel-Crafts catalyst. Reaction of boron trifluoride with boric oxide gives the volatile trimer $(BOF)_3$.

Diboron tetrafluoride, B_2F_4. Best prepared by treating boron monoxide with sulphur tetra-fluoride. Contains a B—B bond, reacts ex-plosively with oxygen.

Fluoro derivatives of some of the higher boranes and carboranes are also known.

Boron hydrides. A group of compounds of the formulae: B_2H_6 (m.p. −165·5°, b.p. −92·5°), B_4H_{10} (m.p. −119·9°, b.p. 16°), B_5H_9 (m.p. −46·1°, b.p. 58·4°), B_5H_{11} (m.p. −123·4°, b.p. 63°), B_6H_{10} (m.p. −42·3° b.p. 108°), B_9H_{15} (m.p. 2·6°), $B_{10}H_{14}$ (m.p. 99·7°, b.p. *ca.* 213°), $B_{20}H_{16}$ (m.p. 196°-198°). A mixture of boron hydrides was formerly prepared by the action of acid on magnesium boride but good yields are obtained by treatment of boron trifluoride with lithium aluminium hydride. This latter method gives diborane, B_2H_6 and the other hydrides are obtained by pyrolysis followed by vacuum distillation. The hydrides are all decomposed at red heat into boron and hydrogen. They are decomposed by alkalis into boric acid and hydrogen, are attacked more or less readily by water and oxygen, and react readily with the halogens and ammonia (see Borazole). All the hydrides react as unsaturated compounds and have three centre bonds. Diborane reacts with sodium hydride to form sodium borohydride,

$NaBH_4$ (*q.v.*) Many other borohydride anions and substituted boron hydrides and borohydrides are known. See Adams, 'Boron, Metallo-Boron Compounds, and Boranes'.

Boron hydrides could be used industrially as high energy fuels, sources of pure boron for coating, and as vulcanizing agents.

Boron iodides. *Boron tri-iodide*, BI_3, is prepared by passing hydrogen iodide mixed with BCl_3 vapour through a red-hot tube; m.p. 43°, b.p. 210°. It has very similar properties to boron trichloride.

Boron sub-iodide, B_2I_4, is prepared by the action of an electrical discharge on boron tri-iodide vapour.

Boron nitride, BN. Prepared by the action of nitrogen or ammonia on boron at white heat. There seem to be three modifications, (a) with a graphite structure, (b) an amorphous, rather reactive form, (c) an extremely hard form with a diamond structure. Chemically, forms (a) and (c) are very inert. Boron imide, $B_2(NH)_3$, prepared by heating the amide, and boron amide, $B(NH_2)_3$, prepared by passing boron trichloride vapour into liquid ammonia, are also known.

Boron, organic derivatives. Many compounds are known in which boron is bonded directly to a carbon atom. They are readily prepared by the action of Grignard reagents on boron halides. Sodium tetraphenylborate, $NaBPh_4$, is an important reagent for potassium.

Boron oxides. *Boron monoxide*, BO. Prepared by heating a mixture of boron and boron trioxide to 1050° *in vacuo*. Boron monoxide sublimes on to the cooler parts of the apparatus. It disproportionates to boron and boron trioxide at 450° and reduces water.

Boron trioxide, B_2O_3. A white glassy solid, which is prepared by ignition of boric acid. It combines with water to reform boric acid. The oxide appears amphoteric, a phosphate, BPO_4, and various sulphates being known. There is, however, no evidence that these substances contain a boron cation and they are probably oxy-complexes.

Boron phosphate, BPO_4. A stable white solid, prepared by evaporating and igniting a mixture of boric and phosphoric acids.

Borosilicates. Derivatives of one of a group of complex anions containing boron trioxide and silica. Borosilicates are found as minerals (e.g. danburite, $CaO \cdot 2SiO_2 \cdot B_2O_3$), and may also be prepared by fusing together boron trioxide, silica, and a metallic oxide. They form an essential constituent of glasses containing both boron oxide and silica (e.g. Pyrex glass). Glasses may also be prepared from boron trioxide and silica, without the addition of a basic oxide.

Bosch, Carl (1874-1940). Born in Cologne, Bosch graduated in Leipzig in 1898 and then worked at the Badische Anilin und Soda Fabrik. Later he became director of the Kaiser Wilhelm Gesellschaft. He was responsible for the development of Haber's syntheses of ammonia and studied catalysts for high pressure reactions. He shared the Nobel Prize for Chemistry with Bergius in 1931.

Bose, Sir Jagadis Chunder (1858-1937). Born at Mymensingh, Bengal, Bose was educated at Calcutta, Cambridge, and London. After returning to India he joined the staff of Presidency College, Calcutta, from which he retired as professor-emeritus; he also founded the Bose Research Institute, of which he was Director. Elected F.R.S. in 1920, Bose made important contributions to plant physiology.

Boundary layer. When a fluid flows over a surface, due to the frictional resistance there is a layer of fluid in the immediate vicinity of the surface which has a velocity smaller than that in the bulk of the fluid. This is known as the boundary layer. In the part of the layer nearest the surface flow is laminar, that is, the layers of fluid move parallel to each other and there is no mixing between them. Transfer of heat or material across the boundary layer can only occur by the relatively slow process of molecular diffusion, and it is therefore of the greatest technical importance in that it determines the heat and mass transfer properties of the system.

Bourdelin, Claude (1695-1775). Professor of chemistry at Jardin des Plantes, Paris.

Bournonite, $PbCuSbS_3$. Orthorhombic; hardness, $2\frac{1}{2}$, spr.gr. 5·8. Colour lead-grey with metallic lustre. Almost every crystal shows twinning. The composition of the mineral is very constant. Good specimens have been found in the Harz mountains, Cornwall, Hungary, and elsewhere.

Bouveault-Blanc reduction. The reduction of esters to alcohols by nascent hydrogen generated from sodium, and most usually, ethyl alcohol.

$$RCO_2R' + 4[H] \rightarrow R \cdot CH_2OH + R'OH$$

Bowl classifier. This classifier consists of a shallow bowl with a concave bottom. The suspension is fed to the centre near the liquid surface and liquid containing only fine particles overflows from the edge of the bowl. Coarse particles fall to the bottom of the bowl and are raked towards the central discharge by means of ploughs.

Boyle, Hon. Robert. Born at Lismore, Ireland, in 1626; the seventh son of the Earl of Cork; educated at Eton and on the Continent. In 1654 he became a member of the Invisible College, out of which grew the Royal Society. He published his 'Sceptical Chymist' in 1661. He seems to have recognized the difference between elements and compounds; he isolated methyl alcohol from the products of the destructive distillation of wood, and also isolated acetone; he died in 1691. See Thorpe's 'Essays.'

Boyle's law. The volume of a quantity of gas is inversely proportional to the pressure, if the temperature remains constant. This law is exact at low pressures but at high pressures all gases are slightly less compressible than Boyle's law states. See van der Waals' equation.

Bradykinin. A nonapeptide occurring in normal blood plasma in combination with an α_2-globulin as *bradykininogen*. Bradykinin is released from this inactive form by the action of trypsin or of snake venoms. It is extremely potent in increasing capillary permeability (concentrations of 10^{-9} g/ml are active), and together with histamine is associated with shock and inflammatory reactions. The term 'plasma kinin' includes bradykinin and the associated, closely related decapeptide, kallidin: the structures have been established.

Bradykinin:
Arg.Pro.Pro.Gly.Phe.Ser.Pro.Phe.Arg.

Kallidin:
Lys.Arg.Pro.Pro.Gly.Phe.Ser.Pro.Phe.Arg.

Brady's reagent. A solution of 2,4-dinitrophenylhydrazine sulphate in methanol. Gives characteristic crystalline yellow to deep red products with aldehydes and ketones. See 'Characterisation of Organic Compounds', by Wild.

Bragg, Sir William Henry (1862-1942). Born at Wigtown, Cumberland, Bragg was educated at King William's College, Isle of Man, and Trinity College, Cambridge. He held the following appointments: professor of mathematics and physics, Adelaide (1886); Cavendish professor, Leeds (1909); Quain professor of physics, University of London (1915); Fullerian professor of chemistry, Royal Institution (1933), and Director of the Davy-Faraday Research Laboratory. He was elected F.R.S. in 1906, and created K.B.E. in 1920 and was awarded the O.M. in 1931. By the development of the X-ray spectrometer he was able to elucidate many problems of the arrangement of atoms and crystals. With his son, William Lawrence Bragg, he shared in 1915, the Nobel Prize for Physics. He was President of the Royal Society, 1935 to 1940. See *Nature, Lond.*, 1942, **149**, 346.

Bragg, Sir William Lawrence (1890-   ). Born at Adelaide, Bragg was educated at St. Peter's

College and the Universities of Adelaide and Cambridge. He was appointed lecturer in natural sciences, Cambridge (1914), Langworthy professor of physics, Manchester (1919), Director of the National Physical Laboratory (1937), Cavendish professor of experimental physics, Cambridge (1938), and Fullerian professor at the Royal Institution (1953-1965). He was elected F.R.S. in 1921. He shared the Nobel Prize for Physics in 1915 with his father, Sir W. H. Bragg, with whom he was associated in researches upon crystal structure.

Bragg's equation. When a beam of monochromatic X-rays of wavelength λ impinges on a crystal, strong scattering occurs in certain directions only: this is the phenomenon of X-ray diffraction (*q.v.*). The condition for diffraction is that the path difference between waves scattered from successive planes of atoms in the crystal must equal an integral number of wavelengths, n ($n=1,2,3, \ldots$). This condition is expressed by the equation derived by W. L. Bragg in 1912, viz. $n\lambda = 2d \sin \theta$, where d is the distance separating successive planes in the crystal and θ is the angle which the incident beam of X-rays makes with the same planes.

Brand, Hennig (seventeenth century). A native of Hamburg, Brand in 1669 obtained the element phosphorus from the residue left on the evaporation of urine. See 'Discovery of the Elements' (Weeks), p. 336.

Brass. A copper base alloy containing up to 40% zinc. There are two main groups of alloys: (a) the α brasses contain up to 30% zinc; the structure is single-phase α-solid solution which is very ductile and so is suitable for severe cold forming, e.g. thin sheet, wire, tubes, cartridge cases, etc., (b) the $\alpha\beta$ brasses contain about 40% zinc; the structure is two-phased ($\alpha + \beta$) since the solubility of zinc in copper has been exceeded. The β phase is not a simple lattice and so is stronger than α but is lacking in ductility making this alloy unsuitable for cold shaping. It is widely used for castings of all sizes and also for hot forming, particularly extrusion. Additions of small quantities of other metals give improved properties; e.g. tin gives improved corrosion resistance in *Admiralty* metal containing 70% Cu, 29% Zn, and 1% Sn, and in *Naval brass* containing 60% Cu, 39% Zn, and 1% Sn. *Manganese bronze* contains approximately 59% Cu, 40% Zn, and 1% Mn, which acts as a deoxidizer for the production of sound castings; this alloy is much used for large castings such as ships propellers. Easy-machining brasses are based on the 60% Cu, 40% zinc alloy with the addition of 2% Pb. The lead is insoluble in brass and forms a dispersion of fine globules which act as chip breakers. This leaded alloy is sometimes referred to as *Muntz metal*. Aluminium additions up to 3% give high-tensile brasses.

Brassidic acid, $C_{22}H_{42}O_2$,

$$CH_3 \cdot [CH_2]_7 \cdot CH:CH \cdot [CH_2]_{11} \cdot COOH$$

Crystallizes in plates, m.p. 61·9°, d_4^{20} 0·85, n_D^{20} 1·4435. It is the *trans* isomer of erucic acid, and can be prepared from it by treatment with nitrous acid.

Brauner, Bohuslav (1855-1935). The grandson of the chemist Neumann, Brauner was born at Prague, where he received his early education at the Czech Technische Hochschüle and the German University. Later he studied under Bunsen (Heidelberg), and Roscoe (Manchester). In 1882 he was appointed lecturer at the Charles University, Prague, and in 1897 he became professor. His original work dealt with problems associated with Mendeléeff's periodic system, particularly the separation and atomic weight determinations of the rare earths. See 'Chem. Soc. Mem. Lect.,' 1935, 1876.

Braunite. Brown manganese oxide (Mn_2O_3), which usually contains some silica. It has a sub-metallic lustre, a brown-black streak, and is brittle. Sp.gr. 4·75-4·82. Hardness 6-7. It is used (i) as a source of manganese, (ii) as a colour for multi-coloured bricks, pottery, etc.

Brazilite, ZrO_2. A variety of baddeleyite, found in Brazil.

Brazing metal. See Solder.

Bredt's rule. In bridged bicyclic and polycyclic systems with small or medium sized rings, it is not possible to introduce a double bond at the bridgehead atom. This is a consequence of the compound being unable to accommodate angle strain and/or bond deformation.

Breunnerite. An impure form of magnesite ($MgCO_3$) containing 5-30% of iron carbonate; also known as giobertite and mesitite. It is usually light-coloured when fresh, but darkens on exposure, sp.gr 3·0-3·45 It occurs in Austria, Czechoslovakia, Canada, India, and the Urals. Used (i) for the manufacture of magnesite bricks, for which purpose the iron oxide present acts as a bond and produces stronger (though less refractory) bricks than those made of purer magnesite, (ii) as a source of magnesia.

Brewster, Sir David (1781-1868). Born at Jedburgh, Brewster was educated for the Church at Edinburgh University. Handicapped by nervousness, he gave up divinity in favour of physics. In 1838 Brewster became Principal of the United Colleges at St. Andrews, and in 1859 of Edinburgh University. He was one of the founders of the British Association. Much of his research was upon the properties of light. He was elected F.R.S. in 1815, awarded the Rumford gold and silver medal in 1818, and knighted in 1832. See 'Home Life of Brewster,' by Gordon (1869).

Bright stock. A lubricating oil of high viscosity prepared by a combination of refining processes, e.g. solvent de-asphalting, dewaxing, acid treatment, and percolation through active clays and earths.

Brilliant green, Basic Green. Bis (*p*-diethylamino)-triphenylmethyl hydrogen sulphate.

$$(SO_4H)^-$$

Glistening golden crystals, soluble in water and alcohol to give a deep green solution. It is prepared from diethylaniline and benzaldehyde. It is a green dye with powerful bactericidal properties and is used as an antiseptic and disinfectant.

Brillouin zones. The electronic theory of metals divides the electronic states of the metal into a series of zones of different energy. These zones are known as Brillouin zones.

Brin's (oxygen) process. An obsolete commercial method of preparing oxygen. See Barium oxide.

Brinell hardness. See Hardness.

Britannia metal. A ternary alloy containing 90-95% tin, 4·5-9% antimony, and 1% copper. It is used for tableware and ornamental plate.

British thermal unit (Btu). This is the most commonly used industrial heat unit, and is the amount of heat required to raise 1 lb of water through 1°F under specified conditions. Since the specific heat of water varies, particularly with temperature, the actual value of a Btu is dependent on the conditions chosen as standard. The value corresponding to the international table calorie is 1055·06 joules, and this is the value used by the British Standards Institution.

Brix scale. See Hydrometer.

Brodie, Sir Benjamin Collins (1817-1880). Born in London, Brodie was educated at Harrow and Oxford, and in Liebig's laboratory at Giessen. Here he commenced investigations on beeswax, which he continued after returning to England, and for which he was awarded a Royal Medal of the Royal Society in 1850. In 1855 he was appointed Waynflete professor of chemistry in Oxford University, where he remained until his retirement in 1873. His extensive researches included the discovery of the peroxides of the organic radicals and confirmed Odling's formula for ozone. He was President of the Chemical Society in 1859-61.

Bromal, Tribromoacetaldehyde, $CBr_3 \cdot CHO$. An oily liquid, d 3·34, b.p. 174°. Miscible with alcohol and ether; a crystalline hydrate is formed with water. Prepared by passing bromine into a mixture of paraldehyde and ethyl acetate, or by the action of bromine on alcohol. Decomposed by alkalis to give bromoform and a formate. Forms alcoholates with alcohols.

Bromal hydrate, Tribromoethylidene glycol, $CBr_3CH(OH)_2,H_2O$. Crystallizes in colourless prisms, m.p. 53·5°. Soluble in water and alcohol. Prepared by adding water to bromal. Distillation converts it to bromal.

Bromelin. A potent proteolytic enzyme obtained from the stems of *Ananas comosus* (the pineapple). It has a depolymerizing effect on the fibrin matrix and operates over a wide pH range.

Bromic acid, $HBrO_3$. By dissolving bromine in hot concentrated caustic alkali, a bromate and a bromide are produced. These salts may be separated by fractional crystallization. Bromates may also be prepared by electrolytic oxidation of bromine solutions. Silver bromate, formed by precipitation between silver nitrate and a bromate, gives free bromic acid on treatment with bromine. By evaporation on a water-bath, a 5% or, in a vacuum desiccator, a 50% solution may be obtained. Bromic acid is colourless, decomposes readily into bromine and oxygen, and is a powerful oxidizing agent.

Bromates are usually only sparingly soluble in water. On heating they decompose to give a bromide and oxygen. Perbromates are unknown. A mixture $NaBrO_3 + 2NaBr$ is used under the name 'bromine salt' in the extraction of gold.

Bromides. Metals such as iron and zinc dissolve in hydrobromic acid with the formation of bromides. The bromides of most other elements are obtained by direct interaction of the element with free bromine. The alkali bromides are obtained directly from bromine and caustic alkali or technically from iron bromide, a by-product in the preparation of bromine.

The chief bromides used in medicine are those of ammonium, potassium, and sodium. Bromides are used internally for their sedative action on the nervous system.

Bromine, Br. At.wt. 79·916, At.no. 35. A dark red, almost black liquid, d 3·188, m.p. $-7·2°$, b.p. 58·2°. Solid is dark red. The red vapour, poisonous and of irritating odour, contains Br_2 molecules.

The chief sources of bromine are the ocean, the Dead Sea, certain brines in America, and the residual liquors of the Stassfurt deposits. In bromine manufacture these liquors are mixed with chlorine and (if necessary) sulphuric acid, the former displacing the bromine. If the resulting solution is sufficiently rich in bromine it is removed by steam stripping, the vapours being condensed to yield the crude material. If it is not, air is blown through the chlorinated solution and the bromine removed from the emerging air stream by scrubbing with sodium carbonate solution or water containing sulphur dioxide. This effects a concentration of the bromine which may then be liberated by chlorine and removed by steam.

The element is very reactive, combining with many elements to form bromides, and in solution acts as a very powerful oxidizing agent. It rapidly adds on to the double bond of unsaturated organic compounds, and forms a large number of important brominated derivatives, many of which are used as disinfectants. It forms a number of compounds with the other halogens, e.g. BrCl, BrF, BrF_3, BrF_5, and IBr. Its chief industrial use is in the manufacture of ethylene dibromide, which is used in the manufacture of anti-knock fluids. Elementary bromine is a very active corrosive poison.

Bromine fluorides. *Bromine monofluoride*, BrF, m.p. $-33°$, b.p. 20°, is formed by the interaction of bromine and fluorine, but readily decomposes to the tri- and pentafluorides. *Bromine trifluoride* BrF_3 m.p. 8·8°, b.p. 126°, is prepared similarly. It is a yellow liquid which has found great use as a combined fluorinating agent and non-aqueous solvent.

Bromine pentafluoride, BrF_5, m.p. $-60·5°$, b.p. 40·8°, is obtained by passing a mixture of fluorine and bromine trifluoride through a copper tube heated to 200°.

Bromine oxides. *Bromine monoxide*, Br_2O, is formed by the action of bromine on specially prepared mercuric oxide or by the thermal decomposition of bromine dioxide, m.p. $-17·5°$. This oxide probably gives hypobromous acid with water.

Bromine dioxide, BrO_2, is made by passing bromine and oxygen through a cooled discharge tube.

Higher oxides are formed by the action of ozone on bromine. These are solids of composition $BrO_{2·0-3·0}$. All bromine oxides are unstable at room temperature and give bromine and oxygen on warming.

Bromoacetic acid, $CH_2Br \cdot COOH$. A white crystalline solid, m.p. 50°, b.p. 208°. Soluble in water and alcohol. Prepared by the action of dry bromine on dry acetic acid in presence of small amounts of red phosphorus. Produces sores upon the skin; used in chemical syntheses. See Reformatski reaction.

Bromoacetone, $CH_3CO \cdot CH_2Br$. A colourless

liquid which rapidly becomes violet in colour; it is a powerful lachrymator; d^{23} 1·634, b.p. 136°/725 mm. Slightly soluble in water; miscible with alcohol or acetone. Manufactured by treating aqueous acetone with bromine at 30°-40°; it is usual to add sodium chlorate to convert the hydrobromic acid formed by the reaction back to bromine. It is not very stable and decomposes on standing. Used as a tear gas.

Bromobenzenes. *Monobromobenzene*, C_6H_5Br, b.p. 155°, sp.gr. 1·517 at 0°; prepared from benzene by direct bromination in the presence of a carrier (iodine, iron or aluminium chloride) or by treatment of the diazonium compound with cuprous bromide. Used for making diphenyl and diphenyl ether and derivatives, and for introduction of a phenyl group into a molecule via a Grignard reagent; the halogen atom can be removed by treatment with magnesium, sodium, or copper. The disubstituted derivatives $C_6H_4Br_2$ *o-dibromobenzene*, m.p. 7·8°, b.p. 224°, and *p-dibromobenzene*, m.p. 89°, b.p. 219°, also yield substituted diphenyl derivatives by removal of halogens. All bromobenzenes are insoluble in water but soluble in organic solvents.

Ortho   Para

Bromoform, Tribromomethane, $CHBr_3$. A colourless liquid, d^{15} 2·90, m.p. 8°; b.p. 151° (slight decomposition). Sparingly soluble in water; miscible with alcohol and ether. Prepared by the action of bromine and sodium hydroxide on alcohol or acetone, or by warming bromal with alkalis. Decomposed by light and air more readily than chloroform; stabilized by 4% alcohol. Converted to carbon monoxide and potassium bromide by potassium hydroxide.

Bromoform has anaesthetic properties similar to those of chloroform. It is chiefly used for treating whooping cough, being administered as a syrup.

Bromonaphthalenes, $C_{10}H_7Br$.

α-Bromonaphthalene, m.p. 5°, b.p. 279°.
β-Bromonaphthalene, m.p. 59°, b.p. 282°.

The α-isomer can be prepared by the direct action of bromine on naphthalene. The β-isomer is obtained by treating diazotized β-naphthylamine with cuprous bromide. α-Bromonaphthalene is used as a standard for refractive index measurements; also as an immersion fluid in the determination of the refractive index of crystals.

Bromoplatinic acid, Bromoplatinous acid. See Platinum bromides, complex.

N-Bromosuccinimide, NBS, $C_4H_4BrNO_2$. A white solid, m.p. 178°. It is soluble in water and benzene, but only slightly soluble in carbon tetrachloride and hexane. Primarily it is of interest as a brominating agent which will replace activated hydrogen atoms in benzylic or allylic positions, and also those on a carbon atom α to a carbonyl group. Activating influences can produce nuclear substitution in a benzene ring and certain heterocyclic compounds; this reagent also finds use in the oxidation of secondary alcohols to ketones.

Bromothymol blue, Dibromothymolsulphonphthalein. One of the sulphonphthalein group of indicators. It is used in 0·04% aqueous solution to which is added 3·2 ml of 0·05 *M* sodium hydroxide per 0·1 g of indicator. Its pH range is 6·0 (yellow) to 7·6 (blue).

Brønsted, Johannes Nicolaus (1879-1947). Brønsted was born at Varde, Denmark, and educated at Copenhagen, where he was professor of chemistry and Director of the Physico-chemical Institute at the University, and professor of physical chemistry at the Danish Technical College. His researches dealt with an extensive range of physico-chemical subjects, including papers on the kinetic properties of ions, catalysis and nitramide.

Bronze. Originally denoted an alloy of copper and tin. The tin addition hardens and strengthens the copper. 5% Tin forms a solid solution used as cold-formed strip or wire for high strength or spring material. The 10% tin alloy (with 2% zinc as a deoxidizer) is known as *Gun metal*, a casting alloy with good wear resistance due to the presence of a hard eutectoid constituent; it is used for slow-moving bearings, bushes, and gear and worm drives. *Phosphor bronze* has slightly superior properties; 0·2% phosphorus is added to the 5% tin alloy while up to 1% may be added to the 10% tin alloy. *Aluminium bronze* is a copper-based alloy containing about 10% Al, up to 5% Ni, and 5% Fe. It is difficult to cast but is one of the stronger copper base alloys with a tensile strength of about 40 t.s.i. It has good corrosion resistance, wear and abrasion resistance. Much used in marine components, particularly pumps and impellers. It may be quenched and tempered. *Beryllium bronze* contains 2% beryllium. This is a precipitation hardening alloy with a tensile strength of 75 tons per in^2. It is much used for electrical spring contacts: it may also be used for the manufacture of non-sparking tools.

Brookite. A titanium dioxide (TiO_2) which occurs as dark orthorhombic crystals. The oxygen atoms are in hexagonal close packing. Sp.gr. 4·0. Hardness 5-5·5. Refractive index max. 2·700, min. 2·583. It occurs in gneiss and schists of the Alpine type and as detrital mineral.

Brosyl. The trivial abbreviation for the *p*-bromobenzenesulphonyl group: hence brosylate, etc.

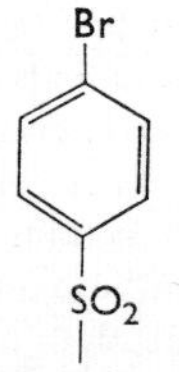

Brown, Alexander Crum (1838-1922). Born in Edinburgh, Brown was educated at the Royal High School, Edinburgh, at Mill Hill School, and at the Universities of Edinburgh, London, Heidelberg, and Marburg. He occupied the chair of chemistry at Edinburgh University from 1869 till 1908. His investigations were chiefly upon types and radicals, on the theory of isomerism and the organic compounds of sulphur. He was elected F.R.S. in 1879. See *J. Chem. Soc.* 1923, 3422. See Crum Brown's rule.

Brownian movement. When a colloidal sol is observed in the ultramicroscope the particles, which are brightly lit against a dark ground, appear to be in rapid and random movement. This can also be seen with the smallest particles visible in the ordinary microscope, and was termed the Brownian movement after its discoverer (Brown, 1827), who first observed it with a pollen suspension. The Brownian movement becomes more intense the greater the degree of dispersion, and is due to the impact on the dispersed particles of the molecules of the dispersion medium. As the particles increase in size, the probability of unequal bombardment from different sides decreases, and eventually collisions from all sides cancel out and the Brownian movement becomes imperceptible at a particle size of about 3-4 μ. The Brownian movement thus gives a concrete proof of the correctness of the kinetic picture of molecular dimensions, and from the characteristics of the movement, Perrin calculated Avogadro's number N, obtaining a value in agreement with that calculated by other methods.

Brown ring test. Nitrates can be identified by the brown colour formed at the interface when a solution mixed with ferrous sulphate solution is allowed to come into contact with concentrated sulphuric acid. The brown colour is due to an iron-nitrosyl complex.

Brucine, $C_{23}H_{26}N_2O_4$. Brucine is an alkaloid

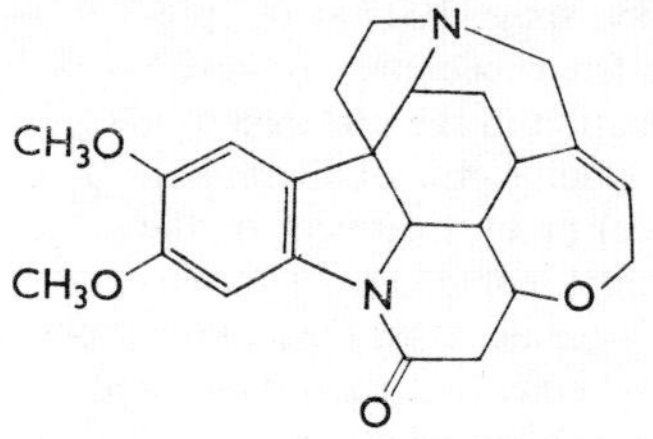

found with strychnine in *nux vomica* and other plants. It crystallizes in white prisms with four molecules of water, m.p. 105° (178°, when anhydrous). Insoluble in water, soluble in alcohol. Laevorotatory. It can be distinguished from strychnine, of which it is the dimethoxy derivative, by the deep red colour it gives with nitric acid. It is poisonous, but less so than strychnine.

Brucite, $Mg(OH)_2$. A white to green mineral crystallizing in the rhombohedral system, the crystals being tabular or foliated, or sectile, with a pearly lustre and perfect cleavage; sp.gr. 2·4. Hardness 2-3. There is one molecule in the unit cell. Brucite has a layer-lattice structure, the OH groups being in hexagonal close packing. Each layer consists of two sheets of OH parallel to the basal plane (001) with a sheet of Mg atoms between, each Mg atom lying between six OH groups. Each OH is linked to three Mg atoms on one side, and fits into three OH of the next layer.

On heating, brucite forms cubic crystals of periclase (MgO).

Brunswick black. A black air-drying paint used as a protective coating for metal work, obtained by dissolving pitch or bitumen in volatile solvents. A cheap variety consists of a solution of pitch in white spirit.

Brunswick green. This green pigment is a mixture of Prussian blue and chrome yellow, obtained by mixing solutions of lead acetate, ferrous sulphate, potassium ferrocyanide, and sodium dichromate in presence of ground barytes as diluent. Different proportions give colours of various shades, and paints produced with it are reasonably permanent, but gradually become bluer on exposure. See Brit. Standard 303.

Bubble-cap plate, Bubble-cap tray. A vapour-liquid contacting device used in distillation and absorption columns. The plate is perforated by a number of holes on the top sides of which are mounted short vertical tubes called *risers*. Over each riser is mounted a bell-shaped cap whose lower edge is slotted or serrated, and the level of liquid on the plate is such that the lower edges of the caps dip beneath it. Vapour travelling up the column passes through the risers where the *bubble-caps* break up the streams into chains of bubbles; intimate vapour-liquid contact is thereby achieved.

Bubble-cap plates are probably still the most widely used plates, but are tending to be replaced by simpler and cheaper types of comparable efficiency. See Plate column.

Bubble chamber. A device for the detection of particles in nuclear chemistry, which consists of a chamber containing a superheated liquefied gas through which the particle passes. Any ionizing radiation is detected by the formation of gas bubbles in the liquid. See Wilson cloud chamber.

Bucherer reaction. Bucherer discovered that the interconversion of β-naphthol and β-naphthylamine through the action of alkali and ammonia could be facilitated if the reaction was carried out in the presence of bisulphite at about 150°. This reaction is exceptional for the ease with which an aromatic C—O bond is broken. It is not of general application, and is most commonly used in the preparation of β-naphthylamine by heating β-naphthol with strong solutions of ammonium sulphite and ammonia for 8 hours at 150° It is probable that the reaction depends upon the addition of bisulphite to the normally unstable keto-form of β-naphthol, and subsequent displacement of —OH by —NH₂, e.g.

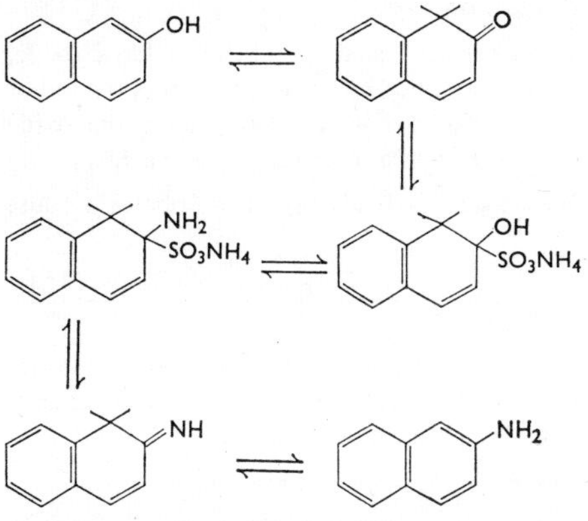

Buchner, Eduard (1860-1917). Buchner studied chemistry and biology in Munich, his native town, and worked for five years as assistant to von Baeyer. His interest was largely in fermentation problems, though he taught analytical and pharmaceutical chemistry at Tübingen. He received the Nobel Prize in chemistry in 1907 for his biochemical researches and in particular for showing that alcoholic fermentation could take place in a cell-free extract of yeast.

Buchucamphor, Diosphenol, $C_{10}H_{16}O_2$. The crystalline solid which separates from oil of buchu leaves, from various species of *Barosma*. It has the constants, m.p. 83°, b.p. 109°-110°/10 mm. The molten substance has $d_4^{99\cdot2}$ 0·9542, $n_D^{99\cdot8}$ 1·4607. It can be obtained by oxidation of menthone with ferric chloride in acetic acid solution. It gives an intense green coloration with ferric chloride. It forms a phenylurethane of m.p. 113°-114°.

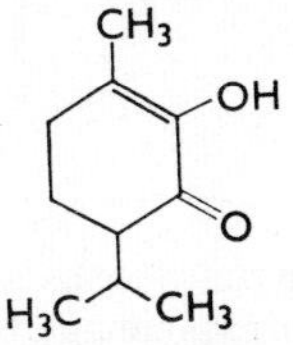

Bucket elevator. A machine for elevating particulate solids consisting of a series of buckets attached to an endless chain or chains. At the lower end the buckets are dragged through the material, picking it up, at the upper end they are emptied by being inverted.

Buffer solutions. It is often desirable to prepare a solution of definite pH, made up in such a way that this pH alters only gradually with the addition of alkali or acid. Such a solution is called a buffer solution, and generally consists of a solution of a salt of a weak acid in the presence of the free acid itself, e.g. sodium acetate and acetic acid. The pH of the solution is determined by the dissociation equilibrium of the free acid:

$$\frac{[H^+][CH_3COO^-]}{[CH_3COOH]} = K.$$

The sodium acetate, which is largely dissociated, serves as a source of acetate ions, which combine with any hydrogen ions which may be added to the solution to yield more of the acetic acid. The addition of hydrogen ions has therefore much less effect on such a solution than it would have on water. In a similar manner, the solution of the salt of a strong acid and a weak base, in the presence of the weak base, has a pH that is insensitive to additions of alkali.

Bufotalin, $C_{26}H_{36}O_6$. A steroid genin isolated

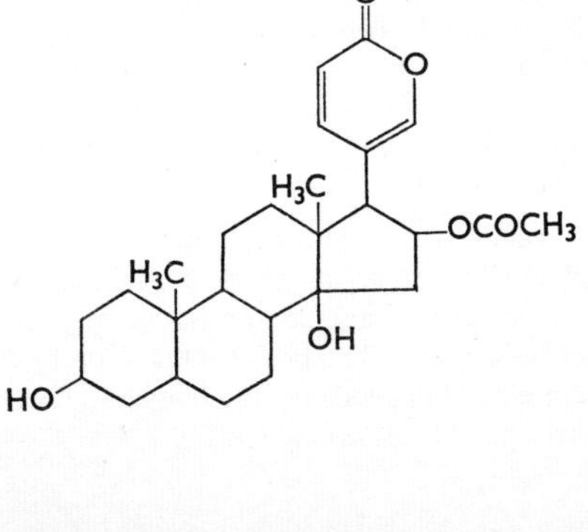

from the venom of the toad, *Bufo vulgaris*, in which it occurs as its suberylarginine ester, bufotoxin.

Bufotenin. 5-Hydroxy-3-dimethylaminoethyl-indole, m.p. 146°-147°, found in the venoms of

Bufotenin

several species of toads, together with the corresponding betaine, bufotenidin. It has vasoconstrictor action causing a rise in blood pressure.

Bufotoxin, $C_{40}H_{60}N_4O_{10},H_2O$. A conjugated steroid genin, occurring in toad venoms and composed of bufotalin esterified with suberyl-arginine, $C_{14}H_{26}N_4O_5$.

$$HO_2C[CH_2]_6CO \cdot NH \cdot [CH_2]_3-NH-C-NH_2$$
$$\qquad\qquad | \qquad\qquad\qquad\qquad ||$$
$$\qquad\qquad CO_2H \qquad\qquad\qquad NH$$

Buhrstone mill. One of the oldest types of size-reduction equipment, this mill is still used for the grinding of grain and the fine grinding of various minerals and other materials. It consists essentially of two round, flat stones, one stationary and the other slowly revolving, between which is fed the material to be ground. The surfaces of both stones are dressed with grooves in such a way that material works its way from the central feed point to the edges, grinding taking place through a shearing action.

Buna rubbers. A name for synthetic rubbers based on polymerized butadiene; thus Buna N and Buna S refer to butadiene-acrylonitrile (see Nitrile rubber) and styrene-butadiene (*q.v.*) copolymers respectively; these synthetics can be vulcanized in a similar manner to natural rubber, their molecules being unsaturated.

Bunsen, Robert Wilhelm (1811-1899). Bunsen was born and received his early education at Göttingen. Later he studied at Berlin, Paris, and Vienna. He held various teaching posts prior to his appointment in 1852 to the chair of chemistry at Heidelberg. His work upon the cacodyl compounds first brought him into prominence. With Kirchhoff he introduced the spectroscope into mineral analysis, and was instrumental in discovering the elements caesium and rubidium. See Mem. Lect., *J. Chem. Soc.*, 1900, 513.

Buoyancy balance. This generally consists of a hollow silica globe mounted on one arm of a sensitive balance, and counterpoised by a small massive cylinder. The position taken up by the beam clearly depends on the buoyant effect of the gas surrounding the bulb. The density of a gas or vapour may thus be determined by observing the pressure at which the gas must be maintained in the gas-tight balance case in order just to maintain the beam of the balance in equilibrium. Alternatively, the weight of an object placed on the end of the beam remote from the bulb may be determined by noting the pressure of gas necessary to preserve equilibrium. Such a balance, made entirely of silica, is capable of extraordinary precision, and may be sensitive to as little as 10^{-11} g.

Burette. A burette is an apparatus used for measuring the quantity of a liquid or gaseous substance employed in a chemical operation. In volumetric analysis the burette generally consists of a vertical tube, graduated in fractions of a millilitre, provided with a tap at the lower end, by means of which the amount of liquid which is allowed to flow from the graduated tube may be controlled. In more precise work, a weight burette is employed. It consists of a flat-bottomed flask provided with a ground stopper, and a narrow side limb provided with a ground glass cap. The burette is weighed before and after pouring out the requisite amount of liquid from the narrow side-limb.

In gas analysis the burettes are generally vertical graduated tubes provided with a tap at the upper end. The lower end is connected by means of rubber tubing to a reservoir containing mercury or water, by means of which the pressure on the gas enclosed between the tap and the liquid surface may be adjusted and ascertained. This form of burette was devised by Hempel. The Bunte gas burette has an additional tap at the lower end.

Burger's vector is a measure of the crystal lattice displacement resulting from the passage of a dislocation.

Burnt oxide. A steel-grey form of ferric oxide, Fe_2O_3, obtained by strong ignition of the red or brown oxide. The ignition renders the oxide crystalline and almost insoluble in acids.

Butacaine, $C_{18}H_{30}N_2O_2$. Its sulphate, a white

crystalline powder, m.p. 100°-103°, slowly soluble in water, soluble in alcohol and acetone, is used as a local anaesthetic.

Butadiene, 1,3-Butadiene, C_4H_6,

$$CH_2:CH \cdot CH:CH_2$$

A colourless gas, b.p. $-5°$. Prepared by passing the vapours of 1,3-butylene glycol, butylene oxide, or cyclobutanol over heated catalysts. Manufactured by the catalytic cracking of *n*-butylenes (obtained during certain refinery operations) or the catalytic dehydrogenation of butane. Also made by the dehydrogenation of ethanol to acetaldehyde, followed by the condensation of ethanol and acetaldehyde. When heated with sodium or certain other substances it polymerizes to a rubber-like material. Used for the preparation of artificial rubbers. Also oligomerized to 4-vinylcyclohexene-1 by heat and to cyclo-octa-1,5-diene and isomeric forms of 1,5,9-cyclododecatriene and higher oligomers by certain transition metal catalysts. Forms complexes, e.g. butadiene–$Fe(CO)_3$, with metal compounds.

Butadienes. Conjugated butadienes are unsaturated hydrocarbons containing the grouping

$$\text{C=C-C=C}$$

. The simplest member, C_4H_6,

is a gas, the substituted butadienes are liquids or solids which with alkyl substituents, readily polymerize to rubber-like solids. They are formed by removal of water or halogen from suitable glycols or chloroparaffins, or in certain cases from acetylenes. They are characterized by great reactivity. Combination occurs with either one or two molecules of halogens, halogen acids, or hypochlorous acid, and also with dinitrogen tetroxide and sulphur dioxide. They can be identified readily by spectroscopic techniques, especially ultra-violet, and by their reaction with maleic anhydride (Diels-Alder reaction) to give derivatives of tetrahydrophthalic anhydride. See Butadiene, Chloroprene, Isoprene.

Unconjugated butadienes, i.e. buta-1,2-diene, CH_2=C=CH—CH_3, also exist; see Allenes.

Butaldehydes, Butyraldehydes, C_4H_8O. *Normal butaldehyde*, $CH_3CH_2CH_2CHO$, is a colourless liquid with a pungent odour, d_{20}^{20} 0·8048, b.p. 75·4°. Sparingly soluble in water; miscible with alcohol and ether. Manufactured by reduction of crotonaldehyde with hydrogen and a metallic catalyst, or by passing the vapour of normal butyl alcohol over heated copper oxide. Forms a bisulphite compound with sodium bisulphite: oxidized to butyric acid. Polymerizes in the presence of zinc chloride to parabutaldehyde. Used in the preparation of rubber accelerators.

Isobutaldehyde. A colourless liquid with a

$$\text{H}_3\text{C}\diagdown_{\text{CHCHO}}$$
$$\text{H}_3\text{C}\diagup$$

pungent odour; d^{20} 0·7938, b.p. 63°-64°/757 mm. More soluble in water than n-butaldehyde. Prepared by oxidation of isobutyl alcohol. Forms a sparingly soluble bisulphite compound. It is oxidized in air to isobutyric acid.

Butane, C_4H_{10}. This hydrocarbon is the lowest member of the series to exhibit chain (nuclear) isomerism, there being two possible isomers.

n-Butane $CH_3CH_2CH_2CH_3$. A colourless gas with a faint odour, b.p. −0·3°. It occurs in natural gas, and is obtained in large amounts during the cracking of petroleum. For chemical properties see Paraffins. Used in refrigeration plant; it is also compressed in cylinders for use as an illuminant, or for heating purposes. It has a high calorific value.

iso-Butane is a colourless gas, b.p. −10·28. It also occurs in natural gas and petroleum gas and may be separated from n-butane by fractional distillation under pressure.

Butenandt, Adolf (1903-   ). Born in Wesermünde, Butenandt studied under Windaus in Göttingen and became director of the organic chemical and biochemical laboratory there in 1930. Later he worked at Danzig, in Berlin, Tübingen and Munich. His chief fame rests on the work on the isolation and characterization of sex hormones, and for this he shared a Nobel Prize in 1939.

Butenes. See Butylenes.

Butlerov, Alexander Michailowitsch (1828-1886). Professor in St. Petersburg, prepared a number of synthetic hexoses and a variety of tertiary alcohols.

Butobarbitone, $C_{10}H_{16}N_2O_3$, 5-Butyl-5-ethylbarbituric acid. A white crystalline powder,

$$\text{C}_2\text{H}_5 \quad (\text{CH}_2)_3 \cdot \text{CH}_3$$

slightly soluble in water, soluble in 2 parts of alcohol, and in 10 parts of ether; m.p. 122°-124°.

It is prepared by condensing ethyl butylethylmalonate with urea. It is an intermediate acting barbiturate, and as it is more active than barbitone it can be given in smaller doses. It is used as a sedative and hypnotic.

Butter of antimony. See Antimony trichloride.

Butyl, Iso. The group

$$\text{H}_3\text{C}\diagdown_{\text{CH—CH}_2-}$$
$$\text{H}_3\text{C}\diagup$$

Butyl, Normal, *n*-Butyl-. The group

$$CH_3CH_2CH_2CH_2-$$

Butyl, Secondary, sec.-Butyl-. The group

$$CH_3CH_2CHCH_3.$$

Butyl, Tertiary, tert.-Butyl-, t-Butyl. The group

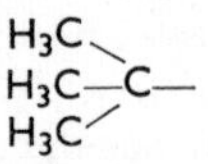

Butyl acetates. There are four esters corresponding to the four butyl alcohols. They are colourless liquids with fruity odours: the normal, iso-, and secondary butyl acetates are important solvents for cellulose lacquers. *Normal butyl acetate,* $CH_3CH_2CH_2CH_2O \cdot OCCH_3$; d^{20} 0·8826, b.p. 126°. Sparingly soluble in water; miscible with alcohols and acetone. *Isobutyl acetate,* $(CH_3)_2CHCH_2O \cdot OCCH_3$; d^{20} 0·8712, b.p. 118°. Slightly soluble in water; miscible with alcohols and acetone. *Secondary butyl acetate,* d^{25} 0·8648, b.p. 112°-113°. Manufactured by heating butylene with acetic and

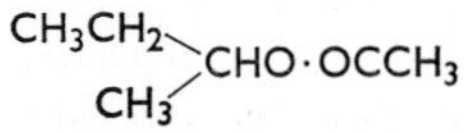

sulphuric acids in water. *Tertiary butyl acetate,* $(CH_3)_3CO \cdot OCCH_3$; d^{20} 0·8958, b.p. 96°.

Butyl alcohols, $C_4H_{10}O$. There are four butyl alcohols; three are colourless liquids with peculiar odours and one is a solid. The liquid alcohols are important solvents for resins and lacquers; they are used to prepare butyl acetates, also important lacquer solvents: other butyl esters are used in artificial flavouring essences and perfumes. *Normal butyl alcohol, 1-Butanol, Propyl carbinol,* $CH_3CH_2CH_2CH_2OH$. Inhalation of its vapour causes coughing; d^{20} 0·8098, b.p. 117·4°. Slightly soluble in water (9%); miscible with alcohols and esters. Forms constant-boiling mixture with water (b.p. 92°). Manufactured by reduction of crotonaldehyde with hydrogen and a metallic catalyst. It forms esters with acids and is oxidized first to butaldehyde and then to butyric acid. *Isobutyl alcohol, Isobutanol, Isopropyl carbinol,* d^{15} 0·8058, b.p. 108°. Slightly soluble in water; miscible with

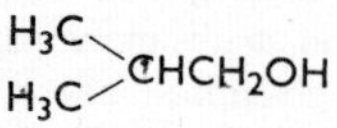

alcohols and esters. Occurs in fusel oil. Oxidized by potassium permanganate to isobutyric acid; dehydrated by strong sulphuric acid to isobutylene. *Secondary butyl alcohol, 2-Butanol, Methylethyl carbinol,* d^{20} 0·808, b.p. 100°.

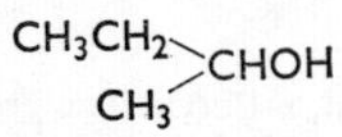

Slightly soluble in water (12%); miscible with alcohols and esters. Manufactured from the butane-butylene fraction of the gas from the cracking of petroleum; this is led into hot sulphuric acid, which converts the butylene

to butyl alcohol. It is oxidized to methylethyl ketone. *Tertiary butyl alcohol, Trimethyl carbinol, Tertiary butanol.* Crystallizes in

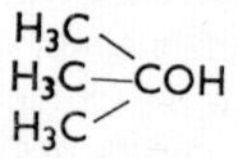

colourless prisms, m.p. 25·5°, b.p. 83°. Soluble in alcohol and acetone. Prepared by absorbing isobutylene in sulphuric acid, neutralizing and steam distilling the liquor. Converted to isobutylene by heating with oxalic acid. Forms constant-boiling mixture with water.

Butylamines, Aminobutanes, $C_4H_{11}N$. There are four of these amines corresponding to the four butyl alcohols. They are colourless liquids with ammoniacal or fish-like odours, miscible with water to give alkaline solutions. *Normal butylamine 1-Aminobutane* $CH_3CH_2CH_2CH_2NH_2$. d^{15} 0·742 b.p. 78°. Manufactured by heating normal butyl alcohol with ammonia in the presence of silica gel, or by passing crotonaldehyde, hydrogen, and ammonia over a suitable catalyst. Forms a crystalline hydrochloride, m.p. 195°. *Isobutylamine, 1-aminoisobutane,* d^{25} 0·724, b.p. 68·9°. Forms a crystalline hydrate,

$C_4H_{11}N$, H_2O, m.p. 74°. Prepared by heating isobutyl alcohol with ammonia in the presence of zinc chloride. Forms hydrochloride, m.p. 177°-178°. *Secondary butylamine, 2-aminobutane.* $CH_3CH_2CH(NH_2)CH_3$. d^{20} 0·724, b.p. 63°. Occurs in the oil of *Cochlearea officinalis* in an optically active (+)-form, $[\alpha]_D^{20}$ +7·42°. The inactive (±)-form is obtained by heating sec-butyl alcohol with ammonia and a suitable catalyst. *Tertiary butylamine, 2-aminoisobutane,*

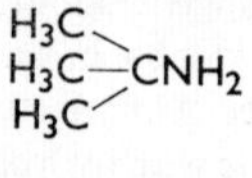

d^{15} 0·7004, b.p. 46·4°.

Butyl cellosolve. A trade name for Ethylene glycol monobutyl ether.

Butyl chloral, Trichlorobutaldehyde, $C_4H_5Cl_3O$, $CH_3CHCl \cdot CCl_2 \cdot CHO$. A colourless oil with an odour resembling that of chloral; d^{20} 1·3956, b.p. 164°-165°/750 mm. Forms a crystalline hydrate with water; miscible with alcohol and ether. Manufactured by the action of chlorine on acetaldehyde or paraldehyde, or by chlorinating crotonaldehyde previously saturated with hydrogen chloride.

Butylenes, Butenes, C_4H_8. Colourless gases with unpleasant odours. There are three isomers obtained from the appropriate butyl alcohol. All three are present in the gas from the cracking of petroleum. *α-Butylene, Butene-1*, $CH_3CH_2CH:CH_2$. Prepared by passing the vapour of normal butyl alcohol over heated alumina. *β-Butylene, Butene-2*,

$$CH_3CH:CHCH_3$$

Prepared by heating secondary butyl alcohol with sulphuric acid. It occurs as two geometrical

$$\begin{matrix} H_3C \\ H_3C \end{matrix} C:CH_2$$

isomers. *Isobutylene, Isobutene.* Prepared by heating tertiary butyl alcohol with oxalic acid.

For general reactions see Olefins. The butylenes are used to prepare secondary butyl alcohol.

Butylene glycols, $C_4H_{10}O_2$. There are five glycols of this formula, and three of them are capable of existing in optically active forms. They are colourless, rather viscous liquids. *α-Butylene glycol*, 1,2 butylene glycol, $CH_3CH_2CH(OH)CH_2OH$, $d°$ 1·019, b.p. 192°-194°. Has a sweet taste, and is soluble in water, but sparingly soluble in ether. Prepared by heating 1,2 dibromobutane with sodium hydroxide solution. *β-Butylene glycol*, 1,3 butylene glycol, $CH_3CH(OH)CH_2CH_2OH$ has been obtained optically active, $[\alpha]_D^{22}$ +7·5°, b.p. 60°-65°/0·8 mm.; ($\pm$)-form, b.p. 204°. Soluble in water; insoluble in ether. Manufactured by reduction of aldol or by the action of yeast on aldol. Used to prepare butadiene. *ψ-Butylene glycol*, 2,3 butylene glycol, $CH_3CH(OH)CH(OH)\cdot CH_3$ The glycol produced by fermentation consists largely of the optically inactive meso-form, while the synthetic glycol is mainly the optically inactive ($\pm$)-form; $d°$ 1·048, b.p. 177°-180°. Soluble in water. Manufactured by the fermentation of potato mash or molasses by organisms of the *Aerobacter* and *Aerobacillus* groups. Used to prepare butadiene. *α.δ-Butylene glycol*, 1,4 butylene glycol, $CH_2(OH)CH_2CH_2CH_2OH$, has an unpleasant odour of leeks; $d°$ 1·011, b.p. 202°-203°. Prepared by the reduction of succinic dialdehyde. *Isobutylene glycol*, $(CH_3)_2C(OH)CH_2OH$, b.p. 177°. Prepared from isobutylene dibromide or chlorohydrin by the action of sodium hydroxide solution.

tert.-Butyl hypochlorite, $(CH_3)_3COCl$. A yellow liquid with a lachrymatory action, which is prepared by passing chlorine into an aqueous alkaline solution of tert.-butyl alcohol. It may be distilled, b.p. 77°-78°, but is liable to decompose violently if overheated, or exposed to light or rubber. It is used for N- and C-chlorinations (reaction similar to N-bromosuccinamide) and for dehydrating alcohols.

Butyl rubber. A copolymer of isobutylene and isoprene (1%-3%) that can be vulcanized in the normal way with sulphur. Butyl rubber has less than 1/40th of the gas permeability of natural rubber and for this reason finds wide use in tyre inner tubes. It is resistant to atmospheric ozone and so can be used out-of-doors in black sheet form for roofing and as a water impermeable membrane to prevent seepage from reservoirs.

Butyric acids, $C_4H_8O_2$. Two acids are known. *Normal butyric acid*, $CH_3CH_2CH_2COOH$, is a colourless syrupy liquid with a strong odour of rancid butter; d^{20} 0·9590, b.p. 162°. Miscible with water, alcohol, and ether; insoluble in solutions of calcium chloride. It occurs in butter as the glycerol ester. Prepared by oxidation of normal butyl alcohol or by the fermentation of sugary or starchy materials by *B. subtilis, Granulobacter saccharobutyricum,* and other organisms. It is volatile in steam. Boiling with nitric acid converts it to succinic acid. Crystalline salts are formed with metals and are mostly soluble in water. The silver salt is only slightly soluble. *Isobutyric acid, Dimethylacetic acid* $(CH_3)_2CH\cdot COOH$, is a colourless syrupy liquid with an unpleasant odour; d^{20} 0·9503, b.p. 154°. Soluble in 5 parts of water; miscible with alcohol and ether. Prepared by the oxidation of isobutyl alcohol with potassium dichromate and sulphuric acid. Its crystalline metallic salts are more soluble in water than the corresponding salts of normal butyric acid.

γ-Butyrolactone, $C_4H_6O_2$. A colourless liquid with a pleasant odour: $d°$ 1·144, b.p. 206°, 89°/12 mm. It is miscible with water, alcohol, and ether and is volatile in steam. A number of preparations have been described from tetrahydrofuran, from vinylacetic acid, and from acetylene and formaldehyde. Converted to butyric acid by hot alkalis and to succinic acid by oxidation with chromic acid. It is used as a solvent for various polymers and as an intermediate in the preparation of, e.g. polyvinylpyrrolidone and piperidine.

Butyrone, Di-n-propylketone, $C_7H_{14}O$, $(CH_3CH_2CH_2)_2CO$. A colourless odorous liquid; d^{15} 0·8205, b.p. 144°. Slightly soluble in water; miscible with alcohols, amyl acetate, and ether. Manufactured by heating calcium butyrate. It does not form bisulphite compounds. Used as a solvent for resins, particularly glyptal and vinyloid resins, and lacquers.

Butyryl-. Groups formed from the butyric acids by removal of the—OH group. *Normal butyryl-*, $CH_3CH_2CH_2CO—$. *Isobutyryl-*, $(CH_3)_2CHCO—$.

C

Cacodyl, $C_4H_{12}As_2$. A colourless liquid with

$$H_3C \diagdown \quad \diagup CH_3$$
$$\qquad As\!-\!As$$
$$H_3C \diagup \quad \diagdown CH_3$$

an intensely powerful, nauseating odour, b.p. 170°. It ignites spontaneously in air to give cacodyl oxide, $(CH_3)_2As \cdot O \cdot As(CH_3)_2$. Cacodyl is prepared by heating dimethylarsenic chloride, $(CH_3)_2AsCl$, with zinc in an atmosphere of carbon dioxide; dimethylarsenic chloride is prepared by reducing cacodylic acid with sodium hypophosphite in the presence of hydrochloric acid. Cacodyl reacts with chlorine, sulphur, and nitric acid to give cacodyl chloride, sulphide, and nitrate respectively.

Cacodylic acid or **Dimethylarsinic acid,** $As(CH_3)_2O \cdot OH$. A colourless, poisonous, crystalline compound. It is readily obtained by distilling arsenious acid with potassium acetate. Its salts, particularly the sodium salt, have been used in medicine.

Cadaverine, Pentamethylenediamine,

$$H_2N \cdot [CH_2]_5 \cdot NH_2$$

A syrupy fuming liquid, b.p. 178°-180°. Soluble in water and alcohol. Cadaverine is one of the ptomaines, and is found, associated with putrescine, in putrefying tissues, being formed by bacterial action from the amino-acid lysine. It is found in the urine in some cases of the congenital disease cystinuria. The free base is poisonous, but its salts are not.

Cadinene, $C_{15}H_{24}$. A sesquiterpene of very wide

distribution, which forms the main component of oil of cubebs. It also occurs in galbanum, cade, and other oils. It forms a dihydrochloride of m.p. 117°-118°. When purified by means of this latter, cadinene has b.p. 134°-136°/11 mm, d_4^{20} 0·9819, n_D^{20} 1·5079, $[\alpha]_D$ −125·2°. The hydrocarbon from West Indian sandal-wood oil showed b.p. 138°-140°/13 mm, d^{16} 0·9260, n_D^{16} 1·50934, $[\alpha]_D$ +38·72°. Cadinene is very stable, and is unaltered by heating under pressure at 330°. It is isomerized by treatment with acetic acid and by other means, forming isocadinene, which yields no crystalline hydrochloride, and which has been isolated from cade oil and also prepared synthetically from nerolidol and from bisaboline.

Cadinol, $C_{15}H_{28}O$. (−)-Cadinol is present in oil of cubebs and (+)-cadinol in galbanum oil. A mixture of cadinols is also found in West Indian sandal-wood oil. It is a tertiary alcohol which gives cadinene dihydrochloride with hydrochloric acid. (+)-Cadinol is probably a mixture of 3 isomerides. It has b.p. 155°-156°/12 mm, d_4^{14} 0·9665, n_D^{14} 1·5054, $[\alpha]_D$ +7·7°. (−)-Cadinol has b.p. 153°-155°/10 mm, d^{20} 0·9727, n_D^{20} 1·508, $[\alpha]_D$ −54°.

Cadmium, Cd. At.wt. 112·41, At.no. 48; m.p. 321°, b.p. 767°, d 8·64. A soft, bluish-white metal, which 'rustles' on bending. The crystal structure of cadmium (and of zinc) is a distortion of hexagonal close packing in which the six neighbours in the plane of the atom are at 2·973 Å with six far neighbours at distances of 3·286 Å. The cell dimensions are $a=2·973$, $c=5·605$ Å, and the distortion is due to part covalency in the metal lattice.

Cadmium occurs in the rare mineral greenockite, CdS, but the principal sources are the zinc ores; blende contains 2-3% Cd, calamine up to 3%. The average value is less than 0·5%.

Cadmium is much more volatile than zinc, and is found in the first portions of the dust collecting in the receivers of zinc furnaces (in which zinc ores containing cadmium are reduced). The distillate may contain 20% or more of Cd as the brown oxide, CdO, together with zinc oxide. Finally, the product is distilled with charcoal in small iron or clay retorts. In America much cadmium is extracted from the fumes from lead and copper furnaces, and from the vat residues in electrolytic zinc refining.

The vapour density corresponds to the atomic form Cd. The metal is used in a number of alloys, as an amalgam in the Weston standard cell, and in very thin layers as a protective coating on iron and steel. Cadmium compounds are exceedingly toxic.

Cadmium alloys. Copper containing up to 1% Cd is used for overhead tramway wires. Aluminium containing 0·5-5% Cd is used for casting. Cadmium can also replace tin in antifriction alloys and solders. In conjunction with tin and bismuth it forms a number of very fusible alloys, with melting-points below 100° (see Bismuth alloys). Cadmium plating is commonly used to impart corrosion resistance.

Cadmium chloride, $CdCl_2$. Obtained by dissolving the oxide, hydroxide, sulphide, or carbonate in hydrochloric acid. The principal hydrate is $2CdCl_2$, $5H_2O$, but $CdCl_2$, $4H_2O$ and $CdCl_2$, H_2O are known.

The crystal structure of cadmium chloride is of the layer lattice type. (*q.v.*).

The halogen salts are readily soluble in water, but are only very feebly ionized in solution. Complex ions such as $CdCl_4^=$ and $CdI_4^=$ are produced, but the ionization is in any case very small. Cadmium chloride forms adducts with many ligands—e.g.

$$CdCl_2(pyridine)_2 , CdCl_2 \cdot 6NH_3.$$

Cadmium metal dissolves in cadmium chloride to give dark-coloured melts which contain Cd^i species.

Cadmium, organometallic compounds. Compounds of the type R_2Cd are prepared by the action of organo lithium derivatives or Grignard reagents with $CdCl_2$. They are less sensitive to oxygen than the corresponding zinc derivatives.

They are used directly in reaction with acid chlorides to give ketones

$$R_2Cd + R'COCl \rightarrow R'COR.$$

Cadmium oxide, hydroxide. The hydroxide, $Cd(OH)_2$, is precipitated by the addition of caustic alkali to a solution of a cadmium salt. It is insoluble in excess of alkali, but dissolves in ammonia, forming a complex $Cd(NH_3)_4(OH)_2$. Ignition of the hydroxide or carbonate, or burning the metal in air, gives the oxide CdO. The oxide varies in colour from brown-red to black, the colour depending on the mode of preparation. The colour arises from lattice defects. Cadmium oxide has been used as a high-temperature resistor material.

Cadmium red, orange, and scarlet. The colour is due to cadmium sulpho-selenides prepared by precipitating a solution of cadmium sulphate with barium sulphide in the presence of selenium, forming co-precipitated pigments containing cadmium sulphide, cadmium selenide, and barium sulphate which are furnace-treated after precipitation. The colours are available in a variety of shades, fast to light, insoluble, and having good resistance to acid, alkali, and heat. As pigments they are extremely soft and easily ground, with low oil absorption.

Cadmium sulphate. $CdSO_4$. Normally obtained as one of the hydrates $3CdSO_4 \cdot 8H_2O$, or $CdSO_4 \cdot H_2O$; the anhydrous salt is prepared by heating to 105°. It is the most widely used cadmium salt.

Cadmium sulphide, CdS. Obtained as a bright yellow precipitate by passing hydrogen sulphide into a very weakly acid solution of a cadmium salt. The colour of the precipitate is affected by the acid concentration; it is obtained in a red form from more strongly acid solutions, and may on occasion be precipitated green. CdS is not precipitated from acid solutions and cadmium is separated from copper by precipitation, as the sulphide, from solutions containing cyanide ions. CdS has both the wurzite and zinc blende structures. It is used as a pigment and in the manufacture of fireworks.

Cadmium yellow. Cadmium sulphide as it occurs naturally as greenockite. It is available in a variety of hues and some zinc sulphide may be present in the greener shades.

Caesium, Cs. At.no. 55, At.wt. 132·91; m.p. 28·5°, b.p. 670°. Caesium occurs in very small quantities in saline deposits but the most important source is the rare silicate mineral, pollucite.

Caesium is a typical alkali metal, and is the most electropositive metal known. The compounds of caesium are all very similar to those of sodium and potassium. The alkali metals can be separated as their salts by fractional crystallization or by ion exchange resins.

Caesium forms a single series of unipositive derivatives. These are typical alkali metal compounds.

Caesium compounds emit electrons if exposed to light or ultra-violet rays, and this property is made use of in the manufacture of certain photoelectric cells.

Radio-caesium, ^{137}Cs, is an important fission product, and is used in deep-ray therapy.

Caesium chloride. This compound has given its name to a very important crystal structure type for compounds AX. In the structure of caesium chloride the caesium ions occur at the corners and the chloride ions at the centres of the cubic unit cells. Each ion is therefore

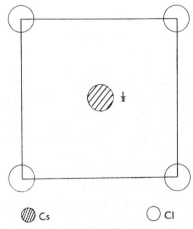

       Cs   Cl

Caesium chloride structure

surrounded by eight of the opposite kind. A number of halides, cyanides, and hydrosulphides crystallize with this structure, e.g. the low temperature forms of CsCl, CsBr, and CsI, and CsCN, TlCN, CsSH, etc. It is also the structure of a considerable number of alloys, e.g. AgLi, HgTl, MgTl, etc.

Caffeic acid, 3,4-dihydroxycinnamic acid,

$$CH=CH \cdot CO_2H$$

$C_9H_8O_4$. Yellow crystals, soften 195°, decompose 223°-225°. Soluble in alcohol. It occurs free in clematis, and is obtained by the alkaline decomposition of certain tannins.

Caffeine, $C_8H_{10}N_4O_2$.   1,3,7-Trimethyl-

xanthine, an alkaloid occurring in tea, coffee, and guarana, from which it may be prepared by extraction. It is also manufactured by the methylation of theobromine, and by the condensation of cyanoacetic acid with urea. It crystallizes in long white needles with one molecule of water, or anhydrous from organic solvents; m.p. (anhydrous) 235°, sublimes at 176°. Very soluble in hot water, at 25° soluble in 46 parts water, 53 parts alcohol, 375 parts ether, 6 parts chloroform. Odourless, and with a very bitter taste. Caffeine is used medicinally as a stimulant and diuretic, and as a constituent of cola drinks.

Cage mill. See Squirrel cage disintegrator.

Cahours, Auguste (1813-1891). Professor of chemistry in Paris. Discovered amyl alcohol, allyl alcohol, anisole, and tin tetraethyl.

Cailletet, Louis Paul (1832-1913). Born at Chatillon-sur-Seine, Cailletet worked in his father's ironworks. Throughout his lifetime he was an enthusiastic research worker, particularly upon the liquefaction of gases. In 1877 he liquified oxygen and later hydrogen, nitrogen, and air.

Cairngorm. See Quartz.

Cajuputol. See 1,8-Cineole.

Calamine. Zinc carbonate, occurring naturally as a mineral, is called calamine in Britain and smithsonite in the United States. Hemimorphite, a hydrated zinc silicate $ZnSiO_4,H_2O$, was formerly called electric calamine in Britain and calamine in America.

Medicinal calamine is a basic zinc carbonate, suitably coloured with ferric oxide. It was formerly prepared from the native carbonate, but is now obtained by precipitation. It is used, either in lotions or as the powder, for sun-burn, sore skins and dermatitis.

Calandria evaporator. See Short-tube vertical evaporator.

Calciferol. See Vitamin-D.

Calcite. A form of calcium carbonate ($CaCO_3$) which occurs as colourless, white, or grey hexagonal crystals and as amorphous grains. In the massive condition it forms limestone, marble, chalk. The crystals have many local names, including calcspar, Iceland spar, dogtooth spar. The crystal structure is rhombohedral with four molecular units per unit cell. Hardness 3, sp.gr. 2·71. Calcite is attacked by most cold dilute acids. Calcite is the most stable form of calcium carbonate and is distinguished from aragonite by its crystalline form and cleavages and by not being coloured red on boiling with cobalt nitrate.

Calcium, Ca. At.no. 20, At.wt. 40·08. A white, malleable metal; d_4^{25} 1·545, m.p. 810°, b.p. 1175°. At ordinary temperatures metallic calcium crystallizes with the face-centred cubic structure ($a=5·56$ Å), but at temperatures above 450° changes over into a close-packed hexagonal structure, $a=3·98$, $c=6·52$ Å. Calcium does not occur native, but its compounds are distributed extensively throughout the earth. The most abundant is the carbonate $CaCO_3$, occurring in massive form as limestone, chalk, etc. In combination with magnesium carbonate it forms dolomite. Gypsum is naturally occurring calcium sulphate, $CaSO_4$, $2H_2O$. Phosphates, silicates, and halides also occur naturally.

The metal is obtained by the electrolysis of the fused chloride. Technically, a fused mixture of 100 parts $CaCl_2$, together with 16·5 parts of fluorspar, CaF_2 (to reduce the temperature of fusion) is used. The electrolytic bath is made of carbon, the bath itself acting as anode. To prevent the metal forming a suspension in the molten chloride, the cathode is slowly screwed up as the calcium accumulates and the calcium is drawn out into the form of an irregular rod, 20-30 cm in diameter, protected from oxidation by a layer of chloride. The metal is obtained pure by sublimation or distillation in vacuum. Calcium may be made directly by electrothermic reduction of the oxide by carbon.

Calcium is a soft, silvery, malleable metal; it tarnishes rapidly on contact with the air, and combines directly with halogens, sulphur, etc. It burns in oxygen with the formation of the oxide CaO. It reacts violently with water, although the pure metal is only slowly attacked by fuming nitric acid.

Although the quantity of calcium used industrially is small, it is increasing. The metal is used as a deoxidizer in steel manufacture, in some valves, and in small proportions in certain bearing alloys.

Calcium acetate, $Ca(C_2H_3O_2)_2 \cdot 2H_2O$. Colourless needles, soluble in water. The dihydrate changes to the monohydrate at 84°. It is prepared by neutralizing acetic acid with lime or calcium carbonate, and is used in the preparation of other acetates and in calico printing.

Calcium aluminates. Mixed oxides of calcium and aluminium. There are three important calcium aluminates: (i) monocalcium aluminate, CaO, Al_2O_3, m.p. 1605°; (ii) tricalcium aluminate, 3CaO, Al_2O_3; and (iii) tricalcium penta-aluminate, 3CaO, $5Al_2O_3$. A variable mixture of calcium aluminates, with 3CaO, Al_2O_3, largely preponderating, forms *ciment fondu;* they are also present in Portland cement, and to a very small extent in some glasses and slags.

Calcium bromide, $CaBr_2$. Very similar to the chloride. It has m.p. 760° and forms a hexahydrate, the solubility of which is 140 g in 100 g water at 25°.

Calcium carbide, CaC_2. Prepared commercially by the action of an electric arc on a mixture of coke and calcium oxide in an electric furnace. The commercial product is greyish black and is used in the production of acetylene, for the reduction of metal oxides and for the manufacture of calcium cyanamide. The pure compound is colourless. The crystal structure is based on a sodium chloride lattice with C_2^{2-}, acetylide ions replacing the chloride ions.

Calcium carbonate, $CaCO_3$. Occurs naturally to an enormous extent. It is dimorphous, crystallizing in the rhombohedral system as calcite, and in the rhombic system as aragonite. In the massive form calcite occurs as marble, limestones, calcspar, and chalk. Aragonite occurs in coral. In combination with magnesium carbonate it forms dolomite, $MgCO_3$, $CaCO_3$.

Calcium carbonate precipitated from cold lime-water by carbon dioxide has the calcite structure; from hot lime-water crystals of aragonite are produced. Calcite is the stable form at ordinary temperatures and pressures. Above 400° aragonite is transformed into calcite.

Calcium carbonate is soluble in water containing carbonic acid, owing to the formation of the acid carbonate $Ca(HCO_3)_2$. One litre of water dissolves 13 mg calcite, or in the presence of carbon dioxide 100 times as much.

Calcium chloride, $CaCl_2$. This occurs naturally as tachydrite, $CaCl_2$, $2MgCl_2$, $12H_2O$, and in sea and mineral waters. Is prepared by dissolving the carbonate or oxide in hydrochloric acid. From the aqueous solution crystals of the hexahydrate $CaCl_2$, $6H_2O$ (m.p. 30°) separate. On heating to 200°, water is evolved and a white porous mass of the dihydrate remains. On heating to 400° in a stream of hydrogen chloride and cooling in nitrogen the anhydrous salt is obtained, m.p. 772°. The tetra- and monohydrates are also known. Calcium chloride is very soluble in water and alcohol, the concentrated solutions having low freezing-points. A solution containing 30 g $CaCl_2$ in 100 g H_2O freezes at $-55°$.

The anhydrous chloride reacts with dry ammonia to give the series of compounds

$$CaCl_2, nNH_3,$$

where $n = 1$, 2, 4, 8. With methyl and ethyl alcohols the compounds $CaCl_2 \cdot nROH(n=3$ and 4) are formed.

Commercially, calcium chloride is obtained from natural brines or from the waste liquor from the ammonia-soda (Solvay) process. It is used for de-icing of roads, dust control and as an antifreeze in concrete mixes. Its solutions, known as 'brines', are used in refrigeration plants.

Calcium citrate, $(C_6H_5O_7)_2Ca_3$, $4H_2O$. The calcium salt of citric acid; acid salts also exist. It crystallizes as white needles, which are sparingly soluble in cold water, and less soluble in hot. By treating it with sulphuric acid, citric acid is obtained.

Calcium cyanamide. $CaCN_2$. Prepared by the action of nitrogen on calcium carbide at about 1000°. Calcium cyanamide is used extensively as a fertilizer either directly or after treatment with superheated steam. On hydrolysis it gives ammonia and is converted to urea in the soil. It is phytotoxic. Calcium cyanamide has also been used as a source of cyanides; the latter can be obtained by fusion with sodium chloride at 1200°. Contains the $[NCN]^{2-}$ ion.

Calcium feldspars. Feldpathic minerals containing lime as their chief base. The most important are anorthite, CaO, Al_2O_3, $2SiO_2$, and the various plagioclase feldspars, the base in the latter consisting partly of sodium oxide and partly of calcium oxide.

Calcium fluoride, CaF_2. Occurs naturally as fluorspar. It has m.p. 1330°, solubility 25 mg per litre of water at 18°. It is used in optical systems for ultra-violet and near infra-red radiation, to which it is transparent. It is also used to lower the melting-points of fused calcium chloride and cryolite baths in the preparation of calcium and aluminium respectively. For structure see Fluorspar.

Calcium gluconate, $Ca(C_6H_{11}O_7)_2$, H_2O. The calcium salt of D-gluconic acid. It is a white powder, soluble in 30 parts of cold water and 5 parts of boiling water. It is widely used in the treatment of milk fever in cows and has other veterinary uses. It is used medicinally in cases of calcium deficiency and for certain other conditions, such as the treatment of lead poisoning.

Calcium glycerophosphate,

$$CaC_3H_5(OH)_2PO_4, 2H_2O$$

A white powder, soluble in about 50 parts of water, insoluble in alcohol. Prepared from glycerophosphoric acid. It is administered for neurasthenia and debility and is a constituent of many proprietary nerve tonic foods.

Calcium hydride, CaH_2. A white solid, prepared by passing hydrogen over metallic calcium at a temperature of 400°-500°. With the very fine metal powder obtained from a solution of calcium in liquid ammonia combination takes place at room temperature. It gives off hydrogen on treatment with water, and has been used for this purpose under the name of 'hydrolith.' It is also used as a reducing agent in metallurgical processes.

Calcium hydroxide, slaked lime, $Ca(OH)_2$. Calcium oxide reacts vigorously with water with the evolution of much heat and the formation of calcium hydroxide, $Ca(OH)_2$. If quicklime is treated with just sufficient water so that it crumbles to a fine, dry, white powder, slaked lime is produced. On shaking the paste formed from quicklime with excess of water, with water, a suspension called milk of lime of formed. A clear solution of the hydroxide in water is known as lime-water.

Slaked lime is used chiefly in the preparation of mortar. This consists of a thick paste of slaked lime with three to four times as much sand as quicklime originally taken. Lime made from magnesian limestone slakes slowly and gives a powdery mixture with water; it is called a 'poor lime' as distinguished from a 'fat lime,' which gives a paste with water. The hardening of mortar consists in the evaporation of the moisture, or its absorption in the bricks, and the slow conversion of the hydroxide into carbonate by atmospheric carbon dioxide. No combination occurs between the lime and the silica.

Calcium iodide, CaI_2. Very similar to the chloride. It has m.p. 740° and forms a hexahydrate, m.p. 42°, the solubility of which is 204 g in 100 g water at 20°.

Calcium lactate,

$$(CH_3 \cdot CHOH \cdot COO)_2Ca, 5H_2O$$

A white powder soluble in 20 parts of water, slightly soluble in alcohol. It is used medicinally for the same purposes as calcium gluconate. It is often prepared as an equimolecular

mixture with sodium lactate, known as calcium sodium lactate, in which form the calcium is said to be more readily assimilated.

Calcium nitrate, $Ca(NO_3)_2, 4H_2O$. This is formed by neutralizing nitric acid with limestone, or by passing oxides of nitrogen into milk of lime, until the nitrite in the mixture is decomposed. The salt forms very deliquescent monoclinic crystals, soluble in alcohol. This salt is present in the soil, and serves as a plant food.

Calcium oxalate, CaC_2O_4. Colourless cubic crystals, insoluble in water. Soluble in hydrochloric acid, but not in acetic acid. It is precipitated with one molecule of water of crystallization on adding a calcium salt to an oxalate. It becomes anhydrous at 180° and reabsorbs water on exposure to air. On gentle ignition it gives calcium carbonate and on heating to redness calcium oxide. It is widely distributed in the vegetable kingdom, occurring in rhubarb and other plants, frequently as small crystals. It is one of the least soluble of calcium salts, and is used in the estimation of calcium.

Calcium oxide, lime, quicklime, CaO. A white amorphous material, d 3·32, m.p. 2570°, which crystallizes with the sodium chloride structure. It is produced when calcium carbonate is heated to temperatures above 650°. The reaction $CaCO_3 \rightleftharpoons CaO + CO_2$, is reversible, and if the carbon dioxide produced is swept away, e.g. by a current of air, the reaction goes to completion.

Commercially, lime is produced by heating limestone to a temperature between 900° and 1200°. Various types of kiln are used. Rotary kilns consist of long, slightly inclined, revolving steel cylinders, lined with firebrick and fired from outside. They take a fairly small feed, less than $2\frac{1}{2}$ in. in size. Vertical shaft kilns consist of a short, wide, steel stack lined with firebrick into the top of which limestone is fed, working its way downwards and being removed from the bottom as lime. These kilns may either be heated by gases from a separate firebox next to the kiln or a mixed feed of limestone and coal may be used; the latter arrangement results in a high thermal efficiency but the lime is contaminated.

Compared with rotary kilns, vertical shaft kilns take a larger feed (6 in. to 8 in. lumps), have lower fuel costs, greater flexibility and a lower capital cost. Rotary kilns are expensive but have a high throughput and can handle fine material. Kilns using a fluidized bed technique are coming into use.

The type of limestone used in a kiln depends on the purpose for which the lime is required. Thus lime for chemical purposes needs to be of fairly high quality, while that for the sulphite pulp industry and certain building operations should contain some magnesium oxide.

Although much lime is used in building and agriculture, the principal consumers, in at least, are the technologically advanced countries the chemical process industries. Thus large quantities are used in the manufacture of sodium carbonate and caustic soda, steel, refractories, calcium carbide, glass, pulp and paper, and sugar; it is also employed in the treatment of water and sewage and in ore concentration and refining.

Calcium peroxide. Formed as the hydrate, CaO_2, $8H_2O$, by precipitating limewater with hydrogen peroxide. From concentrated solutions, or above 130°, anhydrous CaO_2 is precipitated. It is manufactured by compressing slaked lime and sodium peroxide, and washing with iced water. It is used as an antiseptic.

Calcium phosphates. The orthophosphate, $Ca_3(PO_4)_2$, is formed as a white flocculent precipitate by adding sodium phosphate, Na_2HPO_4, to a solution of calcium chloride made alkaline with ammonia. The precipitate is nearly insoluble in water, but is soluble in the presence of carbon dioxide. A suspension in water is converted by boiling into an insoluble basic and a soluble acid salt.

Calcium hydrogen phosphate is formed by mixing solutions of calcium chloride and sodium phosphate; the precipitate is hydrated

$$CaHPO_4, 2H_2O.$$

By dissolving either of the preceding salts in aqueous phosphoric acid, crystals of tetra-hydrogen calcium phosphate,

$$CaH_4(PO_4)_2, H_2O$$

are obtained on spontaneous evaporation. It is the principal active ingredient of super-phosphates (*q.v.*).

Calcium polysulphides. Sulphur dissolves in hot milk of lime or in solutions of the hydro-sulphide with the formation of a reddish-yellow solution, probably containing the sulphides between CaS_2 and CaS_7. The constitution of this solution and the preparation of individual polysulphides are unknown.

Calcium sulphate, $CaSO_4$. Occurs as anhydrite in limestone or rock-salt, or more commonly as the dihydrate gypsum, $CaSO_4$, $2H_2O$. The transparent form of gypsum is called selenite, the fibrous form satin spar, and the opaque form alabaster.

Anhydrous calcium sulphate exists in two forms: (a) natural anhydrite or the substance formed by dehydrating gypsum at temperatures above 650°, which is soluble in water only with difficulty; (b) a soluble form which may be produced by dehydrating gypsum at 60°-90°

over phosphorus pentoxide. The insoluble variety is used in the form of a fine powder as a filler for paper and other materials. The soluble form readily absorbs moisture and is a very efficient drying agent for gases and organic liquids.

The hemihydrate $2CaSO_4 \cdot H_2O$ is formed by heating gypsum at 128°, and is known as 'plaster of Paris'. When mixed with water heat is evolved and the mass quickly solidifies, expanding slightly. For this reason it is widely used for making plaster casts and moulds, particularly in the ceramics industry. Large quantities are used by the building industry in plaster, plaster board, etc.

Gypsum is used as a soil additive and, in a finely ground form known as 'terra alba', as an inert additive to pharmaceuticals, insecticides and other materials.

Gypsum and anhydrite are also employed as raw materials for the production of sulphuric acid.

Calcium sulphide, CaS. This is formed by heating gypsum with charcoal at 1000°. Is easily obtained by passing hydrogen sulphide into lime-water; it is only sparingly soluble, but dissolves in presence of excess H_2S with the formation of the hydrosulphide, $Ca(HS)_2$. Impure calcium sulphide is luminescent after exposure to light; it is used as a depilatory.

Calcium sulphite, $CaSO_3$. Formed as a white precipitate by passing sulphur dioxide through lime-water, or by adding a sulphite solution to one of $CaCl_2$. It dissolves in excess of sulphurous acid with the formation of $Ca(HSO_3)_2$. Solutions of calcium bisulphite are used for sterilizing purposes and for dissolving the lignin in wood pulp in paper manufacture. The sulphite solutions on standing deposit crystals of the dihydrate $CaSO_3$, $2H_2O$.

Calcium superphosphate. See Superphosphates.

Calder-Fox scrubber. A separator for precipitating entrained liquid droplets in gases, particularly for the removal of sulphuric acid mists in the manufacture of that acid. The scrubber, which is fitted into an enlargement of the line carrying the gases, consists of two types of plate. The *agglomerator plates* contain a number of small holes in forcing itself through which the gas acquires a high velocity and turbulence. This causes coalescence of the droplets. The *collector plates* which follow are also perforated, but the design is such that a thin film of liquid runs down them. This acts as an efficient filter and the liquid droplets are removed from the gas.

Caldwell, George Chapman (1834-1907). Born at Framingham, Massachusetts, Caldwell studied at Harvard and Göttingen. After short periods at Columbia College and Antioch College, he became professor of chemistry at the State Agricultural College of Pennsylvania. In 1868 he was appointed professor of agricultural chemistry at Cornell University, where he was for 29 years Head of the Department of Chemistry, retiring as professor-emeritus in 1902. His book on agricultural chemical analysis was the first in the English language on this subject. He was President of the American Chemical Society in 1892.

Caledon Jade Green X, Vat Green 1, 12,12-′di-methoxydibenzanthrone. A green vat dye

giving beautiful bright shades of extremely high all-round fastness, which dyes successfully on cotton and silk.

Calgon. See Hexametaphosphates.

Caliche. Impure sodium nitrate (Chili saltpetre).

Californium, Cf. At.no. 98. Isotopes of californium ranging in mass from 244 to 254 have been obtained by neutron or alpha bombardment of lower mass isotopes or by the bombardment of uranium targets with carbon or nitrogen ions. The most stable isotopes are ^{249}Cf and ^{251}Cf with half-lives of 470 and 800 years respectively. Californium is separated from other elements by ion-exchange procedures. No solid compounds of californium are known; from tracer studies in solution it is believed that the only oxidation state is $+3$.

Calomel. See Mercurous chloride.

Calomel electrode. The hydrogen electrode is not easy to use as a general standard for laboratory use, and it is often replaced by a calomel electrode which has a constant potential known in terms of that of the hydrogen electrode. It consists of a pool of mercury covered with a paste of mercurous chloride (calomel) and mercury, in contact with a standard solution of potassium chloride saturated with mercurous chloride. The potential of the cell is developed on the mercury, and a suitable contact is made with it by means of a platinum wire. Three types of calomel electrode have been used, viz with 0·1 M, 1·0 M, and saturated potassium chloride. Their respective potentials in volts on the hydrogen scale at 25° are: $-0·3338$, $-0·2800$, $-0·2415$.

Calor gas. (Trade name). A heating gas normally sold in cylinders for domestic and industrial use.

Calorific value. The calorific value of a substance is the amount of heat, usually expressed in the form of large or kilogramme calories, given out on the complete combustion of one gram of the substance. The value is of importance chiefly for fuels and foodstuffs. The calorific value of food-stuffs represents the energy value of the food, and hence is of importance when working out diets. That of carbohydrates is taken as 4·1 calories per g, and of fats 9·3 calories per g. That of proteins is about 5·7 calories per g, but proteins are not completely oxidized in the body and the physiological heat value for proteins is taken as 4·1 calories per g.

Calorific values are determined by burning a sample in an atmosphere of compressed oxygen in a heavy metal cylinder called a 'bomb.' The sample is ignited electrically, and the heat evolved on burning is measured.

Calorimeter. A device for the measurement of the heats of chemical reactions. Early forms of the apparatus used thermometers to measure temperature changes but they suffered generally from large radiation losses. In the modern calorimeter, Dewar vessels are generally employed and thermocouples or thermistors are used as sensing elements. Water equivalents are derived by heating a standard resistance in the calorimeter with known current for a measured time. Using micro-calorimeters temperature changes of $5 \times 10^{-5°}$ and 10^{-6} °C may be detected.

Calorizing. The process for coating or impregnating a surface of steel, iron, copper, etc., with aluminium. The article to be treated is packed in aluminium powder mixed with alumina and heated to about 1000° in a current of hydrogen. Articles so treated show a high resistance to many corrosive materials, and are not easily oxidized at high temperatures.

Calumba. The dried, transversely cut slices of the root of *Jateorhiza palmata*, a plant growing in East Africa. It contains three alkaloids, columbamine, palmatine, and jateorhizine, and three bitter principles, columbin, chasmanthin, and palmarin. Calumba has bitter tonic properties, and its preparations are used in treating dyspepsia.

Calvin, Melvin (1911-   ). Born in Minnesota, Calvin studied at Michigan College of Mining and Technology and at the University of Minnesota. He joined the staff of the University of California in 1937. He received the Nichols Medal in 1958 and a Nobel Prize in 1961 for his work on the photosynthetic cycle.

Campesterol, $C_{28}H_{48}O$, 24α-methylcholesterol,

m.p. 158°, $[\alpha]_D$ − 33° in chloroform. Occurs with β-sitosterol in many plant lipids, e.g. rapeseed oil, wheat-germ oil, and soya-bean oil.

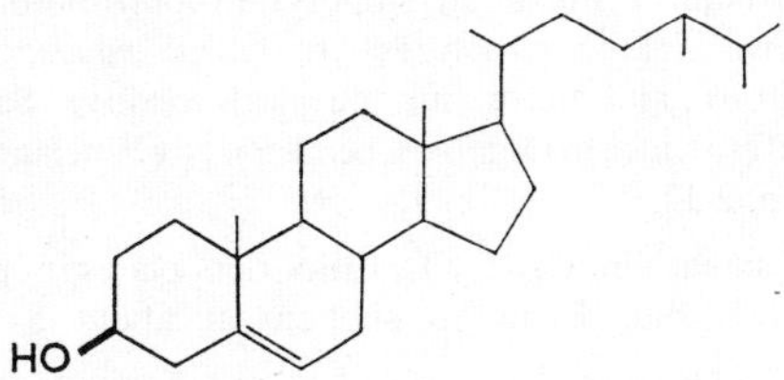

Camphane, $C_{10}H_{18}$. The parent hydrocarbon of the camphor group. It is obtained by suitable reduction of bornyl chloride or isobornyl chloride with sodium in alcoholic solution, or of bornyl iodide with zinc dust in acetic-hydriodic acid. It crystallizes in six-sided plates of m.p. 153°-154°, b.p. 160°-161°, is very volatile and smells like borneol. It is optically inactive, and is chemically very inert.

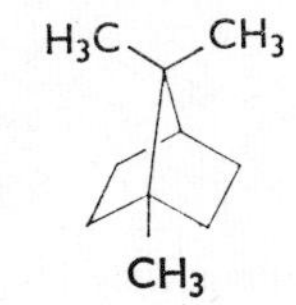

Camphene, $C_{10}H_{16}$. (−)-Camphene is present in citronella and valerian oils, and in French and American turpentine, and the (+)-form in ginger, rosemary, and spike oils. It is produced artificially by the elimination of hydrogen chloride from bornyl chloride (artificial camphor) or from isobornyl chloride, by the dehydration of borneol and isoborneol, and by the action of acetic anhydride on bornylamine. Optically active camphene is obtainable by these methods; for example, (+)-bornyl chloride yields (−)-camphene. Camphene is a crystalline solid of m.p. 51°-52°, b.p. 158·5°-159·5°, d_4^{54} 0·084224, n_D^{54}1·5514. It has probably not been prepared in an optically pure state, but values $[\alpha]_D$ +103·9° and −84·9° (in ether) have been recorded. On oxidation camphene gives a variety of products according to the conditions, including camphor, a dibasic acid, camphenic acid, $C_{10}H_{16}O_4$, and an isomeric hydroxy-acid, camphenylic acid.

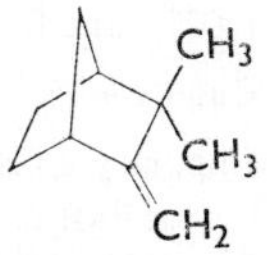

Camphor, $C_{10}H_{16}O$. Camphor occurs naturally in the (+)-, (−)- and (±)-forms. Ordinary commercial camphor is (+)-camphor, from the wood of the camphor tree, *Cinnamonum camphora*, mainly from Formosa.

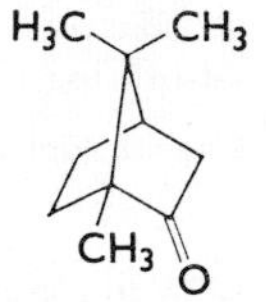

(−)-Camphor occurs in the oil from the leaves of *Blumea balsamifera* and (±)-camphor in the oil from *Chrysanthemum sinense* var. *japonicum*. Camphor is of great technical importance, being used in the manufacture of celluloid and explosives, and for medical purposes. It is not only obtained from natural sources, but is also manufactured, using pinene as the raw material. The camphor produced artificially is known as synthetic camphor, and is usually optically inactive. In the process of manufacture pinene is first converted into bornyl chloride by hydrochloric acid; this is then converted into camphene, which is either directly oxidized to camphor or is hydrated to isoborneol, which is then oxidized to camphor. Camphor crystallizes in thin plates, and sublimes readily at room temperatures. It has m.p. 178·5°-179°, b.p. 209·1°, $d°$ 1·000. In ethyl alcohol $[\alpha]$ ±44·22° (c=20). Camphor can be identified by the preparation of the oxime, m.p. 119·5°, or the semicarbazone, m.p. 245°. On gentle oxidation, for example, with nitric acid, it forms a dibasic acid, camphoric acid, $C_{10}H_{16}O_4$. On reduction, for example, with lithium aluminium hydride, it forms borneol. On dehydration, for example, with phosphorus pentoxide, it forms *p*-cymene. A large number of camphor derivatives have been prepared, including halogen, nitro and hydroxy derivatives and sulphonic acids.

Camphor is much used medicinally as a carminative and stimulant. It is injected in olive oil solution in cases of circulatory collapse. It is a popular remedy for colds and is a constituent of many linaments. Camphorated oil is a 20% solution in olive oil.

Camphorene, $C_{20}H_{32}$. Probably

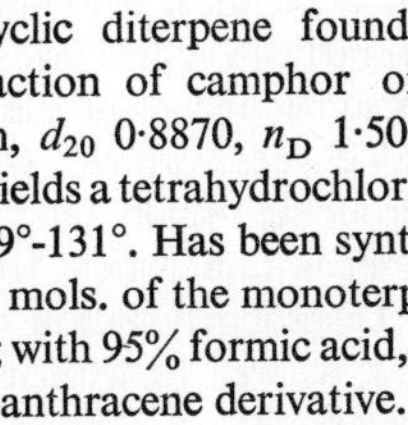

A monocyclic diterpene found in the high boiling fraction of camphor oil, b.p. 177°-178°/6 mm, d_{20} 0·8870, n_D 1·50339. Optically inactive. Yields a tetrahydrochloride, $C_{20}H_{36}Cl_4$ of m.p. 129°-131°. Has been synthesized by the union of 2 mols. of the monoterpene, myrcene. On boiling with 95% formic acid, it is converted to a hydroanthracene derivative.

Canada balsam. An oleoresin obtained from the pine *Abies balsamea*. It is a pale yellow viscous liquid, soluble in most organic solvents. Dissolved in xylene, it is used for mounting microscope slides.

Canal rays. See Positive rays.

Canaline, $C_4H_{10}N_2O_3$. An amino-acid, formed,

$$NH_2 \cdot O \cdot CH_2 \cdot CH_2 \cdot CH \cdot COOH$$
$$|$$
$$NH_2$$

together with urea, by the action of the liver enzyme canavanase on canavanine.

Canavanine, $C_5H_{12}N_4O_3$. An amino-acid, m.p.

$$\begin{array}{c} HN \\ \diagdown \\ C \cdot NH \cdot O \cdot CH_2 \cdot CH_2 \cdot CH \cdot COOH \\ \diagup | \\ H_2N NH_2 \end{array}$$

184°, isolated from jackbean meal. Soluble in water and hot alcohol. $[\alpha]_D^{20} + 7 \cdot 90°$. It is split by the action of the enzyme canavanase in the liver to urea and canaline.

Cane sugar. The common name for sucrose (*q.v.*). Beet sugar is chemically identical.

Cannel coal. A form of coal rich in spores and pollen grains formed in open water from carboniferous algae and plankton, and characterized by the high yields of rich gas, oil, and tar obtained on destructive distillation. Hence the former preferred use of such coals (including 'Bogheads' and 'Torbanites') in gas works, particularly in Scotland, where such types are frequently found.

Cannizzaro, Stanislao (1826-1910). Born in Palermo, a student of both medicine and chemistry and an ardent patriot, Cannizzaro shared in the rebellion of 1847 and, in 1860, while professor at Genoa, he joined Garibaldi and his famous Thousand. In 1861 Cannizzaro became professor of chemistry at his native town, and in 1872 at Rome. A brilliant organic chemist, his most memorable achievement was the elucidation of the meaning and importance of Avogadro's hypothesis. See 'Mem. Lect.,' *J. Chem. Soc.*, 1912, 1677.

Cannizzaro reaction. Two molecules of certain aldehydes, under the influence of dilute alkalis, will interact, so that one is reduced to the corresponding alcohol, while the other is oxidized to the acid; thus, benzaldehyde gives benzyl alcohol and benzoic acid. Most aldehydes behave in this manner under suitable conditions, but those aldehydes which contain the —CH_2CHO grouping usually tend to undergo the aldol condensation when treated with dilute alkalis. Disproportionation occurs with these aldehydes, as well as with most others, under the influence of the acetic acid bacteria, or by living tissues such as the liver or spleen. Aluminium ethoxide or isopropoxide also induce dismutation and carry it a stage further, so that the *ester* is produced by union of the acid and the alcohol. Raney-nickel has been found to act as a catalyst for the dismutation of aldehydes in alkaline solution.

Canonical form. A single structure based on classical valency theory cannot be written for the benzene molecule but instead a number of structures of very similar energy, e.g. the

Kekulé structures, can be envisaged. The resonance theory suggests that the actual structure is a *hybrid* to which the Kekulé structures make an important contribution. The Kekulé structures are called *canonical forms* and have no physical reality. See 'Resonance in Organic Chemistry', by Wheland, pp. 2-12.

Cantharidin, $C_{10}H_{12}O_4$. Colourless plates, m.p. 218°, but begins to sublime at about 84°.

Practically insoluble in water, slightly soluble in alcohol. Soluble in alkalis. It is the active principle of the dried beetle *Cantharis vesicatoria*, found in Southern Europe, and other insects, from which it is prepared by extraction. It is used for blistering the skin to withdraw fluid, in warming plaster, which contains 0·02%, and for stimulating the growth of hair.

Caoutchouc. Natural rubber. See Rubber.

Capillary condensation. When a substance wets the wall of a capillary tube in which it is contained, and possesses a concave meniscus, the vapour pressure above the meniscus is less than that in contact with a plane surface of the liquid at the same temperature. This is expressed by the equation

$$\log_\epsilon \frac{p}{p_s} = 2\frac{\sigma v}{rRT}$$

(p is the pressure at the concave surface, p_s the normal vapour pressure at the same absolute temperature T, σ the surface tension, r the radius of the capillary tube, R the gas constant, and v the mol. volume of the liquid). There is thus a considerable tendency for a vapour to condense in the fine capillaries of a porous material such as charcoal. Capillary condensation is certainly the mechanism of the sorption of water by silica gel, and probably also at higher humidities by charcoal, but it is unsatisfactory as a general theory of physical adsorption.

Capric acid, *n***-Decanoic acid,** $C_{10}H_{20}O_2$.

$$CH_3 \cdot [CH_2]_8 \cdot COOH.$$

Crystallizes in needles, m.p. 31·5°, b.p. 268°-270°, soluble in alcohol and ether, practically insoluble in water. A fatty acid, occurring in wool as the potassium salt, as esters in fusel oil, and as glycerides in cows' and goats' milk and coconut and palm oils.

Caproic acid, *n***-Hexanoic acid,** $C_6H_{12}O_2$,

$CH_3 \cdot [CH_2]_4 \cdot CO_2H$. An oil, m.p. $-3 \cdot 4°$, b.p. 205°, slightly soluble in water. It occurs as glycerides in the milk of cows and goats, in coconut oil and palm oil.

Caprolactam, $C_6H_{11}NO$. Is prepared by Beckmann rearrangement of cyclo-hexanone oxime. It has m.p. 68°-70°, b.p. 139°/12 mm. On heating it gives polyamides. Used in the manufacture of nylon.

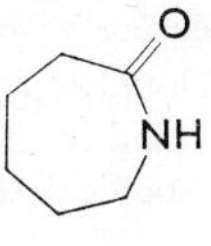

Capryl alcohol, secondary Octyl alcohol, Octanol-2, $C_8H_{18}O$. A colourless liquid with a

$$CH_3[CH_2]_5CHOH$$
$$|$$
$$CH_3$$

strong odour. It can be obtained in optically active forms, $[\alpha]_D^{17} \pm 9 \cdot 9°$, d^{20} $0 \cdot 8216$, b.p. 86°/20 mm. The optically inactive ($\pm$)-form is prepared by distilling castor oil with concentrated sodium hydroxide solution, d^{25} $0 \cdot 8188$, b.p. $179 \cdot 5°$. It has a marked effect in lowering the surface tension of aqueous solutions, and is used as a foam-reducing agent.

Caprylic acid, n-Octanoic acid, $C_8H_{16}O_2$, $CH_3 \cdot [CH_2]_6 \cdot COOH$; m.p. 16°, b.p. 239°, soluble in alcohol and ether, sparingly soluble in hot water. A fatty acid occurring free in sweat, as esters in fusel oil, from which it is most easily prepared, and as glycerides in the milk of cows and goats and in coconut and palm oils.

Capsanthin, $C_{40}H_{58}O_3$. A carotenoid pigment

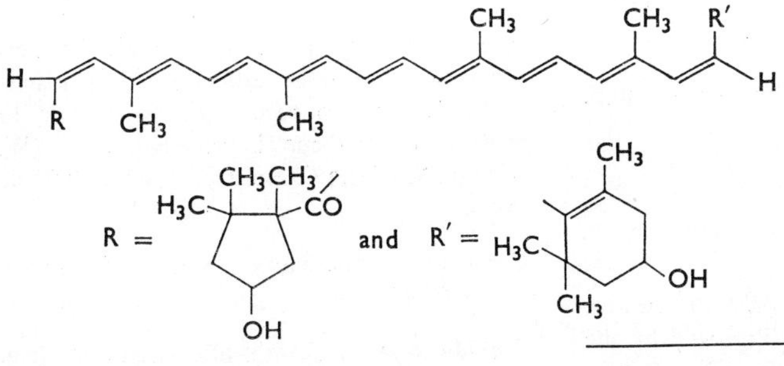

present in the form of esters in paprika. It is a dark red crystalline powder, m.p. 177°-178°. Soluble in acetone and chloroform, slightly soluble in alcohol, insoluble in water.

Capsicum, or chillies. The dried ripe fruit of *Capsicum minimum*. It contains the intensely pungent principle capsaicin, which has the formula:

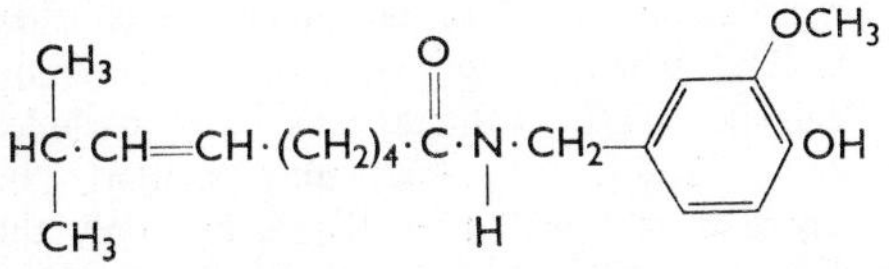

Capsicum is used internally as a digestive stimulant and carminative and as a linament or ointment for external application as a counter-irritant, particularly in lumbago and rheumatism.

Captan, $C_9H_8Cl_3NO_2S$, N-trichloromethylthio-tetrahydropthalimide. Has fungicidal properties. It is prepared by condensing perchloro-

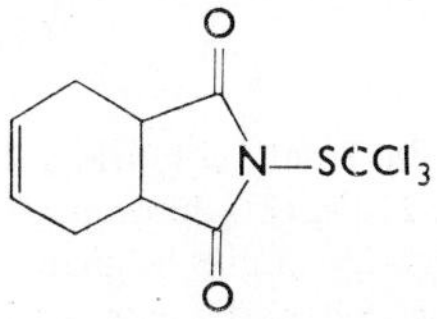

methyl mercaptan and tetrahydrophthalimide, which is obtained by the action of ammonia on tetrahydrophthalic acid. It is a stable, crystalline compound, m.p. 172°, white when pure, and is insoluble in water and soluble in chlorinated solvents. Captan is of low mammalian toxicity, and is non-phytotoxic. It controls *Botrytis* (strawberry mould) and *Venturia inequalis* (apple and pear scab).

Caramel. The brown substance obtained by heating cane sugar or other carbohydrate materials. It chemical nature is unknown, and its reactions vary with its method of preparation. It is soluble in water and is used as a colouring agent for foodstuffs and drinks.

Carane, $C_{10}H_{18}$. A saturated dicyclic hydro-carbon which has not been found in nature. ($-$)-Carane has been obtained by the distillation of pulegone hydra-zone with potassium hydroxide and ($+$)-carane similarly from ($-$)-carone hydrazone. It is also formed by hydrogenation of ($+$)-Δ^3-carene in presence of platinum black. B.p. $169 \cdot 5°$, d_0^{20} $0 \cdot 8411$, n_D^{20} $1 \cdot 4567$, $[\alpha]_D$ $+57 \cdot 64°$, $-47 \cdot 06°$.

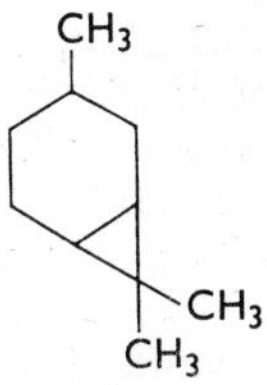

Caraway. Commonly called caraway seeds,

caraway is the dried ripe fruit of *Carum carvi*, and its medicinal properties are due to the aromatic constituents of the volatile oil contained in its vittae. See Oil of caraway.

Carbachol, carbamylcholine chloride,

$$C_6H_{15}ClN_2O_2.$$

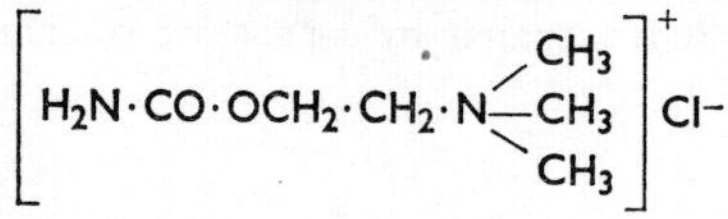

$$\left[H_2N\cdot CO\cdot OCH_2\cdot CH_2\cdot N{\overset{\overset{\displaystyle CH_3}{|}}{\underset{\underset{\displaystyle CH_3}{|}}{-}}}CH_3 \right]^+ Cl^-$$

Crystallizes in small colourless hygroscopic prisms, m.p. 210°-212° (decomp.), very soluble in water, slightly soluble in alcohol. Prepared from β-chlorethyl carbamate and trimethylamine. It has a physiological action similar to that of acetylcholine, but more prolonged, as it is less readily hydrolysed. It is used for intestinal atony following operations, and can be given orally.

Carbamic acid, $H_2N\cdot COOH$. This acid is not known in the free state, but salts and esters of it exist. The most readily obtainable salt is ammonium carbamate, formed by the action of dry carbon dioxide on dry ammonia. Commercial ammonium carbonate contains appreciable quantities of ammonium carbamate. Esters of carbamic acid are called urethanes.

Carbamido-. The name given to the group —NHCONH₂ in organic compounds.

Carbamyl-. The name given to the group —CONH₂ in organic compounds.

Carbanilide, $C_{13}H_{12}N_2O$. Silky needles, m.p.

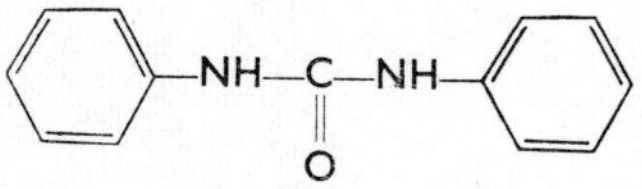

235°, b.p. 260°. Slightly soluble in water, readily in alcohol and ether. Prepared by the action of phosgene upon aniline.

Carbanions, $R_3C^\ominus$. Produced by cleavage of certain carbon-hydrogen, carbon-halogen, carbon-metal, and carbon-carbon bonds. They are mostly of low stability, and react rapidly with air, water, etc. In many cases the existence of these negatively charged species may only be inferred. The delocalization of charge (unshared electron pair) over multiple bond systems increases their stability: e.g. triphenylmethyl sodium and cyclopentadienyl sodium are stable in the absence of potentially electrophilic reagents.

Carbarsone, p-carbamidophenylarsonic acid, $C_7H_9AsN_2O_4$. A white powder, m.p. 190° (decomp.), slightly soluble in water and alcohol, soluble in alkalis. It is prepared by heating p-aminophenylarsonic acid with urea, and is used in the treatment of amoebic dysentery.

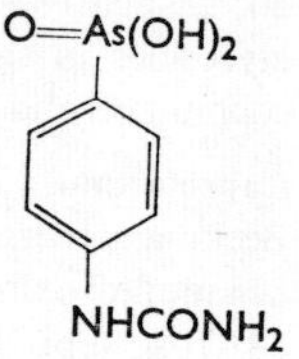

Carbazole, $C_{12}H_9N$. Occurs with anthracene in

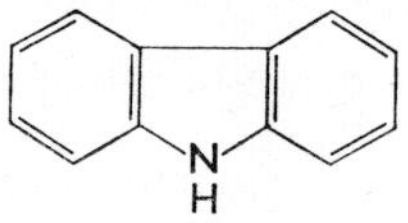

the solid which separates from anthracene oil. It is used in the preparation of Hydron Blue R, a vat dyestuff of unknown constitution. Carbazole crystallizes in colourless leaflets, m.p. 238°, b.p. 335°. Insoluble in water and sparingly soluble in most organic solvents. It sublimes easily.

Carbene, R_2C. A transient and highly reactive species, containing a formally divalent carbon atom. The existence of carbenes has been largely inferred from their reaction with alkenes (leading to cyclopropane derivatives) and other reagents which can trap the intermediate. Produced by photolysis of diazoalkanes or by

an α-elimination of HX from $\overset{\displaystyle H\quad R}{\underset{\displaystyle X\quad R}{\diagup C\diagdown}}$. The

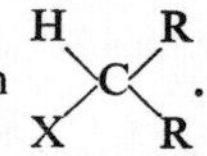

reaction of base with haloforms under Riemer-Tiemann conditions, and the Arndt-Eistert synthesis are two reactions now known to proceed *via* carbene intermediates. See W. Kirmse, 'Carbene Chemistry,' 1963, Academic Press.

Carbethoxy-. The name given to the group —CO·OCH₂CH₃ in organic compounds.

Carbide formers. Certain alloy additions (e.g. manganese, chromium, molybdenum, tungsten, titanium, vanadium and niobium) form stable carbides in steel. Such carbides confer wear resistance when present in a relatively coarse form or creep resistance when present in a fine coherent form.

Carbides. The carbides of the alkali and alkaline earth metals (e.g. Li_2C_2, Na_2C_2, CaC_2) may be regarded as 'salts' of acetylene, which they produce when treated with water. Common 'carbide' is the calcium salt. The carbides Be_2C, Al_4C_3, SiC, etc., may similarly be regarded as 'salts' of methane, but only the first two give methane on treatment with water. Magnesium carbide, Mg_2C_3, gives propyne on hydrolysis. Other carbides, e.g. Fe_3C, Cr_3C_2, W_2C, are interstitial compounds, and the stoicheiometries show no relation to the normal oxidation states of the element or to simple hydrocarbons. The electronegative elements form normal covalent carbides (e.g. CF_4, CS_2).

Carbimazole, 2-ethoxycarbonylthio-1-methyl-iminazole, $C_7H_{10}N_2O_2S$. A white crystalline powder insoluble in water, sparingly soluble in alcohol; m.p. 123°. It is prepared from 2-mercapto-1-methyliminazole and ethyl chloroformate. Carbimazole is an antithyroid drug, and is used in the control and treatment of thyrotoxicosis.

Carbinol. A name for methyl alcohol, introduced by Kolbe in 1860 as a basis for the systematic naming of monohydric alcohols. See Alcohols and Methyl alcohol.

Carbitols. The trivial name given to the mono-alkyl ethers of diethylene glycol, e.g. butyl-carbitol, $C_4H_9OCH_2CH_2OCH_2CH_2OH$. See also Cellosolve and Diethylene glycol mono-ethyl ether.

Carbohydrases. Enzymes which act on carbohydrates; included are the amylases, glycosidases, cellulase, and certain phosphorylases.

Carbocyclic. A generic term relating to organic compounds which are considered to be derived from one or more rings of carbon atoms, e.g. benzene, naphthalene, diphenyl.

Carbodiimides. See Dicylohexylcarbodiimide.

Carbohydrates. One of the principal classes of naturally occurring organic compounds. An approximate formula is $(CH_2O)_x$ and for various values of x include sugars, starches and cellulose, each essential to plant and animal life. They are produced in plants as the results of photosynthesis, the chlorophyll catalysed combination of carbon dioxide and water under the influence of light. The simple carbohydrates are mono-, di- or polysaccharides, having repeating units usually containing 5 or 6 carbon atoms joined through oxygen linkages. For example, sucrose and lactose are disaccharides which are simple carbohydrates; cellulose, a polysaccharide, is a polymer containing approximately 2000-3000 glucose units per molecule. The basic sugar skeleton of carbohydrates, involving hydroxyl groups, gives them their properties such as water solubility and sweet taste. As many carbon atoms are asymmetric the carbohydrates can exist in many stereochemical and structural modifications.

Carbohydrazide, $C_3H_8N_2O_2$,

$$H_2N \cdot NH \cdot CO \cdot O \cdot C_2H_5$$

White crystals, m.p. 153°-154° (decomp.). Very soluble in water, insoluble in alcohol and most organic solvents. It forms crystalline salts with many acids. It can be made by reacting hydrazine hydrate with diethyl carbonate.

Carbolan dyes. These are a range of acid dyes, often possessing brilliant shades, introduced by I.C.I. in 1933. They have high fastness to light and milling and belong either to the monoazo or anthraquinone class. The improved fastness to wet treatments results from the introduction of one or more long-chain alkyl groups (C_4 to C_{20}) into the molecule.

Carbolan Violet 2R (C.I. Acid Violet 51)

The method of application to wool is similar to that of the acid milling dyes, 3% of ammonium acetate being the usual dye-bath addition. Carbolan dyes also have affinity for silk and for polyamide fibres.

Carbolic acid. An old name for phenol (*q.v.*).

Carbomethoxy-. The name given to the group —$CO \cdot OCH_3$ in organic compounds.

Carbon, C. At.no. 6, At.wt. 12·010, m.p. 3600°. Occurs in both the free and combined states. The crystalline forms are graphite, m.p. 3600°, and diamond. For the crystal structures of diamond and graphite see under those headings. Coal has a carbon content dependent on its age and locality. Carbon dioxide occurs in the atmosphere, and also in the combined form in carbonates (limestone, marble, etc.). All living organisms contain carbon, whereby it occupies a unique position in the series of elements. The number of compounds containing carbon probably exceeds the number formed by all other elements.

The following varieties of amorphous carbon are usually described: charcoal from wood, sugar, etc.; lampblack, soot, or acetylene black; animal charcoal, bone charcoal, and ivory black; coke, coal, and anthracite; gas carbon; and electrode carbon. These are all black and opaque, the density and hardness depending on the conditions of formation. X-ray diffraction shows that they all contain microcrystalline material.

Carbon when alloyed with iron forms steel.

Between 0·1 and 1·1% is commonly added giving a progressive increase in strength from about 20 to 55 t.s.i. High carbon (1·1%) in steel forms relatively coarse carbides which provide wear resistance.

Carbonates. The salts of the weak acid, carbonic acid, H_2CO_3. This group of compounds includes many minerals and compounds of great technical importance (e.g. $CaCO_3$, Na_2CO_3, $ZnCO_3$, etc.). The bicarbonates (or acid carbonates) are formed by replacing only one of the two hydrogen atoms in carbonic acid by a metal atom, as in sodium bicarbonate, $NaHCO_3$, and calcium bicarbonate, $Ca(HCO_3)_2$.

The carbonates of the alkali and alkaline earth metals are stable, but those of certain metals, e.g. Cr^{3+}, Fe^{3+}, are hydrolysed readily and completely to the hydroxide. Some metals, e.g. Pb, Cu, Zn, form basic carbonates such as white lead, a compound of variable composition approximating to $2PbCO_3 \cdot Pb(OH)_2$.

Carbonation. The reaction between an organic substrate and carbon dioxide. It is a term frequently applied to such reactions of Grignard reagents and alkali metal organometallic reagents.

Carbon black. This name is applied to a wide range of technologically useful materials based on the incomplete combustion of natural gas or petroleum oil. Different varieties or grades are spoken of as Channel, Furnace, or Thermal Decomposition blacks; these vary in many particulars notably in colour value and particle size. Very large quantities of these materials are used in rubber manufacture, in the paint, ink, polish, and related industries, and for decolourizing.

Carbon dating. ^{14}C is continuously formed in the atmosphere by the reaction $^{14}N + ^1n \rightarrow ^{14}C + ^1H$. The ^{14}C exchanges with ^{12}C in living organisms, but exchange ceases on death when the radioactive ^{14}C content decays with a half-life of 3,760 years. Hence the age of a once-living material may be established by determining the amount of ^{14}C.

Carbon disulphide, CS_2. A colourless, highly refractive liquid with a pleasant ethereal odour. The commercial product usually has a most disagreeable odour owing to the presence of other sulphur compounds in small amount; d^{20} 1·266, m.p. $-111·6°$, b.p. $46·25°$. Very sparingly soluble in water, miscible with alcohol and ether. Manufactured by heating sulphur and wood charcoal together, or by reacting methane with sulphur vapour over a catalyst. By subjecting the technical grade material to fractional distillation or distillation over lime, a pure material with only a trace of odour may be obtained. It is an excellent solvent for oils, waxes, rubber, sulphur, and phosphorus, but its use as a solvent is decreasing owing to its high toxicity and inflammability. Used in the manufacture of viscose silk and carbon tetrachloride; also for the preparation of xanthates used in the flotation of ores.

Carbon fluorides. Many carbon fluorides are known and are, in general, extremely inert substances. For details of preparations and derivatives see Fluorocarbons. Unsaturated fluorocarbons such as tetrafluoroethylene C_2F_4, have been prepared; the action of fluorine on graphite gives $(CF)_n$.

Carbonic acid, H_2CO_3. A very weak dibasic acid, which is formed when carbon dioxide is dissolved in water. Attempts to concentrate its solutions result in decomposition into carbon dioxide and water. A solution of carbon dioxide in water contains much hydrated carbon dioxide. The anhydrous acid can be prepared in ether at $-30°$. The acid forms two series of salts, the normal carbonates (e.g. $CaCO_3$, K_2CO_3) and the acid carbonates or bicarbonates (e.g. $Ca(HCO_3)_2$, $KHCO_3$).

Carbonic anhydrase. A fundamentally important enzyme which reversibly catalyses the reaction $H_2O + CO_2 \rightleftharpoons H_2CO_3$ in an organism. In respiration, it catalyses the formation of carbon dioxide from bicarbonate in the blood vessels of the lung, whereas in kidney function it promotes the formation of carbonic acid. Carbonic anhydrase is widely distributed and has been isolated *inter alia* from red blood cells, kidney tubules, and the pancreas. The enzyme molecule contains zinc as a prosthetic group.

Carbonium ions. Positively-charged species containing a trivalent carbon atom R_3C^+. They exhibit a broad spectrum of reactivity and stability, the latter decreasing in the order tertiary > secondary > primary. They are postulated as intermediates in many reactions, e.g. the dissolution of alkenes in strong acids, the dehydrohalogenation of alkyl halides, and certain solvolytic reactions. Many carbonium ions may be detected by spectroscopic (n.m.r.) methods; tropylium and triphenylmethyl carbonium ions are stable and may easily be isolated. All carbonium ions have a strong affinity for nucleophiles, e.g. water.

Carbonization. See Destructive distillation.

Carbon oxides. *Carbon monoxide*, CO. A colourless and odourless gas (b.p. $-190°$; m.p. $-205·1°$), which is formed in the incomplete combustion of carbon or carbon compounds, by the interaction of carbon dioxide with carbon at $900°$-$1000°$, or, in the laboratory, by the action of concentrated sulphuric acid upon anhydrous formic acid. The gas is also formed, together with hydrogen, in the high-temperature decomposition of steam by coke. This mixture with hydrogen is known as water gas. Carbon monoxide burns in the air or in oxygen with a pale blue flame, and can give rise to violent explosions when ignited in air in suitable proportions. Ignition may be produced by a free flame, a spark, or by a surface heated to *circa* 600°. See Blue water gas.

Carbon monoxide reacts chemically as a reducing agent—thus it will reduce the oxides of metals such as lead or iron to the metal at an elevated temperature. It is the active reducing agent in a number of metallurgical processes. It will reduce iodine pentoxide to iodine at 90°. This reaction is used in analysing gaseous mixtures containing carbon monoxide. It is only sparingly soluble in water. Carbon monoxide is absorbed by an ammoniacal solution of cuprous chloride; the compound $CuCl.CO.H_2O$ is formed. With many transition metals carbonyls are formed. It reacts directly with chlorine to form phosgene.

Carbon monoxide is very poisonous, forming a very stable complex with haemoglobin, which is then not available to effect a transfer of oxygen.

Although carbon monoxide is a chemical of great industrial importance it is not much used in the pure form. Thus in metallurgical processes it is mixed with nitrogen and other gases, and in organic manufacturing processes with hydrogen. Commercially, pure carbon monoxide is obtained from gases containing it by absorption under pressure in solutions of ammoniacal copper salts, or by low-temperature separation processes. The concentrated gas is used in the purification of nickel and other metals and in organic syntheses.

Carbon dioxide, CO_2. A colourless gas which has a faint smell and a sharp taste. On cooling at atmospheric pressure, the gas passes directly into a white solid, the vapour pressure of which equals 1 atmosphere at −78·5°. Liquid carbon dioxide may be obtained at pressures above one atmosphere. The gas occurs in various natural sources, and plays an essential part in animal respiration and the growth of green plants. It is produced in the complete combustion of carbon or carbon compounds, but is most conveniently prepared in the laboratory by heating heavy metal carbonates or alkaline earth carbonates or bicarbonates, or by the action of dilute acids on metal carbonates or bicarbonates. Carbon dioxide is soluble in water, which dissolves approximately its own volume of the gas at 15°. Aerated waters are charged with carbon dioxide under pressure. Carbon dioxide is the anhydride of carbonic acid, H_2CO_3, but

the aqueous solution of carbon dioxide contains mainly hydrated carbon dioxide. Carbon dioxide is readily detected by the formation of a white precipitate of calcium carbonate on bubbling it through lime-water (a solution of calcium hydroxide in water). With excess of carbon dioxide the initial precipitate redissolves, with formation of calcium bicarbonate, $Ca(HCO_3)_2$. In gas analysis, carbon dioxide is absorbed by sodium hydroxide solution, with which it reacts to form sodium carbonate.

On a commercial scale carbon dioxide is obtained from flue or kiln gases by absorption in a suitable solution, such as sodium or potassium carbonate, mono- or triethanol-amine, followed by regeneration by the action of heat; the gas is then purified and liquified. It is also obtained as a by-product in the manufacture of alcohol by fermentation. Carbon dioxide is largely used as refrigerant. At one time the solid 'dry ice', produced by the free evaporation of the liquid at a pressure slightly below the triple point, was preferred to the liquid for this purpose, but of recent years the position has been reversed. The other large outlet for carbon dioxide is the manufacture of mineral waters. Lesser uses are in coal-mining, and as a chemical reagent, fire extinguisher and inert gas.

Carbon suboxide, C_3O_2. A toxic gas with a pungent odour, which can be condensed to a liquid boiling at −6·8° and freezing at −111·3°. It is prepared by dehydrating malonic acid with phosphorus pentoxide *in vacuo* at 140° to 150°. The gas is stable if stored in dry glass apparatus. On heating to 200° it is partly decomposed into carbon dioxide and carbon and partly polymerized. It explodes when mixed with oxygen and sparked. With cold water it forms malonic acid, and is thus to be regarded as the anhydride of this acid. With ammonia it forms malonamide, $CH_2(CONH_2)_2$.

Carbon selenide, Carbon diselenide, CSe_2. This is a golden-yellow liquid, m.p. −45·5°; b.p. 124°, obtained in 50% yield when a mixture of hydrogen selenide and carbon tetrachloride is passed through a glass tube heated to 500°. Better yields are obtained by the action of methylene chloride vapour on selenium at 550°-600°. It burns with difficulty in air or oxygen, and decomposes rapidly in daylight.

Carbon sulphoselenide, CSSe. A yellow oil, m.p. −85°, b.p. 83·9°/749 mm, obtained by the action of carbon disulphide vapour on ferrous selenide at 650°.

Carbon sulphotelluride, CSTe. A yellowish solid, m.p. −54°, prepared by passing an arc between electrodes made of a mixture of tellurium and graphite, the discharge occurring under carbon disulphide. The liquid is very photo-sensitive.

Carbon tetrabromide, CBr_4. A lustrous white crystalline solid (m.p. 93·7°, b.p. 189·5°, with slight decomposition) which is formed by the action of bromine on carbon disulphide in the presence of iodine. It is insoluble in water, but dissolves readily in alcohol, ether, or chloroform.

Carbon tetrachloride, Tetrachloromethane, CCl_4. A colourless liquid with a pleasant odour; d^{20} 1·594, m.p. −22·9°, b.p. 76·7°. Almost insoluble in water, miscible with most organic liquids. Manufactured by the action of chlorine on carbon disulphide or by the chlorination of methane and other aliphatic hydrocarbons. Although dry carbon tetrachloride is quite stable, it is partially decomposed into phosgene and hydrochloric acid when heated in presence of water. Moist carbon tetrachloride will attack metals for this reason. Fuming sulphuric acid acts on it to give phosgene and chlorosulphonic acid; with phenols and sodium hydroxide, the sodium salts of phenol carboxylic acids are formed. The most important commercial use of carbon tetrachloride is in the manufacture of chlorofluorohydrocarbons ('Arctons' and 'Freons'); it was formerly widely used as a solvent, but has tended to be replaced by perchloroethylene and trichloroethylene. It is also used as a fumigant and in fire extinguishers. It is relatively toxic. Although generally considered inert, carbon tetrachloride is, in fact, a very reactive substance.

Carbon tetrafluoride, CF_4. Prepared by the action of fluorine on Carborundum or most carbon-containing compounds. M.p. −183·5°, b.p. −128°. A very inert gas which can be decomposed only under the most drastic conditions.

Carbon tetraiodide, CI_4. Prepared as dark red crystals by interaction of carbon tetrachloride and methyl iodide in the presence of aluminium chloride. It decomposes on heating but sublimes *in vacuo* between 90° and 100°; d^{20} 4·32.

Carbon value. A measure of the tendency of an oil to form carbon when used as a lubricant. Usually determined by heating the oil sample strongly in the absence of air and determining the weight of the solid residue. Both the methods commonly used, the Conradson and Ramsbottom tests, depend upon this principle, but in neither case is the correlation with practical results satisfactory.

Carbonylate ions. Ions containing anionic or cationic metal carbonyl groupings. Metal carbonylate anions are generally prepared by the action of base or an alkali metal on the carbonyl, e.g.

$$Mn_2(CO)_{10} + pyridine + Na \rightarrow [Mn(CO)_5]^- \text{ ion}$$

Cations are prepared by the action of a Lewis acid and a co-ordinating group on the carbonyl halide, e.g.

$$Mn(CO)_5Cl + AlCl_3 + CO \rightarrow [Mn(CO)_6]^+$$

These groupings generally obey the effective atomic number rule (*q.v.*).

Carbonylation. The reaction of an organic or intermediate organometallic compound, with carbon monoxide gas. Acetylenes will react with carbon monoxide in the presence of a metal carbonyl (e.g. $Ni(CO)_4$) and water to give acrylic acids ($R \cdot CH{=}CH \cdot CO_2H$), with alcohols ($R'OH$) to give acrylic esters

$$R \cdot CH{=}CH \cdot CO_2R'$$

and with amines ($R'NH_2$) to give acrylic amides ($R \cdot CH{=}CH \cdot CO \cdot NHR'$). Using alternative catalysts, e.g. $Fe(CO)_5$, acetylenes and carbon monoxide will produce cyclopentadienones or hydroquinols. A variation of this reaction is hydroformylation (the Oxo reaction) (*q.v.*).

Carbonyl chloride (Phosgene), $COCl_2$. A colourless gas which is highly poisonous and has a smell resembling that of fresh hay. It forms a colourless mobile liquid, b.p. 8·2°, m.p. −118°, d 1·43. It is formed by exposing a mixture of carbon monoxide and chlorine to bright sunlight, or passing a mixture of the two gases over heated charcoal. It is manufactured by the latter method. Carbonyl chloride is readily soluble in acetic acid, benzene, or toluene, but is decomposed by water into hydrochloric acid and carbon dioxide. It reacts with ammonia to form a mixture of urea, $CO(NH_2)_2$, and ammonium chloride. This reaction may conveniently be carried out in toluene solution, the urea being separated from the ammonium chloride by dissolving it in warm alcohol. Carbonyl chloride is a chemical of great industrial importance. Most of it is utilized for the manufacture of toluene diisocyanate, used for polyurethane plastics, but it is also used for the insecticide 1-naphthyl-*N*-methylcarbamate and for polycarbonates.

Carbonyl halides of the other halogens as well as mixed carbonyl halides are known.

Carbonyl group. The name given to the $\diagdown C{=}O$ group in such compounds as aldehydes, ketones, metallic carbonyls, and phosgene. For the general reactions of this group see Aldehydes and Ketones.

Carbonyloxime. See Fulminic acid.

Carbonyls. These are co-ordination compounds

between carbon monoxide and a metal. Binary carbonyls have been found for the elements V, Cr, Mo, W, Mn, Tc, Re, Fe, Ru, Os, Co, Rh, Ir, Ni, and Pt. Compounds containing carbonyl groups are formed by these elements and Ti, Nb, Ta, Pd, Cu, Ag, and Au. The carbonyls form many derivatives, the carbonyl hydrides and carbonyl halides being the simplest. Other coordinating groups such as cyclopentadiene, tertiary phosphines, dipyridyl, and nitric oxide can replace the carbon monoxide in carbonyls. The carbonyls contain carbon-metal bonds, although carbonyl groups can act as bridges between metal atoms.

Organic molecules containing C=O groups, e.g. ketones, are also called carbonyl compounds.

Carbonyl selenide, COSe. A colourless gas, with an abominable odour, prepared by passing a rapid stream of carbon monoxide over selenium heated to dull redness; m.p. $-122\cdot2°$, b.p. $-20°$.

Carbonyl sulphide, carbon oxysulphide, COS. A colourless odourless gas (b.p. $-50\cdot2°$, m.p. $-138\cdot2°$), which is formed when carbon monoxide and sulphur vapour are passed through a hot tube, or, alternatively, by the action of dilute sulphuric acid (H_2SO_4, 5 vols.; H_2O, 4 vols.) on ammonium thiocyanate at $20°$. The gas is moderately soluble in water ($0\cdot8$ ml in 1 ml of H_2O at $13\cdot5°/1$ atm.), and readily soluble in toluene. The aqueous solution is slowly decomposed, the products of hydrolysis being carbon dioxide and hydrogen sulphide. Carbonyl sulphide is an inflammable gas and forms an explosive mixture with oxygen. The products of its oxidation are carbon dioxide and sulphur dioxide. Oxidation is also readily effected by bromine water or acidified potassium permanganate, when the products are carbon dioxide and sulphuric acid. The gas is absorbed by dilute aqueous or alcoholic potash, and a mixture of potassium sulphide and carbonate is formed.

Carboranes. Derivatives of the boron hydrides in which a C atom replaces a B—H group. Generally prepared by the action of acetylene on a boron hydride.

Carborundum. The trade name for silicon carbide (*q.v.*), produced by The Carborundum Co. Ltd., but the term is widely used for silicon carbide from other sources.

Carbowaxes. Trade name for a wide range of waxy polyethylene glycols of the general formula $HOCH_2(CH_2OCH_2)_xCH_2OH$, soluble in water and in polar organic solvents. Carbowax 1000 has average molecular weight 950-

1050; Carbowax 6000 has average molecular weight 6000-7500, but the numerical correspondence does not always hold.

Carboxy-. A prefix denoting that the substance in question contains a carboxyl group.

Carboxyhaemoglobin. The compound of haemoglobin with carbon monoxide, the carbon monoxide being combined by co-ordination, as is the oxygen in oxyhaemoglobin. The avidity of haemoglobin for carbon monoxide is much greater than for oxygen; human haemoglobin has 500 times as great an affinity for carbon monoxide as for oxygen. This is the reason for the toxicity of carbon monoxide, which prevents haemoglobin from carrying oxygen to the tissues.

Carboxylase. An enzyme present in yeasts, bacteria, and plants, but not found in animal tissues. In the presence of its coenzyme, co-carboxylase, which is the diphosphate of thiamine, it catalyses the decarboxylation of α-keto acids, in particular pyruvic acid, which is converted to acetaldehyde. The enzyme β-carboxylase catalyses the reversible breakdown of oxalacetic acid to pyruvic acid and carbon dioxide. Other carboxylases are also known, e.g. isocitrate decarboxylase.

Decarboxylases, which are highly specific for individual amino acids, decarboxylate these to amines. They are found chiefly in bacteria, but also in animal tissues. Pyridoxal phosphate acts as their coenzyme.

Carboxyl group. The group in organic compounds.

$$-C\diagup_{\diagdown OH}^{O}$$

Carboxylic acids. Organic compounds containing one or more carboxyl (—COOH) groups; the number of these groups is indicated by the prefixes mono-, di-, tri- etc. These acids are much weaker than the mineral acids such as hydrochloric, but they are partially ionized in aqueous solution and will liberate carbon dioxide from metallic carbonates and bicarbonates. The strength of the acid is markedly affected by the nature of the remainder of the molecule. They form salts with metals and with organic bases, and form esters with alcohols. Anhydrides of the type

$$\begin{array}{c}-C{=}O\\ \diagdown O\\ -C{=}O\end{array}$$

are formed from most acids by elimination of a molecule of water between two carboxyl groups. This elimination may be either inter- or intra-molecular. The hydroxyl (—OH) group is replaceable by halogens to give acyl halides.

The acids are formed by oxidation of the corresponding alcohol or aldehyde; by heating nitriles with alkalis; or by treating Grignard reagents with carbon dioxide and decomposing the product with sulphuric acid. Many of these acids occur naturally in the plant and animal kingdoms either free, or as salts or esters.

Carbromal, Uradal, α-bromo-α-ethylbutyryl-carbamide, $C_7H_{13}BrN_2O_2$. White crystals,

$$(C_2H_5)_2 \cdot CBr \cdot CONHCONH_2$$

m.p. 116°-118°, very slightly soluble in water, soluble in 18 parts of alcohol. Prepared by the action of α-bromo-α-ethylbutyryl bromide on urea. It is a sedative and hypnotic and is useful in insomnia.

Carburetted water gas, C.W.G. During peak periods of gas consumption blue water gas is enriched by the addition of oil gas. The oil is sprayed on to the top of red-hot chequered brickwork in the carburettor. The gas formed by the cracking of the hydrocarbon is 'fixed' by passing with the blue water gas through another chamber called the superheater. The oil gas has a calorific value of 1600-1800 Btu/ft.[3] and 1 gallon of oil yields 70-80 ft.[3] of gas and about 15% of C.W.G. tar. The process is very flexible compared with coal gas manufacture.

A typical C.W.G. has the composition:

Carbon monoxide	30·5%
Hydrogen	38·0%
Carbon dioxide	5·5%
Nitrogen	7·0%
Methane	14·0%
Unsaturated hydrocarbons	5·0%

Carbylamine reaction. A qualitative test for primary amines carried out by warming the suspected amine with chloroform and an alcoholic solution of potassium hydroxide. Under these conditions primary amines produce the intensely nauseating odour characteristic of the carbylamines. Sometimes used as a test for chloroform, but it is not specific, as bromoform, iodoform, and chloral also react in the same manner.

Carbylamines, Isocyanides, Isonitriles. Organic compounds, R—NC, analogous to carbon monoxide in bonding but having an R—N in place of oxygen. They are colourless liquids, having a toxic and highly disagreeable odour. Sparingly soluble in water, but miscible with most organic solvents. They may be prepared by treating alkyl halides with silver cyanide, but more conveniently by dehydration of formamides (RNH·CHO) with phosphorus oxychloride in the presence of base; the reaction between a primary amine, chloroform, and alcoholic potash generates a carbylamine which is a useful test, but of limited preparative value. They are reactive substances; acids cause decomposition to a primary amine and formic acid. Heating at 100°-200° causes isomerization to cyanides. They are oxidized by sulphur to *iso*thiocyanates and by mercuric oxide to *iso*cyanates. Reaction with carbonyl compounds and amines gives derivatives of α-amino acids. They form compounds with hydrochloric acid and chlorine; their stable complexes with transition metals are analogous to the metal carbonyls.

Carbyloxime. See Fulminic acid.

Carcinogens. Substances capable of causing the

I

II

III

Its calorific value is approximately 500 Rtu/ft.[3] (gross).

development of malignant cells in animals. Carcinogenic hydrocarbons include 1,2,5,6-

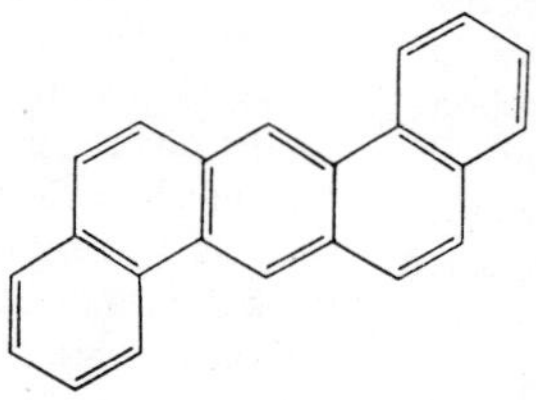

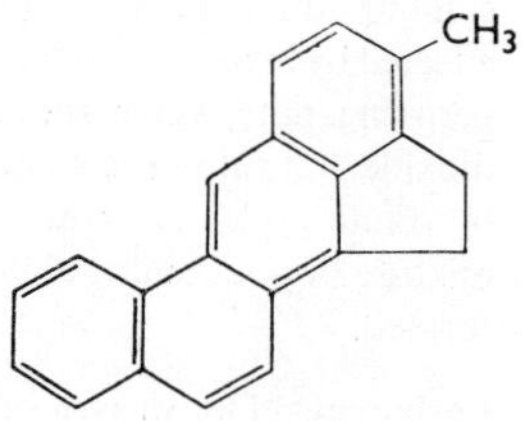

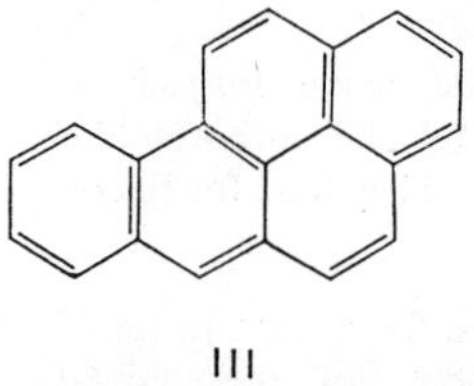

dibenzanthracene (I), methylcholanthrene (II) and benzo(a)pyrene (III): the last occurs in tar and soot and is largely responsible for the occupational skin cancer associated with long exposure to these materials. Many other compounds have been shown to produce tumours in test animals, e.g. 2-naphthylamine, 2-nitrofluorene, N-nitroso-N-methylurethane and β-propiolactone.

Cardamon. The dried seeds of *Elettaria cardamomum* kept in the capsular fruit until required for use. Cardamom possesses aromatic and carminative properties and is administered with purgatives and other aromatic substances.

Cardiac aglucones. Digitalis and related heart poisons found in plants are glycosides which on hydrolysis break down to a carbohydrate and a genin or cardiac aglucone. The cardiac aglucones are chemically related to the sterols and include strophanthidin and digitoxigenin.

Δ^3-Carene, $C_{10}H_{16}$. A dicyclic terpene, the (+)-form of which occurs in Swedish and Finnish oils of turpentine, in various pine-needle oils, and many other essential oils, whilst the (−)-form has been found in oil from the rhizomes of *Kaempferia galanga* and in an oil from *Pinus sylvestris*. It is a colourless oil with a sweet and penetrating smell. The (+)-form has b.p. 168°-169°/705 mm, d_{30}^{30} 0·8586, n_D^{30} 1·469, $[\alpha]_D$ +7·69°. It forms a slightly soluble nitrosate melting with decomposition at 147·5°. It oxidizes and resinifies rapidly in the air. It gives a fugitive purple-green coloration with sulphuric acid in acetic anhydride solution. When treated with hydrochloric acid, it forms sylvestrene dihydrochloride.

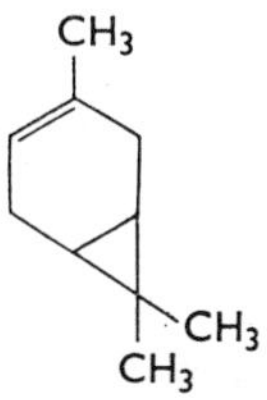

Δ^4-Carene, $C_{10}H_{16}$. A dicyclic terpene, the (+)-form of which is found in the oils from various Andropogon grasses, in German pine-needle oil, in Finnish and Swedish turpentine oils, and various other products. It is a colourless oil of pleasant smell with the following constants: b.p. 165·5°-167°/707 mm, d_{30}^{30} 0·8552, n_D^{30} 1·474, $[\alpha]_D^{20}$ +62·2°. It yields no crystalline derivatives. When heated to 280° under pressure it forms sylvestrene and α-terpinene.

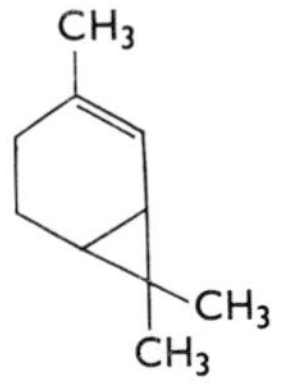

Carius method. The quantitative determination of sulphur and halogens in covalent compounds may be accomplished by complete destruction of the compound by conc. nitric acid to halide and sulphate ions. Estimation of

precipitated silver halide or barium sulphate is then possible.

Carmine. A red lake pigment obtained by extracting cochineal with boiling water and precipitating the extract with alumina. It is insoluble in water, oils, and ordinary organic solvents, but gives a deep crimson solution with caustic alkalis and ammonia. It fades on exposure to sun and air. The modern equivalent is known as alizarin carmine, a lake prepared from 1,2-dihydroxyanthraquinone.

Carminic acid, $C_{22}H_{20}O_{13}$. The colouring matter

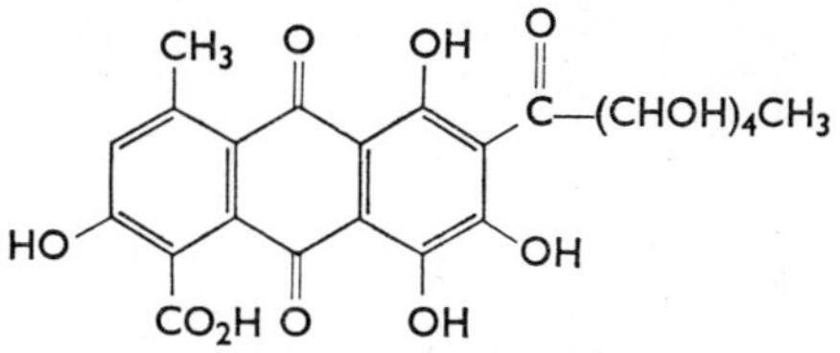

of cochineal. It crystallizes in red prisms, soluble in hot water, moderately soluble in alcohol. Decomposes at 135°; pH indicator: 4·8 yellow; 6·2 violet. Used as a stain.

Carnallite, KCl, $MgCl_2$, $6H_2O$. One of the principal components of the extensive evaporite deposits at Stassfurt and in Alsace, New Mexico, and Texas. When pure it is white and translucent, but is usually pink or red owing to the presence of iron. It is an important source of potassium salts.

Carnauba wax is the dried exudation from the leaves of the South American copaiba palm. These are dried in the sun, cut, and treated with boiling water, the wax collecting on the surface. The crude wax is yellow or dirty green, brittle, and very hard. Pure carnauba wax has d^{15} 0·99, m.p. 84°-91°. The principal constituent is melissyl cerotate. It is used in many polishes and varnishes, as when mixed with other waxes it makes them harder and gives more lustre.

Carnitine, α-Hydroxy-γ-butyro-betaine, $C_7H_{15}NO_3$. A laevorotatory, water-soluble

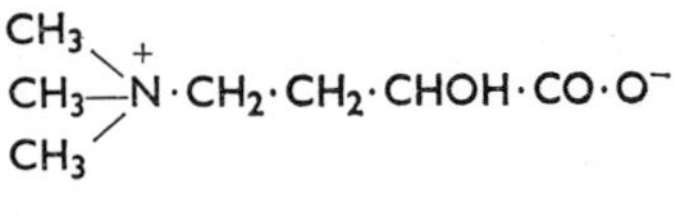

base, present in muscle.

Carnosine, β-Alanylhistidine, $C_9H_{14}N_4O_3$.

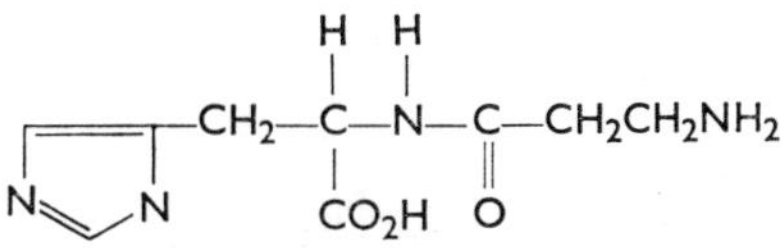

A dipeptide crystallizing in colourless needles, m.p. 246°-250°, with decomposition. Soluble in water. $[\alpha]_D$ +21°. A strong base. It is present in mammalian muscle, and the fact that it contains an amino-acid, β-alanine, not found in proteins, indicates that it has probably some specific action, but which is not known.

Carnot, Nicolas Léonhard Sadi (1796-1832). Born at Paris, Carnot was educated at the École Polytechnique, and served before and after the battle of Waterloo in the Engineers. Lord Kelvin, in 1848-1849, was instrumental in proving how Carnot, ahead of his period, realized the true nature of heat, and had noted down many of the best modern methods for determining its mechanical equivalent. 'Carnot's principle' is one of the fundamentals in thermodynamics.

Carnotite. A naturally occurring hydrated vanadate of uranium and potassium of variable composition. An important ore of uranium, especially in the carnotite-bearing sandstones of Colorado and Utah.

Carnot's cycle. A hypothetical scheme for an ideal heat engine. With its aid Carnot proved that the maximum efficiency for the conversion of heat into work depends only on the two temperatures between which the heat engine works, and not at all on the nature of the substance employed.

Caro's acid. See Permonosulphuric acid.

Carone, $C_{10}H_{16}O$. A saturated dicyclic ketone obtained by treating dihydrocarvone hydrobromide with alcoholic potash at 0°. Both (+)- and (−)-forms have been prepared from the corresponding dihydrocarvone hydrobromides. When distilled at normal pressures it boils at about 210° with partial decomposition and conversion to carvenone. Its constants are: b.p. 99°-100°/15 mm, d_4^{20} 0·9567, $n_D^{18·8}$ 1·4787, $[\alpha]_D$ +173·8°, −169·5°; (+)- and (−)-carone form semicarbazones of m.p. 167°-169° and the racemic form yields a semicarbazone of m.p. 178°.

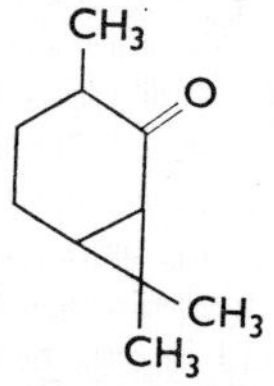

Carotene, $C_{40}H_{56}$. Carotene is one of the most important of the colouring matters of green leaves. It is found in all plants and in many animal tissues. It is the chief yellow colouring matter of carrots, of butter, and of yolk of egg. It exists in several forms, the most common being β-carotene, with the formula

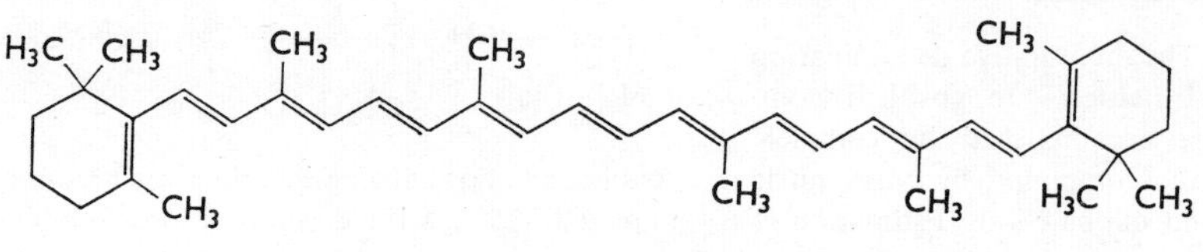

It forms reddish-brown crystals, m.p. 181°-182°, insoluble in water, sparingly soluble in alcohol and ether, soluble in benzene and petroleum ether. It is optically inactive.

α-Carotene has an unsymmetrical structure with the ring shown herewith replacing one of the rings in the β-carotene formula. It is dextrorotatory.

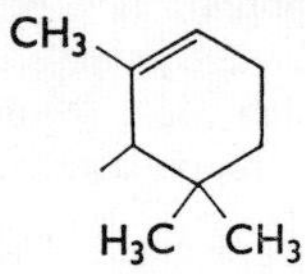

Carotene is important physiologically in that it is the precursor of vitamin A. Carotene present in the food is transformed into vitamin A in the liver, and hence carotene can replace the vitamin, although most rich sources of carotene also contain vitamin A in the free state.

Carotenoids. These are pigments related to carotene which occur in plants, particularly in the leaves, and in certain animal tissues. They include the hydrocarbons carotene and lycopene and their related hydroxyl compounds, the xanthophylls, as well as other less important pigments. They are soluble in fats and fat solvents, and give characteristic blue colours with sulphuric acid and with antimony trichloride. See 'Carotenoids' by Karrer and Jucker.

Carothers, Wallace Hume (1896-1937). Born in Iowa and educated at Tarkio College, Missouri, and the University of Illinois, Carothers held various academic posts before joining the Du Pont Company in 1928 in charge of fundamental research in organic chemistry. An expert in polymerization reactions, Carothers was responsible for the preliminary work that lead to the development both of chloroprene and of nylon.

Carragheenin is the dried extract from the edible

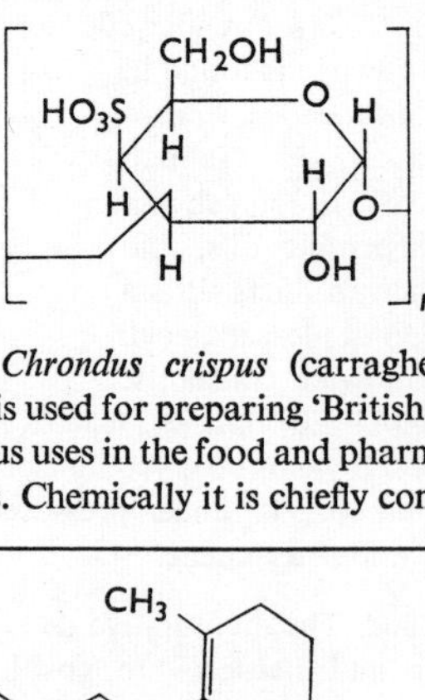

seaweed *Chrondus crispus* (carragheen, Irish moss). It is used for preparing 'British agar' and has various uses in the food and pharmaceutical industries. Chemically it is chiefly composed of

120

polymerized sulphated D-galactopyranose units, but other residues are also present.

Carron oil. An emulsion prepared from equal volumes of linseed oil and lime water, used as a first-aid treatment for burns.

Carvacrol, 2-Hydroxycymene, $C_{10}H_{14}O$. A colourless liquid, m.p. 0.5°, b.p. 237°-238°.

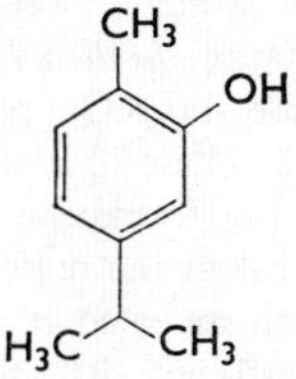

Sparingly soluble in water, soluble in alcohol, ether, and alkalis. It is a constituent of many essential oils.

Carvenone, $C_{10}H_{16}O$. An unsaturated cyclic ketone isomeric with carone (q.v.) from which it may be prepared. Reduction gives carvomenthol (q.v.). A liquid, b.p. 232°-234°, n_D 1.4805, $[\alpha]_D$ −2.1°; it gives a semicarbazone, m.p. 200°-201°.

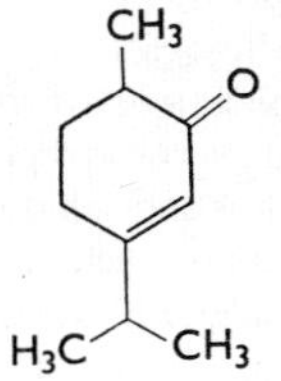

Carveol, $C_{10}H_{16}O$. A monocyclic terpene alcohol, obtained by the autoxidation of limonene in moist air and found in small quantity in caraway oil. It forms carvone on oxidation with chromic acid. Its constants are: b.p. 226°-227°/757 mm, d^{15} 0.9578, n_D^{15} 1.4961. Its crystalline phenylurethane has m.p. 94°-95°.

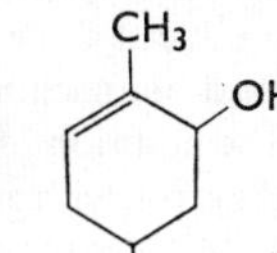

Carvestrene. The racemic form of sylvestrene.

Carvomenthol, $C_{10}H_{20}O$. A monocyclic terpene alcohol, which does not occur in nature. It contains 3 asymmetric carbon atoms and can therefore exist in 8 optically active and 4 racemic forms. It can be obtained by the reduction of carvone, carvenone, carvotanacetone, and carvomenthone. It has the following constants: b.p. 220°, d^{22} 0.904, n_D^{22} 1.4636. It forms a phenylurethane of m.p. 74°-75°.

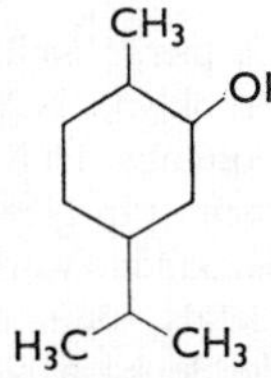

Carvone, $C_{10}H_{14}O$. This compound is a ketone derived from the terpene, dipentene. It occurs in both (+)- and (−)-forms; (+)-carvone is the main constituent of caraway and dill oils, whilst (−)-carvone is the chief constituent of spearmint and kuromoji oils. Carvone is a colourless oil with a very characteristic smell, b.p. 230°, $d_4^{18.7}$ 0.961, $[\alpha]_D^{20}$ ±62.3°. It forms a crystalline compound with H_2S which may be used for its separation.

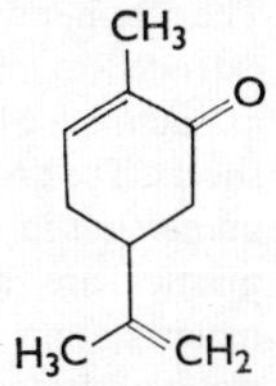

Caryophyllene, $C_{15}H_{24}$, the sesquiterpene hydrocarbon which is the main hydrocarbon constituent of oil of cloves. It is a colourless oil, b.p. 123°-125°/10 mm, and forms a nitroso chloride of m.p. 177°. It is readily converted into isocaryophyllene which has a cis configuration for the endocyclic double bond.

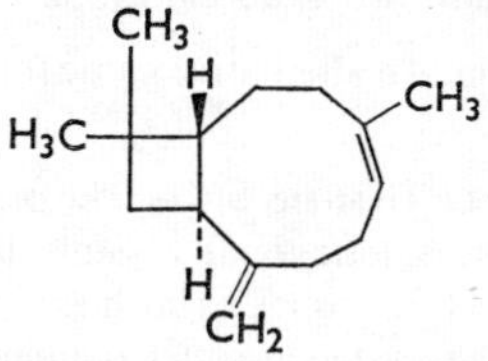

Cascara sagrada. The dried bark of Rhamnus purshiana, an American shrub. The freshly dried bark has emetic properties, and it is necessary to keep it for at least a year before use, during which time these properties disappear. Cascara sagrada has a very unpleasant bitter taste; it contains the free anthroquinone emodin, and iso-emodin, aloe-emodin, and chrysophanol, besides glycosides. It is a mild purgative which acts by irritating the mucosa of the large intestine.

Case hardening. A process for producing a hard, resistant surface on a tough core for steel components such as gear wheels, splines, etc. The component is manufactured from a low carbon (tough) steel. It is then heated to about 910° in an atmosphere rich in carbon; i.e. in a hydrocarbon gas or packed in charcoal. The carbon diffuses into the surface of the steel to a depth of about 0.05 in., forming a high carbon surface which is subsequently quenched to martensite for maximum hardness and wear resistance.

Casein. A phosphoprotein, occurring as a suspension of calcium caseinate in mammalian milk. It can be isolated as an alkali-soluble white powder by treatment of cows' milk with either mineral acid or with rennet. The former gives 'acid casein' which is used medicinally, in food preparations, in adhesives and distempers, and for paper treating. 'Rennet casein' is the form used for the production of casein plastics. The casein, mixed with water and colour, is hot-extruded to give rods which can either be used as such, sliced, or further hot-pressed to give sheets. The processed casein is then hardened by immersion in dilute formalin solution. Casein plastics are available in light colours; the materials machine well, but have very poor water resistance. For many years, this type of cheap plastics material has been used for the manufacture of buttons, buckles, handles, pen and pencil sets, etc.

Casing head gas. Natural gas evolved from crude petroleum at the well head.

Cassel brown. See Vandyke brown.

Cassel yellow. See Lead chlorides.

Cassiopëium. An alternative name for Lutetium (*q.v.*).

Cassiterite or **Tinstone**, SnO_2. The principal ore of tin. Forms tetragonal crystals having the rutile structure (*q.v.*). Hardness $6\frac{1}{2}$, sp.gr. $6\cdot4$-$7\cdot1$. The crystals are often twinned, possessing a strong refraction and adamantine lustre. Colourless when very pure but usually brown or black owing to the presence of impurities, especially iron. It occurs as vein tin usually at the junction of granitic masses and slates, and in alluvial deposits as stream tin.

Casting. The process of producing metal shapes by pouring the liquid metal or alloy into a prepared mould. Such moulds are normally of bonded sand. In *diecasting* an alloy steel mould is used. This gives a more accurate casting with better surface finish. In *pressure diecasting* the liquid alloy is forced into the metal mould under high pressure, thus ensuring good filling of the mould. Zinc and aluminium alloys are ideal for such a process in the mass production of small fittings or toys.

Cast Irons. Cast irons are widely used because of their cheapness, ease of casting, and machinability. They consist basically of iron with 2·5-4% carbon. In this form all the carbon is present as Fe_3C, making the material brittle and only of use for wear resistance. The fracture is whitish, giving it the name *white iron*. The addition of about 1·5% silicon causes most of the carbon to separate as graphite flakes in a matrix of pearlite. This is known as *grey iron* because of the appearance of the fracture. This iron is not so brittle as the white form but has poor strength due to the large flakes of graphite. Innoculating additions are generally made to refine these flakes and so improve the properties. The most recent development has been the addition of magnesium to cause the formation of graphite spheroids in place of flakes. Since spheroids do not constitute planes of weakness, these *Spheroidal graphite* (*S.G.*) cast irons have properties almost as good as steel with the good casting properties of cast iron. They may be heat treated to give a matrix of pearlite for strength or ferrite for toughness and ductility. Other alloy additions include phosphorus for ease of casting for decorative work, and nickel, copper, chromium and molybdenum in various proportions for strength, wear resistance and corrosion resistance. *Malleable cast irons* were developed before the S.G. irons and are still very much used. These irons are cast as white iron to avoid the formation of the graphite flakes which weaken the material. This brittle white iron is then annealed at about 1000° C for many hours, until the brittle Fe_3C decomposes to form iron and graphite. Since the graphite is forming in the solid state it forms spheroids or rosettes which do not have the same weakening and embrittling effect as flakes. In *Blackheart malleable* the graphite is present as rosettes. In the *Whiteheart* process the annealing is carried out under strongly oxidizing conditions so that most of the carbon is oxidized out, leaving a material similar to 0·6% carbon steel.

Alloy cast irons. Alloy additions are made to cast irons to improve the properties for particular purposes. Alloy cast irons can be used in engineering applications where plain cast iron is unsuitable and may even replace steel for some components such as crankshafts. The proportion of carbide formers, such as chromium and molybdenum, to graphitizers, such as copper nickel and silicon, must be carefully considered. With graphitizers in effective excess, the normal machinable grey cast iron containing graphite is produced while with carbide formers in excess a hard unmachinable white iron is produced. The addition of 1·5% Ni and 0·4% Mo gives a grey iron with a tensile strength of about 25 t.s.i. 1·5% Cr gives a white martensitic iron unless nickel is high. This iron is very hard and wear resistant; it is unmachinable and must be cast to shape. High nickel, 15-20%, with up to 6% Cu and 2% Cr, gives a non-magnetic austenitic grey iron with good corrosion resistance. Up to 5% silicon may be added to these austenitic irons for resistance to corrosion and chemicals.

Castner, Hamilton Young (1859-1899). Born in Brooklyn, N.Y., Castner was educated at Columbia University. He became an analytical chemist in New York, but in 1886 he came to England to work a cheap process for making the metals sodium and potassium. In 1891 he developed a new process for the isolation of sodium by the electrolysis of brine and established the Castner-Kellner Company to work the process. Kellner was an Austrian who had also been interested in the same problem. See *J.S.C.I.*, 1899, pp. 901, 986.

Castor oil. The fixed oil expressed from the seeds of *Ricinus communis*. It consists almost entirely of the glyceryl esters of ricinoleic acid. It is miscible with alcohol, has d 0·958 to 0·969, n_D^{20} 1·477-1·481, $[\alpha]_D^{20}$ not less than 3·5°. It is a mild purgative and is used in ophthalmic practice to allay pain and as a solvent for alkaloids which are to be applied to the eye.

Cast phenol-formaldehyde resins. The resins are produced by an initial alkaline condensation of phenol with high molecular proportions of formaldehyde. The resins are cast into lead or glass moulds and hardened by heat treatment for some days. The hardened material can be sliced, machined, and polished. It is used for the production of buttons, brush handles, and desk sets. A special type of cast resin has been developed for templates and metal pressing jigs and dies.

Catalase. Enzymes which destroy hydrogen peroxide are collectively termed catalase. They are found in almost all living tissues, and have been obtained as red-brown crystals. They are conjugated proteins, with haematin or related substances as the prosthetic group, and their activity is related to the oxidation and reduction of the iron in the molecule.

Catalysis. The term catalysis was introduced by Berzelius to describe processes in which the rate of reaction is influenced by a substance that remains chemically unaffected; the substance is known as a catalyst. If the reaction is hindered the added substance is called a negative catalyst; the word catalyst implies acceleration of the process. Catalytic changes may be homogenous or heterogenous, but all comply with two main criteria:

(1) Although it affects the rate at which equilibrium is obtained in a reversible reaction, the catalyst does not affect the position of the equilibrium as this would go against the laws of thermodynamics.

(2) The catalyst can, theoretically, be recovered unchanged chemically at the end of the reaction; it may be changed physically.

The action of catalysts is often ascribed to the formation of intermediate compounds by the catalyst, which under the conditions of the experiment are only of transient existence. For example, the action of manganese dioxide in facilitating the decomposition of potassium chlorate may be considered to undergo the following changes:

$$2MnO_2 + 2KClO_3 = 2KMnO_4 + Cl_2 + O_2$$
$$2KMnO_4 = K_2MnO_4 + MnO_2 + O_2$$
$$K_2MnO_4 + Cl_2 = 2KCl + MnO_2 + O_2.$$

In other cases, when the intermediate compound theory cannot be simply applied, the action of a catalyst may be explained by adsorption theory, as, for example, in the union of hydrogen and oxygen on the surface of platinum. It is assumed that combination is preceded by the adsorption of one or both the reactants on the surface of the catalyst, where they are brought into closer contact, and their effective concentration is thereby increased, so that the reaction is facilitated. Moreover, the actual process of adsorption may yield a certain amount of energy which may be available for promoting the reaction and the substances adsorbed may be bound atomically to the surface. The adsorption theory finds a wide application to those catalytic reactions involving the use of catalysts which are in a different phase from the reactants, e.g. reactions between gases or liquids on solid catalysts.

Catechol, $C_6H_6O_2$. Colourless crystals, m.p. 105°, b.p. 240°. Soluble in water, alcohol, ether, benzene, and alkalis. An alkaline solution gives a green coloration with ferric chloride, which turns brown on standing in air. Strong reducing agent.

It can be obtained from catechu, a natural dye, or prepared by fusing *o*-benzenedisulphonic acid with caustic soda. It is used as a photographic developer.

Catechu. A dried aqueous extract prepared from the leaves and shoots of *Uncaria gambier*, a plant growing in the Malay Archipelago. It occurs in small pale brown cubes and contains catechin and catechutannic acid. Catechin, white needles, m.p. 93°-95°, sparingly soluble in water and in alcohol, has the formula

Catechu is a powerful astringent and is used chiefly for diarrhoea.

Catenation. The tendency of an element to form ring or chain compounds by forming bonds with other atoms of the same element. Carbon has the greatest tendency to catenation.

Cathepsin. A generic name originally applied to intracellular enzymes of animal metabolism, e.g. the proteases of lysosome (*q.v.*). The term is now used for proteolytic enzymes which are active at pH 5-7: they are mostly intracellular.

Cathode. The electrode in electrolysis which carries the negative charge is termed the cathode, and it is on this electrode that the positive ions, such as copper, are liberated.

Cathode glow. See Glow discharge.

Cathode rays. The electrons of varying velocities which travel towards the cathode in a low pressure gas discharge (less than 0·01 mm).

Cathodic protection. A method used to prevent the corrosion of submerged or underground metal work in situations such as ships, piers, boiler installations, water cooling or supply systems and underground pipe-lines. It is based on the fact that there is no solution of metal ions from the cathode of a cell, since the cathode is more negative than the electrode potential for the particular metal. For example a moored ship may be made the cathode of a cell by suspending magnesium anodes some 15 ft. below the ship and short circuiting them to the hull. This is not effective in fresh water due to its poor conductivity. A direct current supply may be used in place of galvanic anodes. Thus for an underground pipeline, a negative lead may be connected to the pipeline while the positive lead is connected to a graphite or scrap iron anode some little distance away. The moist soil acts as the electrolyte.

Cation. The positively charged ion which moves towards the cathode during electrolysis.

Caustic potash. The common name for potassium hydroxide.

Cavendish, Henry. The son of Lord Charles Cavendish and grandson of the Duke of Devonshire; born at Nice in 1731, and educated at Cambridge. In 1764 he determined the specific heat of various metals and other solids, but this information was not published until later. He investigated carbon dioxide and the nature of the hardness of water. He determined with great care the composition of air, and showed that in addition to oxygen and nitrogen it contained about 1% of another gas, now known to be argon. He discovered the composition of water, and determined the weight of the earth; died in 1810. See Thorpe's 'Essays.'

Cavitation. This is a phenomenon sometimes encountered in centrifugal pumps. When a liquid enters such a pump it undergoes a reduction in pressure which may, in certain cases, be sufficient for vaporization to occur or for dissolved gases to come out of solution. The collapse of the bubbles so formed can cause mechanical damage to the pump, and apart from

this there is a loss of performance. It may be avoided by maintaining an adequate pressure at the pump suction.

Cedrene, $C_{15}H_{24}$. Found in cedar-wood oil

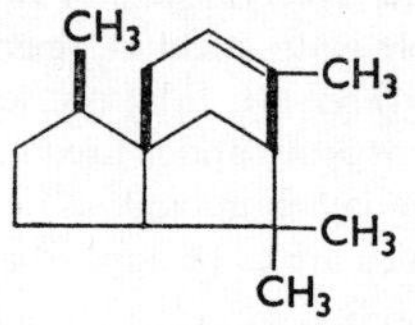

and can be prepared by the reduction of the alcohol, cedrol (cedar-wood camphor). Cedrene is a viscous oil of b.p. 121°/12 mm, d_4^{17} 0·9367, n^{17} 1·5030, $[\alpha]_D$ −52·8°. A specimen prepared from cedrol had $[\alpha]_D$ −85·57°. On oxidation with chromic acid it forms a ketone, cedrone, $C_{15}H_{22}O$, which yields a semicarbazone of m.p. 242°-243°.

Cedrol, cedrenol, $C_{15}H_{26}O$. A constituent of the

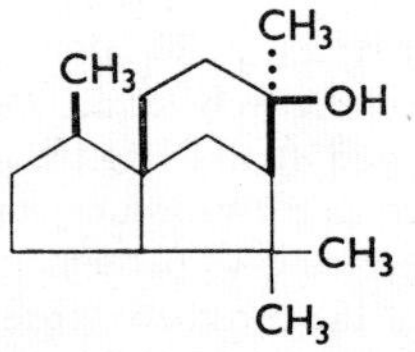

oleoresin of cypress and eastern red cedar. M.p. 103°-104°, $[\alpha]_D$ +10°, slightly soluble in water.

Celestine. Native strontium sulphate, $SrSO_4$. The mineral generally forms colourless or yellowish orthorhombic crystals, sp.gr. 3·9, hardness 3-3·5. Some specimens have a sky-blue colour, to which the name is due. Crystals of celestine are isomorphous with those of barytes. It is an important commercial source of strontium compounds.

Cell. In electrochemistry, cells are used as sources of electrical energy. They consist of two electrodes dipping into one or more electrolyte solutions. If the electrodes are in separate solutions electrical contact between solutions is achieved either by a salt bridge or by use of a porous disc. The electrodes may be of the same metal as the electrolyte solution or of another material, e.g. platinum. The e.m.f. of a cell is measured potentiometrically.

Cell dimensions. See Crystal structure.

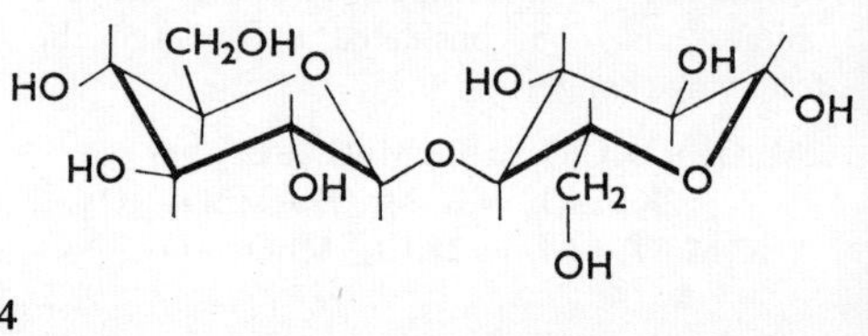

Cellobiose, $C_{12}H_{22}O_{11}$. 4-[β-D-Glucopyranosido]-D-glucopyranose. Its crystalline β form has m.p. 225° and $[\alpha]_D$ +14° (initial), +35° (final). It is the disaccharide that forms the repeating unit of cellulose, but it has never been found naturally *per se* or as a glycoside.

Cellophane. A transparent cellulose in the form of sheets, prepared by extruding cellulose xanthate solution through a long, narrow slit into a bath of acid. Cellophane swells and softens when immersed in water, but may be rendered waterproof by a varnishing process. It is widely used as a wrapping material for foodstuffs, cigarettes, etc. The name is a registered trade mark.

Cellosolve. A trade name for ethylene glycol monoethyl ether.

Cellosolve acetate. A trade name for ethylene glycol monoethyl ether acetate.

Cellular plastics. A generic term used to describe the various forms of foamed and expanded plastic materials. Cellular plastics may be subdivided into four groups: (i) open cell flexible, (ii) open cell rigid, (iii) closed cell flexible, and (iv) closed cell rigid. Such materials have received wide application as packaging materials, thermal insulators and for lightweight, foam-cored partitions and roofings. The more important cellular plastics are expanded polystyrene, rigid and flexible polyurethane foams, cellular polyvinyl chloride, expanded polyethylene, and foamed urea and phenolic resins.

Celluloid. A thermoplastic composition based on cellulose nitrate (11% nitrogen) plasticized with camphor. Celluloid is strong and may be obtained in transparent, translucent, opaque, coloured and variegated patterns; it is easily shaped and machined but it is very inflammable and tends to yellow on ageing. Celluloid film is produced by a special solvent-casting process.

Cellulose, $(C_6H_{10}O_5)_x$. The chief constituent

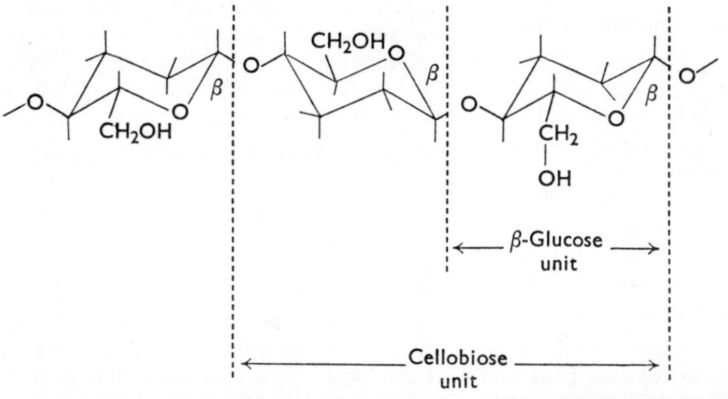

It is a polymer of glucose, with over 3500 repeat units in a chain. The glucoside linkage is β, whereas in starch it is α.

Strong acids completely hydrolyse cellulose to glucose; very mild hydrolysis gives hydrocelluloses with shorter chains and lower viscosity and tensile strength. Under special conditions a large yield of cellobiose is obtained.

Cellulose dissolves in strong mineral acids, in caustic soda, and in cuprammonium solution. It forms a triacetate, a trinitrate, and ethers with methyl, ethyl, and benzyl alcohol; all of these are of great industrial importance. Its largest use is in the rayon industry. Wood pulp and cotton linters are the most important sources from which it is prepared commercially.

Cellulose acetate plastics. Cellulose, in the form of cotton linters or purified wood pulp, is acetylated by, for example, treatment with acetic anhydride in the presence of acetic acid using sulphuric acid as catalyst. Complete acetylation gives substantially the chloroform-soluble cellulose triacetate which is normally ripened to obtain an acetone-soluble product (53·5% acetic acid) for use in plastics. Cellulose acetate with a plasticizer such as dimethyl phthalate is worked by the celluloid technique to give sheet material. Cellulose acetate moulding and extruding material is made by compounding cellulose acetate with placticizers, dyes, and lubricants, etc. Cellulose acetate plastics may be injection-moulded, extruded, sliced, and hot shaped, and are widely used in the production of combs, buckles, brush backs, spectacle frames, and toys. Continuous lengths of cellulose acetate film are made by a solvent-casting process and are used for home cinema film. Cellulose acetate is also widely used in rayon manufacture.

Cellulose ethers. Treatment of alkali-cellulose with aryl- and alkyl-halides gives cellulose

β-Glucose unit

Cellobiose unit

of the cell wall of all plants, and the most abundant organic substance found in nature.

ethers which may be used for plastics and surface coating materials. Ethyl cellulose is the chief ether used industrially: when compounded with suitable plasticizers it can be fabricated by the celluloid technique, by injection moulding, and by casting. Ethyl cellulose plastics have better resistance to chemical attack and better low temperature flexibility than cellulose ester materials. Methyl cellulose is water-soluble and is used as an emulsifying, sizing, and priming material.

Cellulose nitrate. See Nitrocellulose.

Cement. A substance used to make other substances cohere. There are many kinds of cement, but they may be divided into two main groups: (1) cements used to bind together numerous particles so as to form a coherent mass of considerable strength, and (2) those used to unite two or more separate masses (e.g. portions of a broken article); this second class includes glues and various organic cements. Cements in the first group include Portland cement, *ciment fondu*, Keene's cement, and many others. Cements which form a plastic paste with water and set hard on standing are known as hydraulic cements. Cements are also known by their chief constituent, as calcareous cements, aluminous cements, siliceous cements; also by their characteristic property as acid-resisting cements, quick-setting cements, rapid-hardening cements; by their reputed origin, as Roman cement, and by their fancied resemblance to some other material, as Portland cement which was, at one time, supposed to resemble Portland stone. Cements which can be used at high temperatures, e.g. for repairing furnaces, are known as refractory cements. The term 'cement' is also used for any argillaceous limestone capable of producing cement when sintered.

Cements are made by heating a mixture of limestone and clay to about 1400°. The product is ground with gypsum. Chemically cements consist of a mixture of calcium silicates and aluminates.

Cement, aluminous. See Aluminous cement and Ciment fondu.

Cement gun. A device for spraying a semi-fluid mixture of Portland or other cement with sand or grog and water on to a surface which it is desired to cover or into cracks or fissures which it is wished to fill. It consists essentially of a cylindrical container, a flexible hose with nozzle, and a supply of compressed air. The material used in this device is sometimes known as gunite; it is really a fine concrete.

Cement, quick-setting. A variety of Portland cement which, when made into a soft paste with water, rapidly sets and forms a hard mass. In this respect it is distinguished from similar cements which require a longer time before

setting. The difference depends on a slight difference in composition and in the heat-treatment in the kiln. The setting time can also be reduced by the addition of very small proportions of calcium chloride to the water used. Quick-setting cements are often troublesome to use and most slow-setting cements are safer in unskilled hands. Care must be taken not to confuse 'quick-setting' with 'rapid-hardening.'

Cement, rapid-hardening. A term applied to Portland and other cements which (after setting) attain so large a proportion of their maximum hardness that the product (concrete) may be used in three or four days instead of a month, as was the case before rapid-hardening cements were made. The rapidity or slowness of hardening depends partly on the composition and heat-treatment of the cement clinker, but also, to a large extent, on the fineness of the grinding. There is no necessary relation between the rate of setting and the rate of hardening so that a slow-setting cement may harden rapidly.

Cement, Scott's. See Cement, selenitic.

Cement, selenitic. A product obtained by calcining an argillaceous limestone, so as to form a hydraulic lime, and adding to this about 5% of finely ground plaster of Paris. It is also known as Scott's cement.

Cementation process of steel manufacture. This is the oldest commercial method of manufacture. Bars of refined wrought iron are embedded in charcoal and kept in an air-free furnace at a yellow heat for about ten days, the appearance of the fracture of trial bars withdrawn from time to time deciding the actual time. After firing, the bars are then allowed to cool slowly, taking about a week. The bars are now known as 'blister steel.' They are broken into short lengths and sorted according to fracture. These are then welded together and drawn under the hammer to obtain homogeneity. The result is called 'single shear steel,' and if once again cut up and rewelded 'double shear steel.' The final treatment consists in melting down in crucibles and casting into ingots giving 'crucible cast steel.' The process is now obsolete.

Cementite. A carbide of iron having the chemical formula Fe_3C. It is a hard, brittle substance, and crystallizes in thin plates. It is practically insoluble in α-iron, but relatively very soluble in γ-iron. In alloy steels cementite refers to the solid solution formed by the carbides of metals, other than iron, in Fe_3C. Microscopically cementite is white, like ferrite, and a suitable etching agent, such as alkaline sodium picrate, is required to show up the cementite from the ferrite. The eutectoid pearlite is ferrite and cementite.

Centre of symmetry. See Symmetry elements.

Centrifugal attrition mills. See Ring-roller mills.

Centrifugal grinders. See Ring-roller mills.

Centrifugal pump. This is the most widely used pump in the chemical and process industries. It consists of a rotor having a number of curved vanes which rotates at high speed inside a flat cylindrical casing. Round the edge of this casing is a ring-shaped chamber of circular cross-section called a *volute*. Liquid enters the centre of the casing along the rotor axis and is swept along the vanes of the rotor into the volute, where it is decelerated and the kinetic energy which has been acquired is converted to pressure energy. Discharge is through a tangential outlet in the volute.

The centrifugal pump is simple in construction and may be fabricated from a wide range of corrosion-resistant materials. It can be driven directly from an electric motor, and may be operated against a closed delivery without harm. On the other hand, it will not give a high pressure unless several stages are used, and is efficient over a limited flow range only.

Centrifugal separators. See Centrifuges.

Centrifugation. Separation of substances by means of a centrifuge.

Centrifuges. These are machines which employ centrifugal force to obtain high rates of sedimentation or filtration in order to separate a solid and a liquid or two immiscible liquids. The mixture to be separated is contained in a cylindrical *bowl* which is rotated at high speed. If the walls of the bowl are permeable (*perforate bowl*) the liquid will drain through, if not, two layers will be formed.

Perforate bowl centrifuges are used chiefly for

develop higher centrifugal fields than filtering centrifugals and therefore have higher speeds of rotation. The bowl is not perforated and the clear liquid leaves over a circular weir at the end. Many centrifuges of this type are continuous; this is achieved by incorporating a helical screw conveyor inside the bowl which scrapes the solid along the walls to the discharge ports.

Centrifuges for separating liquids require high centrifugal fields or must be so designed that the droplets have only to settle through a small distance. The *tubular bowl centrifuge* has a long bowl of small diameter and revolves at very high speeds (about 15,000 r.p.m.). The *disc bowl centrifuge* has a bowl containing a vertical array of conical discs set close together, and revolves at rather lower speeds than the previous type. Although the centrifugal field is less, the droplets have only to settle through a distance less than the distance between discs, say 1/32 in. In both types the heavier liquid flows to the outside of the bowl and the light liquid to the inside. Operation is invariably continuous. See also Ultracentrifuge.

Cephalin, Kephalin. Cephalins are phosphatides found associated with lecithins in all animal and vegetable tissues, and resembling lecithins in most respects, but are less soluble in alcohol and less easily hydrolysed by acids and alkalis. They are white, brittle solids, very hygroscopic and forming colloidal solutions with water. At least three different types of cephalin exist; one is phosphatidyl ethanolamine (with ethanolamine replacing choline in the lecithin molecule); a second is phosphatidyl serine (with the serine attached to the phosphate residue through its hydroxyl group); a third type contains inositol.

Cephaloridine, Ceporin. A useful semisynthetic

Cephaloridine

the filtration and dewatering of coarse materials such as crystals (*filtering centrifugals*). The bowl axis is normally vertical, and the bowl may be driven from above or below. Although batch-wise operation is widely employed labour requirements are high. For this reason automatic batch and continuous machines have been developed, in which loading and unloading of the machine is either automatic or continuous.

Sedimentation centrifuges are used to separate finely divided solids from liquids. They have to

antibiotic derived from cephalosporin C. It is almost non-toxic and has a wide spectrum of activity, especially against Gram-negative organisms and strains of *Staphylococcus aureus* which are resistant to penicillin.

Cephalosporin. C. An antibiotic produced by *Cephalosporium acremonium* (Abraham and Newton, 1955). The cephalosporin nucleus is resistant to penicillinase and is more stable than penicillins towards acid, but has weaker antibacterial activity. However, it may be converted via 7-aminocephalosporanic acid, followed by N-acylation, into semisynthetic antibiotics

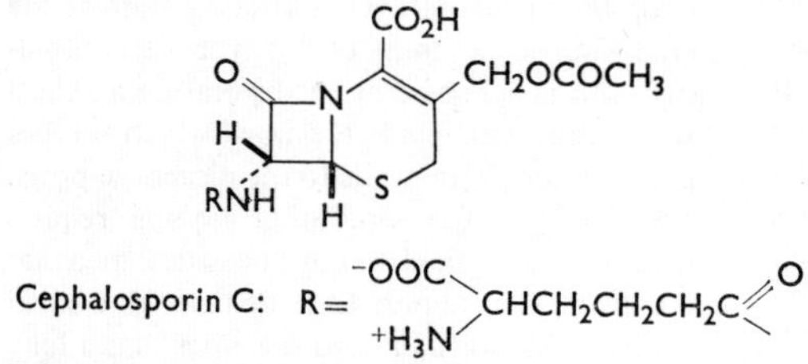

Cephalosporin C: R= ^-OOC $\diagdown$ $CHCH_2CH_2CH_2C$ $\diagup$ O
^+H_3N

7-Aminocephalosporanic acid: R=H

having a wide range of useful activity: examples are cephaloridine (Ceporin, trade name) (*q.v.*) and cephalothin (Keflin, trade name) (*q.v.*). A total synthesis of cephalosporin C has been achieved (Woodward, Nobel Lecture, 1965).

Cephalothin, Keflin. A useful semisynthetic antibiotic derived from cephalosporin C.

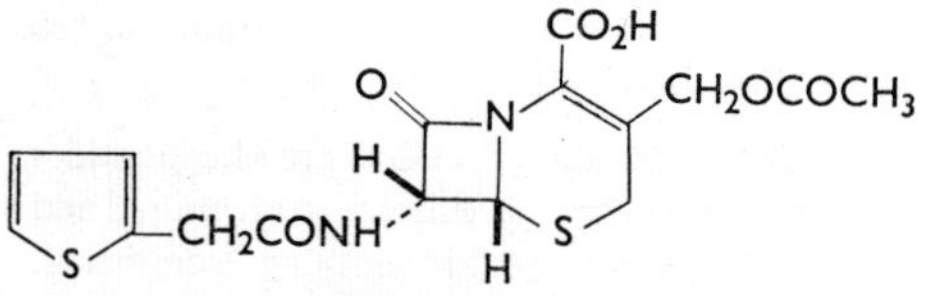

Cephalothin

Cerebron, See Phrenosin.

Cerebronic acid. See Phrenosinic acid.

Cerebrosides, Galactolipid(e)s, Galactolipin(e)s. A group of substances of a glycoside nature which on hydrolysis give galactose, the base sphingosine, and a fatty acid. They occur chiefly in brains in company with sphingomyelin, from which they cannot easily be separated, as they resemble it in chemical and physical properties. Among the cerebrosides are phrenosin, kerasin, and nervone.

Ceresin, Cerasin. A white, odourless, waxy solid used as a substitute for beeswax in ointments and polishes. It is obtained from ozokerite by various processes. The melting-point varies from 60° to 80° according to source and method of purification.

Cerium, Ce. At.no. 58, At.wt. 140·13, *d* 6·771, m.p. 795°, b.p. 3470°. The metal is cubic close-packed below −150°, *a*=4·85 Å; hexagonal close-packed to −10°, *a*=3·68, *c*=11·92 Å; cubic close-packed to 795°, *a*=5·1604 Å. Cerium is the commonest of the rare-earth elements but is, in general, a typical member of that group. Cerium oxides have been obtained in large quantities after the extraction of thorium from monazite sand; the metal has been used in many alloys, notably mischmetal (*q.v.*). The metal oxidizes very readily and ignites at 320°.

Cerium alloy. Another name for pyrophoric alloy.

Cerium compounds. Cerium (III) salts are typical rare-earth compounds (*q.v.*). They are colourless. Cerium (IV) salts (ceric) are obtained from ceric oxide, CeO_2, they are generally yellow-orange in colour.

Cerium (IV) oxide is obtained from cerous oxide by heating in air. Ceric oxide dissolves in concentrated hydrochloric acid to give a yellow solution containing *chloroceric acid*, H_2CeCl_6; the tetramethylammonium salt $(NMe_4)_2CeCl_6$ has been prepared. Anhydrous *cerium (IV) sulphate*, $Ce(SO_4)_2$, is prepared by dissolving ceric oxide in concentrated sulphuric acid; double sulphates such as *cerium (IV) ammonium sulphate*, $Ce(SO_4)_2·2(NH_4)_2SO_4·2H_2O$ are also known. Cerium (IV) sulphate and its derivatives are used in volumetric analysis as standard oxidizing agents. Cerium (IV) nitrate cannot be isolated but very stable complex nitrates, $M_2Ce(NO_3)_6$ are formed with alkali metal nitrates and have been used in the separation of cerium from the other rare-earths. *Cerium (IV) fluoride*, CeF_4, can be made by the action of fluorine on cerium (III) fluoride at 500°-600°.

Cermets. Pressed or sintered ceramic-metal mixtures, e.g. $Cr—Al_2O_3$ and $Si—SiC$, which have been developed for use in jet engines and other high temperature applications. They are composed of inorganic substances and metal constituents which may be bonded together mechanically or chemically.

Cerotic acid. The trivial name for hexacosanic acid, $CH_3·[CH_2]_{24}·COOH$ (m.p. 88°). It occurs free in beeswax and carnauba oil and esterified with ceryl alcohol and other higher alcohols in wool fat, Chinese wax, and many other waxes.

Cerulean blue. A fine light blue pigment consisting of cobalt stannate (containing also silica and calcium sulphate) obtained by precipitating from a solution of cobalt nitrate and sodium stannate, and heating the precipitate.

Cerussite, $PbCO_3$. Native lead carbonate, of some importance as a lead ore. It forms orthorhombic crystals with an adamantine lustre, sp.gr. 6·5, hardness 3-3½, and occurs in the upper oxidized zones associated with galena veins.

Ceryl alcohol, $C_{26}H_{54}O$.

$$CH_3 \cdot [CH_2]_{24} \cdot CH_2OH.$$

Colourless crystals, m.p. 79°. It occurs as esters in various waxes, ceryl palmitate being the chief component of opium wax and ceryl cerotate of Chinese wax.

Cetane. The trivial name for the straight chain hydrocarbon, hexadecane, $C_{16}H_{34}$. It has m.p. 18°, b.p. 280°.

Cetane number. A means of expressing the ignition quality of a diesel fuel, defined as the percentage of cetane in the mixture of cetane and α-methylnaphthalene which matches the fuel under test in ignition characteristics.

Cetoleic acid, $C_{22}H_{42}O_2$. A straight chain, unsaturated fatty acid, with one double bond in the 11-12 position. It is abundant in certain shark liver oils, and found also in other fish oils.

Cetrimide, cetyltrimethyl ammonium bromide, CTAB, $[C_{16}H_{33}N(CH_3)_3]^+Br^-$. The commercial product is made by the condensation of cetyl bromide with trimethylamine, and contains other alkyl ammonium bromides. It is a creamy-white powder, soluble in water to give a readily foaming solution. It is one of the group of cationic detergents and wetting agents, which act by causing a lowering of the surface tension of the solution. It is also a potent bactericide and is particularly suitable for sterilizing the skin.

Cetyl alcohol, Hexadecanol, $C_{16}H_{34}O$.

$$CH_3 \cdot [CH_2]_{14} \cdot CH_2OH.$$

Colourless crystals m.p. 49°. It occurs as esters in various waxes, the most important being cetyl palmitate, which is the chief component of spermaceti. It forms a mono-molecular layer on water and its use has been suggested to reduce evaporation from reservoirs in hot countries.

CFR engine. A type of variable compression petrol engine in which the octane number of a fuel may be determined by direct comparison with a series of standard fuels of known octane numbers. The intensity of knock is in this case indicated by a bouncing pin, the movements of which follow the changes of pressure in the cylinder, the pin being so adjusted that it remains stationary in the absence of knocking.

Chabazite. See Zeolites.

Chadwick, Sir James (1887-   ). After working at the Cavendish Laboratory, Chadwick was in 1935 appointed professor of physics at Liverpool University. He was awarded the Nobel Prize for Physics in 1935 for his discovery of the neutron and other work in atomic physics. He was Master of Gonville and Caius College, Cambridge, 1948-58.

Chain reactions. Bodenstein and Lind (1906) studied the hydrogen-bromine reaction and concluded that the reaction was not of simple kinetic order. Their rate expression

$$\frac{d[HBr]}{dt} = \frac{k_1[H_2][Br_2]^{\frac{1}{2}}}{k_2 + [HBr]/[Br_2]^{\frac{1}{2}}}$$

(where k_1 and k_2 are constants) was later interpreted by means of the chain reaction mechanism:

(a) $Br_2 \rightarrow 2Br\cdot$
(b) $Br\cdot + H_2 \rightarrow HBr + H\cdot$
(c) $H\cdot + Br_2 \rightarrow HBr + Br\cdot$
(d) $H\cdot + HBr \rightarrow H_2 + Br\cdot$
(e) $2Br\cdot \rightarrow Br_2$

The first stage (a) of the reaction represents the dissociation of a few molecules of bromine into bromine atoms. These atoms then react (b) with hydrogen molecules. In step (c) bromine atoms are again formed and these can now repeat step (b) in the chain propagation. Both steps (b) and (c) lead to production of HBr, and since bromine atoms are regenerated the process can be repeated many thousands of times. Reaction (d) leads to an inhibition in the chain reaction and step (e) represents the chain termination.

The reaction between hydrogen and chlorine is also thought to be of this type and many organic free radical reactions (e.g. the decomposition of acetaldehyde) proceed via chain mechanisms.

In nuclear chemistry, a fission reaction (see Atomic energy) may be initiated by a neutron and may also result in the production of one or more neutrons which if they reacted in like manner could start a chain reaction. Normally, 'moderators' such as cadmium rods which absorb neutrons are placed in the reactor to control the rate of fission.

Chair form. See Conformation.

Chalcedony. A somewhat fibrous form of precipitated or colloidal silica which is formed in a manner similar to flint and chert. It is generally regarded as amorphous, but X-ray analysis shows that it has a structure similar to quartz, though it shows no inversion at 575° and is more easily converted, by heating, into a form of low specific gravity (probably cristobalite). At 800° it is converted into quartz and tridymite, the former being converted into tridymite on further heating. Pure chalcedony is white, but most specimens are tinted. Sp.gr. 2·55-2·58, hardness 7. Refractive index, max. 1·543, min. 1·532. A bad conductor of electricity, it has a low thermal expansion. Onyx and agate are similar.

Chalcocite or **Copper glance**, Cu_2S. Native cuprous sulphide crystallizing in the orthorhombic system. Iron-black with metallic lustre, hardness $2\frac{1}{2}$, sp.gr. 5·7. Widely distributed in veins of copper ore.

Chalcogens. The elements oxygen, sulphur, selenium, tellurium and polonium, of group 6 of the periodic table, are sometimes collectively called chalcogens.

Chalcopyrite or **copper pyrites**, $CuFeS_2$. The most important ore of copper; tetragonal, hardness 4, sp.gr. 4·2. Brassy yellow in colour with a metallic lustre. The ratio of iron to copper varies.

Chalk. A naturally occurring form of calcium carbonate.

Chalkone, **Benzalacetophenone,** $C_{15}H_{12}O$.

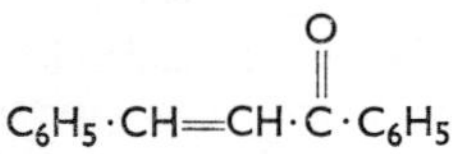

$$C_6H_5 \cdot CH{=}CH \cdot \overset{\overset{\displaystyle O}{\|}}{C} \cdot C_6H_5$$

Crystallizes in pale yellow prisms, m.p. 58°, b.p. 345°-348°. Insoluble in water, moderately soluble in alcohol, more soluble in ether. It can be prepared by condensing acetophenone and benzaldehyde in the presence of sodium ethoxide.

Chalybite, Siderite, $FeCO_3$. Occurs as yellow-brown crystals, as a yellow or brown film covering other minerals, or as large concretionary masses. It is found in large quantities as clay ironstone in association with clay and carbonaceous matter. Sp.gr. 3·7-3·9, hardness 3·5-4·5. The crystals are rhombohedral.

Chamber press. See Filter press.

Chaptal, Jean Antoine Claude, Comte de Chanteloup (1756-1832). Born at Nogaret, Lozère, Chaptal, the son of an apothecary, studied chemistry at Montpellier, where in 1871 he was appointed professor. With an inheritance he established a chemical works and in 1793 took over management of the saltpetre works at Grenelle. He received from Napoleon the title of Comte. He was a pioneer in the application of chemistry to industry.

Chardonnet, Comte Hilaire de. Comte de Chardonnet, a French chemist, exhibited, in 1889, a material derived from cellulose, imitative of natural silk. He established a works at Besancon and was the first to produce artificial silk on the industrial scale.

Charge transfer complexes. Complexes in which there is weak interaction between the donor and the acceptor properties which are generally induced in the acceptor. Examples of charge transfer complexes include the complexes formed between aromatic derivatives and halogens.

The class is really indistinguishable from true complexes. Charge (electron) transfer takes place in all complexes.

Charge transfer spectrum or band. An absorption band which corresponds to complete transfer of an electron from one atom to another.

Charpy test. See Impact resistance.

Char value. A measure of the tendency of a kerosine when burning in a lamp to deposit char on the wick. Normally expressed as the quantity of charred substances deposited in the course of a burning test carried out in a specially designed lamp and extending over a period of 24 hours.

Charles, Jacques Alexandre César (1746-1823). Born at Beaugency, Loiret, Charles abandoned his position as a clerk in the ministry of finance and took up scientific study. He was the first successfully to use hydrogen for filling balloons and also investigated the expansion of gases. In 1785 he was elected to the Academy of Sciences.

Charles's law. This law states that at constant pressure the volume of a given mass of gas varies directly with the absolute temperature.

Chaulmoogra oil. The oil expressed from the ripe seeds of *Taraktogenos kurzii*, or the similar products from *Hydnocarpus wightiana* and *Gynocardia odorata*—all trees indigenous to India and the Malay peninsula. The oil, d^{25} 0·935-0·960, $[\alpha]_D$ +48° to +60°, solidifies below 25°. It is composed principally of glycerides of chaulmoogric and hydnocarpic acids, and was formerly important in the treatment of leprosy, but has been superseded by other drugs.

Chaulmoogric acid, $C_{18}H_{32}O_2$. A fatty acid

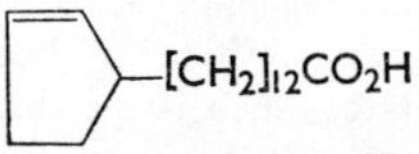

$$\text{[structure]}-[CH_2]_{12}CO_2H$$

occurring as glycerides in chaulmoogra oil. It crystallizes in colourless leaflets, m.p. 68·5°, soluble in ether and chloroform; $[\alpha]_D$ +62° in chloroform. It was used in the treatment of leprosy.

Cheddite. Explosive composed of ammonium perchlorate, dinitrotoluene, and castor oil.

Chelate compound. A compound in which a co-ordinate link or links causes the formation of a closed ring of atoms is termed a chelate compound; beryllium acetylacetonate contains two chelate rings.

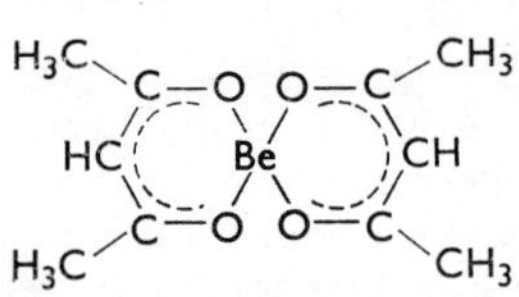

Chemical development. The term applied in photography to the process in which the silver ions of the halide grains of an emulsion are reduced to silver by a developing agent, usually under alkaline conditions. This process is used in most practical forms of photography, and the developing action is generally limited to the exposed grains.

Chemical potential. A thermodynamic property introduced by J. W. Gibbs. Loosely, it may be described as a measure of the 'intensity' of a chemical substance in a given system (e.g. solution or mixture). Mathematically, if the total Gibbs free energy G of a system increases by an increment dG when an infinitesimal quantity, dn_A mole, of component A is added to the system under conditions of constant temperature and pressure, the chemical potential of A in the system, denoted μ_A, is given by $\mu_A = (dG/dn_A)_{P,T}$; μ is therefore sometimes called the partial molar free energy. Chemical potential is a valuable function in the theory of heterogeneous equilibria, since it can readily be proved that, if such a system is not initially at equilibrium, substances will tend to pass from one phase to another (e.g. solid dissolving or crystallizing) until a uniform chemical potential is attained for each substance in every phase.

Chemical toning. See Toning.

Chemiluminescence. A number of chemical reactions are accompanied by emission of light, e.g. the oxidation of yellow phosphorus. The process is the reverse of the ordinary photochemical one, in which reactions are caused to take place by exposing the reactants to light, and is termed chemiluminescence. The light emitted by the fire-fly or glow-worm, and indeed ordinary luminous combustion, are examples of this very common phenomenon.

Chemisorption. In many cases the adsorption of a material at a surface is irreversible and essentially chemical in nature, resulting in the formation of a surface compound. An example of this is given by the carbon-oxygen system. Carbon readily adsorbs oxygen, but on evacuation the gas cannot be recovered. If the charcoal is heated, the oxygen is finally obtained in the form of oxides of carbon. Films of oxygen on the surface of metals are also of this type. See Adsorption.

Chemotaxonomy. The study of the chemical constituents of plants, animals and other organisms as a guide to their phylogeny and classification. See, e.g., 'Chemotaxonomie der Pflanzen', by R. Hegnauer, vols. 1-3, *et seq.*, 1962.

Chemotherapy. A term defined by Ehrlich as the selective destruction of pathogenic organisms within a host by the use of chemicals. It is now enlarged to include chemical methods of treatment of cancer and other diseases of uncertain aetiology. Important chemotherapeutic drugs include mepacrine, proguanil, the sulphonamides, the penicillins, and numerous other antibiotics.

Cheshunt compound. Used for the prevention of 'damping-off' of seedlings. It is made by mixing 2 parts by weight of copper sulphate and 11 parts of ammonium carbonate, and is a violet powder, soluble in water, containing cuprammonium sulphate. It is applied to seed-containing soil at a dilution of 1 g. to 2 gallons of water.

Chevreul, Michel Eugène (1786-1889). Born at Angers, where his father was a physician, Chevreul was educated at Paris. In 1813 he was appointed professor of chemistry at the Lycée Charlemagne and subsequently Director of Gobelins' tapestry works. In 1830 he became professor of organic chemistry at the Natural History Museum, of which he was appointed Director in 1860. His classical researches upon animal fats made possible the soap and candle industries. In 1826 he was elected a Member of the Academy of Sciences and in 1857 awarded the Copley Medal of the Royal Society.

Chicle. This gummy resin is obtained from the tree *Achras sapota*, growing in Mexico and Central America. It is rubber-like and is quite soft at 49°. It is used in the manufacture of chewing gum, adhesive plasters, electric cable insulation (with rubber), and waterproof varnishes, and as a modelling material.

Chile saltpetre. See Sodium nitrate.

Chillies. See Capsicum.

Chimyl alcohol, Cetyl-α-glyceryl ether, $C_{19}H_{40}O_3$.

$$CH_3 \cdot [CH_2]_{15} \cdot O \cdot CH_2 \cdot CHOH \cdot CH_2OH.$$

Colourless crystals, m.p. 61°. A constituent of the liver oils of elasmobranch fishes, also isolated from bull and boar testes.

China clay, kaolin. A white powdery material arising from the decomposition of feldspar in granite rocks by chemically active fluids (pneumatolysis) or surface weathering. It can either be residual (i.e. *in situ* as in Cornwall) or transported (sedimentary deposits bearing no relation to the rocks on which they rest). The clay is washed from the decomposed rock in Cornwall by a stream of water and purified by the controlled settling out of impurities. China clays from various sources differ somewhat in their physical properties. Its chief uses are in the paper trade, in pottery manufacture, and as a filler in the textile and paint industries; there are many minor uses. See Kaolinite.

China-stone. A granitic rock containing partially kaolinized feldspar. Obtained from Cornwall, hence sometimes known as Cornish Stone. It is used as a flux in ceramics.

Chinese blue. A name formerly applied to various blue pigments, but now it usually means a form of Prussian blue, either used alone or mixed with a white pigment.

Chinese wax. The secretion, consisting chiefly of ceryl cerotate $CH_3[CH_2]_{24} \cdot CO \cdot O[CH_2]_{25}CH_3$, deposited by certain insects (*Coccus* spp.) on the branches of a species of ash tree in W. China. Used commercially in making candles, polishes, etc. and in textile processing.

Chinosol, 8-hydroxyquinoline sulphate $(C_9H_7NO)_2 \cdot H_2SO_4$. A systemic fungicide. It is a

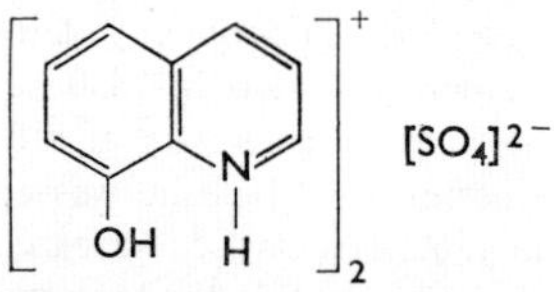

yellow crystalline powder, m.p. 175°-178°, and is soluble in water and alcohol. Alkalis liberate the free base 8-hydroxyquinoline.

Chitin. A structural polysaccharide in which

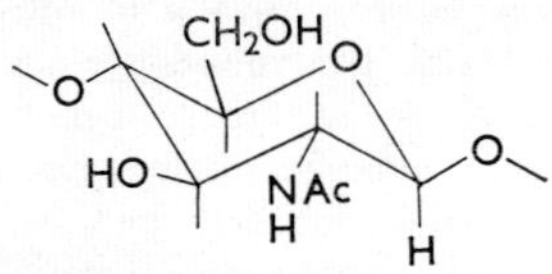

N-acetyl-D-glucosamine units are linked in the β-(1→4)-positions. As 'native chitin', in association with proteins and other materials, it forms the integument of Crustacea, insects and fungi. Chitin is very resistant to acid hydrolysis but is attacked by the widely distributed enzyme chitinase: the disaccharide chitobiose has been isolated.

Chitinase. One of the enzymes found in the digestive juices of the snail and in mould fungi. Able under certain conditions to hydrolyse chitin, the skeletal carbohydrate of the Crustacea, and also of fungi, the final product being N-acetyl glucosamine. It is not the same as emulsin. It also attacks synthetic glycosides of acetylglucosamine. The presence of the acetyl group is essential for its activity.

Chitosamine. See Glucosamine.

Chittenden, Russell Henry (1856-1943). Born at New Haven, Connecticut, Chittenden studied at Yale University and at Heidelberg. In 1882 he became professor of physiological chemistry in the Sheffield Scientific School, Yale University,

and in 1898 its director. His researches on diet and the physiology of digestion were among the first scientific studies of these subjects, and showed that health could be maintained on a low protein dietary. An inspired teacher and author of numerous books and papers, Chittenden exercised a great influence on the development of physiological chemistry in the United States. See *J. Biol. Chem.*, 1944, **153**, 329.

Chloral, trichloroacetaldehyde, $CCl_3 \cdot CHO$. A colourless oily liquid with a pungent odour; d^{20} 1·512, b.p. 98°. Miscible with water, alcohol, and ether. Manufactured by the action of chlorine on alcohol; the product of this reaction is chloral alcoholate, which is then decomposed with sulphuric acid and the chloral distilled off. It is also made by the chlorination of acetaldehyde. When allowed to stand, it changes slowly to a white solid. Additive compounds are formed with water (see Chloral hydrate), ammonia, sodium bisulphite, alcohols, and certain amines and amides. Oxidized by nitric acid to trichloroacetic acid. Decomposed by alkalis to chloroform and a formate: this is a convenient method of obtaining pure chloroform. It is used almost exclusively for the manufacture of DDT. It gives a blue colour when gently warmed with a solution of pyrogallol in 65% sulphuric acid. It is also used as a hypnotic. Another hypnotic related to chloral is triclofos sodium, the monosodium salt of 2,2,2-trichloroethyl dihydrogen phosphate.

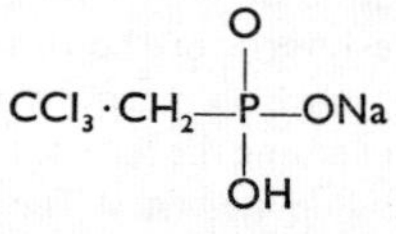

Chloralamide. See Chloralformamide.

Chloralformamide, chloralamide, $C_3H_4Cl_3NO_2$, $CCl_3CH(OH)NH \cdot CHO$. A colourless crystalline solid, m.p. 115°. Soluble in water, alcohol, and ether. Manufactured by warming chloral with formamide, and recrystallizing the product from water. When heated with water above 60°, it decomposes into chloral and formamide: decomposed by alkalis to chloroform, ammonia, and a formate. It is not affected by dilute acids. It is used in the treatment of delirium tremens. Its effect resembles that of chloral hydrate, but it is somewhat slower in action and is considered to be safer.

Chloral hydrate, trichloroethylidene glycol, $C_2H_3Cl_3O_2$

. Crystallizes in large, colourless prisms having a peculiar odour; m.p. 57°, b.p. 97·5°. Very soluble in water, alcohol, and ether;

less soluble in chloroform. Manufactured by adding the calculated amount of water to chloral. For other properties see Chloral. Its chief use is as a hypnotic. A complex of chloral hydrate and phenazone in the molecular proportions of 2:1 is known as dichloralphenazone, and is widely used as a hypnotic.

Chlorambucil, γ - [p - di - 2 - chloroethylamino-phenyl] **butyric acid,** $C_{14}H_{19}Cl_2NO_2$. A white

$$Cl \cdot CH_2 \cdot CH_2$$
$$Cl \cdot CH_2 \cdot CH_2 \Big\rangle N - \bigcirc - [CH_2]_3 \cdot COOH$$

crystalline powder, insoluble in water, soluble in many organic solvents. It is a nitrogen mustard (*q.v.*) and has been administered orally in the treatment of chronic lymphatic leukaemia.

Chloramine, NH_2Cl. Formed by the action of sodium hypochlorite on ammonia and separated by distillation under reduced pressure; m.p. $-66°$. Chloramine is liable to explode. Chloramine reacts with excess hypochlorous acid to give hydrazine.

Chloramine T, sodium p-**toluenesulphon-chloroamide,** $C_7H_7ClNNaO_2S$, $3H_2O$. White crystals, which lose water at $100°$ and decompose suddenly at $175°$-$180°$. Soluble in 7 parts of water and 12 parts of alcohol. Prepared from p-toluenesulphonamide and sodium hypochlorite. It is a powerful antiseptic and is used in dilute aqueous solution for washing wounds.

$$CH_3$$
$$NaO - \overset{\|}{\underset{\|}{S}} = O$$
$$N - Cl$$

Chloramphenicol, Chloromycetin, $C_{11}H_{12}Cl_2$ N_2O_5. Colourless needles or elongated plates,

$$O_2N - \bigcirc - CH(OH) \cdot CH \cdot CH_2OH$$
$$\underset{NH \cdot CO \cdot CHCl_2}{|}$$

m.p $150°$, soluble in alcohol and acetone, sparingly soluble in water; $[\alpha]_D^{25}$ $-25 \cdot 5°$ in ethyl acetate, dextrorotatory in alcohol. It is an antibiotic, produced by the submerged fermentation of *Streptomyces venezuelae*, and by synthesis starting from p-nitrobromaceto-phenone. It is very stable to heat and changes in pH, and the fact that the molecule contains a nitro group and chlorine atoms is very unusual for a natural product. It is used very effectively in the treatment of typhus, typhoid, and other diseases caused by a wide variety of organisms, including some caused by rickettsia and viruses.

Chloranil, tetrachloro-p-benzoquinone, $C_6Cl_4O_2$, The fungicidal properties of chloranil were discovered in 1937, it is mainly used as a seed protectant. It forms yellow crystals, m.p. $290°$, which sublime when heated, insoluble in water. Prepared by oxidizing phenol with an acid and potassium chlorate.

Chlorates. Salts of chloric acid. See Sodium chlorate.

Chlorazide, N_3Cl. A colourless, highly explosive gas, prepared by the action of a hypochlorite on sodium azide in a weakly acid medium, e.g. boric acid.

Chlorbutol, 2,2,2-trichloro-1,1-dimethylethanol, $CCl_3C(CH_3)_2OH$. Crystallizes with a variable amount of water in colourless crystals with a musty camphorous odour and taste. Volatile at ordinary temperatures, m.p. $77°$, b.p. $167°$; soluble in 130 parts of water and 1 part of alcohol. It is prepared by heating acetone and chloroform with potassium hydroxide. Chlorbutol has a mild sedative and local analgesic action, resembling that of chloral hydrate. It is used for treating persistent hiccough, in whooping cough, and in nasal drops for relieving catarrh.

Chlordane, $C_{10}H_6Cl_8$. Chlordane is a technical

product containing 1,2,4,5,6,7,10,10-octachloro-4,7,8,9 - tetrahydro - 4,7 - endomethyleneindane, and is made by condensation of hexachloro-cyclopentadiene with cyclopentadiene followed by further chlorination of the product. The technical product is a brown liquid which is soluble in organic solvents, and insoluble in water, and consists of a mixture of isomers (60-75%) and related compounds. The pure isomers of chlordane are white solids.

Chlordane is a persistent insecticide, non-phytotoxic and of low toxicity to mammals.

Chlorex process. See $\beta\beta$-Dichloroethyl ether.

Chlorhexidine, $C_{22}H_{30}Cl_2N_{10}$. Prepared by the interaction of hexamethylenebisdicyandi-amide and 4-chloroaniline. The dihydrochloride is a white crystalline powder, m.p. about $225°$ (decomp.). It is sparingly soluble in water and in alcohol.

It is used as an antiseptic and skin sterilizing agent.

Solid bromine and iodine form similar molecular crystals. Free chlorine was first prepared by

$$Cl—\langle C_6H_4\rangle—NH—\underset{\underset{NH}{\|}}{C}—NH—\underset{\overset{NH}{\|}}{C}—NH—[CH_2]_6—NH—\underset{\overset{NH}{\|}}{C}—NH—\underset{\underset{NH}{\|}}{C}—NH—\langle C_6H_4\rangle—Cl$$

Chloric acid, $HClO_3$. Most readily obtained by the action of sulphuric acid on barium chlorate. The filtered solution may be concentrated in vacuum over sulphuric acid until it contains about 40% $HClO_3$. On further concentration the acid decomposes into chlorine, oxygen and perchloric acid. It has a pungent smell, similar to that of nitric acid, and strong acidic and bleaching properties. The most important salt is sodium chlorate (*q.v.*).

Chloride of lime. See Bleaching powder.

Chlorides. Formed by all elements of the periodic table except the noble gases. Electropositive elements form salts but the chlorides of the non-metals and many transition metals show appreciable covalent character. Most covalent chlorides are hydrolysed by water with the liberation of hydrogen chloride. Chlorides are prepared by the action of hydrogen chloride or chlorine on individual elements or their derivatives such as oxides. Anhydrous chlorides may be obtained by the action of acetyl chloride or thionyl chloride.

Chlorinated rubber. Compounds containing varying proportions of chlorine up to about 68 % w/w (corresponding to the formula $C_{10}H_{12}Cl_8$) are formed by reacting rubber, in the solid form, in solution, or as latex, with chlorine, the reaction being partly addition and partly substitution. The products are of considerable technical importance and are prepared commercially by the reaction of chlorine with rubber dissolved in carbon tetrachloride. Chlorinated rubber is soluble in benzene and its homologues, chloroform, carbon tetrachloride, and some other chlorinated solvents, and certain esters, but is insoluble in petrol and alcohol. The material is stable for long periods at room temperature, but loses hydrogen chloride on heating. One of the most important properties of chlorinated rubber is its stability to acids, alkalis, water, and oxidizing agents. Its chief use is in corrosion-resistant and non-flammable paints. It is used also as an impregnating agent, as an adhesive, and as a paint resin. See Halogenated rubbers.

Chlorine, Cl. At.no. 17, At.wt. 35·457; m.p. $-101°$, b.p. $-34·11°$. Crystalline chlorine consists of molecules Cl_2, the Cl—Cl separation within the molecule being 2·02 Å. at $-160°$.

Scheele in 1774 by the action of hydrochloric acid on manganese dioxide. The elementary nature of the gas was demonstrated by Davy in 1810.

The chief source of chlorine is common salt, sodium chloride, NaCl. Chlorine is readily obtained by the oxidation of hydrochloric acid, with oxygen and a catalyst, or manganese dioxide. Technically chlorine is obtained by the electrolysis of brine; caustic soda and hydrogen being produced at the same time. The gas is easily liquefied by compression (6 atm) and is stored and sold in steel tanks or cylinders.

Chlorine is a greenish-yellow, poisonous gas. The density corresponds to the formula Cl_2. Thermal dissociation occurs at 1000°; the gas is 21% dissociated at 1400°. Chlorine is a very reactive element, combining directly with hydrogen and most metals and non-metallic elements except nitrogen, oxygen, and carbon. The gas is soluble in water, a small fraction reacting chemically to give hypochlorous acid. Chlorine is widely used in the chemical industry for chlorinations, also in water sterilization and pulp and paper manufacture.

Chlorine fluorides. *Chlorine pentafluoride*, ClF_5. Made by the combination of chlorine and fluorine at high temperatures. Only slowly hydrolysed by water.

Chlorine trifluoride, ClF_3; m.p. $-76°$, b.p. 12·1°. A colourless gas formed by interaction of chlorine and fluorine. It is an extremely powerful fluorinating agent, converting most elements to fluorides. ClF_3 is an efficient method of transporting fluorine which, in the elementary state, is difficult to handle.

Chlorine fluoride, ClF, m.p. $-156°$, b.p. $-100·8°$, is prepared similarly. Readily dissociates to the elements.

Chlorine hydrate. Crystallizes from solutions of chlorine in cold water, and has the composition $Cl_2·7·27H_2O$. It has a clathrate structure with chlorine molecules occupying holes in the water lattice. Chlorine slowly reacts with water to give hypochlorite and chloride ions.

Chlorine oxides. Chlorine forms four oxides, the formulae, melting points, and boiling points of which are as follows:

	Cl_2O	ClO_2	Cl_2O_6	Cl_2O_7
m.p.	$-116°$	$-59°$	$3.5°$	$91.5°$
b.p.	$2°$	$11.0°$	$203°$ (calc.)	$80°$

The first of these oxides, Cl_2O, is a brownish-yellow explosive gas, formed by passing dry chlorine over mercuric oxide. It is absorbed by water, forming a solution of hypochlorous acid, HOCl. Chlorine dioxide, ClO_2, is formed by adding concentrated sulphuric acid to potassium chlorate at a low temperature, or by heating potassium chlorate at 70° with crystalline oxalic acid. It is a dangerously explosive compound. It dissolves in water to give a mixture of chlorous and chloric acids, and with alkalis yields a mixture of chlorites and chlorates. It is widely used as a bleach in the wood-pulp and milling industries. The oxide Cl_2O_6 has been prepared by mixing ozonized oxygen with a stream of oxygen carrying chlorine dioxide. The heptoxide, Cl_2O_7, is obtained by dehydrating perchloric acid, $HClO_4$, with phosphorus pentoxide. Both Cl_2O_6 and Cl_2O_7 are dangerously explosive.

Chlorine oxyfluorides. *Chloryl fluoride*, ClO_2F, is prepared by the action of bromine trifluoride on potassium chlorate. It forms salts, probably containing the ClO_2^+ ion, with acid fluorides such as boron trifluoride. *Perchloryl fluoride*, ClO_3F, is prepared by electrolysis of sodium perchlorate in anhydrous hydrogen fluoride. It is an inert gas, m.p. $-146°$, b.p. $-46.7°$.

Chlorites. A group of green scaly ferromagnesium minerals with the typical formula $5(Mg, Fe)O \cdot Al_2O_3 \cdot 3SiO_2 \cdot 4H_2O$. In many respects similar to the micas with sheets of linked SiO_4 tetrahedra, but they contain no alkalis. They are often secondary minerals resulting from the alteration of pyroxenes, amphiboles and biotite.

The word is also used for the salts of chlorous acid (q.v.).

Chloroacetic acids, *Monochloroacetic acid.* $CHCl \cdot COOH$, forms large colourless crystals which readily absorb water vapour. It exists in three solid modifications, α, m.p. 63°; β, m.p. 55·6°; γ, m.p. 50°, the β modification is the one normally obtained. B.p. 189°. Soluble in water, alcohol, chloroform, and benzene. Manufactured by heating trichloroethylene with sulphuric acid, or by treating glacial acetic acid with chlorine in the presence of red phosphorus, sulphur, or acetic anhydride. Reacts with ammonia to give glycine, and with many types of organic compounds. It is largely used as a chemical intermediate, particularly in the manufacture of the chlorophenoxyacetic acid weedkillers, thiocyanate insecticides and various pharmaceuticals.

Dichloroacetic acid,

$$CHCl_2COOH$$

is a low-melting solid. d^{20} 1·563, m.p. 5°-6°, b.p. 194°. Prepared by the action of copper powder on trichloroacetic acid or by the action of sodium cyanide on chloral hydrate.

Trichloroacetic acid, CCl_3COOH, is a crystalline solid which rapidly absorbs water vapour; m.p. 58°, b.p. 196·5°, very soluble in water, alcohol, or benzene. Manufactured by the action of chlorine on acetic acid at 160° in the presence of red phosphorus, sulphur, or iodine. It is decomposed into chloroform and carbon dioxide by boiling water. It is a much stronger acid than either the mono- or the dichloro-acids and has been used to extract alkaloids and ascorbic acid from plant and animal tissues. It is a precipitant for proteins and may be used to test for the presence of albumin in urine. The sodium salt is used as a selective weed-killer.

Chloroacetone, $CH_2Cl \cdot CO \cdot CH_3$. A colourless liquid whose vapour is a powerful lachrymator; d^{16} 1·162, b.p. 119°. Soluble in water, alcohol, or ether. Manufactured by treating acetone with bleaching powder or chlorine. It is used as a tear gas and is usually mixed with the more potent bromoacetone.

Chloro acids. Complex chloro acids are formed by most elements of the periodic table by solution of oxides or chlorides in concentrated hydrochloric acid. Potassium salts of many of the acids are precipitated from solution when potassium chloride is added to a solution of the chloro acid. For individual acids see under the appropriate metal halides.

p-**Chloroaniline,** C_6H_6ClN. Forms colourless rhombic prisms, m.p. 70°-71°, b.p. 232·3°. Insoluble in water, soluble in organic solvents. Volatile in steam. Basic and forms a sulphate sparingly soluble in cold water. It is prepared by reducing *p*-nitrochlorobenzene with iron and hydrochloric acid.

Chlorobenzene, C_6H_5Cl. Colourless liquid, b.p. 132°, sp.gr. 1·106 at 20°. Insoluble in water, miscible in all proportions with organic solvents. Nitrates in the *o*- and *p*-positions.

Prepared by the direct chlorination of benzene in the presence of an iron catalyst. Largely used as an intermediate in the manufacture of other chemicals, particularly phenol, DDT and aniline.

Chlorocarbonic ester. See Chloroformic ester.

Chlorochromates, $MCrO_3Cl$. Obtained by treating dichromates with concentrated hydrochloric acid or by adding chromyl chloride to a saturated solution of a metal chloride. The salts contain the tetrahedral anion CrO_3Cl^-; the free acid is unknown. The solutions decompose on boiling to chlorine and chromium (III) salts. Another series of chlorochromates of type $M_2^I CrOCl_5$ results from the action of concentrated HCl and alkali metal chloride on CrO_3 at $0°$.

Chlorocresol. C_7H_7ClO, *p*-chloro-*m*-cresol.

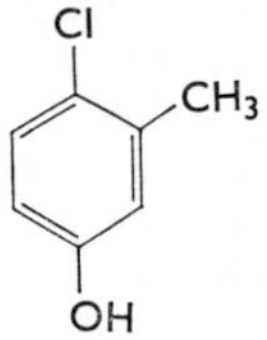

Colourless crystals, m.p. $64°-66°$. Sparingly soluble in water, soluble in alcohol. Used as an antiseptic and preservative in solutions for injection.

Chlorocruorin. A respiratory pigment, red in concentrated and green in dilute solutions, found in the plasma of certain polychaete worms. It is a protein combined with a pigment group, which is composed of a porphyrin, resembling haem, combined with iron, and it gives rise to a series of compounds corresponding to methaemoglobin, haematin, etc. Like haemoglobin it exists in an oxidized and a reduced form.

2-Chloroethyl alcohol. See Ethylene chlorohydrin.

Chloroform, Trichloromethane, $CHCl_3$. A colourless liquid with a sweet, pleasant odour; d^{15} $1·498$, b.p. $60°-61°$. Very slightly soluble in water; the solution has a sweet taste. A constant-boiling mixture (b.p. $56°$) is formed with $2·5\%$ water. It is miscible with most organic liquids. Manufactured by the chlorination of methane. It is oxidized by air and sunlight to phosgene; the addition of a small amount of alcohol prevents this. It is not inflammable but will burn when mixed with alcohol. When heated with sodium hydroxide it yields sodium formate and carbon monoxide. Some compounds crystallize from it with chloroform of crystallization. It is an excellent solvent for oils, fats, waxes, rubber, and many other organic substances. It can be detected by the nauseating odour of phenyl isocyanide produced when it is warmed with aniline and potassium hydroxide. Bromoform, iodoform, and chloral also give this carbylamine reaction.

Chloroform is a potent volatile anaesthetic; a vapour concentration of $2-3\%$ is suitable for inducing, and $1-2\%$ for maintaining anaesthesia. It is today only used for short operations.

Orally it is used as a carminative, and externally as a rubefacient and counter-irritant. Medical applications, however, account for only a small proportion of chloroform consumption, and it is used principally for the manufacture of chlorofluorohydrocarbon refrigerants ('Arctons' and 'Freons') and certain polymers.

Chloroformic ester, Chlorocarbonic ester, Ethyl chloroformate, Ethyl chlorocarbonate, $ClCOOCH_2CH_3$. A volatile liquid with an unpleasant odour; d^{20} $1·135$, b.p. $94°-95°$. Prepared by the addition of ethyl alcohol to cooled phosgene. It is very reactive and unites with many organic compounds containing —OH groups to give carbethoxy-derivatives. Reacts with ethyl alcohol to give diethyl carbonate and with ammonia to form urethane. Used in organic syntheses.

Chlorogenic acid, $C_{16}H_{18}O_9$. A condensation

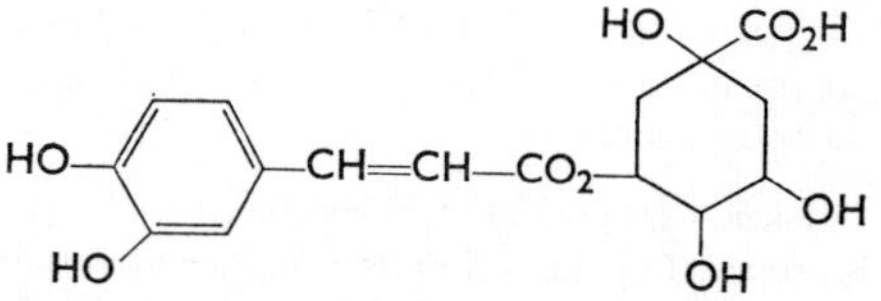

product of caffeic and quinic acids that is widely distributed in plants. It loses hydrogen in the presence of an oxidase to give a green pigment which is itself easily reduced.

Chlorohydrins. Organic compounds containing the group:

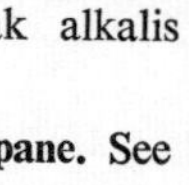

They are formed by treating compounds containing a double bond with chlorine water, or by treating glycols or olefin oxides with hydrochloric acid. They are converted to glycols when heated with weak alkalis such as sodium bicarbonate.

Chlorohydroxypropane. See Propylene chlorohydrins.

Chloroisopropyl alcohol. See Propylene chlorohydrins.

Chloromethane. See Methyl chloride.

Chloromethylation. The introduction of the —CH_2Cl group into aromatic, especially activated aromatic, compounds using hydrogen chloride, formaldehyde and anhydrous zinc chloride. *See* Mannich reaction.

$$R—H + CH_2O + HCl \rightarrow R—CH_2Cl + H_2O$$

Chloromycetin. A trade name for chloramphenicol.

Chloronaphthalenes. *α-Chloronaphthalene.* Colourless refractive liquid, b.p. $263°$, sp.gr.

1·202 at 15°. Prepared by direct chlorination of naphthalene in the presence of ferric chloride. Used as in industrial solvent.

Other chlorinated naphthalenes. The other monochloronaphthalene (β-), the ten theoretically possible dichloronaphthalenes, and the fourteen trichloronaphthalenes have all been prepared, generally from the corresponding amino-derivatives by diazotization and treatment with cuprous chloride. They are of no industrial importance, but form a convenient set of reference compounds for the determination of the orientation of the substituents in an unknown naphthalene compound.

Chlorophenol red, Dichlorophenolsulphonphthalein. One of the sulphonphthalein group of indicators. It is used in 0·04% aqueous solution after neutralization with sodium hydroxide. Its pH range is 4·8 (yellow) to 6·4 (red).

Chlorophyll. Chlorophyll is the green colouring matter of plants. Two chlorophylls are present in plants, *chlorophyll a*, $C_{55}H_{72}MgN_4O_5$, which is obtained as a blue-black powder, and *chlorophyll b*, $C_{55}H_{70}MgN_4O_6$, a dark-green powder. Both are soluble in alcohol and ether. Chlorophyll *a* has the formula:

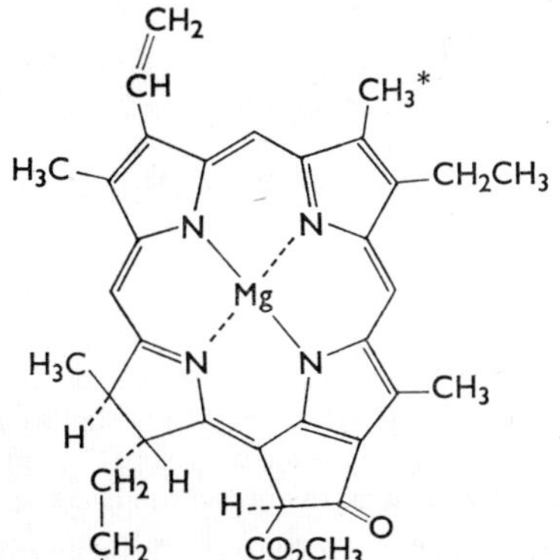

$$R = C_{29}H_{39} \quad \text{(Phytol)}$$

The methyl group marked with an asterisk is replaced by an aldehyde group in chlorophyll *b*. The ratio of chlorophyll *a* to chlorophyll *b* in green leaves is about 3 to 1, and the two pigments can be separated by extracting a solution of them in petroleum ether with methyl alcohol in which chlorophyll *b* is preferentially soluble. Treatment of chlorophyll *a* with acids removes the magnesium atom, replacing it by two hydrogen atoms, and gives an olive-brown solid, phaeophytin *a*,

$$C_{32}H_{32}ON_4 \Big\langle \begin{array}{l} COOCH_3 \\ COOC_{20}H_{39} \end{array}$$

Hydrolysis of this splits off phytol, and gives phaeophorbide *a*,

$$C_{32}H_{32}ON_4 \Big\langle \begin{array}{l} COOCH_3 \\ COOH \end{array}$$

Similar compounds are obtained from chlorophyll *b*. Alkaline degradation of chlorophyll yields a series of phyllins—magnesium porphyrin compounds—the final member of the series being aetiophyllin, and treatment of the phyllins with acids gives porphyrins, resembling, but not identical with, those obtained from the animal blood pigments.

Chlorophyll is present in all green plants, and is essential to the life of the plant, as it acts as a catalyst in the photosynthesis of carbohydrates from carbon dioxide and water.

Crude chlorophyll is prepared commercially from alfalfa meal or nettles by extraction with alcohol and partition into benzene. It is used as a colouring matter, particularly for foods and pharmaceutical products. It has been synthesized.

Chlorophyllase. An enzyme belonging to the esterase or fat-splitting class. It acts to split off phytol from chlorophyll in ethanolic solutions, and is widely distributed in leaves.

Chloropicrin, CCl_3NO_2. A colourless liquid; the vapour is lachrymatory and highly toxic; d^{20} 1·654, b.p. 112°. Insoluble in water, miscible with alcohol or acetone. Manufactured by treating sodium picrate with chlorine, or calcium picrate with bleaching powder. It is stable to cold acids or alkalis, but decomposed by reducing agents such as sulphides. It has been used in gas warfare. It is used as an insecticide, parasiticide, and for disinfecting cereals.

Chloroplasts. Photosynthetic processes in green plants take place within the chloroplasts, which are subcellular bodies or *organelles* containing chlorophylls, carotenoids, plastoquinones and other required factors. Light energy absorbed by the pigments leads to the release of electrons, with the aid of which ATP is produced through the intermediacy of plastoquinones.

Chloroplatinic acid, Chloroplatinous acid. See Platinum chlorides, complex.

Chloroprene, β-**Chlorobutadiene,** C_4H_5Cl, $CH_2:CCl\cdot CH:CH_2$. A colourless liquid, d_{20}^{20} 0·9583, b.p. 59·4°. Sparingly soluble in water; miscible with most organic liquids. Manufactured by treating vinylacetylene with hydrochloric acid at 30° in the presence of cuprous ammonium chloride. Changes to a rubber-like solid in ten days at 25°; this polymerization is 700 times as rapid as that of isoprene. Used to prepare synthetic rubbers which are resistant to oil and are not affected by ozone, e.g. neoprene.

2-Chloropropane. See Isopropyl chloride.

2-Chloropropyl alcohol. See Propylene chlorohydrins.

3-Chloropropylene glycol. See Glycerol monochlorohydrins.

Chlorostannates. Salts of chlorostannic acid, H_2SnCl_6, $6H_2O$. Ammonium chlorostannate, $(NH_4)_2SnCl_6$, known commercially as 'pink salt', was formerly used as a mordant in dyeing. See Tin chlorides.

Chlorosulphuric acid, $SO_2Cl(OH)$. A colourless liquid, m.p. $-80°$, b.p. $151°$, obtained by the direct combination of SO_3 and HCl; also by distilling concentrated sulphuric acid with phosphorus pentachloride or phosphorus oxychloride. It reacts violently with water to form sulphuric and hydrochloric acids. It may be used as a chlorinating or sulphonating agent.

Chlorothiazide, $C_7H_6ClN_3O_4S_2$. A white

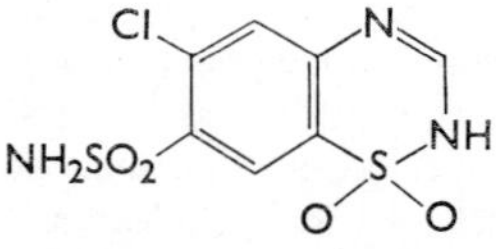

crystalline powder, almost insoluble in water and in alcohol, insoluble in chloroform and ether. Slightly soluble in acetone, soluble in solutions of the alkali hydroxides.

It is used as a diuretic against oedema and hypertension.

Chlorotoluenes, C_7H_7Cl. *o-Chlorotoluene.*

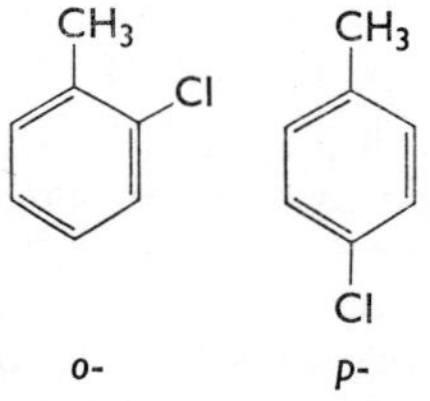

Colourless oil, b.p. $159°$, sp.gr. $1·0881$ at $15°$. M.p. $-34°$.

p-Chlorotoluene. Liquid, b.p. $162°$, sp.gr. $1·075$ at $15°$. M.p. $7·4°$.

The two monochlorotoluenes are prepared together by the direct chlorination of toluene in the presence of a catalyst. The mixture can be separated by sulphonation with 93% sulphuric acid, which only affects the *o*-chloro-compound, followed by separation and regeneration of the *o*-chlorotoluene by hydrolysis. *o*-Chlorotoluene is the more important of the two and is also easily prepared from *o*-nitrotoluene, by diazotization and treatment with cuprous chloride, or by chlorinating toluene-*p*-sulphonyl

chloride followed by removal by hydrolysis of the sulphonic group.

o-Chlorotoluene is used as a source of *o*-chlorobenzaldehyde.

2-Chlorotrimethylene glycol. See Glycerol monochlorohydrins.

Chlorous acid. This acid, $HClO_2$, is unknown in the pure state. It is formed in solution, together with chloric acid, by dissolving chlorine dioxide in water. Chlorine dioxide reacts with sodium dioxide, Na_2O_2, forming sodium chlorite, $NaClO_2$, and free oxygen. Numerous metallic chlorites have been prepared by double decomposition, the lead and silver salts being insoluble in water. Chlorites are fairly stable in alkaline solution. In the solid state they decompose on heating, or may detonate on heating or shock. Mercuric chlorite is one of the least stable. Either in the solid state or in solution the chlorites behave as powerful oxidizing agents. Sodium chlorite is widely used in industry as a bleach.

Chlorpromazine, Largactil, $C_{17}H_{19}ClN_2S \cdot HCl$. A white or cream-coloured powder m.p. $194°$-$197°$. It is soluble in water, in alcohol and in

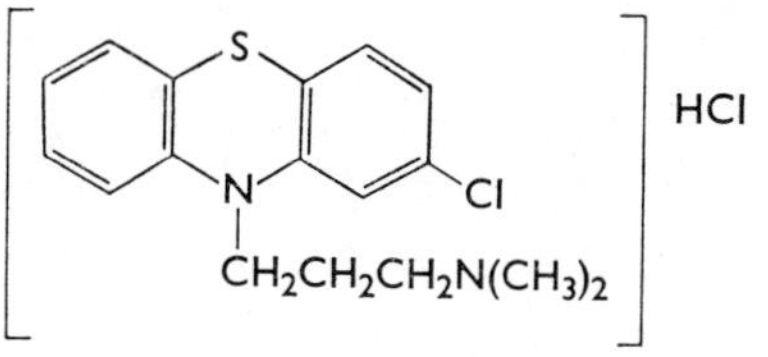

chloroform, Insoluble in benzene and in ether. It is a major tranquillizer, also an anti-emetic. The chlorine-free compound *promazine* (trade name Sparine) $C_{17}H_{20}N_2S \cdot HCl$ is slightly less sensitizing, and is widely used as a minor tranquillizer and as an adjunct to anaesthesia.

Chlorpropamide, Diabenese, *N*-4-chlorobenzenesulphonyl-*N'*-propylurea, $C_{10}H_{13}ClN_2O_3S$. A white crystalline powder, insoluble in water,

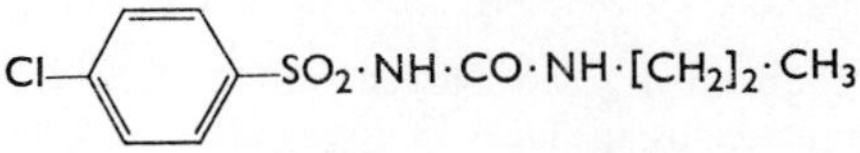

soluble in 12 parts of 95% alcohol. It is a hypoglycaemic substance, taken orally in the treatment of diabetes.

Chlortetracycline. See Tetracyclines.

Chlorthiamid. The common name for 2,6-dichlorothiobenzamide, $C_7H_5Cl_2NS$, a herbicide with a high level of biological activity.

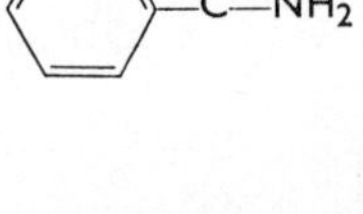

It is an off-white crystalline solid, m.p. 151°-152°.

Chlorthiamid is used for selective weed control in transplanted rice, fruit and vines and also for industrial total weed control.

Cholane ring system. The C_{24} skeleton of the

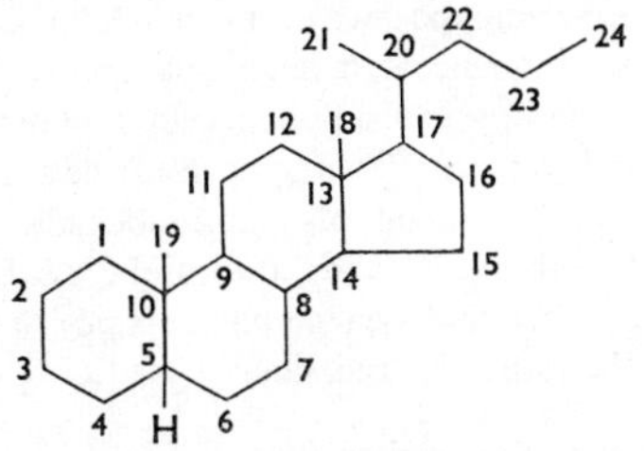

common bile acids, numbered as shown. The hydrocarbon depicted is 5β-cholane, m.p. 90°, which has the *cis*-ring junction as found in the major natural bile acids.

Cholanic acids, $C_{24}H_{44}O_2$. 5β-Cholanic acid

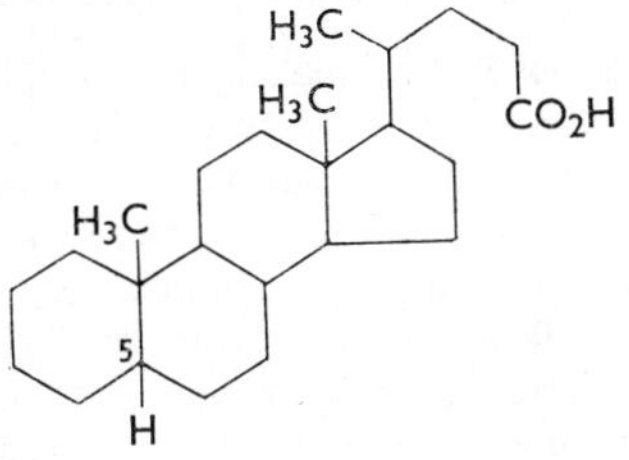

(as shown), a reduction product of the commoner bile acids, has the *cis*-ring junction. It crystallizes from acetic acid, m.p. 164°, $[\alpha]_D$ +22° in chloroform. The epimeric 5α-cholanic acid, formerly known as *allo*cholanic acid, has m.p. 170°, $[\alpha]_D$ +22°.

Cholestanol, $C_{27}H_{48}O$. The trivial name for 5α-

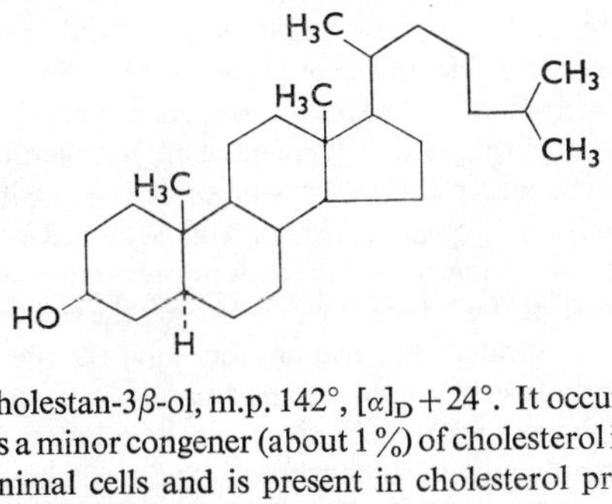

cholestan-3β-ol, m.p. 142°, $[\alpha]_D$ +24°. It occurs as a minor congener (about 1%) of cholesterol in animal cells and is present in cholesterol prepared commercially from spinal cord.

Cholesterol, Cholest-5-en-3β-ol, $C_{27}H_{46}O$. Crystallizes as the monohydrate from dilute alcohol; loses the water at 70°-80° and has m.p. 149°, $[\alpha]_D$ −39° in chloroform. Almost insoluble in water, soluble in hot ethanol and most other organic solvents. Forms an insoluble digitonide, also a crystalline dibromide which is useful for purification: the free sterol may be regenerated by treatment with zinc dust.

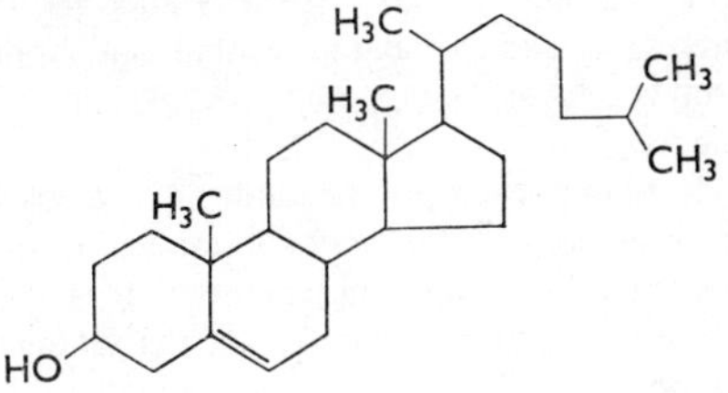

Cholesterol is the principal sterol of animals, and is found in free and esterified forms in all parts of the animal body. It was first isolated from gallstones but is an essential constituent of blood, brain, nervous tissue, liver, and the adrenal glands. Cholesterol is obtained commercially from beef spinal cords by extraction with ethylene dichloride, also from wool 'wax' in which it occurs with lanosterol (*q.v.*).

Cholesterol is synthesized by animals from acetate units via mevalonic acid, squalene and lanosterol. In addition to its own biological functions, it is of extreme importance as precursor of the other steroids required in animal metabolism, notably the bile acids, the sex hormones, and the adrenocortical hormones; it is also the source of endogenous vitamin D.

Cholesterol has been found in algae and some plants, but the typical sterols of higher plants have alkyl groups at C_{24}. See Stigmasterol, β-Sitosterol.

See 'Cholesterol', ed. R. P. Cook, Academic Press, 1958.

Cholic acid, $C_{24}H_{46}O_5$. Cholic acid is 3α,7α,12α-

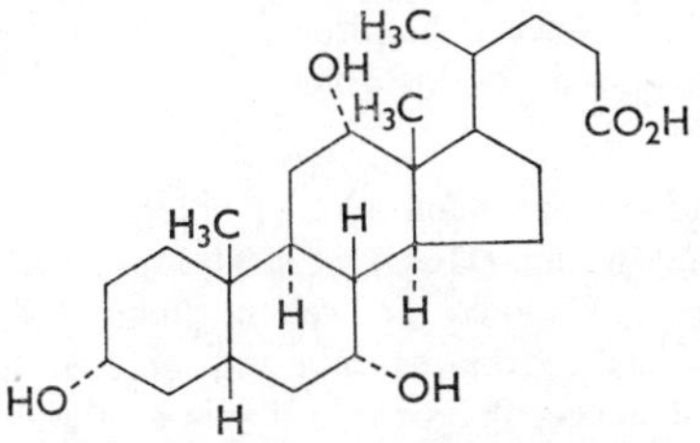

trihydroxy-5β-cholanic acid. It crystallizes from water as the monohydrate. Anhydrous form, m.p. 195°, $[\alpha]_D$ +37°. Sparingly soluble in water, ether and benzene; moderately soluble in alcohol and acetone; readily soluble in acetic acid.

Mammalian bile contains sodium salts of 'conjugated' bile acids, e.g. glycocholic acid and taurocholic acid, in which cholic acid is combined (amide linkage) with glycine and taurine respectively.

Choline,   Trimethyl-2-hydroxyethylammonium hydroxide.

$$[(CH_3)_3NCH_2 \cdot CH_2OH]^+OH^-$$

A colourless syrup crystallizing with difficulty to a hygroscopic mass. Strongly alkaline. It is present as a constituent of lecithin in all animal and vegetable tissues, and less commonly as the free base.

It is important in the body as, except for methionine, it is the only substance known to take part in methylating reactions. It is sometimes regarded as a member of the vitamin-B group.

Choline sulphate occurs in fungi (up to 0·2% of the dry mycelium by weight), lichens and red algae. Its biosynthesis appears to be limited to plants and higher fungi.

Choline-esterase. An enzyme able to hydrolyse acetylcholine to acetic acid and choline; it is widely distributed in the tissues. Acetylcholine is the substance in the body by means of which the para-sympathetic nerves produce their effect, so that an enzyme able to destroy it or synthesize it from the components is of considerable interest. The enzyme itself is specifically and reversibly poisoned by a number of urethanes allied to eserine, and by the fluorophosphonates. It acts on other esters of choline.

Cholylglycine. See Glycocholic acid.

D-**Chondrosamine,   2-amino-2-deoxy-D-galactose,** $C_6H_{13}NO_5$. It can be crystallized as the hydrochloride. It is obtained from chondroitin, the constituent of cartilage and tendons. Chondroitin, which is usually sulphonated, is a polymer containing   N-acetylchondrosamine and D-glucuronic acid.

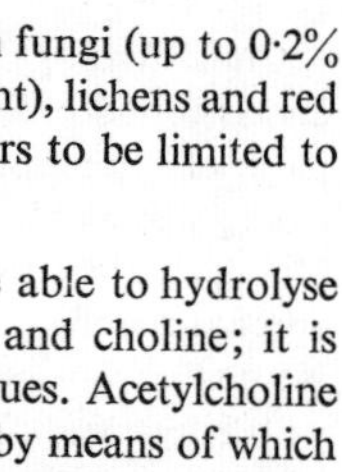

Chorionic gonadotropin. Human chorionic gonadotropin (HCG) is a glycoprotein hormone, of molecular weight about 100,000, produced by the placenta and excreted in the urine during pregnancy. It has a stimulating effect on the development of the gonads and may be estimated by its action on the ovaries of immature female rats. Its excretion is one of the surest tests for early pregnancy. HCG is of therapeutic value in the treatment of hypogonadism and sterility. Serum gonadotropin is a similar preparation from the serum of pregnant mares. See also Gonadotropic hormones.

Chorismic acid, $C_{10}H_{10}O_6$. Crystallizes as the monohydrate, m.p. 148°-149°, $[\alpha]_D$ −295°. An intermediate in aromatic biosynthesis via the

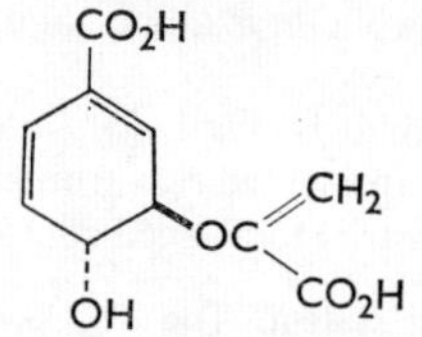

'shikimic acid pathway'. From shikimic acid (q.v.) the sequence is through 5-phosphoshikimic acid, 3-enolpyruvylshikimic acid 5-phosphate, to chorismic acid. This appears to be the final common precursor of p-aminobenzoic acid, p-hydroxybenzoic acid, anthranilic acid (and tryptophan), and (via prephenic acid) (q.v.) of phenylalanine and tyrosine.

Chroman. A strongly refractive liquid, b.p. 214°-215° (749 mm) which smells like peppermint. It may be regarded as the parent of a number of important classes of compounds derived from the γ-pyrone skeleton (e.g. flavone, xanthone) and the important chroman derivatives called the tocopherols (vitamin E).

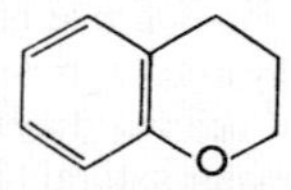

Chromates. Salts of the unknown acid H_2CrO_4. Acid chromates of the type $KHCrO_4$ are not known but anionic polymerization occurs to give the dichromate, $Cr_2O_7^{2-}$, and higher anions. These all contain oxygen bridges.

Normal potassium chromate, K_2CrO_4, is yellow and isomorphous with potassium sulphate. Both this salt and the dichromate, $K_2Cr_2O_7$, are non-deliquescent and crystallize without water. The corresponding sodium salts are Na_2CrO_4, $10H_2O$ and $Na_2Cr_2O_7$, $2H_2O$, and are deliquescent. Ammonium dichromate decomposes violently on heating, evolving nitrogen and steam and leaving a green mass of Cr_2O_3. The chromates of the heavy metals are, in general, insoluble.

The chromates are used extensively as oxidizing agents, in the tanning industry, and in the photographic and printing industries. Sodium dichromate and sodium chromate are obtained from chromite by calcining the ore with sodium carbonate in the presence of air at 1100°, when sodium chromate is formed. This is leached from the resulting mass, aluminium precipitated by treatment with sodium dichromate, the solution concentrated by evaporation and the decahydrate crystallized out. Sodium dichromate is obtained from sodium chromate solution by treatment with sulphuric acid. Sodium sulphate crystallizes out preferentially and the dichromate is obtained in a fairly pure state.

Chromatography, chromatographic analysis. The process for the separation of the constituents of a mixture of chemicals by passing a solution of the mixture or its vapour through a column

140

of absorbent material. The constituents of the mixture are absorbed at different rates on the absorbent, and so layers or bands of pure chemicals build up. The volumes or areas of each can be measured by suitable means, or they may be separated mechanically or recovered by leaching with solvents. The method may therefore be used for the analysis of mixtures or for the separation and recovery of the constituents of a mixture. The latter method is used industrially in the preparation of various fine chemicals.

The name was originally given because the bands which separated were identified colorimetrically. Modern developments have rendered the term an inappropriate one.

One later development is paper chromatography in which strips of filter paper are used as the adsorbent. A solution of a mixture is applied to a corner of the paper and washed down with a solvent. The paper may subsequently be turned perpendicularly and the chromatogram developed in two dimensions using another solvent. This method has been used for the separation and identification of amino-acids in mixtures, the positions of the amino-acids on the paper being shown by spraying with ninhydrin, and has many other uses.

Thin layer chromatography uses a thin layer of absorbent deposited on a suitable surface. It is used as a method of handling small samples and reactions can be carried out directly on the plate.

Another important development is that of gas-liquid or vapour phase chromatography. Here the stationary phase consists of a liquid, for example a silicone oil, on a column of a solid carrier, which is kept at a suitable temperature. The mixture of materials to be analysed is injected at the top of the column, volatilized, and carried through in a stream of inert gas, such as nitrogen or helium. The appearance of the separated components is detected at the bottom of the column, usually by making use of some physical property, e.g. thermal conductivity. This technique is extremely valuable for the separation and identification of mixtures of many components, and also as a criterion of purity of materials.

Chrome alum, $K_2SO_4 \cdot Cr_2(SO_4)_3 \cdot 24H_2O$. A typical alum. Used to harden gelatin. See Gelatin hardeners.

Chrome green. See Chromium oxides.

Chrome orange. See Lead chromates.

Chrome yellow. See Lead chromates.

Chromic acid. A name incorrectly used for chromium trioxide.

Chromite, $FeCr_2O_4$. Occurs as brownish-black

octahedral crystals and in massive form with a granular and compact structure. Sp. gr. 4·3, hardness 5-6, m.p. 2180°. It has the spinel structure. Chromite is the only commercial source of chromium, and is also used in the manufacture of ferrochrome, chromium compounds, and (with a suitable binder) chrome refractories.

Chromites. Chromites (III), containing $[Cr(OH)_6]^{3-}$ ions are formed when Cr_2O_3 dissolves in excess of base. Mixed oxides
$$M^{II}Cr_2O_4$$
having spinel structures are formed by fusing the appropriate oxides. Mixed oxides of Cr(IV), e.g. $M_2^{II}CrO_4$ and Cr(V), e.g. $M_3^{II}(CrO_4)_2$ are also known. The action of a KOH melt on K_2CrO_4 gives a green solution containing the CrO_4^3, hypochromate ion.

Chromium, Cr. At.no. 24, At.wt. 52·01; m.p. 1903°, b.p. 2475°, d^{25} 7·188. Crystallizes in the body-centred cubic structure, $a = 2\cdot8839$ Å.

Discovered in 1797 by Vauquelin and by Klaproth in the mineral crocoisite, a lead chromate, $PbCrO_4$.

Chromium metal does not occur native. The most important mineral is chromite, or chrome-ironstone, $FeCr_2O_4$, a spinel. Rarer minerals are chrome-ochre, Cr_2O_3, and chrometite, Fe_2O_3, Cr_2O_3.

The technical production of the metal is carried out in two stages; the chromite ore is fused with alkaline carbonate, the chromate extracted with water, converted to dichromate by means of acid, and finally reduced to the green oxide, Cr_2O_3; the sesquioxide is then reduced with aluminium in a thermite reaction. The chromium prepared by this process is 99·5% pure. Pure chromium, or chromium plate, is obtained by the electrolysis of solutions of the trioxide, CrO_3. A finely divided chromium, which is pyrophoric, is obtained by heating chromium amalgam *in vacuo*. The trioxide has also been reduced to the metal by carbon in an electric arc, and by hydrogen at 1500°.

Chromium is a hard, crystalline, but malleable metal, silver-white, with a bluish tinge in colour. It is very resistant to oxidation, and is used as a protective coating for many metals. It dissolves slowly in dilute sulphuric and hydrochloric acids, forming in the absence of air blue solutions of chromium (II) salts. It is readily soluble in concentrated acids, although in concentrated nitric acid it becomes passive. Passivity is also induced by exposure to air or dipping in chromic acid. It finds wide application in plating. It is a common alloy–additive to steel. Added to low carbon steels 3-25% chromium provides corrosion resistance. In medium carbon steels 1% chromium improves the hardenability and the strength. In high carbon steels 1-18%

chromium is added to form hard carbides for wear resistance.

Chromium compounds. Chromium forms two series of salts of oxidation states +3 and +2. It also forms an acidic oxide, chromium trioxide, CrO_3, giving rise to the salts known as chromates and dichromates. A rather less stable chromium (IV) dioxide is also known.

Chromium compounds are used for making pigments, in tanning, dyeing metal treatment and corrosion control, as oxidizing agents in organic syntheses.

Chromium complexes. Chromium (III) forms a very large number of complexes, the most common ligands containing nitrogen, oxygen, and sulphur. The chromium ammines very closely resemble the cobalt (III) ammines. Chromium (II) complexes are less stable.

Chromium bromides. *Chromic bromide*, $CrBr_3$. This forms hydrates, e.g. green

$$[Cr(H_2O)_4Br_2]Br \cdot 2H_2O$$

and violet $[Cr(H_2O)_6]Br_3$, very similar to the corresponding chlorides.

Chromous bromide, $CrBr_2$. A white solid, very soluble in water, prepared by the action of hydrogen bromide on chromium in the absence of air.

Chromium carbonyl, $Cr(CO)_6$. Prepared by the action of carbon monoxide under pressure on chromic chloride and a reducing agent. It is a white powder, m.p. 149°. It is extremely stable both thermally and chemically.

Chromium chlorides. *Chromium (IV) chloride*, $CrCl_4$. This is formed as a gas by interaction of chromic chloride and chlorine at 600°-700° followed by rapid cooling. It begins to decompose at −80°.

Chromic chloride, $CrCl_3$. Anhydrous chromic chloride is obtained by passing chlorine over chromium or a mixture of chromic oxide and carbon heated to redness. The peach-blossom coloured, scaly crystals volatalize at 1065°. They are insoluble in water, unless a trace of chromous chloride is present.

Three crystalline hydrates are known, $[Cr(H_2O)_6]Cl_3$ is violet; $[Cr(H_2O)_5Cl]Cl_2 \cdot H_2O$ is green; $[Cr(H_2O)_4Cl_2]Cl \cdot 2H_2O$ is green. These complexes are good examples of co-ordination isomerism.

Chromous chloride. The anhydrous salt is obtained by heating chromic chloride in hydrogen, or metallic chromium in hydrogen chloride. It forms silky white needles. The vapour density at 1300° corresponds to Cr_2Cl_4 but some dissociation occurs at 1600°. The hydrated salts are obtained by reducing potassium dichromate with zinc and hydrochloric acid, precipitating the chromium (II) as the acetate, dissolving this in

concentrated hydrochloric acid at 0° in an atmosphere of hydrogen, and finally precipitating the blue crystalline tetrahydrate by hydrogen chloride gas. The following hydrates are known:−6 aq. (blue); 4 aq. (blue); 3 aq. (pale blue); 2 aq. (pale green). Chromous chloride is a powerful reducing agent and is extensively used as such.

Chromium fluorides. *Chromium hexafluoride.* A red volatile material prepared by the action of fluorine at high temperature and pressure on a lower fluoride.

Chromium pentafluoride, CrF_5. A red, fairly volatile solid obtained by the action of fluorine on a chromium compound. Complex fluorides, $MCrOF_4$, are prepared by the action of bromine trifluoride on dichromates.

Chromium tetrafluoride, CrF_4. A brown amorphous solid prepared by the action of fluorine on a chromium compound. Complex fluorides, M_2CrF_6, are prepared by the action of fluorine on a mixture of alkali metal salt and chromium salt.

Chromium trifluoride, CrF_3. The anhydrous salt is obtained by the action of hydrogen fluoride on Cr_2O_3. Many hydrates and complex fluorides of the types M_3CrF_6 and $M_2CrF_5 \cdot H_2O$ are known.

Chromium difluoride, CrF_2. A green solid, made by the action of hydrogen fluoride on chromium. A complex, $KCrF_3$, is known.

Chromium hydroxide (III). Obtained by precipitating a chromium (III) solution with caustic soda, potash, or ammonia; it is a pale green flocculent precipitate. The purity of the product depends on the conditions of precipitation; in hot solutions with ammonia the reaction is quantitative, but there is little evidence for the true hydroxide, $Cr(OH)_3$, as distinct from the hydrated oxide, $Cr_2O_3 \cdot nH_2O$. In the cold, in the presence of a large excess of ammonia, chromammines are formed, e.g.

$$[CrCl(NH_3)_4(H_2O)]Cl_2$$

which impart to the solution a pink colour. The hydroxide dissolves in concentrated alkali to form chromites (*q.v.*).

Chromium oxides. *Chromous oxide*, CrO. This is prepared by oxidizing chromium amalgam with air. At high temperatures hydrogen reduces it to the metal.

Chromic oxide, Cr_2O_3. Is obtained as a green powder by ignition of the hydroxide, ammonium dichromate, mercurous chromate, or sodium dichromate with sulphur. Cr_2O_3 is an amphoteric oxide giving $[Cr(H_2O)_6]^{3+}$ and $[Cr(OH)_6]^{3-}$ species with acids and bases respectively. Chromic oxide is very refractory (m.p. 1990°), and is used to give a green colour to glass and porcelain. It is also used as a permanent green oil paint (chrome-green). See Viridian.

Chromium trioxide, Chromic anhydride, CrO_3. Obtained as a red crystalline precipitate by the action of concentrated sulphuric acid on a solution of a chromate or dichromate. It is a deliquescent material, $d\,2·7$, m.p. 198°, forming a dark red liquid, solidifying on cooling to a reddish-black mass with a metallic lustre. At 420° it loses oxygen, giving chromic oxide, Cr_2O_3. Chromium trioxide is a powerful oxidizing agent, and is used for this purpose in many reactions. The aqueous solution contains chromate (VI) ions.

Chromium trioxide is an important industrial chemical, largely used for metal treatment. Thus it is employed in chromium plating, the anodizing of aluminium, stripping oxide scale from copper and brass, forming corrosion-resistant coatings on metals, and as a corrosion inhibitor.

Chromium peroxide, CrO_5. A blue peroxide, stabilized by complexing by ether, extracted into ether when chromates are treated with hydrogen peroxide in acid solution.

Chromium dioxide, CrO_2. A black solid, prepared by the action of oxygen on chromium trioxide or chromic oxide at 420°-450° and 200-300 atm.

Chromium sulphates. *Chromic sulphate.* Obtained in violet crystals by dissolving chromium (III) hydroxide in sulphuric acid. On precipitating the aqueous solution with alcohol, octahedra of $Cr_2(SO_4)_3$, $18H_2O$ are deposited. Violet salts occur with 18, 9, 3, and 0 H_2O; there are green salts with 6 and 0 H_2O, and an anhydrous form of peach-blossom colour. Chromic sulphate combines with sulphates of the alkali metals, forming alums. Ordinary chrome alum has the formula

$$K_2SO_4.\,Cr_2(SO_4)_3,\,24H_2O$$

and is obtained by reducing a solution of potassium dichromate in sulphuric acid.

Chromous sulphate can be prepared as a blue hydrate with 5 and 7 molecules of water by electrolytic reduction of a solution of chromic sulphate.

Chromophore. In Witt's theory of colour it is a group responsible for the colour of the compound, i.e. in practice for causing absorption in the visible region of the spectrum, e.g. $-C=C-$, $-C=O$, $-N=N-$; chromophores are thus groups containing multiple bonds. See the chapter by E. A. Braude in 'Determination of Organic Structures by Physical Methods,' edited by E. A. Braude and F. C. Nachod.

Chromoproteins. A class of conjugated proteins related to haemoglobin and consisting of a protein combined with a pigment molecule such as haem and acting as respiratory carriers or catalysts.

Chromosomes. Linear, fibre-like bodies, enclosed in fixed numbers by the nuclei of all cells, which are responsible for the storage and reproduction of genetic information (hereditary transmission), and in sex cells also for the determination of sex. The principal structural components are nucleic acids.

Chromotropes. A class of azo wool dyes derived from chromotropic acid. When dyed on wool as acid dyes, they yield various tones of bright red shades having reasonable fastness to light but poor washing fastness. If after-mordanted (after-chromed) the shade changes remarkably and various tones of dark blue (navy blue to deep purple) are obtained. As these shades still have good light fastness and also good wet fastness, they are in extensive use for dyeing wool piece goods.

Chromotropic acid, 1,8-dihydroxynaphthalene-3,6-disulphonic acid, $C_{10}H_8O_8S_2$. When pure it crystallizes in colourless needles with two molecules of water. Soluble in water. It is used as a component for azo dyes, and as a reagent for the determination of titanium and formaldehyde.

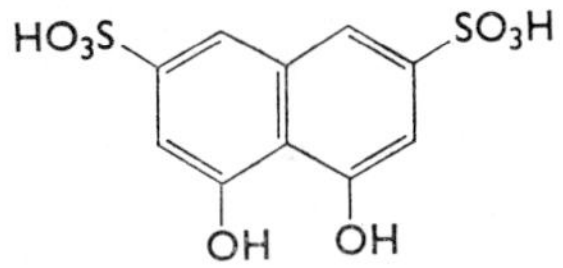

Chromous acetate, $[Cr(O_2CCH_3)_2]_2·2H_2O$. A red insoluble compound prepared by the action of sodium acetate on an aqueous solution of chromous chloride. It is the most stable chromium (II) compound; the structure shows a Cr—Cr bond.

Chromyl chloride, CrO_2Cl_2; b.p. 115·7°, m.p. $-96·5°$, $d\,1·9$. Obtained by distilling a mixture of sodium chloride and potassium dichromate with concentrated sulphuric acid. The dark red vapour evolved condenses to a nearly black liquid. It is decomposed violently by water with the production of chromic and hydrochloric acids. Chromyl chloride is a powerful oxidizing agent, exploding in contact with phosphorus, and inflaming sulphur and many organic substances. It is used in the Étard reaction in which it combines with an organic compound and, on hydrolysis, gives aldehydes or ketones. The vapour density is normal, corresponding to the formula CrO_2Cl_2, the acid chloride of chromic acid.

Chromyl compounds. Derivatives containing the CrO_2 grouping. Chromyl chloride is the best known compound but a fluoride, nitrate, bromide, and cyanate have been prepared. See *Chemical Reviews*, 1958, **58**, 1.

Chrysamine G, Direct Yellow 1. A yellow direct

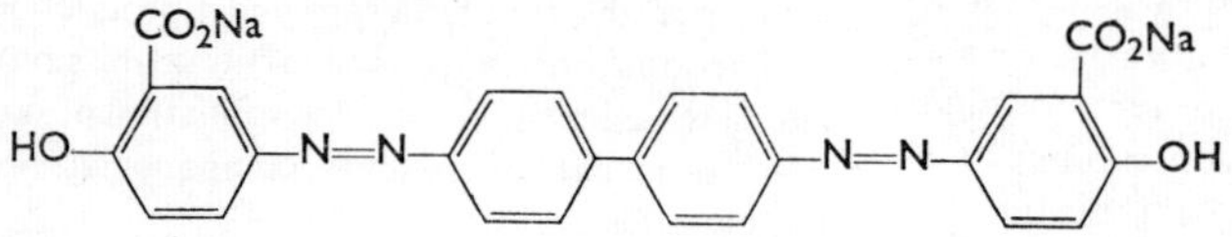

m.p. 117·5°. Soluble in alcohol and ether, sparingly soluble in water. The commercial product is the hydrochloride, which forms

cotton dyestuff, obtained by tetrazotizing one mole of benzidine in hydrochloric acid solution and reacting this with two moles of salicylic acid in alkaline solution.

It was the first direct yellow cotton dyestuff to be obtained and dyes unmordanted cotton from a soap bath.

Chrysanthemum carboxylic acids. These are the acids, esters of which are the active constituents

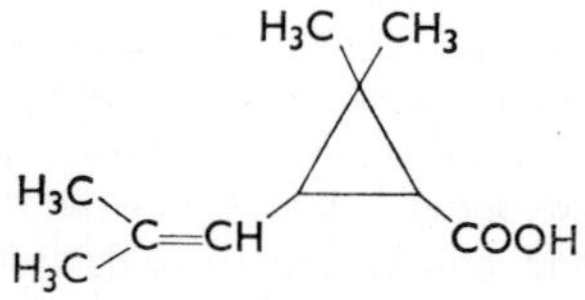

Chrysanthemum monocarboxylic acid

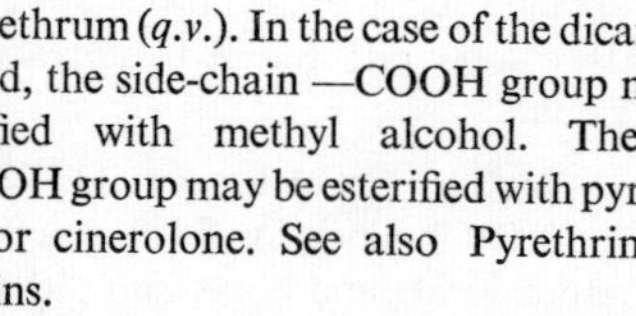

Chrysanthemum dicarboxylic acid

of pyrethrum (*q.v.*). In the case of the dicarboxylic acid, the side-chain —COOH group may be esterified with methyl alcohol. The ring —COOH group may be esterified with pyrethrolone or cinerolone. See also Pyrethrins and Cinerins.

Chrysene, $C_{18}H_{12}$. Crystallizes in colourless

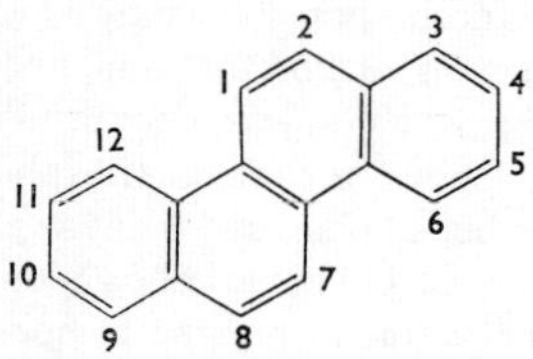

plates, m.p. 254°, b.p. 448°. Soluble in hot benzene and sparingly soluble in alcohol. It occurs in the highest boiling fraction of coal tar. A characteristic picrate is formed.

Chrysoidine, C.I. Basic Orange 2, **2,4-diaminoazobenzene,** $C_{12}H_{12}N_4$. Pale yellow crystals,

blackish-green prisms. It is prepared by the interaction of benzene diazonium chloride and *m*-phenylenediamine. It is employed as a

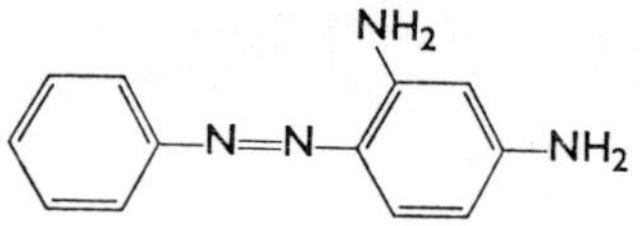

dyestuff for cotton treated with tannin. It has been used as a photographic desensitizer and as a light filter.

Chrysotile. A variety of asbestos (*q.v.*).

Chylomicrons. Fat droplets which can be observed in the blood serum after the ingestion of moderate amounts (1-2 oz) of fats.

Chymotrypsins. An important group of proteolytic enzymes, produced in the pancreas from inactive chymotrypsinogen, and activated by trypsin (*q.v.*). Chymotrypsins are major proteases of the intestine, effecting the digestion of casein and other dietary proteins. They are used clinically as anti-inflammatory agents for internal and external applications. Chymotrypsins act specifically on phenylalanine and tyrosine residues in the proteins.

Ciba dyes. See Acenaphthenequinone.

Ciment fondu. A hydraulic cement made by heating a suitable mixture of limestone and alumina (bauxite) until it sinters or even melts, cooling, and then reducing to powder. It sets slowly but hardens rapidly so that it is largely used where time is an important factor. It shows on analysis, lime 40%, alumina 40%, silica 10%, and impurities 10%. Sp.gr. 3·0. It is highly resistant to sea-water and to waters containing sulphates in solution. It has several advantages over Portland cement, but is more expensive. Recently it has been used as a refractory cement for repairing furnaces, retorts, etc.; for this purpose it is mixed with grog and water so as to form a soft paste. See Aluminous cement.

Cinchocaine, $C_{20}H_{29}N_3O_2$. A white powder, m.p. 63·5°-65·5°, almost insoluble in water, soluble in acids and in oils.

Its hydrochloride, which can be obtained as

white, hygroscopic crystals, soluble in water and alcohol, is used as a local anaesthetic.

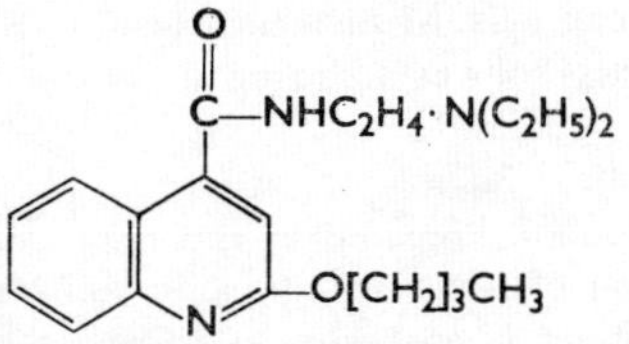

Cinchona. The dried bark of various species of *Cinchona*. It owes its medicinal properties to its alkaloidal contents, chief among which are quinine, cinchonidine, quinidine, and cinchonine. Cinchona has the actions of quinine, but other preparations are preferred in the treatment of malaria as it is bitter and astringent. Cinchona preparations have been used as tonics.

Cinchonidine, $C_{19}H_{22}N_2O$. The stereoisomer

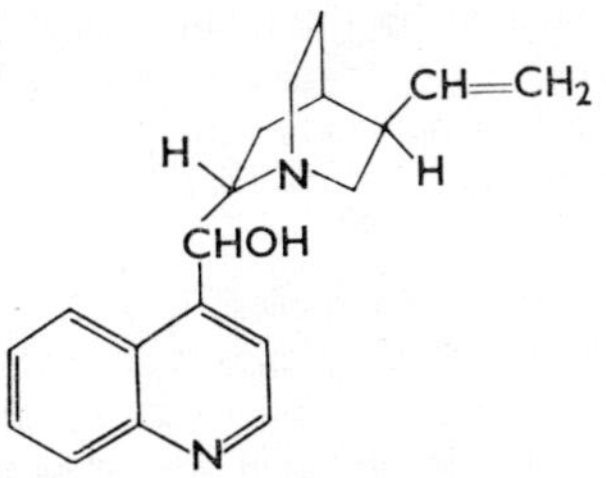

of cinchonine, and is also obtained from cinchona. Its physiological action resembles that of quinine, but like cinchonine it increases the reflexes and causes convulsions in large doses. Prisms, m.p. 210°, $[\alpha]_D^{20}$ −190·2° in alcohol.

Cinchonine, $C_{19}H_{22}N_2O$. Colourless needles, m.p. 255°. Practically insoluble in water, more

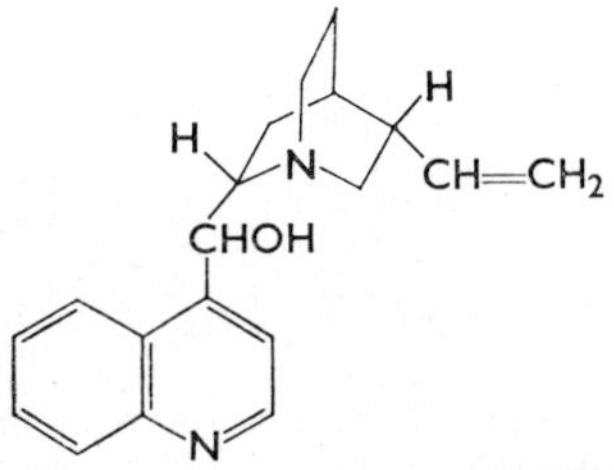

soluble in alcohol; $[\alpha]_D$ +229° in alcohol. Cinchonine is one of the cinchona alkaloids and is used to a small extent instead of quinine for patients who exhibit an idiosyncrasy to the latter. It increases reflexes, and in large doses it may cause convulsions.

Cinchophen, 2-phenylquinoline-4-carboxylic acid, $C_{16}H_{11}NO_2$. White crystals, insoluble in water, soluble in 120 parts of alcohol; m.p.

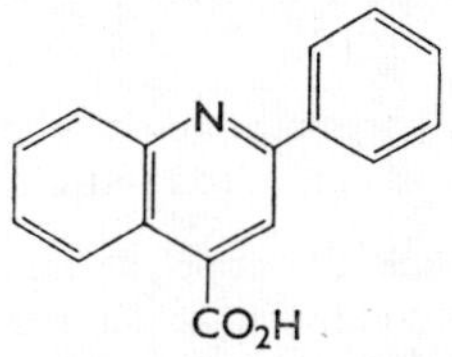

214°-217°. It is prepared by condensing isatin with acetophenone in the presence of alkali. It is used medicinally for rheumatism and gout, as it increases the rate of excretion of uric acid, but it may have a toxic action on the liver.

1,8-Cineole, Eucalyptol, Cajuputol, $C_{10}H_{18}O$. A very widely distributed constituent of essential oils; of commercial importance, as it is often considered as the active constituent of medicinal eucalyptus oil. Amongst other oils it is present in wormseed oil, cajuput oil, and in various eucalyptus oils, including that from *Eucalyptus globulus*. It is a colourless, viscous oil of characteristic camphorlike smell. M.p. −1°, b.p. 174·4°, d^{15} 0·930, n^{15} 1·4584. It possesses great chemical stability.

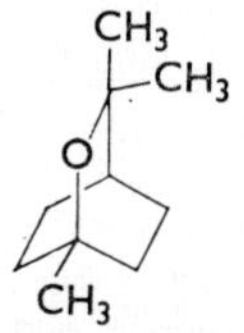

It forms a number of addition compounds; e.g., with resorcinol, $2(C_{10}H_{18}O)$, $C_6N_6O_2$, m.p. 80°-85°, and with *o*-cresol, $C_{10}H_{18}O$, C_7H_8O m.p. 55·5°. It forms a crystalline compound with phosphoric acid of the formula $C_{10}H_{18}O$, H_3PO_4. In medicine it is used for the same purposes as eucalyptus oil, from which it is obtained by fractionation or freezing.

Cinerins. Constituents of pyrethrum (*q.v.*).

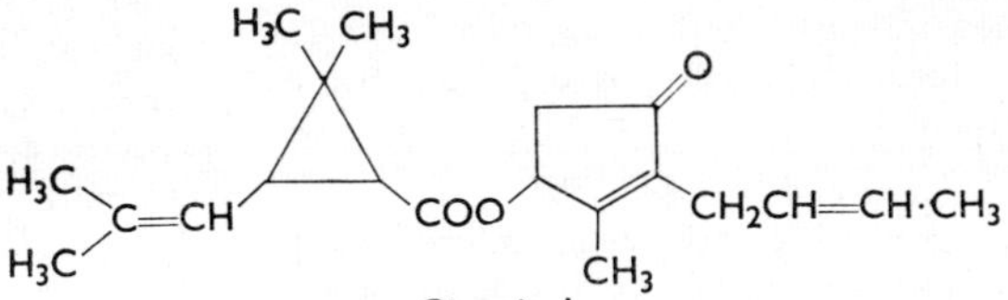

Cinerin I

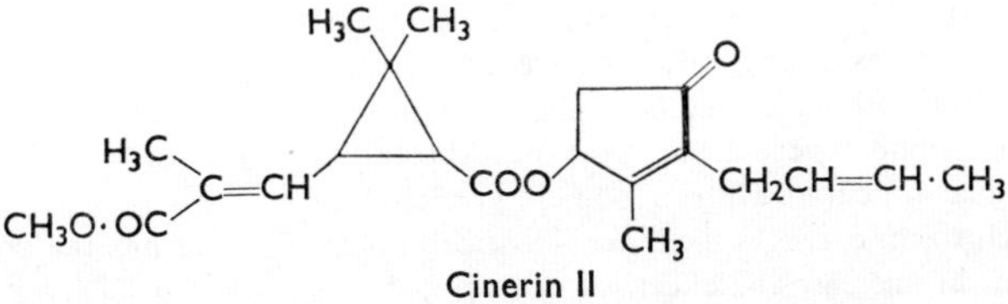

Cinerin II

145

Cinerin I is the ester of cinerolone and chrysanthemum monocarboxylic acid, and cinerin II is the ester of cinerolone and chrysanthemum dicarboxylic acid monomethyl ester.

Cinerolone. The ketonic alcohol, esters of

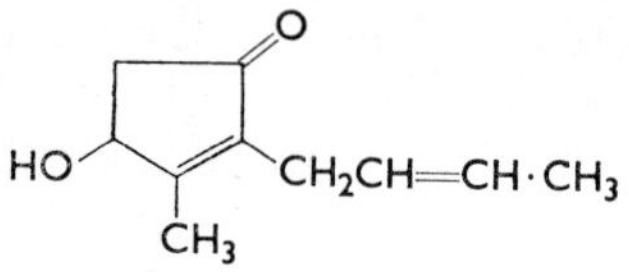

which with chrysanthemum carboxylic acids are the cinerins (*q.v.*). See Pyrethrins.

Cinnabar, HgS. The principal ore of mercury. It occurs naturally in bright red hexagonal crystals, hardness $2\frac{1}{2}$, sp.gr. 8·2, with strong birefringence, high refractivity, and rotatory polarization.

Cinnamic acid, $C_9H_8O_2$. Colourless crystals,

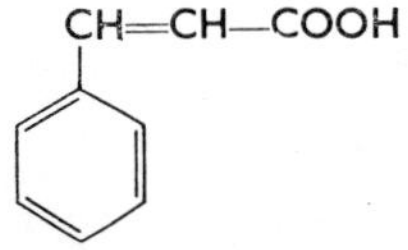

m.p. 133°, b.p. 290°. Soluble in alcohol and hot water, insoluble in cold water. Decarboxylates on prolonged heating. Oxidized by nitric acid to benzoic acid. Ordinary cinnamic acid is the *trans* isomer.

Prepared by heating benzaldehyde with sodium acetate and acetic anhydride or with ethyl acetate and sodium ethoxide. Occurs in storax, or liquid amber, as the ester cinnamyl cinnamate made from cinnamyl alcohol, $C_6H_5\cdot CH{=}CH\cdot CH_2OH$.

Circular dichroism. In the Cotton effect distinct changes in the polarization angle are seen as a function of wavelength. This is due to differences in the specific extinction coefficients for the left- and right-handed polarized light. As a linearly-polarized light wave passes through a substance the differing adsorptions cause an elliptically polarized wave to be produced. This phenomenon is known as circular dichroism. The magnitude of the effect is expressed by the equation

$$\phi = \pi/\lambda(\eta_l - \eta_r)$$

where ϕ is the ellipticity (in radians) of the emerging beam and η_l and η_r are the absorption indices of the left- and right-handed circularly-polarized light respectively. When the ellipticity is plotted as a function of wavelength, a curve is given with a maximum corresponding to the wavelength of zero angle in the optical rotatory dispersion curve. Optical isomers give circular dichroism curves which are identical except that in one case the effect is positive, i.e., ϕ is positive throughout whereas for the other isomer the effect is negative.

Citraconic acid, Methylmaleic acid, $C_5H_6O_4$. A colourless solid crystallizing in fine needles, m.p. 91° (decomp.). Soluble in water and alcohol. Prepared by the addition of water to citraconic anhydride. It loses water when heated and forms the anhydride. Reduced by hydrogen to pyrotartaric acid. Electrolysis of the acid yields propyne.

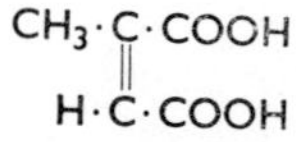

When a saturated solution in ether and chloroform is treated with a little bromine and placed in sunlight, crystals of mesaconic acid are slowly deposited.

Citraconic anhydride, Methylmaleic anhydride, $C_5H_4O_3$. A colourless solid, m.p. 7°, b.p. 213°. Soluble in ether. Prepared by the rapid distillation of anhydrous citric acid. Combines with water to give citraconic acid.

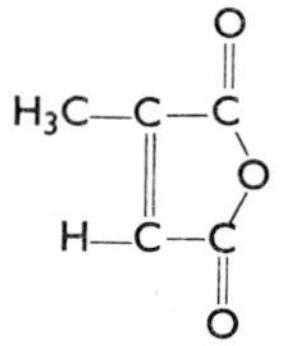

Citral, $C_{10}H_{16}O$. A terpene aldehyde. A volatile oil of pleasant odour forming the main constituent of lemon-grass oil from *Cymbopogon flexuosus,* and also found in other essential oils. Lemon-grass oil is an important article of commerce. The citral found in natural products is a mixture of cis- and trans-isomerides, known as *citral*-a and *citral*-b. *Citral*-a (geranial), which is the main constituent of the aldehydic fraction of lemon-grass oil, has the constitutional formula

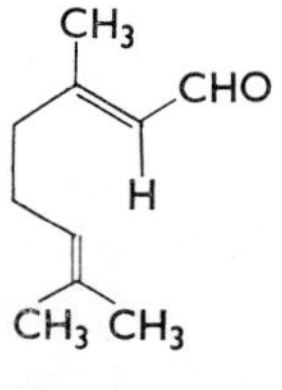

It is separated from *citral*-b as a sodium bisulphite compound. It has b.p. 118°-119°/20 mm, d^{20} 0·8898, n_D^{20} 1·4891. Its semicarbazone melts at 164°. *Citral*-b (neral) is separated from *citral*-a by means of its lesser reactivity with cyanoacetic acid. It has the constitutional formula

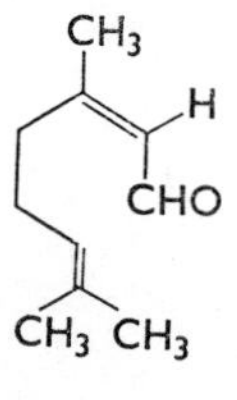

and has the constants: b.p. 117°-118°/20 mm, d^{20} 0·8888, n_D^{20} 1·4891. Its semicarbazone melts at 171°. When heated with dilute sulphuric acid citral forms *p*-cymene. Citral can be condensed with acetone to form a ketone, pseudoionone, $C_{13}H_{20}O$, which is technically important, as it is readily convertible into α- and β-ionone. Pseudoionone itself has no characteristic smell.

Citric acid, $C_6H_8O_7$. Crystallizes from water below 36·6° in large colourless prisms containing one molecule of water of crystallization; above this temperature the acid crystallizes in the anhydrous form, m.p. 153°. Very soluble in water and alcohol; less soluble in ether. It occurs in the juice of citrus fruits and in beets, cranberries, and certain other acid fruits. Lemon juice contains 5-6% citric acid, and was at one time the source of the acid. It is now manufactured by the fermentation of sugar by moulds of the *Aspergillus niger* group. The acid is tribasic, and forms three series of salts; the citrates of the alkali metals are soluble, but the neutral citrates of calcium and barium are insoluble. When heated to 175° it loses water to give aconitic acid: at higher temperatures aconitic and citraconic anhydrides are formed. Oxidation with potassium permanganate or heating with fuming sulphuric acid gives acetone dicarboxylic acid. When heated with an acid solution of mercuric sulphate and a little potassium permanganate it gives a white precipitate (Denige's test). It is used extensively in the soft drinks industry.

```
CH2COOH
|
HOC—COOH
|
CH2COOH
```

Citronellal (Rhodinal), $C_{10}H_{18}O$. An optically active terpenic aldehyde. Its (+)-form is found in Ceylonese citronella oil and in various eucalyptus oils, and the (−)-form in Javanese citronella oil and in the oil from *Pinus Jeffereyi*. It is easily reduced to citronellol. The physical constants vary according to the method of preparation but typical figures are b.p. 82°/2 mm, d_{20}^{20} 0·8682, $[\alpha]_D^{20}$ +9·19°. It forms a semicarbazone of m.p. 82·5°.

Citronellol (Rhodinol), $C_{10}H_{20}O$. Citronellol occurs in rose oil, geranium oil, and in citronella oils from Ceylon and Java. Citronellol has also been prepared by the reduction of citronellal with sodium amalgam and acetic acid. (+)-Citronellol from Java citronella oil has the following constants: b.p. 103°/5 mm, d^{15} 0·8604-0·8629, n_D^{22} 1·4565-1·4579, $[\alpha]_D$ +2·7° to +2·32°, whilst (−)-citronellol from geranium

oil has b.p. 114°-115°/12 mm, d^{22} 0·856-0·862, n^{20} 1·456, $[\alpha]_D$ −4·2°. Rhodinol is obtained from the same sources as citronellol, and probably has the same constitution as (−)-citronellol.

Citrulline, α-**Amino-δ-ureidovaleric acid,** $C_6H_{13}N_3O_3$. Crystallizes in prisms, m.p. 222°.

```
        O
        ‖
H2N—C—NH—[CH2]3—CH—CO2H
                    |
                    NH2
```

Soluble in water, insoluble in alcohol. Citrulline is an intermediate stage in the cycle of events in urea production in the body; it is formed from ornithine, ammonia, and carbon dioxide; it then combines with more ammonia to form arginine, and the arginine breaks down to ornithine and urea.

Claisen condensation. Condensation of an ester with another ester, a ketone, or a nitrile under the influence of sodium ethoxide, sodium, or sodamide, with the elimination of an alcohol. The result is the formation of a β-ketonic ester, ketone, or nitrile respectively, e.g.

$CH_3COOC_2H_5 + HCH_2COOC_2H_5 \rightarrow$
$CH_3COCH_2COOC_2H_5 + C_2H_5OH.$
ethyl acetoacetate

The reaction is of general application and of great importance, and a large number of syntheses have been effected by its use.

Claisen reaction. Condensation of an aldehyde with another aldehyde or a ketone in the presence of sodium hydroxide, water being eliminated. Thus benzaldehyde and acetaldehyde give cinnamic aldehyde, $C_6H_5CH:CH\cdot CHO$, and benzaldehyde and acetone give either monobenzylidene acetone, $C_6H_5CH:CHCOCH_3$, or dibenzylidene acetone,

$$C_6H_5CH:CHCOCH:CHC_6H_5$$

according to the quantities taken. It is probable that in all cases a hydroxy compound is first formed, which then loses water.

Clapeyron-Clausius equation. A thermodynamic expression applying to any 2-phase equilibrium for a pure substance (e.g. solid-liquid, liquid-vapour, etc.). The *exact* equation is

$$dP/dT = L/T\Delta V$$

where P is the pressure, T the absolute temp., L the molar latent heat of phase change and ΔV the corresponding change of molar volume. If one phase is a vapour, the expression reduces to

$$\ln P = C - L/RT$$

where P is now the vapour pressure of the liquid

147

or solid (R being the gas const.). C is a constant for the substance.

Clarain. A macroscopic constituent of coal which occurs in bands of varying thickness and stratified parallel to the bedding plane. It breaks at right angles to the bedding plane and is less friable than vitrain. Under the microscope it shows a striated appearance which is due to fragments of plant tissue existing in different stages of disintegration, and the translucency will depend on the extent of this disintegration. Cuticles, spores, and resin bodies may also be seen.

As defined at the various International Stratigraphical Conferences at Heerlen, 1937-1957, Clarain is one of the four rock types present in coal, the others being Vitrain, Durain and Fusain (*q.v.*). These rock types must be distinguished from the distinctive petrological units of coal called 'macerals' by being separable by physical means, e.g. by hand picking. The macerals which are present in the rock–type clarain include vitrinite, fusinite, and exinite.

Clarification. The removal from a liquid of small amounts of suspended matter with the object of obtaining a clear product. Clarification may be achieved by filtration, centrifugation, or by the use of a clarifier.

Clarifier. Continuous clarifiers are used for the treatment of trade wastes, domestic sewage and dilute suspensions. They consist of large tanks with continuous feed and outflow in which the suspended matter is allowed to settle. A raking mechanism drags the settled sludge to a discharge point. Clarifiers are generally similar to thickeners except that they handle smaller quantities of solids.

Clark, Thomas (1801-1867). Born at Ayr, Clark was educated at Ayr Academy. In 1826 he was appointed lecturer in chemistry at Glasgow Mechanics' Institute, but gave up this post in order to study medicine at Glasgow University where he graduated in 1831. From 1833 till 1860 Clark was professor of chemistry, Marischal College, Aberdeen. Expert in the subject of water purification, he introduced the use of calcium hydroxide for softening water. See 'The Teaching of Chemistry in the Universities of Aberdeen' (Findlay), p. 18.

Clark, William Mansfield (1884-1964). Clark was born at Tivoli, New York, and educated at Williams College and at the Johns Hopkins University. From 1910 to 1920 Clark was a chemist in the U.S. Department of Agriculture, which he then left to become professor of chemistry of the Hygienic Laboratory of the U.S. Public Health Service. From 1927 to 1952 he was professor of physiological chemistry at Johns Hopkins Medical School, Baltimore. He carried out fundamental work on hydrogen-ion concentration and on oxidation-reduction equilibria. See *Ann. Rev. Biochem.*, 1962, **31**, 1.

Clarke, Frank Wigglesworth (1847-1931). Born at Boston, Massachusetts, Clarke was educated at Harvard University. After being professor of chemistry and physics at Howard University (1873-1874), and at the University of Cincinnati (1874-1883), he was appointed chief chemist of the United States Geological Survey in 1883. His chief work was on physico-chemical constants, in particular on the re-calculation of the atomic weights, and on geochemical data. He was President of the American Chemical Society in 1901.

Classification. The process of separating a mixture of particles into two or more fractions according to size or density. Examples are the size classification of the product from the grinding of a homogeneous substance (e.g. calcined anthracite), and the separation of the metalliferous constituents from siliceous material following the grinding of a metallic ore.

Classifier. An apparatus which effects a separation on the basis of particle size by utilizing free settlement. Examples of this type of plant are the Spitzkasten and Dorr classifiers.

Clathrate compounds. Molecular compounds formed by the inclusion of molecules of one type in holes in the lattice of another. Organic compounds, particularly nitro-compounds and quinol, form lattices which are able to take up small molecules such as the rare gases. One of the best known clathrate compounds is the nickel ammonia cyanide benzene clathrate.

Claude process. A process similar to the Linde process (*q.v.*) for the liquefaction of air, except that additional cooling is produced by allowing the expanding gas to do external work.

Claudogens. A term proposed (Petrow, 1960) for steroids capable of inhibiting ovulation, or otherwise limiting fertility.

Clausius, Rudolf Julius Emmanuel (1822-1888). Born at Köslin in Pomerania, Clausius studied at the Gymnasium, Stettin, and Berlin University. He was appointed professor of physics, Berlin Engineering School (1850), Zurich Polytechnic and University (1855), and Würzburg (1867). Mathematical rather than experimental, his interests lay towards molecular physics. With Clerk Maxwell he put the kinetic theory of gases on a mathematical basis.

Clausius-Clapeyron equation. See Clapeyron-Clausius equation.

Clausius-Mosotti law. The relationship

$$P = \frac{D-1}{D+2} \cdot \frac{M}{d},$$

wherein P is the molecular polarization of a substance, D its dielectric constant, M its molecular weight, and d its density, is termed the Clausius-Mosotti law.

Clay. Used chiefly as the name of those portions of the earth's crust which occur as a plastic paste or can be converted into such a paste by grinding and mixing with water. Chemically, clays are aluminosilicates which do not form large crystals, but commercially and agriculturally the term has so wide a meaning as to be almost indefinable. Some china clays, for example, are almost devoid of plasticity, which is usually regarded as the chief characteristic of clays.

Clays, when dried and ground to powder, can be suspended in water and remain in suspension indefinitely, though the coarser particles of associated minerals settle fairly rapidly. Much less water is needed to effect the suspension if a very small proportion (0·2-0·5%) of sodium carbonate or other alkali is added. Such suspensions are used as a means of casting clay articles in plaster moulds. In dilute suspensions the particles are kept in motion by forces producing the Brownian movement, but in more concentrated suspensions the Brownian movement ceases and a gel may be formed.

Clays are sometimes classified as Na-clays, Ca-clays, H-clays, etc., according to the predominant ion of an easily replaceable nature. On washing H-clays with a solution containing metallic ions, the hydrogen is replaced by alkali or alkaline earth-ions or, occasionally, by iron ions.

Primary or residual clays are found at the place of their formation as distinct from secondary or sedimentary clays, which have been transported, usually by water, and redeposited. Primary clays are chiefly composed of kaolin (china clay) or montmorillonite and similar minerals, and are not very plastic. The particles are usually (but not always) coarser than those of secondary clays. Primary clays are usually associated with other minerals formed from the same rocks as the clay, and can be separated by washing. Primary clays are chiefly used in the manufacture of porcelain (china ware), and as inert fillers in the paper, textile, paint, and chemical industries.

Secondary clays are fine-grained and plastic. Ball clays, which are used to introduce plasticity into pottery mixtures, are of this type.

Clément, Nicholas (1779-1841). A native of Dijon, Clément became professor of applied chemistry at the Conservatoire des Arts-et-Métiers, Paris. He carried out numerous investigations in conjunction with Desormes, their principal achievements being the elucidation of the true nature of carbon monoxide and substantial improvements in the manufacture of sulphuric acid by the chamber process.

Clemmensen reduction. Aldehydes and ketones may be reduced to the corresponding hydrocarbons by heating them with amalgamated zinc and hydrochloric acid. This method, due to Clemmensen, has received wide application, and has been successfully employed for the reduction of aliphatic and aromatic aldehydes and ketones, cyclic ketones, and hydroxyaldehydes and ketones.

Clève, Per Theodor (1840-1905). Born at Stockholm, the son of a merchant, Clève was educated at the University of Uppsala. After studying for a time with Wurtz in Paris, he was appointed professor of chemistry at Uppsala. He was interested alike in chemistry, geology, botany, and hydrography but his fame rests chiefly on his discoveries among the rare earths. He discovered the element thulium, and was an independent discoverer of holmium. See *Chem. Soc. Mem. Lect.*, 1906.

Cleveite. A variety of the mineral uraninite consisting largely of uranium oxides but containing up to 10% rare earths. Cleveite is generally black, and has sp.gr. 7·5, hardness 5·5. It frequently contains appreciable quantities of helium, part of which is liberated by strong heating.

Clève's acids. A mixture in approximately equal proportions of 1-naphthylamine-6-sulphonic acid and 1-naphthylamine-7-sulphonic acid. The corresponding nitro-acids are

obtained by nitrating naphthalene-2-sulphonic acid and are then converted into Clève's acids by reduction. They are used as components in the production of black direct cotton dyestuffs.

Climbing film evaporator. See Long-tube vertical (L.T.V.) evaporators.

Closed circuit grinding. A method of grinding whereby the whole of the product is subjected to some form of size classification, e.g. screening, and the oversize material returned to the mill together with fresh feed. Compared with *open circuit grinding*, where the material is passed through the mill once only, for a specified maximum product size this method gives a more uniform product, a greater production rate and a smaller power consumption.

Close size range. A size range in which there is little difference in size between the largest and smallest particles.

Cloud chamber. See Wilson chamber.

Cloves. The dried unexpanded flower buds of *Eugenia caryophyllus*, a tree cultivated in Zanzibar. The medicinal properties of this drug lie chiefly in its volatile oil—oil of cloves—of which it contains up to 20%. It is a stimulant and carminative.

Cloxacillin. See Penicillin.

Clupadonic acid, $C_{22}H_{34}O_2$. A straight chain fatty acid with 5 double bonds. It is a pale yellow oil with a fishy smell, which is a major component of fish oils and the oils of marine animals.

Clupeine. A protein, belonging to the protamine class, found in the sperm and testicles of the herring. On hydrolysis, it gives about 90% of the amino-acid arginine. Its molecular weight is probably under 10,000.

Coacervation. Under certain circumstances a lyophilic (hydrated colloid) sol may be made to separate into two immiscible liquid phases, each of which has a different concentration of the disperse phase. This process is known as coacervation, the resulting liquids, coacervates. A typical example of coacervation is the action of alcohol on protein sols at 50°.

Coagel. Gels are formed by the partial coagulation of hydrated colloidal sols. In the case of gelatin and many other hydrophilic colloids, the gel is a continuous jelly formed by lowering the temperature. On the other hand, gelatinous precipitates such as those of the metallic hydroxides are formed by coagulation of the initially formed sol in a chemical double decomposition. The term gel is usually extended to cover such cases, but sometimes gels formed in this way by coagulation are named coagels. Amongst coagels are not only the gelatinous precipitates, but also the continuous, rigid silica gel. See Colloids, Gel, Hydrophilic colloid.

Coagulation. The stability of a colloidal particle is due to its surface electric charge, or its possession of a hydration sheath, or both. Any effect, chemical or physical, which removes these causes of stability produces coagulation. Thus the passage of an electric current through a colloidal sol makes the particles move to the electrodes. There they are discharged and coagulated. The electrical precipitation of smokes and mists is due to a similar action.

The action of small quantities of electrolytes in coagulating hydrophobic (i.e. unhydrated)

colloids is important. The colloid is coagulated by the adsorption of ions of charge opposite to that which it carries. Thus an arsenic sulphide sol (negative) can be coagulated by unipositive cations, but dipositive cations are more efficient and tripositive cations much more so, the latter producing coagulation even at great dilutions. The addition of a large excess of the coagulant may stabilize a sol of opposite charge to that of the initial colloid, by adsorption of a large excess of (in the above example, positive) ions. Other coagulating influences include ultrasonic vibrations, ultra-violet light, and boiling (as in denaturization of proteins); the two latter effects are essentially chemical. Hydrated or hydrophilic colloids are also coagulated by electrolytes, but only in high concentrations. This effect is termed 'salting out' (*q.v.*) in contrast to the simple adsorption effect outlined above. See Colloids, Electrophoresis, Peptization, 'Salting out'.

Coal. A naturally occurring solid fuel which exists in the form of seams at varying depths below the earth's surface. It has been formed by the arrested bacterial decay of trees that grew 40-300 million years ago, followed by chemical processes of condensation and polymerization under the influence of temperature, pressure, and time. By these processes the differences between the original woody material and anthracite, the highest ranking coal, can be explained.

The changes have been gradual and continuous and the products comprise a well defined series. The rank of any member of the series may be defined as the degree of chemical change that has taken place. As the rank increases the carbon content increases from about 50 to 95%, and the oxygen content decreases from about 40 to 3%. The calorific value increases from about 8,000 to 15,000 Btu/lb through the range of coals: peat—lignites—bituminous—semi-bituminous and carbonaceous coals—to the anthracites.

The properties of the various coals in this ranking will vary considerably and many are used only for specific purposes, e.g. central-heating, steam-raising, domestic fires, metallurgical coke, gas works, and producer practice.

Coal is classified in many different ways according to its chemical and physical properties or its botanical nature. The National Coal Board classification depends on the volatile matter and coking characteristics. The standard A.S.T.M. method used in the U.S.A. depends on the proximate analysis, which is a series of empirical determinations of moisture, volatile matter, ash, and calorific value.

Coal briquettes. By briquetting coal fines into blocks or ovoids a more adaptable product for burning is obtained. The raw coal is ground and mixed with the 'binder' (usually coal-tar pitch or bitumen) which has also been ground. The mixture is then fed into the steam kneading apparatus, heated with superheated steam. The plastic material may be further intimately mixed in a roller mill, and is then fed into the press at a temperature of about 80°-90° where the briquettes are pressed out. Other briquetting processes are used, including pressing without a binder at extremely high pressures and the addition of binder by hot spraying.

Coal gas. See Town gas.

Coalite process. The oldest and most successful process for the low-temperature carbonization of coal. The temperature of carbonization is about 600°. The usual by-products of low-temperature carbonization are obtained and the yield of products from 1 ton of coal is approximately:

Smokeless fuel	14 cwt.
Crude coal-tar oil	18 galls.
Crude petrol from gas	3 galls.
Gas equivalent to	30 therms.
Ammonium sulphate	4 lb.
Aqueous ammonia liquor	20 galls.

Coal-tar pigments. This term generally means the metallic lakes or insoluble metallic salts of organic dyestuffs.

Coated paper. For the purpose of producing a fine surface for printing, paper is coated with a colloidal mix, consisting of a finely dispersed mineral such as kaolin, satin white, etc., with an adhesive such as glue, casein, or starch. Additional materials are added to give plasticity to the coat, to harden the protein, and to prevent frothing. The preparation, application, and drying of such materials is strictly in accordance with colloidal principles.

Cobalt, Co. At.no. 27. At.wt. 58·94, m.p. 1492°, b.p. 3100°. Metallic cobalt has a hexagonal close packed structure below 417°, $a=2·51$, $c=4·07$ Å, $d=8·85$, cubic-close-packed structure to the m.p. $a=3·54$ Å, $d=8·80$. Discovered in 1735 by Brandt in the blue glass called smalt.

Occurs to a small extent as the arsenide, $CoAs_2$, known as speiss cobalt or smaltite. Cobalt is also found as cobalt glance,

$$[Co, Fe, As, S]$$

and as cobalt bloom, $Co_3(AsO_4)_2, 8H_2O$. The principal commercial sources of cobalt are the silver ores, containing arsenides and sulphides, of Cobalt City, Ontario, and the manganese ores containing about 2% cobalt oxide of New Caledonia. The ores are subjected to successive roastings to remove impurities and the metal is finally precipitated as the hydroxide. The metal is prepared by reducing the oxide with carbon.

Cobalt is a tenacious, silvery-white metal, which is readily polished and shows a high lustre. It oxidizes slowly on heating in air. In the finely divided state it will adsorb about 100 volumes of hydrogen. The metal dissolves slowly in dilute sulphuric and hydrochloric acids, and readily in nitric acid. In the latter acid it can become passive. Finely divided cobalt acts as an effective catalyst for hydrogenation reactions. It is a constituent of many alloys.

Cobalt acetates. Red monoclinic crystals of cobaltous acetate tetrahydrate,

$$Co(C_2H_3O_2)_2, 4H_2O$$

are obtained by crystallizing a solution of cobalt carbonate in acetic acid. The red anhydrous salt is prepared by the action of acetic anhydride on $Co(NO_3)_2, 6H_2O$. Cobalt (II) acetate is used as a drier in paints. A green solution of Cobalt (III) acetate, $Co(C_2H_3O_2)_3$, is obtained by electrolytic oxidation of a solution of anhydrous Cobalt (II) acetate in acetic acid.

Cobalt alloys. The most important alloys of cobalt are the *Stellites*, which contain up to 30% chromium, up to 18% tungsten and up to $2\frac{1}{2}\%$ carbon. This gives a constitution of hard chromium and tungsten carbides in a softer matrix of cobalt. The less hard alloys are used as wear-resistant welded deposits on components such as valves while the harder alloys may be fabricated by sintering to form cutting tools. *Vitallium* is a cobalt base alloy containing about 20% chromium and small quantities of carbide-forming elements. The carbides impart high temperature strength making the alloy suitable for very high temperature service. Up to 10% cobalt is added to high-speed tool steel to impart high-temperature strength to the matrix; the metal is also an important constituent of permanent-magnet alloys.

Cobaltammines. Cobalt (II) is oxidized to cobalt (III) ammines when a solution of a cobalt (II) salt is exposed to air in the presence of ammonia. The species present in solution have ammonia molecules co-ordinated to the metal.

The cobalthexammines contain the ion $[Co(NH_3)_6]^{+++}$ and may be obtained by the method outlined above. This cation forms well-defined salts with nearly every inorganic acid. In this group the ammonia may be replaced by such compounds as hydroxylamine $[Co(NH_2OH)_6]^{+++}$, ethylenediamine,

$$[Co(NH_2 \cdot CH_2 \cdot CH_2 \cdot NH_2)_3]^{+++}$$

propylenediamine and many other organic amines. The ammonia molecules may also be partly or entirely replaced by water molecules, giving ions such as $[Co(NH_3)_5H_2O]^{+++}$, $[Co(NH_3)(H_2O)_5]^{+++}$, and finally

$$[Co(H_2O)_6]^{+++}$$

When ammonia is replaced by a negative ion, the charge on the complex changes. Thus replacing one ammonia group by a chloride, hydroxyl, or nitro group gives the doubly charged complexes

$$[Co(NH_3)_5Cl]^{++}, [Co(NH_3)_5OH]^{++}$$

and $[Co(NH_3)_5(NO_2)]^{++}$; these are the pentammines. The ammonia, in a similar way to the hexammines, may be replaced by ethylenediamine, etc.

Triammines have three NH_3 groups replaced by neutral or negative groups. Such compounds as cobalttrichlorotriammine $[CoCl_3(NH_3)_3]$ are known.

Cobalt bloom. Cobalt arsenate. See Arsenic.

Cobalt blue. A mixed oxide of cobalt and aluminium made by precipitating solutions of cobalt chloride or nitrate and alum with sodium carbonate. It is a very permanent pigment used by artists.

Cobalt carbonyl. By heating cobalt at 150° in carbon monoxide at 30 atm. pressure orange-red crystals of cobalt carbonyl, $Co_2(CO)_8$, (m.p. 51°) are obtained. At 60° it forms $Co_4(CO)_{12}$, giving black crystals from a solution in benzene.

Cobalt compounds. Simple cobalt (II) compounds contain the Co^{2+} ion, but it is very doubtful if the cobaltic Co^{3+} ion exists as such except in complexes. In its compounds cobalt shows oxidation states of 0, 1, 2, 3, and 4.

Cobalt cyanides (complex). Cobalt (II) cyanide, $Co(CN)_2, 3H_2O$, precipitated by the addition of potassium cyanide to a solution of a cobalt salt, is soluble in excess of cyanide, forming a yellow solution from which purple crystals of $K_6Co_2(CN)_{10}$ can be obtained. The solution absorbs hydrogen with formation of the $[Co^{III}(CN)_5H]^{3-}$ ion. On boiling in acid solution, oxidation occurs and potassium cobalticyanide, $K_3Co(CN)_6$, is formed.

Cobalt fluorides. *Cobalt (II) fluoride*, CoF_2. A pink solid prepared by dehydrating the hydrates, which are known with 2, 3, and 4 molecules of water. Solubility at 25°, 1·4 g per 100 g water. A perovskite type salt, $KCoF_3$, is known.

Cobalt (III) fluoride, CoF_3. A green powder prepared by electrolytic oxidation of cobaltous fluoride in hydrofluoric acid solution, when it separates with $3\frac{1}{2}$ molecules of water, or as a brown anhydrous powder by the action of fluorine on anhydrous cobalt (II) chloride. It is used as a fluorinating agent, particularly for replacing

the hydrogen atoms of organic derivatives by fluorine. Complexes $M_3^ICoF_6$ are known.

Cobalt (IV) fluoride is not known but the complex Cs_2CoF_6 has been prepared by the action of fluorine on Cs_2CoCl_4.

Cobalt green, Rinmann's Green. A furnaced pigment consisting substantially of zinc oxide and cobalt oxide (11-12%) with phosphate introduced by using sodium phosphate as the precipitant. It is used in painting porcelain.

Cobaltic. Containing cobalt (III) species.

Cobalt nitrites (complex). Potassium nitrite gives, with a solution of a cobalt (II) salt acidified with acetic acid, a yellow precipitate of potassium cobaltinitrite, $K_3Co(NO_2)_6$. The salts $KAg_2Co(NO_2)_6$ and $K_2AgCo(NO_2)_6$ are less soluble than the potassium salt. Thus a solution of sodium silver cobaltinitrite is sufficiently sensitive to detect one part of potassium in 10,000 parts of water.

Cobaltocene, di-π-cyclopentadienyl cobalt (II), $(C_5H_5)_2Co$. A fairly unstable derivative formed with π-$C_5H_5Co(CO)_2$ by the action of cyclopentadiene on cobalt carbonyl. Easily oxidized to the stable $[(C_5H_5)_2Co]^+$ ion.

Cobaltous. Containing cobalt (II) species.

Cobaltous bromide, $CoBr_2$. Very similar to the chloride. The anhydrous salt is green; a blue dihydrate and a red hexahydrate are also known. Cobalt (II) bromide is very soluble in water.

Cobaltous chloride. The solutions of cobalt, or the oxide, in hydrochloric acid give on evaporation dark red crystals of cobaltous chloride hexahydrate, $CoCl_2, 6H_2O$. The anhydrous salt and the monohydrate, obtained by heating, are blue in colour. Aqueous solutions of the chloride are pink, but become blue on the addition of hydrochloric acid. Cobaltic chloride, $CoCl_3$, is unknown.

Cobaltous iodide. CoI_2. Formed from the elements, and is normally obtained as a black hygroscopic mass, which gives a pink solution in water. By sublimation a yellow form, which gives a colourless water solution, is obtained. The cause of this isomerism is unknown. Red hydrates have 9 and 6, and green ones 4 and 2, molecules of water.

Cobaltous nitrate. Obtained by dissolving cobalt in nitric acid, the solution on evaporation yields pink crystals of hexahydrate,

$$Co(NO_3)_2, 6H_2O$$

Hydrates with 9, 3, and 2 molecules of water are also known.

Cobaltous sulphate. Formed by dissolving the metal, or the oxide, in sulphuric acid; it crystallizes on evaporation as the heptahydrate,

$CoSO_4$, $7H_2O$, isomorphous with nickel and iron (II) sulphates. The solution at 50° deposits $CoSO_4$, $6H_2O$, isomorphous with zinc sulphate, $ZnSO_4$, $6H_2O$. A tetrahydrate and the rose-red anhydrous salt are known.

Cobalt oxides. *Cobalt (II) oxide*, CoO. The addition of caustic potash to a solution of cobalt (II) nitrate gives a bluish-violet precipitate, which on boiling is converted into pink, impure cobalt (II) hydroxide, $Co(OH)_2$. On heating the hydroxide out of contact with air, olive-green cobalt (II) oxide is formed. This oxide is also formed by the ignition of cobalt sulphate, nitrate, or carbonate in an inert atmosphere or *in vacuo*. Cobalt (II) oxide oxidises readily, even at 100°, to form Co_3O_4. It is readily reduced by hydrogen to the metal. CoO has the NaCl structure.

Cobalt (III) oxide, Co_2O_3. Co_2O_3 cannot be obtained pure although a hydrate, $Co_2O_3 \cdot H_2O$, is formed as a brown powder by oxidizing Co_3O_4 and precipitating with alkali.

Tricobalt tetroxide, Co_3O_4. Obtained, as a black powder, by the ignition of the other oxides, nitrate, carbonate, or sulphate in air. It has a spinel structure. Is readily reduced to the metal by hydrogen, the reaction commencing at 900° and is very rapid and complete at 1100°. May also be reduced by aluminium.

Cobalt (IV) oxide. CoO_2. Obtained, as a dark brown precipitate, by the oxidation of a cobalt salt with chlorine, bromine, or iodine in alkali hydroxide. This oxide is very unstable, passing, even on continued washing, into Co_3O_4. Cobalt dioxide is acidic, a cobaltate (IV), Ba_2CoO_4, has been reported.

Cobalt yellow. See Aureoline.

Cocaine, benzoylmethylecgonine, $C_{17}H_{21}NO_4$.

Colourless prisms, m.p. 98°. Very slightly soluble in water, soluble in 10 parts of alcohol; $[\alpha]_D^{20} -15.83°$ in chloroform. It is obtained from coca, either by direct purification, or by acid hydrolysis of the mixed alkaloids to ecgonine, which is then methylated and benzoylated. Coca consists of the dried leaves of *Erythroxylum coca* and *Erythroxylum truxillense*, shrubs growing in Bolivia and Peru.

Cocaine is the oldest of the local anaesthetics.

It has toxic actions, and is habit-forming when taken internally. See Ecgonine.

Cocarboxylase. See Carboxylase.

Cochineal. Cochineal is the dried body of the female insect *Dactylopius coccus*. It is ground to a powder and is largely soluble in water and alcohol. The deep red colour of cochineal is due to carminic acid, of which it contains about 10%. Cochineal was in the past used for dyeing silk and wool. It is used as a colouring matter for foodstuffs and drugs, and as an indicator.

Cockscomb pyrites. See Marcasite.

Co-current. When two streams of material are brought into contact with each other with the object of transferring either heat or matter between them, if the streams move in the same direction flow is said to be co-current. See also Counter-current flow.

Codeine, Methylmorphine, $C_{18}H_{21}NO_3$. Colourless crystals with one molecule of water, m.p.

155°. Soluble in 120 parts of water, more soluble in alcohol; $[\alpha]_D -137.75°$ in alcohol. Prepared by methylating morphine or directly from opium. It is a mild hypnotic and sedative and is not habit-forming. It is useful in the treatment of coughs.

Cod-liver oil. The oil expressed from the fresh liver of the cod, *Gadus callarias*. It is a pale yellow liquid, d_{20}^{20} 0.917-0.924, slightly soluble in alcohol, miscible with organic solvents. It contains about 1000 units of vitamin A activity per g and about 100 units of antirachitic activity per g. It is a valuable source of the above vitamins and other food factors, and is used in the prevention and cure of rickets in growing children.

Coenzyme A. An important coenzyme which effects transfer of acyl groups (other than formyl). Acetyl-coenzyme A (usually abbreviated to acetyl-CoA) and malonyl-CoA are particularly important biosynthetic intermediates.

Structurally, coenzyme A is composed of adenosine-3',5'-diphosphate and pantetheine phosphate moieties, with a pyrophosphate linkage. Pantetheine is made up of pantoic acid, β-alanine, and mercaptoethylamine—i.e. of pantothenic acid (*q.v.*) and mercaptoethylamine.

Pantothenic acid is a vitamin because it is a necessary component of coenzyme A. See also Acetyl-coenzyme A.

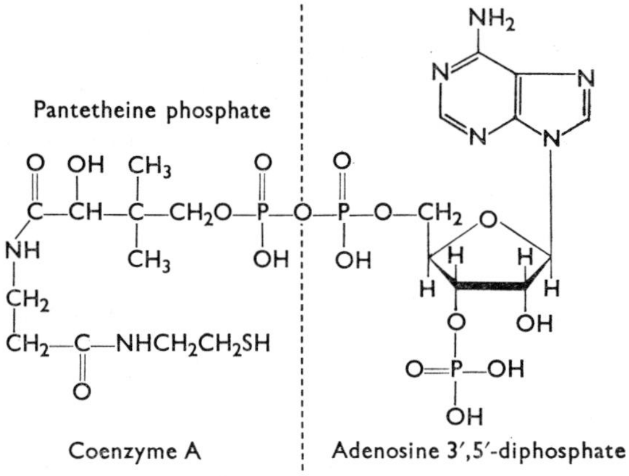

stage in the formation of a proper precipitate in a solid solution. Coherent precipitates are one of the major factors in high-strength alloys,

Pantetheine phosphate

NH$_2$

$$O=P-OH$$
$$|$$
$$OH$$

Coenzyme A

Adenosine 3′,5′-diphosphate

Coenzymes. Defined as small thermostable molecules that are necessary for the action of enzymes. This term will include certain metals, but the word has come to be used only for substances which play a known part in the reaction catalyzed by the enzyme. The difference between coenzymes and prosthetic groups (defined as the non-protein portions of enzymes) is one of degree rather than of kind, depending on the firmness of the combination of the protein, thus the haematins are usually referred to as prosthetic groups and the phospho-pyridine nucleotides as coenzymes, though both play essentially similar parts in biological oxidations.

Coenzymes may be classified into three main groups:

(1) *Coenzymes effecting transfer of hydrogen.* These include the pyridine nucleotides, nicotin-amide-adenine dinucleotide and nicotinamide-adenine dinucleotide phosphate; the flavin nucleotides such as flavin-adenine dinucleotide; and lipoic acid.

(2) *Coenzymes effecting transfer of groups.* Examples of this class are adenosine triphos-phate (ATP), biotin, coenzyme A, and pyridoxal phosphate.

(3) *Coenzymes effecting isomerisation.* Pyri-doxal phosphate also falls into this class, in respect of its catalysis of the enzymic decarboxy-lation of amino-acids.

Coherent precipitate in a solid alloy system is one which is still bonded directly to the parent lattice and so does not have a distinct grain boundary. The activation energy for the forma-tion of such a precipitate is thus less, since no new grain boundary has to be formed, and so such precipitates are normally an intermediate

particularly at high temperatures. They impart strength by interfering with the slip process or, more correctly, dislocation movement.

Coke. The dense product left in the retort or coke-oven after a suitable coal has been carbonized. The size and nature of the final residue will depend on many factors, e.g. rate, temperature, and duration of carbonization, width of oven, and type of coal. The coke will vary in colour from a dark matte appearance to the more desirable bright silvery lustre. The material should have a light metallic ring when dropped.

Coke is used for many purposes: blast-furnace work, foundry work, central heating, and boiler installations; the use to which it is placed will determine the properties most desir-able. In most cases it should have a low ash (less than 10%), low sulphur and phosphorus contents, and should also contain a low percent-age of moisture. Importance is attached to its reactivity, porosity, and hardness since these determine its suitability for domestic, central heating, or metallurgical purposes.

Coke oven. The modern by-product oven is an horizontal rectangular chamber from 30 to 45 ft. long, 10 to 20 ft. high, and from 11 to 22 in. wide. It is closed at each end by a cast iron or steel door with firebrick lining. These doors are removed by winches or by a removing and clamping device.

The charge of coal (10-30 tons) is either fed in via charging holes in the top of the oven or compressed in a box in a stamping machine and transferred directly, in the form of a single cake, into the oven through the doors. Batteries of upwards of 30 ovens are built, separated from each other by single or double flues in which the gas is burnt to heat the ovens. This gas may be either part of the purified coke-oven gas or, when this is required for other purposes, producer or blast-furnace gas may be used.

The air required for combustion is preheated in chequered brickwork (regenerators) which runs beneath the ovens either the length of the battery or under each individual oven. For alternating intervals of about half an hour one half of these regenerators are being heated at the expense of the sensible heat in the burnt gases leaving the flues, and the other half is giving up its heat to the incoming air or gas prior to combustion. At the end of each period the procedure is reversed.

The crude coke-oven gas leaves the top of the ovens by means of the ascension pipes and enters the hydraulic main which carries it to the by-product recovery plant. At the end of the coking period (12-24 hours) the coke is discharged by the 'ram' either directly on to the coke bench, where it is cooled first by the Darby cooler and then by water from hoses, or on to the coke car, which takes it to the quenching tower, where it is sprayed with cold water.

There are several varieties of by-product coke ovens, the most common being: horizontal, regenerative or waste-heat; vertical, recuperative or regenerative. The original Beehive type of oven is still found in some countries. It gives no by-products.

Coking coal. The commercial value of a coke depends on the extent to which it satisfies the requirements of the process for which it is to be used: e.g. in foundries, blast furnaces, lime kilns, or for domestic use, and will depend on its purity, size, strength, and structure. These physical characteristics will be determined by: (a) the coal used and the state in which coal is charged into oven or retort; (b) the type of oven used for carbonizing; (c) the control of the oven, e.g. flue temperatures, time of carbonization; (d) the subsequent treatment of the coke after discharge.

The coal on carbonizing must shrink adequately to permit of easy discharge from the oven. A coal may be classed as a coking coal if when carbonized by a commercial method in a commercial type of oven it will give a marketable coke. A coal which in itself may not be a coking coal will often in combination with another type of coal give rise to a good coke.

Colchicine, $C_{22}H_{25}NO_6$. It crystallizes in pale yellow needles, m.p. 155°, very soluble in water and alcohol, $[\alpha]_D^{17}$ −120·7°. It is an alkaloid obtained from colchicum, which is the dried corms and seeds of the meadow saffron, *Colchicum autumnale.* Large doses are poison-

ous; in small doses it is used in the treatment of gout. Colchicine is important biologically for its capacity to arrest cell division, and is used to

produce polyploid mutants of plants and animals.

Cold working. See Work hardening.

Colistin. See Polymyxins.

Collagen. A protein of the scleroprotein class which is the most important constituent of the connective tissue of animals. It is also a structural element of skin, cartilage and the scales of fish. The molecules (14×2900 Å) appear to comprise a triple helix of linear polypeptide strands, composed of glycine, proline and hydroxy-proline. When collagen is boiled with water, the strands separate and undergo some hydrolysis, affording gelatin. The conversion of collagen to leather involves the formation of cross linkages between collagen molecules. See A. G. Ward, *J. Roy. Inst. Chem.,* 1964, **88**, 406.

Colligative properties. Those properties of solutions which are independent of the nature of a solute, and dependent only on the number of particles (atoms, molecules, or ions) present, are called colligative properties, e.g. vapour pressure, osmotic pressure, elevation of boiling-point, depression of freezing-point.

Collodion. A nitrocellulose containing 10·5-12·3% of nitrogen, widely used as a base for lacquers, in which a ketone or ester may be used as the solvent. Many esters particularly suitable as nitrocellulose solvents have been developed. Addition of certain resins to the lacquer improves the gloss and adhesiveness of the nitrocellulose film left on drying. The term 'collodion' is sometimes applied incorrectly to nitrocellulose lacquers. See Nitrocellulose.

Colloidal electrolyte. Many colloidal materials react as if they consisted of numbers of giant polyvalent ions in equilibrium with the corresponding number of simple ions of opposite sign. Thus the sodium salts of the lower fatty acids behave as normal weak electrolytes, dissociating into simple anions and cations; as we pass to higher members of the series, association begins to take place and colloidal character is assumed. The anion is no longer a discrete fatty acid anion but consists of an aggregate of fatty acid anions, together with undissociated neutral salt molecules; it is a giant polyvalent ion, dissociating at the surface and compensated by an equal number of sodium ions in close proximity to the giant ion. This is a general picture of a colloidal electrolyte, to which class the soaps and many dyestuffs belong. On passing an electric current through the above system, the outer sodium ions move to the cathode, the giant ions to the anode. Since these latter contain undissociated salt molecules, it follows that some of the sodium migrates to the anode. The rate of movement of the giant ions is little different from that of simple ions and transport number determinations can be carried out normally. See also Polyelectrolyte.

Colloid mills. These are devices for producing colloidal suspensions or emulsions where the particle and droplet sizes are less than one micron. By producing very high shearing forces within the fluid they perform size reduction and dispersion at the same time. These forces may be obtained in various ways.

In the disc type mill the mixture of solid and liquid or of the two liquids is passed between a pair of discs with only a small clearance between them which rotate at high speed relative to each other. The feed is to the centre and the product is discharged from the periphery into the surrounding casing. In the valve and orifice types the mixture, after being forced at extremely high velocity through an orifice, strikes a breaker ring. The combination of shearing and impact produces a disintegrating action.

Colloid mills are used in the paint industry, and in the pharmaceutical and food-processing industries.

Colloids, the colloidal state. In 1860 Graham differentiated between substances which, in solution, were able to penetrate a dialysis membrane and those which were retained. The former (soluble salts, acids, cane sugar, etc.) he termed crystalloids, the latter (gelatin, albumin, etc.) colloids. Colloids are further characterized by a slow rate of diffusion and by the fact that the path of a beam of light is illuminated on passage through a colloidal solution. These properties indicate that particles of greater than molecular size exist in such solutions, and a substance is now defined as being in the colloidal state if its particles, of approximate size between 1 and 100 mm, are dispersed in a continuous medium. Colloids are thus intermediate between coarse suspensions on the one hand and molecular or ionic solutions on the other. The lines of demarcation are indefinite, fine suspensions showing some colloidal effects, whilst large molecules are essentially colloidal in behaviour.

As it is now possible by choice of suitable conditions to prepare most compounds in this form, the colloid state should be considered as a physical state in which all substances can be made to exist. Nevertheless, it is still convenient to regard as colloids many materials such as proteins, vegetable fibres, rubber, etc., which are most stable or occur naturally in the colloidal state.

As the subdivision of a solid progresses, its specific surface increases greatly, and hence its adsorptive properties become pronounced. In the colloidal state the properties of surface are all-important, and it is possible to define a colloidal system as one in which surface properties predominate over chemical constitution. See also Brownian movement, Coagulation, Colloidal electrolyte.

Cologne yellow. See Lead chromates.

Colophony. See Rosin.

Colour couplers. Couplers are compounds, the anions of which can react under basic conditions with developer (p-dialkylaminoaniline derivatives) to give dyes as oxidation products. Compounds which fulfill these requirements are the phenols, α-naphthols and molecules containing a reactive methylene group, e.g. benzoylacetanilide and cyanoacetylcoumarone. Couplers may also be substituted in the reactive position with displaceable groups such as azo dye residues to give masking coloured couplers used in negative/positive systems to compensate during print exposures for the unwanted light absorption of the negative image dyes.

Colour development. Photographic colour development is a process in which developer oxidation products, formed in the emulsion layer where silver ions are reduced, are used to form dyes either by direct combination with another molecule of oxidized developer (primary colour development), or by the oxidized developer reacting with a new molecular species known as a colour coupler ($q.v.$) to give a dye of the required absorption (secondary colour development). All multicoloured processes employ the latter system.

Colour Index. The first publication dealing with dye classification to receive international recognition was 'Farbstoff Tabellen', by Schultz and Julius, published in 1888. This arranged about 280 known dyes according to their chemical constitution, and by 1914 the fifth edition had been published in which the number of listed dyes reached 1000.

This reflects the German supremacy in dye-making during the above period, but after the First World War the dye-making industry in Great Britain revived, and in 1924 a Colour Index was published by the Society of Dyers and

Colourists, Bradford, in which 1316 dyes were arranged according to their chemical constitution, following the pattern of Schultz and Julius. Very little information of methods of application or fastness properties was included but nevertheless the first edition of the Colour Index was a most valuable work and soon became a standard work of reference throughout the world for dye-makers, dye-users and official bodies.

A supplement appeared in 1928 but the years of industrial depression, followed by the outbreak of war, delayed any further development in Great Britain, although a seventh edition by Schultz and Julius was published in 1931, which listed 1471 known dyes. Towards the end of the Second World War the Society of Dyers and Colourists took up the matter of publishing a second edition of the Colour Index, and sought and obtained the collaboration of the A.A.T.C.C. (American Association of Textile Chemists and Colorists).

This edition was to be much more comprehensive than the first edition and was planned to consist of three parts, viz. Part I (2 volumes) containing all the known commercial names under which a dye is sold; equivalents being grouped together with details of their application and fastness properties, (31,500 entries): Part II (1 volume) giving the known constituents of 3595 dyes, and linking these up with Part I references: Part III (1 volume) containing the commercial names index, details of fastness tests, conversion tables, etc.

Dyemakers throughout the world were invited to supply information and apart from the U.S.S.R. the response was practically complete. After 13 years of arduous labour the final volume (Part III) was published in 1958 and it has now become the custom to indicate the Colour Index (C.I.) number when referring to any known dye. The value of the Colour Index for industrial, commercial, research and official purposes is immense. For example in some countries, officials in customs, licensing and patent offices, demand C.I. numbers for dyes or pigments and refuse to recognize those for which no C.I. designation or number can be quoted.

The Colour Index is being kept up to date and in 1963 a Supplement was published which included information on about 1250 new dyes, as well as adding to or amending the information given in the second edition.

Columbite. (Fe, Mn) (Nb, Ta)$_2$O$_6$ in which Nb preponderates over Ta. The members of the series are orthorhombic, opaque, dark brown or black, and range in sp.gr. from 5·3 (columbite) to 7·3 (tantalite). It is the main ore of niobium,

and occurs widely in granites, pegmatites, and heavy alluvials.

Columbium, Cb. An alternative name for niobium (q.v.), not now officially recognized, but still widely used in America.

Comassie Navy Blue, Acid Blue 113. A disazo dye of formula

It is an acid dye which is cheap, easy to apply and has good fastness to light and washing but not to sulphur bleaching. It is widely used in wool dyeing for producing navy blue shades.

Combining volumes, law of. See Gay-Lussac's law.

Combustion. The term, as usually employed, refers to the combination of substances with oxygen with evolution of heat and light (e.g. the burning of phosphorus or of carbon monoxide in air or oxygen). In its wider sense it also includes certain reactions in which oxygen does not participate, such as the burning of phosphorus or of sodium in chlorine. The term slow combustion refers to oxidation reactions taking place with a comparatively small rise in temperature, attributable to the inherent slowness of reaction, or to a deficit of one or other of the reactants. Oxidation reactions taking place without light emission are also sometimes classed as slow combustion. The term catalytic combustion is used to describe oxidation reactions taking place at a catalytic surface, either with or without the evolution of light.

Complex. Any compound in which the bonding is by interaction of the electrons of the donor with empty orbitals of the acceptor. In some complexes the electron flow may take place in both directions simultaneously—see Backbonding. The interaction may take place between charged or uncharged species.

Complex ion. A complex ion is formed by the co-ordination of other ions or molecules to an ion to form a stable charged entity. Thus the Co^{3+} ion and ammonia give the Co(NH$_3$)$_6^{3+}$ complex whilst the Fe^{3+} ion and cyanide ions give the Fe(CN)$_6^{3-}$ complex. Depending upon the stability of the complex a solution of a complex salt may or may not give the reactions of the individual components of the complex. It should be noted that hydrated salts generally contain aquo-complexes e.g. [Cu(H$_2$O)$_4^{2+}$] and that the anions of oxy-salts may be considered as being complexes formed by (mostly hypothetical) positive ions and oxide ions, e.g. the NO_3^- ion as N^{5+} and $3O^{2-}$.

Complexone. See Sequestering agent.

Component. Findlay defined the number of components in a system as the smallest number of independently variable constituents by means of which the composition of each 'phase' participating in the state of equilibrium can be expressed in the form of a chemical equation. E.g. in a closed vessel containing $CaCO_3$, CO_2, and CaO, there are three molecular species, but $CaCO_3 = CaO + CO_2$, hence the number of components is not three, but two. The system is a two-component system.

Compound. The usage of chemists in respect of the word compound is not perfectly definite; all would agree that gunpowder is a mixture and common salt a compound. Not much difficulty is found with a compound with a fixed composition such as salt, cane-sugar, or water. It is not so easy to learn the orthodox usage in connexion with substances the composition of which may vary by infinitesimal changes, the properties of the substance probably also varying in the same way. Glass, steel, red lead, white lead, and starch are examples of such substances; in them every atom is attracted by all the adjacent atoms so as to make a uniform or very nearly uniform solid; such bodies are clearly not mere mechanical mixtures; they are chemical compounds of varying or indefinite composition; the feldspars and many other silicates also have no definite composition; similarly many plastics and other polymers are chemically combined right through and must be considered as chemical compounds of varying composition; alloys such as pewter and brass are compounds not mere mixtures. It is impossible to give a definition of compound that is of any value, and there are intermediate states in between the typical compound and the typical mixture. The topic concerns crystal structure, polymerization, colloids, and liquids. The vagueness of the term must be borne in mind in defining a molecule as the smallest possible unit of a chemical compound.

Compounding. A term used to describe the mixing processes used to obtain a homogeneous mixture of a polymeric material with various additives. The choice of additives will be influenced by the end properties required, their effect on processing and the cost level required for the final product. The term is applicable to both rubber and plastics compositions. In rubber compounding many different materials are incorporated with the raw rubber, in order to modify properties such as mechanical strength, hardness, abrasion resistance, resist-

ance to tear, ageing resistance, colour, electrical properties, and so on. The types of compounding ingredients include vulcanizing agents (*q.v.*), accelerators, activators, reinforcing and inert fillers, anti-oxidants, softeners, extenders and colourants. Plastics compounding is normally less complex an operation, since fewer additives are involved. General additives for thermoplastics materials may be anti-oxidants, ultraviolet light absorbers, heat stabilizers and colourants. Specific additives include, for example, plasticizers for polyvinyl chloride, cellulose acetate and celluloid; and rubbers for polystyrene (SBR), polyvinyl chloride (nitrile) and polyethylene (butyl) to improve toughness. Thermosetting resins require the addition of curing agents and hardeners or catalysts to facilitate curing by cross-linking, as well as major amounts of fillers.

Compressors. These are machines for compressing gases. Although all gas pumping equipment produces some degree of compression, the term is normally reserved for those machines whose primary function is to produce a considerable increase in pressure, as distinct from those, such as fans, where the primary object is movement of the gas. There are three main types of compressor:

Reciprocating compressors work on the same principle as the familiar bicycle pump. Their throughput is not particularly high, but they can produce very high pressures, up to 50,000 lb/in.^{2}.

Rotary compressors have members rotating inside a casing, and compression is brought about by pockets of gas being forced along between a member and the casing, or between two members, into the high pressure discharge. They are used for handling moderate volumes of gases at pressures up to 75 lb/in.^{2}.

Centrifugal compressors work in a similar manner to centrifugal pumps (*q.v.*). Several stages are required to produce an appreciable pressure rise. They can handle large volumes and produce pressures up to 500 lb/in.^{2}. See also Fans.

Conant, James Bryant (1893-   ). Conant, formerly President of Harvard University, is a graduate of that university. From 1928 till 1933 he was Sheldon Emery professor of organic chemistry. His researches cover a wide field, in particular free radicals, oxidation-reduction, haemoglobin, and chlorophyll. He was awarded the Chandler Medal, Columbia University, in 1932. See *Science*, 1946, **103**, 191.

Concentrated. A concentrated solution is one which contains a high proportion of the dissolved substance. Sometimes the term is applied not to the solution, but to a solute itself, e.g. concentrated hydrochloric acid, when it has a similar significance, and implies a concentrated solution of hydrogen chloride.

Concentration. See Solution.

Concentration cell. The potential of a piece of metal immersed in a solution containing its ions (see Electrode potential) depends on the concentration of the ions. Thus a cell may be set up which derives its electromotive force from the difference in concentration of solutions of the same electrolyte surrounding the two electrodes. Any cell which depends on this principle is called a concentration cell.

Conchoidal fracture. A fracture of a solid devoid of all appearance of crystalline structure, being made up of a series of shell-like curved surfaces. Such fractures are commonly encountered in amorphous glassy materials.

Condensation reactions involve addition of one molecule to another molecule with the elimination of a simple molecule such as water, ammonia, an alcohol, etc., e.g. the Claisen condensation.

Condensers. These are heat exchangers used for condensing vapours, the heat normally being removed by cooling water. Surface condensers of the *shell and tube* type are usual, but *barometric* and *jet condensers*, which are direct contact devices, are commonly used for water vapour.

Conductiometric titration. A titration in which the equivalence point is ascertained by observing the changes in conductivity of the solution. See also Electrometric titrations.

Conductivity. The property of a substance by virtue of which the substance allows the passage of an electric current is termed the conductivity.

The reciprocal of the resistance of a circuit is called the conductivity. The reciprocal of the specific resistance is the specific conductivity or conductance of a substance.

The conductivity of a solution containing 1 gram equivalent of solute when measured between two large parallel electrodes at a distance of 1 cm apart is called the equivalent conductivity Δ.

$$\Delta = \frac{1000\,K}{c}$$

where K=specific conductance and c=concentration in g equiv. per litre.

Condy's fluid. A disinfectant solution of calcium and potassium permanganates.

Cone crusher. See Conical crusher.

Conessine, $C_{24}H_{40}N_2$, a steroidal alkaloid found in Kurchi bark from a tree native to India and Africa. Plates m.p. 125°, $[\alpha]_D^{20}$ +25° in alcohol.

Sparingly soluble in water. Used medicinally for amoebiasis.

Configuration. The term describing the spatial arrangement of atoms or groups. Used for example when discussing the *cis* and *trans*, *syn* and *anti* forms of isomeric molecules. See Isomerism.

Conformation. The term usually restricted to the potentially dynamic spatial arrangements of atoms or groups in a molecule which may be in equilibrium with other conformations. No single conformation constitutes a discrete and isolable substance under usual conditions, in contrast to configurational isomers. Two extreme conformations of ethane are the *eclipsed* and *staggered* forms, which are easily interconvertible by rotation about the C—C bond. Cycloalkanes present alternative aspects

staggered   eclipsed

of conformational differences. For example cyclohexane molecules exists as rapidly interconverting species with *boat* or *chair* conformations, and it is not possible to separate these, although at room temperature the chair conformation is considerably more stable and comprises more than 99% of the equilibrium mixture.

chair   boat

A monosubstituted cyclohexane, e.g. methylcyclohexane, exists theoretically in two isomeric forms with a chair-form ring, and the methyl substituent either *axial* or *equatorial*. Since these rapidly interconvert through a process known as *ring inversion*, physical separation of the isomers is not possible. Physical evidence suggests that the equatorial form of methylcyclohexane predominates over the axial form. *Cis-trans*-isomers of cyclohexane derivatives have the additional possibility of conformational isomerism.

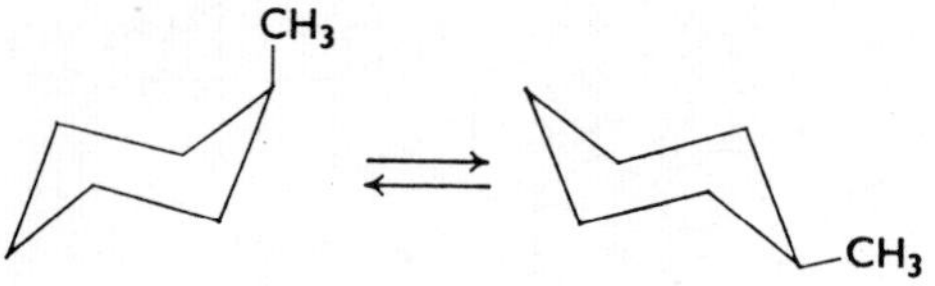

axial   equatorial

Congo red, Direct Red 28. A water soluble direct cotton dyestuff, the sodium salt of

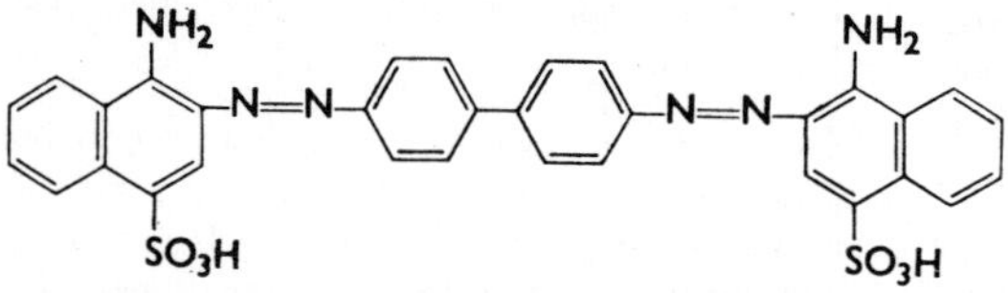

It is prepared by the action of tetrazotized benzidine on naphthionic acid. It is red in neutral and blue in acid solution with a colour change at pH 3-5. It is used as an indicator (0·5% solution in 25% alcohol). It has haemostatic properties and is injected in cases of haemorrhage from the kidneys and urinary tract and is used also for the diagnosis of amyloid disease.

Congorubin number. As a quantitative measure of the protective action of a colloid, Wo. Ostwald has proposed the following as an alternative to the gold number. The congorubin or rubin number is the amount of protective colloid in grams which, when added to 100 ml of a congorubin sol, prevents a change of colour when the latter is made 160 millimolar with respect to potassium chloride. Congorubin was chosen as being a sol which changed colour noticeably on coagulation and was as different as possible from gold in its constitution. The congorubin numbers of a series of hydrophobic sols are in the same order as the gold numbers of the same sols.

Conical crusher, Cone crusher. This is generally similar to the gyratory crusher (*q.v.*) except that it does not take such a coarse feed and gives a much finer product. It also operates at rather higher speeds.

Coniferin, $C_{16}H_{22}O_8$. The glucoside of coniferyl alcohol, present in fir trees, is of importance as the starting-point for the synthesis of vanillin which is formed from it by oxidation with chromic acid. It has m.p. 185°, $[\alpha]_D -67°$.

Coniferyl alcohol, $C_{10}H_{12}O_3$. Crystallizes in prisms, m.p. 73°-74°. Insoluble in water,

moderately soluble in alcohol, soluble in ether and in alkalis. It occurs to a small extent in wood and is a constituent of the glycoside coniferin.

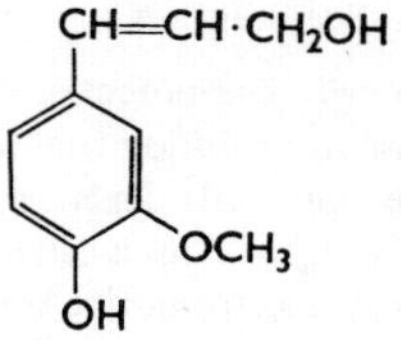

It is commercially important as it can be oxidized to vanillin. It resinifies with mineral acids.

Coniine, $C_8H_{17}N$. A colourless liquid with a penetrating odour, m.p. $-2°$, b.p. 166°-167°. Slightly soluble in cold water, less soluble in

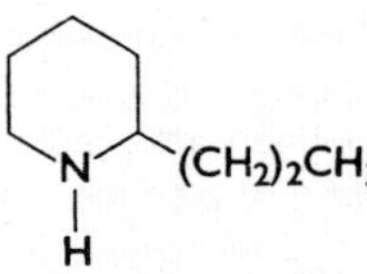

hot. Soluble in alcohol; $[\alpha]_D^{19} +16°$. One of the alkaloids obtained from hemlock. It is very poisonous.

Coning and quartering. A means whereby large quantities of a sample are made into more convenient smaller samples. A cone of the material is built by shovelling around the periphery towards the apex; the sample is flattened and divided into four along two diameters which intersect at right angles. Each pair of opposite corners is shovelled into a separate heap and one of them rejected.

The process is repeated until the required quantity of sample, consistent with the size of the individual particles comprising the total bulk, is obtained.

Conjugate base. According to T. M. Lowry and J. N. Brønsted, the relationship between an acid and base may be expressed in the form:

$$A \rightleftharpoons H^+ + B$$
acid   proton base

where A is the acid and B is its conjugate base. From this it follows that the conjugate base of an acid is its anion.

Conjugate double bonds. See Diolefins.

Conjugate solutions. Solutions of two substances in one another (e.g. phenol in water and water in phenol), which are in equilibrium at a given temperature.

Conradson carbon test. See Carbon value.

Conservation of energy, Law of the. In systems of constant mass, energy can neither be created nor destroyed. One form of energy may disappear, but another takes its place. Thus the energy possessed by a hammer may be converted into heat on striking a surface. Energy can be converted from one form to another, but it cannot be annihilated. Helmholtz (1847) enunciated this principle in the following form: 'In all processes occurring in an isolated system, the energy of the system remains constant.' This is the law of the conservation of energy. Energy and mass are interconvertible.

Conservation of matter, law of. This law, which was understood by the Greeks, was first clearly formulated by Lavoisier in 1774; it stated that matter can neither be destroyed nor created. It is now known that the emission of radiation must be accompanied by a loss of mass, equal to E/c^2, where E is the energy of the radiation and c the velocity of light. E/c^2 is usually small compared with the masses of material used in ordinary chemical manipulation. There is a conservation of mass and energy considered together. See Atomic energy.

Constantan. An alloy of about 45% Ni and 55% Cu with a comparatively high resistance and a low resistance-temperature coefficient. It is used extensively for winding electrical resistances, but care must be taken not to strain the constantan wire as cold working has a marked effect on its electrical properties. With either copper, iron, silver, etc., it forms a thermocouple with a comparatively large E.M.F. Alloys that have similar properties are manganin (4% Ni, 84% Cu, 12% Mn) and eureka (composition similar to constantan).

Constant boiling mixture. See Azeotropic mixtures.

Constant proportions, law of. Proust (1799) concluded, from the analysis of a large number of compounds, that the proportion of each element present in a chemical compound is fixed and constant, i.e. the composition of a pure chemical compound is independent of the method by which it is prepared. This constitutes the law of constant proportions, or constant composition. In fact, many compounds have a fair range of compositions—see Defect structures.

Contact process. See Sulphuric acid.

Continuity of state. As the temperature is increased towards the critical point, the properties of liquids and vapour become increasingly alike, until at the critical temperature they are identical. Although the change liquid to vapour or vice versa is normally discontinuous, a gradual transition is possible. Thus if carbon dioxide, initially at one atmosphere and 20°, is isothermally compressed to 100 atmospheres the appearance of liquid and disappearance of vapour are sharply defined, i.e. the change vapour to liquid is discontinuous. If carbon dioxide is taken under the same initial conditions, and first heated to 40°, isothermally compressed to 100 atmospheres, and then cooled to 20° the same (liquid) state is reached as before, but no discontinuity can be observed.

Continuous counter-current decantation. A method employed in the continuous washing of finely divided solids to free them from impurities. Usually carried out in a series of continuous thickeners, the solids to be washed passing through them in series and being diluted after each settling by a weaker solution flowing in the reverse direction.

Continuous spectrum. The occurrence of well-defined lines (see Line spectrum), or of bands (see Band spectrum) consisting of well-defined lines, is explained on the quantum hypothesis by the assumption that electronic, vibrational, and rotational energy changes in a molecule can only occur in definite steps, each step corresponding with an integral number of energy units (quanta). Certain changes, e.g. the dissociation of a molecule, are not quantized processes. Hence, if light is emitted during the occurrence of such a process, its frequency no longer has definite values, but may take any value over a continuous range of frequencies. The spectrum of such a system is no longer broken into discrete lines or bands, but appears to be continuous. A continuous spectrum is characteristic of an unquantized process, such as dissociation.

Continuous thickeners. These are machines for the continuous thickening of suspensions. They generally consist of a large, shallow, cylindrical tank into which the suspension is introduced a little way below the liquid surface. Clarified liquid overflows from the top of the tank into a trough running round the edge, while the thickened liquid flows out through a central discharge at the bottom. Solids which settle out are dragged continuously towards this latter discharge point by a raking mechanism carried by two large rotating arms.

Continuous thickeners are extensively used in the metallurgical industries and may be up to several hundred feet in diameter.

Contraction rings—Buller's firing trial rings. These are used as a more accurate method of measuring the work done during the firing of a ceramic kiln than is obtained by Seger or Orton cones or Holdcroft's pyroscopes. The rings consist of thin discs, $2\frac{1}{2}$ in. in diameter, and made of an unfired ceramic body. When heated, they contract to a degree that depends upon the rate of heating and the temperature reached. The contraction (or expansion) is measured by an accurate gauge and, for high rates of heating, the scale of temperature is divided into 65 units equal to $960° + 7°$ per scale unit.

Convergence frequency. See Convergency limit.

Convergency limit. The lines in a spectrum represented by a given series (e.g. the Balmer series) become closer and closer together as the wave-length of the lines becomes shorter, and eventually approach a limit, known as the convergency limit, which may be expressed as a frequency, or wave-number, the convergence frequency.

Converting. The term applied in metallurgy to an oxidation process carried out on a molten charge in a vessel termed a converter. The oxidation is effected by blowing air through the charge which is kept molten by the heat of oxidation, no fuel being used.

Conveyor. A machine for the continuous transport of articles or particulate solids from one part of a factory to another. Descriptions of some of the more important types are given under Apron conveyor, Belt conveyor, Drag-link conveyor, Flight conveyor, Redler conveyor, Screw conveyor, Vibrating conveyor. See also Bucket elevator, Skip hoist, Air conveying, Hydraulic conveying.

Convolvulin, $C_{54}H_{92}O_3$. One of the glycosides of jalap root. It has m.p. 150°, $[\alpha]_D -35·3°$, and is hydrolysed to glucose (4 mols.), rhamnose (2 mols.), and convolvulinolic acid which is 3,12-dihydroxyhexadecanoic acid. The roots of several species of the convolvulaceae family have long been used as purgatives. See Jalapin and Pharbitin.

Cooke, Josiah Parsons (1827-1894). Cooke was born at Boston, Massachusetts, and educated at Harvard, where he later (1850) became Erving professor of chemistry and mineralogy. He wrote numerous books, and among his many investigations, which are mainly mineralogical in character, his determination of the atomic weight of antimony is notable, while his theory of the numerical relation between the atomic weights was a precursor of the periodic system.

Cooling towers. These are towers used to cool water for use in condensers and coolers. Water and atmospheric air are contacted, usually counter-currently, and evaporation of water

into the unsaturated air results in cooling. Three main types of cooling towers are in use:

The *natural draught cooling tower* is widely used for cooling large quantities of water. It consists of a shell of concrete with an hyperbolic profile. The bottom section contains wooden grids over which the water is sprayed, but most of the tower is empty. The additional height is necessary in order to obtain a chimney effect and suck air into the tower.

Mechanical draught cooling towers are employed for smaller quantities of water. They are generally square in cross-section and air is sucked or blown through them by a fan.

Atmospheric cooling towers have an open structure which allows air to pass through the sides of them and so effect cooling.

Co-ordinate bond. The linkage of two atoms by a pair of electrons, both electrons being provided by one of the atoms (the donor). The co-ordinate bond is formally identical with the covalent bond. An atom capable of accepting the electrons is an acceptor, the molecule donating the electrons is the donor or ligand. Co-ordinate linkages occur widely in inorganic complexes. See Valency, theory of.

Co-ordination compound. A compound containing a co-ordinate bond or bonds is termed a co-ordination compound. See Valency.

Co-ordination isomerism. Isomerism in co-ordination compounds. The isomerism is in terms of the actual arrangement of the atoms.

Co-ordination number. The number of groups or ions immediately surrounding any given molecule or ion in a crystal. Also, in complexes, the total number of co-ordinating and covalently bonded groups surrounding the central atom.

Copaene, $C_{15}H_{24}$. A sesquiterpene hydrocarbon obtained from oil of copaiba:

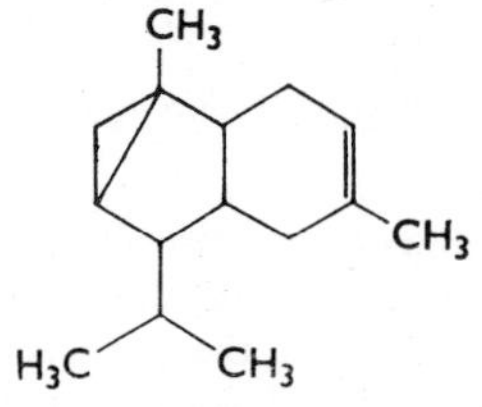

It has b.p. 114°-114·5°/10 mm, d_4^{25} 0·9055, n_D^{25} 1·4887, $[\alpha]_D -13°$.

Copolymer. A complex polymer, resulting from the polymerizing together of two or more different monomers or monomer combinations. A copolymer is a true compound and often has properties quite distinct from those expected of a physical mixture of the separately polymerized component monomers. Industrially important copolymers include vinyl chloride-vinyl acetate copolymer, and styrene-butadiene copolymers.

Graft copolymers are those produced by allowing one monomer to polymerize in the presence of a different polymer, in such a way that the new polymer grows from the established one.

Copper, Cu. At.no. 29, At.wt. 63·542, d 8·96, m.p. 1083°, b.p. 2582°. Crystallizes in the cubic system with the face-centred cubic structure, $a = 3·6153$ Å at 18°, the interatomic distance is 2·551 Å. This metal has been known from very early times; specimens of cast copper from Egypt and Babylonia dating back to $c.$ 4000 B.C. have been discovered. It appears later, alloyed with tin, in bronze; bronze working was practised in Egypt as early as 2500 B.C.

Native copper occurs in masses and in veins traversing sandstone in Sweden, the Ural Mountains, and in large quantities in the vicinity of Lake Superior. It usually contains small quantities of silver, bismuth, and lead. Cuprous oxide, Cu_2O, occurs as cuprite; cupric oxide, CuO, occurs in smaller amounts as tenorite or melaconite. The minerals malachite,

$$CuCO_3, Cu(OH)_2$$

(bright green), and azurite, $2CuCO_3, Cu(OH)_2$ (bright blue) are found in the Urals, and are used in works of art. In combination with sulphur copper is widely distributed, although in relatively small amounts, in the forms of chalcocite, Cu_2S, and covellite, CuS. The commonest ores are copper pyrites or chalcopyrite, $CuFeS_2$, and erubescite (or bornite), Cu_3FeS_3. These two latter minerals and the native copper from Lake Superior are the principal sources of the world's copper.

Pure copper is very malleable and ductile; it can be rolled into sheets, hammered into thin leaves, and drawn into wire. The metal may be spun on a lathe in the production of seamless vessels. Small quantities of impurities reduce the malleability of the metal. In air copper rapidly tarnishes, becoming covered with a very thin adherent film of oxide or sulphide. This causes the bright rose colour of the metal to deepen to brown. Prolonged exposure to moisture and air produces a green film of basic sulphate (verdigris). On heating in air, the metal is readily oxidized and the product forms scales which are black on the outside, due to cupric oxide, CuO, but red on the side in contact with the metal, due to cuprous oxide, Cu_2O. The metal is not attacked by non-oxidizing acids. Concentrated oxidizing acids attack it vigorously.

The chief source of copper is the sulphide ore deposits, which are first crushed and concentrated by flotation. The rich concentrate is smelted in reverberatory furnaces with fluxes to produce copper matte. This matte is then blown in a converter to oxidize the sulphur and to remove iron as a slag. This leaves blister copper, which then is fire-refined and cast, either into anodes for further electrolytic refining, or into billets, wire bars, or cakes of fire-refined tough pitch copper.

Copper has a high electrical conductivity, can be easily worked, and is used in chemical plant and in the food industries, but has been replaced in many cases by aluminium and stainless steel. It is a constituent of a large number of alloys such as brasses, bronzes, etc. When small amounts are added to cast iron it greatly increases the fluidity of the metal, thus simplifying the casting of large and intricate units.

Copper compounds. The cupric compounds (dipositive) are the more stable, and include all the common salts. The cuprous compounds (unipositive) are easily oxidized to the cupric state, in many cases even by exposure to the air. Simple soluble cuprous salts immediately disproportionate on contact with water; the hydrated cupric ion, $Cu(H_2O)_4^{2+}$, is blue, but the unhydrated ion and the cuprous ion are colourless. Some tripositive copper compounds, e.g. K_3CuF_6, are known.

Copper acetate $[Cu(OOCCH_3)_2 \cdot H_2O]_2$. A dimeric compound with a copper-copper bond and further bridging between the metal atoms by acetate groups.

Copperas. See Iron sulphates.

Copper carbonates. Many basic cupric carbonates are known. The most important are the minerals malachite, $CuCO_3, Cu(OH)_2$, and azurite, $2CuCO_3 \cdot Cu(OH)_2$. Addition of dilute sodium carbonate solution to dilute copper sulphate gives a precipitate of a basic carbonate. Cupric hydroxide dissolves in alkali carbonate solution to give the complex anion $Cu(CO_3)_2^{2-}$.

Copper chlorides, *Cupric chloride,* $CuCl_2$. The anhydrous salt is obtained by heating copper in excess of chlorine, or by heating the hydrate in a current of hydrochloric acid gas at 150°. Prepared by these methods, it is a dark brown material; a yellow form is obtained by dehydrating the dihydrate, $CuCl_2, 2H_2O$, with concentrated sulphuric acid. The hydrate is obtained in emerald green crystals by the evaporation of a solution of cupric oxide dissolved in concentrated hydrochloric acid. Only very dilute solutions exhibit the blue colour of the hydrated cupric, $Cu(H_2O)_4^{2+}$, ion; concentrated solutions are green, or in the presence of excess hydrochloric acid, yellow. These colours are due to the presence of the ions $CuCl^+$ and $CuCl_4^{2-}$ respectively; other complex ions are also known in solution.

Cuprous chloride, $CuCl$. Prepared by reducing a solution of cupric chloride in hydrochloric acid with copper or sulphur dioxide and precipitating the cuprous chloride by dilution with water. It is a white powder, m.p. 430°, having like cuprous bromide and iodide, the zinc-blende structure (*q.v.*). In moist air the cuprous chloride decomposes, partially to cuprous oxide and cupric chloride, and partially to a cupric oxychloride $3CuO \cdot CuCl_2 \cdot 3H_2O$. It is soluble in ammonia and in the complete absence of air a colourless solution of the cuprammine chloride $Cu(NH_3)_2Cl$, H_2O is formed. The colourless solutions in hydrochloric acid and ammonia readily absorb oxygen, cupric salts being formed, carbon monoxide with formation of the unstable compound $CuClCO$, $2H_2O$, and acetylene with the formation of a red precipitate of cuprous acetylide, Cu_2C_2.

Copper chromite. A catalyst, a mixed oxide of copper and chromium, obtained by igniting copper ammonium chromate under controlled conditions: barium is frequently added to prevent poisoning of the catalyst. It is used to bring about the reduction of carbonyl groups (e.g. ketones to alcohols, esters to alcohols) and does not encourage reduction of the benzenoid nucleus: alkenes are reduced slowly.

Copper cyanide, *Cuprous cyanide*, CuCN. The addition of potassium cyanide solution to one of cupric sulphate gives a yellow precipitate of unknown composition, which has been formulated as cupric cyanide. This rapidly decomposes with the evolution of cyanogen and the formation of white cuprous cyanide, CuCN. It is soluble in potassium cyanide solution, forming a colourless solution of potassium cuprocyanide, $K_3Cu(CN)_4$.

Copper glance. See Chalcocite.

Copper hydride, *Cuprous hydride*, CuH. An unstable brownish-yellow precipitate obtained by reducing a copper sulphate solution, containing a little sulphuric acid, with a hypophosphite at 70°. It evolves hydrogen with concentrated hydrochloric acid.

Copper hydroxide, *Cupric hydroxide*, $Cu(OH)_2$. Crystalline $Cu(OH)_2$ may be prepared by adding ammonia to a boiling solution of copper sulphate until the green precipitate becomes blue. The precipitate is well washed, and digested with moderately concentrated caustic soda at 20°-40°, and finally filtered, washed, and dried. The precipitate obtained by adding caustic alkali to a cupric salt solution is a basic salt, e.g. $CuSO_4$, $3Cu(OH)_2$. On boiling this blue hydroxide, it is converted to black $4CuO$, H_2O.

Orange-red *cuprous hydroxide* is formed by the electrolysis of a sodium chloride solution between copper electrodes.

Copper iodide, *Cuprous iodide*. The stable iodide of copper. It is formed, as a white precipitate, by the addition of potassium iodide solution to one of copper sulphate. The reaction is quantitative, and the iodine liberated may be titrated against standard sodium thiosulphate solution.

Copper naphthenates. Copper salts of naphthenic acids—carboxylic acids obtained from crude petroleum oils—are used as wood preservatives. The product is a green, unpleasant smelling liquid, which has the combined fungicidal properties of naphthenic acids and copper. Copper naphthenates are very toxic to plants.

Copper nitrate, *Cupric nitrate*, $Cu(NO_3)_2$. Formed by dissolving the metal, oxide, or carbonate in dilute nitric acid; on evaporation blue, deliquescent, prismatic crystals of the trihydrate, $Cu(NO_3)_2$, $3H_2O$ are produced. At low temperatures a hexa- and a nonahydrate are formed. On heating, the salt loses water and nitric acid, forming a basic salt, $Cu(NO_3)_2$, $3Cu(OH)_2$. Continued heating gives the oxide. Anhydrous cupric nitrate may be obtained from a solution of copper in liquid NO_2 and ethyl acetate; it is appreciably volatile.

Copper oxides, *Cupric oxide*, CuO. This is formed by the prolonged heating of the metal in air or oxygen, or by ignition of the nitrate. It is a black solid, stable up to its melting-point (*c.* 1150°), but then evolves oxygen and leaves a solution of cuprous oxide in copper. It is readily reduced by hydrogen, carbon, or organic substances to the metal. The oxide is soluble in dilute acids, blue solutions of cupric salts being formed.

Cuprous oxide, Cu_2O. Red cuprous oxide, Cu_2O, is precipitated by the partial reduction of alkaline cupric salt solutions. On treatment with sulphuric acid, cupric sulphate is formed, accompanied by metallic copper. The oxide is used to some extent in the production of a cheap ruby glass.

Copper pyrites. See Chalcopyrite.

Copper sulphates, *Cupric sulphate*, $CuSO_4$. The commonest cupric salt, usually known as copper sulphate. Crystallizes from water in blue triclinic crystals of the pentahydrate,

$$CuSO_4, 5H_2O$$

called blue vitriol or blue-stone. Obtained by dissolving cupric oxide in dilute sulphuric acid or the metal in hot concentrated acid. Obtained industrially by leaching copper ores with sulphuric acid or by treating copper with hot dilute sulphuric acid in the presence of air. Several hydrates are known; on exposure to air the pentahydrate effloresces to a pale blue powder of the trihydrate $CuSO_4$, $3H_2O$. At 100° the monohydrate is formed. On heating to 260° most of the water is expelled; a small amount remains even up to the decomposition temperature (736°). The product formed by dehydration at 260° is used in the detection of traces of moisture. The principal commercial use for cupric sulphate is in agriculture. It is also used in water treatment and wood preservaiton.

Cuprous sulphate is prepared by the action of methyl sulphate on cuprous oxide.

Copper sulphide, *Cupric sulphide,* CuS. A black solid obtained by heating copper powder with excess of sulphur at a temperature below 440°, or by precipitating a solution of a cupric salt with hydrogen sulphide. In the moist state it is rapidly oxidized by air to the sulphate. It is slightly soluble in yellow ammonium sulphide. Cupric sulphide is less stable than cuprous sulphide, and loses sulphur when gently heated alone or in hydrogen.

Cuprous sulphide, Cu_2S, is obtained by heating together copper and sulphur in the absence of air. It is a black solid.

Coproporphyrin. See Porphyrins.

Coprostanol, Coprosterol, $C_{27}H_{48}O$. Systematic

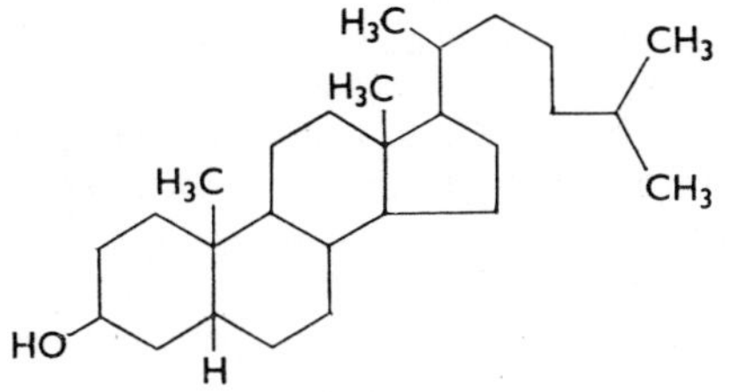

name 5β-cholestan-3β-ol. Needles from methanol, m.p. 101°-102°, $[\alpha]_D$ +28° in chloroform. It is a metabolite of cholesterol found in faeces, being formed by the action of intestinal bacteria on cholesterol. Analogous sterols arise in the same way from phytosterols in the diet.

Cordite. See Propellants.

Corrosion. Most metals and alloys are attacked by oxygen, moisture and acids. Some are attacked by alkalis. The process of attack is called corrosion. Corrosion may result in a uniform attack which is generally not very serious; it may attack preferentially, particularly at grain boundaries, resulting in severe weakening of the metal without much visible deterioration; it may attack locally at areas where conditions are varied resulting in perforation; finally it may produce a passive oxide layer as on chromium and aluminium which gives protection from further corrosion. There are two main types of corrosion: atmospheric oxidation and tarnishing in dry air, which is not serious, and electrolytic corrosion under conditions of mois-

ture or submersion. Any two areas on a metal or alloy surface not chemically and physically identical can act as anode and cathode. Thus two phases in an alloy such as steel act as microanodes and cathodes. The anode reaction is solution of metal or corrosion $M-2e\to M^{++}$ for a dipositive metal. The cathode reaction is by hydrogen evolution in acid solution or oxygen reduction in neutral solution. Differential aeration is a common cause of corrosion. If one area of a metal has a higher oxygen potential than another, then it becomes cathodic

$$\tfrac{1}{2}O_2 + H_2O + 2e \to 2OH^-$$

making the area of low oxygen potential anodic with consequent corrosion. Thus corrosion is more severe under deposits of silt or in general where an area is loosely covered. Underground corrosion is caused by (a) electrolytic cells, the moist soil acting as electrolyte, (b) by stray electric currents from earthing points, etc., and (c) by anaerobic bacteria which in the presence of iron and traces of $CaSO_4$ depolarize the microcathodes with the production of H_2S. The main methods combating corrosion are (a) treatment of water systems with inhibitors; (b) cathodic protection; (c) protection by paint, plating, phosphating, etc. See also Rusting, Cathodic protection.

Corrosive sublimate. See Mercury chlorides.

Corticotropin, ACTH, Adrenocorticotropic hormone. A polypeptide hormone, comprising 39 amino-acid residues in known sequence, secreted by the anterior lobe of the pituitary gland. It is obtained commercially from the glands of cattle, sheep and pigs. Corticotropin stimulates the adrenal cortex, promoting the metabolism of cholesterol to corticosteroid hormones: the concentration of these in the circulating blood is one of several factors influencing the production of corticotropin.

Cortisone, $C_{21}H_{28}O_5$. White crystals, m.p. 215°

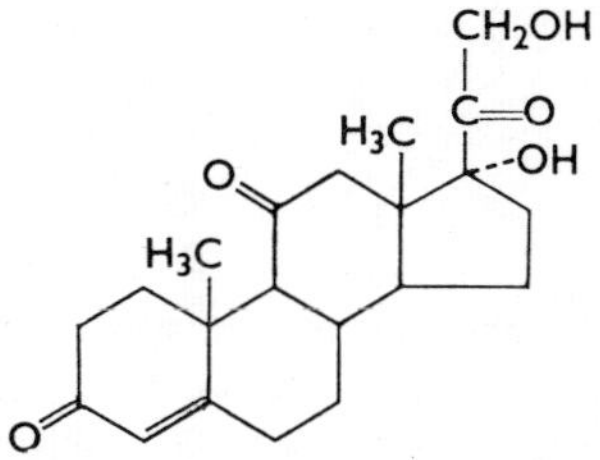

(decomp.), $[\alpha]_D$ +248° in alcohol. Almost insoluble in water. It is usually made as the monoacetate, which has m.p. 245°-246°, $[\alpha]_D$ +186° in acetone, +218° in chloroform, +208 to +219° in dioxan, is almost insoluble in water, more soluble in organic solvents.

Cortisone is a hormone produced by the cortex of the adrenal glands.

It is used for replacement therapy but has only a transient action. It removes the inflammatory features of rheumatoid arthritis, but does not check the underlying disease; it is used in various diseases of the eye, and is an anti-allergic and antifibroplastic agent.

Corundum, αAl_2O_3, a crystalline variety of alumina. Three varieties of this mineral are known: ruby, sapphire, and emery. The first two of these have been known for many centuries. Good crystals are found in Ceylon, Burma, Switzerland, Montana, India, and elsewhere. The crystals are hexagonal. Hardness 9, sp.gr. 3·9-4·1. Corundum is usually blue, with a vitreous lustre; it is dichroic with a strong refraction. The blue varieties are known as sapphires, the red varieties as rubies.

Emery is an impure corundum mixed with magnetite. The melting-point of corundum exceeds 1950°. It is non-magnetic, and a very poor conductor of electricity. Articles, such as crucibles, made of corundum, are highly resistant to corrosion at high temperatures, and are very insensitive to sudden changes in temperature.

Cosmic radiation. Certain radiations, always present in the earth's atmosphere, are called cosmic rays or ultra-radiation. They are possessed of extraordinary penetrating power, and great energy. The pure cosmic rays seem to be positively charged particles with energies of the order 10^9 electron volts; they are very possibly protons. On arrival in the earth's atmosphere they give rise to secondary radiations in which are found most of the elementary particles.

Cotarnine, $C_{12}H_{15}NO_4$. Cotarnine is tautomeric

and can react according to either formula. It exists as colourless needles, m.p. 132°-133°, with decomposition. Sparingly soluble in water, soluble in alcohol. It is an oxidation product of narcotine.

Cotton effect. In his investigation into the optical properties of transition metal tartrate compounds, Cotton (1895) noted a connexion between light absorption and rotatory power. Within the absorption band, there was shown to be anomalous rotatory dispersion. In the

figure, the broken line represents an absorption band and the full line the rotatory dispersion curve. It is seen that as the wavelength decreases

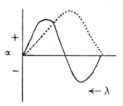

the rotation angle increases, passes through a maximum and then decreases, passing through zero angle at the wavelength corresponding to the maximum of absorption. On proceeding to lower wavelengths, the angle falls till it passes through a minimum and then rises again. This phenomenon is known as the Cotton effect. This effect has been confirmed for many coloured compounds as well as for colourless substances with bands in the ultra-violet region of the spectrum. See Optical rotatory dispersion, Circular dichroism.

Cottrell precipitator. A common name for the single-stage electrostatic precipitator. See Electrostatic precipitators.

Coulomb. This is the unit quantity of electricity; 96,494 coulombs, one Faraday, are required to deposit or ionize a gram equivalent of any element. See Faraday's laws of electrolysis.

Coulometer. A device by which the amount of charge passing in an electric circuit may be measured. A silver coulometer comprises a solution of silver nitrate into which two platinum electrodes are dipped. As the current is passed silver is deposited at the cathode and the resulting gain in weight can be equated to the charge passed.

$$1 \text{ coulomb} = 1·118 \times 10^{-3} \text{ g silver.}$$

o-Coumaric acid, *o*-hydroxycinnamic acid, $C_9H_8O_3$. Colourless crystals, m.p. 108°, ob-

tained by boiling coumarin with sodium ethoxide. Irradiation of *o*-coumaric acid produces coumarinic acid (*q.v.*). The stable form of the acid is the trans form.

Coumarin, $C_9H_6O_2$. Colourless rhombic crystals, m.p. 70°, b.p. 290°. Insoluble in cold water, soluble in hot water, alcohol, ether, and hydrocarbon solvents.

Occurs in the Tonka bean, of which it is the

odorous ingredient. Prepared synthetically by heating salicylaldehyde with acetic anhydride and sodium acetate. It is the δ-lactone of coumarinic acid. Hydrolysis with caustic alkali produces coumaric acid (*q.v.*). It is largely used in perfumery.

Coumarin glycosides are widely distributed in

plants. The aglucones consist of hydroxy-coumarins containing 1, 2, or 3 hydroxyls or their methyl ethers.

The best known are skimmin, aesculin, daphnin, scopolin, fabiatrin, and fraxin. In each instance the sugar is glucose attached at positions 6, 7, or 8.

Coumarinic acid, *o*-hydroxyallocinnamic acid, $C_9H_8O_3$. An unstable acid which spontaneously

forms a δ-lactone, coumarin, when the free acid is generated from its salts.

Coumarone. See Benzfuran.

Coumarone and Indene resins. These are usually prepared from coal-tar naphtha of boiling range 150°-200°. Tar acids and bases are first removed from the naphtha, which is then treated with a small amount of strong sulphuric acid to polymerize the coumarone, indene, and other similar unsaturated substances. The resinous layer so produced is then separated and purified. According to the conditions of extraction these resins may have melting-points from 50°-150°. They are usually brittle, brownish-yellow resins soluble in aromatic hydrocarbons. They are used chiefly in varnishes, rubber, and chewing gum.

Counter-current flow. When two streams of material are brought into contact with each other for the purpose of transferring either heat or matter between them, if the streams move in opposite directions flow is said to be counter-current. Counter-current operation is used in preference to co-current operation wherever possible, because for a given set of operating conditions it results in a greater transfer of heat or matter. See Co-current.

Counter-ions. The charge on the surface of a colloidal particle is compensated by an equal and opposite (ionic) charge in the liquid in immediate contact with it, the system as a whole being uncharged. These compensating ions which surround the charged particles are termed counter-ions. The counter-ions do not form a rigid layer round the charged sol particle but a diffuse layer in which their density decreases with distance from the interface. See Colloids; Electrical double layer.

Counters. Apparatus for the detection and quantitative estimation of radioactivity. The various particles (α, β, γ) produce ionizations in a gas between two charged electrodes; current produced is detected and shows the passage of one particle. Depending upon the voltages used and the amplification system α and β particles can be differentiated. Geiger counters and proportional counters have a filling of inert gas plus about 10% organic gas (methane). A proportional counter can be used to measure the energy of the incoming particle. Other counters in use involve the measurement of the ionization produced in an ionization chamber. Techniques not involving the collection of ions are the cloud chamber where the trace of a particle is recorded photographically as fog droplets in a gas saturated with vapour, and scintillation counters where the impact of an ionizing particle causes a flash of light in the scintillator. The original scintillator was zinc sulphide but modern instruments use organic materials such as anthracene or have the zinc sulphide crystals made more efficient by the addition of such impurities as boron.

Couper, Archibald Scott (1831-1892). Born near Glasgow, Couper studied classics at Glasgow and Edinburgh Universities. His studies in chemistry, undertaken later in Berlin and Edinburgh, were interrupted by ill-health. Couper's great contribution to science, his theory of molecular structure, was essentially the same as that of Kekulé but was not made public until a month after Kekulé had announced his theory.

Courtois, Bernard. Born in 1777 at Dijon; at the age of eighteen he entered the pharmacy of Frémy at Auxerre, and he afterwards studied chemistry under Fourcroy, Thenard, and Séguin. He returned to Dijon in 1804, and was busy with the manufacture of saltpetre and soda. He discovered iodine in 1812; its application to medicine was due to Dr. Coindet of Geneva. He died in 1838. See *Chem. & Ind.*, 1931, 316.

Covalency maximum. The maximum number of atoms which can be covalently bonded to an atom or ion of an element. It depends upon the number of orbitals available to accommodate the electrons from the central atom and from atoms forming covalent or co-ordinate links with that atom. In general these atoms can only go into shells which have very similar energies, thus the 4s, 4p, and 3d shells can be filled together, but the 2p and 3s shells cannot. The maximum covalency of hydrogen is one (though it can form a weak linkage known as a hydrogen bond between two atoms), of the atoms Li-F four, and of the atoms Na-Y six. For heavier atoms the maximum covalency is probably nine or ten.

Covalent bond. The linkage of two atoms by the sharing of two electrons, one contributed by each of the atoms. In practice the electrons are only shared equally when the atoms are identical, and in most covalent bonds the electrons are held to a greater extent by one atom than by the other. Covalent links are formed where electrovalent linkages would involve the interaction of small, highly charged cations with large diffuse anions. See Valency, theory of.

Covalent radius. The equilibrium distance between two atoms joined by a covalent bond of a given type (i.e. single, double, or triple) is found to be constant within close limits. The distance C—C in diamond, for example, is 1·54 Å. and the same distance is found in normal and cyclic saturated hydrocarbons. In general an interatomic distance A—B is the arithmetic mean of the values A—A and B—B, and a set of covalent radii may be drawn up such that the sum of any two gives the distance between the corresponding atoms for covalent binding. These values are half the interatomic distances in the elements except for very electronegative elements (e.g. fluorine). The departures from additivity are used to define electronegativity.

Cracking. The thermal decomposition of a petroleum fraction into substances of lower molecular weight. Cracking processes are the source of olefins which are intermediates in the manufacture of petroleum chemicals. Sometimes a catalyst is present which reduces the reaction temperature and modifies the type of hydrocarbon found in the products.

Cream of tartar. See Potassium hydrogen tartrate.

Creatine, Methylguanidineacetic acid, $C_4H_9N_3O_2$.

$$
\begin{array}{cc}
HN & CH_3 \\
\parallel & | \\
H_2N—C—N—CH_2CO_2H &
\end{array}
$$

Crystallizes in prisms with one molecule of water, which it loses at 100°. It decomposes at 291°. Sparingly soluble in cold water and alcohol, more soluble in hot water. Creatine is present in the muscles of all vertebrates; in mammals and birds there are about 450 mg of creatine per gram of muscle, in reptiles and amphibians rather less. It plays an important part in the cycle of chemical changes involving muscular contraction; phosphagen, a creatine phosphoric acid ester, breaks down to creatine and phosphoric acid, which recombine during the recovery process. It is excreted in the urine of children, and spasmodically by women, particularly after pregnancy. It is also excreted during starvation, in certain fevers, and in general whenever muscular breakdown is occurring. Normally creatinine is the form in which creatine is excreted. Creatine is formed in the body by the methylation (by methionine) of glycocyamine.

Creatine phosphate. See Phosphagen.

Creatinine, Methylglycocyamidine, $C_4H_7N_3O$.

Crystallizes in prisms with two molecules of water, m.p. 260°, with decomposition. Soluble in water and sparingly soluble in alcohol. Creatinine is the internal anhydride of creatine, and is formed from creatine by heating an acid solution of it. In alkaline solution the reverse change occurs. It is found in the urine, about 1 to 2 g being excreted daily by an adult man or woman, and the amount is remarkably constant, the actual quantity being roughly proportional to the body muscular tissue. This constancy shows that it is a breakdown product of the body tissues and not of foodstuffs. It is easily detected and estimated by the orange colour it gives with sodium hydroxide and picric acid.

Creep. In metals and alloys creep is a very slow yielding which takes place generally at high temperatures, over a long period of time, under a load considerably less than that which causes yielding in a normal tensile test. The process is diffusion controlled and failure is intercrystalline.

Creosote. Coal-tar creosote (creosote oil) is a fraction obtained in tar distillation that distils between 200° and 280°. It has a characteristic odour and contains a mixture of hydrocarbons, phenols, and other aromatic derivatives. It is used for the preservation of timber, for softening pitch, and as a fuel.

Medicinal creosote is a mixture of phenols, chiefly guaiacol and creosol (4-methyl-2-methoxyphenol), obtained by distillation of wood-tar. It has sp.gr. 1·037-1·087, b.p. 205°-225°, is almost colourless with a characteristic odour, and is a strong antiseptic, less toxic than phenol. It is used as an inhalent, an expectorant, and a gastro-intestinal antiseptic.

Cresol red, *o*-cresolsulphonphthalein. One of the sulphonphthalein group of indicators. It is used in 0·04% aqueous solution to which is added 5·3 ml of 0·05 M. sodium hydroxide per 0·1 g of indicator. Its pH range is 7·2 (yellow) to 8·8 (red).

Cresols, C_7H_8O. The cresols are colourless

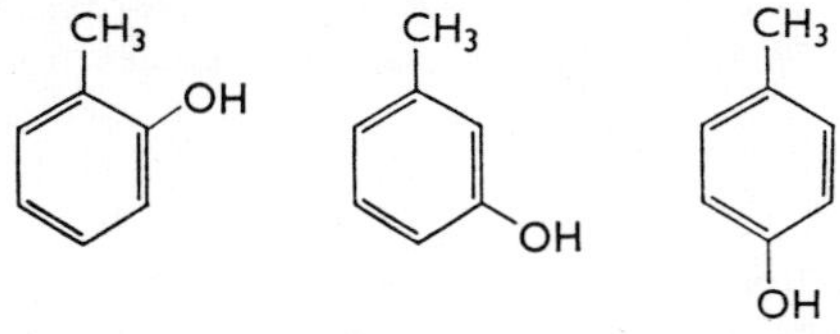

o   *m*   *p*

o-Cresol, m.p. 31°, b.p. 191°.
m-Cresol, m.p. 12°, b.p. 203°.
p-Cresol, m.p. 35°, b.p. 202°.

liquids or crystalline solids. They are volatile in steam, and are converted into toluene by fusion with zinc dust. They occur in the coal-tar fraction, b.p. 185°-220°, and this is one of the two principal sources; the other is cracked naphtha, which contains a certain proportion of cresylic material.

Usually prepared from the corresponding sulphonic acids by alkali fusion, or from the aminotoluene by treatment with nitrous acid followed by boiling. Both *o*- and *p*-cresol are used as end components in a few azo-dyes.

A mixture of the cresols is used as an antiseptic under the name of cresylic acid. It has b.p. 185°-203°, and is obtained as a high-boiling fraction in the purification of phenol. It contains 40% *m*-, 35% *o*-, and 25% of *p*-cresols. It is more powerful than phenol and less toxic. The chief commercial uses for the cresols are for the manufacture of phenolic resins and the plasticiser tricresyl phosphate.

Cresylic acid. See Cresols.

Cristobalite, SiO_2. A form of silica which is readily produced by heating quartz to a high temperature, especially in the presence of a catalyst such as ferric oxide or sodium phosphate. It occurs naturally as pseudo-cubic crystals, but the form prepared by heating quartz is cubic; sp.gr. 2·33, refractive index 1·487. There are two allotropic forms, α and β, with a transition temperature between 200° and 275°. The crystal lattice of the β or high tempera-

ture form contains 8 molecules in the unit cell, $a=7·12$ Å. Cristobalite is more readily dissolved by hydrofluoric acid than any other crystalline form of silica. Between 1470° and 1710° (m.p.) it is the stable crystalline form of silica.

In the low-temperature modification, the Si atoms are arranged like the C atoms in diamond, each being at the centre of four neighbours. The O atoms appear to be midway between the Si atoms, but their position may not be quite regular. The density is less than that of quartz.

Critical humidity. The humidity at which the vapour pressure at the surface of a solid or solution is equal to the partial pressure of water in the atmosphere. Thus at humidities above the critical value water will tend to be absorbed and below the critical value moisture will be lost to the atmosphere.

Critical phenomena. The temperature above which it is impossible to liquefy a gas, no matter what pressure is applied, is called the critical temperature. At this temperature the minimum pressure necessary to cause liquefaction is the critical pressure. The volume occupied by one gram-molecule of the gas at the critical temperature and pressure is the critical volume.

Critical solution temperature. The temperature at which the mutual solubility of two phases becomes equal. In the case of phenol and water, for example, on mixing the two substances two layers are formed, one of which is a solution of phenol in water and the other a solution of water in phenol. The solubility of each substance in the other increases with rise of temperature until, at the critical solution temperature, the two layers become identical and there is only one phase. This temperature is also known as the consolute temperature.

Crocein acid, $C_{10}H_8O_4S$. Obtained by sulphonating β-naphthol with a small quantity of

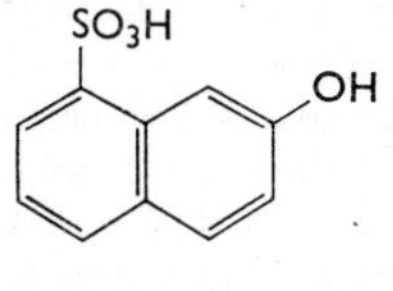

sulphuric acid at a low temperature.

Couples with diazotized bases to give valuable azo-dyes. Also used as a source of crocein yellow, a nitrated crocein acid.

Crocetin, $C_{20}H_{24}O_4$.

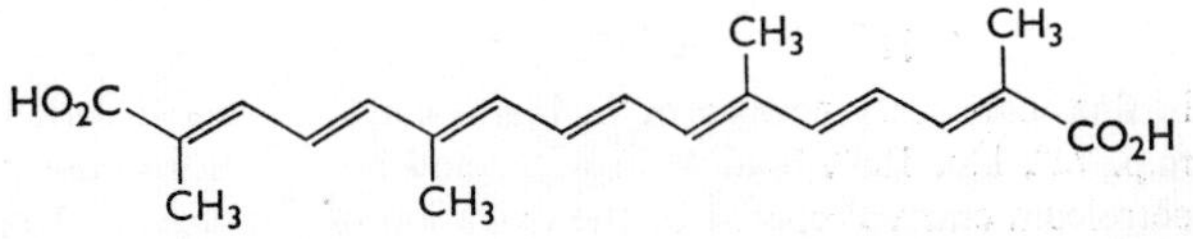

Crystallizes in brick-red rhombs, m.p. 285°, sparingly soluble in most organic solvents, soluble in pyridine. Its digentiobiose ester, crocin, is the colouring matter of saffron, from which it can be extracted with alcohol. Crocetin methyl ester plays a part in the reproduction of a unicellular algae: whether male or female gametes are formed depends on the ratio of the *cis* and *trans* isomers of the compound.

Crocidolite. A variety of asbestos (*q.v.*).

Crookes, Sir William (1832-1919). Crookes was born and educated in London; in 1851 he was appointed assistant to Hofmann at the Royal College of Chemistry. In 1859 he published the first number of the *Chemical News*, of which he remained sole editor until 1906. F.R.S. in 1863, and knighted in 1897, he received the O.M. in 1910. Noted for his researches in spectroscopy and radioactivity, Crookes invented the radiometer, the spinthariscope, and a special glass largely opaque to heat rays and to ultra-violet light. He discovered the element thallium in 1861. See 'Life of Sir William Crookes,' by Fournier d'Albe (1923).

Crookes's dark space. See Glow discharge.

Cross, Charles Frederick (1855-1935). Born at Brentford, Cross was educated at King's College, London, and later studied at Zurich and Owens College, Manchester. An English consulting chemist, he made a world-wide reputation among pulp and paper makers. With E. J. Bevan he discovered, in 1892, viscose which made possible the artificial silk industry. In 1916 Cross was awarded the Society's Medal of the Society of Chemical Industry, and in the following year was elected F.R.S. See *J. Chem. Soc.*, 1935, 1337.

Crotonaldehyde, C_4H_6O, $CH_3 \cdot CH:CH \cdot CHO$. A colourless liquid with a pungent odour; its vapour is lachrymatory; d^{15} 0·8575, b.p. 104°. Moderately soluble in water; volatile in steam; miscible with alcohol, acetone, and ether. Manufactured by the thermal dehydration of aldol. May be oxidized to crotonic acid and reduced to crotonyl alcohol and *n*-butyl alcohol; oxidized by oxygen in the presence of vanadium pentoxide to maleic anhydride. It is an intermediate in the production of normal butyl alcohol from acetaldehyde.

Crotonic acids, 2-Methylacrylic acids, $C_4H_6O_2$. The two crotonic acids are geometrical isomers. *α-Crotonic acid, trans–crotonic acid,* crystallizes

$$H_3C \diagdown / H$$
$$C=C$$
$$H \diagup \diagdown COOH$$

in fine, colourless needles or in large plates; m.p. 72°, b.p. 180°. Soluble in water and hot petroleum ether. Prepared by the oxidation of crotonaldehyde or by heating the substance formed by the action of acetaldehyde on malonic acid. Reduced by zinc and sulphuric acid to normal butyric acid. Oxidized by potassium permanganate to dihydroxybutyric acid. Reacts with chlorine to give αβ-dichlorobutyric acid, and with hydrogen bromide to give β-bromobutyric acid.

Isocrotonic acid, β-crotonic acid, cis-crotonic acid, crystallizes in colourless needles from

$$H_3C \diagdown / COOH$$
$$C=C$$
$$H \diagup \diagdown H$$

petroleum ether; m.p. 14·5°, b.p. 169°; 74°/15 mm. Soluble in water and petroleum ether. Prepared by distilling β-hydroxyglutaric acid under reduced pressure. Converted to α-crotonic acid by heating at 180°, or by the action of bromine and sunlight on an aqueous solution.

Crotonyl. The name given to the group
$$-COCH:CHCH_3$$
in organic compounds.

Crotyl. The name given to the group
$$-CH_2CH:CHCH_3$$
in organic compounds.

Crotyl alcohol, C_4H_8O, $CH_3CH:CHCH_2OH$, is a colourless liquid; d 0·8726, b.p. 118°. Soluble in water (17%). Prepared by the reduction of crotonaldehyde.

Crum Brown's rule as to substitution in benzene derivatives is a good working guide but must not be taken as universal. This rule states that a substance C_6H_5A yields the *meta* disubstituted product if the compound HA can be oxidized directly to HOA; otherwise a mixture of the *o*- and *p*-compounds will be obtained.

Crushing and grinding. Although these terms are widely used in connexion with particle size reduction, they do not have precise meanings. In general *crushing* refers to operations where it is principally compressive forces that bring about size reduction, *grinding* to operations where other mechanisms, e.g. attrition, shearing, are also important. Because machines for producing a fine product normally employ more than one mechanism, operations of this type are usually referred to as grinding. See also Size reduction equipment.

Crushing rolls. Reduction in size may be effected by passing the material between two heavy rollers rotating in opposite directions. The pressure between the rollers is maintained by spring loading; the space between the rolls may be varied to secure a product of the required degree of fineness. Crushing rolls are simple in construction and do not give too high a proportion of fine product. They cannot achieve a high degree of size reduction, a feed/product size ratio of 4 to 5 being typical, and if a large reduction is required it is necessary to operate two or more sets of rolls of different sizes in series. They are sometimes known as smooth roll crushers.

Cryohydric point. The point of intersection of the two curves showing respectively the effect of additions of a substance B on the melting-point of a second substance A, and the effect of additions of A on the melting-point of B. Since the effect of additions of a foreign substance is to lower the melting-point, the cryohydric point will be below the melting-point of either pure component. The cryohydric point is also known as the eutectic point. The solid which separates from a melt at the cryohydric point is a mixture, and is known as the cryohydrate or eutectic.

Cryolite, Na_3AlF_6, is fairly common and occurs massive at Ivigtut, West Greenland. It is monoclinic, sp.gr. 2·97, hardness $2\frac{1}{2}$, m.p. 977°; it changes into a cubic form at 570°. Much commercial cryolite is made artificially.

It is used chiefly as a flux in the isolation of aluminium and as an opacifying agent for glass, ceramic glazes, and enamels.

Cryptone, $C_9H_{14}O$. Isolated from various

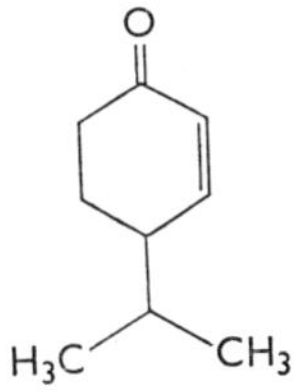

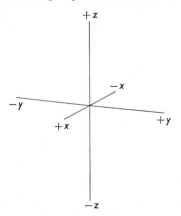

eucalyptus oils, and also obtained by the aerial oxidation of β-phelandrene. (−)-Cryptone has b.p. 98°-100°/10 mm, n_D^{20} 1·4841, $[\alpha]_D$ −119·3°.

Crystal. A discrete solid particle bounded by definite faces intersecting at definite angles, and showing certain symmetry characteristics. The external form of such a crystal is now known to be due to an ordered arrangement of atoms or molecules or ions within the bulk of the solid.

Crystal drawing. Crystals are drawn in a con-

ventional projection and in a conventional position. In dealing with crystals belonging to the cubic system the x axis does not point to the eye of the observer, but is rotated clockwise through an angle of 18° 26′, the tangent of which is 1/3; the y axis is not drawn at right angles to the vertical c axis because the eye is supposed to be elevated at an angle of 9° 28′, the tangent of which is 1/6. The axes are therefore drawn as shown.

Crystal-field theory. A theory of valency which attempts to explain the optical and magnetic properties of compounds and, particularly, complexes, in terms of a central ion surrounded by other ions.

Crystal habit. A term used to denote the relative development of different types of face on crystals which are of the same class.

Crystalline state. A form of the solid state in which there is an ordered arrangement of atoms or molecules or ions in the solid, which is characteristic of each solid, and may give rise to bounding faces of the crystal showing a characteristic symmetry, and intersecting at definite angles.

Crystallization. The removal of a solid from solution by increasing its concentration above the saturation point in such a manner that the excess solid separates out in the form of crystals.

Crystallizer. A plant for producing crystals. In the case of a material with a large temperature coefficient of solubility this may take the form merely of a tank equipped with an agitator and cooling coils, in cases where supersaturation has to be produced by evaporation the crystallizer may be a slightly modified evaporator. Normally, however, more specialized equipment is used. For descriptions of some of the more important types of crystallizer, see Double-pipe crystallizer, Howard crystallizer, Oslo crystallizer, Swenson-Walker crystallizer, Vacuum crystallizers, Wulff-Bock crystallizer.

Crystallographic axes. See Crystal symmetry.

Crystal nucleus. A minute crystal which serves as a centre of formation for larger crystals and without which these latter would not be formed. For example, crystallization of a supersaturated solution may be induced by formation of crystal nuclei through mechanical shock, inoculation with dust, etc.

Crystals, liquid. A number of solid substances, e.g. ammonium oleate and p-azoxyanisole, have the property of melting, on heating, to give a cloudy liquid, which changes at a higher temperature to a clear liquid. The cloudy liquid is doubly refracting, and is called a liquid crystal, or, more generally, is said to be in the mesomorphic state. Substances which form liquid crystals have molecules which are either long or flat. It is believed that in the mesomorphic state the liquid is composed of discrete groups of such molecules. Such groups may be oriented in the liquid by the application of a magnetic field.

Crystal structure. The arrangement of atoms and molecules in a crystal, as revealed by X-ray and electron diffraction methods.

A characteristic of a crystal is that the atoms, molecules, or ions are arranged in a regular way in three dimensions. It follows that if we start from an arbitrary origin in the crystal and proceed in any direction we shall arrive, after travelling a certain distance, at a point with the same environment as the point of origin. We may perform this process in two other directions and find the corresponding 'repeat distances.' These three axes of reference, defined as x, y, and z, and the three repeat distances, a, b, and c, define a parallelopiped which contains a representative portion of the crystal structure, and which if indefinitely repeated in those directions will reproduce the crystal. A characteristic parallelopiped is termed the '*unit cell*', and the repeat distances or *cell dimensions* (the sides of the unit cell) are written a, b, and c, corresponding to the x, y, and z axes. The angles between the axes taken in pairs, are called α, β, and γ (between yz, zx, and xy respectively). The choice of axes in the crystal is not arbitrary, except in the triclinic system, but is determined by the positions of the symmetry elements. The shape of the unit cell, and hence the constants required to define it, depends on the symmetry of the crystal, and the following table summarizes the data required in the various systems:

Triclinic	$a, b, c, \alpha, \beta, \gamma$.
Monoclinic	a, b, c, β $(\alpha=\gamma=90°)$.
Orthorhombic	a, b, c, $(\alpha=\beta=\gamma=90°)$.
Hexagonal and	a $(=b), c$, $(\gamma=120°,$
Trigonal	$\alpha=\beta=90°)$.
Tetragonal	a $(=b), c$, $(\alpha=\beta=\gamma=90°)$.
Cubic	a $(=b=c)$, $(\alpha=\beta=\gamma=90°)$.

Crystal symmetry. A term describing the regularities in the position and arrangement of faces and edges of a crystal. Such regularities are defined in terms of planes of symmetry, axes of symmetry, and centres of symmetry. A plane of symmetry divides the crystal into two identical halves, each of which is the mirror image of the other. An axis of symmetry is an imaginary line drawn through the crystal in such a way that, on rotating the crystal about this line as axis, the crystal presents an identical aspect to the observer more than once in a complete rotation. If the same aspect is presented four times (as would be the case for a cube

rotated about a line through the centres of opposite faces) the axis is called an axis of fourfold symmetry. Similarly, we may have axes of two-, three-, and six-fold symmetry. A crystal has a centre of symmetry if like faces are arranged in matched pairs in corresponding positions on opposite sides of a point. There are a limited number of possible arrangements of planes, centres, and axes of symmetry, which lead to a classification of crystals according to crystal systems (*q.v.*). In order to describe the external form of crystals three crystallographic axes are chosen. One face, making intercepts on all the axes, is taken as the standard or parametral face to which all other faces are referred. The description of crystal symmetry given above refers to the macroscopic crystal. The symmetry elements are also present in the unit cell, where they act on the atoms in the cell.

Crystal systems. According to their symmetry crystals are placed in one of the seven crystal systems: cubic, tetragonal, hexagonal, trigonal, orthorhombic, monoclinic, and triclinic. For the characteristics of each of these systems see Crystal structure and the separate headings, (e.g. Cubic system).

Crystal violet. See Methyl violet.

Cubic close-packing. One of the two simplest

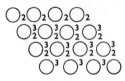

◯	layer 1 and 4
2	layer 2
3	layer 3

ways of packing equal spheres to occupy the minimum volume per sphere, the other being hexagonal close-packing (*q.v.*). Each sphere has twelve equidistant neighbours and, as its name implies, the arrangement has cubic symmetry. In the cubic unit cell the atoms occupy the corners and mid-points of all the faces, whence the alternative description—face-centred cubic structure. Some of the more important metals crystallising with this structure are: Cu, Ag, Au, Al, γ-Fe, β-Co, β-Ni, and Pt.

Cubic system. A term used to describe crystals having three equal crystallographic axes at right angles. Such crystals are sometimes referred to as belonging to the regular system. Cubic crystals are characterized by the presence of four three-fold axes in the directions of the cube diagonals, but additional axes and planes of symmetry may be present up to a maximum of thirteen axes of symmetry (6 two-fold, 4 three-fold, and 3 four-fold) and nine planes of symmetry. The unit cell in the structure of a cubic crystal is a cube and is defined by the length a of its side. Three simple cubic forms are the cube itself, the tetrahedron, and the octahedron. Sodium chloride and many metals crystallize in cubes, while the alums crystallize as octahedra. See also Crystal symmetry.

Cumene, Isopropylbenzene, C_9H_{12}. Obtained commercially by the reaction of benzene with propylene in the presence of a catalyst such as hydrogen fluoride. It has b.p. 152°, $d^{20}_{4}0\cdot8618$, $n^{20}_D 1\cdot4915$. Oxidation via a peroxide allows a commercially valuable route to acetone and phenol.

Cumyl-α-hydroperoxide, $C_9H_{12}O_2$. This commercially important intermediate is obtained by passing air through liquid cumene in the presence of a trace of a basic catalyst. On treatment with acids it gives phenol and acetone.

Cupellation. The term given to a process for obtaining either gold and/or silver from their mixture with an easily oxidizable metal, such as lead. The method is a very old one. In modern practice the alloy is heated in a furnace of the reverberatory type lined with bone ash and a strong current of air passed over it. The lead or other metal forms an oxide, leaving the valuable component behind. If the original alloy contained both silver and gold they have to be submitted to some further process such as 'parting' if their separation is required. Formerly the desilverizing of lead was accomplished by cupellation, but for economical production lead with less than 8 oz. of silver per ton was useless. Modern methods are the Pattinson's and Parkes's processes.

Cupferron, Ammonium N-nitrosophenylhydroxyl-amine. $\overset{+}{N}H_4 O\overset{-}{N}(NO)C_6H_5$. A reagent originally suggested for use in the detection of copper, but now used for the separation of iron, titanium, and zirconium which it precipitates from acid solutions. Cupferron is a brownish-white crystalline substance, soluble in water.

Cupola. A small blast furnace used in a foundry for preparing metal for casting. Pig iron and scrap are used, whereas iron ore is used in larger blast furnaces.

Cuprammonium. The deep blue complex ion $Cu(NH_3)_4{}^{++}$, prepared by adding excess ammonium hydroxide to a solution of a cupric salt. A cuprammonium solution has the property of dissolving cellulose, and is used in one of the processes of rayon manufacture.

Cuprene, Carbene. A solid polymerization product of acetylene which exists as a dark coloured, flocculent powder or in granular lumps, resembling cork. Manufactured by heating acetylene at 200°-400° in the presence of copper, nickel, or iron, metal or oxide. Used in blasting cartridges and as a substitute for charcoal in black powder and other explosives; also used instead of charcoal for decolorizing liquids.

Cupric. Copper (II) species.

Cuprite, Cu_2O. This is sometimes called red copper ore. The crystals are of the cubic system, in octahedra or cubes, and do not display twinning. Hardness $3\frac{1}{2}$, sp.gr. 6. Bright red colour with an almost metallic lustre. It is found in Cornwall, Arizona, Russia, France, and other localities.

Cupron. See Benzoin.

Cuprous. Copper (I) species.

Curare. An extract prepared from the bark of various species of *Strychnos*. It was originally used as an arrow poison by South American Indians, and contains the poisonous alkaloid curarine. When injected subcutaneously it paralyses the motor nerve endings, and in large doses death rapidly occurs from failure of respiration. See Tubocurarine chloride.

Curie. The standard unit of radioactivity. The quantity of substance which gives the same number of disintegrations as 1 g of radium ($3\cdot6 \times 10^{10}$ disintegrations per second).

Curie (Sklodovska) Marie, (1867-1934). Born in Warsaw, Marie Sklodovska was educated by her father, professor of physics at Warsaw, and later at Paris. She married Pierre Curie in 1895. Jointly with her husband she was awarded in 1903 the Davy Medal of the Royal Society, and in 1904 they, jointly with Becquerel, were awarded a Nobel Prize. In 1906 she succeeded her husband as professor of physics at the Sorbonne, Paris, and in 1911 was awarded the Nobel Prize for chemistry. One of the pioneers in radioactivity, her work in that sphere is historic. She was the first Director of the Radium Institute in Paris. See Mem. Lect., *J. Chem. Soc.*, 1935, 654.

Curie-Joliot, Irène (1896-1956). Daughter of Marie Curie and wife of Frédéric Joliot, Irène Curie assisted her mother and later her husband in work on natural and artificial radioactivity. She shared the Nobel Prize for chemistry with her husband in 1935.

Curie-Weiss law. Pierre Curie (1895) showed that

the magnetic susceptibility per mole of a substance may be represented by the equation

$$\chi = C/T$$

where C is called the Curie constant; χ is composed of both diamagnetic and paramagnetic contributions. Not all substances conform to this expression and a more general relationship known as the Curie-Weiss law,

$$\chi = \frac{C}{T-\theta}$$

is used; θ is the Weiss constant and is characteristic for a particular substance.

Curium, Cm. At.no. 96. Isotopes of curium of mass from 238 to 259 can be prepared by the action of α-particles on ^{239}Pu or of accelerated carbon ions on ^{232}Th. ^{242}Cm and ^{244}Cm have been used in chemical research but the heavier isotopes have very long half-lives and would be more suitable for this purpose if they were more accessible. Curium is separated from other elements by ion-exchange or solvent extraction procedures. Metallic curium has been prepared by reduction of CmF_3 with barium at 1275°; it is a silvery, malleable metal which appears to undergo rapid corrosion even at room temperature. Curium is extremely radioactive and hazardous to health. Curium metal has a hexagonal close-packed structure, m.p. 1340°.

Curium compounds. On account of the intense radioactivity of curium very few compounds are known. Two *curium oxides*, Cm_2O_3, white, and CmO_2, black, are known. *Curium trifluoride*, CmF_3, is insoluble in water. *Curium tetrafluoride*, CmF_4, has been prepared by the action of fluorine on CmF_3.

Curtius, Theodor (1857-1928), professor of chemistry at Heidelberg, discovered hydrazine in 1887 and the tetrazine derivatives in 1906; he also investigated the polypeptides.

Curtius transformation. An alternative to the Hofmann transformation for obtaining an amine from an ester via the hydrazide, azide, and isocyanate. Thus ethyl acetate is converted into methylamine by the following series of reactions:

$CH_3COOC_2H_5 + NH_2NH_2 \rightarrow CH_3CONH \cdot NH_2$ in hot alcohol.
$CH_3CONH \cdot NH_2 + HNO_2 \rightarrow CH_3CO \cdot N_3$ in aqueous solution at 0°.
$CH_3CO \cdot N_3 \rightarrow CH_3 \cdot NCO + N_2$ on warming.
$CH_3 \cdot NCO + H_2O \rightarrow CH_3NH_2 + CO_2$ on boiling with dilute acid.

Alternatively, the azide may be boiled with alcohol to convert it into the urethane, and the latter then hydrolysed with dilute acid. In general, the Hofmann method is rather more convenient, but the Curtius method must be employed when the compound in question is attacked by alkalis or easily brominated.

Cut-back asphaltic bitumen. Bitumen which has been rendered fluid by the addition of a diluent such as white spirit, kerosine, or creosote before addition of the mineral aggregate in the preparation of road surface dressings.

Cutin. A component of the waterproof covering or cuticle of the outer cellulose wall of plants. It is composed of a mixture of unsaturated fatty acids that have undergone oxidation and condensation, and of soaps and esters of such substances.

Cyanamide, NH_2CN. A colourless, crystalline deliquescent solid, m.p. 41°, which is readily soluble in water, alcohol, or ether, but only sparingly soluble in carbon disulphide, benzene, or chloroform. It is prepared by the action of mercuric oxide on thiourea or by passing carbon dioxide over heated sodamide. Cyanamide behaves as a very weak acid, and both acid and normal salts (e.g. $NaHNCN$ and Na_2NCN) are known. The calcium salt, calcium cyanamide, $CaNCN$, is prepared by the action of nitrogen on calcium carbide at a high temperature. With strong acids cyanamide also acts as a base and forms salts, but they are decomposed by water. Cyanamide is hydrolysed to urea by the action of dilute acids. With hydrogen sulphide it forms thiourea and, with ammonia, guanidine.

Cyanates. Salts of cyanic acid, HNCO. They are readily formed by heating a cyanide with a metallic oxide, when the latter is reduced to the free metal (e.g. $KCN + PbO = KNCO + Pb$). When acidified, solutions of cyanates liberate free cyanic acid, which is rapidly hydrolysed ($HNCO + H_2O = NH_3 + CO_2$). Ammonium cyanate, which is produced by mixing concentrated aqueous solutions of potassium cyanate and ammonium chloride, is transformed on heating into the isomeric substance, urea ($NH_4CNO \rightarrow (NH_2)_2CO$).

Cyanic acid, HNCO. A mobile, volatile liquid, with a smell resembling that of glacial acetic acid, which is formed by distillation of cyanuric acid, $C_3N_3(OH)_3$. Above 0° the acid changes rapidly into a solid polymer, known as cyamelide. Cyanic acid in aqueous solution is rapidly hydrolysed to ammonia and carbon dioxide. There are two alternative modes of formulating cyanic acid, viz. $HO \cdot C \equiv N$ or $NH = C = O$. The second of these, known as isocyanic acid is believed to represent the constitution of the free acid although alkyl derivatives of unambiguous constitution are known corresponding to each of the two formulae. The salts of this acid are known as the cyanates or isocyanates.

Cyanides. The salts of hydrocyanic acid. This is a weak acid and the cyanides of the alkali metals are hydrolysed in solution and show an alkaline reaction. The solubility of the metallic cyanides in water parallels that of the chlorides; silver cyanide, for example, being insoluble in water whereas the cyanides of the alkali and alkaline-earth metals are readily soluble. Mercuric cyanide, on heating, forms cyanogen. Many cyanides, particularly those of the transition elements, react with excess alkali cyanide to give complex cyanides containing metal-carbon bonds. Cyanides are extremely poisonous.

Cyanidin. The glucose free product obtained as

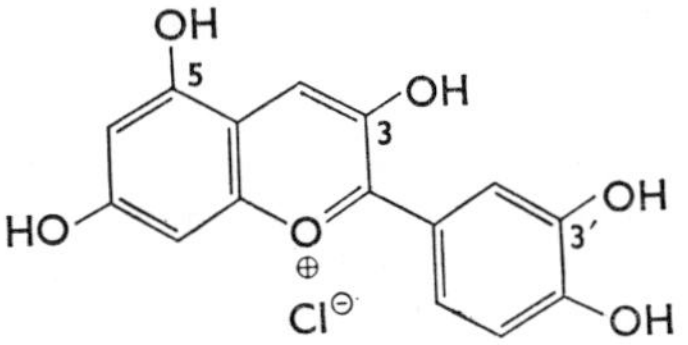

the chloride $C_{15}H_{11}ClO_6$ in a brown-red crystalline form by hydrolysis (HCl) of cyanin.

Cyanin. The anthocyanin of the cornflower and the rose. It is the 3,5-diglucoside of cyanidin. On the other hand mekocyanin

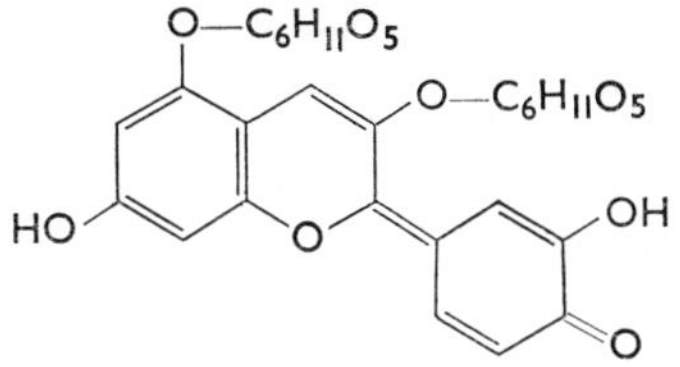

obtained from the poppy is the 3-bioside of cyanidin. Other cyanidin anthocyans are:

Chrysanthemin (asterin) present in the chrysanthemum, aster, blackberry, and elderberry; this is the 3-monoglucoside.

Peonin from the peony is a 3-bioside of 3′-methylcyanidin (peonidin).

Cyanine dyes. This class of dyes is of great importance in the photographic industry in providing many of the most powerful spectral sensitizers. They have found few other applications, being generally fugitive to light, but a limited number have interesting properties for textile and pharmaceutical applications. They are cationic dyes with a conjugated polymethine chain between two heterocyclic nitrogen-containing rings. The essential conjugation is of the extended amidinium type. The sensitization band moves to longer wavelengths as the polymethine chain is extended. Many useful dyes incorporate indolenine, benzoxazole, benzothiazole, benzoselenazole, pyridine and quinoline heterocyclic ring systems in their structures.

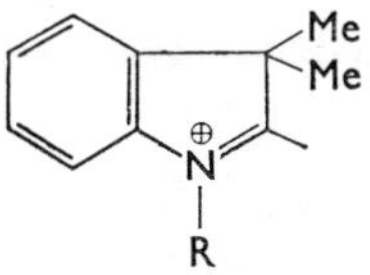

Indoleninium

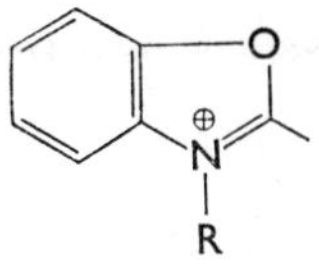

Benzoxazolium

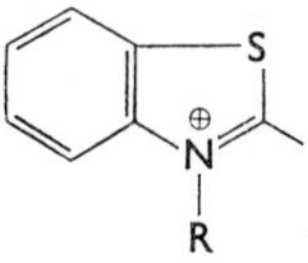

Benzothiazolium

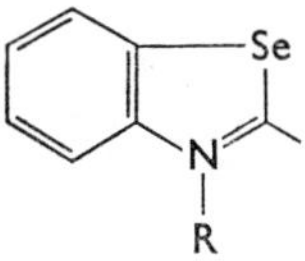

Benzoselinazolium

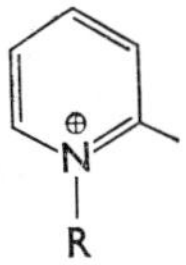

2-Pyridinium

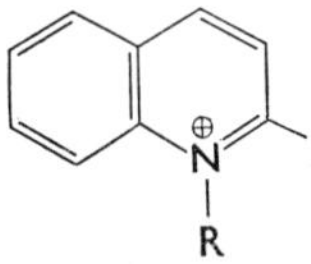

2-Quinolinium

Dyes representative of sub-classes of the

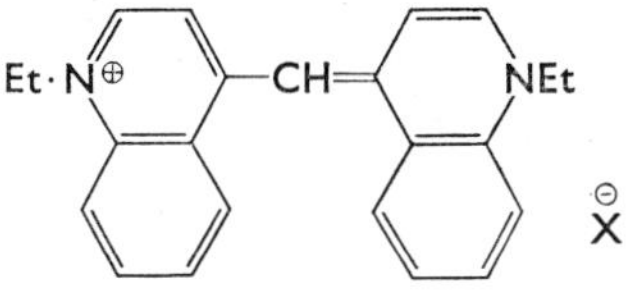

Cyanine (blue)

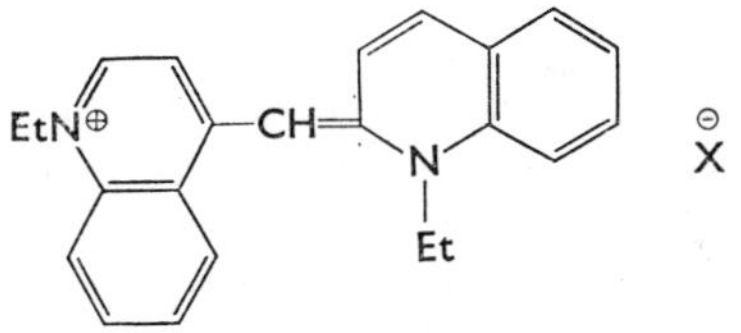

Isocyanine, Ethyl Red (magenta)

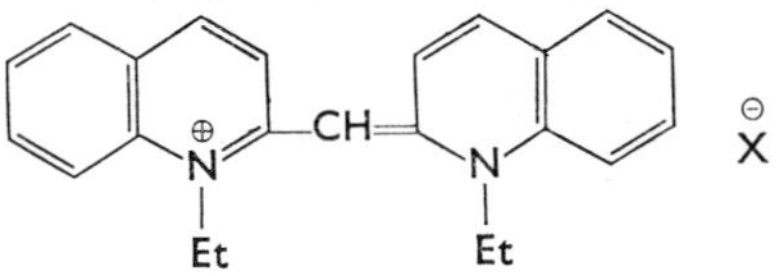

Pseudoisocyanine, pseudocyanine (red)

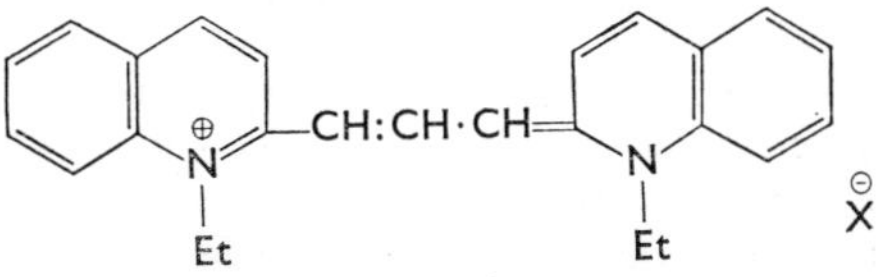

Pinacyanol (blue)

175

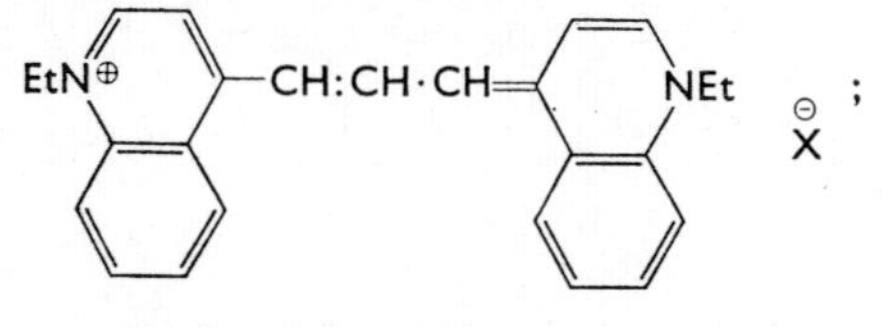

Kryptocyanine (blue-green)

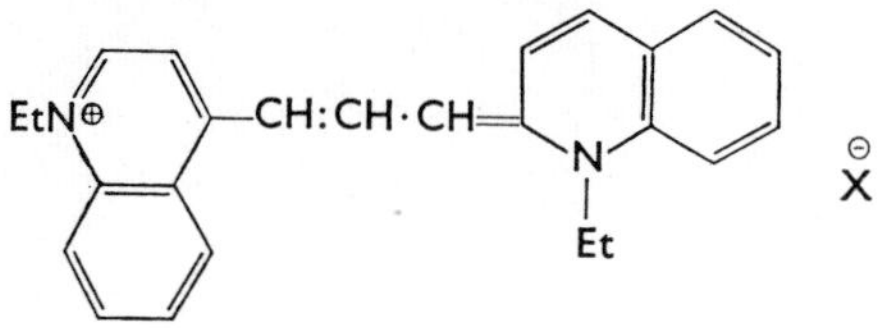

Dicyanine (blue)

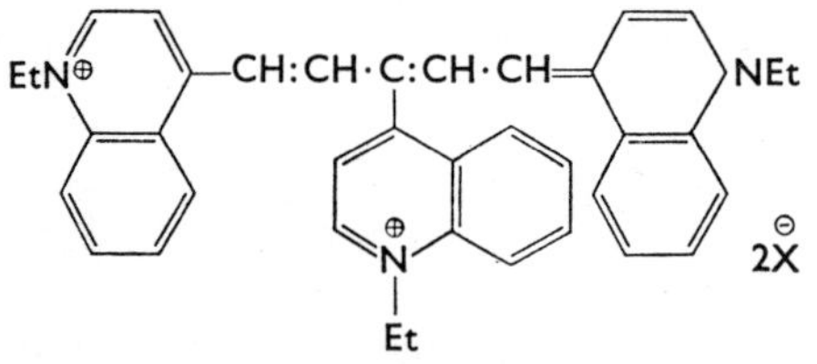

Neocyanine (green)

cyanines include cyanine (4,4′-cyanine), iso-cyanine (2,4′-cyanine), pseudocyanine (2,2′-cyanine) and their higher vinylogues. Neo-cyanine, a tri-nuclear dye, is an infra-red sensitizer which is effective beyond 800 mμ. The name cyanine, meaning dark blue, was given by Williams to the amyl analogue of the 4,4′-cyanine, which he isolated in 1856. See also Spectral sensitizers, J-Sensitization, Panchromatic sensitization.

Cyanite. See Kyanite.

Cyanoacetic acid, $NC \cdot CH_2COOH$. Crystallizes in large prisms which liquefy on exposure to atmospheric moisture, m.p. 66°. Very soluble in water, alcohol, and ether. Prepared by adding sodium cyanide to a solution of sodium chloroacetate. The sodium cyanoacetate so formed is acidified with sulphuric acid and the cyanoacetic acid extracted with benzene. It decomposes at 160° into carbon dioxide and acetonitrile. Concentrated acids or alkalis convert it to malonic acid. Condenses with aldehydes to give unsaturated α-cyano acids or unsaturated nitriles. It forms metallic salts which are either amorphous, or crystallize with difficulty. The ethyl ester is used in organic syntheses.

Cyanoacetic ester, Ethyl cyanoacetate, $C_5H_7NO_2$, $NC \cdot CH_2COOCH_2CH_3$. A colourless liquid, d^{20} 1·063, b.p. 207°, 97°/16 mm. Insoluble in water, soluble in alcohol and benzene. Prepared by boiling cyanoacetic acid with ethyl alcohol and sulphuric acid. Reacts with ammonia to give cyanoacetamide. Like acetoacetic ester, it

will react with sodium and the product will combine with halogen compounds such as alkyl bromides. It may be used to replace malonic ester or acetoacetic ester in many syntheses.

o-**Cyanobenzamide,** $C_8H_6N_2O$. Colourless needles, m.p. 173°. Readily soluble in alcohol and acetone. On heating to its m.p. it is converted into imidophthalimide, m.p. 203°. Readily hydrolysed to phthalic acid.

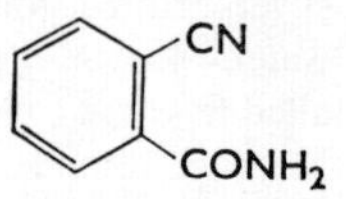

Prepared by the partial dehydration of phthalamide with acetic anhydride.

It has a limited use in the preparation of the phthalocyanine pigments into which it is readily converted on heating with metallic salts.

Cyanocobalamine. See Vitamin B$_{12}$.

Cyanoethylation. A particular example of a Michael reaction (*q.v.*). Certain nucleophiles, especially carbanion species, readily add across the double bond of acrylonitrile, forming a cyanoethyl derivative. For example, in the presence of a base, acetone can undergo cyanoethylation to give mono-, di-, or tri-cyanoethylation products.

$$CH_3COCH_3 \rightarrow CH_3COCH_2CH_2CH_2CN \rightarrow$$
$$CH_3COCH(CH_2CH_2CN)_2 \rightarrow$$
$$CH_3COC(CH_2CH_2CN)_3$$

The base used is most often benzyltrimethylammonium hydroxide, but aqueous or ethanolic alkali is suitable. In addition to compounds with active methylene groups, primary and secondary amines, alcohols and phenols can undergo cyanoethylation. See Acrylonitrile.

Cyanogen, C_2N_2. A colourless gas which condenses to a colourless liquid (b.p. $-21 \cdot 1°$, m.p. $-27 \cdot 92°$). It has a characteristic smell of bitter almonds and is very poisonous. Water dissolves 4·95 times its volume of the gas at 0°. Cyanogen is produced by heating mercuric cyanide, $Hg(CN)_2$, to a dull red heat. A brown non-volatile powder is formed at the same time. This is a polymer of cyanogen and is called paracyanogen. Cyanogen is an inflammable gas and burns with a pink flame. It is absorbed by sodium or potassium hydroxide solution, forming a mixture of cyanide and cyanate. The hydrolysis of cyanogen is exceedingly complex; oxamide, ammonium oxalate, ammonium formate, and urea being among the products.

Cyanogen bromide, BrCN. A colourless crystalline solid (m.p. 52°, b.p. 61°) which is very poisonous. It is formed by the action of bromine on a cyanide or on hydrocyanic acid. It is stable in the pure state but polymerizes rapidly to cyanuric tribromide, $(CNBr)_3$, in the presence of a trace of hydrobromic acid. It is decomposed slowly by water, in which it is appreciably soluble (5-6%). It is rapidly decomposed by alkalis, forming a mixture of cyanate and bromide.

Cyanogen chloride, ClCN. A colourless mobile liquid (m.p. $-6\cdot9°$, b.p. 13°) which is formed by the action of chlorine on a solution of potassium cyanide and zinc sulphate. It is exceedingly poisonous. When stored in the liquid state it is stable, but in the presence of a trace of hydrochloric acid it polymerizes to solid cyanuric trichloride $(CNCl)_3$. It is decomposed by alkalis to yield metallic chlorides and cyanates. With ammonia it forms ammonium chloride and cyanamide, $NH_2 \cdot CN$. It is hydrolysed by aqueous hydrochloric acid to give ammonium chloride and carbon dioxide. It is moderately soluble in water (approx. 6%). It has no action on metals at ordinary temperatures, but gives addition compounds with some metal halides.

Cyanogen fluoride, FCN. A colourless gas best prepared by pyrolysis of cyanuric fluoride at 1300°. It is stable at low temperatures but polymerizes at room temperature.

Cyanoguanidine. See Dicyandiamide.

Cyanohydrins. Organic compounds containing the group shown. They are formed by the action of hydrogen cyanide on aldehydes or ketones, or by the addition of sodium cyanide to a cooled suspension of the bisulphite compound of an aldehyde or ketone. They are split up by alkalis to give a cyanide and the original compound; mineral acids convert them to α-hydroxycarboxylic acids.

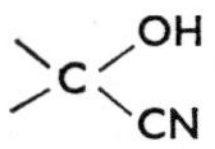

Cyanophoric glycosides. Those glycosides containing hydrocyanic acid which is split off on hydrolysis; they are of frequent occurrence in plants. Amygdalin is the best known.

Several glycosides of mandelonitrile are found, viz.:

1. Prunasin = (+)-form, m.p. 147°-150°, $[\alpha]_D$ $-26\cdot9°$.
2. Prulaurasin = racemic form, m.p. 120°-122°, $[\alpha]_D$ $-52\cdot7°$.
3. Sambunigrin = (−)-form, m.p. 151°, $[\alpha]_D$ $-76\cdot3°$.
4. Dhurrin = p-hydroxymandelonitrile glycoside.

Others are lotusin, linamarin, vicianin.

Cyanoplatinites, Cyanoplatinates. See Platinum cyanides, complex.

Cyanuric acid, $C_3H_3N_3O_3$. A stable crystalline substance sparingly soluble in water. It may be prepared by heating urea above its melting-point, or by hydrolysis of cyanuric chloride.

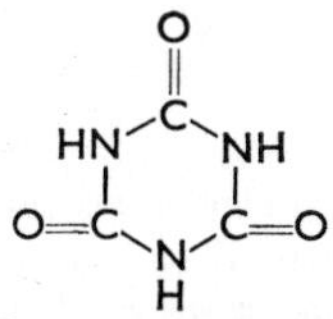

Esters with the alkyl group attached to the nitrogen atoms are known.

Cyanuric azide, C_3N_{12}. A crystalline solid, insoluble in water, soluble in acetone and benzene; m.p. 94°; decomposes, often with detonation, above 100°. It has a cyclic structure similar to cyanuric chloride, and is prepared by adding cyanuric chloride to a solution of sodium azide. It is a sensitive detonator but not suitable for use in large quantities.

Cyanuric chloride, $C_3N_3Cl_3$. M.p. 145°, b.p. 190°. A cyclic compound prepared by the polymerization of cyanogen chloride or industrially from chlorine, hydrocyanic acid, and hydrochloric acid.

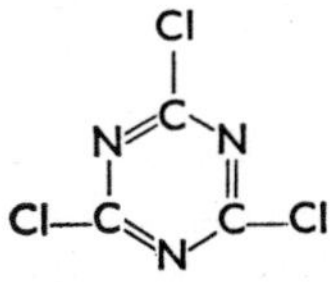

Cyanuric chloride is extensively used in the dyestuffs, pharmaceuticals, plastics, and explosives industries.

Cyanuric fluoride $(FCN)_3$. Prepared by fluorinating cyanuric chloride with any fluorinating agent. A toxic material.

Cyclamate sodium. The sodium salt

$$(C_6H_{12}NO_3SNa)$$

of N-cyclohexylsulphamic acid, itself obtained by sulphonation of cyclohexylamine, is used as a non-nutritive (low calorie) sweetening agent. It is said to be about 30 times sweeter than cane sugar (weight for weight). The calcium salt, $Ca^{2+}[C_6H_{12}NO_3S]_2$, also has culinary applications as a substitute for sugar.

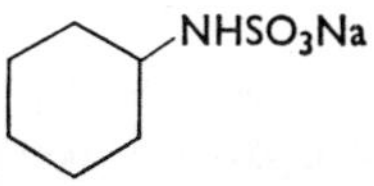

Cyclenes. Cyclic hydrocarbons containing one or more double bonds.

Cyclethrin, $C_{21}H_{28}O_3$, 3-(2-cyclopentenyl)-2-methyl-4-oxo-cyclopent-2-yl chrysanthemum monocarboxylate. Has similar chemical properties to the pyrethrins (q.v.). An insecticide of low mammalian toxicity; it is more effectively synergized than is allethrin.

Cyclic. Cyclic compounds are compounds which contain a closed ring system, such as the cyclohexane ring, as opposed to the open chain aliphatic compounds. Cyclic compounds can be subdivided into homocyclic compounds, in which the ring is composed only of carbon atoms, and heterocyclic compounds, in which the ring is composed of atoms of more than one kind.

Cyclic processes. A system which has undergone a series of changes and as a result is found to be in its original state is said to have completed a cycle. The whole series of changes is a cyclic process.

Cyclized rubbers. Cyclic isomers of natural rubbers. In general they are hard, thermoplastic, and non-elastic. See Plioform resins and Thermoprenes.

Cyclizine, $C_{18}H_{22}N_2$. 1-Diphenylmethyl-4-methylpiperazine, obtained as the hydrochloride, trade name Marzine, which is a white crystalline powder, m.p. 285°, sparingly soluble

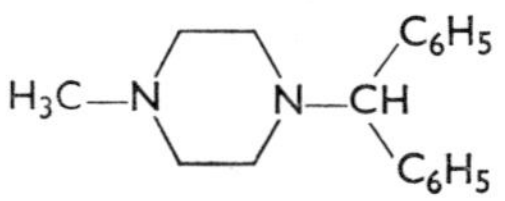

in water and alcohol. It is prepared from diphenylmethyl chloride and 1-methylpiperazine. It is an anti-histamine drug with a strong anti-emetic action, used for the prevention and treatment of nausea and vomiting, e.g. in motion sickness, radiation sickness, and pregnancy. It has a rapid action and gives side effects in only few people.

Cyclobarbitone, $C_{12}H_{12}N_2O_3$. A white crystalline powder, almost insoluble in cold water, sparingly soluble in hot water, soluble in alcohol; m.p. 173°. Prepared by condensing urea with ethyl cyanoethylcyclohex-1-enyl acetate, and hydrolysing the product. It is a short-acting barbiturate, used in treating insomnia.

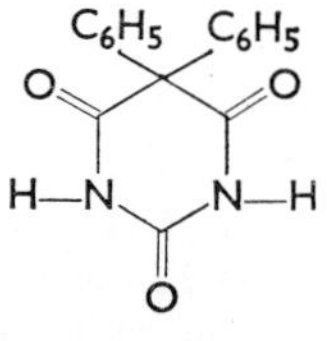

Cyclobutane, C_4H_8. A colourless gas which burns with a luminous flame. Insoluble in water, soluble in acetone or alcohol; b.p. −15°. Prepared by treating 1,4 dibromo-butane with metallic sodium. Reduced to *n*-butane by hydrogen at 200° in presence of nickel catalysts.

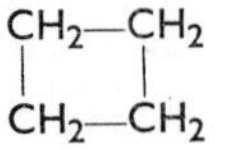

Cyclohexane, C_6H_{12}. A colourless liquid, m.p. 6·5°, b.p. 81°, d^{20} 0·7791. Insoluble in water; miscible with many organic solvents. Occurs in Russian petroleum. Manufactured by the reduction of benzene with hydrogen

in the presence of a nickel catalyst. It is inflammable. Used as a solvent for oils, fats, and waxes, and also as a paint remover. For stereochemistry of cyclohexane see Conformation.

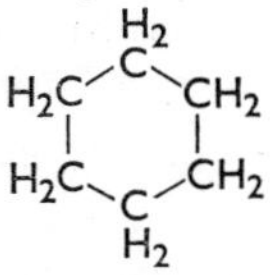

Cyclohexanol, Hexalin, Hexahydrophenol, $C_6H_{12}O$. A colourless liquid, m.p. 24°, b.p. 161°, d^{20} 0·9624. Moderately soluble in water; miscible with many organic solvents. Readily absorbs water vapour. Manufactured by heating phenol with hydrogen under pressure in the presence of suitable catalysts. Oxidized to adipic acid; dehydrogenated to cyclohexanone. Reacts with aluminium chloride and many other reagents to give cyclohexene. Used in the manufacture of celluloid, detergents, and printing inks.

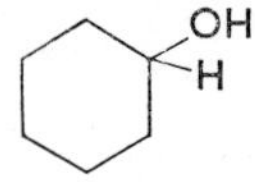

Cyclohexanone, $C_6H_{10}O$. A colourless liquid with a strong peppermint-like odour, d^{20} 0·9478, b.p. 155°. Slightly soluble in water; miscible with most organic solvents. Manufactured by passing the vapour of cyclohexanol over a heated copper catalyst. Volatile in steam. Oxidized to adipic acid. Used in the manufacture of adipic acid, nitrocellulose lacquers, celluloid, artificial leather, and printing ink.

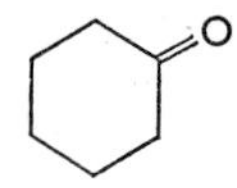

Cycloheximide (trade name Actidione),

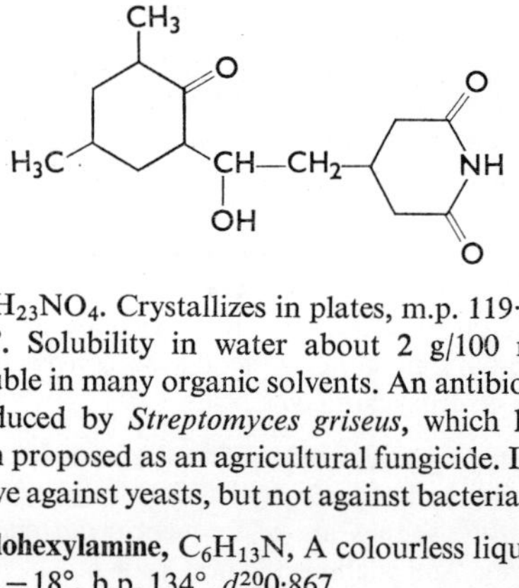

$C_{15}H_{23}NO_4$. Crystallizes in plates, m.p. 119·5°-121°. Solubility in water about 2 g/100 ml. Soluble in many organic solvents. An antibiotic produced by *Streptomyces griseus*, which has been proposed as an agricultural fungicide. It is active against yeasts, but not against bacteria.

Cyclohexylamine, $C_6H_{13}N$, A colourless liquid, m.p. −18°, b.p. 134°, d_4^{20}0·867, miscible with water, volatile in steam. It can be extracted from aqueous solution by hydrocarbons. It is a strong base and is used as a solvent for dyestuffs, as an acid inhibitor in degreasing baths, and for other industrial purposes.

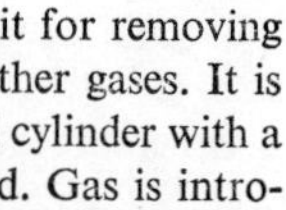

Cyclone separator. This is a unit for removing suspended solids from air or other gases. It is usually in the form of a vertical cylinder with a flat top and a conical lower end. Gas is introduced at high velocity through a tangential inlet near the top, and the swirling motion that results causes the particles to be thrown out against the walls by centrifugal force. The motion of the gas is such that the solids are carried into the conical end from where they may be discharged; the clean gas leaves through an axial outlet at the other end. Because the movement of particles into the conical end is not dependent on gravity, cyclones may be, and frequently are, mounted horizontally.

The cyclone separator is the most widely used type of dust collection plant, being simple and cheap. It is very effective provided the proportion of particles below 10 μ is not too large.

Cyclonite,   **Cyclotrimethylenetrinitramine,**

$C_3H_6N_5O_6$. Prepared by nitrolysis of hexamethylenetetramine. It is a white crystalline powder, m.p. 202° (decomp.), soluble in acetone, insoluble in water, alcohol, and petroleum ether. It is an explosive, more powerful than TNT, but considerably more sensitive. It has therefore to be diluted with wax or mixed with TNT to render it acceptable for filling into ammunition. The mixtures are comparable in sensitivity but more powerful than TNT. See Nitroamines.

1,5-Cyclo-octadiene, C_8H_{12}. The *cis,cis*-isomer is obtained by a catalytic dimerization of butadiene using, for example, certain complex derivatives of nickel carbonyl. It is a colourless, mobile liquid with terpene-like odour, b.p. 150·9°, m.p. −69·5°. The *trans, trans*-isomer is also known.

Cyclo-octatetraene, COT, C_8H_8. A golden-yellow liquid, m.p. −7°, b.p. 42-42·5°/17 mm, d^{20} 0·9206, n_D^{20} 1·5290. First obtained by Willstätter from pseudopelletierine, COT is now prepared by the polymerization of acetylene at moderate temperature and pressure in the presence of nickel salts. The molecule is non-planar and behaves as a typical cyclic olefin, having no aromatic properties. It may be catalytically hydrogenated to cyclo-octene, but with zinc and dilute sulphuric acid gives 1, 3, 6- cyclo-octatriene. It reacts with maleic anhydride to give an adduct, m.p. 166°, derived from the isomeric structure bicyclo-4,2,0-octa-2,4,7-triene (I):

(I)   (II)

Halogens add to COT and also give bi-cyclic products (II). COT and its derivatives undergo other interesting ring-contraction reactions. See J. W. Copenhaver and M. H. Bigelow, 'Acetylene and Carbon Monoxide Chemistry.'

Cyclo-octene, C_8H_{14}. Obtained in its most

stable *cis* form by the partial hydrogenation of *cis,cis*-1,5-cycloöctadiene. It is a colourless liquid with a terpene-like odour, b.p. 144°, m.p. −16·5°. Oxidation with potassium permanganate produces suberic acid.

Cyclopentadiene, C_5H_6. A colourless liquid with a sweet, distinctive smell, b.p. 41·5°-42·0°, n_D^{16} 1·4463, d_4^{25} 0·7966. It is insoluble in water, but soluble in all organic solvents.
Obtained during the cracking of petroleum hydrocarbons, and from the distillates produced in the carbonization of coal. It polymerizes very readily on standing at room temperature to dicyclopentadiene (m.p. 32·5°) and higher polymers, via an intermolecular Diels-Alder reaction. These are a more convenient form for handling cyclopentadiene which is easily regenerated by 'cracking' the oligomers. One hydrogen atom of the methylene group is acidic; sodium dissolves in ethereal cyclopentadiene solutions with the evolution of hydrogen, yielding $C_5H_5^-Na^+$ which is colourless to pink in the absence of air. The cyclopentadienyl anion $C_5H_5^-$ is an aromatic system. Fulvenes (*q.v.*) are produced in basic media from ketones or aldehydes. Cyclopentadienylides (*q.v.*) are produced with many metals. It undergoes typical Diels-Alder reactions; used in the preparation of plastics and certain insecticides.

Cyclopentadienylides. Metal derivatives of cyclopentadiene. These derivatives of the transition metals are often extremely stable and are formed by Grignard reactions, by the reaction between sodium cyclopentadienylide and the metal halide, or by other methods used in producing organometallic derivatives. They may be uncharged (ferrocene, $(C_5H_5)_2Fe$) or exist as charged ions, $(C_5H_5)_2Fe^+$, $(C_5H_5)_2Nb^{2+}$. Cyclopentadienyl halides, e.g. $(C_5H_5)_2TiCl_2$, and carbonyls, e.g. $C_5H_5V(CO)_4$, are known. Indene forms similar derivatives. In most of these derivatives the ring systems have considerable aromatic character. In the transition metal compounds the ring system is often π-bonded symmetrically to the metal (sandwich compound). In the alkali metal cyclopentadienylides the anion is present as such. Cyclopentadienylides of metals such as tin have a 6 metal-carbon bond.

Cyclopentadienylmanganese tricarbonyl, $C_8H_5MnO_3$

A volatile yellow solid, m.p. 77°, with a camphoraceous odour, is completely air stable and soluble in organic solvents. An example of a so-called 'half-sandwich' compound, the C_5H_5 ring undergoes electrophilic substitution. The methyl compound $CH_3C_5H_4Mn(CO)_3$ is of some technical interest as a fuel additive [AK-33X—Ethyl Corporation of America].

Cyclophanes. Benzene derivatives bridged

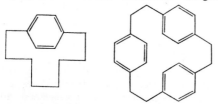

[8] Paracyclophane   [2,2,2]-Paracyclophane

between para- and/or meta-positions with methylene groups; hence paracyclophane, etc. It is not usual to include the ortho-derivatives since alternative names based on conventional ring systems are possible. The value of the prefix [m] indicates the number of methylene groups in the ring whilst the number of prefixes [m, n, etc.] refers to the benzene rings in the structure, i.e [8]-paracyclophane, [2,2,2]-paracyclophane. Systems based upon heterocyclic molecules are also known. See Brandes H. Smith, 'Bridged Ring Systems', Academic Press, 1964.

Cyclophosphamide, $C_7H_{15}Cl_2N_2O_2P \cdot H_2O$. A

fine, white crystalline powder, m.p. 49·5°-53°. Soluble in water and in alcohol. Slightly soluble in ether.

It is a cytotoxic agent used in the treatment of neoplastic disease, e.g. breast cancer.

Cyclopropane, Trimethylene, C_3H_6. A colourless gas with a sweetish odour, b.p. −34·5°, d_{20}^{20} 0·61. It is prepared by treating 1, 3-dibromo-propane with zinc. It is the most powerful of the gaseous anaesthetics, non-irritant and non-toxic to the liver and kidneys,

but it is a respiratory depressant. Deep anaesthesia is produced by 20-25% mixed with 75-80% of oxygen.

Cycloserine, 4-amino*iso***ooxazolidin-3-one,** $C_3H_6N_2O_2$. Colourless crystals, m.p. 156°, solubility 1 part in 10 of water. An amino acid having antibiotic activity isolated from *Streptomyces* species. It has been used as a tuberculostatic drug, but toxic side reactions occur, and bacterial resistance frequently develops.

Cyclotron. The cyclotron is an apparatus devised by Lawrence in America and Gerthsen in Germany by means of which charged atomic particles, e.g. protons, are accelerated by passing them repeatedly through the same electric field. Thus, 10,000 volts may be made to do the work of 1,000,000 volts, and produce protons of very high velocity and hence of great energy.

Cymarin, $C_{30}H_{44}O_9$. M.p. 130°, $[\alpha]_D$ +23°. It consists of cymarose and strophanthidin, $C_{23}H_{32}O_6$. When combined with a molecule of glucose the glycoside is known as k-strophanthin. Other similar glycosides are periplocymarin, which is made up of cymarose and periplogenin, $C_{23}H_{34}O_5$, and sarmentocymarin made up of sarmentogenin, $C_{23}H_{34}O_5$, and an isomeric sugar sarmentose.

All these are strophanthus glucosides with specific cardiac action; they are present in the seeds of *Strophanthus* and *Apocynum* species. Probably most of them are combined with a further molecule of glucose as in the digitalis glycosides.

Cymarose, 3-methyldigitoxose, $C_7H_{14}O_4$. Obtained on hydrolysis of cymarin. It has m.p. 93°, $[\alpha]_D^{21}$ +53°.

$$CH_3-\overset{H}{\underset{OH}{C}}-\overset{H}{\underset{OH}{C}}-\overset{H}{\underset{OCH_3}{C}}-CH_2-CHO$$

Cymenes, Isopropylmethylbenzenes, $C_{10}H_{14}$. p-Cymene is a colourless liquid, d^{20} 0·8570, b.p. 177°. Insoluble in water; miscible with organic solvents. Occurs in many essential oils, such as cumin, thyme, and chenopodium. Obtained from the oil in the waste liquors of the sulphite wood pulp process. Prepared by heating camphor with zinc chloride, or from oil of turpentine. Oxidized by chromic acid to terephthalic acid and by nitric acid to p-toluic acid. Used as a thinner for paints and in the manufacture of thymol.

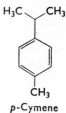

p-Cymene

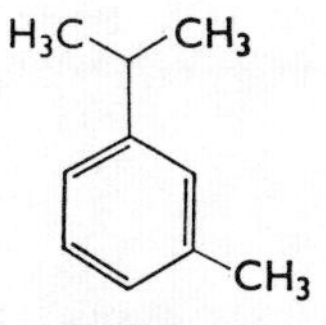

m-Cymene 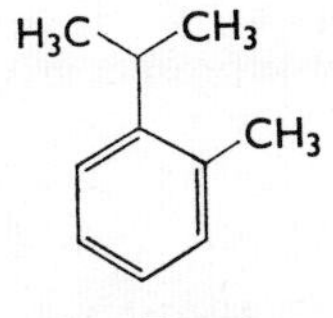   o-Cymene

m-Cymene is a colourless liquid, d^{20} 0·8696, b.p. 176°. Oxidized to isophthalic acid.

o-Cymene is a colourless liquid, d^{20} 0·876, b.p. 175°.

Cysteine, α-Amino-β-thiolpropionic acid, $C_3H_7NO_2S$. Cysteine is a reduction product of

$$HS—CH_2·CH·COOH$$
$$\quad\quad\quad\quad | $$
$$\quad\quad\quad\quad NH_2$$

cystine. It is the first step in the breakdown of cystine in the body, one molecule of cystine splitting to give two molecules of cysteine. Cysteine is soluble in water, giving a laevorotatory solution, but it is very unstable, being oxidized on standing in air to cystine.

Cystine, Dicysteine, $C_6H_{12}N_2O_4S_2$. Crystallizes

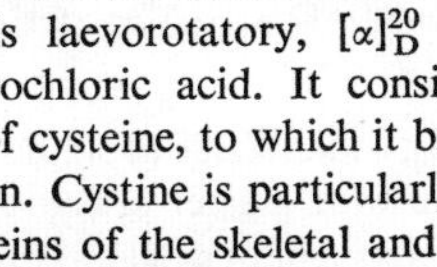

$$CH_2—S—S—CH_2$$
$$|\quad\quad\quad\quad\quad | $$
$$CH·NH_2\quad CH·NH_2$$
$$|\quad\quad\quad\quad\quad | $$
$$COOH\quad\quad COOH$$

in hexagonal plates, decomposing at 258°-261°. Sparingly soluble in cold water, more soluble in hot, insoluble in alcohol. The naturally occurring substance is laevorotatory, $[\alpha]_D^{20}$ −206°, in dilute hydrochloric acid. It consists of two molecules of cysteine, to which it breaks down on reduction. Cystine is particularly abundant in the proteins of the skeletal and connective tissues of animals and in hair and wool, from which it is most readily prepared.

Cytidine. See Nucleosides.

Cytochrome. A widely distributed respiratory catalyst associated with the oxidative processes of living cells. It is found in all cells capable of active metabolism. It is a mixture of four haemochromogens, differing in their porphyrin groups, and called cytochromes a_1, a_3, b, and c. Cytochrome b is autoxidizable and unstable. Cytochrome c is present in the greatest amount and has been the most thoroughly studied. It is very stable and is oxidized only by cytochrome oxidase, which uses atmospheric oxygen to convert the iron in the molecule from the ferrous to the ferric state. The cytochrome system is reduced by the dehydrogenases, and thus acts as an oxygen carrier to them.

Cytochrome oxidase. The same as indophenol oxidase and Warburg's respiratory enzyme, and may be identical with cytochrome a_3.

Cytosine, 2-oxy-6-aminopyrimidine, $C_4H_5N_3O$.

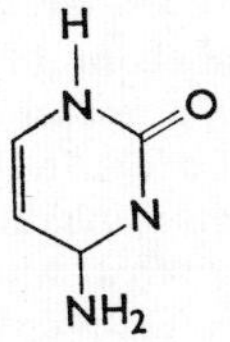

Crystallizes in plates with 5 molecules of water. Soluble in hot water, sparingly soluble in alcohol. Decomposes at 320°-325°. A hydrolysis product of nucleic acid.

Cytotoxic agents. Chemicals injurious to living cells. The term is applied especially in connexion with cancer chemotherapy. Many cytotoxic agents are bifunctional alkylating agents, e.g. mustard gas, nitrogen mustards. See also Chlorambucil and Myleran.

D

2,4-D, 2,4-dichlorophenoxyacetic acid,

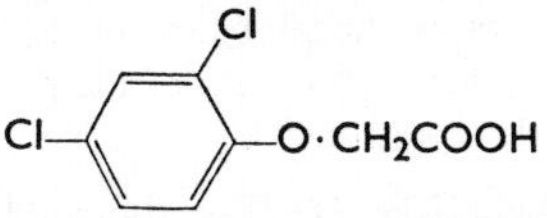

$C_8H_6Cl_2O_3$. A selective growth-regulator herbicide for use against broad-leaved plants. It is made from 2,4-dichlorophenol and sodium monochloroacetate, and is a white solid melting at 138°, insoluble in water and soluble in alcohols and alkalis. It is also used as its esters and amine salts, these having greater solubilities than the acid itself in water. 2,4-D is harmless to mammals at the normally used concentrations. See also the related compounds 2,4,5-T and MCPA.

Dacron. A trade name (Dupont) for polymerized ethyleneglycol terephthalate. See Terylene.

Dakin's solution. An antiseptic solution containing chlorinated lime, sodium carbonate, and boric acid, and yielding between 30% and 40% of available chlorine. It is used as an antiseptic irrigant for wounds.

Dale, Sir Henry Hallet (1875-   ). Dale was born in London and educated at the Leys School and the University, Cambridge. From 1904 till 1914 he was Director of the Wellcome Physiological Research Laboratories. His numerous researches lie in the fields of biochemistry and pharmacology. Elected F.R.S. in 1914, he was created C.B.E. in 1919, and knighted in 1932. He was Director of the National Institute for Medical Research 1914-1942, Fullerian professor of chemistry at the Royal Institution 1942-1946, President of the Royal Society, 1940-1945. He was awarded the O.M. in 1944 and shared the Nobel Prize for medicine in 1936.

Dalton, John, was born in Cumberland in 1766, and became a teacher of science at the Manchester New College. In 1800 he became the secretary of the Philosophical Society of Manchester. He discovered what is known as Dalton's law of partial pressures (*q.v.*). In the first few years of the nineteenth century he came to the conclusion that every chemical element consists of an immense number of identical atoms, and that chemical combination consists in the combination of one or two atoms of one element with one, two, or three or more atoms of another element or other elements. This theory was published by Thomson in 1807 and by Dalton in 1808, and was gradually accepted as the only possible explanation of the facts. He died in 1844.

Dalton's law of partial pressures. The total pressure which is exerted by a mixture of gases is equal to the sum of the pressures which the gases would exert if each was separately contained in the volume occupied by the mixture. Thus in a mixture of gases, the total pressure, P, is equal to the sum, $p_1 + p_2 + p_3 + \ldots$, of the partial pressures of the constituents.

Dambonitol, $C_8H_{16}O_6$. The dimethyl ether of inositol (*q.v.*), m.p. 195°, occurs in Gabon rubber and in the latex of *Castilloa elastica*.

Daniell, John Frederic (1790-1845). A native of London, Daniell became first professor of chemistry at King's College on its foundation in 1831. He invented the Daniell cell, and his observations on the electrolysis of salts supported the theories of their constitution put forward by Davy and Dulong, in contrast to those of Berzelius. His meteorological work is also of importance, and during his career he was awarded all the medals in the gift of the Royal Society, of which he became a Fellow in 1813.

Daniell cell. The e.m.f. of the Daniell Cell is 1·10 V and is virtually independent of temperature.

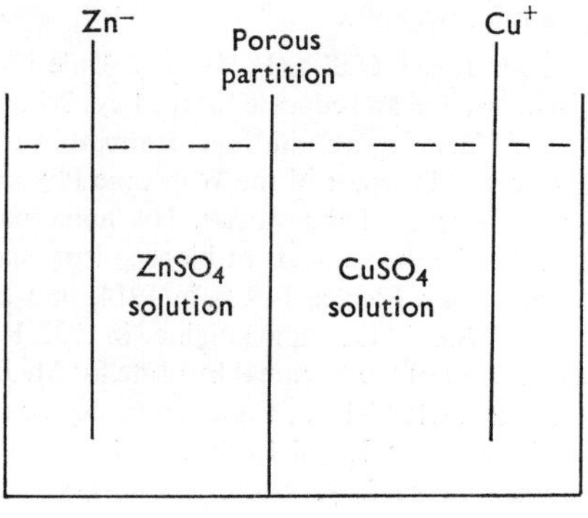

Dapsone, $C_{12}H_{12}N_2O_2S$. A white crystalline powder, existing in two forms, m.ps. 178·5° and

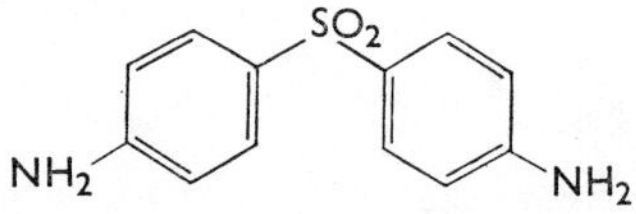

180·5°. Insoluble in water, soluble in alcohol. Prepared by treating 4-chloronitrobenzene with sodium sulphide, oxidizing the product, and reducing the sulphone obtained.

It is bacteriostatic, and is used in the treatment of leprosy. It is given orally, and is liable to give unpleasant side effects.

Davy, Sir Humphry. Born in Penzance in 1778. He discovered the intoxicating properties of nitrous oxide, and was engaged by the newly created Royal Institution of London as lecturer in chemistry. He experimented on galvanism, and in 1807 prepared potassium and sodium by the electrolysis of potash and soda. He also was the first to prepare calcium, barium, and strontium. He showed in 1810 that chlorine, already discovered by Scheele, was an element. He invented the miner's safety lamp, which has saved thousands of lives, and is still in use. He was knighted in 1812, and later made a baronet. He died in 1829.

2,4-DB, 4-(2,4-dichlorophenoxy)butyric acid,

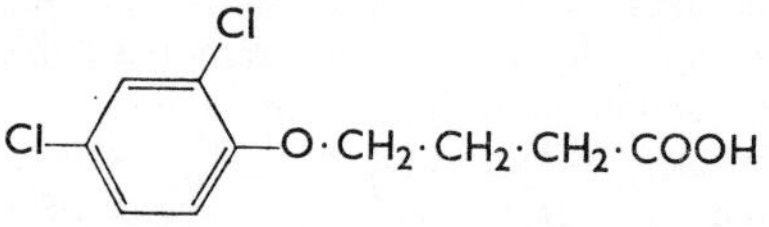

$C_{10}H_{10}Cl_2O_3$. A herbicide of similar properties to 2,4-D, but with greater selectivity. It forms colourless crystals of m.p. 117°-119°.

D-D. The trade name for a dark, volatile liquid containing 1,3-dichloropropene and 1,2-dichloropropane, obtained as a by-product in allyl chloride manufacture. It is used for soil treatment against nematodes (eelworms), and is toxic to mammals and plants.

DDT, Dichlorodiphenyltrichloroethane, m.p.

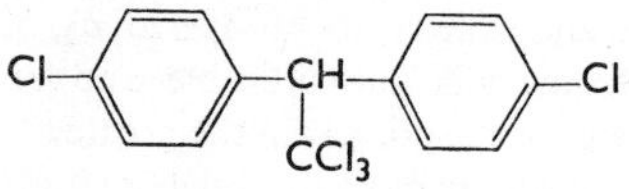

108.5°. Ordinary DDT contains about 15% of the 2,4'-isomer, and is prepared from chloral, chlorobenzene, and sulphuric acid. DDT is insoluble in water and soluble to varying extent in organic solvents. It is non-phytotoxic to most plants. It is a powerful and persistent insecticide, but has recently been found to be stored in the bodies of animals and birds.

Deacon, Henry (1822-1877). Born in London,

Deacon left school at the age of 14, and became apprenticed to the firm of Messrs. Galloway & Sons Ltd., mechanical engineers. A family friendship with Faraday created an interest in chemistry, to which he applied his inventive mind. Later Deacon became associated with the firms Nasmyth & Gaskell, Messrs. Pilkington Plate Glass Works, and Hutchinson's Alkali Works. In 1855 he entered into a partnership with Gaskell and established an alkali works at Widnes. He invented, among other processes, the Deacon process for the manufacture of chlorine by oxidation of hydrogen chloride with oxygen at 450°. See *J. Chem. Soc.*, 1877, 494.

Deactivating collision. See Deactivation.

Deactivation. Deactivation implies the process involved in diminishing or removing entirely the chemical activity of a substance. Thus clean platinum considerably accelerates the combination of sulphur dioxide and oxygen to yield sulphur trioxide, Traces of arsenic destroy this activity. The platinum is said to be poisoned, or deactivated. Again in a photochemical reaction a molecule absorbs light. It possesses more energy than an ordinary molecule, and is therefore more reactive. It may, however, collide with another molecule, and transfer its energy without reacting. The first molecule has been deactivated. The collision in which the molecule lost its energy is a deactivating collision.

Deaeration. Removal of oxygen and other dissolved gases from solvents by physical or chemical means. Carried out on a large scale from boiler feed water with a view to reducing corrosion.

De-asphalting. The removal of asphaltic constituents from a residual lubricating oil stock by precipitation with light solvents, usually propane.

Debye, Peter Joseph Wilhelm (1884-1966). Born in Maastricht and studying in Munich, Debye was a lecturer there before holding professorships at Zurich, Utrecht, Göttingen and Leipzig. In 1935 he became director of the Kaiser Wilhelm Institute for Physics in Berlin. In 1940 he emigrated to the United States and became professor at Cornel. He is renowned for his work on polar molecules, dipole moments and molecular structure and worked with Hückel on problems of solution. He gained the Nobel Prize for chemistry in 1936.

Debye-Hückel theory. In 1923 P. Debye and E. Hückel published a classic paper in which a mathematical theory of the coulomb interactions between ions of an electrolyte in solution was developed. The theory was successful in explaining the abnormal osmotic properties (activity coefficients) at least for very dilute

solutions and it formed a landmark in physical chemistry. Subsequent work has led to only minor refinements of the Debye-Hückel theory, owing to the mathematical difficulty of the problem. See Harned and Owen, "The Physical Chemistry of Electrolytic Solutions," 3rd edn. 1957 (Reinhold, New York).

Decaborane-14, See Boron hydrides.

Decalin, decahydronaphthalene, $C_{10}H_{18}$. As the

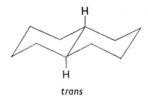

trans

cis

two rings are not in the same plane, two stereoisomers of decalin exist. The *cis* form has m.p. $-51°$, b.p. 193°, d_{20}^{20} 0·893-0·898. The *trans* form has m.p. $-36°$, b.p. 185°, d_4^{20} 0·870-0·872. The *cis* form can be quantitatively converted into the *trans* form by the action of aluminium chloride. Commercial decalin is manufactured by the high-pressure hydrogenation of naphthalene at high temperatures, and contains 90% *cis* and 10% *trans* decalin. The two forms can be separated by fractional distillation. Decalin is used as a solvent.

Decantation. The removal of a liquid from a suspension or from an immiscible heavier liquid, while leaving the latter in the original container.

Decarboxylases. See Carboxylase.

Decay constant. Radioactive decay follows an exponential law $N = N_0 e^{-\lambda t}$, where N is the number of atoms present at time t, N_0 is the number of atoms present at time 0, and λ is the decay constant. First-order reactions follow a similar exponential law.

Decoctions. Decoctions are pharmaceutical solutions made by boiling a drug with water and filtering.

Decomposition voltage. The smallest voltage which will cause the appreciable electrolysis of an electrolyte is termed the decomposition voltage. It depends not only on the electrolyte, but also on the nature of the metal forming the electrodes.

Decyl alcohols, $C_{10}H_{21}OH$. These are of considerable commercial importance, being used in the manufacture of plasticisers and detergents. They are manufactured by the oxo reaction (*q.v.*), a mixture of nonenes being first converted by carbon monoxide and hydrogen to decanals, which are then hydrogenated to yield a mixture of decyl alcohols. The composition of the product depends on the composition of the feed, the most common commercial grade being 'isodecanol', a mixture of ten-carbon branched-chain primary alcohols with a narrow boiling range.

n-Decyl alcohol is manufactured by the polymerization of ethylene in the presence of aluminium triethyl. Aluminium trialkyls are formed, which are oxidized to the alkoxides and then hydrolysed by sulphuric acid to a mixture of straight-chain alcohols. From these *n*-decyl alcohol may be fractionated, though it is usual to market a mixture of alcohols. Pure *n*-decyl alcohol is a colourless liquid with a sweet fat-like odour, m.p. 7°, b.p. 233°, d_4^{20} 0·830, insoluble in water, soluble in alcohol.

De-emulsification. Emulsions of oil and water formed in various operations often need special mechanisms or plant to separate the two liquids. The process is called de-emulsification, or demulsification, and involves breaking the emulsion by physical or chemical means. The chemical methods depend on the opposing action of various emulsifiers on one another. Thus the addition of a sulphonated emulsifying agent to an emulsion may cause it to break. Little is known about this effect, which is strictly specific.

Some emulsions can be broken by mere mechanical treatment; others coagulate in the presence of electrolytes; whilst others can be broken electrically by the passage of high voltage alternating current.

Defect structures. An ionic lattice in which there is a hole at a point which should be occupied by an ion or atom. Electrical neutrality in an ionic lattice is preserved by an alteration of oxidation state in another ion in the lattice, by placing an extra ion in the crystal surface, or by putting an extra ion in a normally unoccupied position. Defect structures show anomalous physical properties, particularly density, colour, and electrical conductivity, and are in general non-stoicheiometric in their composition.

Degeneracy. When different wave functions have the same energy they are said to be degenerate. For example, in the first-row transition metal ions, the five 3*d* orbitals are equivalent in energy in the free ion and are said to be five-fold degenerate. When a crystal field is applied the degeneracy is removed.

Degree of hydrolysis. The degree of hydrolysis of a salt is defined as the fraction of the total salt hydrolysed by water. Thus, if in a solution of the salt AB, 90% of it is hydrolysed to yield the base AOH and the acid BH, the degree of hydrolysis is 0·90. It may be expressed also as a percentage, i.e. 90%.

Degrees of freedom. From the standpoint of the phase rule, the number of degrees of freedom which a system possesses is the number of variable factors, temperature, pressure, and concentration of the components, which must be fixed in order to define completely the condition of the system. E.g. if the pressure and temperature of a given mass of gas are fixed, the volume of the gas must have a definite value. The system has, therefore, two degrees of freedom.

In connexion with statistical mechanics (e.g. the theory of specific heats of gases) a degree of freedom means an independent mode of absorbing energy by movement of atoms. Thus a monatomic gas has three translational degrees of freedom. Polyatomic molecules have in addition vibrational and rotational degrees of freedom.

Dehumidification. The removal of condensable vapour from a vapour-gas mixture by condensation, absorption or adsorption. The term is most frequently applied to the removal of water vapour from air.

Dehumidification equipment. Dehumidification of an air supply is normally carried out by cooling, either by refrigeration or direct injection of cooling water. In the latter case the quantity of water and the size of the individual drops is much larger than in humidification practice since the primary consideration is not dispersion of the water but provision of sufficient cooling surface. Adequate provision must be made to remove all entrained water before the air leaves the plant.

If small quantities of dry air are required, the dehumidification may be carried out by chemical means, using concentrated sulphuric acid or any other suitable absorbent.

Dehydro is a prefix for an organic compound indicating the presence of less hydrogen. Often considered to be synonomous with anhydro- (*q.v.*).

Dehydroacetic acid, 6-Methylacetopyranone, $C_8H_8O_4$. Crystallizes in colourless needles,

m.p. 109°, b.p. 270°. Soluble in hot water and alcohol. Prepared by boiling acetoacetic ester for several hours and then distilling off the unchanged ester. It is formed from keten by polymerization in the presence of zinc bromide. Forms a crystalline sodium salt; the parent acid is unstable and always reverts to the lactone form shown above. It is reconverted to acetoacetic ester by boiling alcoholic potassium hydroxide. Reduced by hydrogen iodide to dimethylpyrone.

Dehydrogenases. The enzymes responsible for removing hydrogen from many substances in biological systems. The revised nomenclature of enzymes requires that the term 'oxidoreductase' be used in the systematic name. Convenient trivial names are still based on the name of the substrate, as for example glucose dehydrogenase, alcohol dehydrogenase, lactate dehydrogenase, etc. Some dehydrogenases, such as succinic dehydrogenase, are highly specific; others, such as aldehyde dehydrogenase, act on a variety of substrates. Very few of the dehydrogenases can transfer hydrogen to molecular oxygen: in general, one of the pyridine nucleotide coenzymes (NAD or NADP), or occasionally other hydrogen acceptors, are required for activity.

Dehydrothiotoluidine, $C_{14}H_{12}N_2S$. Crystallizes

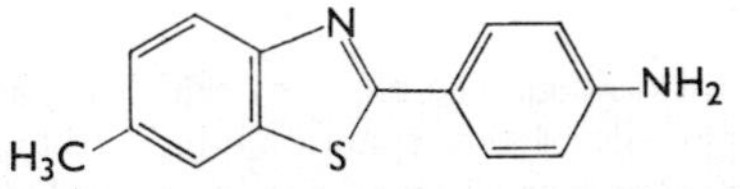

from alcohol in iridescent yellow prisms, m.p. 194·8°, b.p. 434°. It is insoluble in hot or cold water, moderately soluble in benzene and hot alcohol, more so in acetic acid. It gives a mono- and di-hydrochloride.

It is prepared, together with a similar compound of higher molecular weight, primuline (*q.v.*), by heating together sulphur and *p*-toluidine in the proportion of two atoms to two molecules. The reaction is carried out at 170°-210°, and much hydrogen sulphide is evolved. It is isolated by direct distillation out of the melt.

It is used as a first component in azo-dyes. The dyes thus obtained are direct cotton colours. It can be directly sulphonated with sulphuric acid to give a product which is also much used as a first component of direct cotton azo-dyes. In the latter case the sulphonated compound has direct affinity for the fibre, and it can first be dyed and then diazotized and coupled *in situ*. In this way improved fastness properties are obtained.

De La Rue, Warren (1815-1889). Born in Guernsey, De La Rue studied at the College of St. Barbe, Paris, and later, after entering his father's business, took a course of practical chemistry at the Royal College of Science. In

conjunction with H. Müller, with whom he invented the silver chloride battery, he carried out numerous chemical investigations of a varied nature, and also a series of experiments on electrical discharges in gases, etc., but for a considerable time his chief interest lay in astronomy. A Fellow of the Royal Society, and an original member of the Chemical Society, he was President of the latter body in 1867-1869 and again in 1879-1880.

Deliquescence. When a salt absorbs moisture from the atmosphere and proceeds to dissolve in the absorbed water, it is said to be deliquescent. This will only occur if the vapour pressure of water over the solid is less than that of the air surrounding it.

Delocalization. In the benzene molecule the six π electrons are situated in molecular orbitals which are delocalized over the six carbon atoms. If instead of this, three π bonds had been formed at particular carbon atoms, the energy of the benzene molecule would have been higher than it is. The extent to which the molecule is stabilized by this electronic displacement is called the delocalization energy.

Delphinin. The anthocyanin (*q.v.*) pigment of the larkspur and many other plants. On hydrolysis it gives delphinidin, two molecules of glucose and *p*-hydroxybenzoic acid.

Delphinine. An alkaloid related to aconitine (*q.v.*).

Delrin. A trade name used to describe a range of plastics materials based on polyformaldehyde (*q.v.*).

Delta bonding. Lateral overlap of two *d* orbitals to form a bond. Postulated in metal-metal bonds.

Delta rays or **δ-rays.** When α-particles are absorbed by matter, δ-rays are emitted. They consist of electrons moving with relatively small velocities compared with those of β-particles.

Demarçay, Eugène Anatole (1852-1904). Born in Paris, Demarçay was educated at the Lycée Condorcet and the École Polytechnique. He was assistant at the Polytechnique for a time, but gave up the appointment in favour of research. The discoverer of the element europium, he carried out investigations on the terpenes and on the volatility of metals.

Demeton-methyl. See Metasystox.

Denaturants. Substances added to dutiable articles to render them unfit for human consumption, so that they may be used for other purposes without having to pay duty. For denatured alcohol see Methylated spirit. Tea which is to be used for the extraction of caffeine is denatured with lime and asafoetida, while tobacco to be used for fumigation of insect pests is treated with moss litter and crude bone oil.

Denaturation. The denaturation of proteins means the irreversible change in solubility and other properties that occurs when a protein is heated. It is believed to be due more to a change in molecular architecture than in chemical composition.

Dendrite. A tree-like crystal formation. Crystallisation or solidification of e.g. a pure metal starts at a nucleus and proceeds more rapidly in certain axial directions. From these primary branches secondary branches are formed at periodic intervals, and these in turn produce further branches. In this way a skeleton crystal or dendrite is formed. The interstices between the branches are finally filled in with solid, which in a pure metal is indistinguishable from the skeleton. In alloys, which on solidification form solid solutions, the solid deposited varies in composition, and, unless equilibrium is established and diffusion is complete, the final structure shows evidence of the dendritic mode of growth. The skeleton will be richer in the higher melting point metal, and will etch differently to the metal deposited in the interstices. Such a structure is known as a 'cored structure.'

Dendritic salt. Sodium chloride which has crystallized in a dendritic form (i.e. a spiky crystalline form). It is less dense than normal rock salt, does not cake so easily, dissolves more quickly.

Dense media separation. Materials of different specific gravities may be separated by the use of a liquid intermediate in density, in which one will sink and the other float. Liquids of high specific gravity, suitable for the separation of minerals by this means, may be obtained by producing a stable suspension of a finely divided dense material such as magnetite or ferrosilicon in water. The technique is known as dense media separation and is used for such processes as coal cleaning and the concentration of metallic ores.

D-2-Deoxyribose, Desoxyribose, $C_5H_{10}O_4$. The sugar isolated by hydrolysis of DNA. Colourless

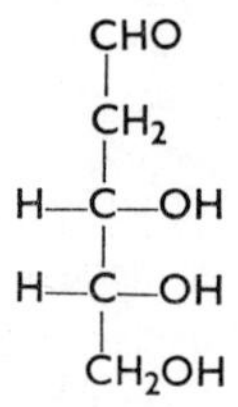

```
        CHO
         |
        CH₂
         |
   H—C—OH
         |
   H—C—OH
         |
        CH₂OH
```

crystals, m.p. 91°, soluble in water. Exhibits mutarotation, final $[\alpha]_D^{22} - 56 \cdot 2$ in water.

Dephlegmator. See Partial condenser.

Depot fat. The reserve stores of fat in animals,

deposited in adipose tissue and normally undergoing metabolism relatively slowly. Depot fat is important in nutrition because of its high calorific value.

Depression of freezing-point. The freezing-point of a pure solvent is depressed by the addition of a solute. The depression is proportional to the concentration of solute in the solution. The depression caused by 1 g molecule of solute in 1 litre of solvent is called the *molecular depression constant*, and has a definite value for each solvent.

Depsides. The depsides are simple compounds with tannin-like properties formed by the condensation of the carboxylic group of one phenolcarboxylic acid with a hydroxyl group of a similar acid. Thus:

$$HO \cdot C_6H_4 \cdot COOH + HO \cdot C_6H_4 \cdot COOH$$
$$\rightarrow HO \cdot C_6H_4 \cdot COO \cdot C_6H_4 \cdot COOH$$

They are called didepsides, tridepsides, polydepsides, etc., depending on the number of phenol groups they contain.

Derris. Obtained from the root of the Far-Eastern shrub *Derris elliptica*, and originally used as a fish poison; contains rotenone (*q.v.*). It is applied as a dust, and is used as an insecticide.

Desensitization. The effect by which a photographic silver halide emulsion is induced to lose sensitivity over all or part of its spectral sensitivity range is termed desensitization.

Practically, desensitizers are used in a predeveloper bath, or in the developer, to allow subsequent processing to be carried out in relatively bright light. For this purpose, the desensitizer must neither attack the latent image nor inhibit development. Such compounds as anthraquinone-2-sulphonic acid, its derivatives and carboxylic acid analogues, pinakryptol green, pinakryptol yellow and phenosafranine, can be used. Generally, oxidizing agents are desensitizers, and their action is to convert silver and silver sulphide sensitivity specks into silver salts. Thus, chromic acid and mercuric chloride are powerful desensitizers, also destroying latent image. Most sensitizing dyes, although enhancing long wavelength sensitivity, reduce the overall emulsion sensitivity and so are also desensitizers.

Desmosterol, $C_{27}H_{44}O$. 24-Dehydrocholesterol,

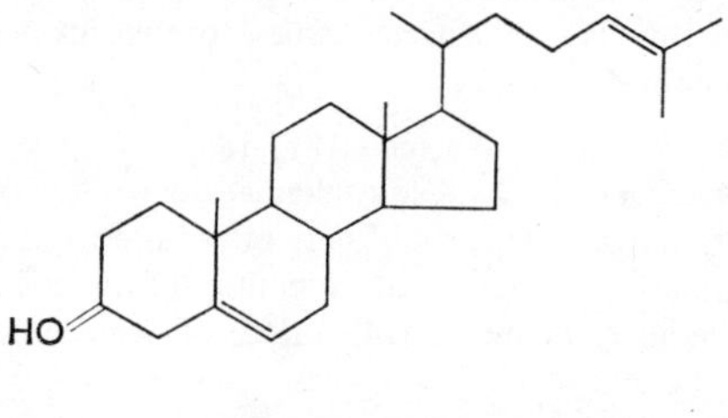

a naturally occurring companion of cholesterol first isolated from chick embryo, and from rat skin. Desmosterol is a close biogenetic precursor of cholesterol, and certain drugs lead to its accumulation in the blood.

Desmotropism. A term now taken to be synonymous with tautomerism.

Desormes, Charles Bernard (1777-1862). After teaching at the École Polytechnique, Paris, Desormes became a chemical manufacturer at Verberie, Oise. See Clément.

Desoxycorticosterone, $C_{21}H_{30}O_3$. Occurs in the adrenal cortex and has been prepared in

numerous ways from other steroids. Plates, m.p. 141°-142°, $[\alpha]_D^{22} + 178°$ in alcohol. Soluble in alcohol, acetone, etc. Used medicinally as the acetate for adrenal insufficiency, especially in veterinary applications.

Destructive distillation, Carbonization. These are names given to the process of distillation of organic solids or liquids in which the substance distilled decomposes in whole or in part during the process, leaving a solid or viscous liquid in the still. Only the decomposition products that are volatile at the temperature of distillation pass to the condenser, and of these only those condense that are liquid at atmospheric temperature. The process is typified by the carbonization of coal, peat, wood, or oil shale, and by some older processes for the destructive distillation of crude petroleum oils.

Detergent oil. Lubricating oil used in internal combustion engines. Possesses sludge dispersing properties by reason of the addition of special dopes.

Detergents. Surface active agents which besides being good wetting agents are capable of removing dirt (usually grease) from a variety of surfaces. Not all wetting agents are good detergents since the ability to prise the dirt away from its substrate and to hold it in sufficiently stable dispersion until it can be flushed away is an additional requirement not possessed by all wetting agents. Commercial detergents, besides containing the essential surface active ingredient, often have 'builders' added to prevent re-deposition of the detached dirt on to the substrate, to increase 'whiteness' (optical

bleaches), and to give an attractive colour or perfume, etc.

Detonating gas. A common name for the mixture of hydrogen with half its volume of oxygen which is produced by the electrolysis of water and explodes violently, with re-formation of water, when ignited.

Detonation. If the compression ratio of a petrol engine is progressively raised a point is reached at which the combustion ceases to be practically noiseless and a sharp metallic hammering is heard. This is known variously as pinking, knocking, or detonation. The exact nature of the change in the combustion process is not precisely understood, but the knocking appears to be due to a sudden increase in the rate of combustion causing high-pressure gas waves to strike the cylinder walls.

Detoxication (Detoxification). A general term for the biochemical transformations which occur in the metabolism of foreign organic compounds by an organism, not necessarily resulting in decreased toxicity. See Williams, 'Detoxication Mechanisms', London, 1959.

Deuterium, D. At.no. 1, At.wt. 2·013. An isotope of hydrogen which, because of the relatively high difference in masses, has markedly different physical and chemical properties. The bracketed values below are the data for certain physical properties of molecular hydrogen and its compounds, and the unbracketed values those for the deuterium analogues: b.p. $-249·7°$ $(-252·8°)$; b.p. of D_2O, 101·4° (100·0°); b.p. DCl, $-81·5°$ $(-85·0°)$; m.p. D_2O, 3·8° (0·0°); m.p. C_6D_6, 6·8° (5·5°); density at 25°, 1·105 (0·997); temp. of max. density, 11·6° (4·0°); ionic product at 25°, $1·8 \times 10^{-15}$ $(1·0 \times^{-14})$. Deuterium was first detected spectroscopically. Its isolation depends on the observation made by Washburn and Urey (1932) that the water remaining after the destructive electrolysis of water is relatively richer in deuterium oxide than the starting material. Ordinary water contains approximately 1 part in 4500 of deuterium oxide. As a result of the operation of physical processes (e.g. preferential evaporation of H_2O), small variations in this ratio are observed in water obtained from certain natural sources. The abundance of D_2O is usually estimated from density determinations.

Deuterium and its compounds react at different rates from normal hydrogen compounds. Deuterium compounds have been used as tracers in the investigation of chemical and biological reactions. Deuterium oxide (heavy water) is used as a moderator in atomic piles.

Deuteroporphyrin. See Porphyrins.

Deuton (Deuteron). The nucleus of the deuterium

atom. It is related to deuterium as the proton is related to hydrogen, and like the proton has proved a valuable agent for producing artificial disintegration by bombardment.

Devarda's alloy contains 45% aluminium, 50% copper, and 5% zinc. Nitrates in strongly alkaline solution are reduced quantitatively to ammonia on addition of the finely divided alloy. Since the ammonia can be distilled off and determined by titration, Devarda's alloy is used in the volumetric determination of nitrates.

Developed colours. See 'Ingrain' dyes.

Developers, photographic. See Aminophenol developers, Colour development.

Development accelerators. Development accelerators are compounds such as potassium nitrate, laurylpyridinium bromide and urea which are added to photographic developer solutions in order to increase the rate of development. The effect is due either to a softening of the protective colloid, gelatin, around the developing crystal, or to an alteration of the potential of the charge barrier (zeta potential) associated with the crystal. Either mechanism facilitates access of the negatively charged developer ion to the grain surface.

Development centres. Development centres are areas of the silver halide crystal occupied by discrete silver specks (see Latent image) from which reduction of the exposed grain to metallic silver commences. Other minute foreign particles dispersed in gelatin can also function as development centres in conditions favourable to physical development (*q.v.*).

Devitrification. Numerous amorphous solids like glass are really strongly supercooled liquids. They have, therefore, a tendency to crystallize, but the change is retarded by their high viscosity. Under certain conditions, crystallization does set in, and the glass becomes opaque through the appearance of crystals. The process is termed devitrification.

de Vries, Hugo (1848-1935). Born at Haarlem and educated at Leyden, Heidelberg, and Würzburg, de Vries was in 1871 appointed lecturer at the University of Amsterdam, and in 1881 became professor. A botonist, de Vries was responsible for some pioneer observations on osmosis.

Dewar, Sir James (1842-1923). Born at Kincardine-on-Forth, Dewar became a pupil of Lyon Playfair (Edinburgh), and Kekulé (Ghent). In 1875 he was appointed Jacksonian Professor of Natural Experimental Philosophy at Cambridge, and in 1877 he became, in addition, Fullerian professor of chemistry at the Royal Institution. He was knighted in 1904. Possessed of a mind which was original and impatient, his scientific work covered a wide field. He liquefied numerous gases and invented the vacuum flask. See Royal Institution Lecture (H. E. Armstrong), January, 1924.

Dewaxing. The removal of waxes from lubricating oil stocks. It is usually carried out by filtration at low temperatures after dilution with solvents such as methyl ethyl ketone.

Dew point. That temperature at which liquid first appears when a mixture of vapours is cooled, assuming the system is in equilibrium.

Dew point hygrometer. An instrument for the determination of dew point in which a highly polished surface is cooled by circulation of cold water or some other means. The highest temperature at which condensation will occur gives the dew point of the mixture.

Dexamethasone, $C_{22}H_{20}FO_5$. Prepared by par-

tial synthesis. White to tan crystals or crystalline powder, m.p. $\sim 255°$. Almost insoluble in water, soluble at 20° in 42 parts alcohol, $[\alpha]_D^{20} + 72°$ to $+80°$ (1% w/v in dioxan).

It is an adrenocortical steroid similar to cortisone, only more potent.

Dexamphetamine, Dexedrine. The dextrorotatory isomer of amphetamine.

Dextran. A mucilaginous polymer of glucose made by certain bacteria. It has mol.wt. between 30,000 and 250,000, and has both 1-4 and 1-6 linkages with branches about every five units, giving it considerable resistance to hydrolysis by enzymes. It is manufactured by the fermentation of sucrose with *Leuconostoc mesenteroides* and similar organisms and is refined by acid hydrolysis. It can be used as a plasma substitute in blood transfusions, as an emulsifying and thickening agent, and as a stabilizer for ice creams.

The sodium salts of sulphuric acid esters of dextran are used as anticoagulants for the same purposes as heparin.

Dextrins. Dextrins are intermediate products formed during the hydrolysis of starch to sugars. They can be divided into three classes: amylodextrins, which give a blue colour with iodine and are soluble in 25% alcohol, erythrodextrins, giving a red colour with iodine and soluble in

55% alcohol, and achroodextrins which give no colour with iodine, and are soluble in 70% alcohol. They are soluble in water and strongly dextrorotatory. Dextrins are manufactured by the action of heat and hydrolytic agents on wet or dry starch and are used as adhesives.

Dextropimaric acid, $C_{20}H_{30}O_2$. Present in French colophony; m.p. 211°-212°, $[\alpha]_D + 60°$ (in ethanol). It has the structure shown. On hydrogenation it gives the dihydro compound m.p. 240°-241°. Laevopimaric acid, obtained from the same sources, has a different carbon skeleton but it, like dextropimaric acid and abietic acid, gives retene on dehydrogenation.

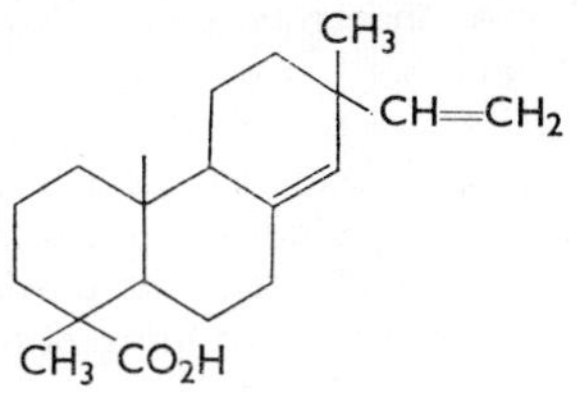

Dextrose. See Glucose.

De-zincification. A form of corrosion in brasses resulting in the removal of zinc from the alloy and its replacement by a porous deposit of copper. Small quantities of tin or arsenic are often incorporated to remedy de-zincification; as in Admiralty metal 70/29/1 and Naval brass 61/38/1.

Diacetin. See Acetins.

Diacetone. See Diacetone alcohol.

Diacetone alcohol, $C_6H_{12}O_2$, $HOC(CH_3)_2CH_2COCH_3$. A colourless, odourless liquid; d^{25} 0·9306, b.p. 166°. Manufactured by treating acetone with lime, or sodium or barium hydroxides. It is readily decomposed by acids and strong alkalis. It is used as a lacquer solvent, particularly for brushing lacquers, as it evaporates slowly. It is also used as a dye-solvent in the printing trade.

Diacetoneamine, $C_6H_{13}NO$. A colourless,

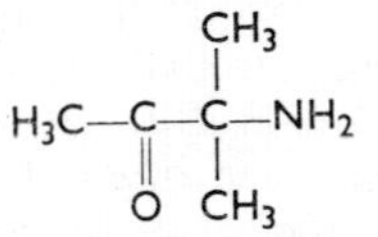

strongly basic liquid, b.p. 25°/0·2mm. Moderately soluble in water; miscible with alcohol and ether. Manufactured by treating mesityl oxide with ammonia, or by passing ammonia gas into boiling acetone. It is isolated as the diacetoneamine acid oxalate, a colourless crystalline substance, m.p. 126°-127°. Decomposes on heating to mesityl oxide and ammonia. Reacts with sodium nitrite, forming diacetone alcohol.

Forms derivatives of γ-piperidone with aldehydes. Used in the synthesis of β-eucaine.

Diacetyl, Biacetyl, $C_4H_6O_2$, $CH_3COCOCH_3$. A greenish-yellow liquid with a powerful odour; d^{15}_{15} 0·9904, b.p. 88°. Miscible with water, alcohol, and ether. It occurs in bay and other essential oils, and also in butter. It is formed in small amounts when tartaric acid, sugar, and starch are charred by heat. Prepared by leading vinylacetylene into a solution of mercuric sulphate in sulphuric acid, and decomposing the insoluble product with hydrochloric acid at 95°-100°. Other methods include the oxidation of 2,3-butylene glycol with oxygen at 270° in the presence of a copper catalyst, and the distillation of a solution of acetoin in 50% ferric chloride. It is volatile in steam. Reduced to 2,3-butylene glycol by yeast; oxidized by hydrogen peroxide to acetic acid. Forms dimethylglyoxime with hydroxylamine. When treated with syrupy phosphoric acid, a crystalline compound, $C_4H_6O_2, 2H_3PO_4$, is formed. Detected by conversion to dimethylgloxime, the addition of a soluble nickel salt then produces a red colour. Hardening results from the addition of diacetyl to photographic gelatin. Its action is believed to be due to the formation of xyloquinone.

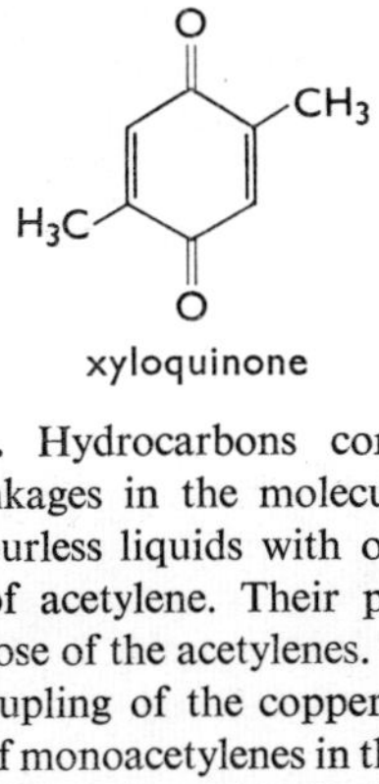

xyloquinone

Diacetylenes. Hydrocarbons containing two acetylene linkages in the molecule. They are mobile, colourless liquids with odours resembling that of acetylene. Their properties are similar to those of the acetylenes. They are prepared by coupling of the copper or Grignard derivatives of monoacetylenes in the presence of cupric chloride. Diacetylene itself is conveniently obtained by treating 1,4-dichlorobut-2-yne with sodamide in liquid ammonia.

Diagonal relationship. An apparent similarity between elements of the main groups of the Periodic Table that are related to one another, diagonally. Thus Li resembles Mg; Be, Al; and B, S. The similarity is brought about by the equivalence in size of the pairs of atoms in their combining forms.

Dialysis. The comparatively large particles (1-100 mμ) of a colloidal sol, in contrast to molecules or ions, are unable to diffuse rapidly or to pass through membranes of parchment, collodion, etc. By enclosing an impure sol within such a membrane (dialyser), which is supported

DIAMAGNETISM

DIAPHORASE

in pure (and preferably flowing) water, impurities of a crystalloid nature are gradually removed. This process, which is the standard method of purification of colloidal sols, was termed dialysis by Graham. See Colloids, Ultrafiltration, Electrodialysis.

Diamagnetism. The property of a substance that causes expulsion of lines of magnetic force. This results in a lower number of lines of magnetic force passing through the substance than would pass through the corresponding position in space.

1,2-Diaminoethane. See Ethylenediamine.

1,5-Diaminopimelic acid, $C_7H_{14}N_2O_4$. Crystallizes in fine white needles, m.p. over 305°, moder-

$$HO_2C—\underset{\underset{H}{|}}{\overset{\overset{NH_2}{|}}{C}}—[CH_2]_3—\underset{\underset{H}{|}}{\overset{\overset{NH_2}{|}}{C}}—CO_2H$$

ately soluble in water, soluble in acids and alkalis, insoluble in alcohol and other organic solvents. The D, L, and *meso* forms are all found in protein hydrolysates of bacterial origin, and diaminopimelic acid is believed to be peculiar to bacterial proteins. It is an intermediate in the biosynthesis of lysine.

Diamond. A crystalline form of carbon, and one of the hardest and most infusible substances known. It has d 3·520, n_D 2·417. In a crystal of

Important sources in South Africa are the basic igneous rock known as kimberlite and alluvials. The valuable diamond may be colourless or faintly coloured, but must be transparent. The heavily coloured forms, known as carbonado or bort, are of no value as gems, but are used for rock drills, for lathe tools, and when powdered for cutting and polishing clear diamonds. In cutting, the natural crystalline form is obliterated and an artificial shape, which gives rise to a large amount of internal reflexion producing the 'fire' of the stone, produced. The diamond is extremely hard, and stands highest in Mohs's scale of hardness. It possesses a high refractive index, and dispersive power. It is relatively much more transparent to X-rays than are its imitations.

Diamond is very resistant to chemical reagents; potassium dichromate and sulphuric acid attack it with the formation of CO_2. It burns in air or oxygen at 700° to carbon dioxide, leaving scarcely any ash; some forms of bort may leave as much as 4·5% ash.

Recent work on the effect of very high temperature and pressure on graphite in the presence of a metal catalyst has resulted in synthetic diamonds big enough for many industrial uses, but the cost of production is high.

Diamond black F, Mordant black 5. The dyestuff is prepared by diazotizing *p*-aminosalicylic acid and combining the diazonium compound with

$$C_6H_3(OH)(COOH)·N:N·C_{10}H_6·N:N·C_{10}H_5\overset{\diagup SO_3H}{\diagdown OH}$$

diamond every carbon atom is linked tetrahedrally to four others, as shown in the accompanying figure. The structure has cubic symmetry ($a=3·56$ Å) and the C—C distance is 1·54 Å, equal to that found in saturated hydrocarbons.

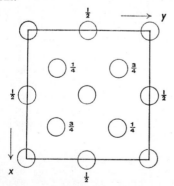

This mineral, which in its transparent varieties is a most beautiful and costly gem, has been known from very early times.

α-naphthylamine. The aminoazo-dyestuff thus produced is diazotized and combined with α-naphthol-γ-sulphonic acid.

Diamorphine, Heroin, $C_{21}H_{23}NO_5$. Diacetylmorphine, with both hydroxyl groups acetylated. It is almost insoluble in water and is used in the form of its hydrochloride which is soluble in 2·5 parts of water and 13 parts of alcohol and has m.p. 231°-232°. It is prepared by the action of acetic anhydride on morphine. It resembles morphine in action, but is more powerful. The dangers and effects of addiction are worse than those of morphine and diamorphine should only be used when less dangerous analgesics and cough depressants have proved inadequate.

Diaphorase. A flavoprotein enzyme concerned in the Krebs cycle at the stage of decarboxylation of α-oxoglutaric acid to succinic acid. It requires thiamine pyrophosphate and lipoic acid as coenzymes: diaphorase effects the dehydrogenation of the resulting dihydrolipoic acid by hydrogen transfer to NAD.

Diaphragm valve. A valve for controlling the flow of liquids and gases, in which the closing action is effected by a flexible diaphragm being pushed down against a ridge running across the valve body. This valve is widely used in the chemical industry because no moving parts other than the diaphragm come into contact with the fluid, and it is therefore relatively easy to make it corrosion-resistant.

Diaspore. A variety of hydrated aluminium hydroxide of formula $Al_2O_3 . H_2O$. The crystals are orthorhombic with two molecules in the unit cell. The oxygen atoms are in a close-packed arrangement with each Al in an octahedral hole and each O shared by three Al atoms. The hydrogen atoms appear to be between two oxygen atoms and there is very strong hydrogen bonding. On heating, diaspore forms corundum. Sp.gr.3·4, hardness 6·5-7. The crystals are white, grey, or greenish-yellow, with a pearly lustre. They often occur as tabular scales or bladed and foliated. Some types of bauxite consist essentially of diaspore.

Diastase. See Amylase.

Diastereomers. Stereoisomeric structures which are not enantiomers. For example, mesotartaric acid and either one of the optically-active tartaric acids are said to be diastereomeric and differ only in the configuration at one carbon

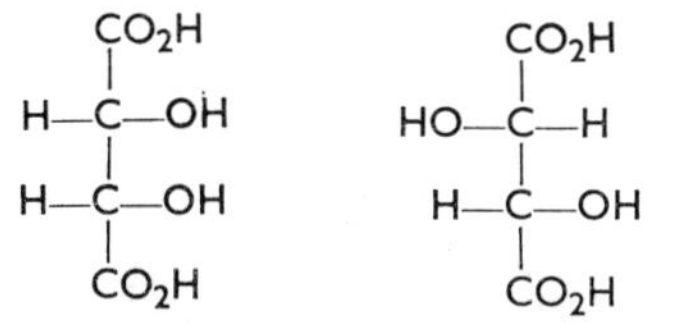

Mesotartaric acid	d- or l-Tartaric acid
CO_2H	CO_2H
H—C—OH	HO—C—H
H—C—OH	H—C—OH
CO_2H	CO_2H

atom. Unlike enantiomers, diastereomers usually have substantially different chemical and physical properties.

Diatomic molecule. A molecule with two atoms, e.g. HCl.

Diatomite or **Kieselguhr.** The siliceous remains of minute diatoms consisting of opaline silica. The particles are hollow and the material is thus used as an absorbent (with nitroglycerin it forms dynamite). Other uses, varying with the shape of the diatoms, are for polishing, as a filtering and decolorizing medium, and in heat-insulating compositions. Tripolite is a compact form.

Diatrizoic acid. See Acitrizoic acid.

Diazald. A trade name for N-methyl-N-nitrosotoluene-p-sulphonamide, $C_8H_{10}N_2O_3S$. A white crystalline solid, m.p. 60°, it is a con-

venient and easily stored source of diazomethane, which can be liberated by alkaline saponification.

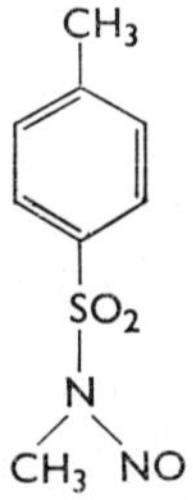

Diazinon, $C_{12}H_{21}N_2O_3PS$. Diethyl 2-isopropyl-4-methyl-6-pyrimidinyl phosphorothionate. A

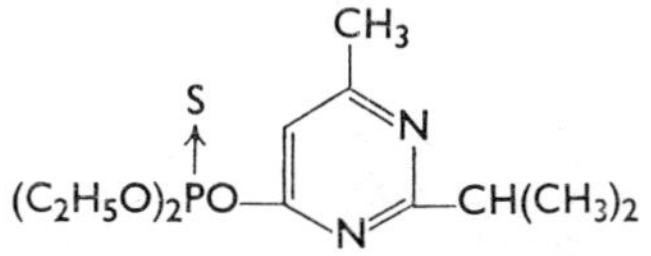

compound which shows high activity against insects, particularly house flies. It is made by reaction of diethyl phosphorochloridothionate $[(EtO)_2P(S)Cl]$ with the intermediate pyrimidine, itself made from ethyl acetoacetate and isobutyramidine. When pure it is a colourless liquid, b.p. 83°-4°/0·002 mm, but the technical (90%) material is brown. Soluble in organic solvents, insoluble in water.

Diazoacetic ester, Ethyl diazoacetate,

$$C_4H_6N_2O_2$$

$N_2CHCOOCH_2CH_3$. A yellow oil; d^{24} 1·083, b.p. 84°/61 mm. Sparingly soluble in water, soluble in alcohol, ether, and benzene. Prepared by treating a solution of ethyl glycinate hydrochloride with sodium nitrite and sulphuric acid at 0°. The ester is extracted with ether and distilled under reduced pressure. It decomposes explosively if distilled at atmospheric pressure, or if treated with concentrated hydrochloric or sulphuric acid. When treated with alkalis it forms nitrogen-containing ring compounds. Forms glycollic acid on boiling with water. Reacts with alcohols to give alkoxy-acetic esters, and with aldehydes to give β-keto-esters. Esters of unsaturated acids react with it, forming pyrazoline carboxylic esters; these lose nitrogen on heating to give derivatives of cyclopropane. Used in organic syntheses.

Diazoamino-compounds. These compounds are most conveniently prepared by the condensation of a diazonium salt with a primary or secondary amine in the presence of sodium acetate, e.g.

$$C_6H_5N_2Cl + NH_2 \cdot C_6H_5 = C_6H_5 \cdot N_2 \cdot NH \cdot C_6H_5$$
diazoaminobenzene

The diazoamino-compounds are usually yellow in colour, and do not dissolve in acid;

they can usually be isolated and crystallized without decomposition. When treated with nitrous acid two molecules of diazonium salt are formed. The most important reaction is the intramolecular conversion into an azo compound when warmed with an amine and its hydrochloride, e.g. diazoaminobenzene when warmed with aniline containing aniline hydrochloride gives p-aminoazobenzene.

$$\text{C}_6\text{H}_5-\text{N}{=}\text{N}-\overset{\text{H}}{\text{N}}-\text{C}_6\text{H}_5 \longrightarrow$$

$$\text{C}_6\text{H}_5-\text{N}{=}\text{N}-\text{C}_6\text{H}_4-\text{NH}_2$$

Diazo compounds. An indiscriminate name covering the diazoalkanes, diazonium salts and azo compounds.

Diazonium compounds. An important class of compounds containing the characteristic group —N≡N— in which one valency is satisfied by an aromatic and the other by a non-aromatic group.

The diazonium salts are by far the most important diazo-compounds. These are salts derived from the base R—N≡N—OH, e.g. benzene diazonium chloride, $C_6H_5—N≡N^+Cl^-$.

They are prepared by the action of nitrous acid on aromatic amines. The amine is dissolved in excess of mineral acid and sodium nitrite is added slowly until a slight excess of nitrous acid is present. The reaction is usually carried out in ice-cold solution. The solution then contains the diazonium salt of the mineral acid used. This process is called diazotization.

The diazonium salts usually decompose when warmed with water to give a phenol and nitrogen. When treated with cuprous chloride, cuprous bromide, or potassium iodide, the diazo group is replaced by chlorine, bromine, or iodine respectively (Sandmeyer reaction). A diazonium sulphate and hydroxylamine give an azoimide.

The most important reaction of the diazonium salts is the condensation with phenols or aromatic amines whereby intensely coloured azo compounds are formed. The phenol or amine is called the secondary component, and the process of 'coupling' with a diazonium salt

$$\text{C}_6\text{H}_5-\text{N}_2^{\oplus}\text{Cl}^{\ominus} + \text{C}_6\text{H}_5-\text{OH} \longrightarrow$$

$$\text{C}_6\text{H}_5-\text{N}{=}\text{N}-\text{C}_6\text{H}_4-\text{OH}$$

is the basis of manufacture of all the azo dyestuffs. The entering azo group goes into the p-position of the benzene ring if this is free, otherwise it takes up the o-position, e.g. diazotized aniline coupled with phenol gives benzeneazophenol. When only half a molecular proportion of nitrous acid is used in the diazotization of an aromatic amine a diazoamino compound is formed.

Diazomethane, N_2CH_2. A yellow gas with a peculiar musty odour. It is very poisonous. Very soluble in ether. Prepared by treating a mixture of nitrosomethylurea and ether with cold concentrated potassium hydroxide solution. The resulting ethereal solution is a convenient form in which to handle diazomethane. It is a very reactive substance, and forms methyl chloride with hydrochloric acid, acetonitrile with hydrogen cyanide, and methyl esters with organic acids. It reacts with acyl chlorides to give diazoketones, and with esters of unsaturated organic acids to give pyrazoline carboxylic acids. With aldehydes a mixture of a methyl ketone and an olefin oxide is formed; the proportions depend upon the conditions of the reaction and upon the aldehyde used. Alcohols react slowly or not at all, but phenols form methyl ethers. It is a useful reagent in organic syntheses. See Arndt-Eistert synthesis.

Dibasic acid. An acid which has two replaceable hydrogen atoms, and therefore yields two series of salts, is termed a dibasic acid, e.g.H_2SO_4, which yields $NaHSO_4$ and Na_2SO_4.

1, 2, 5, 6-Dibenzanthracene, $C_{22}H_{14}$. Crystallizes

in silvery leaflets, m.p. 262°. A carcinogenic substance obtained from coal tar.

Dibenzene chromium, $C_{12}H_{12}Cr$. Brown-black crystals, m.p. 284°-285°, which are rapidly oxidized by air, moderately soluble in organic solvents, but insoluble in water. It is an example of a sandwich compound, but although diamagnetic does not undergo the reactions associated with ferrocene. It is of possible interest for vapour-phase chromium plating work. Analogous systems (charged or uncharged) based upon other metals are known. See Arene-metal complexes.

Dibenzyl, $C_{14}H_{14}$. It forms colourless crystals m.p. 52°, b.p. 284°. It is insoluble in water,

slightly soluble in alcohol, soluble in carbon disulphide.

It can be obtained by the action of sodium or copper upon benzyl chloride, by the action of aluminium chloride upon benzene and ethylene dichloride or by heating benzoin or benzil.

It is readily oxidized by chromic acid to benzoic acid. When it is heated to 500° some stilbene is formed.

Diborane. See Boron hydrides.

Dibromochloropropane. 1,2-Dibromo-3-chloro-propane, $ClCH_2Br-CHBr-CH_2Cl$. A heavy liquid, b.p. 196°, insoluble in water but miscible with organic solvents. It is used as a nematocide.

1,2-Dibromoethane. See Ethylene dibromide.

Dibutyl phthalate. See Phthalic esters.

Dicarboxylic acids. Organic acids containing two of the acidic carboxyl $(-COOH)$ groups. They form both acidic and neutral salts and esters; some give anhydrides by loss of a molecule of water between the two carboxyl groups. Many occur naturally as the free acid or an ester. They are generally prepared by the oxidation of a glycol, hydroxy-acid or hydroxy-aldehyde, or by hydrolysis of a dinitrile or cyano-acid.

Dichloralphenazone. See Chloral hydrate.

Dichloroacetic acid. See Chloroacetic acids.

Dichlorobenzenes, $C_6H_4Cl_2$.

o-Dichlorobenzene, b.p. 179°.
m-Dichlorobenzene, b.p. 172°.
p-Dichlorobenzene, m.p. 53°, b.p. 174°.

Colourless, insoluble in water, readily soluble in organic solvents.

The o- and p-isomers are manufactured by the direct chlorination of benzene in the presence of iron as a catalyst, the resulting mixture being separated by fractional distillation. The m-isomer may be obtained by isomerization of the o- or p-compound in the presence of a catalyst.

p-Dichlorobenzene is the most important of the three compounds, being used largely as a moth repellant and air deodorant. o-Dichloro-benzene is used as a dye intermediate, insecticide, solvent and for various other purposes. The m-isomer is not of commercial importance.

$\beta\beta'$-Dichlorodiethyl sulphide. See Mustard gas.

Dichlorodifluoromethane, CCl_2F_2. B.p. $-30°$. Manufactured by the action of hydrogen fluoride on carbon tetrachloride using antimony penta-chloride as a catalyst. Known commercially as Freon-12 or Arcton-12. Widely used as a refrigerant and aerosol propellant. It is much less toxic than carbon tetrachloride.

1,2-Dichloroethane. See Ethylene dichloride.

Dichloroethenes. See Dichloroethylenes.

Dichloroethylenes, Dichloroethenes, $C_2H_2Cl_2$. There are three of these compounds. *1,1-Di-chloroethylene, asymmetrical dichloroethylene,* $CH_2=CCl_2$, is a colourless liquid, b.p. 37°. Insoluble in water, miscible with alchol and hydrocarbons. Prepared by heating 1,1,1- or 1,1,2-trichloroethylene with excess lime at 70°-80°. Polymerizes readily to an insoluble solid.

Acetylene dichloride, 1,2-dichloroethylene exists in two geometrically isomeric forms. *Cis-*1,2-dichloroethylene, and *trans-*1,2-dichloro-ethylene, are both formed when acetylene

cis   trans

tetrachloride is heated with water and zinc at 100°. The product contains about 80% of the cis-form. When a mixture of equal volumes of acetylene and chlorine is passed over activated carbon at 40° the trans-form is the chief product. Cis-form, d^{15} 1·289, b.p. 60°; trans-form, d^{15} 1·265, b.p. 49°. They are insoluble in water but are miscible with hydrocarbon solvents and are very similar in properties to trichloroethylene; are not affected by moisture or alkalis. They are used as substitutes for ether in fat extraction, as solvents e.g. for rubber, and have been used in a synthesis of thioindigo.

$\beta\beta$-Dichloroethyl ether, $(ClCH_2CH_2)_2O$. A colourless liquid with a chloroform-like odour; d^{20} 1·222, b.p. 178°. Insoluble in water but miscible with most organic solvents and oils. Manufactured by treating ethylene chloro-hydrin with chlorine and excess ethylene at 80°; or by heating ethylene chlorohydrin with strong sulphuric acid at 100°. Reacts with amines to give morpholines and with sodium tetrasulphide to give rubber-like plastics. It reacts with fused potassium hydroxide to give divinyl ether. Used as solvent in the chlorex process for dewaxing mineral oils, and for removing grease from textiles.

Sym-Dichloroisopropyl alcohol. See Glycerol dichlorohydrins.

Dichloromethane, Methylene chloride, CH_2Cl_2. A colourless liquid with a chloroform-like odour; d^{15} 1·337, b.p. 41°. Insoluble in water, miscible with hydrocarbon solvents. May be prepared by heating chloroform with zinc, alcohol and hydrochloric acid; manufactured by the direct chlorination of methane. Decomposed by water at 200° to give formic and hydrochloric acids. Largely used as a solvent, particularly for paint removal, dissolving cellulose acetate and degreasing. It is somewhat toxic.

1,2-Dichloropropane. See Propylene dichloride.

2,3-Dichloropropyl alcohol. See Glycerol dichlorohydrins.

Dichlorvos, dimethyl-2,2-dichlorovinylphosphate,

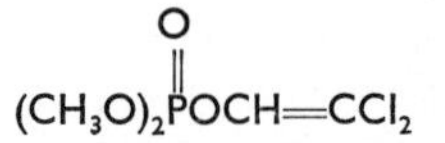

$$(CH_3O)_2\overset{O}{\overset{\|}{P}}OCH\!=\!CCl_2$$

$C_4H_7Cl_2O_4P$. A compound of high insecticidal activity, particularly against the house fly. It was first found as an insecticidal impurity in a sample of Dipterex and is now made from dimethyl-1-hydroxy-2,2-trichlorophosphonate by dehydrochlorination and rearrangement. It is a liquid, b.p. 120°/14 mm, slightly soluble in water but slowly hydrolysed in the solution. Active in the vapour phase. Of importance in protection of stored products and in domestic and animal health outlets. See J. G. Attfield and D. A. Webster, *Chem. and Ind.*, 1966, 272.

Dichromates. Polymeric chromate anions containing the $[O_3CrOCrO_3]^{2-}$ anion. See Chromates.

Dicophane. The official pharmacopoeial name for DDT.

Dicoumarol, dicoumarin, $C_{19}H_{12}O_6$. A white

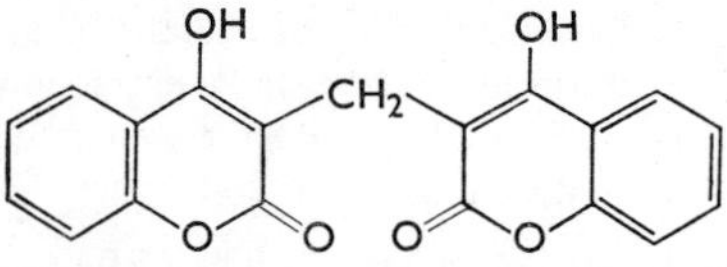

microcrystalline powder, m.p. 285°-293°, slightly soluble in water, soluble in strong alkalis. Prepared by the action of formaldehyde on 4-hydroxycoumarin, which is made from methyl salicylate. It delays coagulation of the blood through reducing the prothrombin content, and is used in the treatment of thrombosis. This effect was discovered when the formation of dicoumarol from coumarin in improperly cured sweet clover silage was found responsible for a haemorrhagic disease of cattle.

Dicyandiamide, cyanoguanidine, $C_2H_4N_4$, $H_2N\cdot C(NH)\cdot NH\cdot CN$. A colourless crystalline solid, d^{14} 1·405, m.p. 209°, soluble in water and alcohols. It is prepared commercially by the dimerization of cyanamide in the presence of bases, and is used in the manufacture of plastics and other products.

Dicyclohexylcarbodiimide, $C_{13}H_{22}N_2$. Crystalline solid, m.p. 35°-36°, b.p. 154°-156°, prepared by oxidizing N,N'-dicyclohexylthiourea with mercuric oxide in carbon disulphide solution. Used as a mild dehydrating agent, especially in the synthesis of peptides from amino-acids.

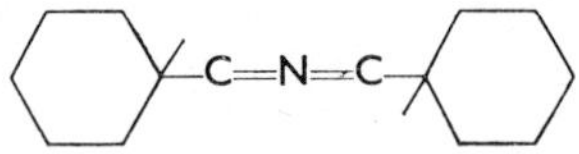

Diecasting. See Casting.

Dieldrin. The approved common name for the

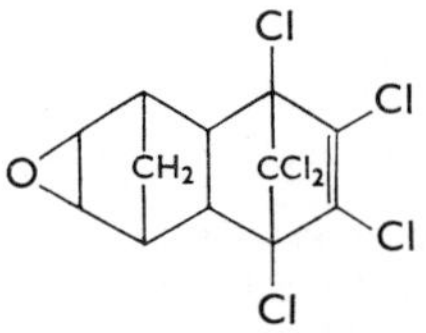

insecticidal product containing not less than 85% of 1,2,3,4,10,10-hexachloro-6,7-epoxy-1,4,4a, 5,6,7,8,8a-octahydro-exo-1,4-endo-5,8-di-methanonaphthalene ($C_{12}H_8Cl_6O$). The pure substance is a white solid, m.p. 175°-176°, but the technical material is pale brown. Dieldrin is the epoxy derivative of aldrin from which it is prepared by epoxidation with peracetic or perbenzoic acid, and is insoluble in water, soluble in aromatic solvents and slightly soluble in paraffins. It has a high contact and stomach toxicity to most insects, and is very persistent. Due to the fact that organochlorine compounds such as dieldrin are stored in the bodies of birds and mammals, their use is now much restricted.

Dielectric constant. The force F between two electric charges e, separated by a distance r in a vacuum, is given by $F = \dfrac{e^2}{r^2}$. In any other medium this relationship becomes $F = \dfrac{e^2}{Dr^2}$, where D is a characteristic of the medium called the dielectric constant. Dielectric constants are generally measured by comparing the capacity of a condenser filled with the medium with that of the same condenser filled with air, for the capacity C of a condenser $= \dfrac{DQ}{V}$, where Q is the charge and V the potential, and the dielectric constant of air is close to unity.

Diels, Otto (1876-1954). Born in Hamburg and

trained at the University of Berlin, Diels held several posts there before becoming in 1916 professor of chemistry and Director of the Chemical Institute at the University of Kiel. He shared the Nobel Prize for Chemistry for 1950 with his former pupil Kurt Alder for their work on diene synthesis. Diels was the discoverer of carbon suboxide, and worked on sterols and other aspects of organic chemistry.

Diels-Alder reaction. See Diene synthesis.

Diels' hydrocarbon, γ-**Methylcyclopentenophenanthrene,** $C_{18}H_{16}$. The fundamental hydrocarbon on which the structure of the sterols and

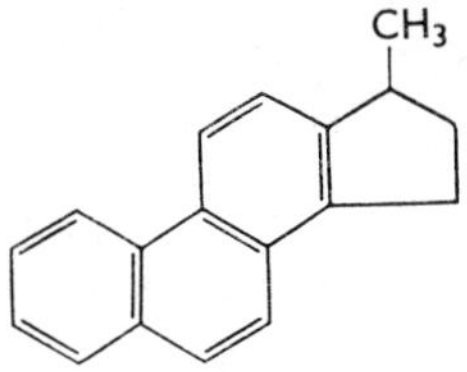

related compounds is based. It can be obtained by heating cholesterol with selenium. Its constitution has been confirmed by synthesis.

Dienes. Organic compounds containing two carbon to carbon double bonds.

Diene synthesis, Diels-Alder reaction. The Diels-Alder reaction constitutes one of the most useful synthetic organic chemistry procedures, and describes the 1,4 addition of an alkene or alkyne (dienophile) across a conjugated diene. Its general nature was first recognised in 1920 by Euler and Josephson; an intensive study of the reaction by Diels and Alder earned them the Nobel Prize in chemistry in 1950. An example is the addition of acrolein to buta-1,3-diene to give $\varDelta^4$-tetrahydrobenzaldehyde. The dieno-

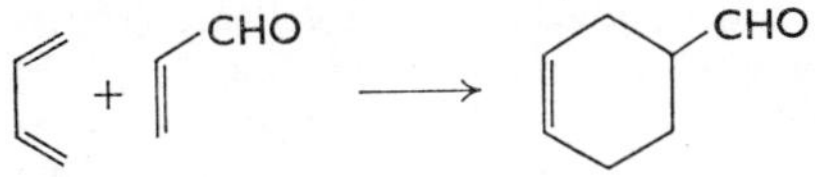

phile should be substituted with electron-attracting groups such as $-\overset{\overset{\text{O}}{\|}}{C}-R$, $-CN$, $-CF_3$, $-NO_2$, to enhance its reactivity, and the conjugated diene should have a *cis*-configuration. The reaction is often spontaneous when the two substances are mixed, and is a useful procedure for the identification of dienes. Its utility in synthesis arises from the stereospecific

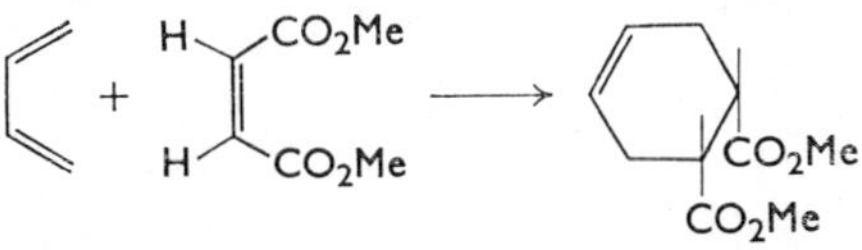

course it follows, i.e. the addend from dimethylmaleate is also *cis*. Addition to cyclic dienes, e.g. cyclopentadiene, may give *endo* or *exo*

products; often the *endo* adduct is produced first but slowly isomerizes to the more stable *exo* adduct; e.g. for maleic anhydride and cyclopentadiene.

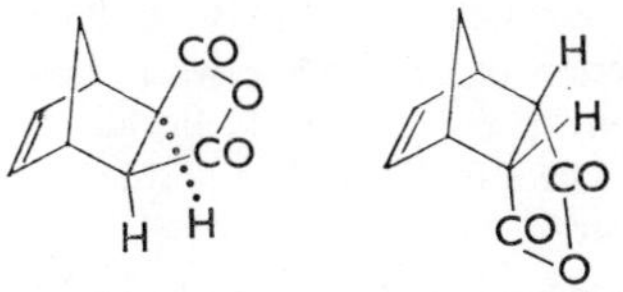

exo adduct   endo adduct

Diene value. This denotes the degree of unsaturation in fats; it is determined by heating the fat with a solution of maleic anhydride in acetone.

Dienoestrol, $C_{18}H_{18}O_2$. A colourless crystalline powder, m.p. 233°, insoluble in water, soluble in

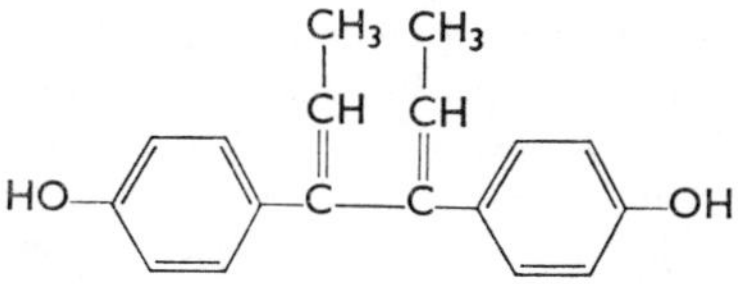

alcohol and in organic solvents. It is prepared by reducing *p*-hydroxypropiophenone and dehydrating the pinacol thus obtained.

It has oestrogenic properties, and is used for the same purposes as stilboestrol, for instance, in the suppression of lactation.

Diesel fuel. Fuel used for compression ignition engines. The composition varies for different types, but is essentially that of gas oil (*q.v.*).

Dieterici's equation. This is a modification of van der Waals equation, in which account is taken of the pressure gradient at the boundary of the gas. It is written

$$p(v-b) = RTe^{-a/RTv}.$$

where a and b are constants characteristic of each gas; at relatively low pressures it is identical with van der Waals equation.

Diethanolamine. See Ethanolamines.

Diethylamine. See Ethylamines.

Diethylcarbamazine, $C_{10}H_{17}NO_3$. Used as the

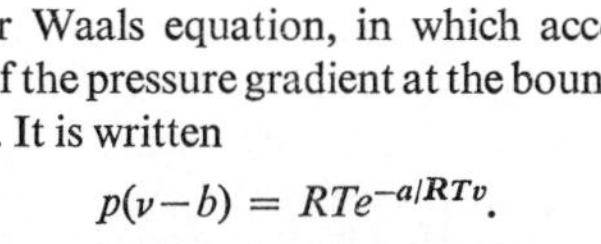

acid citrate, $C_{16}H_{29}N_3O_8$ which is very soluble in water, soluble in hot alcohol, sparingly soluble in cold, m.p. 137°. Prepared by condensing piperazine with diethylcarbamoyl chloride, followed by methylation, and conversion to the acid citrate.

Diethylcarbamazine is used for the treatment of filarial infections, and may be taken orally. It is useful in some cases of elephantiasis.

NN′-Diethyl-NN′-diphenylurea, $C_{17}H_{20}N_2O$.

$$CH_3 \cdot CH_2 \underset{C_6H_5}{\overset{C_6H_5}{N—CO—N}} CH_2 \cdot CH_3$$

A white, crystalline solid, m.p. 79°. Prepared by the reaction of ethylaniline with phosgene or with methylphenylcarbamyl chloride. It is used as a stabilizer for smokeless powders and as a plasticizer.

Diethyldithiocarbamic acid. A colourless,

$$CH_3CH_2 \underset{CH_3CH_2}{\overset{}{N \cdot C}} \overset{S}{\underset{SH}{}}$$

unstable, crystalline solid. Soluble in water and alcohol. Prepared by adding first diethylamine and then carbon disulphide to ice-cold alcohol. The acid crystallizes out on evaporation of the solution. Forms salts with metals and organic bases. The sodium salt is obtained by neutralizing the crude acid with sodium hydroxide and recrystallizing the product from 90% alcohol. This salt gives a brown complex with copper salts which is soluble in carbon tetrachloride, and is used as a means of determining copper. The zinc and diethylamine salts are used as accelerators in the vulcanization of rubber.

1,4-Diethylene dioxide. See Dioxan.

Diethyleneglycol, 2,2′-dihydroxydiethyl ether, $C_4H_{10}O_3$, $(HOCH_2CH_2)_2O$. A colourless and almost odourless liquid; d. 1·1185, b.p. 244·5°. Miscible with water, alcohol, and chloroform; insoluble in benzene and carbon tetrachloride. Readily absorbs moisture from the atmosphere. It is obtained as a by-product in the manufacture of ethylene glycol by the hydration of ethylene oxide. Manufactured by heating ethylene glycol with ethylene oxide. It is a solvent for cellulose nitrate, but not for the acetate. Used as a softening agent for textile fibres, as a solvent for certain dyes, and as a moistening agent for glues, paper, and tobacco. Its esters and ethers are used as solvents and plasticizers in lacquers.

Diethyleneglycol dinitrate (DEGN),

$$C_4H_8N_2O_7,$$

$O(CH_2CH_2ONO_2)_2$. A synthetic material formed by the nitration of diethyleneglycol. When pure it is a viscous, colourless, odourless liquid; m.p. −11·5°. It has been used to replace nitroglycerin in propellant manufacture. It is much less sensitive to initiation than nitroglycerin, and has an increased gelatinizing power for nitrocellulose, hence it gives rise to less danger and greater ease and rate of production in the manufacture of propellants. It is, however, more volatile than nitroglycerin, and is considered in some quarters to be more toxic. It also contains less oxygen than nitroglycerin

and consequently has a lower calorific value and contributes less energy to the final decomposition.

Diethyleneglycol monoethylether, Carbitol, $C_6H_{14}O_3$, $CH_3CH_2OCH_2CH_2OCH_2CH_2OH$.
A colourless liquid with a pleasant odour; d_{20}^{20} 0·9902, b.p. 202°. Miscible with water and most organic solvents. Manufactured by heating ethylene oxide with ethylene glycol monoethyl ether under pressure. Used in the preparation of nitrocellulose lacquers and laminated glass. It may be used to replace ethyl alcohol in the determination of the saponification value of fats and waxes.

Diethyl ether. See Ether.

Diethyl oxalate, Oxalic ester, $C_6H_{10}O_4$. A colourless liquid; d^{20} 1·0785, b.p. 185·4°, 85°/11 mm. Sparingly soluble in water; miscible with alcohol and ether. Prepared by distilling a mixture of oxalic acid, alcohol, and carbon tetrachloride. The water formed by the reaction is carried off as the low-boiling mixture of water, alcohol, and carbon tetrachloride. The residue of ester is distilled under reduced pressure. Decomposed by heating with water or dilute alkalis into oxalic acid and ethyl alcohol. Reacts with ammonia to give oxamide. Condenses with other esters in presence of sodium. Used in organic syntheses.

$$\overset{COOCH_2CH_3}{\underset{COOCH_2CH_3}{|}}$$

Diethyl oxide. See Ether.

Diethyl phthalate. See Phthalic esters.

Diethyl succinate. See Ethyl succinate.

Diethyl sulphate, $(C_2H_5)_2SO_4$. A colourless liquid with a faint ethereal odour; d_{20}^{20} 1·180, b.p. 208° (slight decomp.), 96°/15 mm. Insoluble in water, miscible with alcohol, ether, and benzene. Manufactured by leading ethylene under pressure into 100% sulphuric acid, and then distilling off the diethyl sulphate under reduced pressure; it may also be separated by the addition of water and removal of the insoluble ester. It is decomposed by boiling water. Reacts with hydroxy-compounds and amines to give ethers, esters, amines, and imines. One ethyl group reacts at temperatures between 50° and 100°, while both react at about 150°. Used as an ethylating agent in organic syntheses.

Diethyl sulphide, Ethyl sulphide, $(CH_3CH_2)_2S$. A colourless liquid with an ethereal odour when pure; usually it has a strong garlic-like odour; d^{20} 0·8368, b.p. 92°. Insoluble in water, soluble in alcohol and ether. Prepared by the action of potassium hydrogen sulphide on ethyl chloride or potassium ethyl sulphate. When heated at 400°-500° it forms thiophene. Oxidized by nitric acid to diethyl sulphoxide, $(C_2H_5)_2SO$, and diethyl sulphone. It forms complexes with metallic salts.

Diethyl sulphone, $C_4H_{10}O_2S$, $(C_2H_5)_2SO_2$. Crystallizes in colourless plates; m.p. 73°-74°, b.p. 248°. Soluble in water and benzene; insoluble in petroleum ether. Prepared by the oxidation of a solution of diethyl sulphide in acetic acid with hydrogen peroxide or potassium permanganate. It is very stable.

Differential flotation. The separation of a complex ore containing several finely divided minerals by the addition of specific reagents to a suspension of the ore in water, enabling the components to be removed one at a time by froth flotation.

Diffraction pattern. The pattern obtained on a photographic plate, consisting of a more or less symmetrical arrangement of rings or spots, or both, and formed by the passage of X-rays or electrons through a crystalline substance, or by their reflexion from a crystalline surface. Patterns consisting of diffuse rings are obtained with non-crystalline materials. In its more general sense, a diffraction pattern is the pattern observed in a process of optical diffraction, e.g. with a diffraction grating.

Diffusion. In any gaseous mixture or liquid solution which is kept at a uniform temperature, the composition eventually becomes uniform throughout the system, no matter what the original distribution was. This is explained on the basis of the kinetic theory of molecules, the spontaneous molecular motion leading to uniform distribution being termed diffusion.

Graham showed that the rate of diffusion of different gases through a porous diaphragm was inversely proportional to the square roots of their densities; this is the basis of a method of separation of gases, and has been applied successfully to the separation of hydrogen and deuterium.

A diffusion mechanism is also used in dialysis (q.v.) as a means of separating colloids from crystalloids. The rate of diffusion of molecules in gels is practically the same as in water, indicating the continuous nature of the aqueous phase. The diffusion of gases into a stream of vapour is of considerable importance in diffusion pumps.

Diffusion may also take place, although slowly, between solids; thus a nickel coating on a nickel-plated copper wire will diffuse into the copper at a measurable rate at 800°.

Diffusion pump. This is a non-mechanical pump used for the production of the very high vacua required in such operations as molecular distillation. Gas is drawn through the pump inlet into a stream of oil or mercury vapour from a heater, and forced towards the exit by molecular bombardment. The heavy vapour is condensed and returned to the heater, while the gas is removed from the exit by a backing pump.

Difluorodiazines, N_2F_2. See Nitrogen fluorides.

Difluoromethane, CH_2F_2. A gas, b.p. $-51·6°$, used as an azeotropic mixture with other fluorocarbons as a refrigerant.

Digilanids. These are the primary glycosides of digitalis. *Digitalis lanata* contains digilanids A, B, and C; the corresponding deacetylated purpurea glycosides are found in *D. purpurea*.

Digilanid A, $C_{49}H_{76}O_{19}$, is made up of digitoxose (3mols.), glucose (1 mol.), acetate and digitoxigenin. Mild alkali hydrolyses the acetyl group, while enzymes remove the glucose, leaving digitoxin, which is converted by complete acid hydrolysis into digitoxose and digitoxigenin.

Digilanids B and C are similar, but the aglucones are gitoxigenin and digoxigenin respectively.

Digitalin, $C_{36}H_{56}O_{14}$. M.p. 229°, $[\alpha]_D + 14·2°$. It is composed of digitalose, glucose and digitaligenin: it crystallizes in needles, and is obtained from German commercial digitalin. It is used for the preparation of solutions to be administered by hypodermic injection. Its action is that of digitalis, and it is employed where immediate action is necessary to avoid cardiac failure, or in cases where oral administration is inadmissible.

Digitalis. Consists of the dried leaves of *Digitalis purpurea*, the common foxglove. It is a valuable heart tonic, and causes the heart to beat more slowly, more strongly, and more regularly; it thus increases the flow of blood and at the same time rests the heart's muscles. Digitalis also exerts a diuretic action due to the increased supply of blood to the kidneys. Digitalis preparations are standardized by biological methods of assay.

Digitalis owes its properties to the glycosides it contains. These are present in this and related plants as a complex mixture containing several sugars including the unusual sugars digitalose and digitoxose. The aglucones or genins are steroids. For the individual glycosides see Digitalin, Digitonin, Digitoxin, Gitonin, Gitoxin, Oleandrin, and Digilanids.

Digitalose, 3-methyl-D-fucose, $C_7H_{14}O_5$. The

sugar constituent of digitalin. It has m.p. 106°, $[\alpha]_D + 106°$.

Digitonides. Molecular complexes formed between digitonin and a variety of hydroxylic compounds. The sparingly soluble digitonides formed by 3β-hydroxysteroids facilitate their separation from 3α-epimers. Cholesterol (*q.v.*) may be determined gravimetrically or spectrophotometrically as its digitonide.

Digitonin, $C_{55}H_{90}O_{29}$. It consists of 4 galactose units with xylose and digitogenin. It is the principal constituent of commercial digitalin, and crystallizes in crusts of slender needles. It is poisonous but has not the same action on the heart as digitalis. M.p. 235°.

Digitoxigenin, $C_{23}H_{34}O_4$. A cardiac aglucone obtained by hydrolysing digitoxin.

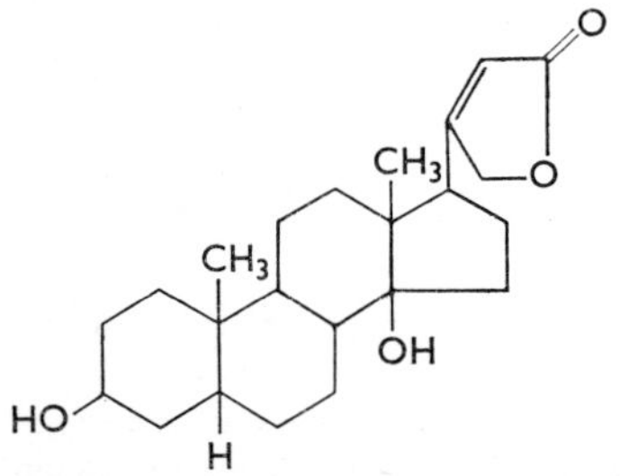

Digitoxin, $C_{41}H_{64}O_{13}$. The chief constituent of the mixture of glycosides obtained from digitalis leaf. It is composed of three digitoxose units and digitoxigenin. It is a white crystalline powder, soluble in alcohol, insoluble in water, m.p. 263°, $[\alpha]_D + 33°$. It is used for the same purposes as digitalis leaf, but is absorbed to a much greater extent and gives less gastric irritation.

Digitoxose, $C_6H_{12}O_4$. The 2-desoxy sugar present in several of the heart-specific glycosides of the foxglove. M.p. 112°, $[\alpha]_D + 46°$.

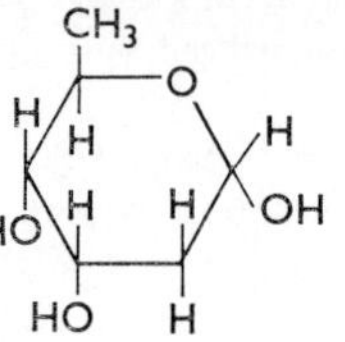

Diglyme. An abbreviated name for the dimethyl ether of diethylene glycol, $C_6H_{14}O_3$.
$CH_3 \cdot O \cdot CH_2 \cdot CH_2 \cdot O \cdot CH_2 \cdot CH_2 \cdot O \cdot CH_3$. It is a colourless liquid, b.p. 160°, miscible with water, lower alcohols, acetone, benzene, hexane, trichloroethylene, and other solvents, and with a number of polymers. It displays all the properties of an ether, and is useful as a high-temperature solvent.

Digol. The trivial name for diethyleneglycol, $O(CH_2CH_2OH)_2$ (*q.v.*).

Digoxin, $C_{41}H_{64}O_{14}$. A glycoside obtained from the leaves of *Digitalis lanata* which contains three digitoxose units and digoxigenin. It forms colourless crystals, insoluble in water and chloroform, soluble in alcohol, m.p. 265°, $[\alpha]_D + 13°$. It is absorbed more rapidly than digitalis and is used instead of it when more rapid action is required.

Dihydrocarveol, $C_{10}H_{18}O$. An optically active monocyclic terpene alcohol, the (−)-form of which occurs in caraway oil. It is formed by the reduction of carvone with sodium and alcohol. It contains 3 asymmetric carbon atoms, and the alcohol prepared from (+)- or (−)-carvone is a mixture of stereoisomers. (−)-Dihydrocarveol from caraway oil shows the following constants; b.p. 100°-102°/7-8 mm. d^{15} 0·9368, n^{20} 1·4836, $[\alpha]_D$ −6·14°. (+)-Dihydrocarveol, prepared by the reduction of (+)-carvone shows b.p. 222°-225° and 112°/14 mm, d^{20} 0·927, n_D 1·48168, $[\alpha]_D$ +30·56°.

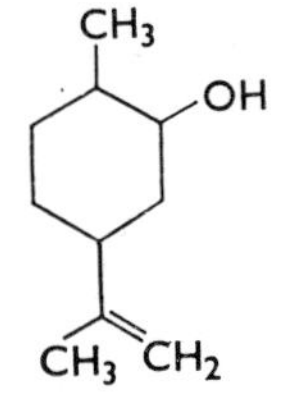

Dihydrocarvone, $C_{10}H_{16}O$. An optically active terpene ketone, the (−)-form of which is present in caraway oil. (−)-Dihydrocarvone is formed by the reduction of (+)-carvone with zinc dust in the presence of alkali. It contains two asymmetric carbon atoms, and should therefore exist in two (+)- and two (−)- forms, and in two racemic forms. In actual fact, only one (+)- and one (−)-form, together with the corresponding racemic form, have been recorded. It is a colourless oil of aromatic odour. A sample of the natural ketone showed the constants: b.p. 221°/735·5 mm, d^{15} 0·9797, n_D^{20} 1·47107, $[\alpha]_D$ −16·8°. It forms characteristic oximes, and can be separated in the form of a crystalline compound with sodium bisulphite.

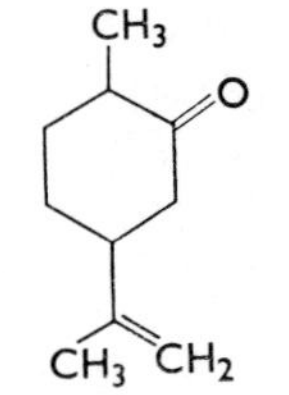

Dihydroxyacetone. Crystallizes as the monomer, m.p. about 80°, but this on standing changes to the dimer, m.p. about 115°. It is soluble in water,

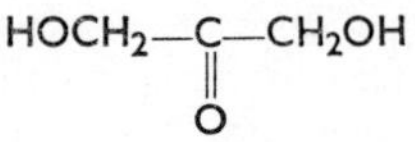

$$HOCH_2-\underset{\underset{O}{\|}}{C}-CH_2OH$$

hot alcohol, or ether, insoluble in petroleum ether. It is obtained by the action of certain *acetobacter* on glycerol. It is a strong reducing agent and forms an insoluble bisulphite compound.

2,2′-Dihydroxydiethyl ether. See Diethylene glycol.

Dihydroxymalonic acid. See Mesoxalic acid.

3,4-Dihydroxyphenylalanine (Dopa), $C_9H_{11}NO_4$.

HO—⟨⟩—CH_2—CH—CO_2H with NH_2, and a second HO group.

Crystallizes in prisms, m.p. 282°, with decomposition. Soluble in water, insoluble in alcohol. The naturally occurring substance is laevorotatory, $[\alpha]_D^{20} - 14\cdot28°$. It is an amino-acid isolated from various plant sources, but not found in the animal body. It is formed from tyrosine as the first stage in the oxidation of tyrosine to melanin.

1,2-Dihydroxypropane. See Propylene glycol.

Dihydroxytartaric acid, $C_4H_6O_8$, is a colourless,

$$HO_2C \cdot C(OH)_2 \cdot C(OH)_2 \cdot CO_2H$$

crystalline solid, m.p. 114°-115°. Soluble in water, alcohol, and ether. Prepared by treating dihydroxymaleic acid with bromine in glacial acetic acid solution and evaporating the liquor after adding a little water. Also prepared by treating tartaric acid with a mixture of nitric and sulphuric acids; the resulting tartaric acid dinitrate is neutralized with sodium carbonate and allowed to stand. Sodium dihydroxytartrate is slowly precipitated. The acid behaves in some ways as if it were a diketo-acid. Forms esters of diketosuccinic acid with alcohols. Decomposes when heated above its melting-point, giving tartronic acid, carbon dioxide, glyoxal, and oxalic acid. Forms an osazone with phenylhydrazine. The sodium salt is very insoluble, and is used as a means of estimating sodium.

3,5-Diiodotyrosine, Iodogorgic acid,

$C_9H_9I_2NO_3$. Pale, straw-coloured needles, m.p. 198°. It is found in certain marine organisms, such as corals and sponges, and in the thyroid gland, where it is believed to be the precursor of thyroxine. About half the total iodine of the thyroid gland is present as diiodotyrosine and the thyroid hormone is probably a compound of diiodotyrosine, thyroxine, and other amino-acids.

Diisopropyl ether. See Isopropyl ether.

Diisopropylideneacetone. See Phorone.

Diketen, $C_4H_4O_2$. A colourless highly lachrymatory liquid, b.p. 127°, m.p. $-6\cdot5°$. It is manufactured from acetone *via* keten. It reacts with alcohols and amines to give acetoacetic esters and amides respectively.

Diketones. Organic compounds containing two keto ($>C{=}O$) groups. They are classified according to the number of carbon atoms separating the two keto groups. α- Or 1,2-diketones are formed from their mono-oximes, the isonitrosoketones, by boiling with dilute sulphuric acid. The aliphatic α-diketones are yellow oils with pungent odours, while the aromatic diketones are crystalline solids. They react characteristically with o-phenylenediamines to give quinoxalines; they form mono- and di-oximes with hydroxylamine and osazones with hydrazines. β- Or 1,3-diketones $R \cdot CO \cdot CH_2 \cdot CO \cdot R$ are obtained by the reaction between an ester and a ketone in the presence of metallic sodium or sodamide. They show acidic properties and form metallic salts, many of which are insoluble in water but soluble in organic solvents. These diketones can exist in keto and enol forms like acetoacetic ester. They react with phenylhydrazine to give pyrazoles, and with hydroxylamine to give iso-oxazoles. They form very stable derivatives (see, e.g., Acetyl-acetonates) with metals. γ- Or 1,4-diketones ($R \cdot CO \cdot CH_2 \cdot CH_2 \cdot CO \cdot R$) are formed by treating acetoacetic ester in the form of its sodium derivative with α-bromoketones and hydrolysing the product. They readily form ring compounds.

2,5-Diketopiperazine, Glycine anhydride,
$C_4H_6N_2O_2$. Crystallizes in plates, subliming at 260°; sparingly soluble in water; hydrolysed by alkalis or mineral acids to glycylglycine. It and substituted diketopiperazines are formed by the condensation of amino-acids, and are obtained in small quantities on the hydrolysis of proteins.

Diketosuccinic acid. Not known in the free

$$HO_2C{-}C{-}C{-}CO_2H$$

with two O atoms double-bonded.

state. Its esters are formed by treating dihydroxytartaric acid with alcohols and a mineral acid. Saponification of these esters gives dihydroxytartaric acid.

Dilatancy. Certain pastes or suspensions (e.g. starch moistened with water) seem to become harder when they are subjected to shearing; in extreme examples, pastes, which are 'wet' enough to flow as a viscous liquid when allowed to stand, will temporarily crumble like a dry, brittle solid if suddenly stirred. This rheological phenomenon, called dilatancy, is the opposite of thixotropy (*q.v.*). It is explained by the friction of the particles against one another; when they are left undisturbed, the particles roll over one another and settle down into minimum volume, but when the medium is subjected to shear, they are forced into a less dense packing and the available fluid is insufficient to fill the interstices. Hence, the material seems dry and hard.

Dilatometer. An apparatus for measuring small changes of volume of a liquid, solution or solid immersed in a liquid. It usually consists of a cylindrical glass bulb with attached capillary tube, and change of volume of the contents of the bulb is noted by observing the movement of the meniscus in the capillary. Dilatometry is useful for determining transition temperatures, rates of reaction, polymerization, etc.

Dilute. A solution is said to be dilute when it contains only a small proportion of the dissolved substance.

Dilution, infinite. The equivalent conductivity (Λ) of dilute electrolyte solutions increases as the solution is further diluted. If Λ is extrapolated to zero concentration, the limiting value, Λ_0, is termed the equivalent conductivity at infinite dilution.

Dimedon, Dimethyldihydroresorcinol,
$C_8H_{12}O_2$. Greenish-yellow needles or prisms, m.p. 148°-149°, sparingly soluble in cold water. It is used as a method of fixing and identifying aldehydes with which it gives crystalline condensation products, and for detecting alcohol after it has been oxidized to acetaldehyde. The crystalline solid, if formed, is filtered off, dried, and identified by m.p. determination.

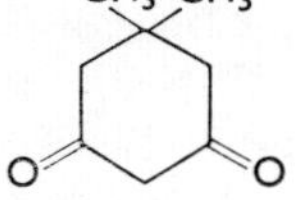

Dimefox. Bis(dimethylamino)phosphorofluoridate, or bis(dimethylamido)fluorophosphine oxide, $C_{14}H_{12}FN_2OP$.
An extremely poisonous, persistent, systemic insecticide, which is usually applied to the roots of plants. It is a colourless, mobile liquid of b.p. 67°/4 mm, miscible with water and most organic solvents, and is prepared from dimethylamine, phosphoryl chloride and potassium fluoride. Dimefox is resistant to hydrolysis and is destroyed by bleaching powder, which is the generally used decontaminant.

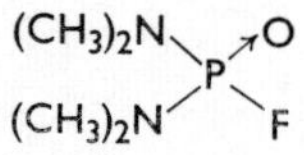

Dimenhydrinate, $C_{17}H_{22}NO \cdot C_7H_6ClN_4O_2$ (trade name Dramamine). The 2-diphenyl-methoxyethyldimethylamine salt of 8-chlorotheophylline. Slightly soluble in water, soluble in alcohol, chloroform, benzene; m.p. 104°. An antihistamine used in the treatment of motion

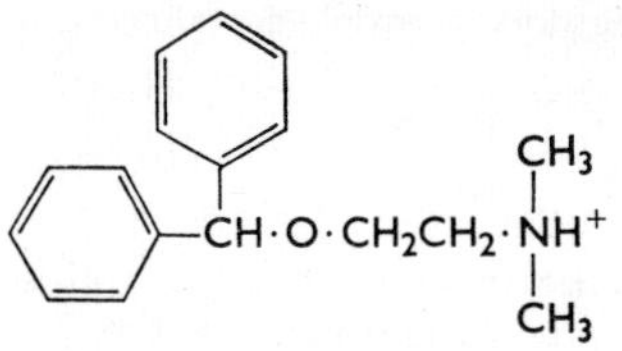

cation

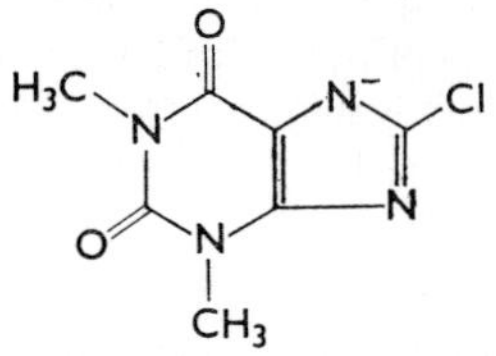

anion

sickness and the prevention of emesis due to other causes.

Dimer. A compound formed by the addition polymerization of two molecules of a monomer.

Dimercaprol. The official pharmacopoeial name for BAL.

Dimethoate. O,O-Dimethyl(N-methylcarbamoylmethyl)phosphorothiolothionate,

$$(CH_3O)_2\overset{\uparrow}{P}SCH_2CONHCH_3$$

$C_5H_{12}NO_3PS_2$. Also known by the trade name 'Rogor'. A systemic insecticide effective against house flies, aphids, mites, leafminers and other insects. The pure substance is a white solid, m.p. 44°-46°, slightly soluble in water, and soluble in most organic solvents. It is prepared by reaction of an alkali metal salt of $(CH_3O)_2P(S)SH$ with N-methyl-α-chloroacetamide. Although toxic to mammals, it is less so than many other organophosphorus insecticides. It is unstable towards alkalis.

Dimethyl acetylenedicarboxylate, $C_6H_6O_4$, $CH_3OOC \cdot C{\equiv}C \cdot COOCH_3$. A lachrymatory liquid, b.p. 195°-198°, which is extensively used as a dienophile in Diels-Alder reactions.

cis-**Dimethylacrylic acid.** See Tiglic acid.

Dimethylamine. See Methylamines.

m-**Dimethylaminophenol,** $C_8H_{11}NO$. Forms colourless needles, m.p. 87°, b.p. 265°-268°. Insoluble in water, easily soluble in alcohol, ether, and benzene. It dissolves in acids and alkalis.

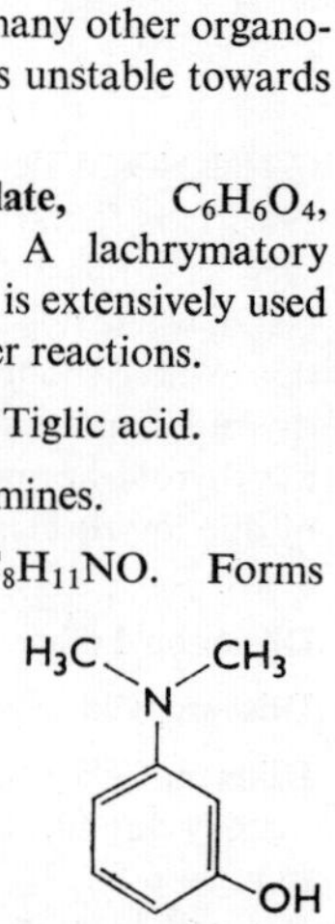

It is prepared by caustic soda fusion of dimethylaniline-*m*-sulphonic acid, or by heating in an autoclave at 125° a mixture of resorcinol, dimethylamine sulphite and dimethylamine solutions.

Other *m*-(alkylamino)phenols are commonly used, and are prepared by analogous methods. They are used as intermediates in the preparation of pyronine and rhodamine dyestuffs.

Dimethylaniline, $C_8H_{11}N$. Colourless oil of characteristic smell, b.p. 193°, density at 20° 0·9575. Insoluble in water, miscible with most organic liquids, volatile in steam, soluble in dilute acid solutions.

It is prepared by heating aniline with methyl alcohol and a little sulphuric acid at 215° in an autoclave.

It condenses with benzaldehyde to give the leuco base of a triphenylmethane dye, malachite green. With formaldehyde gives diphenylmethane derivatives. Nitrous acid gives *p*-nitrosodimethylaniline. Used as a solvent and as a second component in a few azo-dyes.

2,3-Dimethylbutadiene, *βγ*-**Dimethylbutadiene,**

$$H_2C{=}C{-}C{=}CH_2$$
$$\;\;\;\;\;\;\;\; | \;\;\; |$$
$$\;\;\;\;\;\;\;CH_3 \;\; CH_3$$

C_6H_{10}. A colourless liquid, d^{20} 0·7262, b.p. 69·5°. Insoluble in water; miscible with hydrocarbon solvents. Manufactured from acetone by converting this to pinacone and passing its vapour over heated potassium hydrogen sulphate. Exhibits the typical properties of diolefins. Forms a crystalline compound with maleic anhydride, which has m.p. 78°–79°. Slowly changes to a rubber-like substance; the change is hastened by contact with metallic sodium or peroxides. Used in the manufacture of artificial rubber.

Dimethylformamide, DMF. A colourless liquid, b.p. 153°, m.p. −61°, n_D^{25} 1·4269, d_4^{25} 0·9445, miscible with water in all proportions. It is an excellent solvent (dielectric constant at 25°, 36·71) for a large variety of organic and inorganic materials and is widely used as a reaction medium. It can act as a catalyst in certain substitution, elimination and addition reactions; synthetic applications include syntheses of aldehydes (with phosphorus oxychloride) and amines (Leuckart reaction). It is used as a solvent for lacquers, adhesives, dyes, etc.

Dimethylglyoxime, Diacetyl dioxime, $C_4H_8N_2O_2$. Crystallizes in colourless, shining needles, m.p. 234°; begins to sublime at 215°. Insoluble in water; soluble in alcohol. Prepared by the action of hydroxylamine on diacetyl, or by treating methyl ethyl ketone with

$$CH_3 \cdot C{:}NOH$$
$$\;\;\;\;\;\;\; |$$
$$CH_3 \cdot C{:}NOH$$

ethyl nitrite and hydrochloric acid. The diacetyl mono-oxime so formed is then treated with sodium hydroxylamine monosulphonate at 70° and the dimethylglyoxime filtered off. It slowly polymerizes; condenses with *o*-phenylenediamine to give quinoxaline derivatives. Forms a dark-red crystalline solid when added to a solution of a nickel salt. This is insoluble in water and acetic acid, but soluble in mineral acids and alcohol. Under appropriate conditions dimethylglyoxime can be used for the detection and estimation of bismuth, copper, cobalt and palladium. Also used for rot-proofing of certain fibres.

1,1-Dimethylhydrazine, Unsym-dimethylhydrazine $(CH_3)_2NNH_2$. A highly inflammable hygroscopic yellow liquid which fumes in air; m.p. −58°, b.p. 64°, d_{25}^{25} 0·782. It is miscible with water and organic solvents. Prepared industrially from dimethylamine and ammonia in the presence of suitable catalysts. Used in rocket fuels. Corrosive to skin and mucous membranes.

Dimethyl oxalate. See Methyl oxalate.

Dimethyl phthalate. See Phthalic esters.

2,2-Dimethyl-2-silapentane-5-sulphonate, (DSS), $(CH_3)_3SiCH_2CH_2CH_2SO_3Na$. Has been described as a useful water-soluble internal reference for use in PMR spectroscopy (see G. V. D. Tiers and R. I. Cook, *J. Org. Chem.*, **26** (1961) 2097). At the usual reference concentration (0·3–1%) the methyl protons appear as a sharp singlet at 10·00 *τ* but the methylene group protons are a low, broad, featureless multiplet.

Dimethyl sulphate, $(CH_3O)_2SO_2$. A colourless and odourless liquid. Its vapour is extremely poisonous, and any of the liquid spilled on the skin should be washed off with dilute ammonia; d^{15} 1·335, b.p. 188°. Insoluble in water, soluble in alcohol, ether, and benzene. Prepared by adding absolute methyl alcohol to chlorosulphonic acid cooled to −10°. The ester is distilled under reduced pressure. A good methylating agent, it reacts with amines and ammonia to give methylamines, with phenols to give methyl ethers and with organic acids to give methyl esters. If the reaction is carried out below 100°, only one CH_3 group reacts, but at about 140° both groups react.

Dimethyl sulphite, $(CH_3O)_2SO$. A colourless liquid with a faint odour; d_0^0 1·242, b.p. 126°. Insoluble in water, miscible with alcohol, ether, and benzene. Prepared by boiling methyl alcohol with thionyl chloride and distilling the product. Decomposed by boiling water to methyl alcohol and sulphur dioxide. It reacts with organic acids, amines, and alcohols to give methyl esters, methylamines, and methyl ethers. Used as a methylating agent in organic syntheses; it has the advantage that the sulphurous acid produced in these reactions breaks up into water and sulphur dioxide, which can readily be removed.

Dimethyl sulphoxide, DMSO. A colourless, odourless solid, m.p. 18°, b.p. 189°, which is somewhat hygroscopic but a powerful broad spectrum solvent (dielectric constant=48·9 at 20°) for a wide variety of inorganic and organic reactants. Saturated aliphatic hydrocarbons are virtually insoluble in DMSO. Possessing apparently very low toxicity it has found several promising new uses in biology and medicine, especially for low-temperature preservation. The chemical reactions are those of a typical lower aliphatic sulphoxide. With sodium hydride a salt of the anion $[CH_3SOCH_2]^-$ is produced (dimsyl sodium). The anion has several synthetic uses being a powerful nucleophile. Produced by the oxidation of dimethyl sulphide, obtained from Kraft pulping liquors. Many solutes readily ionize in DMSO, which allows extremely high rates of reaction.

Dimorphism. The property possessed by certain crystalline materials of existing in two distinct crystalline forms; such substances are said to be dimorphous.

m-Dinitrobenzene, $C_6H_4N_2O_4$. Forms colourless crystals, m.p. 89·8°, b.p. 302°. Readily soluble in alcohol and benzene, insoluble in water. Very poisonous.

It is prepared in good yield by the direct nitration of benzene or nitrobenzene, only small quantities of the o- and p-dinitro-compounds being produced.

It is much used as an intermediate in the preparation of m-nitroaniline and m-phenylenediamine.

4,6-Dinitro-o-cresol (DNOC), $C_7H_6N_2O_5$. A

yellow crystalline solid, m.p. 86°, with insecticidal, ovicidal and herbicidal properties, prepared from o-cresol by sulphonation followed by nitration. DNOC is almost insoluble in water but soluble in most organic solvents, and forms water-soluble salts with organic and inorganic bases. Due to its herbicidal properties its application for insect control is limited to dormant

sprays. It is poisonous to mammals, and animals should be kept away from sprayed areas for at least two weeks.

Dinitrogen tetroxide. See Nitrogen oxides.

2,4-Dinitrophenylhydrazine, $C_6H_6N_4O_4$. A violet-red crystalline solid, m.p. 197° (decomp.), insoluble in water, sparingly soluble in alcohol. Prepared from 2,4-dinitrochlorobenzene and hydrazine in boiling alcohol. It is an important reagent for aldehydes and ketones (Brady's reagent).

2,4-Dinitrotoluene, $C_7H_6N_2O_4$. Forms colourless needle-shaped crystals, m.p. 71°. Sparingly soluble in cold alcohol and ether, easily soluble in benzene.

It is prepared by the nitration of the mixture of mononitrotoluenes obtained by mildly nitrating toluene.

It is used for the preparation of the corresponding mono- and di-amino-compounds.

Dinoseb. See DNBP.

Diolefins. Hydrocarbons containing two double bonds. They are divided into three classes, according to the position of the double bonds. Compounds of the type —CH=C=CH— are called allenes after the simplest member of the series. They are said to have 'cumulated' double bonds. They react in most cases normally, that is, each double bond is unaffected by the proximity of the other; they are converted by heating into the isomeric acetylenes. Compounds of the type —CH=CH—CH=CH— are said to have 'conjugated' double bonds and react somewhat differently from the other diolefins. For instance, bromine or hydrogen is often added so that a product of the type —CHBr—CH=CH—CHBr— is formed. Also, these hydrocarbons react with maleic anhydride to give derivatives of tetrahydrophthalic anhydride. They show a tendency to form rubber-like polymers. Hydrocarbons not falling into these two classes are said to have 'isolated' double bonds and each reacts normally. See Olefins and Butadienes.

Diorite. A widely distributed igneous rock composed essentially of plagioclase feldspar and hornblende. Extensively quarried for road metal in the Channel Islands and near Mount Sorrel in Leicestershire.

Diosgenin, $C_{27}H_{42}O_3$. M.p. 204°-207°, $[\alpha]_D$ −129° in chloroform. A steroid sapogenin found abundantly in Dioscorea spp. (Mexican yams), and used in very large amounts as one of the principal starting materials for the commercial manufacture of steroid hormones.

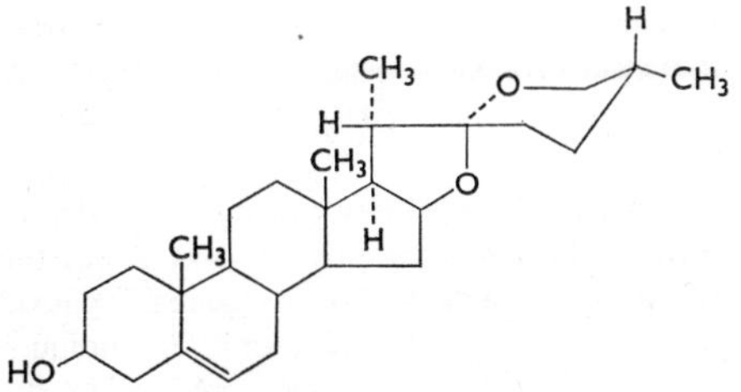

Diosphenol. See Buchucamphor.

Dioxan, 1,4-Diethylene dioxide. A colourless liquid with a faint and not unpleasant odour, d^{20} 1·0329, m.p. 11°, b.p. 101·5°. Miscible with water and organic solvents. Manufactured by heating ethylene glycol with concentrated sulphuric acid or by passing ethylene oxide over solid sodium hydrogen sulphate at 120°. Dioxan is definitely toxic, and possesses a haemolytic action on red blood cells. It forms crystalline complexes with halogens, metallic salts, and nitric and sulphuric acids. Treatment with acetic anhydride in the presence of ferric chloride gives diethylene glycol diacetate. Forms a constant-boiling mixture (b.p. 88°) with 20% water. Used as a solvent for cellulose acetate, resins, waxes, and many organic substances.

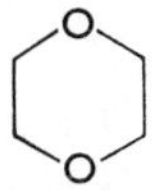

Dipentene. See Limonene.

Diphenan, p-benzylphenyl carbamate, $C_{14}H_{13}NO_2$. A white crystalline powder, m.p.

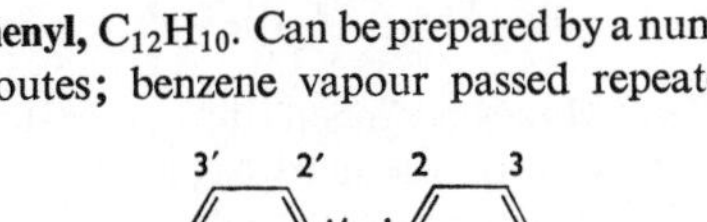

147°-150°, insoluble in water, sparingly soluble in alcohol, soluble in ether. Prepared from p-benzylphenyl chloroformate and ammonia, and used in the treatment of threadworms.

Diphenyl, $C_{12}H_{10}$. Can be prepared by a number of routes; benzene vapour passed repeatedly

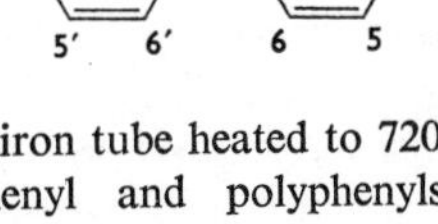

through an iron tube heated to 720° produces much diphenyl and polyphenyls. Bromobenzene when heated with copper powder (Ullman reaction) and the action of chromic or cupric chlorides on phenyl magnesium halide also provide reasonable quantities of diphenyl. It is a volatile, colourless solid which forms large lustrous plates, m.p. 70·5°, b.p. 254°. It is insoluble in water, but soluble in organic

solvents. Uses include its action as a fungistat during shipment of apples and oranges, and as a heat transfer agent.

Diphenylamine, $C_{12}H_{11}N$. Colourless leaflets,

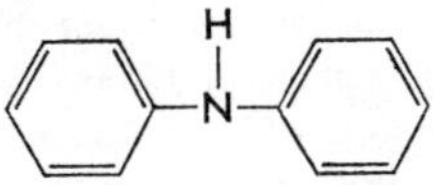

m.p. 54°, b.p. 302°. Insoluble in water, soluble in methyl and ethyl alcohols, and in octane.

Prepared by heating aniline and aniline hydrochloride in an autoclave at 200°.

It is only weakly basic, its salts with mineral acids being hydrolysed by water. Gives a characteristic blue colour when treated in sulphuric acid solution with nitrates or other oxidizing agents. It is also slightly acidic, and gives an N-potassium salt.

Its chief use is as a second component in monoazo dyestuffs.

Diphenylguanidine, $C_{13}H_{13}N_3$. Monoclinic,

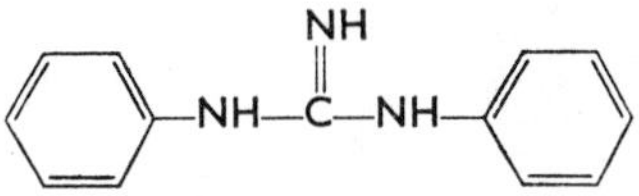

colourless needles, m.p. 147°. Slightly soluble in cold water, easily soluble in alcohol.

Prepared by the action of litharge and ammonia on thiocarbanilide.

Extensively used as a rubber accelerator, particularly when mixed with other accelerators, such as zinc diethyldithiocarbamate.

Diphosgene. See Trichloromethyl chloroformate.

Dipicrylamine, hexanitrodiphenylamine.

$$C_{12}H_5N_7O_{12}$$

Crystallizes from acetic acid in yellow prisms,

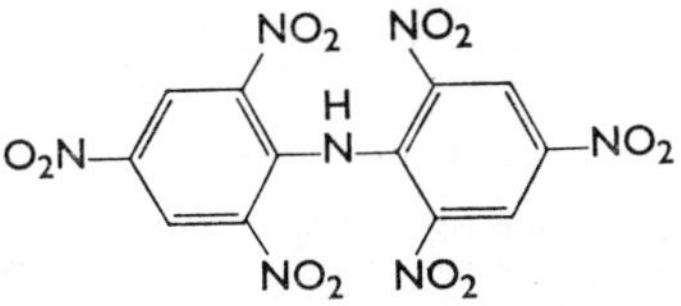

m.p. 234°. It is insoluble in water and ether, but forms water-soluble sodium and ammonium salts. Prepared by treating diphenylamine with nitric acid. It is poisonous and explosive. The formation of an orange red, insoluble potassium salt has been made the basis of a spot test for potassium. The ammonium salt, under the name of aurantia, is used as a dyestuff in certain light filters and as a microscopical stain.

Dipole moment. If in a molecule the centre of action of the positive centre does not coincide with that of the negative centre the molecule may act like a rod carrying a negative and positive charge at either end. Such a molecule will tend to orient itself in an electrical field, and is said to have a *dipole moment* whose magnitude $\mu = es$, where e is the charge on one end, and s the distance separating the charges. Dipole moments give considerable information about the constitution of a molecule. Thus atoms themselves clearly have no dipole moment, because the centre of action of the positive portion (nucleus) is surrounded by a symmetrical arrangement of electrons. In a molecule AB, however, the atom A may have a greater share of the electrons forming the valency bond than has atom B. Hence the molecule has a dipole moment. In more complex molecules consisting of three or more atoms the dipole moment is clearly a measure of the symmetry of their arrangement. It is also possible to determine the moment associated with various linkages, and hence to determine the distribution of polarity in the molecule, and obtain valuable information concerning its structure.

Dipterex. The trade name for dimethyl (1-hydroxy-2,2,2-trichloroethyl)phosphonate,

$$(CH_3O)_2\overset{O}{\underset{|}{P}}CH(OH)CCl_3$$

$C_4H_8Cl_3O_4P$, an organophosphorus insecticide especially active against Diptera (winged insects), and used for the control of flies and cockroaches which have become resistant to certain other insecticides. It is a white solid, m.p. 78°-80°, soluble in water and most organic solvents, and is of low mammalian toxicity. It is made by condensation of chloral with dimethyl hydrogen phosphite, and is decomposed by alkalis.

Diquat, ethylene dipyridylium bromide.

$C_{12}H_{12}Br_2N_2$

A powerful herbicide which is rendered inactive on contact with the soil. Diquat is made by reaction of 2,2'-dipyridyl with ethylene dibromide, and forms yellow crystals, m.p. 335°-340°, containing water of crystallization. It is soluble in water. The main uses of diquat are for plant defoliation and non-selective weedkilling, but although of such high herbicidal activity, it is used in Canada to control corn spurry (*Spergula arvensis*) in oats, the oats quickly recovering from any damage suffered by the application. See also Paraquat.

Diradical. A molecule possessing two separate free electrons, e.g.

$$(C_6H_5)_2\underset{|}{C}\cdot C_6H_4\cdot[CH_2]_4\cdot C_6H_4\cdot\underset{|}{C}(C_6H_5)_2$$

Direct ammonia-recovery process. In order to recover the ammonia present in coal gas the whole of the gas evolved in this process is passed into a bath of sulphuric acid. Ammonium sulphate is formed and recovered as in the semi-direct process (*q.v.*).

Direct or substantive cotton dyes (Salt colours). These substances are for the most part azo-compounds derived from benzidine or from bases which are similar to benzidine in their constitution. They dye cotton and cellulose rayon direct from a neutral bath containing sodium chloride or sodium sulphate. They are inferior with regard to brilliance to basic dyes and to mordant dyes in fastness. Many of these cotton dyes also dye wool, i.e. monosulphonates. They are therefore useful for dyeing wool-cotton union materials. The properties of direct cotton dyes can be correlated with the chemical structure of the dye along definite lines, and are dependent upon the nature of the primary component (diazotized base) rather than on that of the secondary component. They may be divided into three main classes: (1) dyes from tetrazo-compounds; (2) dyes from 'J' acids; (3) dyes from heterocyclic substances. Recently light-fast ranges such as Durazol (I.C.I.), Chlorantin Fast 22 (Ciba), and Sirius Supra (Bayer), have been produced.

Disaccharides. Sugars derived from monosaccharides by the elimination of a water molecule from two monosaccharides.

Disacryl. A polymer of acrolein formed by polymerisation initiated by free radicals. A head-

to-tail vinyl polymer modified by cyclization of most of the aldehyde functions to tetrahydropyran ring systems with some acetal cross-linking.

Disazo dyestuffs. This group can be divided into 'primary' and 'secondary' disazo dyestuffs. The 'primary' are dyes formed by the successive action of two similar or different diazo salts—obtained by the diazotization of monoamines—on an amine, phenol, or aminophenol, whereby the two diazo groups are attached to different carbon atoms of the secondary component. The 'secondary' are compounds made by the combination of diazotized aminoazo dyestuffs with amines and phenols. They are used in the dyeing of wool and cotton. Typical examples are: Naphtol Blue Black, Resorcin Brown, Biebrich Scarlet, Diamond Black F.

Discharge tube. The vessel, usually a glass bulb or tube containing two metal contacts, in which the passage (i.e. the discharge) of electricity occurs through a gas or vapour, is called a discharge tube.

Disc grinder. A machine for fine grinding in which two parallel discs rotate at high speed relative to one another. Material is fed to the centre and works its way outwards under the action of centrifugal force. The discs may be mounted horizontally or vertically and are fitted with renewable grinding surfaces. Sometimes known as an attrition mill.

Dislocation. The observation that pure single crystals are invariably far less strong mechanically than is predicted from the theory of intermolecular forces led to the discovery that all crystals contain various kinds of imperfections.

A dislocation is a line defect in a crystal lattice. An edge dislocation is the boundary of an extra plane of atoms, while a screw dislocation is at the centre of a spiral arrangement of atoms. An applied stress can cause dislocations to move through the crystal, resulting in slip or displacement of the lattice which has been transversed by the dislocation. An edge dislocation causes displacement in the direction of the dislocation movement, i.e. at right angles to the dislocation line, while a screw dislocation results in a shearing movement with the displacement in a direction at right angles to the direction of dislocation movement, i.e. parallel to the dislocation line. When the Burger's vector does not lie in the plane of slip, the dislocation cannot glide and is said to be 'sessile'.

Disperse dyes. These are a class of water insoluble dyes originally introduced for dyeing cellulose acetate, and usually applied from fine aqueous suspensions.

From a chemical standpoint they fall mainly into three classes: (a) nitroarylamine, (b) azo, and (c) anthraquinone. No sulphonic acid groups are present but amino (or substituted amino) groups are usually present.

(a) *Nitroarylamines* are a small group yield-

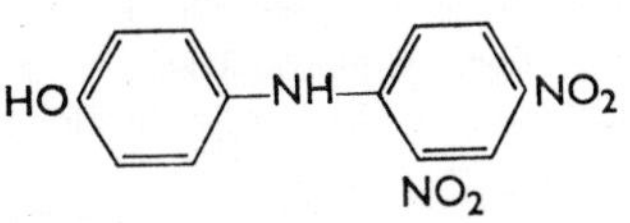

Serisol Fast Yellow A (Y.D.C.), C.I. Disperse Yellow I

ing yellow or orange shades. They were among the earliest disperse dyes.

The fastness to light is moderate but the dye

is still in general use for dyeing acetate rayon and nylon.

(b) *Azo.* A much larger group yielding a full range of shades. An example of the older aminoazo type of dye is Dispersol Diazo Black AS, C.I. Disperse Black 3. It is diazotized on the fibre

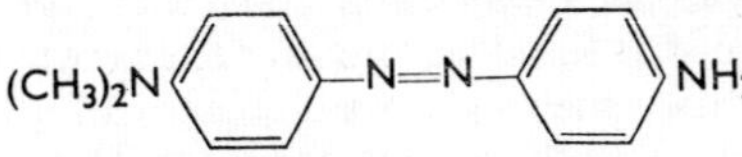

and coupled with 2-hydroxy-3-naphthoic acid to give a bluish-black shade.

A more modern azo dispersed dye is

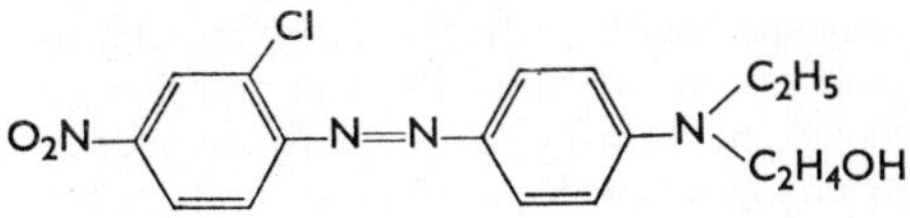

Dispersol Fast Crimson B, Disperse Red 13, a useful dye for acetate rayon giving reddish blue shades of good fastness to light.

(c) *Anthraquinone*—for orange to greenish-blue shades. These are derivatives of α-amino anthraquinones.

1-Aminoanthraquinone itself gives an orange-yellow shade on acetate rayon but is not a commercial dye.

1,4-Diaminoanthraquinone gives a red dye (Duranol Violet 2R, Disperse Violet 1). Very

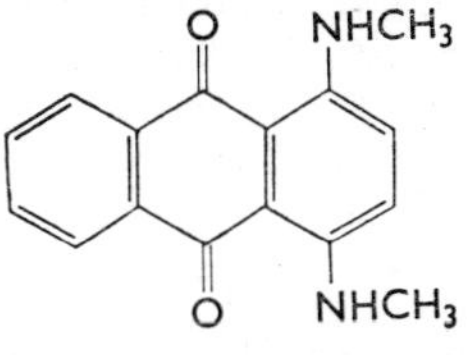

1,4-di(methylamino) anthraquinone
Duranol Brilliant Blue G, Disperse Blue 14

interesting relationships exist between the constitution and the colour of these dyes. Some of the blue and violet aminoanthraquinone dyes are susceptible to 'gas fume fading,' shown by loss of tinctorial value and unpleasant reddening of shade due to the action of oxides of nitrogen resulting from gas combustion. One of the trends, therefore, in modern disperse dye development, is to produce blue dyes which are unaffected by this agency. An example (not an anthraquinone dye) is Artisil Direct Blue GFL, Disperse Blue 20, which is a naphthaquinone-imine derivative, probably

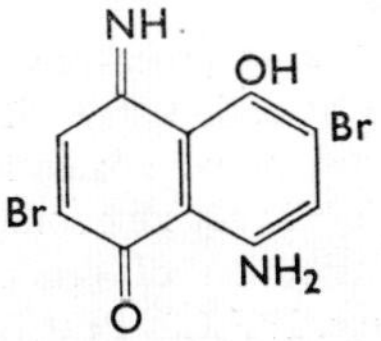

Introduction of a CF_3 group ortho to the susceptible group lowers basicity and gives greater resistance to fading.

The general method of using disperse dyes on acetate rayon is to carefully stir the powder with warm water or, in the case of pastes, gradually to dilute with warm water with stirring. The dye is then added through a fine sieve to the dyebath containing a small quantity of a dispersing or levelling agent. The scoured material is entered at 45°-50°, and the temperature gradually raised to 80° where dyeing continues for $\frac{3}{4}$-1 hour.

Disperse dyes also dye readily on Tricel (cellulose triacetate fibre) by raising the temperature of the dyebath to 100° and on nylon (at 85°). Some disperse dyes dye a different shade on nylon as compared with cellulose acetate, e.g. Serisol Fast Orange GD (similar to C.I. Disperse Orange 3), gives a bright orange shade on cellulose acetate but a dull red on nylon.

Polyacrylic and polyester fibres also dye with disperse dyes although modified dyeing methods have in some cases been found necessary in order to obtain heavy shades. These include high-temperature dyeing, i.e. above 100° under pressure, and the use of carriers such as diphenyl (Tumescal D) and 2-hydroxydiphenyl (Tumescal OP). Although the past few years have shown no outstanding developments in newer types of disperse dyes, there has been steady progress in various directions. This has extended the three chemical types already mentioned, to include methine, ketonimine and aminoketone dyes. The Amichrome dyes are of special interest, as they are pre-metallized disperse dyes which are very suitable for dyeing acrylic fibres.

Progress has been made in producing dyes having higher fastness to sublimation, arising out of the demand for dyed fabrics made from some synthetic fibres, chiefly cellulose triacetate and polyesters, to be pleated at high temperatures. Attention has also been paid to the dyeing of Terylene with disperse dyes and many dye makers now market ranges of these dyes specially chosen for this purpose.

Dispersing agent. A material used in the production of emulsions or dispersions of immiscible liquids or liquid/solid systems. The dispersing agent may lower the surface tension existing between the components (surface tension depressant) or may increase the viscosity of the continuous phase (protective colloid).

Disproportionation. A process in which a compound of one oxidation state decomposes to compounds of two or more oxidation states, e.g. $2Cu^+ \rightarrow Cu + Cu^{2+}$ in aqueous solution. Alternatively a redistribution of groups around a central atom, e.g. $2PF_4Cl \rightarrow PF_3Cl_2 + PF_5$.

Dissociation. The process whereby a molecule is split up into simpler fragments which may be molecules, atoms, free radicals or ions. The term is used particularly in connexion with ionic (electrolytic) dissociation, thermal dissociation, photochemical dissociation.

In the case of molecules in solution or in the gas phase, the extent of dissociation is measured by the dissociation constant K, e.g. when a molecule breaks up to give ions,

$$AB \rightleftharpoons A^+ + B^-$$

$$K = \frac{[A^+][B^-]}{[AB]}$$

where the factors in the brackets represent concentrations or (more accurately) activities.

Disthene. See Kyanite.

Distillation. The process of separating a liquid from a solid or another liquid by vaporising it and then condensing the vapour. See also Fractional distillation.

Distillation column, Distillation tower. The common name for a rectifying or fractionating column. See Rectification.

Distribution law. Another name for the Partition law (*q.v.*).

Disulphiram. See Antabuse.

Diterpene. Diterpenes are unsaturated hydrocarbons of the empirical formula, $C_{20}H_{32}$, which may be considered as dimers of the terpenes. They may contain one or more closed carbon rings. The term is also applied to their simpler derivatives. They are mostly vegetable products. A typical diterpene is α-camphorene. Phytol and abietic acid are diterpene derivatives.

Dithionic acid. See Polythionic acids.

Dithionous acid. See Hydrosulphurous acid.

Dithio-oxamide. See Rubeanic acid.

Dithiothreitol, $C_4H_{10}O_2S_2$. *threo*-2,3-Di-hydroxybutane-1,4-dithiol, a useful water-soluble reagent (Cleland, 1964) for preserving

$$\overset{\displaystyle OH \quad OH}{HS—CH_2—CH—CH—CH_2SH}$$

thiols in the reduced state, and for reducing disulphides quantitatively to dithiols. The *erythro*-isomer is also effective.

Dithizone, diphenylthiocarbazone, $C_{13}H_{12}N_2S$. Obtained as a blue-black solid decomposing at

165°-169°. It is insoluble in water, but soluble in alkalis and chloroform. Prepared by a series of reactions from phenylhydrazine and carbon disulphide. When a chloroform solution of dithizone is shaken with an alkaline aqueous solution of heavy metal salts these metals are extracted into the chloroform layer as dithizonates. The presence of potassium cyanide inhibits the reaction with all metals except lead, bismuth and thallium.

It is used for the extraction and estimation of lead in the presence of heavy metals which would otherwise interfere with normal analytical procedures.

Dithranol, 1,8-dioxyanthranol, $C_{14}H_{10}O_3$. A

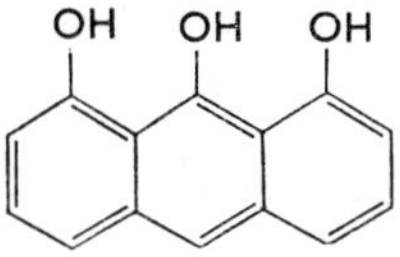

yellow powder, m.p. 174°-178°, insoluble in water, slightly soluble in alcohol, soluble in acetone, benzene, chloroform. It is prepared by the reduction of 1,8-dioxyanthraquinone, and used medicinally for the treatment of psoriasis and other skin diseases.

Divinyl acetylene, C_6H_6.

$$CH_2{=}CH{-}C{\equiv}C{-}CH{=}CH_2.$$

A colourless liquid which turns yellow on exposure to the air; it has a distinct garlic-like odour, d_4^{20} 0·7851, b.p. 83·5°. Manufactured by the controlled, low-temperature polymerization of acetylene in the presence of an aqueous solution of cuprous and ammonium chlorides. It is very dangerous to handle, as it absorbs oxygen from the air to give an explosive peroxide. When heated in an inert atmosphere, it polymerizes to form first a drying oil and finally a hard, brittle resin insoluble in all known solvents. Reacts with chlorine to give a mixture of chlorinated products used as drying oils and plastics.

Divinyl ether, C_2H_6O. $(CH_2{:}CH)_2O$. A colourless, volatile liquid with a characteristic odour, b.p. 28·3°. Insoluble in water; miscible with alcohol and ether. Manufactured by reacting $\beta\beta'$-dichloroethyl ether with fused potassium hydroxide in an atmosphere of ammonia, or by heating the ether under pressure with a solution of potassium hydroxide in ethylene glycol at 210°-240°. It is readily oxidized by light and air to formaldehyde and formic acid: this reaction is inhibited by the addition of 0·01% α-naphthylamine. It slowly polymerizes to a jelly.

Dixon, Harold Baily (1852-1930). Born in London, Dixon was educated at Westminster

School, from which he obtained a classical scholarship to Christ Church, Oxford. There he studied both classics and science and, in 1879, was appointed to a lectureship. In 1886 he went to Manchester as successor to Sir Henry Roscoe at Owens College. His work upon gaseous explosions opened a new era in combustion research. See *J. Chem. Soc.*, 1931, 3349.

DMF. See Dimethyl formamide.

DMSO. See Dimethyl sulphoxide.

DNA. See Nucleic acids.

DNBP, Dinoseb, 2-*sec*-butyl-4,6-dinitrophenol, $C_{10}H_{12}N_2O_5$. A powerful insecticide the application of which, like DNOC, is limited by its phytotoxicity to use on dormant trees. As

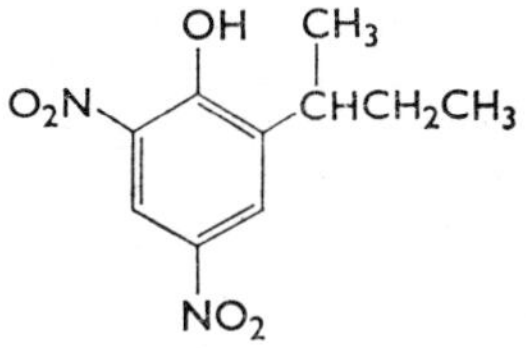

a herbicide it shows selective properties, and its amine salts can be used for weed control in certain crops such as leguminous plants.

DNBP is a yellow solid, m.p. 42° when pure, but the technical material is a red-brown oil. It is insoluble in water but soluble in most organic solvents, and is manufactured either by nitration of *o-sec*-butylphenol, or by sulphonation of phenol, followed by butylation and nitration. It forms salts with organic and inorganic bases, which are yellow to red solids. DNBP is toxic to mammals.

DNOC. See 4,6-Dinitro-*o*-cresol.

Döbereiner, Johann Wolfgang (1780-1849). Born at Hof near Jena, Döbereiner studied pharmacy at Münchberg and early developed great ability for chemical research. In 1810 he was appointed professor of chemistry at Jena. In 1829 he announced the existence of 'triads' among the elements; other problems which he studied included fermentation and pneumatic chemistry.

Doctor treatment. A process employed in the sweetening of petrols and kerosines by treating with a sodium plumbite solution, thus converting mercaptans, which give the product a disagreeable odour, to less noxious compounds.

A modification of this reaction is used to test for the presence of mercaptans in petroleum fractions (the Doctor test).

Dodge crusher. The trade name of a well-known type of jaw crusher (*q.v.*).

Doebner-von Miller reaction. Condensation of an aromatic amine with an aldehyde or ketone in the presence of hydrochloric acid to form a quinoline derivative. This is a general method, and has been used to prepare a large number of substituted quinolines. Thus aniline and paraldehyde give 2-methylquinoline (quinaldine) and *p*-phenetidine.

Dolerite. A widely distributed igneous rock composed essentially of plagioclase feldspar and augite; SiO_2 48-52%. Much quarried for road metal.

Dolomite. The double carbonate of magnesium and calcium, $MgCO_3.CaCO_3$. The purest form of the mineral, sometimes termed 'dolomite spar,' forms colourless or white rhombohedral crystals, sp. gr. 2·85, hardness, 3·5-4. The term is more loosely used for all mixtures of the two carbonates in the very common 'dolomite rock' or magnesian limestone, which is used for building purposes and for the basic linings of Bessemer converters and open-hearth steel furnaces. It is one of the most important raw materials for the production of magnesium and its salts.

Donnan, Frederick George (1870-1956). Born at Holywood, Co. Down, Ireland, Donnan was educated at Queen's University, Belfast, and later studied at Leipzig, Berlin, and London. In 1904 he was appointed professor of physical chemistry and director of the Muspratt Laboratory, Liverpool, and in 1913 became professor of chemistry, University College, London. His researches were in the field of physical chemistry, particularly colloid chemistry. He was elected F.R.S. and created C.B.E. in 1920. In 1928 he was awarded the Davy Medal of the Royal Society. He was President of the Chemical Society 1937-1939. See *Proc. Chem. Soc.*, 1957, 362.

Donnan membrane equilibrium. This concerns the distribution of ions on each side of a membrane separating two portions of a solution of an electrolyte, e.g. NaCl, in water; on one side of the membrane a polyelectrolyte, e.g. a protein, is introduced, the molecules and ions of which cannot pass through the membrane. The distribution of the NaCl on the two sides of the membrane will be unequal and a membrane potential will be established. The theory of such systems, which are of importance in biology, was fully worked out by Donnan.

Donor. See Co-ordinate bond.

Dopa. See 3,4-Dihydroxyphenylalanine.

Dorr agitator. See Air-lift agitator.

Dorrco filter. See Internal drum filter.

Double bond. It is possible for atoms to share two pairs of electrons between them and thus to form a double bond between them. Thus

ethylene, , has a double bond. A double is stronger than a single bond although it is more reactive. More formally a double bond arises from overlap of *p* orbitals of two atoms which are already united by overlap of *s* orbitals. See Pi-bonding, Sigma bonds.

Double layer. See Electrical double layer.

Double-pipe crystallizer. This consists essentially of a length of jacketed pipe with the liquid from which crystallization is occurring flowing through the inner pipe, and a cooling medium flowing in the opposite direction through the annulus. The inner pipe contains a rotating axial shaft with scraper blades attached to it, so that solid deposited on the cold walls is immediately removed. High heat-transfer coefficients result from this continuous scraping action, and the apparatus is thus suitable for highly viscous liquids. It is widely used in the petroleum industry for the crystallizing of paraffin wax.

Double refraction. Having different refractive indices in different crystallographic directions.

Double salt. When equivalent quantities of certain salts are mixed in aqueous solution, and the solution is evaporated, a salt may be formed with physical properties entirely different from those of either of the individuals. For example, solutions of ferrous sulphate and ammonium sulphate yield ferrous ammonium sulphate, $FeSO_4$, $(NH_4)_2SO_4$, $6H_2O$. In aqueous solution, however, the salt behaves like a mixture of the individual sulphates, because any complex ions formed are unstable, and readily dissociate into the simple ions of the original salts in aqueous solution. Such compounds are termed *double salts*, in contra-distinction to complex salts. They are weak, easily dissociated complexes.

Dow, Herbert Henry (1866-1930). Dow was born at Belleville, Ontario, and educated at the Case School of Applied Science. He founded the Dow Chemical Co. to develop the brine of northern Michigan, from which a large range of chemicals, notably bromine and alkalis, is now produced. Awarded the Perkin Medal for 1930.

Dow process. The process for the extraction of magnesium from sea-water by precipitation of the hydroxide by lime followed by solution of the hydroxide in hydrochloric acid.

Dowtherm. Mixtures of high-boiling organic substances used for purposes of heat exchange. Dowtherm A is a eutectic mixture of diphenyl oxide (73·5%) and diphenyl (26·5%); it has the characteristic geranium-like odour of diphenyl oxide, m.p. 12·0°, b.p. 258°. Used for heating over the range 16°-400°. Dowtherm C consists mainly of the various isomers of diphenylbenzene, m.p. 21°-172°, b.p. 316°-427°. Used for heating over the range 159°-420°.

Drag-link conveyor, Drag-chain conveyor. A machine for the conveying of particulate solids, consisting of a trough along which the material is dragged by means of a chain buried in it. The chain links are frequently specially shaped with flat vertical surfaces for propelling the material.

Dramamine. A trade name for dimenhydrinate.

Draper, John William (1811-1882). Born at St. Helens, near Liverpool, Draper studied chemistry at University College, London, but, in 1833, he emigrated to the United States, where he graduated in medicine at the University of Pennsylvania. In 1839 he became professor of chemistry in the University of New York, and from 1850-1873 was president of its medical department. He published numerous researches on photochemistry, and was also known as a writer on historical subjects. See *American Journal of Science*, **23**, 163-166.

Drier, Dryer. A plant or apparatus for drying a material. See also Dryers, industrial.

Drikold. A commercial name for solid carbon dioxide.

Drip point. A term used in laboratory distillation tests; it means the temperature at which the first drop of distillate falls from the end of the condenser.

Dropping-mercury electrode. The electrode consists of a column of mercury passing through a fine capillary and emerging, in small drops, in a solution. It is used in polarography.

Drum dryers. These are used for producing a dry solid from a solution or slurry. The liquid is fed on to a slowly rotating steam-heated drum, where evaporation occurs and a coating of solid is left adhering to the surface. This is removed by a knife. Sometimes two drums are used, set close together and rotating in opposite directions.

By enclosing drying drums in a larger vacuum vessel, vacuum drying may be achieved.

Drummond, Sir Jack Cecil (1891-1952). A graduate of London University, Drummond was appointed director of biochemical research, Cancer Hospital, London, in 1918. Later he became reader in physiological chemistry (1919), and professor of biochemistry (1922) at University College, London. In 1945 he was appointed research director to Boots Pure Drug Co., Ltd. He was knighted in 1944 for his work as scientific adviser to the Ministry of Food. See *J. Chem. Soc.* 1953, 357.

Dryers, industrial. Gases are dried using such equipment as fixed-bed adsorbers and packed absorption columns, while liquids may be dried by distillation. See Adsorption industrial, Gas absorption, Rectification.

In the case of solids a variety of equipment and techniques are used. For descriptions of some of the more important of these see Drum dryers, Freeze drying, Rotary driers, Spray drying, Tray drier, Tunnel drier.

Dry ice. Solid carbon dioxide.

Drying. 1. The removal of small quantities of water from a liquid or gas by physical or chemical means. 2. The removal of water from a solid by applying heat so that evaporation occurs.

In the case of a solid, *drying* also occasionally refers to liquids other than water.

Dry screening. A process in which the moisture content of the material fed to the screening plant has reached equilibrium with the air, or has been reduced by drying until all surface moisture and moisture between particles has been removed, permitting the powder to flow freely.

Duhamel du Monceau, Henri Louis (1700-1782). Born in Paris, Duhamel was both botanist and engineer; for many years he held office as inspector-general of marine. His association with chemistry is due to the fact that he was the first to discover that soda is derived from the same base as common salt.

Dulcin, Sucrol, *p* - Ethoxyphenylurea, $C_9H_{12}N_2O_2$. Colourless crystals, m.p. 171°-172°,

soluble in hot water and organic solvents. It can be prepared by refluxing acetylurea with *p*-phenetidine and other similar methods. It is used as a sweetening agent, being about 200 times as sweet as cane sugar.

Dulcitol, $C_6H_{14}O_6$. The alcohol from galactose,

it is of wide occurrence in plants. It forms monoclinic columns, m.p. 198°, and is optically inactive.

Dulcolux. See Bisacodyl.

Dulong, Pierre Louis. Born in 1785 at Rouen, became professor of chemistry at the École Polytechnique, Paris. In 1811 he discovered nitrogen trichloride. In conjunction with Petit he showed that the specific heats of many elements were in inverse proportion to their atomic weights. He died in 1838 .

Dulong and Petit's law. Dulong and Petit showed that the specific heat of a metallic element multiplied by its atomic weight approximates to 6·2. This is not true of all metals, or of several non-metals at ordinary temperatures, but it is also true of these at high temperatures.

Dumas, Jean Baptiste André (1800-1884). Dumas was born at Alais, in the south of France. After some years spent as an apprentice with an apothecary, he took up the study of physiological chemistry, and rapidly rose to prominence among the leading men of science. He held various teaching appointments, including the chairs of chemistry at the Sorbonne, the École Polytechnique and the École de Médicine. A man of great vitality, he made many important contributions, not only to organic, but to inorganic chemistry.

Dumas' method for determining vapour densities. This method consists in determining the weight of a known volume of vapour contained in a glass bulb.

Dumas' method for the estimation of nitrogen in a compound involves the copper oxide oxidation and subsequent copper reduction of the contained nitrogen, to nitrogen gas, which can be measured.

Durain. A macroscopic constituent of coal which exists in solid bands of varying thickness. It has a finely granular structure with a dull or greyish appearance. The texture is firm or hard.

Under the microscope, microspores and macrospores are sometimes visible but the section may often be only semi-opaque. Two sub-varieties are recognized, grey durains and black durains. The former contain less hydrogen and volatile matter than the latter.

Duralumin. See Aluminium alloys.

Duriron. An iron alloy containing silicon 14-15%, manganese 2-2·5%, carbon 0·8-1·3%, and sulphur 0·05-0·2%. It is particularly resistant to the action of acids and can be used in chemical plant where this property is required.

Dutch metal. An alloy of copper and zinc prepared in leaf form in imitation of gold leaf.

du Vigneaud, Vincent (1901-   ). Born in Chicago and graduating from the University of Illinois, du Vigneaud in 1932 was head of the biochemistry department at George Washington University and in 1938 at Cornell. Working on many aspects of biochemistry, particularly on naturally-occurring sulphur-containing compounds, he was the first to elucidate the structure of and to synthesize a polypeptide—the hormone oxytocin. He was awarded the Nobel Prize for chemistry in 1955.

Dynamites. Nitroglycerin, being too sensitive to shock and friction to be used alone as an explosive, is mixed with other materials to form dynamites, which are much safer to handle. The simplest type of dynamite consists of nitroglycerin mixed with kieselguhr, an inert base, but there are more powerful forms of dynamite which have an explosive base, such as a nitrate mixed with wood meal, etc. Small amounts of calcium carbonate are often added to neutralize any acid formed by decomposition of the nitroglycerin and so improve the keeping properties of the explosive. A disadvantage of most dynamites is the readiness to freeze. Frozen dynamites may not detonate properly and when thawed they tend to exude nitroglycerin. In nonfreezing dynamites for use in cold regions the nitroglycerin is partly replaced by diethyleneglycol dinitrate (*q.v.*).

Dysprosium, Dy. At.no. 66. At.wt. 159·2. *d* 8.536. Dysprosium has the hexagonal close-packed structure, $a = 3·5923$, $c = 5·654$ Å. See Rare earths.

Dysprosium compounds. Dysprosium forms a single series of very pale yellow-green salts, the metal being in the tripositive state. These salts are typical rare-earth compounds (*q.v.*). There is evidence for formation of a complex fluoride containing Dy (IV).

E

Ebonite. Also known as hard rubber or vulcanite. The hard black product made by vulcanizing mixtures in which the rubber:sulphur ratio usually lies between 65:35 and 70:30. Generally less than 4% of the sulphur remains uncombined. The composition approaches the empirical formula, C_5H_8S (rubber hydrocarbon:sulphur::68:32). The material has good chemical and electrical properties.

Ecdysone. An insect hormone, required together with 'Juvenile hormone' (*q.v.*) for larval moulting. Crystalline ecdysone from silkworm pupae

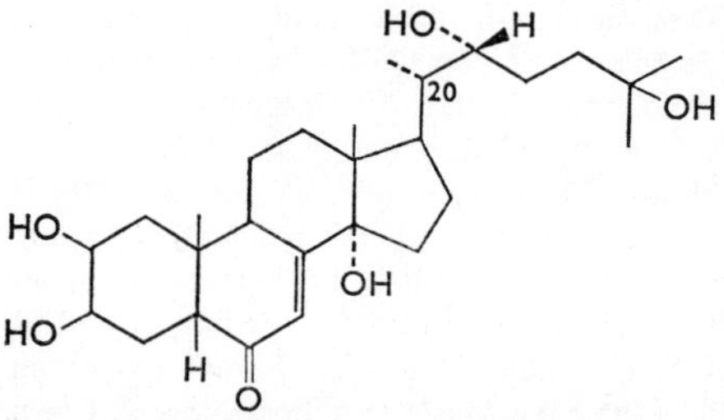

has been shown by degradation, X-ray crystallography, and synthesis to have the structure shown. The related hormone, crustecdysone, from crustaceans, possesses an additional hydroxyl group at C-20. These compounds are of interest as the first natural cholestane derivatives showing high biological activity.

Ecgonine, 3-hydroxy-2-tropanecarboxylic acid, $C_9H_{15}NO_3$. The major portion of the cocaine molecule, from which it may be obtained by hydrolysis with acid. Benzoylation and methylation reconvert it to cocaine. A colourless crystalline material, m.p. 198°, soluble in water, but only sparingly soluble in organic solvents, $[\alpha]_D^{15}$ $-45°$. Although neutral to litmus it forms a stable hydrochloride, m.p. 246°. See Cocaine.

Eclipsed. See Conformation.

Edestin. A protein, belonging to the globulin class, obtained from hemp seeds. It has been obtained crystalline and its molecular weight is about 290,000.

Edge runner mill, Pan crusher. One or more heavy verticle wheels or *mullers*, resting on a stout horizontal pan, are connected by arms to a vertical drive shaft. Rotation of the shaft causes the wheels to travel around the edge of the pan, crushing material fed to it by their weight. This type of mill is suitable for both wet and dry grinding, and can also handle sticky materials such as clays.

EDTA. Ethylenediamine tetra-acetic acid.

Effective atomic number rule. Most generally applied to metal carbonyls and organometallic derivatives the rule states that the total number of electrons available to the element from its own outer shells and by donation of lone pairs from the ligands is equal to the number of electrons of the next rare gas.

Efflorescence. When the vapour pressure exerted by a salt hydrate is greater than the partial pressure of water vapour in the atmosphere, the hydrate loses some of its water of crystallization to the atmosphere. The phenomenon is known as efflorescence.

Effusion. The passage of a gas through an orifice which has a diameter smaller than the mean free path of the gas molecules. The rate of effusion is proportional to the area of the orifice and to the mean velocity of the molecules (and hence to the reciprocal of the square root of the molecular weight of the gas). This principle is employed experimentally for investigating low vapour pressures and the molecular weight of gaseous species (e.g. in high-temperature equilibria); the apparatus used is called a Knudsen cell.

Egyptian blue. An important pigment in Ancient Egyptian times and up to the 7th century A.D. but not now made commercially. It consists of a double silicate of copper and calcium (CaO, CuO, $4SiO_2$ approx.).

Ehrlich, Paul (1854-1915). Ehrlich, the founder of chemotherapy, was born at Strehlen, in Silesia, and educated at Breslau, Strasburg, Freiburg, and Leipzig. In 1878 he became an assistant to v. Frerichs at the Erste Medizinische Klinik der Charité, Berlin. In 1896 he was appointed Director of the Institut für Serumforschung und Serumprüfung at Steglitz, and in 1899 took charge of the Institut für experimentelle Therapie at Frankfurt. He also became Director of the Georg Speyer Haus für Chemotherapie on its establishment in 1906. His discovery of salvarsan was the most remarkable achievement in a long series of outstanding investigations, and in 1908 he was awarded, jointly with Metchnikoff, the Nobel Prize for Medicine.

Eigen function. In wave mechanics, the Schrödinger equation may be written using the Hamiltonian Operator H as

$$H\psi = E\psi$$

Only certain energy values (E) will lead to solutions of this equation. The corresponding values of the wave functions are called eigen functions or characteristic wave functions.

Einstein, Albert (1879-1956). Born in Württemberg of Jewish patents, Einstein took his Ph.D. at the University of Zürich and was appointed extraordinary professor of theoretical physics there in 1909. He revolutionized theoretical physics with the production of the special theory of relativity in 1905. The general theory followed in 1915. In 1915 he was made director of the Kaiser Wilhelm Physical Institute in Berlin. He emigrated to the U.S.A. during the Hitler régime, and became professor of mathematics at the Institute of Advanced Study at Princeton in 1933. He won the Nobel prize for physics in 1921.

Einstein. A unit of radiant energy. If every molecule in a gram molecule of a substance absorbs one quantum of light, the total energy absorbed is $Nh\nu$, where N is the Avogadro number, that is, the number of molecules in one gram molecule, h is Planck's constant, and ν the frequency of the light. $N = 6.06 \times 10^{23}$; $h = 6.548 \times 10^{-27}$ erg sec., and therefore for red light of frequency 4×10^{14}, one Einstein $= 1.588 \times 10^{11}$ ergs. Also, one gram calorie $= 4.184 \times 10^7$ ergs, hence one Einstein $= 3.79 \times 10^4$ calories.

Einstein's law of photochemical equivalence. Before a chemical reaction can be induced by light, the light must be absorbed by some of the molecules present. Einstein proposed that each molecule reacting must be excited by the absorption of one quantum of light. This principle is not easy to test, because the occurrence of secondary reactions following the primary reaction may lead to destruction of many more molecules of the absorbing substance. Thus the apparent reaction induced by a single quantum of light may be much greater than that calculated from Einstein's law. Further, some of the excited molecules may lose their energy by fluorescing, or by colliding with other molecules without reacting, so that the yield of reaction products is only a fraction of that calculated from Einstein's law. The law is, however, considered to hold for the primary act of light absorption.

Einsteinium, Es. At.no. 99. Isotopes of einsteinium of mass ranging from 245 to 256 have been prepared by bombardment of other transuranic elements. The first identification of einsteinium was in the debris from thermonuclear explosions. The most stable isotopes of einsteinium, ^{252}Es and ^{254}Es, have half-lives of 140 and 280 days respectively. As far as can be seen from ion-exchange studies, in solution einsteinium behaves as a typically tripositive actinide ion.

Ejector. A simple non-mechanical device used for the pumping of liquids and gases. Fluid under pressure is fed through a jet into the entrance of a venturi tube. Due to the venturi effect the fluid being pumped is entrained and passes into the venturi tube also. The mixed stream then passes into the discharge line.

Ejectors may be operated by either liquid or gas. Having no moving parts they are relatively easy to make corrosion resistant and are used for moving acids and alkalis. *Steam jet ejectors* are widely used as vacuum pumps, especially with distillation and evaporation plant. The water-operated vacuum pump used in the laboratory is a familiar example of an ejector.

Elaidic acid, $C_{18}H_{34}O_2$.

$$CH_3 \cdot [CH_2]_7 \cdot CH : CH \cdot [CH_2]_7 \cdot COOH$$

Crystallizes in plates, m.p. 46·5°, soluble in alcohol and ether. It is the *trans*-isomer of oleic acid, and is prepared from it by treatment with isomerizing agents, of which 0·3% selenium at 150°-220° is the most effective. The product is an equilibrium with about 66% elaidic acid and 34% oleic acid, from which elaidic acid is obtained by crystallization from acetone.

Elastase. A proteinase of mammalian pancreas named from its ability to hydrolyse elastin. Hydrolysis of peptides by elastase occurs internally at bonds linking amino-acids which possess non-polar (alkyl) side chains.

Elastico-viscosity. See Visco-elasticity.

Elastin. The protein of elastic tissue, ligaments, and arterial walls. It is structurally related to collagen, but contains about 30% each of glycine and leucine and about 15% of proline.

Elastomer. The term used to describe a synthetic polymer which, although chemically different, shows considerable physical similarities to natural rubber (see Rubber).

Electrical double layer. An electrical double layer is generally formed at the interface between two phases. One phase acquires a net positive charge and the other a net negative charge. The first quantitative investigation of this phenomenon was by Helmholtz (1879) who, using a parallel plate condenser as his model, assumed that there existed a compact double layer at the ionised surface. This was later modified by Gouy who suggested that although the inner ionic layer of the double layer is rigid (owing to absorbed or structural ions) the outer layer is more diffuse and extends a few mμ from the surface. Thus a negatively-charged dropping mercury electrode would be surrounded by an ionic sheath in which the proportion of positive ions decreases and that of negative ions increases with increasing distance from the interface. Stern (1924) improved on the model by combining the essential characters of both the rigid and diffuse double layer theories.

Electrochemical equivalent. The weight of an element liberated from its ions or converted into them by unit quantity of electricity (1 coulomb) is called the electrochemical equivalent of the element.

Electrochemical series. Standard electrode potentials of the elements (see Electrode potential) vary from $+3\cdot045$ volts for lithium to $-2\cdot65$ volts for fluorine. The elements may thus be arranged in a series in order of decreasing standard electrode potential.

$$
\begin{array}{ll}
Li \rightarrow Li^+ & +3\cdot045 \text{ V} \\
K \rightarrow K^+ & +2\cdot925 \text{ V} \\
Zn \rightarrow Zn^{2+} & +0\cdot763 \text{ V} \\
Cd \rightarrow Cd^{2+} & +0\cdot403 \text{ V} \\
Ni \rightarrow Ni^{2+} & +0\cdot250 \text{ V} \\
Sn \rightarrow Sn^{2+} & +0\cdot136 \text{ V} \\
Cu \rightarrow Cu^{2+} & -0\cdot337 \text{ V} \\
Cl^- \rightarrow \tfrac{1}{2}Cl_2 & -1\cdot360 \text{ V} \\
Au \rightarrow Au^{3+} & -1\cdot50 \text{ V} \\
F^- \rightarrow \tfrac{1}{2}F_2 & -2\cdot65 \text{ V}
\end{array}
$$

The complete series is called the electrochemical series. The electrode potential is a measure of the tendency of an element to pass into solution in the form of its ions; the more positive the potential, the greater is this tendency. Hence any metal higher up the series will tend to displace from solution the ions of another metal lower down the series, e.g. copper is readily deposited

212

as the metal by placing a piece of zinc or iron in an aqueous solution of copper sulphate.

Electrochemistry. This term has a very wide significance, and is often understood to apply to all branches of science concerned with chemical reactions which are induced by electricity in any form, or which are accompanied by electrical phenomena. Such a definition includes the study of electrolysis, of gaseous reactions occurring in an electrical glow discharge, in an electric spark, or in an electric arc, as well as those processes accompanied by the emission of electrons or ions, e.g. radioactive transformations, and the photo-electric effect. In practice electrochemistry is generally meant to apply to that branch of chemistry concerned with electrolysis, and other like phenomena accompanying the passage of a current through the solution of an electrolyte, or concerned with the behaviour of ions in aqueous solution, or in other ionizing solvents.

Electrode. An electro-conducting body dipping into an electrolyte and exhibiting a certain electrical potential with respect to the bulk of the electrolyte.

Electrode potential. When an electrode of any ion-forming element is placed in a solution containing ions of this element a certain electrical potential is exhibited by the electrode. This is dependent on both electrode and solution and is called the electrode potential of the element. As long as no net current flows between an electrode and solution there exists a state of thermodynamic equilibrium at the electrode, which is said to behave reversibly. The potential of the electrode in this state is called the reversible electrode potential and depends on the concentration of those ions in the solution which are in equilibrium with the material of the electrode. The reversible electrode potential of an element in solution at unit activity of its ions, measured against the reversible electrode potential at unit activity of H_3O^+ ions (taken arbitrarily as zero), is termed the standard electrode potential of the element.

If an appreciable current flows across the boundary between an electrode and solution, thus disturbing the thermodynamic conditions of equilibrium, the electrode is said to be polarized and its potential is then termed 'irreversible'.

The sign given to the potential is arbitrary, but for a reaction $A \to A^+$ which tends to occur spontaneously the sign must be positive. Conversely if $B^+ \to B$ tends to occur spontaneously this potential must be positive.

Electrodialysis. The diffusion of electrolytes through a membrane is considerably accelerated, and the purification of a colloidal sol becomes more rapid if the dialyser compartment is placed between electrodes connected to a source of direct electric current. This process is known as electrodialysis.

Electrodispersion. If an arc is struck between two metal electrodes under the surface of a liquid, particles are torn off the metal and remain colloidally dispersed in the liquid. By this means Bredig prepared colloidal dispersions of most of the metals. This process of electrodispersion is improved if the arc is maintained within a silica tube and the vaporized metal blown through a small hole in front of the arc into the dispersion medium by means of a stream of inert gas. See Colloids.

Electrokinetic potential. This is frequently called the zeta (ζ) potential and is the potential difference across the diffuse part of the double layer, i.e. between the rigid solution layer and the mobile part of the solution adjacent to the bulk solution. See Electrical double layer.

Electrokinetics. Electrophoresis is one of several effects, collectively known as electrokinetic phenomena, which are met in systems with electrical double layers at the interface between a solid and a liquid (generally aqueous) or between one liquid and another. The other effects are electro-osmosis, streaming potential, and sedimentation potential. They all arise from a partial separation of the fixed and mobile parts of the electrical double layer.

Electrolysis. The process of decomposing a substance, usually either molten or in solution, by the passage of an electric current.

Electrolysis, laws of. See Faraday's laws of electrolysis.

Electrolyte. A substance which is dissociated partly or completely into ions in solution, and thus readily permits the passage of an electric current, is called an electrolyte. If an electrolyte has a dissociation constant greater than about 10^{-2} it is termed a strong electrolyte.

Electrolytic dissociation. The process of the formation of ions in solution from an added solute. In the case of solid solutes having an ionic lattice (e.g. NaCl) there is probably a complete dissociation into ions in dilute solution. For other types of solute (e.g. HCl) there is probably an equilibrium between the ions and the undissociated molecules.

Electromagnet. An electromagnet consists of a coil of wire wound round an iron or other metal core. On passing an electric current through the wire, the core behaves exactly like a permanent magnet.

Electrometer. An instrument for detecting and

measuring the magnitude of an electrical charge is termed an electrometer.

Electrometric titrations. During a titration there is a rapid change in the concentration of all reacting species at the end point. An inert electrode immersed in the solution thus shows a rapid change in electromotive force near the equivalence point, which may thus be ascertained by observing the change in e.m.f. of the electrode during the neutralization. The process is called electrometric titration. The method is of especial service when coloured solutions are under examination, when colour indicators are often useless.

Electron. The electron is the ultimate indivisible negative charge, or particle of negative electricity, and forms an integral part of every atom of matter. The mass of an electron is 1/1840 of that of a hydrogen atom.

Electron affinity. The energy released when an ion is formed in the gaseous state by the combination of an atom and an electron, e.g.

$$A + e \rightarrow A^-$$

The electron affinities for the halogen atoms are

$$F = 95, Cl = 86, Br = 84, I = 73 \text{ kcal.}$$

Electron affinities may be calculated using the Born-Haber cycle.

Electron alloys. See Magnesium alloys.

Electron-deficient compounds. A term applied to compounds in which there are apparently insufficient electrons to give every atom a filled-shell electron configuration whilst retaining the maximum number of nearest neighbours around each atom. If theory based on overlap of more than two atomic orbitals (multicentre bonds) is used the bonding in electron-deficient compounds may be rationalized.

Electron density. In the investigation of molecular structure by X-rays the electron density distribution which is calculated is mapped out and contour diagrams made by drawing lines of equal electron density are constructed. Using such diagrams accurate bond lengths may be derived.

In theories of bonding the term is often used to indicate the probability of finding an electron at a particular point.

Electron diffraction. Since all matter has both particle and wave properties the wave properties of electrons may be used in diffraction experiments. They have been used in the determination of molecular structures in the gas-phase and also in the investigation of surfaces.

Electronegativity. The power of an atom in a stable molecule to attract electrons to itself. Thus in covalently bonded hydrogen chloride, HCl,

the electrons are much closer to the chlorine than to the hydrogen. It is measured from the dipole moment and various other functions of the molecules.

Electronic configuration. (a) Atoms. The electronic configuration of an atom is the basis of the properties of the atom: the chemical properties are determined by the electronic configuration of the outer shells. Each electron has four characteristic quantum numbers which are interrelated:

(i) Principal quantum number, represented by n and having values 1, 2, 3 . . .; this denotes the overall size and energy of the electron.

(ii) The azimuthal quantum number, represented by l and having values 0, 1, 2 . . . to $n-1$. This denotes the angular momentum and thus shape of the orbital. Azimuthal quantum numbers with $l = 0$, 1, 2, and 3 are also called s, p, d, and f respectively.

(iii) A magnetic quantum number, represented by m. and having values $-l$, $-l+1$, . . . 0 . . . $l-1$, 1. This denotes the orientation of the orbital. For any value of n there are one s orbital, three p orbitals, five d orbitals, and seven f orbitals.

(iv) A spin quantum number $s = \pm \frac{1}{2}$.

An s orbital is spherically symmetrical and can take a maximum of two electrons with opposing spins. A p orbital has a solid figure-of-eight shape; there are three equivalent p orbitals for each principal quantum number; they correspond to the three axes of rectangular coordinates. The d and f orbitals have more complex shapes; there are five equivalent d orbitals and seven equivalent f orbitals for each principal quantum number, each orbital taking two electrons with opposing spins.

The above definitions must be qualified by stating that for principal quantum number 1 there are only s orbitals; for principal quantum number 2 there are only s and p orbitals; for principal quantum number 3 there are only s, p, and d orbitals; for higher principal quantum numbers there are s, p, d, and f orbitals.

The appropriate number of electrons are placed in the orbitals in order of energy, the orbitals of lower energy being filled first, subject to the proviso that for a set of equivalent orbitals—say the three p orbitals in a set—the electrons are placed one in each orbital until all the orbitals are half filled. The order of energy of orbitals for most nuclei is $1s < 2s < 2p < 3s < 3p < 4s < 3d < 4p < 5s < 4d < 5p < 6s < 4f < 5d < 6p < 7s. . . .$

(b) Molecules. The electronic configurations

of molecules can be built up by direct addition of atomic orbitals (LCAO method) or by considering molecular orbitals which occupy all of the space around the atoms of the molecule (molecular orbital method).

Electronic transition. In an atom or molecule the electrons exist only in certain definite orbitals. The electrons in any orbital are associated with a definite amount of energy characteristic of the orbital. If an electron passes from one orbital to another, an electronic transition is said to have occurred, and is associated with an emission or absorption of energy corresponding to the difference in energy possessed by the electron in the different orbitals.

Electron spin. Electrons have certain properties which can be explained by assuming that they are able to spin, much as the earth spins on its axis. See Multiplet.

Electron spin resonance (e.s.r.). In the absence of any external fields, all spatial orientations of the electron spin are equally probable. On the application of a magnetic field, however, the spins are aligned either parallel or antiparallel to the direction of the magnetic field vector. The energy difference between these two states is $g\beta H$ where g is the Landé factor, β is the Bohr magneton and H is the strength of the applied magnetic field. Boltzmann's law governs the distribution of spins between the two states, and at normal temperatures there is a slight excess in the lower energy state.

In an electron spin resonance spectrometer, transitions between the two states are brought about by the application of the quantum of energy $h\nu$ which is equal to $g\beta H$. The resonance condition is defined when $h\nu = g\beta H$ and this is achieved experimentally by varying H keeping the frequency (ν) constant. E.s.r. spectroscopy is used extensively in organic chemistry in the elucidation of structures of radicals.

Electron transfer reaction. A reaction which involves transfer of electrons from one group to another. In essence this is oxidation and reduction (*q.v.*).

Electron transport. A term referring to the biological function of the respiratory chain as a coupled oxidation-reduction system. The electron-transport particles are small portions of the mitochondria.

Electro-osmosis. If a direct current is passed through a tube of liquid which is fitted with two electrodes, one on either side of a diaphragm, the potential difference between the diaphragm and the liquid manifests itself by a movement of the liquid towards one or other of the electrodes. This phenomenon, which is akin to electro-phoresis (*q.v.*), is termed electro-osmosis. It is

modified by the presence of acids, bases, and salts. The hydrogen-ion concentration at which there is no movement of liquid with respect to the membrane is termed the isoelectric point. See Colloids.

Electrophilic reagents act by acquiring electrons, or a share in electrons, from a foreign molecule; examples are the chlorine molecule and the nitronium ion (NO_2^+). The reagent can frequently only accommodate the extra electrons by undergoing fission, thus acidity is a special case of *electrophilicity*, the affinity for external electrons in general.

Electrophilic substitution involves the exchange of an atom or group in a molecule for an entering electrophile according to

$$R{-}X + E^{\oplus} \rightarrow R{-}E + X^{\oplus}$$

The nitration, sulphonation, and Friedel-Crafts acylation of aromatic compounds (e.g. benzene) are typical examples of electrophilic aromatic substitution.

Electrophoresis. When two electrodes are inserted in a suspension or a colloidal sol and a potential difference applied (small current to prevent disturbances due to electrolysis and gas evolution), the dispersed particles move with respect to the dispersion medium. This movement is termed electrophoresis. There are various methods of measuring electrophoretic velocity, such as the moving boundary method in which the movement of a coloured boundary of the dispersion in a U-tube is observed and microscope methods in which the actual motion of the individual particles across the field of the microscope is measured.

Most solids are negatively charged with respect to water, but hydroxide sols and basic dyes are positive. It must be realized, however, that by the adsorption of ions of the opposite sign, the charge of a colloid may be reversed and with it the direction of electrophoresis.

When the particles of a colloidal sol reach the electrode, they generally coagulate to coarse aggregates. The magnitude of electrophoretic velocity is to some extent a measure of colloidal stability. The potential on the particles is related to the velocity of migration thus:

$$v = \frac{\zeta XD}{3\pi\eta}$$

(v is the velocity, ζ the electrokinetic potential, η the viscosity, X the potential gradient, and D the dielectric constant of the medium).

Electroplating. The deposition of metals from solution in the form of a layer on other metals by the passage of an electric current. The metallic article to be plated is made the cathode in a bath of a solution of an ionised salt of the metal which is to do the plating, and the anode is generally of the same material as the metal in the bath. The process requires careful control, the current density, the pH of the bath, etc., having a marked effect on the adhesion and texture of the deposited metal. The chief metals used for plating are silver, chromium, and nickel.

While electroplating generally denotes metallic plating, any substance which in solution or suspension has an electric charge can under suitable conditions be plated on to a surface. The electroplating or electrodeposition of rubber from colloidal solution is extensively used for lining various articles. The rubber is first plated on and the coating subsequently vulcanized.

Electrostatic precipitators. These are plants for the removal of fine suspended matter from a gas, and depend for their action on the ionization of the gas between two highly charged electrodes. The ions so formed attach themselves to the dispersed particles conferring a charge, with the result that the latter then migrate to the appropriate electrode.

In practice the *discharge electrodes* carry a potential of from 10,000 to 60,000 V, and are in the form of wires or have sharp edges so that an intense electric field may be produced. The *collector electrodes* for the dust or mist are usually earthed and take the form of flat plates, though in large installations they normally consist of vertical pipes surrounding the discharge electrodes. The collector electrodes require periodic rapping to remove precipitated material, or they may be irrigated.

Discharge and collector electrodes are commonly contained in the same unit, such precipitators being referred to as *single-stage* or *Cottrell precipitators*. In some installations ionization and collection occur in different parts of the plant, that is, the two types of electrode are separated, and these are called *two-stage precipitators*.

Electrostatic precipitators are relatively expensive and running-costs high, but collection efficiencies are high also, even for very small particles. Material as small as 0·01 μ may be removed, and they are thus suitable for smokes and fumes.

Electrostatic separation. A method used for the concentration of certain minerals. If particles of two different non-conductors are in contact, one will acquire a positive charge and the other a negative charge, and when subjected to an electric field will be attracted to opposite electrodes. Again, if a conducting and a non-conducting material are in contact with a charged surface, the conductor will acquire a charge of the same polarity as the surface, while

the non-conductor merely acquires a dipole. The conducting material will be attracted towards an electrode of opposite polarity, while the non-conductor will tend to adhere to the surface. Both these effects, which may be operative at the same time, provide the basis for electrostatic separation.

A typical electrostatic separator consists of an earthed rotor in the form of a horizontal cylinder on to which the ground material is fed, with a *static electrode* nearby. There may also be another electrode of the same polarity as the static electrode situated above it, to provide a corona discharge to charge the particles. The fraction that adheres to the rotor is continuously brushed off into a chute, while the fraction which is attracted towards the static electrode falls into another chute.

Electrostatic separation is extensively used for the concentration of tin and titanium ores.

Electro-ultrafiltration. Just as the process of separation of crystalloids from colloids in dialysis can be speeded up by placing electrodes on either side of a dialyser, so that electrolytes are removed by ionic migration, so ultrafiltration can be modified in a similar manner. Electro-ultrafiltration is the quickest but most complicated of the various methods of colloid purification. See Dialysis, Electrodialysis, Ultrafiltration.

Electrovalent compounds. Compounds in which the major bonding is the electrostatic attraction between positive and negative ions. There are no discrete molecules in electrovalent compounds, the ions being packed together in the most efficient way geometrically. Electrovalent compounds are distinguished from covalent compounds by their ionization and conductivity when melted and when dissolved in polar solvents, by their low volatility, solubility in polar solvents, and general insolubility in non-polar solvents.

Electrovalent bond or **Polar bond.** Bonding by electrostatic attraction.

Eledoisin. An extremely powerful vasodilator, isolated from the salivary gland of certain molluscs. The structure of this undecapeptide-amide (see Physalaemin) has been established by degradation and synthesis:

Tyr.Pro.Ser.Lys.Asp.Ala.Phe.Ileu.
Gly.Met.NH$_2$

Element. An element may be defined as 'a substance which cannot be broken down to yield other simpler substances by ordinary chemical methods.' The elements are the basic substances from which all others are built up by chemical combination. The above definition is adequate only in so far as ordinary chemical methods are understood to exclude such processes as lead to the disruption of the nucleus of the atoms which comprise an element, and to avoid possible confusion arising from this ambiguity, an element may be defined as 'a substance which consists wholly of atoms having the same nuclear charge.' A list of the elements with the arrangement of their electrons will be found on pages 218 and 219.

Elements, abundance of. The abundance of elements in the earth's crust is very different from the abundance in the core and the abundance in meteorites and stars. The abundances of the lighter elements in the crust are (expressed relative to $Si = 10^6$):

Li	470	P	3860
Be	22·4	S	1640
B	28·1	Cl	43
C	2710	Ar	10^{-1}
N	108	K	$6·7 \times 10^4$
O	$2·96 \times 10^6$	Ca	$9·17 \times 10^4$
F	3750	Sc	45
Ne	$3·6 \times 10^{-4}$	Ti	9310
Na	$1·25 \times 10^5$	V	240
Mg	$8·7 \times 10^4$	Cr	195
Al	$3·06 \times 10^5$	Mn	1850
Si	10^6	Fe	$9·1 \times 10^4$

Elements of symmetry. A general expression for the symmetry of a molecule, a crystal lattice, or a crystal. The items considered are centres of symmetry, axes and planes of symmetry.

Elementary particles. The fundamental particles found in nature. Those known at present are: neutrino, photon, graviton, electron, positron, mesons, proton, neutron, hyperons (*q.v.*).

Elevation of boiling-point. The boiling-point of a solvent is raised in the presence of a solute. The rise in boiling-point for small concentrations of the solute is proportional to the concentration of solute in the solution. The elevation caused by 1 gram molecule of solute in 1 litre of solvent is called the molecular elevation constant.

Elixirs. Elixirs are aromatic pharmaceutical solutions frequently containing considerable alcohol and used as sweetening or flavouring agents when administering nauseous drugs.

Ellagic acid, $C_{14}H_6O_8$. Crystallizes in needles,

sparingly soluble in water and alcohol, soluble in alkalis. It occurs free and combined in oak

bark and galls, being probably formed in the plant by the hydrolysis of tannin.

Elutriation. The process of separating a material into fractions of various sizes by allowing it to settle against an upward moving stream of fluid, usually air or water. The individual particles will settle through the fluid at a definite velocity, depending on size, density, and a number of other factors. Given a material of uniform density there will be, under any given set of conditions, a certain particle size at which the rate of descent is equal to the velocity of the fluid stream. All particles larger than this will sink to the bottom of the elutriator, and all smaller particles will pass out of the vessel with the fluid stream, and may be recovered by some suitable means.

Emanation. The old name for radon.

Emerald. The grass-green variety of beryl, the colour being due to the presence of traces of chromium.

Emerald green, Paris green, Schweinfürter green. Variants of copper aceto-arsenite, $CuAc_2, As_2O_3, 3CuO$, prepared by reacting verdigris (basic copper acetate) with sodium arsenite and acetic acid. These compounds are no longer used as pigments, but are components of sprays for fruit trees for their insecticidal effect. Since they are readily decomposed to water-soluble arsenic compounds, their application is now very restricted.

Emery. An impure form of corundum (α-Al_2O_3) containing a variable proportion of iron oxide, chiefly in the form of magnetite. It is chiefly obtained from the island of Naxos in the Grecian Archipelago, Asia Minor, and the United States. It is used as an abrasive and polishing agent.

Emetine, $C_{29}H_{40}N_2O_4$. An alkaloid extracted

from ipecacuanha or obtained by the methylation of cephaeline, another ipecacuanha alkaloid. A white amorphous powder, m.p. 74°, $[\alpha]_D^{20} - 50°$ in chloroform. Soluble in most polar solvents, gives a strongly alkaline reaction. Emetine is considered to be a specific for amoebic dysentery, for which purpose it is administered in combination with bismuth iodide, and in addition emetine hydrochloride is injected hypodermically or intramuscularly. It is an

THE ELEMENTS AND THEIR ELECTRONS

Element		Atomic number	Electronic Configuration			
			$1s$	$2s$	$2p$	
Hydrogen	H	1	1			
Helium	He	2	2			
Lithium	Li	3	2	1		
Beryllium	Be	4	2	2		
Boron	B	5	2	2	1	
Carbon	C	6	2	2	2	
Nitrogen	N	7	2	2	3	
Oxygen	O	8	2	2	4	
Fluorine	F	9	2	2	5	
Neon	Ne	10	2	2	6	

Element		Atomic number	$1s$	$2(sp)$	$3s$	$3p$	$3d$	$4s$	$4p$
Sodium	Na	11	2	8	1				
Magnesium	Mg	12	2	8	2				
Aluminium	Al	13	2	8	2	1			
Silicon	Si	14	2	8	2	2			
Phosphorus	P	15	2	8	2	3			
Sulphur	S	16	2	8	2	4			
Chlorine	Cl	17	2	8	2	5			
Argon	Ar	18	2	8	2	6			
Potassium	K	19	2	8	2	6		1	
Calcium	Ca	20	2	8	2	6		2	
Scandium	Sc	21	2	8	2	6	1	2	
Titanium	Ti	22	2	8	2	6	2	2	
Vanadium	V	23	2	8	2	6	3	2	
Chromium	Cr	24	2	8	2	6	5	1	
Manganese	Mn	25	2	8	2	6	5	2	
Iron	Fe	26	2	8	2	6	6	2	
Cobalt	Co	27	2	8	2	6	7	2	
Nickel	Ni	28	2	8	2	6	8	2	
Copper	Cu	29	2	8	2	6	10	1	
Zinc	Zn	30	2	8	2	6	10	2	
Gallium	Ga	31	2	8	2	6	10	2	1
Germanium	Ge	32	2	8	2	6	10	2	2
Arsenic	As	33	2	8	2	6	10	2	3
Selenium	Se	34	2	8	2	6	10	2	4
Bromine	Br	35	2	8	2	6	10	2	5
Krypton	Kr	36	2	8	2	6	10	2	6

Element		Atomic number	$1s$	$2(sp)$	$3(spd)$	$4s$	$4p$	$4d$	$5s$	$5p$
Rubidium	Rb	37	2	8	18	2	6		1	
Strontium	Sr	38	2	8	18	2	6		2	
Yttrium	Y	39	2	8	18	2	6	1	2	
Zirconium	Zr	40	2	8	18	2	6	2	2	
Niobium	Nb	41	2	8	18	2	6	4	1	
Molybdenum	Mo	42	2	8	18	2	6	5	1	
Technetium	Tc	43	2	8	18	2	6	6	1	
Ruthenium	Ru	44	2	8	18	2	6	7	1	
Rhodium	Rh	45	2	8	18	2	6	8	1	
Palladium	Pd	46	2	8	18	2	6	10		
Silver	Ag	47	2	8	18	2	6	10	1	

THE ELEMENTS AND THEIR ELECTRONS—*cont.*

Element		Atomic number	Electronic Configuration											
			(1,2,3)	4*s*	4*p*	4*d*	4*f*	5*s*	5*p*	5*d*	6*s*	6*p*	6*d*	7*s*
Cadmium	Cd	48	28	2	6	10		2						
Indium	In	49	28	2	6	10		2	1					
Tin	Sn	50	28	2	6	10		2	2					
Antimony	Sb	51	28	2	6	10		2	3					
Tellurium	Te	52	28	2	6	10		2	4					
Iodine	I	53	28	2	6	10		2	5					
Xenon	Xe	54	28	2	6	10		2	6		1			
Caesium	Cs	55	28	2	6	10		2	6		1			
Barium	Ba	56	28	2	6	10		2	6		2			
Lanthanum	La	57	28	2	6	10		2	6	1	2			
Cerium	Ce	58	28	2	6	10	1	2	6	1	2			
Praseodymium	Pr	59	28	2	6	10	2	2	6	1	2			
Neodymium	Nd	60	28	2	6	10	3	2	6	1	2			
Promethium	Pm	61	28	2	6	10	4	2	6	1	2			
Samarium	Sm	62	28	2	6	10	5	2	6	1	2			
Europium	Eu	63	28	2	6	10	6	2	6	1	2			
Gadolinium	Gd	64	28	2	6	10	7	2	6	1	2			
Terbium	Tb	65	28	2	6	10	8	2	6	1	2			
Dysprosium	Dy	66	28	2	6	10	9	2	6	1	2			
Holmium	Ho	67	28	2	6	10	10	2	6	1	2			
Erbium	Er	68	28	2	6	10	11	2	6	1	2			
Thulium	Tm	69	28	2	6	10	12	2	6	1	2			
Ytterbium	Yb	70	28	2	6	10	13	2	6	1	2			
Lutetium	Lu	71	28	2	6	10	14	2	6	1	2			
				(1,2,3,4)										
Hafnium	Hf	72		60				2	6	2	2			
Tantalum	Ta	73		60				2	6	3	2			
Tungsten	W	74		60				2	6	4	2			
Rhenium	Re	75		60				2	6	5	2			
Osmium	Os	76		60				2	6	6	2			
Iridium	Ir	77		60				2	6	7	2			
Platinum	Pt	78		60				2	6	8	2			
Gold	Au	79		60				2	6	10	1			
Mercury	Hg	80		60				2	6	10	2			
Thallium	Tl	81		60				2	6	10	2	1		
Lead	Pb	82		60				2	6	10	2	2		
Bismuth	Bi	83		60				2	6	10	2	3		
Polonium	Po	84		60				2	6	10	2	4		
Astatine	At	85		60				2	6	10	2	5		
Radon	Rn	86		60				2	6	10	2	6		
Francium	Fr	87		60				2	6	10	2	6		1
Radium	Ra	88		60				2	6	10	2	6		2

The electronic structures of the remaining elements are in some doubt. Electrons go into 5*f* and 6*d* orbitals but the exact distributions are not known.

irritant to mucous surfaces, and has powerful emetic properties.

Emodins. See Frangulin.

Emulsification. The preparation of a suspension, or emulsion, of one liquid in another.

Emulsifier. (1) Another name for an emulsifying agent. (2) Any machine for producing an emulsion. In some cases a satisfactory emulsion may be produced by the use of a simple mixer, such as a propeller or turbine agitator, but frequently it is necessary to employ a special machine. See Colloid mills.

Emulsifying agent. Dilute suspensions of oil in water behave like typical hydrophobic sols, and it is not possible to increase the concentration of oil unless a stabilizing material is added which decreases the interfacial tension. Such substances, known as emulsifying agents, are generally long-chain compounds containing a hydrophilic (carboxyl or sulphonate) group at one end of the molecule; these become orientated at the interface, the hydrophilic end projecting into the water. There are also solid emulsifying agents (e.g. carbon black) which possess widely different angles of contact for the two phases.

There are two types of emulsion possible for each system; oil-in-water (O/W) and water-in-oil (W/O). Usually a given emulsifying agent will emulsify so as to form only one of these types. An emulsifying agent generally produces such an emulsion that the liquid in which it is most soluble forms the external phase. Thus the alkali metal soaps and hydrophilic colloids produce O/W emulsions, oil-soluble resins the W/O type.

The commonest emulsifying agents are the soaps, which have the disadvantage of coagulating in hard waters. For edible and pharmaceutical emulsions gums of various sorts are employed. Of recent years, large numbers of synthetic organic emulsifying agents have been developed. Many of these are sulphonates or quaternary ammonium compounds.

Emulsin. An enzyme preparation obtained from almonds by extraction with water and precipitation with alcohol, and from many other plant and animal sources. Its chief constitutuent is a β-glucosidase, and it contains other related enzymes.

Emulsion. An emulsion is a disperse system in which both phases are liquids; generally one of the liquids is water or an aqueous solution, and the other an oil or other water-immiscible liquid. With a given pair of liquids (e.g. an oil and water) two distinct types of emulsion are possible according to which forms the dispersion medium. Emulsions in which an oil is dispersed in water are termed oil-in-water (O/W) emulsions;

those in which the water is the disperse phase are water-in-oil (W/O) emulsions. It is possible to have any phase ratio in an emulsified system. Thus naturally-forming emulsions such as that of the condenser water of an engine may contain only a fraction of a per cent. of oil, while semi-solid emulsion pastes may contain 95% of oil dispersed in water. In order to stabilize all but the most dilute emulsions, it is necessary to have present a third substance, the emulsifying agent, to stabilize the system.

The viscosity of an emulsion increases rapidly with the concentration of the disperse phase; very often when the emulsifying agent is not efficient, increase in the concentration of the disperse phase above a certain value causes phase reversal, an O/W emulsion changing to W/O type. The presence of certain ionic substances also brings this about.

Emulsions have innumerable industrial uses; they are used widely as foods and pharmaceutical preparations, cosmetics, horticultural and insecticide sprays, as oil-bound water paints, as lubricants, for spraying of roads, etc.

Emulsion stabilizers (see also Antifoggants). The appearance of fog in photographic materials during storage can be prevented by the addition to the emulsion during manufacture of certain organic compounds known as emulsion stabilizers, which do not cause a loss of sensitivity of the emulsion. These compounds are weakly adsorbed to the grain surface, where they displace the chemical sensitizer (*J. Phot. Sci.*, 1965, **13**, 171).

Emulsoid. An obsolete term for lyophilic colloid.

Enamines. Vinylamines; those having a hydrogen atom on nitrogen are usually unstable

and re-arrange to the corresponding imine, but those with no hydrogen on nitrogen are stable and important synthetic intermediates. These are usually easily prepared from ketones with an α-hydrogen and a secondary amine, e.g. pyrrolidine, with an acid catalyst. Since many

undergo C-alkylation smoothly, and the substituted enamine can be cleaved easily back to a ketone, a facile substitution of the α-position of ketones is possible.

Enantiomorphism. The dextrorotatory and laevorotatory forms of an optically active substance (see Optical activity) are said to be enantiomorphous. Their interrelation is known as enantiomorphism.

Enantiotropy. When red mercuric iodide is heated to 126° it changes to the yellow form, and on cooling below this temperature again, it reverts to the red form. Such a reversible transformation of one polymorph into another, or of one allotrope into another, at a definite transition temperature, is termed enantiotropy.

Enclosure compounds. Clathrate compounds (*q.v.*).

Endo-. A prefix used to describe the orientation

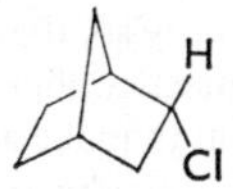

endo-norbornyl   exo-norbornyl
chloride   chloride

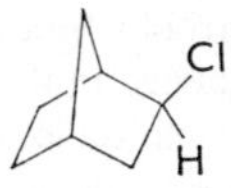

of atoms or groups with respect to the rest of the molecule, especially with polycyclic molecules, but not restricted to these classes. It indicates that the substituent is facing the inside (convex side) of the molecule. In certain instances such identification may be doubtful (see Cookson and Wariyar, *J. Chem. Soc.*, 1956, 2302). The stereochemically related isomer is given the prefix *exo-*.

Endopeptidases. A class of peptide-cleaving enzymes which act at points along the chain rather than at the terminal groups. Typical substrates are proteins and higher polypeptides, and the enzymes are often known as 'proteinases'. Important examples are trypsin, chymotrypsin, and pepsin—all concerned in digestion. See also Exopeptidases.

Endosmosis, electrical. Another name for electrophoresis.

Endothermal. An alternative word for endothermic.

Endothermic, compound or reaction. A reaction in which heat is absorbed is called an endothermic reaction. Likewise an endothermic compound is one which is formed from its elements with the absorption of heat.

End-point. This corresponds with the stage in a titration when the indicator (in its widest sense) undergoes its visible change, corresponding with a definite hydrogen or other ion concentration, or oxidation-reduction potential. It does not necessarily correspond with the equivalence point.

Endrin. The common name for the insecticidal

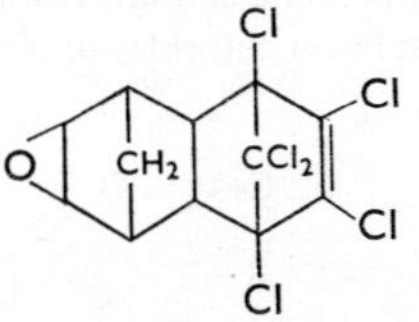

product containing not less than 92% by weight of 1,2,3,4,10,10-hexachloro-6,7-epoxy-1, 4,4a,5,6,7,8,8a-octahydro-1,4-*endo,endo*-5,8-di-methanonaphthalene (the *endo-endo* isomer of the principal constituent of dieldrin) (*q.v.*). It is insecticidally active as a contact and stomach poison for use against a wide range of pests, principally on cotton. It is non-phytotoxic and does not cause taint to crops.

Endrin, like other chlorinated hydrocarbons, is toxic to humans and animals. It is soluble in fat but insoluble in water and can be absorbed by ingestion, inhalation and through the skin. It should therefore be handled with care at all times.

Enediols. Organic compounds containing one carbon-carbon double bond and two hydroxyl groups.

Energy levels. Energy taken up by a molecule, say by the absorption of light, may cause an electron to move from an orbit of lower to one of higher energy; it may increase the energy of rotation of the molecule as a whole, or may increase the energy of vibration of the nuclei of the constituent atoms relative to one another. The changes all occur in accordance with the quantum hypothesis, i.e. the changes in energy are not continuous, but take place only in definite steps. Thus, every electronic orbital is associated with a specific energy value, or energy level. So the rotational and vibrational states have only certain restricted energy values, or energy levels. Diagrammatically, these are usually represented as a series of horizontal, parallel straight lines separated by distances proportional to the differences in energy of the various states.

Enols, or Enolic compounds. The tautomeric forms of certain ketones, particularly those with an α-carbon with a hydrogen atom. They contain the grouping

$$\ce{>C=C-OH}$$

This grouping is also present in phenols, and enols resemble the phenols in several of their reactions. They give deep colorations with ferric chloride solutions and the hydrogen atom of the —OH group is acidic and is replaceable by sodium and other metals. The copper compounds of 1,3-diketones and β-ketonic esters are of this type. The sodium compounds react with alkyl and acyl chlorides to give derivatives of the type

$$>C-C=O$$
$$\quad | \quad | $$
$$\quad R$$

The hydrogen of the —OH group can be replaced by an acyl group if the reaction is carried out in pyridine solution. The amount of the enol in a mixture of the two tautomeric forms can be estimated by treating the mixture with an alcoholic solution of bromine. The keto form does not react under these conditions. See Isomerism.

Enthalpy. The enthalpy (H) sometimes called the heat content of a system is the heat function at constant pressure. The enthalpy change during any process is defined by

$$\Delta H = \Delta E + P \Delta V$$

where ΔE is the energy change, P is the pressure and ΔV the change in volume.

In a chemical reaction the enthalpy change is derived from the equation

$$\Delta G = \Delta H - T \Delta S$$

where ΔG and ΔS refer to the free energy and entropy changes respectively.

Enthalpy is usually expressed in units of kilocalories/mole.

Entrainment. The carrying forward by a stream of gas or vapour of fine liquid droplets. In distillation columns the transport of liquid from one plate to the next by this mechanism can have an adverse effect on separation efficiency.

Entropy. The entropy, S, of any system may be regarded as the degree of disorder occurring in that system, and any change taking place which results in an increase in the disorder is said to be a positive entropy change ΔS. All spontaneous processes are accompanied by an increase in entropy.

Using the transition state theory for chemical reaction rates, expressions can be derived for the free energy and entropy of the activation processes. Ion association and dimerization reactions usually have negative entropies of activation, due to the reduction in the number of particles in the system.

Enzymes. These have been defined (in 'Enzymes' by Dixon and Webb) as 'proteins with catalytic properties due to their power of specific activation'. They catalyse the reactions which take place in the living cell, e.g. the hydrolysis of fats, sugars, and proteins, and their re-synthesis.

They also catalyse the many forms of oxidation and reduction which provide energy for the cell. Enzymes are obtained from plant and animal tissues by extraction with a suitable solvent, preferably after the cell structure has been destroyed by drying or grinding. They can be purified by precipitation and re-solution and by fractional absorption and elution. Many enzymes have been obtained crystalline.

Enzymes often need for their activity the presence of a non-protein portion, which may be closely combined with the protein, in which case it is called a prosthetic group, or more loosely associated, in which case it is a co-enzyme. The presence of certain metals, including iron, magnesium, copper, zinc, manganese, or cobalt, is often necessary for their action.

One outstanding feature of enzymes is that many of them are highly specific. Those that act on carbohydrates are particularly so, the slightest change in the stereochemical configuration of the molecule being sufficient to make a particular enzyme incompatible and unable to effect hydrolysis. Most enzymes work best within a narrow pH range, and are susceptible to a wide variety of substances which act generally as poisons, though sometimes as promoters, according to the enzyme. The activity of most enzymes increases with temperature to a maximum which is often around 40°; at higher temperatures they are rapidly inactivated.

Enzymes are usually classified in terms of the reactions which they catalyse, and were formerly named by adding the suffix 'ase' to the substrate or to the process of the reaction. A very confused nomenclature developed, which is now being replaced by the system recommended by the International Union of Biochemistry in 1964. (See 'Enzyme Nomenclature', in Vol. 13, 2nd edn., of 'Comprehensive Biochemistry', ed. M. Florkin and E. H. Stotz, Elsevier, 1965). The enzymes are classified into groups on the basis of the type of reaction catalysed: this, together with the names of particular substrates, provides a basis for designating individual enzymes. The suffix 'ase' is retained but in a more clearly defined way, attached to the name of the reaction. Enzymes are divided into six main groups as follows:

1. *Oxidoreductases.* This group includes enzymes formerly known as dehydrogenases, oxidases, reductases, peroxidases, oxygenases, hydrogenases, and hydroxylases. The subsidiary names are still accepted as trivial but convenient descriptions.

2. *Transferases.* This includes a variety of group-transferring enzymes: the name of the transferred moiety is incorporated, e.g. methyltransferases (formerly 'transmethylases'). The term 'kinase' is retained as a convenient trivial

name for phosphate-transferring enzymes (phosphotransferases).

3. *Hydrolases.* A large group including phosphatases, sulphatases, amylases, phospholipases (phosphatidases), glucosidases, peptidases, proteinases, etc. which remove groups by hydrolysis.

4. *Lyases.* Enzymes which remove groups from their substrates (not by hydrolysis) leaving double bonds or which add groups to double bonds. This group includes the decarboxylases, certain carboxylases, aldolases, hydratases, dehydratases, etc.

5. *Isomerases.* As well as enzymes formerly known as isomerases, this group includes racemases, epimerases, mutases, etc.

6. *Ligases (Synthetases).* Enzymes which catalyse the linkage of two molecules at the same time as there is breakdown of a pyrophosphate bond in ATP or a similar triphosphate. This group includes mainly enzymes already known as synthetases, but also certain carboxylases.

Eosin C.I. Acid Red 87, or **Eosin A.** The

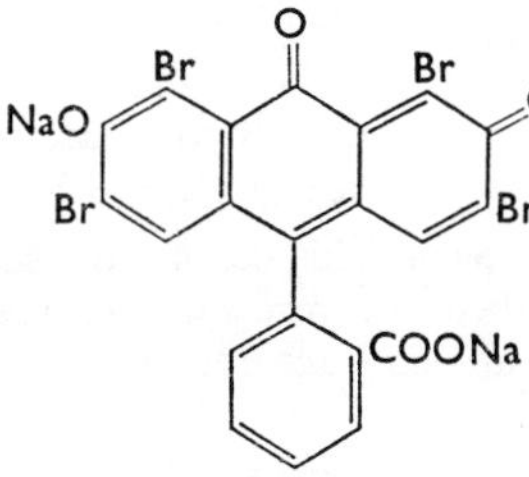

sodium salt of tetrabromofluorescein. It is prepared by the direct bromination of fluorescein. The dye is red, but shows a brilliant fluorescence in ultra-violet light. Spirit-soluble eosin, C.I. Solvent Red 87, and eosin-S are the corresponding methyl- and ethyl-esters respectively. Eosin is used as a constituent of red inks, and as a stain for tissue slices. It has poor light fastness.

Eötvos, Roland von (1848-1919). Born at Budapest, Eötvos was educated there and at Heidelberg. In 1872 he was appointed professor of physics in the University of Budapest. His investigations were mainly upon capillarity, gravitation, and terrestrial magnetism. He constructed the Eötvos balance.

Eötvos equation. This equation states that $\gamma\left[\dfrac{M}{D}\right]^{2/3} = K(T_e - T)$, where γ is the surface tension, M the molecular weight, D the density, T_e the critical temperature, and T the temperature of the liquid at which γ and D were measured, and K a constant which is approximately 2·0 for a few normal liquids.

Ephedrine, $C_{10}H_{15}NO$. Colourless crystals containing about $\frac{1}{2}$ H$_2$O, m.p. 40°, b.p. 225°.

Soluble in water and alcohol. The naturally occurring substance has $[\alpha]_D - 6\cdot3°$ in alcohol. It is obtained from various species of *Ephedra*,

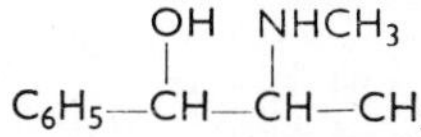

$$\underset{C_6H_5-CH-CH-CH_3}{\overset{OH \quad NHCH_3}{| \quad\quad |}}$$

or may be synthesized. Its physiological action resembles that of adrenaline. It is used to relieve catarrh, asthma, hay fever, and for similar conditions.

Epicamphor (β-**camphor**), $C_{10}H_{16}O$. (−)-Epi-

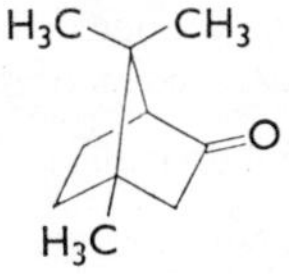

camphor is prepared from methyl-(+)-bornylene-3-carboxylate, which is converted by means of hydroxylamine into (+)-bornylene-3-hydroxamic acid. This latter is converted on heating above its m.p. into (−)-epicamphor and ammonia. The smell of epicamphor differs slightly from that of camphor. Its (+)- and (−)-forms have m.p. 182°. The (±)-form melts at 180°. Epicamphor has b.p. 213° and the recorded $[\alpha]_D$ values (in benzene) are +58·4° and −58·21°.

Epichlorohydrin, 3-chloropropylene oxide, C_3H_5ClO. A colourless liquid with an odour resembling that of chloroform, d^{20} 1·181, b.p. 115°-117°. Insoluble in water; miscible with alcohol and ether. Prepared

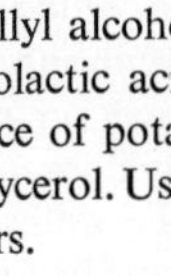

by treating glycerol dichlorohydrins with solid sodium hydroxide at 25°-30°. The epichlorohydrin is extracted with ether and distilled. Reduced by sodium amalgam to allyl alcohol, oxidized by nitric acid to β-chlorolactic acid. Reacts with alcohols in the presence of potassium hydroxide to give diethers of glycerol. Used in the manufacture of glycerol ethers.

Epimerism is a type of isomerism shown by substances which contain several asymmetric centres but differ in the configuration of one only of these.

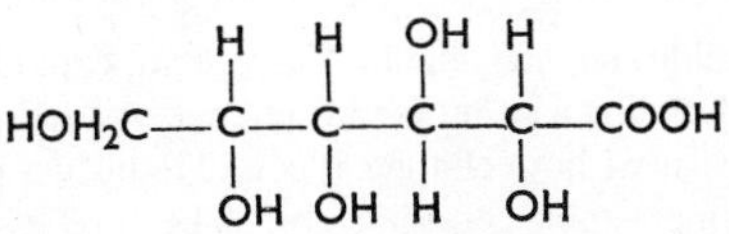

In carbohydrate chemistry the term is restricted to sugars or their derivatives which differ only in the orientation of the groups attached to the carbon atom next to the potential aldehyde group of the sugar or to the corresponding group in the sugar derivative. Thus D-gluconic acid,

and D-mannonic acid,

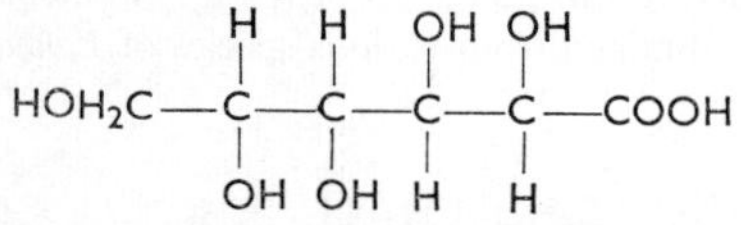

$$HOH_2C \underset{\underset{OH}{|}}{\overset{\overset{H}{|}}{C}} \underset{\underset{OH}{|}}{\overset{\overset{H}{|}}{C}} \underset{\underset{H}{|}}{\overset{\overset{OH}{|}}{C}} \underset{\underset{H}{|}}{\overset{\overset{OH}{|}}{C}} COOH$$

are epimers, and each may be partially converted into the other by heating in pyridine or quinoline, such a process being called epimerization. Dicarboxylic acids such as mucic acid may be epimerized at the carbon atom next to each carboxyl group. The sugars themselves are epimerized to some extent when treated with dilute alkalis, but side-reactions also occur.

Epinephrine. See Adrenaline.

Epoxy. A prefix indicating an —O— bridge in a molecule, e.g. $CH_2\overset{\displaystyle \diagdown O \diagup}{—}CH_2$, epoxyethane.

Epoxy resins. Polyethers formed, for example, by the condensation of epichlorohydrin with diphenylolpropane in the presence of alkali. The intermediate resins (having molecular weights in the range 400-6,000) still contain terminal epoxy groups.

These can be made to react with crosslinking agents such as diethylene triamine, *m*-phenylenediamine, or phthalic anhydride to give clear amber-coloured fully cured products, having outstanding chemical resistance and dimensional stability. Among the more important applications are surface coatings of good adhesion, flexibility, and chemical resistance; solvent-free adhesives which will set at comparatively low temperatures and bond a variety of materials, including glass and metals; glass fibre reinforced laminates of very high strength; and casting and potting resins having low shrinkage during cure. Special derivatives are used, based on epoxy resins modified with polysulphides, polyamines, amino resins, and phenolic resins. Epoxy resins are also known as ethoxyline resins, and glycidyl polyethers.   •

Epsom salts. See Magnesium sulphate.

Equatorial. See Conformation.

Equilibrium constant. See Mass action, Law of.

Equilibrium diagram. A simplification of the boiling-point diagram used in distillation problems. The diagram shows graphically for a liquid mixture the composition of the vapour which is in equilibrium with the liquid. It is widely used in metallography to show the equilibrium between liquid and solid alloys.

Equilibrium, metastable. If a system, capable of undergoing a spontaneous change, nevertheless persists without change, it is said to be in a state of metastable equilibrium. The process of change requires special initiation or catalysis, e.g. crystallization of a super-saturated solution, or combination of oxygen and hydrogen.

Equilenin, $C_{18}H_{18}O_2$. A substance with the

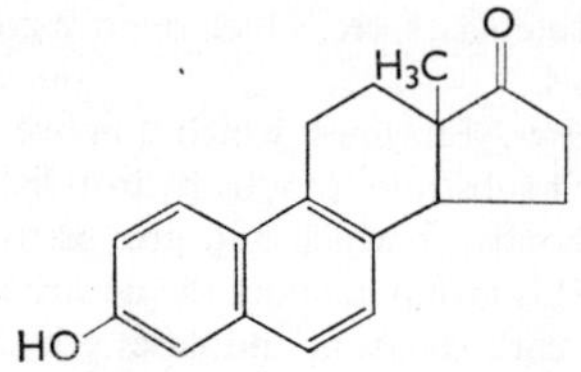

properties of a female sex hormone, but not so physiologically active as equilin; found in the urine of pregnant mares, m.p. 258°-259°, with decomposition. Sparingly soluble in alcohol.

Equilin, $C_{18}H_{20}O_2$. A substance with the

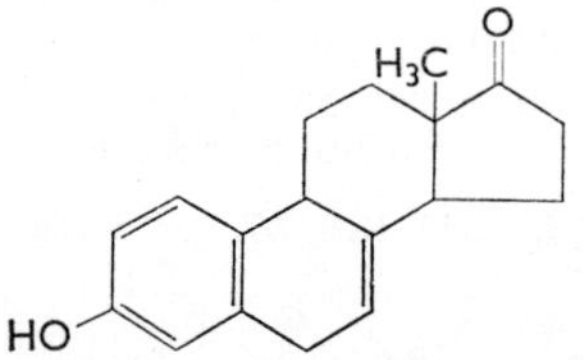

properties of a female sex hormone found in the urine of pregnant mares, m.p. 238°-240°.

Equivalence-point. This denotes the stage in a titration when the reactants are present in equivalent amounts according to the reaction being used.

Equivalent, chemical. The chemical equivalent or equivalent weight of a substance is defined as the weight of the substance which will combine with or displace eight parts by weight of oxygen. Thus, 8 g of oxygen are equivalent to 35·5 g of chlorine. Hence, the equivalent of a substance may also be determined by finding how much of it will combine with or displace 35·5 g of chlorine. In oxidation—reduction reactions, since the equivalent is the number of atoms or ions equivalent to one electron in the reaction, the equivalent weight is the number of grams which are equivalent to a Faraday.

Equivalent conductivity. This is defined as the specific conductance multiplied by the volume in ml containing 1 g equivalent of the electrolyte.

Equivalent proportions, law of. This law states that substances combine together in the ratio of their equivalents. Since many elements exist in a wide variety of oxidation states and many compounds are non-stoicheiometric, the law does not have wide application in its simple form.

Erbium. Er. At.no. 68, At.wt. 167·2, *d* 9·051, m.p. 1497°, b.p. 2900°. Erbium metal has the hexagonal close-packed structure, $a=3·5590$,

$c = 5\cdot592$ Å. It is a typical rare earth element (*q.v.*).

Erbium compounds. Erbium forms a single series of rose coloured salts, the metal having an oxidation state of three. These salts are typical rare earth compounds (*q.v.*).

Erdmann's salt, $NH_4[Co(NH_3)_2(NO_2)_4]$. A typical cobaltammine, which is prepared by the action of ammonium salts and a nitrite on a neutral solution of a cobalt (II) salt, in the presence of air or oxygen.

Ergometrine, Ergonovine, $C_{19}H_{23}N_3O_2$. The water-soluble alkaloid of ergot to which the drug owes much of its physiological activity. It is the chief active constituent of all aqueous preparations of ergot. It is used therapeutically as the acid maleate, which is a white micro-

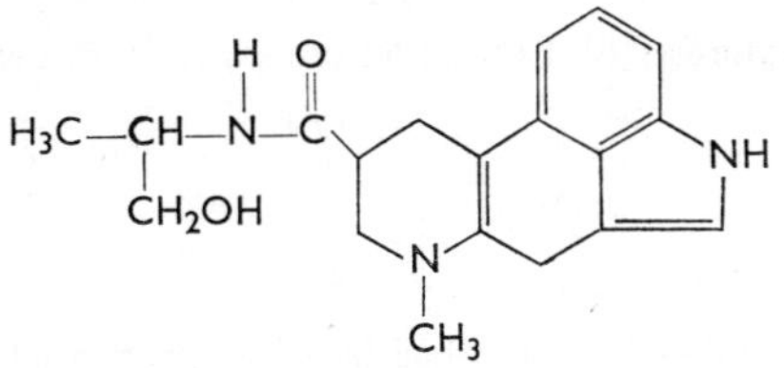

crystalline powder, soluble in water, m.p. 195°-197° (decomp.). It is used to promote uterine contraction and control post-partum haemorrhage. It is administered orally, by intramuscular and intravenous injection. Its physiological effect is similar to that of ergotoxine, but it is more rapid in action and less liable to produce gangrene.

Ergonovine. See Ergometrine.

Ergosterol, 24β-methylcholesta-5,7,22-trien-3β-ol. Crystallizes with one molecule of water

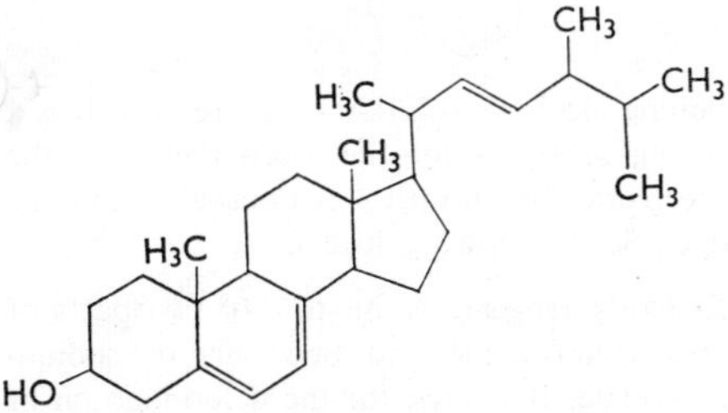

from 95% alcohol, or anhydrous from ether, m.p. 163°, $[\alpha]_D - 133°$ in chloroform. Ergosterol was isolated in 1889 from ergot of rye, and occurs in many yeasts and fungi. It is important as a source of vitamin D_2, which is among a number of products obtained by ultra-violet irradiation.

Ergot. The sclerotium of the fungus *Claviceps purpurea*, which develops in the ovary and replaces the grain of rye. Ergot owes its physiological activity almost entirely to the alkaloids

ergotoxine, ergometrine and ergotamine. It is employed to excite uterine contractions during childbirth, and to check uterine haemorrhage by stimulating the uterine muscles. It is also used as an emmenogogue. The chief galenical preparation is the liquid extract which is standardized on its alkaloidal content.

Ergotamine, $C_{33}H_{35}N_5O_5$. One of the ergot alkaloids, obtained in particular from central European ergots and not in general found with ergometrine. Its tartrate, colourless crytals which soften at 187° and decompose at 192°, is given orally or by injection in the treatment of migraine. Its suggested structure is:

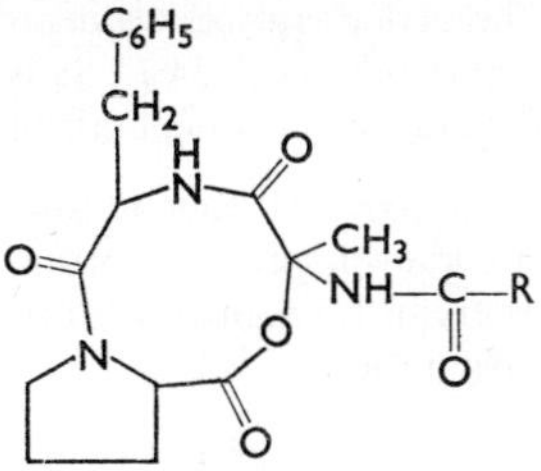

R is lysergyl (see Lysergic acid).

Ergothioneine, Thiolhistidinebetaine. Crystal-

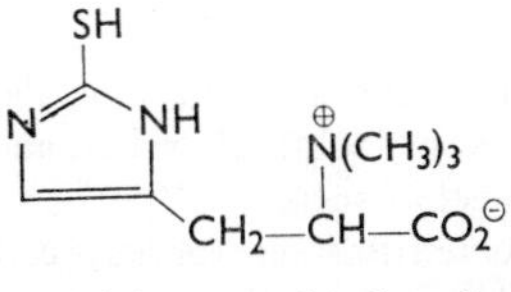

lizes in plates with two molecules of water, m.p. 290°, with decomposition; $[\alpha]_D + 116\cdot5°$. A base present in ergot and in mammalian blood corpuscles. It is a biological transmethylating agent.

Ergotoxine. A mixture of three of the ergot alkaloids, ergocornine, $C_{31}H_{39}N_5O_5$, ergocrystine, $C_{35}H_{39}N_5O_5$, and ergokryptine, $C_{32}H_{39}N_5O_5$. All these have molecules built up of lysergic acid, D-proline, L-phenylalanine and other compounds. Ergotoxine is insoluble in water, but is dissolved by dilute acids, and is usually administered by injection in the form of a solution of the ethanesulphonate. It causes a rise in the blood pressure and produces contraction of unstriated muscle, particularly that of the uterus. Continued administration causes gangrene. Ergotoxine is used in obstetrics to prevent post-partum haemorrhage.

Erlenmeyer, Emil (1825-1900). Professor in Frankfurt, discovered isobutyric acid in 1865, and synthesized tyrosine in 1883.

Erlenmeyer's rule. This originally postulated that all unsaturated alcohols of the types

$$>C{=}CHOH \quad \text{and} \quad >C{=}COH{-}C\!\!<$$

were unstable and that any reaction leading to them would give instead the aldehyde or keto forms

$$>CH—CHO \qquad >CH—CO—C<$$

Later findings have modified the rule, especially when the carbon atoms concerned are connected with carbonyl- or carboxyl-groups, but it still holds good for monohydric unsaturated alcohols.

Erucic acid, $C_{22}H_{42}O_2$.

$$CH_3 \cdot [CH_2]_7 \cdot CH:CH \cdot [CH_2]_{11} \cdot COOH$$

An unsaturated fatty acid belonging to the oleic acid series, occurring as glycerides in rape oil and other vegetable oils, m.p. 34·7°. It is the *cis*-isomer, the *trans*-isomer being brassidic acid.

Erythritol, $C_4H_{10}O_4$. All four tetrose alcohols (tetritols) are known, but the only one to occur naturally is erythritol or mesoerythritol which has the configuration

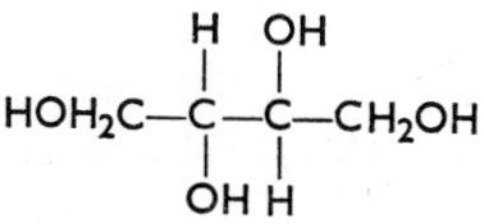

$$HOH_2C—\overset{\overset{\displaystyle H}{|}}{C}—\overset{\overset{\displaystyle OH}{|}}{\underset{\underset{\displaystyle H}{|}}{C}}—CH_2OH$$
$$\qquad\quad \underset{OH}{}$$

It is found in lichens and in some algae. It has m.p. 120°, is very soluble in water, and is about twice as sweet as sucrose.

The other tetritols were formerly called *d*- and *l*-erythritol, but have been renamed L- and D-threitol respectively. A racemic form can also be prepared. They do not occur naturally.

Erythro-. A prefix used to distinguish one

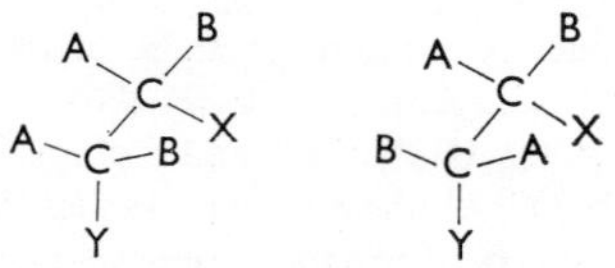

diastereomer from the other *threo* form which is based upon an analogy to erythrose and threose. The erythro diastereomer is defined as the one in which at least two sets of similar substituents on adjacent asymmetric carbons are in the eclipsed configuration.

Erythromycin. An important macrolide (*q.v.*) antibiotic, $C_{37}H_{67}NO_{13}$, produced by *Streptomyces erythreus*. It has a fourteen-membered pentahydroxyketolactone nucleus, with two of the hydroxyl groups linked glycosidically with desosamine (A) and cladinose (B). It is biosynthesized from propionate units.

Erythromycin is active against Gram-positive and certain Gram-negative bacteria, also against

Rickettsia and spirochaetes. It is used for patients who are allergic to or do not respond

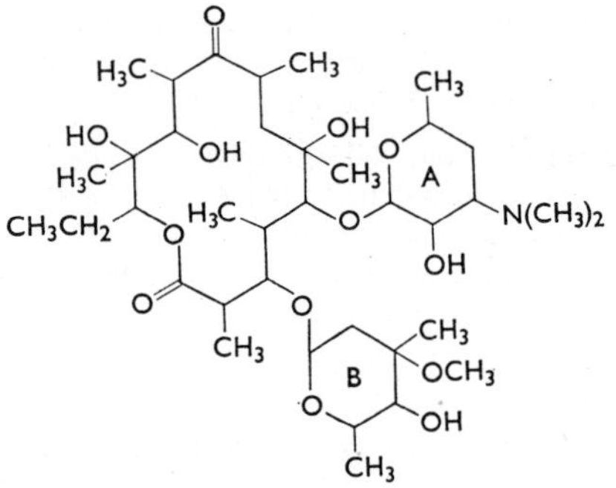

to the more usual antibiotics, such as the penicillins and tetracyclines.

Erythrose, $C_4H_8O_4$. A tetrose sugar, both the

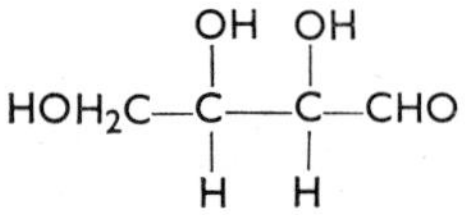

$$HOH_2C—\overset{\overset{\displaystyle OH}{|}}{\underset{\underset{\displaystyle H}{|}}{C}}—\overset{\overset{\displaystyle OH}{|}}{\underset{\underset{\displaystyle H}{|}}{C}}—CHO$$

D- and L- forms of which have been prepared. It has been obtained as a liquid, very soluble in water and alcohol.

Erythrosin. This red dye is prepared by the action of iodine and potassium iodate on a

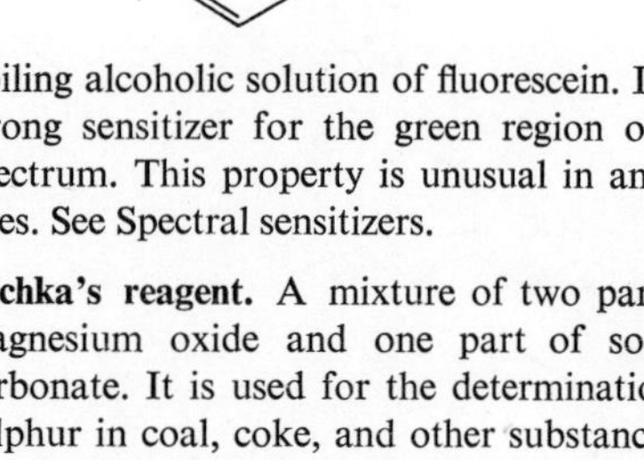

boiling alcoholic solution of fluorescein. It is a strong sensitizer for the green region of the spectrum. This property is unusual in anionic dyes. See Spectral sensitizers.

Eschka's reagent. A mixture of two parts of magnesium oxide and one part of sodium carbonate. It is used for the determination of sulphur in coal, coke, and other substances.

Eserine. See Physostigmine.

Essential fatty acids (EFA). A group of unsaturated acids, which must be in the diet for normal growth. A deficiency of EFA leads to cessation of growth and to skin lesions and necrosis: individual acids show different activity in these respects. Necessary structural features include an all-*cis* arrangement of double bonds, and a 'methylene-interrupted' polyene system.

The principal EFA are linoleic acid (*cis,cis*-

9,12-octadecadienoic acid), for which the term was coined originally (1930); arachidonic acid (*cis,cis,cis,cis*-5,8,11,14-eicosatetraenoic acid); linolenic acid (*cis,cis,cis,*-9,12,15-octadecatrienoic acid); and γ-linolenic acid (*cis,cis,cis*-6,9-12-octadecatrienoic acid). Linolenic acid is sometimes excluded from the class. EFA occur abundantly in most vegetable oils, and to a lesser extent in other dietary fats of animal or marine origin, so that a normal adult diet is unlikely to be deficient in EFA. Infants probably need about 4% of their diet (in terms of calories) as linoleic acid: human milk is a source much richer than cow's milk in this respect.

Esterases. Enzymes which catalyse the hydrolysis of esters. Included are the lipases, phosphatases, sulphatases, and such enzymes as choline esterase.

Ester-gum. See Rosin-ester.

Esterification. The name given to the process of formation of esters by the combination of an acid with an alcohol.

Esters. Organic compounds formed by the union of an acid and an alcohol with elimination of water. They are volatile liquids or low-melting solids and are usually insoluble in water but soluble in alcohol or ether. Many esters have characteristic fruity odours and occur naturally in fruit. As the reaction between an acid and an alcohol is reversible, it cannot be carried to completion unless the water produced is removed. In some cases it is sufficient to have a large excess of alcohol present to secure a good yield of ester; in other cases it is usual to add a liquid such as benzene or carbon tetrachloride to the mixture and to distil off the water in the form of a low-boiling mixture. The reaction between alcohol and acid is very slow at ordinary temperatures, but the ester is formed much more rapidly at higher temperatures and in the presence of a small amount of an acid such as sulphuric, hydrochloric, or benzenesulphonic acid. Esters are also produced by the action of an alcohol on an acid chloride or anhydride; amides also react with alcohols to give esters in the presence of boron fluorides. Some esters may be obtained by the action of an aldehyde on aluminium ethoxide or isopropoxide; the number of aldehydes which undergo this reaction is limited. Methyl and ethyl esters are often conveniently obtained by treating the sodium salt of the acid with methyl or ethyl sulphates. Diazomethane also reacts with organic acids to give methyl esters. Esters can also be prepared by heating an alcohol with the methyl or ethyl ester of the acid; in this case an exchange of alcohols occurs and methyl or ethyl alcohol is formed. Esters are completely decomposed to

acid and alcohol by heating with dilute sodium hydroxide solution. They react with ammonia to give amides; with ketones in the presence of sodamide to give 1,3-diketones and with Grignard reagents to give tertiary alcohols. They are reduced by a mixture of sodium and ethyl alcohol to the alcohol corresponding to the acid of the ester. Used as solvents, flavouring essences, and perfumes; they are also used in many chemical processes.

Estradiol. See Oestradiol.

Étard's reaction. This is a direct method for the production of aromatic aldehydes by the oxidation of the methylated homologues of benzene. It is effected by chromyl chloride, which first gives addition compounds, e.g.

$$C_6H_5CH_3 \cdot 2CrO_2Cl_2.$$

These are decomposed to give the aldehyde and a chromium (III) salt. When benzene homologues with longer side chains are treated with chromyl chloride a ketone is the usual product, but with ethylbenzene a mixture of phenylacetaldehyde and acetophenone is obtained.

Ethane, $CH_3 \cdot CH_3$. A colourless, odourless gas: it forms an explosive mixture with air. B.p. $-88 \cdot 63°$, d^0 $0 \cdot 5719$. It occurs in the gas from petroleum deposits. May be prepared by reduction of ethylene or acetylene by hydrogen under pressure in the presence of a nickel catalyst, or by the electrolysis of a solution of potassium acetate. It has the general properties of the paraffins. Used in low-temperature refrigeration plant.

1,2-Ethanedithiol, $HS(CH_2)_2SH$. A colourless liquid, b.p. 146°, which dissolves easily in alkali and organic solvents. Used in place of 1,3-propane dithiol (*q.v.*) for protecting carbonyl groups.

Ethanol. See Alcohol.

Ethanolamines. The three compounds are low-melting, colourless solids which very readily absorb water and form viscous liquids; they have distinct ammoniacal odours and are strong bases. Soluble in water and alcohol, sparingly soluble in benzene and ether.

Monoethanolamine, 2-Aminoethyl alcohol, 2-hydroxyethylamine, $HOCH_2CH_2NH_2$, d^{20} $1 \cdot 022$, m.p. $10 \cdot 5°$, b.p. $171°$. Is volatile in steam.

Diethanolamine, di-(2-hydroxyethyl) amine, $(HOCH_2CH_2)_2NH$, d^{20} $1 \cdot 097$, m.p. $28°$, b.p. $217°/150$ mm. Not volatile in steam.

Triethanolamine, tri-(2-hydroxyethyl) amine, $(HOCH_2CH_2)_3N$, d_{20}^{20} $1 \cdot 126$, m.p. $21°$, b.p. $277°/150$ mm. Not volatile in steam. The commercial product contains some mono- and di-ethanolamines.

All these compounds are manufactured by

heating ethylene oxide under pressure with concentrated aqueous ammonia. A mixture of the three is obtained, the proportion of each depending on the ammonia/ethylene oxide ratio used, and this is separated by fractional distillation.

The ethanolamines form soaps with fatty acids which are almost neutral in reaction and soluble in benzene. These are of great commercial importance, being used as detergents, emulsifying agents and in the preparation of cosmetics and toiletries. Monoethanolamine is widely used for removing acid constituents such as carbon dioxide and hydrogen sulphide from gas streams. These acid gases are then removed by steam stripping.

Ethene. See Ethylene.

Ethenoid plastics. High molecular weight, usually resinous bodies, obtained by the polymerisation of monomers containing one or two reactive ethenoid linkages CH_2=CHX or by the modification of such polymers. Typical ethenoid monomers are vinyl acetate, vinyl chloride, styrene, isobutylene, ethylene, methyl methacrylate, methyl acrylate, diallyl esters and vinylidene chloride.

Ethenyl, Vinyl. The name given to the group CH_2=CH—.

Ether, Diethyl ether, Diethyl oxide,
$(CH_3CH_2)_2O$. A colourless liquid with a pleasant, characteristic odour; it is very volatile and its vapour forms an explosive mixture with air, d_4^{24} 0·708, b.p. 34·5°. Soluble in water to 7%; soluble in strong sulphuric and hydrochloric acids; miscible with many organic solvents. The preparation of ether from alcohol and sulphuric acid was described by Valerius Cordus in 1540. It is manufactured by passing alcohol vapour into a mixture of 92% alcohol and 78% sulphuric acid at 128°. May also be produced as a by-product in the manufacture of alcohol from ethylene. Commercial ether usually contains small amounts of water, alcohol, aldehyde, and peroxide; it may be purified by standing over solid sodium hydroxide for some days and may be dried over sodium wire or molecular sieves. It is a comparatively inert compound and is an excellent solvent for a great many organic substances. Oxidized by nitric acid to acetic acid. Combines with strong sulphuric acid to give ethyl hydrogen sulphate and with hydrogen iodide to give ethyl iodide. Chlorine reacts violently with ether at ordinary temperatures but forms various chloro-ethers at low temperatures. Crystalline addition compounds are formed with some metallic salts.

Employed for the production of general anaesthesia by inhalation. It is considered one of the safest anaesthetics, but it is essential that it should be pure and free from its very objectionable oxidation products, as these give rise to unpleasant and dangerous after-effects. Ether acts as a carminative to the stomach, and is administered in the form of spirit of ether as a restorative in collapse. It is also injected hypodermically for the same purpose. Medical and pharmaceutical uses account for a relatively small proportion of ether consumption, and it is mainly used as a chemical intermediate and as a solvent for oils, fats, waxes and alkaloids.

Ethereal sulphates. A certain proportion of the sulphur in the urine is present in the form of the ethereal sulphates, which are esters formed by the union of sulphuric acid with phenols. Their excretion is the result of a detoxication mechanism, the esters being much less toxic than the free phenols. The ethereal sulphates have soluble barium and benzidine salts, and can thus be separated from the inorganic sulphates. They are hydrolysed to sulphuric acid and phenols by boiling with acids.

Ethers. Organic compounds of the type R—O—R′, where R and R′ are alkyl or aryl radicals or their derivatives. They are formed by heating the sodium derivative of a hydroxy-compound with an alkyl or aryl halide; or by treating the hydroxy-compound with an alkyl halide in presence of silver oxide. Methyl and ethyl ethers are conveniently prepared by the action of dimethyl and diethyl sulphates on a hydroxy-compound in presence of sodium hydroxide solution. Diazomethane will react with phenols in ethereal solution to give methyl ethers. The simpler aliphatic ethers are manufactured by the action of sulphuric acid on the appropriate alcohol or olefin. They are usually liquids with pleasant odours, but some aromatic and the higher aliphatic ethers are crystalline solids. They are insoluble in water but soluble in alcohol and diethyl ether.

Ethinylation. The reaction between acetylene and organic substrates to produce substances having an intact acetylenic bond; e.g. the reaction of formaldehyde and acetylene to give butyne-1,4-diol, $HOCH_2$—C≡C—CH_2OH.

Ethisterone, Pregneninolone, Ethinyltestosterone,

$C_{21}H_{28}O_2$. A white crystalline powder, insoluble in water, sparingly soluble in alcohol, m.p. 273°, $[\alpha]_D + 33°$ (1% in pyridine). Prepared by treating dehydroepiandrosterone with acetylene and oxidizing the product. It has the properties of progesterone, and is given orally for treating functional uterine haemorrhage.

Norethisterone, 19-norethisterone, m.p. 201°-206° $[\alpha]_D -23°$ to $-27°$ (1% w/v in chloroform) is one of the progestational steroids used in the contraceptive pill.

Ethocaine. See Procaine.

Ethoxy. A prefix used in organic chemistry to denote that the substance contains an ethoxyl, or $CH_3CH_2O—$, group.

Ethoxyl. The name given to the group $CH_3CH_2O—$; also written EtO—.

Ethyl. The name given to the group $CH_3·CH_2—$; often written $C_2H_5—$ and Et—.

Ethyl acetate, Acetic ester, Acetic ether, $CH_3CO_2C_2H_5$. A colourless liquid, d 0·9245, b.p. 77°, with a pleasant fruity odour. Only slightly soluble in water, but miscible with most organic liquids. Manufactured from ethyl alcohol, acetic acid and concentrated sulphuric acid, or from acetylene via acetaldehyde with an aluminium alkoxide as catalyst. It is an extremely useful solvent, especially for cellulose-type varnishes and adhesives; also used for cosmetic applications and as an artificial essence.

Used for the synthesis of acetoacetic ester (*q.v.*).

Ethyl acetoacetate. See Acetoacetic ester.

Ethyl acrylate, $C_5H_8O_2$.

$$CH_2:CHCOOCH_2CH_3$$

A colourless liquid, d^0 0·9283, b.p. 101°. Insoluble in water; miscible with most organic solvents. Manufactured by treating ethylene chlorohydrin with sodium cyanide and heating the β-hydroxypropionitrile so formed with ethyl alcohol and sulphuric acid. Forms a colourless resin on standing. Used in the manufacture of synthetic resins.

Ethyl alcohol. See Alcohol.

Ethylamines. Organic compounds in which one or more of the hydrogen atoms of ammonia are replaced by ethyl groups. They are colourless liquids with strongly ammoniacal odours; they are inflammable and burn with a yellow flame. Manufactured by passing ethylene or ethyl alcohol vapour with ammonia under pressure over heated catalysts. The relative amounts of the three amines formed can be controlled by varying the proportions of ammonia to ethylene or alcohol. They are all three strongly basic in character and show the typical properties of aliphatic amines.

Ethylamine, Monoethylamine, $CH_3CH_2NH_2$, d^{15} 0·6892, b.p. 18·7°; miscible with water, alcohol, and ether. Prepared by reduction of

acetonitrile or by heating ethyl chloride with alcoholic ammonia under pressure. It is a strong base and will displace ammonia from ammonium salts. Forms a crystalline hydrochloride and also crystalline compounds with various metallic chlorides.

Diethylamine, $(CH_3CH_2)_2NH$, d^{18} 0·7108, b.p. 55·5°; very soluble in water, miscible with alcohol and ether. Forms a crystalline hydrate, $[(C_2H_5)_2NH]_2H_2O$. Prepared by the action of a boiling solution of sodium hydroxide on nitroso-diethylaniline. Forms crystalline compounds with many metallic chlorides.

Triethylamine $(CH_3CH_2)_3N$, is an oily liquid, d^{25} 0·7255, b.p. 89·4°; soluble in water, miscible with alcohol and ether. Prepared by heating ethylamine with an alcoholic solution of ethyl chloride under pressure. It is readily oxidized by potassium permanganate.

Ethylation. Processes by which an ethyl group is added to a compound. In aliphatic chemistry this involves the substitution of the hydrogen atom of a hydroxyl, amino, or imino group, and produces an ether or a secondary or tertiary amine respectively. In aromatic chemistry it may also mean the substitution of one of the hydrogen atoms of the ring by the ethyl group; this is carried out by the Friedel-Crafts reaction.

N-Ethyl carbazole. Crystallizes in leaflets, m.p.

67°-68°, very soluble in ether and hot alcohol. It is used as a raw material in making Hydron Blue G.

Ethyl chaulmoograte. An oily liquid, d^{20} 0·900 to 0·905, soluble in alcohol and other organic solvents. It consists of the ethyl esters of the total fatty acids of chaulmoogra oil.

Ethyl chloride, Monochloroethane, CH_3CH_2Cl. A colourless liquid with an ethereal odour; it burns with a green-edged flame, d^0 0·9214, b.p. 12·5°. Sparingly soluble in water; miscible with alcohol and ether. Manufactured by reacting hydrogen chloride with ethylene at 40° in the presence of aluminium chloride using ethylene dichloride as solvent, or by the catalytic or photochemical chlorination of ethane. Reacts with ammonia at 100° to give ethylamine hydrochloride; converted to ethyl alcohol by heating with potassium hydroxide. Forms crystalline products with many metallic chlorides. Its principal use is in the manufacture of lead tetraethyl, for which purpose very large quantities are made.

It is used in medicine solely as an anaesthetic

for minor operations. When inhaled, it is very rapid in its action, but anaesthesia cannot be long maintained on account of the danger of collapse. Ethyl chloride, having a low b.p. is useful for the production of local anaesthesia; it is applied in the form of a fine spray, and its rapid evaporation freezes the part to which it is applied.

Ethyl chlorocarbonate. See Chloroformic ester.

Ethyl chloroformate. See Chloroformic ester.

Ethyl citrate, Triethyl citrate, $C_{12}H_{20}O_7$. A

$$CH_2COOCH_2CH_3$$
$$HOC-COOCH_2CH_3$$
$$CH_2COOCH_2CH_3$$

colourless oil with a bitter taste, d^{20} 1·1369, b.p 185°/17 mm. Sparingly soluble in water; miscible with alcohol and ether. Manufactured by distillation of a mixture of citric acid, alcohol, and sulphuric acid with a solvent such as carbon tetrachloride or benzene. Has the typical properties of an ester. Used as a fixative in perfumery.

Ethyl cyanoacetate. See Cyanoacetic ester.

Ethyl diazoacetate. See Diazoacetic ester.

Ethylene, Ethene, $CH_2{=}CH_2$. A colourless gas with a faint ethereal odour which occurs in natural gas, crude oil and coal gas. M.p. −169°, b.p. −105°. It is manufactured in larger quantities than any other organic chemical, most of it being derived from the vapour-phase cracking of ethane, various petroleum fractions and crude oil. It is also obtained from ethyl alcohol by vapour phase dehydration using an activated alumina catalyst at 350°. May be prepared by dropping alcohol on to syrupy phosphoric acid heated to 220°. It is inflammable and forms an explosive mixture with air. Readily absorbed by concentrated sulphuric acid to give ethyl hydrogen sulphate; if the reaction is carried out under pressure, diethyl sulphate is largely formed, It is dissolved by a solution of mercuric sulphate and is liberated by heating. Absorbed by solutions of potassium permanganate to give ethylene glycol: by dilute chlorine water to give ethylene chlorohydrin. Reduced by hydrogen to ethane. Reacts with hydrogen bromide and hydrogen iodide at 100° to give ethyl bromide and iodide; hydrogen chloride does not react under these conditions. With ammonia under pressure the ethylamines are formed. Reacts with water at 450°, or at lower temperatures in the presence of catalysts, to give ethyl alcohol.

It is given off in minute amounts by ripe apples and has the property of accelerating the ripening of fruit. Used in the manufacture of

ethylene oxide, ethyl alcohol, styrene, ethylene dichloride and ethyl chloride. When polymerized under high pressure, or at lower pressures in the presence of a catalyst, it gives the important plastic material polyethylene (*q.v.*).

Ethylene chlorohydrin, 2-Chloroethyl alcohol, $ClCH_2 \cdot CH_2OH$. A colourless liquid with a faint ethereal odour, d^{20} 1·213, b.p. 129°. Miscible with water, alcohol, and benzene. Forms a constant-boiling mixture (b.p. 96°/740 mm) containing 42·3% chlorohydrin by weight. Manufactured by passing ethylene into dilute chlorine water, or by passing a mixture of ethylene and carbon dioxide into a suspension of bleaching powder in water. It reacts with solutions of sodium bicarbonate to give ethylene glycol and with solid sodium hydroxide to give ethylene oxide; with concentrated sulphuric acid at 100° to give $\beta\beta$-dichloroethyl ether; with ammonia and amines to give aminoethyl alcohols and with sodium salts of organic acids to give glycol esters. It is used in the preparation of these compounds and in the synthesis of phenylethyl alcohol, procaine, and indigo. Also used as an insecticide and for forcing the early sprouting of potatoes.

Ethylenediamine, 1,2 Diaminoethane, $C_2H_8N_2$, $H_2NCH_2 \cdot CH_2NH_2$. A colourless liquid which fumes in air and has a strong ammoniacal odour, d^{15} 0·902, m.p. 11°, b.p. 116°. Soluble in water. Absorbs carbon dioxide and water from the air to give ethylenediamine carbamate. Manufactured by heating ethylene dichloride with ammonia under pressure in the presence of cuprous chloride. It combines with hydrochloric acid to give a crystalline hydrochloride. Forms oil-soluble soaps with fatty acids; these are used as detergents and emulsifying agents. It is also used as a solvent for certain vat dyes and for casein, shellac, and resin. Forms very stable complexes with transition metals, in which it acts as a chelating agent.

Ethylenediaminetetra-acetic acid, EDTA.

$$(HO_2CCH_2)_2N \cdot CH_2 \cdot CH_2 \cdot N(CH_2CO_2H)_2$$

An important compound, which owes its use to its sequestering properties. A polydentate chelating agent. Forms complexes with most elements. The iron complex is used for application to calcifuginous (lime-hating) plants growing in alkaline soils and suffering from iron deficiency.

Ethylene dibromide, 1,2 Dibromoethane, $BrCH_2 \cdot CH_2Br$. A colourless liquid with a sweet odour, d^{20} 2·1816, m.p. 10°, b.p. 131·6°. Insoluble in water; miscible with most organic solvents, Manufactured by passing ethylene through bromine or bromine and water at about 20°. Chemical properties similar to those of ethylene dichloride; when heated with alkali hydroxides, vinyl bromide is formed. Used extensively in petrols to combine with the lead formed by the decomposition of lead tetraethyl, as a fumigant for stored products and as a nematicide. It is toxic to plants so that soil treatments must be carried out at least 8 days before planting.

Ethylene dichloride, 1,2 Dichloroethane,

$$CH_2Cl \cdot CH_2Cl$$

A colourless liquid with an odour like that of chloroform, d_4^{20} 1·257, b.p. 84°. Very sparingly soluble in water; miscible with alcohol, ether, hydrocarbons, essential oils and mineral oils. It is an excellent solvent for fats and waxes. Was first known as 'oil of Dutch chemists'. Manufactured by the vapour- or liquid-phase reaction of ethylene and chlorine in the presence of a catalyst. It reacts with anhydrous acetates to give ethylene glycol diacetate and with ammonia to give ethylenediamine, these reactions being employed for the manufacture of these chemicals. It burns only with difficulty and is not decomposed by boiling water.

Most of the ethylene dichloride produced is utilized for the manufacture of vinyl chloride, which may be obtained from it by pyrolysis or the action of caustic soda. Large quantities are also used in anti-knock additives for gasoline. As a solvent it has been displaced by trichloroethylene and tetrachloroethylene.

Ethylene dinitrate, Ethylene glycol dinitrate, $C_2H_4N_2O_6$, $O_2NOCH_2 \cdot CH_2ONO_2$. A colourless liquid with a sweetish taste and no appreciable odour, d_{15}^{15} 1·496, b.p. 105°/19 mm.; it explodes at 215° when rapidly heated. Slightly soluble (7%) in water; miscible with alcohol, chloroform, and benzene. Manufactured by treating ethylene glycol with a mixture of fuming nitric and sulphuric acids at a low temperature or by passing ethylene into a cold mixture of nitric and sulphuric acids. The nitrate separates as an insoluble layer, and is washed with water and distilled under reduced pressure. It is more volatile than nitroglycerin and its vapour is toxic. Less sensitive to shock than nitroglycerin and a rather more powerful explosive. Used as an explosive of the dynamite type; it is mixed with nitroglycerin to reduce the freezing-point of dynamite.

Ethylene glycol, 1,2 - Dihydroxyethane, $HOCH_2 \cdot CH_2OH$. A colourless, odourless, rather viscous liquid having a sweet taste, d^{20} 1·114, b.p. 197°. Miscible with water, alcohol, and many organic solvents. It readily absorbs up to twice its weight of water vapour from the atmosphere. Manufactured by heating ethylene chlorohydrin with sodium bicarbonate solution at 75°, or by the hydration of ethylene oxide

using very dilute sulphuric acid at 60° or water under pressure at 195°. By far the most important commercial use is in anti-freezes and coolants for engines; smaller quantities are used in manufacture of polyester fibres (e.g. Terylene) and in the manufacture of various esters used as plasticizers.

Ethylene glycol dinitrate. See Ethylene dinitrate.

Ethylene glycol monobutyl ether, Butyl cellosolve, $C_6H_{14}O_2$, $CH_3CH_2CH_2CH_2OCH_2CH_2OH$. A colourless liquid with a pleasant odour, d_{20}^{20} 0·9017, b.p. 171°. Miscible with water and most organic solvents. Manufactured by heating ethylene oxide with n-butyl alcohol in the presence of nickel sulphate as a catalyst. Used as a solvent in brushing lacquers.

Ethylene glycol monoethyl ether, Cellosolve, $C_4H_{10}O_2$, $CH_3CH_2OCH_2CH_2OH$. A colourless liquid with a pleasant odour, d_{20}^{20} 0·9311, b.p. 135°. Miscible with water and most organic solvents. Manufactured by heating ethylene oxide with ethyl alcohol and a catalyst, such as nickel sulphate, or by treating ethylene glycol with diethyl sulphate and sodium hydroxide. Used extensively as a solvent in nitrocellulose lacquers.

Ethylene glycol monoethyl ether acetate, Cellosolve acetate, $C_6H_{12}O_3$,

$$CH_3CH_2OCH_2CH_2OOCCH_3$$

A colourless liquid with a pleasant ethereal odour, d_{20}^{20} 0·9749, b.p. 156°. Soluble in water to 22% by weight; miscible with most organic solvents. Manufactured by heating ethylene glycol monoethyl ether with acetic acid, Used as a solvent in nitrocellulose lacquers.

Ethylene glycol monomethyl ether, Methyl cellosolve, $C_3H_8O_2$, $CH_3OCH_2CH_2OH$, is a colourless liquid with a pleasant odour, d_{20}^{20} 0·9660, b.p. 124·3°. Miscible with water and most organic solvents. Manufactured by heating ethylene oxide with methyl alcohol, either under pressure at 180° or in the presence of a catalyst such as nickel sulphate. Also obtained by treating ethylene glycol with dimethyl sulphate and sodium hydroxide. Used as a solvent for cellulose acetate lacquers and for certain dyes and resins.

Ethylene oxide. A colourless gas with a sweet odour which is somewhat lachrymatory, d 0·887, b.p. 10·5°. Soluble in water and organic solvents. Manufactured by heating ethylene chlorohydrin with milk of lime or caustic soda solution; or by the direct oxidation of ethylene at 250°-300° using a silver catalyst. It forms an explosive mixture with air. Reacts with water in the presence of sulphuric acid to give ethylene glycol and polyethylene glycols; with alcohols and phenols to give ethers of glycol; and with hydrochloric acid to give ethylene chlorohydrin. It reacts with many primary and secondary amines to give hydroxyethylamines; with organic acids to give monoesters of ethylene glycol, and with acid anhydrides to give diesters. It is reduced by hydrogen to ethyl alcohol, and is converted to acetaldehyde by heating at 200°-300° in the presence of alumina. Its principal use is as an intermediate in the manufacture of ethylene glycol, glycol ethers, ethanolamines and similar compounds. It is also used as a fumigant.

Ethylene-propylene rubber (EPR). A high molecular weight random copolymer of ethylene and propylene, devoid of crystallinity at ordinary temperature, that behaves as a typical rubber. It is produced by the use of modified Ziegler catalysts. A trace of a diene monomer is often included in the copolymer to facilitate vulcanization. EPR is very resistant to ageing and has very good mechanical strength.

Ethyl formate, $HCOOCH_2CH_3$. A colourless liquid with the odour of peach-kernels, d^{20} 0·9168, b.p. 54·3°. Insoluble in water; miscible with alcohols, ether, and benzene. Prepared by boiling ethyl alcohol and formic acid in the presence of a little sulphuric acid; the product is diluted with water and the insoluble ester separated and distilled. Used as a fumigant and larvicide for dried fruits, tobacco, and foodstuffs. It is also used in the synthesis of thiamine.

2-Ethylhexyl alcohol, Octyl alcohol, $C_8H_{18}O$.

$$CH_3CH_2CH_2CH_2CHCH_2OH$$
$$| $$
$$CH_2CH_3$$

B.p. 181°, d^{20} 0·8328. Manufactured by heating butyl alcohol with potassium hydroxide and boric oxide at 270°-300°. Used as an anti-foaming agent, as a dispersing agent in the pigment and ceramic industries, and as a means of introducing the 2-ethylhexyl group into other products. Its esters, e.g. with phthalic, stearic, and phosphoric acids, are used as plasticizers. The acrylate on copolymerization with other monomers gives plastics which are 'internally' plasticized. Other esters are used as lubricants, bactericides, fungicides, and insecticides.

Ethyl hydrogen sulphate, Ethylsulphuric acid, $C_2H_6O_4S$. An oily liquid with an acid reaction,

$$CH_3CH_2-O\diagdown_{S}\diagup^{O}$$
$$HO\diagup\diagdown_{O}$$

d^{17} 1·316. Soluble in water and slowly hydrolysed by it to ethyl alcohol and sulphuric acid. Prepared by passing ethylene into concentrated sulphuric acid or by heating ethyl alcohol and

sulphuric acid. Gives ethylene when heated alone, and diethyl sulphate when heated with ethyl alcohol at 140°. Forms crystalline metallic salts which are soluble in water.

Ethylidene. The name given to the group

$$CH_3 \cdot CH\diagdown$$

Ethylidene diacetate. A colourless liquid with a

$$CH_3CH\diagup^{OOCCH_3}_{\diagdown OOCCH_3}$$

characteristic heavy odour, d^{15} 1·073, m.p. 18·9°, b.p. 169°. Manufactured by passing acetylene into glacial acetic acid containing mercuric sulphate. The temperature is kept above 70°; at lower temperatures vinyl acetate is also formed. It is slowly decomposed by water to give acetaldehyde and acetic acid. Decomposed when heated above 150° to give acetic anhydride and acetaldehyde; some vinyl acetate is formed. It is an intermediate product in the manufacture of acetic anhydride from acetylene.

Ethyl iodoacetate, Iodoacetic ester, $C_4H_7IO_2$, $ICH_2COOCH_2CH_3$. A colourless liquid, the vapour of which is a powerful lachrymator, $d^{12·7}$ 1·8173, b.p. 178°-180°. Insoluble in water; miscible with alcohol and ether. Manufactured by warming monochloroacetic ester with potassium iodide in alcoholic solution. It is very similar in its reactions to monochloroacetic ester. It has been used as a lachrymator in shells and grenades.

Ethyl lactate, $C_5H_{10}O_3$.

$$CH_3CHOH \cdot COOCH_2CH_3$$

A colourless liquid with a pleasant odour, d^{19} 1·0308, b.p. 154°; miscible with water and most organic solvents. Manufactured by distilling a mixture of ($\pm$)-lactic acid, ethyl alcohol, and benzene in the presence of a little sulphuric or benzene sulphonic acid. The water produced by the reaction is removed in the distillate and the yield of ester is higher than if no benzene is used. It is a solvent for cellulose nitrate and acetate and also for various resins. Used as a lacquer solvent.

Ethyl orthoformate. See Orthoformic ester.

Ethyl radical. The radical $-CH_2 \cdot CH_3$ made in the free state by the thermal dissociation of $PbEt_4$, or by the photolysis of diethyl ketone. It decomposes to yield CH_3 above 600°.

Ethyl silicate. Sometimes called 'silicon ester'. Has the formula $Si(OC_2H_5)_4$. It is a thin mobile liquid, resembling paraffin in appearance and with a mild ester-like odour, m.p. $-77°$, b.p. 168°, made by reacting alcohol with silicon tetrachloride. It is readily miscible with petrol, alcohol, benzene, or light petroleum. It is not miscible with water, but is slowly decomposed by it to give ethyl alcohol and silicic acid, which dehydrates to an amorphous, very resistant form of silica. It is used for waterproofing stonework, for making precision castings, and for bonding.

Ethyl succinate, Diethyl succinate, $C_8H_{14}O_4$, $CH_3CH_2O_2CCH_2 \cdot CH_2CO_2CH_2CH_3$. A colourless liquid with a faint odour, d^{20} 1·0402, b.p. 217·7°. Insoluble in water; miscible with alcohol and ether. Manufactured by heating succinic acid with alcohol and sulphuric acid. Has the typical properties of an ester. Used as a fixative in perfumery.

Ethylsulphuric acid. See Ethyl hydrogen sulphate.

Ethyne. The systematic name for acetylene.

Eucaine. See Benzamine hydrochloride.

Eucalyptol. See 1,8-Cineole.

Eucalyptus oil. The oil distilled from the leaves of various species of *Eucalyptus*. Its chief constituent is cineole, which is present to the extent of at least 70%. Eucalyptus oil is used chiefly as an antiseptic; it is inhaled for catarrh, and used as a prophylactic for colds and influenza.

Eucarvone, $C_{10}H_{14}O$. A monocyclic ketone obtained by the action of alkali on carvone hydrobromide. It is a colourless oil resembling menthone in smell and with b.p. 88°/10 mm., d_4^{20} 0·9490, n_D^{20} 1·50872.

Eugenol, 4-allyl-2-methoxyphenol, $C_{10}H_{12}O_2$. A colourless liquid, b.p. 254°. Soluble in alcohol and ether, sparingly soluble in water. It is the chief constituent of oil of cloves from which it is obtained by extracting with excess alkali and decomposing with acid. It is also present in oil of bay and oil of cinnamon. It is used in dentistry as an antiseptic dressing and mixed with zinc oxide as a temporary filling. It is a strong antiseptic and is used as a preservative to prevent mould growth.

Euler-Chelpin, Hans von (1873-1964). Born in Augsburg and graduating at the University of Berlin, Euler-Chelpin worked in the laboratories of Nernst, Arrhenius, and van't Hoff. His main studies were in the field of biochemistry, particularly enzymes and co-enzymes. He shared the Nobel Prize in chemistry for 1929.

Europium. Eu. At.no. 63, At.wt. 152·0,

d 5·259, m.p. 826°, b.p. 1439°. Metallic europium has a body-centred cubic lattice, $a=$ 4·578 Å. It is a typical rare-earth element (*q.v.*). The metal is very reactive in air, it is used as a red phosphor in colour television.

Europium forms two series of salts. Europic salts are tripositive and are typical rare-earth compounds (*q.v.*). These salts are pale pink in colour. Europous salts contain the dipositive metal and are pale yellow in colour. They are strong reducing agents.

Europous chloride, $EuCl_2$. Prepared by reduction of $EuCl_3$ in hydrogen at 600°. It is a pale straw-coloured salt and forms a hydrate $EuCl_2 \cdot 2H_2O$, insoluble in concentrated hydrochloric acid. The fluoride, bromide, and iodide are prepared similarly.

Europous sulphate, $EuSO_4$. Can be prepared from europic solutions by reduction with strontium amalgam in presence of sulphuric acid. The europous sulphate is precipitated with the strontium sulphate. The lower oxidation states of europium have been used for the separation of the metal from the other rare-earths.

Eutectic. When a mechanical mixture of substances melts sharply, the mixture is said to be a eutectic or eutectic mixture, and the melting point is the eutectic point.

Eutectic point. The point on the phase diagram of a mixture of substances which represents the melting point and composition of a eutectic is called a eutectic point.

EVA plastics. Plastics based on copolymers of ethylene and vinyl acetate (5-15%). Such materials are more flexible and resilient than normal polyethylene and are used in applications where previously a rubber or plasticized polyvinylchloride might have been used.

Evaporation. All liquids and solids have a characteristic vapour pressure. In a closed vessel, after a sufficient time has elapsed for equilibrium to be established, as many molecules leave the liquid surface to form vapour as return to it from the vapour phase to form liquid. In an open vessel, however, no such equilibrium is set up and if the molecules of vapour immediately over the liquid surface are removed further liquid molecules vaporize to take their place. In this way the liquid bulk is continuously diminished and the process of evaporation occurs. In the chemical and process industries the term normally refers to the removal of water from a solution.

Evaporator. The unit in which low-temperature liquid refrigerant is vaporized in a refrigeration plant is known as an evaporator, but the term is usually confined to plants for the concentration of aqueous solutions by evaporation. The latter may take a variety of forms, but all have a number of features in common:

(a) The evaporator body. This unit holds the solution being concentrated and also provides a space for liquid and vapour to disengage; in some evaporators, featuring low liquid residence times, the body may be quite small.

(b) The heater unit. This is normally of the shell-and-tube type (when it is known as a *calandria*) and may be situated outside or inside the evaporator body.

(c) A device for removing entrained liquid from the steam evolved.

Some of the more important types of evaporator and modes of operation are described under Forced circulation evaporator, Long-tube vertical evaporator, Multiple effect evaporators and Vapour compression evaporator.

Excelsin. A protein, belonging to the globulin class, that can be obtained crystalline from the Brazil nut.

Exchange reactions. These are reactions which occur without any chemical change. In an electron exchange reaction, e.g.

$$Fe^{+2} + Fe^{+3} \rightleftharpoons Fe^{+3} + Fe^{+2}$$

the driving force of the reaction is the positive entropy of mixing and the reaction rate may be determined using radioactive iron. An example of an isotopic exchange reaction is

$$^{16}O_2 + 2H_2{}^{18}O \rightleftharpoons {}^{18}O_2 + 2H_2{}^{16}O$$

and here, due to differences in zero point energy caused by the differing masses of the isotopes, the rates of the forward and reverse reactions are not equal. The equilibrium constant for this reaction is $1 \cdot 012$ at $25°$. Use is made of this fact in the separation of the two isotopes of oxygen.

Many exchange reactions are used for the separation of isotopes.

Excited state. When absorption of energy causes the electrons of an atom or molecule to be transferred to new orbitals of higher energy, the resulting state is called excited.

Exclusion principle. For any atom no two electrons can have all four quantum numbers identical.

Exo-. See Endo-.

Exopeptidases. A class of peptide-cleaving enzymes which act on the terminal amino-acid residues. They are further divided into carboxypeptidases acting on the carboxyl end, and aminopeptidases acting on the amino end of the peptide. Exopeptidases of both types occur in the intestine and are important digestive enzymes. See also Endopeptidases.

Exothermic, Exothermal. Compound or reaction. A reaction in which heat is evolved is called an exothermic reaction. Likewise an exothermic compound is one which is formed from its elements with the evolution of heat.

Explosives. 'Solid, liquid, or gaseous substances which, when submitted to a local initiatory impulse such as shock, friction, sparks, etc., suffer rapid decomposition with the production of a considerable quantity of heat and large volumes of gases which may occupy many times the volume of the original explosive' (Thorpe's Dictionary). The disruptive phenomena associated with the action of explosives are due to the heat evolution, and to the pressure produced by confinement of the hot gaseous decomposition products. The 'violence' of an explosive depends largely on the rate at which the detonation 'wave', once initiated, proceeds through the mass of material. The choice of an explosive for a particular purpose is chiefly governed by the required rate and ease of detonation, and by considerations of safety involved in its use. The three main classes of explosives are:

Propellants (*q.v.*). Explosives which burn at a steady speed and can be detonated only under extreme conditions.

Initiators. Explosives such as mercury fulminate and certain metallic azides which are extremely sensitive to mechanical shock, and are accordingly used in small quantities in detonators to initiate the explosion of larger masses of less sensitive material.

High Explosives. Those explosives which normally burn without undue violence when ignited in an open space, but which can be detonated by a sufficiently large sudden mechanical or explosive shock. They then decompose with explosive rapidity into simple gaseous products such as nitrogen and carbon monoxide or dioxide. This class includes a large number of pure organic substances (such as TNT) which may be used singly or together or mixed with inorganic nitrates. Developments in this field have been towards greater power with the minimum increase in sensitivity. A mixture of cyclonite (*q.v.*) and trinitrotoluene (*q.v.*) for example results in a considerable increase in power but only a very small increase in sensitivity. Since modern conditions demand higher temperature ranges, the question of increasing the melting points of high explosives has assumed greater importance, with the consequence that recent high explosives have contained greater amounts of explosives more resistant to higher temperatures than TNT. Reduction of TNT content beyond a certain point necessitates a pressed filling instead of the more conventional cast filling.

Extender. A compounding ingredient (usually a mineral oil) used in rubbers, primarily to lower the cost but also to soften the vulcanized product. The term is also used to describe plasticizer diluents used, for example, in flexible polyvinyl chloride compositions. In such cases the cheaper extender (a mineral oil, chlorinated wax or chlorinated diphenyl) replaces part of the plasticizer to give a lower cost product without major modification of properties.

External compensation. The state existing in a mixture in equimolecular proportions of the dextro- and laevo-rotatory forms of a given optically active substance. The two components of the mixture produce equal and opposite amounts of rotation of the plane of polarization, with the result that the mixture (usually if examined in solution) will be inactive.

Extinction coefficient. Instead of using the absorption coefficient (κ) as a characteristic of a medium which absorbs light, Bunsen employed the extinction coefficient (α), which is the reciprocal of the layer thickness measured in centimetres, in which the intensity of the incident radiation has been reduced to one-tenth of its original value; $\alpha = 0.4343\kappa$. See Beer's law.

Extract. In solvent refining a portion of the feed is preferentially dissolved by the solvent and is recovered by distilling off the solvent. This constitutes the extract. It is usually highly aromatic in type.

Extraction. The removal of soluble material from a solid mixture by means of a solvent, or the removal of one or more components from a liquid mixture by use of a solvent with which the liquid is immiscible or nearly so. See Leaching, Liquid-liquid extraction.

Extractive distillation. If two substances have boiling points close together, or form an azeotrope, separation by normal fractionation is not feasible. Extractive distillation is a method whereby a third substance is added which decreases the volatility of one compound relative to the other, and makes separation by distillation possible.

The third substance or *solvent* is considerably less volatile than the other two, and is introduced above the feed near the top of the column. From the top of the column one of the substances is obtained in a pure state while the other, mixed with the solvent, is taken from the bottom of the column. A second column is used to separate the other substance from the solvent, the latter being recycled.

Extractive distillation processes are of considerable industrial importance. Examples are the separation of *n*-butane from isobutane using acetone or acrylonitrile as the solvent, and benzene from paraffins using phenol as solvent.

Extra-nuclear electrons. See Electronic configuration.

Extreme pressure lubricant. An oil or grease, containing substances specially introduced to impart an increased film strength, for use in highly loaded gears.

F

Face-centred cubic lattice. A modification of the cubic lattice having, in addition to a point at each corner of the cube, a further point at the centre of each face. See Cubic close-packing.

Factice. A compounding ingredient for rubber made by vulcanizing rape, castor, colza, and linseed oils. Brown factice is made by heating oils with sulphur at 160°-200°, and white factice by slowly adding sulphur chloride to rape or colza oil. Purified factice is of value in separation of lipids by 'liquid-gel' chromatography (see Hirsch, *J. Lipid Research*, 1963, **4**, 1).

FAD. See Flavin-adenine dinucleotide.

Fahl ore. See Tetrahedrite.

Fajans' rules. Electrovalent links are most readily formed (1) by an atom, which yields ions with a low charge (e.g. sodium, which yields the Na^+ ion, should show a greater tendency to form electrovalent links than aluminium, which yields the ion Al^{+++}), and (2) by an atom which yields a large positive ion if it ionizes positively, or a small negative ion if it ionizes negatively (e.g. caesium should form electrovalent links more readily than sodium). Fajans' rules are helpful, but not without exceptions.

Falling film evaporator. See Long-tube vertical (LTV) evaporators.

Fans. This term is restricted to machines for pumping air or gases, frequently in large quantities, against low pressure heads not usually exceeding 0·5 lb/in.^{2}. They are of two main types:

Centrifugal fans have a series of flat or curved blades arranged radially round the central shaft, and work in the same way as centrifugal pumps by imparting kinetic energy to the gas through application of centrifugal force.

Axial flow fans have rotors shaped like marine or aircraft propellers revolving inside a short tube.

Fans find their greatest application in ventilating work, and in supplying air for boilers, furnaces and dryers.

Faraday, Michael (1791-1867). Born at Newington Butts, Faraday became apprentice to a bookbinder. His hungry mind eagerly absorbed the books which passed through his hands until, stimulated by some chemical lectures by Sir Humphry Davy, he entered the service of science. His advance was rapid; laboratory assistant to Davy at the Royal Institution in 1813, F.R.S. in 1824, professor of chemistry in 1827. Amid a varied field of research, his fame rests mainly on his work on voltaic and frictional electricity, on the magnetic rotation of the plane of polarized light, on the electrolytic dissociation of solutions, on his discovery of electric induction and magneto-electric induction, and on his discovery of benzene. See Lives by Tyndall (1868), Bence Jones (1870), and others.

Faraday dark space. See Glow discharge.

Faraday effect. A plane polarized light wave may be considered as consisting of an electric component and a magnetic component at right angles to one another. When a solid or liquid through which a plane polarized wave is passing is placed in a magnetic field, the polarized wave is rotated. This phenomenon is called the Faraday effect. A positive rotation is given when the direction of displacement is the same as that of the magnetizing current. Many organic compounds show large positive effects.

Faraday's laws of electrolysis. In 1834 Faraday deduced the laws of electrolysis which state that (i) the amount of decomposition during electrolysis is proportional to the quantity of current passed, and (ii) for the same quantity of electricity passed through different solutions the extent of decomposition is proportional to the equivalent weight of the element or group liberated.

Farmers' reducer. A solution commonly used to reduce the density of silver in a photographic image. Reducers are oxidizing agents which oxidize silver to a silver salt, this being either water-soluble or converted to a soluble complex. Farmers' reducer is a mixture of potassium ferricyanide and sodium thiosulphate.

Farnesol, $C_{15}H_{26}O$, 3,7,11-trimethyldodeca-trans-2-trans-6,10-trienol, a sesquiterpene alcohol found in many essential oils, notably of ambrette seed, citronella, neroli, palmarosa and rose. B.p. 120°/0·3 mm, d 0·885-0·895, n_D 1·488-1·492. Farnesol may be isolated as its hydrogen

phthalate: it has a characteristic smell and is of value in perfumery. Oxidation affords the aldehyde farnesal, $C_{15}H_{24}O$ (semicarbazone, m.p. 133°-134°). Farnesol is of central importance in the biosynthesis of polyterpenoids including steroids.

Farnesol pyrophosphate is an immediate precursor of squalene (q.v.), the key intermediate in steroid and triterpenoid biogenesis, which arises from the coupling of two farnesol pyrophosphate molecules or of C_{15} units derived therefrom. The numerous types of sesquiterpenoid carbon skeletons represent various modes of cyclization of farnesol (sometimes with rearrangement) and it is probable that farnesol pyrophosphate is also the source of these compounds.

Farnesol derivatives also have 'juvenile hormone' activity.

Fast colour bases. When Naphtol AS and its derivatives began to displace β-naphthol, it was natural to make use of the existing primary amino compounds which were commercially available, in order to extend the range of shades. These were re-named; thus m-nitroaniline became Fast Orange R Base.

Fast colour salts. Since some difficulty has been experienced by dyers in diazotizing fast colour bases for azoic dyeing, many makers supply fast colour salts which are stabilized diazonium salts. These were originally simple substances like Nitrazol C which was diazotized p-nitraniline containing sufficient anhydrous sodium sulphate to combine with the water present. Later the required stability was obtained by coupling the diazotized bases with products like naphthalene sulphonic acids. In spite of certain disadvantages their use greatly simplifies the technique of azoic dyeing as they merely require to be dissolved in cold water (with addition in some cases of acetic acid or other reagent). The naphtholated material is entered into this solution and the colour of the insoluble azo dye develops immediately.

Fast light yellow G, Acid Yellow 11. See Pyrazolone dyes. It is prepared by coupling diazotized

aniline with 1-p-sulphophenyl-3-methyl-5-pyrazolone.

Fast printing green, Mordant Green 4. A nitroso-dye (α-nitroso-β-naphthol, 1,2-naphthaquinone-1-oxime) (A) prepared by the action of sodium nitrite and hydrochloric acid on sodium β-naphtholate. It is used to some extent for printing on an iron mordant, when it forms a vivid green, fast to light. Its water-soluble bisulphite compound is Naphthine S (B) which can be

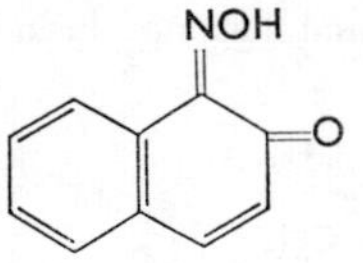

A

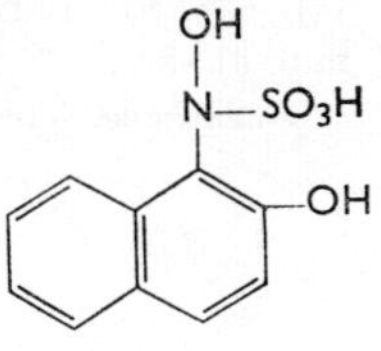

B

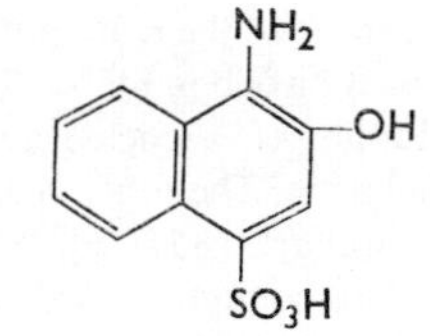

C

reduced by sulphur dioxide and hydrochloric acid to the amino-hydroxy-sulphonic acid (C) which is an important intermediate for chromaeo dyes. α-Nitroso-β-naphthol is used for the estimation of cobalt.

Fast Red A, Acid Red 88. An oxyazo-compound

$$C_{10}H_6{\nearrow}^{SO_3Na}_{\searrow N=N-C_{10}H_6OH}$$

which contains two naphthalene nuclei, and is prepared from diazonaphthionic acid and β-naphthol.

Fatigue of metals. If a specimen of a metal is submitted to a repeated alternating stress it will eventually fail at a stress value well below the critical stress value found by static tests. The failure under this condition is due to 'fatigue'.

Fats. The fats are esters of fatty acids with glycerol with the general formula shown; R^1, R^2, and R^3 may be the same fatty acid residue, but in general the fats are mixed glycerides, each fatty

$$CH_2 \cdot OOCR^1$$
$$CH \cdot OOCR^2$$
$$CH_2 \cdot OOCR^3$$

acid being different. The fatty acids present in the greatest quantity in fats are oleic acid, palmitic acid, and stearic acid. The term 'oil' is usually applied to those glycerides which are liquid at 20°, and the term 'fat' to those that are solid at that temperature.

The fats are mostly insoluble in water and very sparingly soluble in cold alcohol. They are soluble in hot alcohol, in ether, acetone, carbon disulphide, chloroform, carbon tetrachloride, benzene, and other organic solvents. They are hydrolysed to glycerol and fatty acids by boiling with acids and alkalis, by superheated steam, and by the action of certain enzymes, the lipases. If alkalis are used for hydrolysis, the fatty acids combine with the alkalis to form

soaps. Alkaline hydrolysis is therefore sometimes called saponification.

When the fats are heated above 250° they decompose with the production of acrolein, the intense smell of which is one of the best methods for detecting fats. The extraction of fats from tissues is most conveniently carried out by extraction with ether or some other solvent in a Soxhlet apparatus. They can be characterized by their melting-points or solidification-points, and by various chemical methods. See Acid value, Saponification value, Iodine value, Acetyl value, Hehner value, Reichert-Meissl value.

The fats are essential constituents of the food of animals, although conversion of carbohydrates to fats in the animal body does occur. They are partially absorbed from the gut as fats to the lymphatic system and partially hydrolysed by lipases and absorbed as fatty acids which are carried direct to the liver. They are split up in the body principally by oxidation at the β-carbon atom.

Fatty acids. The fatty acids are monobasic acids containing only the elements carbon, hydrogen, and oxygen, and consisting of an alkyl radical attached to the carboxyl group. The saturated fatty acids have the general formula $C_nH_{2n}O_2$. Formic acid and acetic acid are the two lowest members of this series, which includes palmitic acid and stearic acid. There are various series of unsaturated fatty acids:

The oleic acid series, $C_nH_{2n-2}O_2$, with one double bond, of which acrylic acid is the lowest member.

The linoleic acid series, $C_nH_{2n-4}O_2$, with two double bonds.

The linolenic acid series, $C_nH_{2n-6}O_2$, with three double bonds.

There also exist natural fatty acids with four or more double bonds, fatty acids with hydroxy groups in the molecule, and certain cyclic fatty acids.

The lower members of the series are liquids soluble in water and volatile in steam. As the number of carbon atoms in the molecule increases, the melting-points and boiling-points rise and the acids become less soluble in water and less volatile. The higher fatty acids are solids, insoluble in water and soluble in organic solvents.

The fatty acids occur in nature chiefly as glycerides, which constitute the most important part of the fats and oils, and as esters of other alcohols, the waxes. The naturally occurring fatty acids are mostly the normal straight-chain acids with an even number of carbon atoms. They have an open zig-zag chain structure with an angle of 109·5° between three adjacent carbon atoms.

Fehling, Hermann von (1811-1885). Born at Lubeck, Fehling studied chemistry under Liebig. In 1839 he was appointed professor of chemistry at Stuttgart. His name is associated with the solution used for the detection of reducing power in organic compounds and in the quantitative estimation of sugars.

Fehling's solution. A solution of copper sulphate, sodium potassium tartrate, and sodium hydroxide used for estimating reducing sugars. The reagents are kept separate and mixed before use. All Fehling's solutions contain the same amount of copper, and the mixed solution is of such a strength that 10 ml are just reduced by 0.05 g, of glucose, but the quantities of the other reagents can be varied slightly.

Feldspar. A group of aluminosilicates with one or more of the metals potassium, sodium, calcium, or barium as cations. The feldspars are arranged in two groups: the monoclinic feldspars consisting of orthoclase and the rare barium feldspar, celsian; and the triclinic feldspars which include albite, labradorite, oligoclase, anorthite, etc. The alkali feldspars used commercially occur in large crystalline masses in pegmatites. Sp.gr. 2·5-2·9, hardness about 6, m.p. 1160°-1190°. Molten feldspar has a high solvent power for silica and for clay.

Feldspars are used in the ceramic and enamelling industries, particularly in porcelain and in glazes.

Felspar. See Feldspar.

Fenchenes, $C_{10}H_{16}$. A group of terpenes derived chemically from fenchone, in most cases with intramolecular rearrangement, of such a character that their carbon skeletons differ from those of fenchone.

α-Fenchene. This compound is prepared by the distillation of methyl-α-fenchyl xanthate or by the action of nitrous acid on fenchylamine. It is also obtained, admixed with β-, γ-, δ- and cyclo-fenchenes by the dehydration of fenchyl alcohol with potassium bisulphate. (−)-α-Fenchene from (−)-fenchylamine has b.p. 156°-157°, d^{19} 0·869, n_D^{19} 1·4724, $[\alpha]_D$ −32·12°, whilst for (+)-fenchene $[\alpha]_D$ +29° is recorded. It forms a crystalline dibromide, the optically active forms of which have m.p. 87°-88° and the racemic form m.p. 62°.

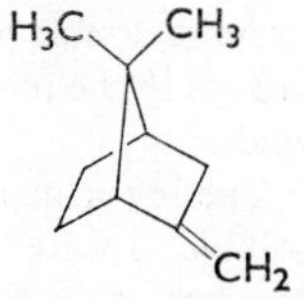

β-Fenchene. This compound is prepared either

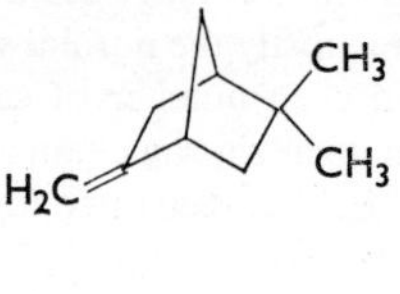

as described under α-Fenchene, or by the action of o-toluidine on (−)-isofenchyl chloride. (+)-β-Fenchene prepared by the latter method has b.p. 150°-153°, d_4^{20} 0·8591, $n_D^{18·6}$ 1·4645, $[\alpha]_D$ +62·91°. It forms a crystalline dibromide, m.p. 81°-82°.

γ-Fenchene. This compound has not been

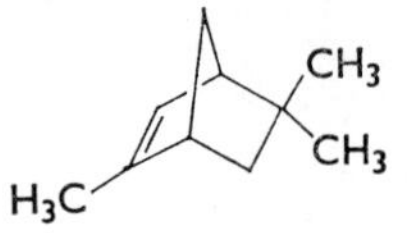

obtained pure. It forms the main portion of the hydrocarbon fraction of b.p. 145°-147°, obtained by the dehydration of α-fenchyl alcohol with potassium bisulphate. The other characteristics of this fraction are: d_4^{20} 0·8547, n_D^{20} 1·4607.

δ-Fenchene. This compound is also known as fenchylene and isofenchylene. It has not been obtained free from cyclofenchene and is present in the lowest-boiling hydrocarbon fraction obtained when α-fenchyl alcohol is dehydrated with potassium bisulphate or by the distillation of isofenchyl xanthate. As obtained from the (−)-xanthate it has b.p. 139°-140°, d_4^{20} 0·8381, n_D^{20} 144·94, $[\alpha]_D$ −68·76° (in alcohol). It forms a nitrosochloride of m.p. 142°.

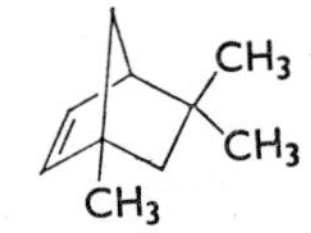

Cyclofenchene (β-Pinolene). This compound is present in the lowest-boiling fraction of the mixture of fenchenes produced by any of the general methods already described. It is also present in the hydrocarbon mixture obtained by the treatment with alkali of the liquid hydrochlorides obtained by the action of hydrogen chloride on pinene. It can easily be obtained pure, as it is very slowly attacked by potassium permanganate, which destroys the accompanying hydrocarbons. It is most simply prepared by treating (+)-fenchone hydrazone with mercuric oxide in presence of alkali. When prepared from (−)-fenchyl alcohol and carefully purified it has b.p. 143°-143·5°/748 mm, d_4^{16} 0·8624, n_D^{16} 1·45370, $[\alpha]_D$ −1·77°.

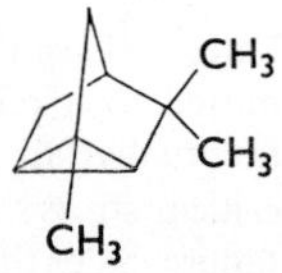

Fenchone, $C_{10}H_{16}O$. A dicyclic ketone of camphor-like smell, the (+)-form of which is an important constituent of fennel oil and of certain lavender oils; the (−)-form is found in thuja oil. On reduction it forms fenchyl alcohol of the opposite optical rotation. It crystallizes easily and has m.p. 5°-6°, b.p. 192°-193°, d^{18} 0·948, n_D^{18} 1·46355, $[\alpha]_D$ +62·76°, −64°. It yields an oxime, the optically active forms of which melt at 164°-165°.

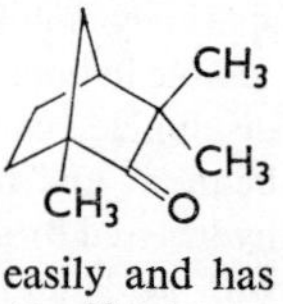

Fenchyl alcohol, $C_{10}H_{18}O$. This secondary

endo-α-   exo-β-

alcohol is produced by the reduction of fenchone with sodium and alcohol; (+)-fenchone yields (−)-fenchyl alcohol and vice versa. Both (+)- and (−)-fenchyl alcohols are each separable into two stereoisomers, endo-α- and exo-β-. (−)-α-Fenchyl alcohol has m.p. 45°, b.p. 210-212°, d_4^{20} 0·9641, $[\alpha]_D + 10·36$ in alcohol. Its hydrogen phthalate has m.p. 146° and its p-nitrobenzoate 108°-109°. (−)-β-Fenchyl alcohol has m.p. 3°-4°, b.p. 91°/18 mm, d^{20} 0·9605, $[\alpha]_{5461} - 27·97°$. Its hydrogen phthalate melts at 153° and its p-nitrobenzoate at 82°-83°. (+)-α-Fenchyl alcohol can also be obtained by the hydration of (−)-pinene with a mixture of acetic and sulphuric acids.

Fennel. The dried ripe fruits of *Foeniculum vulgare* grown in various parts of Europe. It contains a volatile oil—oil of fennel—to which it owes its aromatic and carminative properties. Powdered fennel is a constituent of compound liquorice powder, a mild aperient used for administration to children.

Fenton's reagent. An aqueous solution of a ferrous salt, usually the sulphate, and hydrogen peroxide. The active species appear to be the hydroxyl and hydroperoxyl radicals.

FEP plastics. Named from fluorinated ethylene-propylene, these copolymers of tetrafluoroethylene and hexafluoropropylene have similar properties to polytetrafluoroethylene (q.v.) but possess the distinct advantage of being processable by normal 'melt' techniques.

Fermentation. The term fermentation as generally used means the changes undergone by substances when acted upon by micro-organisms. It was originally applied to the production of alcohol from sugar in the making of beer and wine. It has also been applied, with less justification, to many chemical changes brought about by enzymes so long as the substance referred to is not completely oxidized to carbon dioxide and water. Thus the production of lactic acid in muscle is often spoken of as a fermentation.

In addition to the old-established uses of yeast in bread making, the manufacture of wine and spirits, and brewing, fermentation processes are used in the manufacture of alcohol and other solvents, of various organic acids, of antibiotics, vitamins, certain sterols, and a variety of other substances.

Fermium, Fm. At.no. 100. Isotopes of fermium of mass ranging from 250 to 256 have been prepared by bombardment of other transuranic elements. The first identification of fermium was in the debris from thermonuclear explosions. As far as can be seen from ion-exchange studies, in solution fermium behaves as a typically tripositive actinide ion.

Ferrates (VI). The term ferrates is sometimes used to designate compounds derived from the hypothetical FeO_2 (see under Ferrites). More usually it refers to the better-known series of salts derived from the hypothetical acid H_2FeO_4. These are formed by fusion of the metal with an alkali nitrate or chlorate (though too high a temperature causes decomposition), or when a suspension of ferric hydroxide in caustic alkali is oxidized with chlorine or ozone. Potassium ferrate, K_2FeO_4, forms almost black crystals isomorphous with the sulphate, and soluble in water to a deep red solution which slowly decomposes. Barium ferrate, $BaFeO_4$, is an insoluble purple precipitate.

Ferric compounds. See Iron compounds.

Ferricyanides are salts of hydroferricyanic acid, $H_3[Fe(CN)_6]$, which may be isolated as reddish needles by an appropriate double decomposition, e.g. of the silver salt with hydrochloric acid. Potassium ferricyanide, $K_3[Fe(CN)_6]$, is known as 'red prussiate of potash'. It is formed by the action of excess of potassium cyanide on a ferric salt, but is usually obtained by oxidizing the ferrocyanide with chlorine. It forms dark red crystals which give a yellow solution in water. It is used in the laboratory as a test for ferrous iron, with which it gives Prussian blue. Heavy metal ferricyanides are mostly insoluble precipitates. In alkaline solution ferricyanides have oxidizing properties, and these are occasionally employed in quantitative analysis; an example is the titration of cerium in the presence of excess of potassium carbonate, using potentiometric indication of the end-point.

Ferrifluorides. See Iron fluorides.

Ferrisulphates. See Iron sulphates.

Ferrite. The low temperature (below 910°) body-centred cubic form of iron. It can dissolve only 0·02% carbon in solid solution. It forms solid solutions with many other elements such as Cr, Ni, Si, Mn.

Ferrites. Compounds of iron (III) oxide with a basic oxide. They are insoluble substances of spinel type which are prepared in the dry way, and some of which occur in nature. The term is also applied to salts which contain tetra- and quinque-positive iron, e.g. $BaFeO_3$, which is a black powder formed when barium and ferric hydroxides are heated together in oxygen. It is decomposed by water, oxygen being evolved.

Ferritin. A soluble protein of mammalian tissue, containing over 20% of ferric iron. Together with the less well defined haemosiderin, it comprises most of the non-haem iron stored in liver and spleen. By appropriate treatment the iron may be removed, and apoferritin, a protein of similar crystalline structure to ferritin, is obtained. The ferriprotein thus consists of apoferritin combined with a basic ferric phosphate.

Ferrocene, di-π-cyclopentadienyl iron, bis(cyclopentadienyl) iron, $C_{10}H_{10}Fe$. The prototype of the so-called metallocenes. It is an orange crystal-

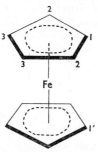

line solid, m.p. 174°, b.p. 249°, which can be sublimed easily, is volatile in steam, soluble in most organic solvents but insoluble in water. Various preparations involving the cyclopentadienyl anion and iron compounds are known, e.g. cyclopentadienyl sodium and ferrous chloride. Syntheses based on substituted cyclopentadienes are possible. It is a diamagnetic material which can be reversibly oxidized to a blue-red dichroic paramagnetic ferricinium cation, corresponding to the loss of one electron. Ferrocene is an extremely reactive aromatic system; it undergoes Friedel-Crafts acylation, sulphonation, metallation, formylation and aminomethylation with ease, but powerful electrophilic agents, such as nitric acid and halogens cause preliminary oxidation to the ferricinium cation: nitro- and halogeno- groups must be introduced by delicate and indirect methods. Hydroxyferrocene is a weaker acid than phenol, and ferrocenylamine is a stronger base than aniline.

Free rotation of the cyclopentadienyl rings about the iron atoms allows the isolation of only one monosubstituted ferrocene derivative but three (1,2:1,3:1,1′) disubstituted derivatives. See 'Chemistry of the Iron-Group Metallocenes', by Myron Rosenblum, Vol. I; J. Wiley, 1965. See also Cyclopentadienylides.

Ferrocyanides. Salts of the acid $H_4[Fe(CN)_6]$, hydroferrocyanic acid, which is precipitated as a white powder on the addition of hydrochloric acid to a concentrated solution of one of its salts. It is soluble in water and also in alcohol and has a strong acid reaction. Potassium ferrocyanide, $K_4[Fe(CN)_6],3H_2O$, 'yellow prussiate of pot-

ash', crystallizes in yellow plates. It is formed by the action of excess of potassium cyanide on a solution of a ferrous salt, and is obtained commercially as a by-product in the purification of coal-gas. There are a large number of processes, all of which involve the absorption of hydrogen cyanide by e.g., ferrous sulphate solution. The iron cyanide derivative may then easily be converted to potassium ferrocyanide, e.g. by treatment first with lime and subsequently with potassium carbonate. The ferrocyanides are stable salts, and the ferrocyanide ion is so little dissociated into its constituent ions that they do not give the reactions for iron and cyanide, and are even non-poisonous. Many of the heavy-metal salts are characteristically coloured precipitates. Thus *copper ferrocyanide* is chocolate brown. It is used as a semi-permeable membrane in work on osmotic pressure, being deposited for this purpose within the pores of a porous pot. *Iron (III) ferrocyanide* is Prussian blue (*q.v.*). *Iron (II) potassium ferrocyanide*, $K_2Fe[Fe(CN)_6]$ is a white precipitate formed from potassium ferrocyanide and a ferrous salt in the absence of air. It is rapidly oxidized to Prussian blue by atmospheric oxygen.

Ferromagnetism. Magnetic behaviour which does not follow the Curie-Weiss Law and is field-strength dependent. There is a characteristic temperature above which the magnetic behaviour is normal.

Ferro-manganese. A variety of pig iron containing 6 to 7% carbon and rich in manganese (80%). It is used for deoxidation and recarburization in steel manufacture. A low grade ferro-manganese containing about 20% Mn is known as 'Spiegeleisen'.

Ferro-molybdenum. An alloy of iron with molybdenum, containing 60% to 65% of molybdenum, which is prepared by reducing molybdenite (MoS_2) with iron and carbon in the electric furnace. It is commonly used as a means of introducing molybdenum into alloy steels and special cast irons.

Ferroprussiates. See Ferrocyanides.

Ferrosilicon, FeSi. Obtained by reducing siliceous iron ore in an electric furnace. Used in the manufacture of silicon steels and to reduce the amount of iron carbide in cast iron.

Ferrous nitroso compounds. Ferrous salts in solution take up nitric oxide with a dark brown colour; on boiling the nitric oxide is driven off again. These compounds are nitrosyl derivatives: the brown compounds are formed during the Brown ring test (*q.v.*).

Ferrous salts. Iron (II) Salts.

Fertilizers. Although any substance which increases production when added to the soil could be called a fertilizer, in practice by fertilizers are usually meant compounds containing nitrogen, phosphorus, or potassium. Ammonium sulphate is the most important nitrogenous fertilizer; sodium nitrate and ammonium nitrate are also extensively used. A mixture of ammonium nitrate and calcium carbonate is sold under the name of Nitro-Chalk. The most important fertilizers containing phosphorus are the superphosphates, which are mineral tricalcium phosphates rendered more soluble by treatment with sulphuric acid. Many mixed fertilizers are now sold, containing various proportions of nitrogen, phosphorus, and potassium.

Ferulic acid, $C_{10}H_{10}O_4$. Crystallizes in needles,

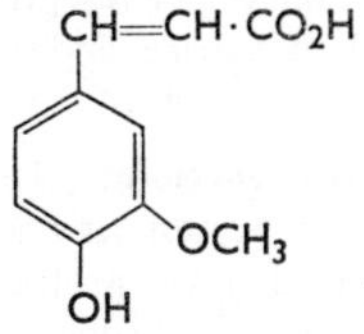

CH=CH·CO₂H

OCH₃

OH

m.p. 174°. Soluble in alcohol and hot water. It occurs in asafoetida as an ester with umbelliferone.

Fibrin. If blood is removed from the blood vessels it rapidly clots. This clotting is essentially due to the conversion of the soluble protein fibrinogen to the insoluble protein fibrin by the action of the enzyme thrombin. Fibrin can be obtained in the form of stringy masses by rapidly whipping freshly drawn blood.

Fibrinogen. A protein of molecular weight about 330,000 occurring in blood plasma (3 mg per ml of human plasma) and essential to the process of clotting. See Fibrin.

Fibroin. A protein belonging to the scleroprotein class, present in silk fibres. It contains a high percentage of glycine and alanine units.

Ficin. A very potent proteolytic enzyme obtained from the latex of tropical trees of the genus *Ficus*. It behaves very similarly to papain and is available commercially. It has been obtained crystalline.

Fick's law of diffusion. According to this law, the rate of diffusion of a substance along a given direction in a medium is proportional to the gradient of its concentration. Thus, the flux (F) of the diffusing substance in the x direction is given by $F = AD(\delta c/\delta x)$, where c is the concentration of the substance at the plane of x, A is the area, and D is a coefficient, depending on the materials and the temperature, called the diffusion coefficient.

Fieser's solution. An aqueous alkaline solution of sodium anthraquinone β-sulphonate ('silver salt') which has been reduced with sodium hydrosulphite. It is used as a scrubbing solution for partially removing oxygen from, e.g., nitrogen gas.

Fillers. Materials incorporated into polymeric compounds (plastics and rubbers) to improve the general properties, to introduce particular characteristics, or to reduce the cost of the compound even though certain physical properties may be somewhat impaired. In rigid materials, fibrous fillers (woodflour, woodpulp, cotton, glass-fibre, asbestos) are incorporated to improve the impact strength. Other fillers are used to increase hardness (slate powder), to improve electrical properties (mica), or to change the density (heavy spar). In synthetic rubbers, fillers are classified as reinforcing fillers, inert fillers, or diluents. In flexible thermoplastics, smaller proportions of inert fillers are used to reduce the cost and sometimes to aid processing.

Filter. An apparatus or plant for carrying out filtration. For descriptions of some of the more important types of industrial filter see Air filters, Bag filter, Filter press, Leaf filters, Rotary drum filters, Sand filter.

Filter-aids. Materials such as diatomite which are added to a suspension of a solid in a liquid to increase the filtration rate. They pack down to beds of high voidage, and therefore increase the porosity of the filter bed if added to the slurry before filtration.

Filter press. This is one of the simplest and most widely used plants for carrying out filtration under pressure. There are two common forms of the press:

The *recessed plate press* or *chamber press* consists of a number of plates the faces of which are recessed and corrugated; filter cloth is fitted over both surfaces of the plates, which are then placed face to face and tightly clamped by means of a screw mechanism. The feed enters under pressure through a channel running through the centre of the press, and passes into all the chambers formed by the recessed plates in parallel. The solid is retained by the filtering medium and forms a cake, the filtrate is discharged through an outlet in the body of the plate. When the cake has completely filled the chambers the press is opened and the solid removed.

In the *plate and frame press* hollow rectangular frames, usually $\frac{1}{2}$ in. to 3 in. thick, alternate with solid plates with serrated surfaces. The filter cloth is placed between each plate and adjacent frame and the assembly clamped together, each frame becoming a thin rectangular chamber bounded on either side by cloth. The slurry is fed through holes in the edges of the frames and the filtered liquid passes along the serrations of the

241

plates to the discharge ports. This type of press has special provision for washing the cake, unlike the previous one.

Filter presses can operate at pressures up to $250 \, lb/in.^2$ and can thus carry out filtrations that would otherwise be slow and difficult. They are simple, cheap, flexible, economical in floor space and can be constructed from a wide range of corrosion-resistant materials. Their principal disadvantages are their high labour requirements and heavy cloth wear.

Filtration. The process of separating a solid from a liquid or gas by use of a membrane or medium which will allow the fluid to pass through but not the solid.

Fine structure. See Multiplet.

Fink, Colin Garfield (1881-1953). Fink was born at Hoboken, New Jersey, and educated at the Universities of Columbia and Leipzig. From 1907 to 1917 he was a research engineer of the General Electric Co. Ltd., and from 1917 to 1921 director of research of the Chile Exploration Co. In 1922 he became head of the department of electrochemistry and professor of chemical engineering at Columbia University. Responsible for numerous developments in applied electrochemistry, Fink was awarded the Perkin Medal in 1934.

Fireclay. A refractory clay consisting mainly of aluminium silicate, suitable for the manufacture of furnace bricks, crucibles, etc., and melting at over 1600°.

Fire-point. That temperature at which a substance, when ignited, first burns freely when the ignition agent is withdrawn.

Fischer, Emil (1852-1919). Fischer was born at Euskirchen in the Rhineland, and studied chemistry under Kekulé at Bonn and Baeyer at Strasburg. He held numerous teaching appointments, including the chairs of chemistry at Erlangen (1882), Würzburg (1885), and Berlin (1892). He was Nobel Prizeman in 1902. One of the foremost organic chemists of the nineteenth century, among the subjects of his research were the sugars, the purine group, synthetic peptides, veronal, and hydrazine. See Mem. Lect., *J. Chem. Soc.*, 1920, 1157.

Fischer, Hans (1881-1945). Born at Höchst a.M., Fischer studied at Lausanne, Marburg, and Munich, where he became a Privat-dozent in 1912. In 1915 he was appointed extraordinary professor, and in the following year went to Innsbruck as professor of applied medical chemistry. In 1918 he went to Vienna in a similar capacity. In 1921 he succeeded Wieland as professor of organic chemistry and Director of the Institute of Organic Chemistry at the Technische Hochschule, Munich. He worked extensively on haemin, the porphyrins, chlorophyll, bilirubin, and the pyrroles, and in 1930 gained the Nobel Prize in Chemistry.

Fischer, Otto Philip (1852-1932). Born at Euskirchen, near Cologne, Fischer studied for a time under Kekulé (Bonn) before proceeding to Strasburg, where he began his researches on the synthesis of hydrocarbons under Baeyer. After a period of work with Liebermann he rejoined Baeyer, then at Munich. Here the Fischer cousins worked on the preparation of the hydrazines. In 1885 Fischer was appointed to the chair of chemistry at Erlangen, a post which he held until he retired in 1925. Fischer investigated the constitution of a number of dyes, prepared the first synthetic alkaloid, kairine, and later studied the photosensitizing dyestuffs of the cyanine group.

Fischer-Hepp rearrangement. The nitrosamines of aromatic secondary amines when treated with hydrochloric acid give nuclear substituted nitrosoamines. Among the benzene derivatives, if the *para* position is free the —NO group displaces the hydrogen atom there; in naphthalene derivatives it enters the α position:

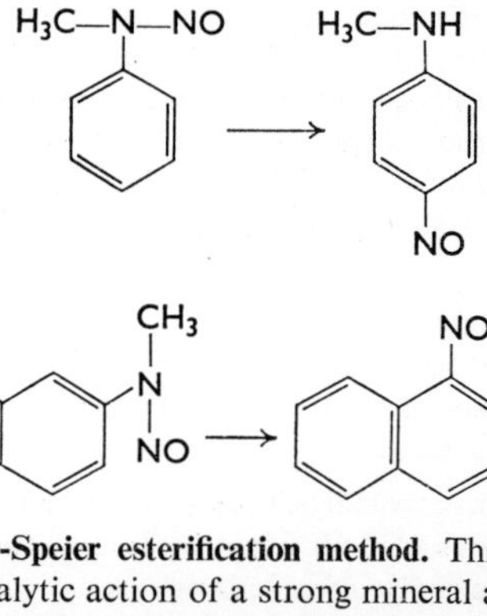

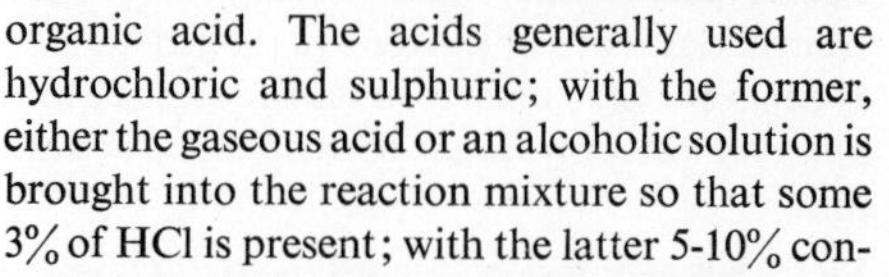

Fischer-Speier esterification method. This uses the catalytic action of a strong mineral acid to effect ester formation between an alcohol and an organic acid. The acids generally used are hydrochloric and sulphuric; with the former, either the gaseous acid or an alcoholic solution is brought into the reaction mixture so that some 3% of HCl is present; with the latter 5-10% concentrated acid by weight is added. The mixture is then refluxed until ester formation is complete.

Fischer-Tropsch synthesis. The reduction and combination of carbon monoxide molecules at elevated temperatures and variable pressures to give alkanes, aldehydes or alcohols according to conditions. Compare Oxo reaction.

Fission products. The products of the fission of the heavy nuclei. The mass numbers of the fission products range from 30 to 160. Fission is generally an asymmetric process, maximum yields occurring for products of mass ~ 90 and mass

~ 140, the distribution of products depending upon the energy of the bombarding particle. Fission products are generally intensely radioactive, most of them decay by β-emission to stable isobars. The separation and disposal of these intensely active materials is a great problem in atomic energy processes.

Fittig, Rudolf (1835-1910). Professor in Tübingen, and later at Strasburg, he discovered diphenyl and synthesized a number of aromatic hydrocarbons; he discovered phenanthrene in 1872, and coumarone in 1883.

Fixation. The removal of unwanted silver halide from a photographic material by solubilization after development is known as fixation. The most widely used fixers are thiosulphates (e.g. hypo). These compounds form water-soluble complex salts with silver halides. Other inorganic fixers include thiocyanates, cyanides, ammonia and concentrated potassium iodide. Organic fixers include thiourea and allylthiourea (thiosinamine). Fixing baths may also include hardeners (chrome alum, potash alum) to toughen the final gelatin layer.

Fixed carbon in coal. This is a figure reported in the proximate analysis of coal and is obtained by subtracting from 100 the combined percentages of moisture, volatile matter, and ash. Fixed carbon should not be confused with the 'carbon content' of the coal, which is determined by ultimate analysis.

Flash photolysis. This is a technique by means of which very fast reactions, usually those involving atoms or radicals may be studied. A powerful

absorption as a function of time using monochromatic light. The advantage of this method over the normal illumination reactions is that very much higher concentrations of the reactive intermediates are formed.

Many reactions in the gas phase have also been studied using this technique.

Flash-point. The temperature, under standardized conditions, at which a liquid begins to evolve inflammable vapours.

Flavanthrene (Flavanthrone), Vat Yellow 1. A

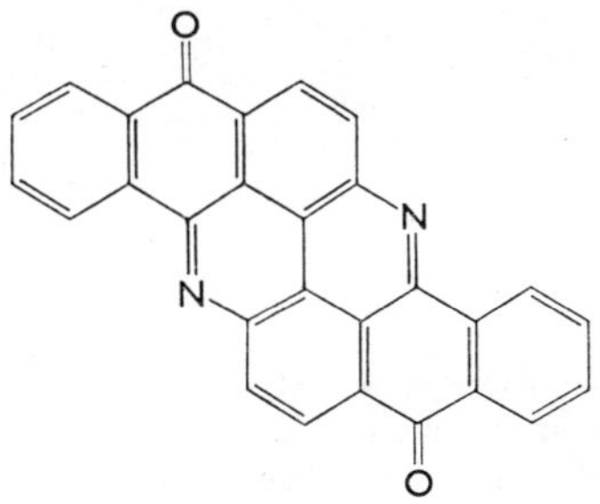

yellow vat dyestuff, manufactured by treating 2-aminoanthraquinone, in nitrobenzene solution, with antimony pentachloride. Is also produced by fusing 2-aminoanthraquinone with caustic potash. It dyes cotton from an alkaline hydrosulphite vat to a blue shade which rapidly changes to a brilliant yellow on exposure to air. The dyeings gradually turn brown on exposure to light, due to phototropic action, but return to the original shade in air after mild scraping.

Flavin-adenine dinucleotide (FAD). The active

(oxidized form)

light flash of very high energy (about 10^5 joules) passing through a solution for a few microseconds causes dissociation, and intermediates may be observed by following changes in their

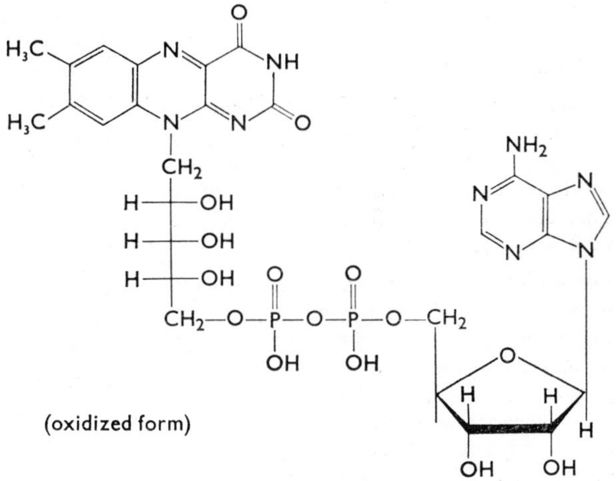

coenzyme or prosthetic group of a large number of flavoprotein enzymes. These take part in a variety of metabolic oxidation-reduction reactions. They may act directly on a substrate, or indirectly by effecting the reoxidation of reduced NAD or NADP.

The reduction of the flavin moiety in FAD and FMN is accompanied by loss of the yellow colour and disappearance of the characteristic absorption at 445 mμ. The reduction-oxidation of flavoproteins can thus be followed spectrophotometrically, if necessary at the same time as that of the pyridine nucleotides which absorb at 340 mμ.

Flavoproteins. A group of proteins which have riboflavin in the molecule of their prosthetic group. Included are Warburg's 'yellow enzyme' and cytochrome reductase, both of which have riboflavin phosphate (flavin mononucleotide) as the prosthetic group, and diaphorase, the prosthetic group of which is flavin-adenine dinucleotide, which has riboflavin phosphate and adenylic acid joined through the phosphate groups. They act as oxygen carriers in biological systems.

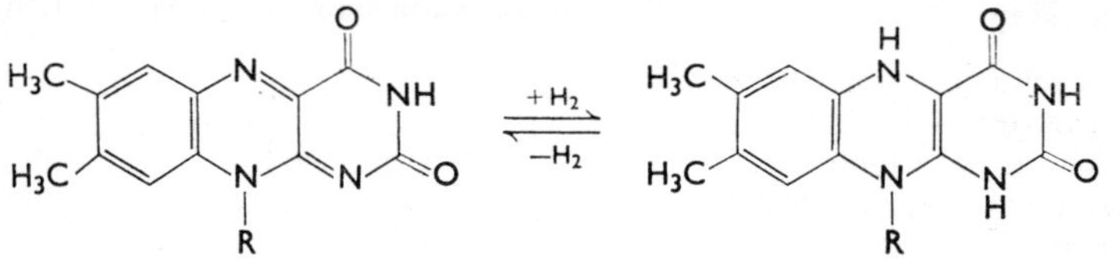

FAD   reduced FAD

Flavin mononucleotide (FMN). Riboflavin-5′-phosphate, the active (coenzyme) component of a number of flavoprotein enzymes, e.g. 'old yellow enzyme'. Most flavoproteins contain flavin-adenine dinucleotide.

Flavone, $C_{15}H_{10}O_2$. Crystallizes in colourless

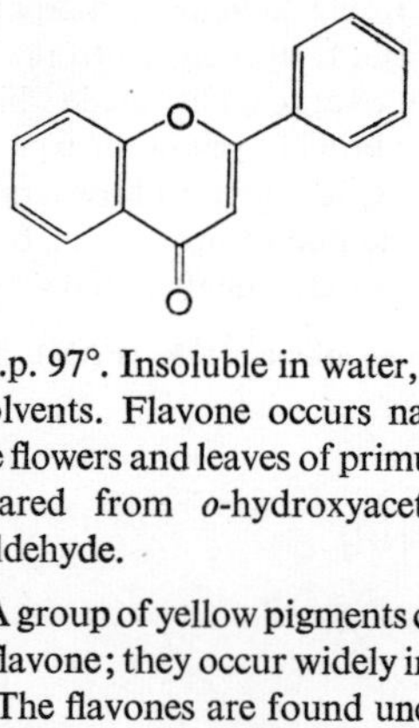

needles, m.p. 97°. Insoluble in water, soluble in organic solvents. Flavone occurs naturally as dust on the flowers and leaves of primulas. It has been prepared from o-hydroxyacetophenone and benzaldehyde.

Flavones. A group of yellow pigments chemically related to flavone; they occur widely in the plant kingdom. The flavones are found uncombined, as glycosides, and in association with tannins. They are mostly crystalline solids, soluble in water and organic solvents.

Flavone glycosides are widely distributed in plants. The sugar residue is either glucose or rhamnose, occasionally a biose sugar. Further isomerization is possible according to which hydroxyl is concerned in the attachment of the sugar. They are, in general, colourless. They include apiin, acaciin, diosmin, lutusin, orobosin.

Flavonol glycosides contain derivatives of flavonol attached to sugar. They include fustin, galangin, kaempferitrin, robinin, datisein, quercitrin, quercetin, incarnatrin, quercimeritrin, serotin, etc. They are very widely distributed in plants.

Flight conveyor, Scraper conveyor. This type of conveyor has one or more chains running in guides and attached to the chains is a series of scrapers or flights. The shape and size of these scrapers is the same as that of the cross-section of the trough in which they move, their motion dragging the material along.

Flint. A compact massive quartz mixed with opaline silica occurring mainly in chalk and obtained from chalk workings. After burning, quenching, and grinding it is used in porcelain manufacture.

Flocculation. The terms flocculation, coagulation, and precipitation are usually used indiscriminately to describe the destruction of a colloidal sol. Sometimes coagulation is intended to indicate the aggregation part of the process and flocculation the resulting sedimentation in accordance with Stokes's law. See Colloids, Coagulation.

Flotation. A method of separation originally evolved for the concentration of sulphide ores in aqueous suspension. The principle involves the formation of a moderately stable foam by addition of a small quantity of a suitable reagent followed by aeration. The particles of sulphide collect in the liquid-air interfaces of the bubbles, the foam may then be removed from the top of the cell, allowed to break down, and the ore concentrate recovered. In this process a number of chemicals are added in small quantities to assist the separation of a mixture of solids suspended in water into its constituents. These include:

(a) *Frothing agents*—used to stabilize the foam to a degree sufficient to enable it to be carried from the flotation cell. Materials generally used for this purpose are mineral or vegetable oils, oleic acid, or higher alcohols, in amounts varying from 0·1 to 0·5 lb/ton of solids present.

(b) *Collectors*—developed originally for the treatment of sulphide ores and used to form a water repellant film on the surface of the sulphide, thus increasing the wetting angle and improving the separation from associated clays. For sulphide ores, sodium ethyl xanthate is often used; soap can be used for the separation of silica from alumina, whilst substituted thioureas float talc from sands. The amounts used are less than 0·3 lb/ton, as amounts above this figure sometimes reverse the effect.

(c) *Activators and Depressors*—used to make the action of collectors more selective in order to separate complex mixtures; pH control is commonly introduced for this purpose and change of pH on either side of 7·0 modifies the wetting angle of the constituents of a mixture in varying degree. More specifically, sodium sulphide is used as an activator for metallic oxides, and sodium cyanide as a depressor of zinc sulphide when lead sulphide is being floated from the mixture. Copper sulphate is an activator for zinc sulphide, and lime is a depressor for iron sulphides.

Flotation cells. In many cases it is possible to produce a froth which will take up the required constituents of a mineral pulp by mechanical agitation. In plant operating on this principle the pulp is beaten into a foam by a high-speed impeller and passes to a separate part of the cell where the froth rises to the surface and is removed by a scraper. The residual pulp normally passes to other cells in series for further treatment to complete the separation.

Fluidization. The suspension of a mass of solid particles in an upward-flowing stream of gas or liquid. The resulting mixture assumes many of the properties of a liquid, e.g. it can transmit hydrostatic forces and solid objects of smaller density will float in it.

Fluidized bed. A bed or mass of particles maintained in a state of fluidization.

Fluidized beds are of great industrial importance and their field of application is constantly widening. Gas-fluidized beds exhibit good solid mixing and high rates of heat transfer in both the vertical and horizontal directions. Because of the uniformity of temperature and the ease of temperature control they are widely used as reactors, especially for the catalytic cracking of heavy hydrocarbons. They are also used for the roasting of sulphide ores and various calcining operations. Liquid-fluidized beds find their major application in Oslo crystallizers.

Fluocinolone acetonide (trade name Synalar). A white crystalline powder, m.p. 245° (decomp.), $[\alpha]_D^{20}$ +92° to +96° (1% w/v in dioxan). It is prepared by partial synthesis. Insoluble in water,

soluble in 10 parts of acetone, in 5 parts of chloroform and in 26 parts of dehydrated alcohol. It is one of the most active topical

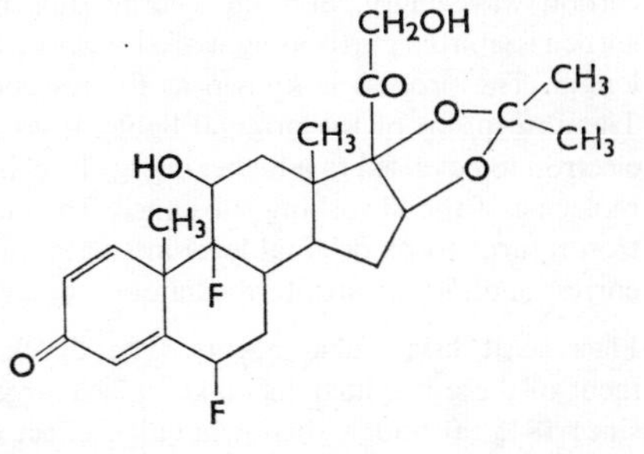

corticosteroids and is widely used in skin diseases.

Fluon. A brand name for polytetrafluoroethylene.

Fluorene, $C_{13}H_{10}$. Forms colourless shining

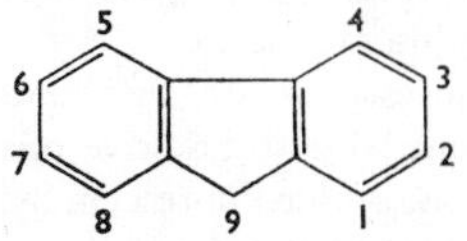

flakes usually showing a violet fluorescence, m.p. 115°, b.p. 294°-295°. It is insoluble in water, slightly soluble in cold alcohol, readily in hot. Easily soluble in ether, benzene, and carbon disulphide. It gives a picrate, m.p. 80°-82°. When heated with caustic potash at 280° a potassium salt is formed in which one of the 9-hydrogen atoms has been substituted. A sodium salt can also be obtained.

Fluorene occurs in coal tar in the fraction, b.p. 295°-310°, from which it can be separated. It can be prepared synthetically by reduction of diphenylene ketone.

Fluorene can be nitrated, sulphonated, and chlorinated.

Fluorescein, Acid Yellow 73, $C_{20}H_{12}O_5$. Crystallizes in red crystals with green iridescence. M.p.

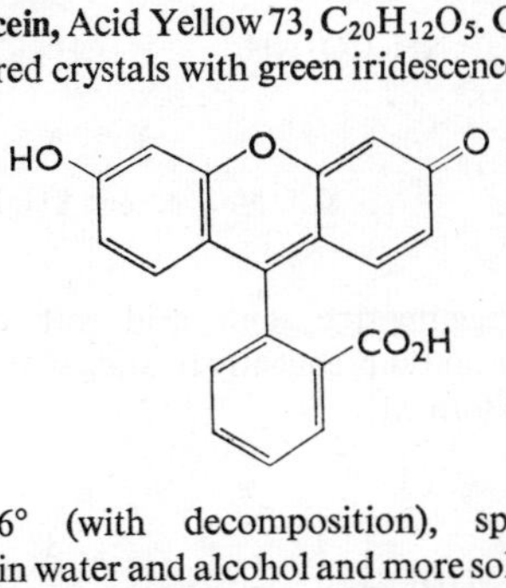

314°-316° (with decomposition), sparingly soluble in water and alcohol and more soluble in acetone. It is made by heating phthalic anhydride with resorcinol. In alkaline solution it shows intense green fluorescence. It is a dyestuff and is used for colouring liquids in various instruments.

The sodium salt, $C_{20}H_{10}O_5Na_2$, is used in

ophthalmic practice to render visible any damaged portions of the cornea.

Fluorescence. Many substances absorb light of a certain wavelength, and the energy thus absorbed is emitted partly as light of a longer wavelength. The process is known as fluorescence. The absorption of the original light causes an electron to be raised to a higher energy level in a molecule of the absorbing substance. The electron returns to its original level in stages, each corresponding with an intermediate energy level.

Fluorescent brightening agents. The development of these products has taken place largely since 1945, although their whitening effect on textiles was mentioned by Krais in 1929. Previously the faint yellowish hue of commercially bleached textile materials was corrected by the use of tinting or blueing agents, e.g. ultramarine or certain blue or violet basic dyes. By subtractive mixing, the effect of this blue or violet on the yellow ground colour gave a grey hue which appeared whiter to the eye.

The fluorescence of the newer products gives a white, due to additive mixing, i.e. the brightness adds blue fluorescent light whereas a tinting agent subtracts yellow light. In daylight, which contains some ultra-violet light, a brilliant white is obtained as the FBA absorbs the ultra-violet and re-emits in the visible spectrum —usually in the blue region. The resultant white is bluish but this may be varied to give greenish, pinkish or neutral whites if desired, depending on the emission wavelengths of the particular FBA used.

Derivatives of 4,4'-diamino-2,2'-stilbene disulphonic acid are widely used for cellulosic and protein fibres. Thus by condensing 1 mol. of this acid with 2 mol. phenylisocyanate there is produced

C.I. F.B.A. 48 was introduced for use on protein fibres from an acid bath. Benzoin is heated with urea and sodium hydrogen sulphate and the product is sulphonated.

C.I. Fluorescent Brightening Agent **48**
(Blankophor WT)

Derivatives of coumarin were among the early FBAs and gave vivid whites although their light fastness was low.

3-methyl-7-hydroxycoumarin

An interesting F.B.A. is a thiazol product which is used for cellulosic fibres and for nylon.

C.I. Fluorescent Brightening Agent **41**
(Uvitex RS)

Many F.B.A.'s have low fastness to light which is a serious disadvantage for textile applications but improved light fastness is found in 5-ring heterocyclic systems including benzoxazole, benzothiazole, furan, thiophene, thiodiazole and oxazole derivatives.

The F.B.A.'s have typical dyestuff structures and in general are used like dyes when applied to textiles. Thus stilbene derivatives are applied to

C.I. Fluorescent Brightening Agent **30**

By reacting the same acid with cyanuric chloride and subsequently treating with aniline, there is formed

cotton from a lukewarm bath containing an electrolyte. Wool and nylon are treated in an acid bath at 40-50° but acrylic and polyester

C.I. Fluorescent Brightening Agent **32**

fibres require high temperatures, e.g. 100°, unless used with carriers in which case temperatures of 50°-75° are satisfactory.

Although F.B.A.'s are very useful on textiles, they are mainly used as ingredients of soaps and detergents and also find wide application in paper making.

Fluorides. The salts of hydrofluoric acid.

Fluorimetry. A method of quantitative analysis which involves the spectrophotometric estimation of the fluorescence produced by a substance in solution.

Fluorinating agents. Any material which will introduce fluorine into another molecule. Typical agents range from fluorine and the halogen fluorides which introduce fluorine by addition, to reagents such as sulphur tetrafluoride and the alkali fluorides which introduce fluorine by replacement of oxygen and other halogens respectively. See the above reagents, Arsenic trifluoride, Antimony trifluoride, Sodium fluoride, Potassium fluoride.

Fluorine, F. At.no. 9, At.wt. 19·00, m.p. $-220°$, b.p., $-188°$. Density at boiling point 1·108. Fluorine is the lightest and most reactive of the halogens. The chief commercial ore is fluorspar, CaF_2, but fluorides are widespread, particularly amongst silicaceous minerals. The element, which was first isolated by Moisson in 1886, is normally obtained by electrolysis of a fused KF/HF mixture using a carbon anode. The hydrogen liberated at the cathode is kept rigidly separated from the fluorine.

For details of various cells in use and for many properties of fluorine see Leech, *Quarterly Reviews*, 1949, **3**, 22. Elementary fluorine, which at normal temperatures is the dimer, F_2, is extremely reactive; reaction occurs immediately with most elements of the Periodic Table and fluorides result. Mixtures of alkali halides and transition metal halides give complex fluorides and by dilution of the fluorine with an inert gas it is possible to partially fluorinate some organic compounds. In general, fluorine, with oxygen, brings out the highest valency shown by the elements. Elementary fluorine is exceedingly toxic but traces of fluorides are essential to life and very beneficial in the prevention of dental decay. Hydrogen fluoride (*q.v.*) is widely used in industry and fluorocarbons (*q.v.*) are of great importance on account of their chemical inertness. Cryolite, Na_3AlF_6, is used in the production of aluminium.

Fluorine oxides. See Oxygen fluorides.

Fluoroacetamide, FCH_2CONH_2. A very poisonous, white crystalline solid, m.p. 108°, soluble in water and alcohols, which has been used as an aphicide and against the blackcurrant big bud mite.

Fluoroacetates. The name is loosely applied to derivatives of monofluoroacetic acid, CH_2FCOOH. The acid itself, its methyl ester, and all derivatives broken down in the body to the acid, are highly toxic substances, behaving as convulsant poisons with a delayed action. They are almost odourless, are difficult to detect chemically, and are very stable.

Sodium fluoroacetate, which is not volatile and not irritating to the skin, is used as a rodenticide under the designation '1080'. It is made from ethyl chloroacetate and potassium fluoride, which react to give ethyl fluoroacetate, which is then hydrolysed with sodium hydroxide in methyl alcohol.

Fluoro acids. Complex fluoro acids are formed by many elements and are, in general, known only as salts, e.g. the fluorotitanates, derived from the hypothetical acid H_2TiF_6. The salts are prepared by the action of fluorine on a mixture of alkali halides and the appropriate metal halides, or by the action of halogen fluorides or anhydrous or aqueous hydrofluoric acid on the appropriate mixture of salts. Most crystallize with closely related structures. By the action of heat on the salts volatile fluorides are obtained; heating an ammonium salt will generally leave a metal fluoride.

With some more electropositive metals, such as magnesium, lanthanum, and uranium, double fluorides are obtained which do not appear to contain discrete fluoro-anions.

Fluorocarbons. A class of organic compounds in which some or all of the hydrogen atoms have been replaced by fluorine. They have very similar freezing and boiling points to the corresponding hydrocarbons but are heavier and have high viscosities and low surface tensions. They are very unreactive and have great thermal stability. Fluorocarbons can be made by fluorination of hydrocarbons with fluorine or inorganic fluorinating agents such as silver (II) fluoride and cobalt (III) fluoride. An important new method of preparation involves the replacement of another halogen, e.g. chlorine, by the action of an alkali halide in a solvent of high dielectric constant. They may also be prepared by fluorination in an electrolytic cell using anhydrous hydrogen fluoride and the substance to be fluorinated as electrolyte. There is a complete new chemistry of the fluorocarbons; derivatives such as trifluoronitrosomethane, CF_3NO; trifluoromethyl isocyanate, CF_3NCO; and organometallics such as $(CF_3)_3P$, and $(CF_3)_2S$ being known. Derivatives of hexafluorobenzene, C_6F_6, show the typical properties of aromatic compounds. Fluorocarbon oils and greases are used under conditions in which ordinary lubricants would be attacked. Perfluoro and perfluorochloro polymers have been used as plastics but moulding is rather difficult. These plastics are extensively used in the chemical industry where corrosive materials are being handled, and in the electrical industry as insulators.

1-Fluoro-2,4-dinitrobenzene, Sanger's reagent, $C_6H_3FN_2O$. M.p. 26° b.p. 137°. Prepared from 1-chloro-2,4-dinitrobenzene and potassium fluoride in nitrobenzene. Soluble in benzene, ether, etc. Used for labelling a terminal amino-acid group of a peptide to aid subsequent identification after degradation.

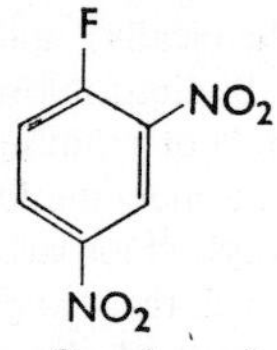

Fluorophosphoric acids. Formed by the controlled hydrolysis of POF_3 and PF_5. Difluorophosphoric acid, HPO_2F_2, forms a series of salts which are very similar to the perchlorates. Monofluorophosphoric acid, H_2PO_3F, may also be prepared by dissolving phosphoric acid in concentrated hydrofluoric acid; its salts resemble sulphates. The esters of H_2PO_3F, the fluorophosphonates, may be prepared by the action of the silver salt on an alkyl halide and in other ways. They are extremely poisonous volatile substances which act by inhibiting the enzyme cholinesterase. They have an immediate action on the brain and lungs and cause a typical constriction of the pupil of the eye. Derivatives have been used as insecticides and suggested as chemical warfare agents (the 'nerve gases'). In addition to these two oxyfluoro acids there is an extensive series of salts containing the hexafluorophosphate, PF_6^-, anion. These also have solubilities similar to those of the perchlorates and are best prepared by the action of a strong fluorinating agent on a mixture of a metal halide and phosphorus pentoxide.

Fluorosilicates. Salts of the unknown acid H_2SiF_6. Prepared by adding a metal fluoride to a solution of silica in hydrofluoric acid. The potassium salt is relatively insoluble. An aqueous solution of H_2SiF_6 results from the action of silica tetrafluoride on water or by dissolving silica in hydrofluoric acid. This aqueous solution is formed as a by-product in the production of superphosphate by the action of concentrated sulphuric acid on minerals which contain apatite.

Fluorosulphinates, MSO_2F. Salts of the unknown fluorosulphinic acid, HSO_2F. Prepared by dissolving alkali fluorides in liquid sulphur dioxide.

Fluorosulphuric acid, HSO_3F. Prepared by distilling a mixture of potassium bifluoride and

oleum, b.p. 162·6°. The hydrolysis of the acid is slow and the anhydrous acid does not attack glass. The fluorosulphates are quite stable and are isomorphous with the perchlorates. Fluorosulphates may also be prepared by the action of peroxydisulphuryl difluoride,

$$FS(O)_2O—OS(O)_2F$$

(prepared by the action of fluorine on sulphur trioxide) on the elements.

Fluorspar, Fluorite, CaF_2. Occurs in crystals of the cubic system, usually in cubes. The cubes are sometimes truncated by faces of {310}. It is usually found as a vein mineral associated with

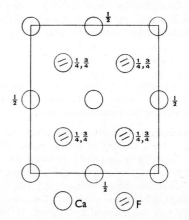

metallic ores. Twinned crystals are common, and in these, where the corners of a cube project, the surrounding 'cube' face is often a very low pyramid with faces such as {32·1·0}. The crystals are usually yellow, blue, green, or violet. Hardness 4, sp.gr. 3·18. In the crystal structure of fluorite, a unit cell of which is shown in the figure, each calcium ion is surrounded by eight fluorine, and each fluorine by four calcium ions. For CaF_2 the length of the side of the cubic unit cell $a = 5·46$ Å. A number of dioxides and difluorides crystallize with this structure and also certain alloys, e.g. $PbMg_2$ and $SnMg_2$.

Fluorspar is the chief commercial mineral source of fluorine and the fluorides. It is also used as a constituent of certain glasses and enamels, and as a metallurgical flux.

Fluothane. A trade name for halothane (q.v.).

Flux. The word has two meanings in metallurgical engineering practice. It may denote a substance added to another to assist the fusion of the latter. The addition of limestone in iron smelting is essentially the addition of a flux, but in this case the flux also helps to form a desirable slag. Flux also denotes a substance used to enable two pieces of metal to be joined together without their becoming oxidized.

FMN See Flavin mononucleotide.

Foamed plastics. See Cellular plastics.

Foams. A foam is a coarse dispersion of a gas in a liquid, most of the phase medium being gas with the liquid in thin laminar sheets between the gas bubbles. Foaming does not occur with pure substances and it is developed by agitation of liquids and gases in the presence of stabilizing agents. These are generally surface-active substances (e.g. lauryl alcohol) which greatly lower the surface tension of the solution and which are themselves strongly adsorbed at the gas/solution interface. This adsorption process must take place very rapidly if break up of the foam is to be avoided. The persistence of different foams ranges from a few seconds (e.g. amyl alcohol solution) to hours and even months (soap and protein solutions). Among the factors thought to be important in foam formation are surface elasticity, surface viscosity and electrical double layer effects.

Foams are used industrially and are important in rubber preparations (foamed-latex) and in fire fighting, where they have the double advantage that aeration reduces the density of the aqueous medium and also that there is a great increase in surface area. This enables the foam to float as a continuous layer across the burning surface, so preventing the evolution of inflammable vapours. Foams are also used in gas adsorption and in the separation of proteins from biological fluids. See Anti-foaming agents.

Folic acid. The name was originally given to a substance present in spinach and other green leaves, which stimulated the growth of certain bacteria. It is now loosely used for several closely related compounds with vitamin activity. Pteroylglutamic acid, which is found in liver and has been synthesized, is used in the treatment of sprue and certain other types of anaemia, and needed for the growth of some bacteria. It has the structure—

Forced circulation evaporator. A widely used and versatile type of evaporator in which the liquid being evaporated is circulated through the heating element by means of a pump. The heating element, which is of the shell-and-tube type, may be either horizontal or vertical, and is normally situated outside the evaporator body, unlike the arrangement in a natural circulation evaporator. The forced circulation results in high rates of heat transfer and also helps to prevent fouling and scaling of the heater tubes, but these advantages are partly offset by the cost of pumping. Forced circulation units are used where the evaporator has to be constructed in an expensive corrosion-resistant material, where a crystalline product is formed or where viscous solutions are encountered.

Formaldehyde, $HCHO$. A colourless gas with a characteristic and pungent odour. Soluble in water to 52%: the commercial solution—formalin—contains about 40% formaldehyde. First prepared by Hofmann in 1867 by passing air and methyl alcohol vapour over a hot platinum wire. It is manufactured by passing methyl alcohol vapour and air over a heated metal or metal oxide catalyst, and to a lesser extent by the oxidation of paraffinic hydrocarbons. It reacts with water to give stable hydrates, called polymethylene glycols, of the type $(CH_2O)_n$, H_2O. In dilute solutions most of the formaldehyde is present as methylene glycol, $CH_2(OH)_2$ or CH_2O, H_2O. In more concentrated solutions, trimethylene glycol $(CH_2O)_3$, H_2O is also present. When formalin is allowed to stand, flocculent masses of paraformaldehyde are precipitated. Its principal use is in the manufacture of urea-, phenol-, melamine- and polyformaldehyde resins. Large quantities are also used in the manufacture of ethylene glycol, pentaerythritol and hexamethylenetetramine.

It is a powerful germicide, whether in solution or vapour. Rooms may be disinfected by spraying the solution or vaporizing paraformalde-

$$HO_2C \cdot [CH_2]_2 \cdot \underset{\underset{CO_2H}{|}}{CH} \cdot NH \cdot CO \underset{}{\bigcirc} NH \cdot CH_2 \cdots$$

It contains a pterin group, a molecule of *p*-aminobenzoic acid, and one glutamic acid residue. Related compounds from other sources and needed by different bacteria contain seven, three, and no glutamic acid residues. Pteroylglutamic acid is a bright yellow crystalline substance, insoluble in cold water and organic solvents, slightly soluble in hot water.

hyde. Dilute solutions are used for sterilizing surgical instruments and as applications in certain skin diseases.

Formaldehyde sodium sulphoxylate,

$$HOCH_2SO_2Na \cdot 2H_2O$$

Formaldehyde hydrosulphite. Obtained as colourless crystals, m.p. 65°, which readily dissolve in water. It is decomposed by dilute acids. Used as a reducing agent in calico printing.

Formalin. See Formaldehyde.

Formamide, $HCONH_2$. A colourless, rather viscous, odourless liquid; it absorbs water vapour, d^{20} 1·134, m.p. 2·5°, b.p. 210° (decomp.). Miscible with water and alcohol; slightly soluble in chloroform and benzene. Manufactured by direct union of carbon monoxide and ammonia under pressure, or by distillation of ammonium formate. It is converted to formic acid or a formate by concentrated acids or alkalis. Forms compounds with metals and with acids. It and its derivatives are good solvents for many organic and inorganic compounds.

Formates. Esters and salts of formic acid.

Formation constant. Another name for stability constant (q.v.)

Formic acid, $H \cdot COOH$. A colourless liquid which fumes slightly and has a penetrating odour, d^{20} 1·220, m.p. 8·4°, b.p. 100·5°. Miscible with water and alcohol; moderately soluble in benzene. It was discovered in 1670 by Rey, who distilled red ants with water. Occurs in sweat and urine, and is said to be present in stinging nettles. Prepared by heating oxalic acid with glycerol, when formic acid distils off. Manufactured by decomposing sodium formate, from the reaction of carbon monoxide and sodium hydroxide, with sulphuric acid; also made by the hydrolysis of methyl formate obtained by reacting carbon monoxide with methanol. It is used in textile dyeing and finishing, in leather tanning, and as an intermediate for other chemicals. It is a good solvent for many organic and inorganic compounds.

Formol titration. A method for estimating carboxyl groups in amino-acids and free carboxyl groups in proteins, devised by Sörensen. Formaldehyde reacts with the amino-groups of amino-acids to give neutral methylene derivatives, thus:

$$R{<}^{NH_2}_{COOH} + HCHO = R{<}^{N:CH_2}_{COOH} + H_2O$$

In the presence of formaldehyde the carboxyl groups can be estimated by titration with alkali. A free amino-group belonging to the guanidine nucleus, as in arginine, does not combine with formaldehyde.

Formoxy. The name given to the group $-O \cdot CHO$.

Formyl. The name given to the group $-OCH$.

Formylation. The introduction of a formyl,

$O{=}C{-}H$, group. Appropriate amines are formylated to give N-formyl derivatives useful for the preparation of isonitriles. Formylation of aromatic compounds may be compared with acylation and allows the introduction of an aldehyde group. Reactions due to Gattermann (q.v.) Gattermann-Koch (q.v.) Reimer-Tiemann (chloroform heated with sodium phenoxide) and Vilsmeier (aromatic compound, phosphorus oxychloride and N-methylformanilide) are suitable methods of formylation.

Forsterite, magnesium orthosilicate,
$2MgO \cdot SiO_2$. Crystals are orthorhombic, sp.gr. 3·3-3·35, hardness 6-7. At 1557° and above forsterite decomposes into clinoenstatite and cristobalite.

Forsterite refractories can be made by heating olivine and magnesite. They resist attack by slag, have a low thermal expansion and are strong.

Fourcroy, Antoine François de (1755-1808). Born in Paris, Fourcroy was first a dramatist, then a doctor of medicine, but in 1784 succeeded Macquer as professor of chemistry at the Jardin du Roi. He wrote two books which were once important, 'Systeme des Connaissances Chimiques' and 'Philosophie Chimique'. See 'Fourcroy, Chemist and Revolutionary', by W. A. Smeaton.

Fractional crystallization. The process of crystallization of part of the material from a solution containing a mixture of two or more substances. The first material to crystallize from such a solution will be enriched in the least soluble component of the dissolved mixture. Such a process, if carried out repeatedly and systematically, may result in the separation of the various components.

Fractional distillation. This is the process of separating a mixture into a series of fractions of different volatilities by means of distillation. The simplest method of doing this is by gradually vaporizing the liquid mixture, and removing and condensing the vapour as it is evolved. During the process the b.p. of the liquid gradually rises, due to loss of more volatile components, and the condensate may be collected in a series of fractions of different boiling ranges. The disadvantage of this method, which is known as *differential distillation*, is that since the vapour evolved at any time is in equilibrium with the boiling liquid, unless there are marked differences in the boiling points of the components separation will be poor. Consequently this method is rarely used outside the laboratory. *Rectification* (q.v.) is much more efficient, and is the fractionation process normally employed. Fractional distillation may be carried out at low temperatures, generally in a vacuum line.

Fractionating column. See Rectification.

Francium Fr. At.no. 87. ^{221}Fr and ^{223}Fr occur

as members of the decay series of heavier elements and various isotopes of mass numbers between 205 and 224 are known, ^{223}Fr, half-life 21 minutes, and ^{212}Fr, half-life 19·3 minutes, are the most stable. Francium is a member of the alkali metals but only tracer studies have been carried out on its chemistry.

Franck-Condon principle. According to this principle, the time occupied by an electronic transition in a molecule is very brief compared with the period of vibration of the constituent atomic nuclei. The principle is of great importance in discussing the energy changes occurring in molecules.

Frangulin, $C_{21}H_{18}O_9$. The glycoside present in the bark of *Rhamnus frangula*; is hydrolysed to rhamnose and emodin which is 1,6,8-trihydroxy-2-methylanthraquinone. The emodins are of medicinal importance, being constituents of rhubarb root. It forms needles, m.p. 228°. A glucofrangulin $C_{27}H_{30}O_{14}$, containing an additional molecule of glucose is known, m.p. 215°. Other rhubarb glycosides are chrysophanein, $C_{21}H_{20}O_9$, and rheochrysin, $C_{22}H_{22}O_{11}$, both derivatives of glucose.

Frankland, Sir Edward (1825-1899). Born at Churchtown in Lancashire, Frankland served as a druggist's apprentice in Lancaster before proceeding to London to enter the laboratory of Dr. Lyon Playfair. He later studied under Liebig and Bunsen. In 1851 he was appointed professor of chemistry at Owens College, Manchester. In 1863 he succeeded Faraday at the Royal Institution and, in 1865, became professor at the Royal College of Chemistry and Royal School of Mines in London. He was elected F.R.S. in 1853, and created K.C.B. in 1897. His early work was upon the theory of valency and the organometallic compounds of zinc, but later he investigated the problems of water supply and purification. See Mem. Lect., *J. Chem. Soc.* 1901, 193.

Frankland, Percy Faraday (1858-1946). Born in London, P. F. Frankland studied at the Royal School of Mines and at Würzburg University. He was professor of chemistry in University College, Dundee, from 1888 to 1894, and in Mason College, Birmingham, from 1894 to 1900, then being appointed professor of chemistry in the University of Birmingham. He became Dean of the Faculty of Science in 1913 and retired as professor-emeritus in 1919. He was President of the Chemical Society in 1911-13 and in 1919 received the Davy Medal of the Royal Society. His chief researches dealt with fermentation and with the bacteriology of air, water, and sewage. See *J. Chem. Soc.*, 1948, 1996.

Franklin, Edward Curtis (1862-1937). Born at Geary City, Kansas, Franklin was educated at the University of Kansas, the Johns Hopkins University, and the University of Berlin. He was appointed professor of chemistry at Kansas University in 1899, and at Stanford University, California, in 1906. He is noted for his brilliant researches upon problems associated with ammonia. See Chem. Soc. Mem. Lect., 1938.

Frank Read source. These sources explain the increase in dislocation density during the cold forming of metals. If a moving dislocation line is pinned at both ends, it will bow out in the middle, spiral back about both pinning points and finally form a closed loop. An active source will form a continuing series of such dislocation loops radiating outwards like ripples in a pond. Each loop will result in a fixed amount of slip or displacement of the lattice, so that considerable plastic deformation can result in ductile metals.

Frasch process. The process for obtaining sulphur in the U.S.A., where the sulphur lies in beds under a dome of rock. Superheated water is forced down a shaft, the sulphur is liquefied and then blown to the surface with compressed air.

Free energy. This is usually referred to as the Gibbs free energy and is represented by G (or sometimes F). It is a function dependent only on the state of the system and is defined by the expression

$$\Delta G = \Delta H - T\Delta S$$

Under conditions of constant temperature and pressure, the free energy change occurring in any system may be written as

$$G = \Delta H - T\Delta S$$
$$= \Delta E + P\Delta V - T\Delta S$$

When a spontaneous change takes place in any system, its free energy decreases and a position of equilibrium is reached when the free energy is a minimum.

ΔG is usually expressed in terms of kilocalories per mole for chemical reactions.

Free radicals. These are molecules or ions with unpaired electrons and hence are generally exceedingly reactive. The most stable free radicals are probably nitric oxide NO, nitrogen dioxide, NO_2, and molecular oxygen, O_2. Organic free radicals have a complete range of stability, those of relatively long life like triphenylmethyl which exist in equilibrium with their dimeric forms in solution; and those of relatively short life like methyl, which demand special techniques for their study. By the action of silver on triphenylmethyl bromide Gomberg obtained a product of empirical formula $(C_6H_5)_3C$, which behaved as a highly unsaturated molecule, and in solution proved to be an equilibrium mixture of $(C_6H_5)_3C\cdot$ and $(C_6H_5)_3C—C(C_6H_5)_3$. Numerous aryl-substituted ethanes have subsequently been prepared, and the degree of their dissociation is found to depend on (a) the nature of the solvent, (b) the concentration and temperature of the solution, and (c) the size and nature of the substituent groups.

The free radicals which have only a transient existence, like —CH$_3$, —C$_2$H$_5$, or —OH, and are therefore usually met with only as intermediates in chemical reactions, can usually be prepared and studied directly only at low pressures of the order of 1 mm, when they may be transported from the place of preparation in a rapidly streaming inert gas without suffering too many collisions with other molecules. They may be frozen and stabilized in glasses and other matrices.

Freeze drying. This is a method of drying heat-sensitive materials by subliming off the moisture. The material is cooled to a temperature in the range $-40°$ to $-10°$ such that all the water freezes, and this is then removed at a pressure of 0·1-2 mm Hg. The advantage of this method is that chemical changes and loss of volatile materials are avoided, and that it does not damage the physical structure of the material. Its disadvantage is its high cost. Freeze drying is mainly used for biological materials and certain food products. It can also be used for the removal of solvents other than water.

Freezing mixture. A mixture used for small-scale refrigeration. Such a mixture may be prepared by adding a soluble salt to a mixture of ice and water. The result is that the temperature of the mixture falls until it approximates to that of the cryohydric-point for the particular mixture.

Freezing-point, depression of. The lowering of freezing-point of a solvent produced by the presence of a dissolved substance. This lowering is proportional to the weight of dissolved substance for small concentrations of the latter. Molecular proportions of different substances usually produce the same lowering. The depression produced by dissolving 1 g molecule of solute in 100 g of solvent is called the molecular depression constant. Typical values of this constant are tabulated below:

Solvent	Molecular Depression Constant
Water	18·5°
Benzene	51·2°
Phenol	53°
Acetic acid	39°
Camphor	400°

Frémy, Edmond (1814-1894). Born at Versailles, Frémy studied chemistry under Gay-Lussac. In 1846 he was appointed professor of chemistry at the École Polytechnique, and in 1850 became professor of chemistry and director of the Muséum d'Histoire Naturelle. His research work covered a wide field, including investigations on the ferrates, stannates, plumbates, ozone, and the colouring matters of flowers. Fremy prepared anhydrous hydrogen fluoride, but failed to isolate fluorine.

Frémy's salt, (KO$_3$S)$_2$NO. A radical salt. Dimerized yellow in the solid state but reversibly dissociated to the purple monomer in aqueous solution. Obtained by oxidation of hydroxylamine disulphonates with alkaline permanganate. Used to oxidize phenols to the corresponding p-quinones.

Frenkel defect. Many factors, e.g. dislocations, interstitial atoms or impurities may contribute to defects in solids. The Frenkel defect is seen when an atom is displaced from its normal lattice site to an interstitial position. This distortion of the system may be regarded as introducing a lattice vacancy into the crystal. These defects are particularly noticeable when small cations are combined with large anions. In silver bromide, for example, at 300° about 0.4% of the silver ions are in interstitial sites. Frenkel defects are used in the interpretation of conductivities in solids.

Freons. A trade name for a group of chlorofluorocarbons. They can be made by treating a suitably chlorinated hydrocarbon with hydrogen fluoride in the presence of an inorganic chloride such as antimony pentachloride. They are inert substances which have been used extensively as solvents, refrigerants, and inert dispersing agents. Individual members are distinguished by numbers; the more important Freons include the following: Freon 12, Dichlorodifluoromethane CCl$_2$F$_2$; Freon 21, Dichlorofluoromethane CHCl$_2$F; Freon 142, 1-Chloro-1,1-difluoroethane CH$_3$CClF$_2$. Also called Geons or Arctons.

Frequency. Normally the number of wavelengths passing a fixed observer per second. Thus the frequency depends on the velocity of the wave motion. Another frequency often used in spectroscopy is the number of complete waves per cm (abbreviation cm^{-1}). This latter figure is merely the reciprocal of the wavelength.

Fresnel, Augustin Jean (1788-1827). Born at Broglie, Normandy, Fresnel was educated at Caen and at the École Polytechnique and the École des Ponts et Chaussées. He served for several years as an engineer. As a physicist his main researches were on problems associated with optics, but his name is linked with chemistry because he discovered the reaction between sodium chloride and ammonium bicarbonate, which forms the basis of the Solvay process for the manufacture of sodium carbonate.

Freundlich, Herbert (1880-1941). A German chemist, Freundlich was appointed professor at Braunschweig University (1911), Berlin University (1923), and Berlin Technische Hochschule (1930). He went to University College, London, in 1933 and to the University of Minnesota in 1938. He carried out many researches upon capillarity and surface chemistry. See *J. Chem. Soc.*, 1942, 646.

Freundlich isotherm. The relationship between the amount of a substance adsorbed and the concentration of the solute is

$$\frac{x}{m} = kc^{\frac{1}{n}}$$

where x is the amount adsorbed, m the weight of adsorbent, c the concentration or pressure, and k and n constants. This equation is empirical, depending on no theoretical assumptions. The values of the constants k and n vary with the system; n is usually between 0·2 and 0·7. The Freundlich equation is successful with adsorption systems of very variable characteristics, such as adsorption from solution and adsorption of gases. It expresses the rapid increase of adsorption with concentration at low concentrations, but is not so successful at higher concentrations.

Friar's balsam. See Benzoin.

Friedel, Charles. He was born in 1832 at Strasbourg and took a degree there in science in 1850. In the following year he went to Paris taking a degree there in physical science in 1855. He was especially interested in mineralogy, but in 1854 entered the laboratory of Wurtz and paid special attention for some years to the ketones and aldehydes. In 1876 became professor of mineralogy at the Sorbonne, and in 1884 succeeded Wurtz as professor of organic chemistry at the Sorbonne. He died in 1899 at Montauban. He is best known for his work in conjunction with Crafts on the Friedel-Crafts reaction. See Chem. Soc. Memorial Lectures, 1893-1900.

Friedel-Crafts reaction. In its broadest sense this reaction covers the acylation and alkylation of aromatic compounds by an electrophilic reagent. For example an acid chloride $RCOCl$ and benzene will react together in the presence of a Lewis acid to give a ketone $RCOC_6H_5$. Alkyl halides, alcohols, and under certain conditions, alkenes, may replace the acyl halide and yield the alkyl-substituted aromatic system. The Lewis acid is usually anhydrous $AlCl_3$, but HF, BF_3, $FeCl_3$, $SnCl_4$ may also be used; these serve to generate the acylium ion $(RCO)^{\oplus}$ or alkyl carbonium ion $R^{\oplus}$ which is the electrophile. Alkyl group rearrangement may occur during reaction, e.g. *n*-propyl bromide may yield an isopropyl substituent.

The reaction is useful for the synthesis of hydrocarbons and ketones, and is used industrially. See 'Friedel-Crafts and Related Reactions', Vols. i-iv. G. A. Olah, Interscience.

Froth flotation. This is the most widely used method of treating minerals to separate the valuable constituents from the accompanying *gangue*. It involves the formation of a moderately stable foam by the addition of a small quantity of a suitable reagent followed by aeration. The bubbles of air adhere preferentially to one of the constituents, and its density is so reduced that it rises to the surface where it is taken off as a froth, leaving the other material behind in the liquid. The desired constituent may collect either in the froth or be left behind to be taken off as the *underflow*. In the process a number of chemicals are added in small quantities to assist the separation. They include:

(a) *Frothing agents*—used to stabilize the foam to a sufficient degree to enable it to be carried from the flotation cell. Materials used for this purpose include pine oil, high alcohols and polypropylene glycol derivatives.

(b) *Collectors and promoters*—these modify the surface of the mineral to be removed in such a way that air bubbles will cling to it. Substances used include xanthates, dithiophosphates, fatty acids, petroleum sulphonates and vegetable and mineral oils.

(c) *Activators*—used to make a mineral surface amenable to the action of a collector. Thus copper (II) ions will render the surface of zinc sulphide active so that it will adsorb xanthates.

(d) *Depressors*—modify the surface of the mineral to be left behind in such a way that it is not affected by the collector of promotor.

Amounts of modifiers used vary widely, but are of the order 0·1-2 lb/ton. The pH value is a critical factor in many separations, and has to be carefully regulated.

Froth flotation cells. Modern cells generally consist of a vessel containing a rotating impeller driven by a vertical shaft. Air is introduced at a point immediately adjacent to the impeller and the action of the latter breaks it up into minute bubbles and mixes it with the *pulp* (the mixture of ground ore and liquid). The foam rises to the surface and is taken off. Operation is continuous. See Froth flotation.

D-**Fructose**, $C_6H_{12}O_6$. The most common ketose sugar. Combined with glucose it occurs as sucrose and raffinose; mixed with glucose it is present in fruit juices, honey, and other products; inulin and levan are built of fructose residues only. In natural products it is always in the furanose form, but it crystallizes in the pyranose form. It crystallizes in large needles, m.p. 102°-104°, $[\alpha]_D$ −133·5° (initial), −92° (final). It is very soluble in water, is twice as sweet as glucose, and in many respects behaves as does glucose.

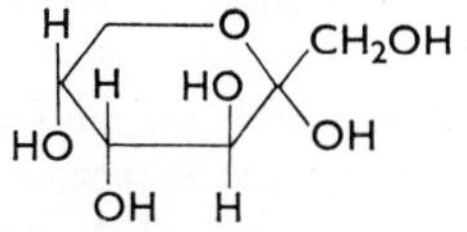

Pyranose form

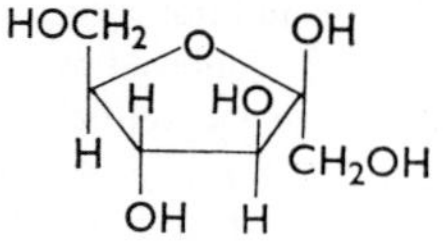

Furanose form

Fuchsin (Magenta), Rosaniline, Basic Violet 14. See Tripenylmethane dyes. It is the higher

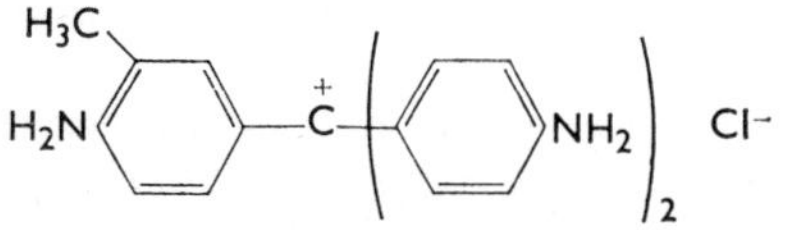

homologue of parafuchsin (the prototype of derivatives of triaminotriphenylmethane), in which one of the phenyl groups has been replaced by a tolyl group. The product of commerce, though chiefly composed of this substance, invariably contains an admixture of parafuchsin as well as the higher homologues. It contains four molecules of water of crystallization.

Fuchsin is prepared by oxidizing a mixture of aniline with *p*-toluidine. The oxidizing process is carried out with nitrobenzene.

Fucidin. The hemihydrate of the sodium salt of fucidic acid, an antimicrobial substance produced by the growth of *Fusidium coccineum*. It is

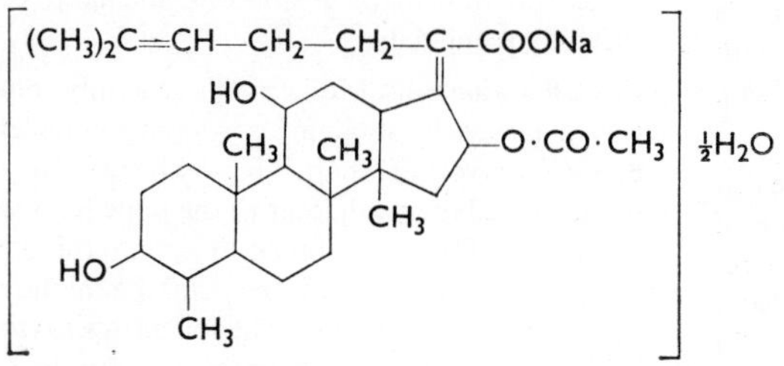

a white crystalline powder, slightly hygroscopic. Soluble at 20° in 1 part of water, $[\alpha]_D +5.5°$ to $+8°$ (3% w/v solution in water+few drops of dilute ammonia). Fucidic acid has a m.p. ~ 192°. It is an antibiotic with activity against Staphylococcal organisms that are resistant to penicillin.

Fucoidin. A polymer of L-fucose sulphate $(C_6H_9O_4SO_3)_n$, which is obtained by extracting brown seaweeds with aqueous solvents. It con-

sists chiefly of α-fucopyranose units, linked through carbon atoms 1 and 2.

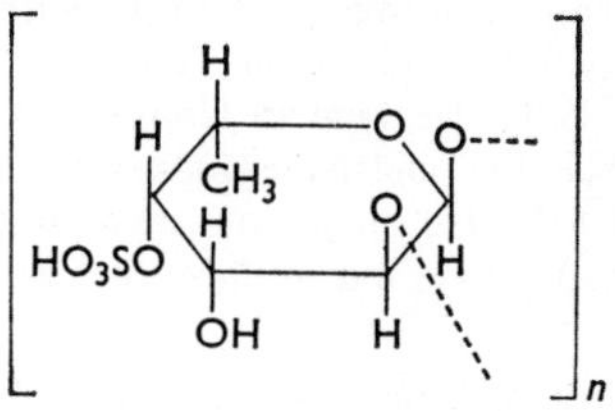

L-Fucose, $C_6H_{12}O_5$. The methyl pentose of gum tragacanth, of the blood group polysaccharides, and of seaweed, where its polymer fucoidin constitutes the cell walls. It crystallizes in microscopic needles, m.p. 145°, $[\alpha]_D -76°$, and has the formula:

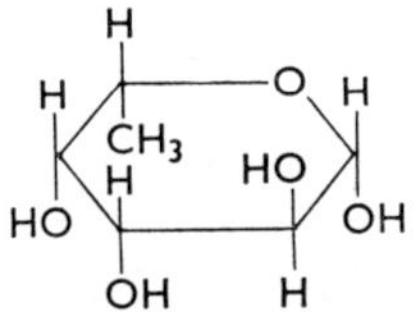

D-fucose has been found in the glycoside jalapin.

Fucosterol, $C_{29}H_{48}O$. The characteristic sterol of seaweeds. It crystallizes in needles from methyl alcohol, m.p. 124°, soluble in most organic solvents, $[\alpha]_D^{20} -41.8°$ in chloroform.

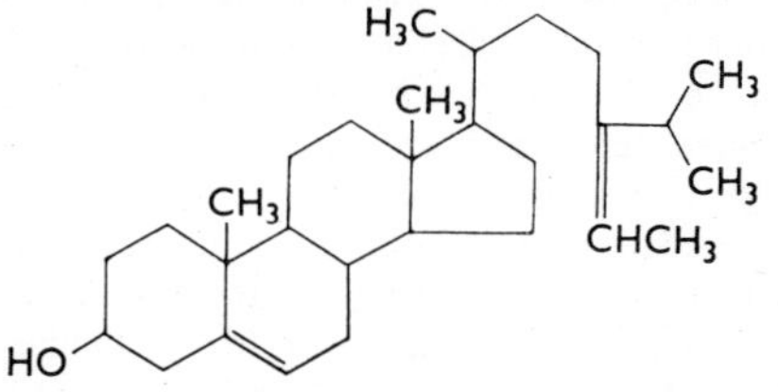

Fucoxanthin. The chief carotenoid pigment of the brown algae. It forms brown-red needles, m.p. 168°.

Fuel oil. A general term applied to an oil used for the production of power or heat.

Fuller's earth. Formerly any detergent clay for fulling cloth; later one valued mainly for its adsorptive properties in decolorizing oils, fats, and waxes, e.g. for lubricants, soaps, and margarine. There are two types: the essential clay mineral of one is montmorillonite, as in the Surrey and Somerset earths in England or in Japanese acid clay; and of the other is attapulgite, worked extensively in Florida and Georgia, U.S.A. ('Floridin') and palygorskite obtained from Spain. The former type is used in making pencils, pigments, ceramics, synthetic bentonite, foundry bonding materials, and activated fuller's earth. Attapulgite is also a useful catalyst in the petroleum industry.

Fulminic acid, Carbonyloxime, Carbyloxime, C=N—OH. An unstable volatile compound with an odour resembling that of hydrogen cyanide; even in solution in ether at low temperatures it is stable only for a short while, and changes to a polymer, metafulminuric acid. The mercury and silver salts are crystalline solids, and are manufactured by dissolving the metal in excess nitric acid and adding ethyl alcohol. These salts are very sensitive to shock, and explode violently. They are used as detonators.

Fulvenes. Hydrocarbons of the general formula shown, where R and R' are hydrogen,

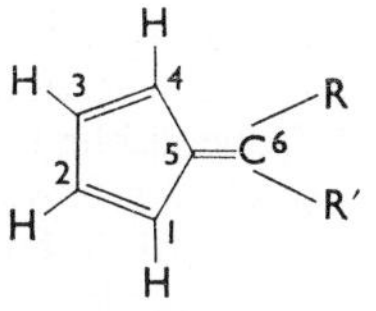

alkyl or aryl groups; compounds based on the fulvene skeleton with groups R and R' other than hydrocarbon residues are also known. They are yellow-orange to deep red-violet compounds, e.g. 6,6-dimethylfulvene is an orange liquid and 6,6-diphenylfulvene is a red-orange solid. The compounds are prepared by base-catalysed condensation of cyclopentadiene and the appropriate keto-compound: they behave as conjugated dienes and peroxidize easily. The parent hydrocarbon fulvene (R=R'=H) is known and is isomeric with benzene.

Fumarase. The enzyme responsible for catalysing the reaction between fumaric acid and water to give (−)-malic acid. It is very widely distributed in living tissues. It has been obtained crystalline and has molecular weight about 224,000.

Fumaric acid, $C_4H_4O_4$. Crystallizes in colourless needles or prisms m.p. 300°–302° in sealed tubes; sublimes above 200° in open vessels. Sparingly soluble in

$$HOOC \cdot CH$$
$$\parallel$$
$$HC \cdot COOH$$

water; soluble in alcohol. It occurs in the common fumitory, in Iceland moss, and in other plants. It can be manufactured by the isomeriza-

tion of maleic acid by heating in the presence of catalysts, or made from carbohydrate sources by the action of *Rhizopus nigricans* or other moulds. When heated to 230° it is converted to maleic anhydride; heated in sealed vessels with water at 150°–170°, it forms (±)-malic acid.

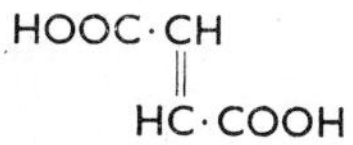

Fumaryl. The name given to the group

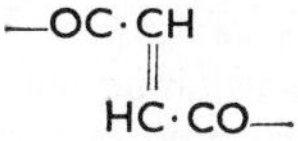

$$—OC \cdot CH$$
$$\parallel$$
$$HC \cdot CO—$$

Furaldehyde. See Furfural.

Furan, Furfuran, C_4H_4O. A colourless liquid, d^0 0·9644, b.p. 32°. Insoluble in water; miscible with alcohol and ether. Prepared by heating furoic acid at its boiling-point. Forms resins in the presence of mineral acids, but is unaffected by alkalis. Reduced by hydrogen to tetrahydrofuran.

Furanose. The term was introduced by Haworth to describe those forms of the sugars which contain a ring of 4 carbons and oxygen. They contain this skeleton and in contrast with the pyranose sugars (*q.v.*) are characterized by their instability. They exist in α and β forms, but the sugars themselves have not been obtained crystalline; they have to be converted into ethylglycosides for crystallization.

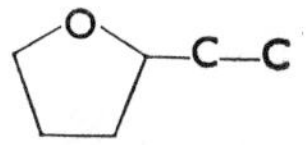

Furazan ring. The ring numbered as shown.

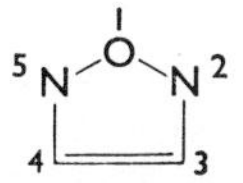

Furfural, Furfuraldehyde, 2-Furaldehyde, $C_5H_4O_2$. A colourless liquid with a peculiar odour; it darkens on exposure to light and air, d^{20} 1·159, b.p. 161·7°. Soluble in 11 parts of water; miscible with alcohol and ether. Volatile in steam. It occurs in many essential oils and in fusel oil. Manufactured by heating corncobs, oat hulls, or other pentosan-containing material with steam under pressure at 180° and fractionally distilling the liquor. Undergoes the Cannizzaro reaction with alkalis to give furoic acid and furfuryl alcohol. Reacts with ammonia to give furfuramide. Oxidized by sodium chlorate in the presence of vanadium pentoxide to give fumaric acid. Forms resins with phenol, aniline, and acetone. Used as a solvent for decolorizing rosin and in the solvent extraction of mineral oils.

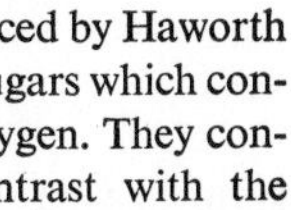

Furfuraldehyde. See Furfural.

Furfuran. See Furan.

Furfuryl-. The group

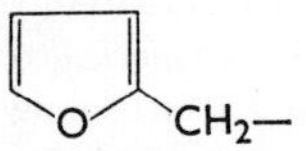

Furfuryl alcohol, $C_5H_6O_2$. A colourless liquid, d^{23} 1·128, b.p. 170°-171°. Miscible with water, alcohol, and ether; exists also in a modification which is insoluble in water. Prepared by the reduction of furfural or by the action of 30% sodium hydroxide solution on furfural in the cold; furoic acid is produced at the same time by the Cannizzaro reaction. Forms resins with mineral acids; it may be stabilized for storage by the addition of 0·5% urea. Reduces solutions of permanganates in the cold. It is poisonous.

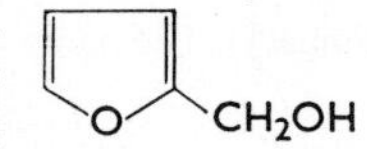

Furfurylidene. The group

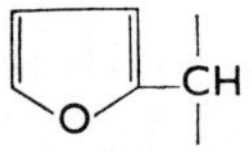

Furil, $C_{10}H_6O_4$. Crystallizes in yellow needles,

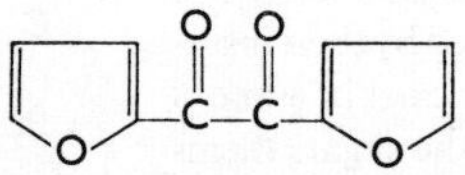

m.p. 165°-166°. Insoluble in water; soluble in benzene and hot alcohol. Prepared by adding furoin to a hot solution of copper sulphate in pyridine. Furil is precipitated by the addition of water.

Furoic acid, α-Furoic acid, Pyromucic acid, $C_5H_4O_3$. A colourless crystalline substance, m.p. 125°-132° (sublimes at 100°), b.p. 230°-232°. Soluble in hot water, alcohol, and ether. Prepared, together with furfuryl alcohol, by the action of 30% sodium hydroxide solution on furfural in the cold. The furfuryl alcohol is removed by extraction with ether and the furoic acid crystallizes out when the solution is acidified. Forms soluble sodium and potassium salts. It is decomposed at its b.p. into furan and carbon dioxide.

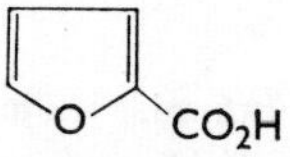

Furoin, $C_{10}H_8O_4$. Crystallizes in colourless

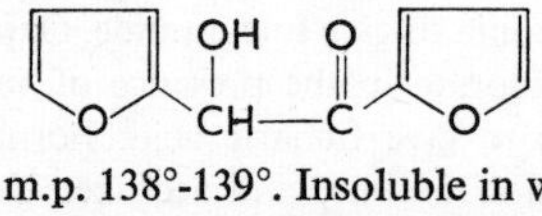

needles, m.p. 138°-139°. Insoluble in water and alcohol, soluble in toluene and hot methyl alcohol. Prepared by boiling a mixture of furfural, alcohol, and water with potassium cyanide: the furoin crystallizes on cooling the liquor.

Furoyl. The name given to the groups

The α configuration is the more common.

Furyl-. The name given to the groups

The α configuration is the more common.

Fusain. A macroscopic constituent of coal which is dull, soft, and like charcoal. It occurs largely as irregular partings or wedges with a fibrous appearance. Under the microscope fusain shows a 'carbonized' cellular structure in which there is little translucent material present. It contains the mineral fusinite.

Fusel oil. A mixture of alcohols obtained as a high-boiling fraction during the distillation of fermentation alcohol. It is formed in small amounts during fermentation from the amino-acids of the proteins present, and its composition depends upon both the material fermented and the yeast used. The chief alcohols present are iso-amyl, active (laevorotatory) amyl, isobutyl, iso-propyl, and normal propyl alcohols. It also contains fatty acids such as capric, caprylic, caproic, butyric, and acetic acids, as well as their esters. Commercial fusel oil boils over the range 105°-137°, and can be fractionally distilled to separate the alcohols it contains. May be detected by the characteristic odour of the isoamyl alcohol present. Used as a source of amyl and isobutyl alcohols.

Fusible white precipitate. See Mercurammine compounds.

Fusidic acid. A steroid antibiotic of clinical value, also of biogenetic interest as the carbon skeleton is that of an un-rearranged cyclosqualene (see Squalene).

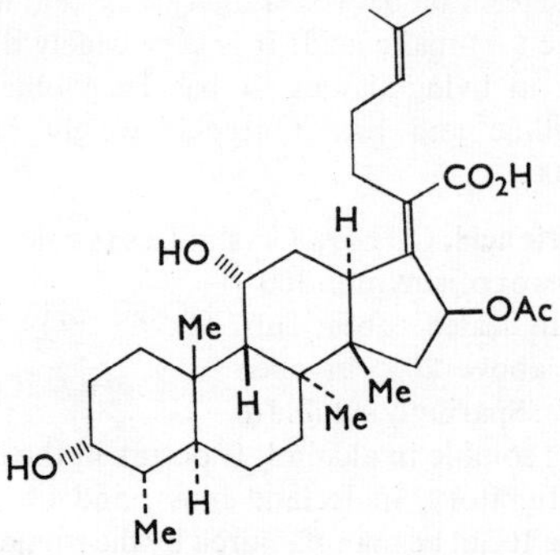

G

Gabriel's reaction. The conversion of a halogen compound into the corresponding amino compound by treatment with potassium phthalimide and subsequent hydrolysis of the intermediate phthalimide compound. Thus chloroacetic acid and potassium phthalimide give phthalimido-acetic acid, which on hydrolysis gives glycine and phthalic acid. The method is of general application and has the great advantage of giving a pure primary amine free from mixture with secondary and tertiary products.

Gadoleic acid, $C_{19}H_{37}COOH$. A fatty acid, belonging to the oleic acid series, occurring as glycerides in cod-liver oil, herring oil, and sperm oil, m.p. about 20°.

Gadolinium, Gd. At.no. 64. At.wt. 156·9, d 7·895, m.p. 1312°, b.p. 3000°. Gadolinium has the hexagonal close-packed structure below 1262° ($a=3·6315$, $c=5·777$ Å) but becomes body-centred cubic above this ($a=4·06$ Å). It is a typical rare-earth element ($q.v.$). Gadolinium is used in microwave ferrites.

Gadolinium compounds. Gadolinium forms a single series of colourless salts, the metal being in the tripositive state. These are typical rare-earth compounds ($q.v.$).

Galactolipid(e)s, Galactolipin(e)s. See Cerebrosides.

Galactans. Polysaccharides which on hydrolysis give galactose. They occur in wood and in many algae. The most important galactan is agar ($q.v.$).

D-**Galactose,** $C_6H_{12}O_6$. An isomer of glucose which is fairly widely distributed in plants. It is a constituent of raffinose and stachyose, of hemicelluloses, of pectin, of gums and mucilages, and of some glycosides. In animals it forms half the lactose molecule and is the sugar found in the brain. Chemically it is very similar to glucose. It has the structure

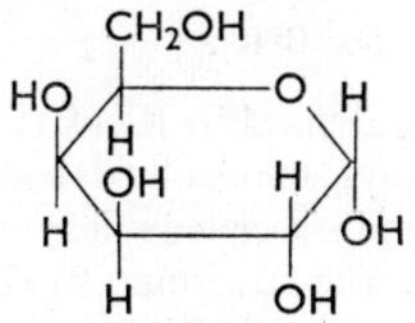

It crystallizes in the pyranose form, m.p. 118°–120° (monohydrate), 165·5° (anhydrous).

L-Galactose is a constituent of agar and other seaweed polysaccharides, and of linseed mucilage.

Galena, PbS. This common ore of lead crystallizes in the cubic system. Hardness $2\frac{1}{2}$. It is bluish-grey or black with a metallic lustre.

Galena crystallizes with the sodium chloride structure.

Gallamine triethiodide, $C_{30}H_{60}I_3N_3O_3$. The triethiodide is a white powder, m.p. 235°, soluble in water, sparingly soluble in alcohol and chloroform, prepared by treating pyrogallol with 1-chloro-2-diethylaminoethane hydrochloride, and treating the product with ethyl iodide. It blocks the transmission of impulses at the nerve-muscle junction, causing paralysis of voluntary muscle. Gallamine triiodide is used to relax muscles in surgical operations.

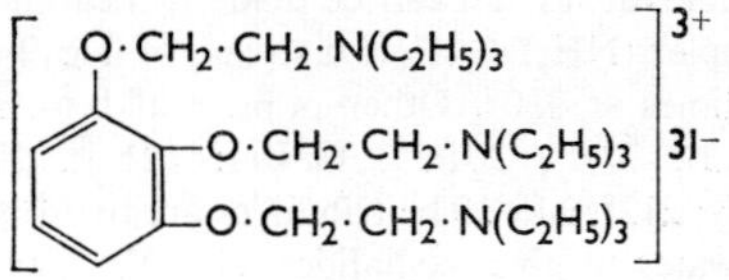

Gallic acid, 3, 4, 5-trihydroxybenzoic acid,

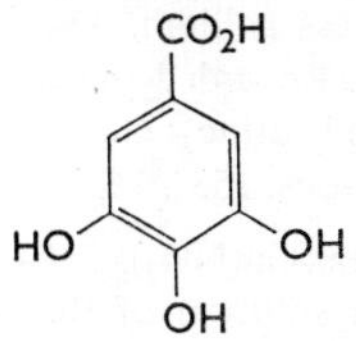

$C_7H_6O_5$. Colourless crystals with one molecule of water, m.p. 253°, sparingly soluble in water and alcohol. It occurs free in woody tissue, in gall-nuts, and in tea, and is a constituent of the tannins, from which it can be obtained by fermentation or by acid hydrolysis. It gives a blue-black colour with ferric salts and is used in the manufacture of inks. On heating it gives pyrogallol.

Gallic acid has a limited use as a dyestuffs intermediate and as a source of medicinals.

Gallium, Ga. At.no. 31, At.wt. 69·72. It is an element which Mendeléeff predicted and to which he gave the name *eka-aluminium*. It is widely distributed, although in very small amounts. It is usually present in zinc and aluminium minerals, but one of the richest sources is the mineral germanite (approx. 0·7% Ga). The element is metallic in appearance and crystallizes in the orthorhombic system. The unit cell containing 8 atoms has the dimensions: $a=4·526$, $b=4·520$, $c=7·660$ Å. It has m.p. 29·75°, b.p. 2230°, d 5·9. The lattice contains Ga_2 units. The metal is unaffected by oxygen at room temperature, and becomes covered with a thin protective coating of oxide when more strongly heated. It reacts very readily with the halogens. Dilute hydrochloric acid attacks the metal in the cold. Dilute nitric acid attacks it on warming. Cold concentrated nitric acid has no action. The metal is dissolved slowly by alkali hydroxides with evolution of hydrogen. Gallium forms a number of alloys (e.g. with aluminium or cadmium) of some use in high-temperature thermometers. The metal is also used in transistors.

Gallium halides. Two series of halides are known, GaX_3 and GaX_2. Of the trihalides, the fluoride is ionic, but the other halides exist, to a large extent, as dimers. The dihalides (X=Cl, Br, I), are ionized and have the structure $Ga(I)[Ga(III)X_4]$, containing uni- and tripositive gallium. The trihalides are prepared from the elements. Hydrated gallic fluoride, $GaF_3 \cdot H_2O$ is obtained from gallic hydroxide and hydrofluoric acid; the anhydrous salt can be made by heating the complex $(NH_4)_3GaF_6$ in a stream of fluorine. It sublimes at 950°. Other m.ps. and b.ps. are: $GaCl_3$, 77·9°, 201·3°; $GaBr_3$; 121·5°, 279°: GaI_3; 212°, 346°. The trihalides are hydrolysed by water to give oxyhalides, GaOX. They are good Friedel-Crafts catalysts. Gallous salts, GaX_2, are prepared by heating the gallium (III) salts with excess gallium. They are strong reducing agents. Recorded m.ps. are (the halides decompose on heating): $GaCl_2$, 170·5°; $GaBr_2$, two modifications, 153°, 165°, GaI_2, 211°.

Gallium nitrate, $Ga(NO_3)$, $3H_2O$. Prepared by evaporating a solution of the oxide in nitric acid. It loses its water of crystallization at 40° and decomposes at 110°.

Gallium nitride, GaN. Prepared by the action of ammonia on the metal at 900°. It is a semiconductor, as are the phosphide and arsenide.

Gallium sesquioxide, Ga_2O_3. This oxide is formed as a white, non-volatile, and non-fusible powder by ignition of the sulphate or nitrate of the element, or by ignition of the hydroxide, $Ga(OH)_3$, which is precipitated by ammonia from solutions of gallium salts. The oxide is dimorphic; the α-form changes to the β-form at 380° (m.p. 1740°). At least two hydrated oxides occur, GaO·OH and $Ga(OH)_3$. Gallium hydroxide is soluble in excess of alkali hydroxides, and partially soluble in excess of ammonia. Gallium oxide is less acidic than that of aluminium, although in many respects it resembles Al_2O_3.

Gallium sulphate, $Ga_2(SO_4)_3$, $18H_2O$. This is obtained by dissolving the metal or its hydroxide in dilute sulphuric acid and crystallizing. It forms colourless crystals. Its aqueous solution undergoes partial hydrolysis on boiling. When gently heated the hydrated salt loses its water and becomes anhydrous. At red heat gallium sulphate is transformed to the sesquioxide. Gallium sulphate forms alums, e.g.

$$(NH_4)_2SO_4, Ga_2(SO_4)_3, 24H_2O$$

when it is crystallized with the sulphates of ammonium, potassium, rubidium, or caesium.

Gallium sulphide, Ga_2S_3. Formed as a yellow crystalline solid by the action of sulphur vapour on metallic gallium. It is decomposed by water, by acids, or by alkalis. Reduction of the sesquisulphide with hydrogen at 400° gives GaS. It is yellow, sublimes *in vacuo* at 800°, m.p. 960°. Further reduction, or interaction of metallic gallium and hydrogen sulphide at high temperature, gives the monosulphide, Ga_2S.

Gallotannic acid. See Tannic acid.

Galls. The dried spherical excrescences from the twigs of *Quercus infectoria* resulting from the deposition of eggs of the gall-wasp. Galls contain a large proportion of gallotannic acid, and are strongly astringent. They are used for the preparation of medicinal tannic acid, and also in ink manufacture. Powdered galls, with or without opium, are a constituent of an ointment and a suppository used for the relief of haemorrhoids.

Galvani, Luigi (1737-1798). Born at Bologna, Galvani studied theology and subsequently medicine at the university there. In 1762 he was appointed lecturer in anatomy in his native town. Galvani owes the wide celebrity of his name to his discoveries in animal electricity rather than in anatomy. In 1791 he observed the convulsive twitching of a frog muscle in contact with two different metals, and thus initiated the study of electrochemistry.

Galvanizing. The coating of steel sheet and other sections with a layer of zinc. The iron is cleaned by pickling with dilute acid and then dipped into a bath of molten zinc, ammonium chloride being used as a flux. The coating is attacked by sea water, by the sulphurous vapours of large towns, and by dilute acids and alkalis; this latter rendering it useless for food-canning purposes.

Cold galvanizing is the process of coating by electrodeposition from a solution of zinc sulphate, using a zinc anode.

Gamma-rays. Electro-magnetic waves of very short wavelength, that is very hard X-rays. They have great penetrating power and are emitted during most nuclear disintegrations.

Gammexane. See BHC.

Gangliosides. Defined by Klenk (1942) as phosphorus-free glycosphingolipids containing sialic acids (*q.v.*), and associated chiefly with brain and nerve tissue. The structure of one ganglioside has been elucidated (Kuhn and Wiegandt, *Chem. Ber.* 1963, **96**, 866).

Gangue. The foreign matter consisting of clay, etc., found associated with ores.

Ganister. A hard siliceous sandstone used for making refractory bricks for lining steel furnaces and converters.

Garnet. A group of minerals crystallizing in

the cubic system of the general formula $R^{2+} R^{3+} (SiO_4)_3$, where R^{2+} is Ca, Fe, Mg, Mn and R^{3+} is Al, Fe, Cr. Some garnets are used as gemstones with colours ranging from yellow-red to deep red and also emerald green. Garnet sand is used as an abrasive.

Garnierite. A hydrated silicate of magnesium and nickel of very variable composition. An important nickel ore. It is soft and friable, bright apple-green in colour, sp.gr. 2·2-2·8, hardness 3-4.

Gas. The gaseous state is the most diffuse state of matter, in which the molecules have an almost unrestricted motion. Thus a gas may be defined as a substance of which the volume increases continuously and without limit as the pressure on it is continuously reduced. This definition does not distinguish a gas from a vapour, and to do this the proviso that the substance is above its critical temperature should be added.

For household gas, see Town gas.

Gas absorption. When a soluble component of a gaseous mixture dissolves in a liquid with which it is in contact the process is known as gas absorption, or frequently simply as absorption. Selective absorption is employed to separate components of mixtures of gases or vapours, e.g. the removal of ammonia from ammonia-air mixtures by absorption in water, or the removal of benzene from coal gas by washing with absorbent oils.

On an industrial scale the process may be carried out by bubbling the gas through the liquid (as in a *plate absorption column*), by spraying the liquid through the gas (as in a *spray column*) or by passing the gas over surfaces wetted by the liquid (as in a packed *absorption tower*). Counter-current flow (*q.v.*) is generally employed. See also Absorption column.

Gas analysis. A mixture of gases may be analysed by:

(1) absorbing each constituent, preferentially by means of a reagent, e.g. carbon dioxide in caustic potash solution, carbon monoxide in acid or alkaline cuprous chloride;

(2) exploding or burning the gas with oxygen or air and measuring both the change in volume and amount of waste gases formed by absorption;

(3) titration as in volumetric analysis, e.g. ammonia and hydrogen sulphide;

(4) by absorbing the gas on a substance which can be weighed both before and after absorption;

(5) by changes in thermal conductivity, e.g. carbon dioxide in flue gas;

(6) by measurement of infra-red or ultra-violet spectra;

(7) by vapour phase chromatography;

(8) by measurement of magnetic susceptibility or other physical property not considered above.

Gas chromatography. A very commonly used process for the separation and identification of fairly volatile materials (b.p. up to 400°). The substances to be separated are distributed between a carrier gas and an inert liquid which will generally be absorbed on an appropriate surface.

Gas cleaning. The removal of suspended particles of liquid or solid from a gas stream with the object of purifying it. Some of the more important types of equipment for doing this are described under Air filters, Bag filter, Calder-Fox scrubber, Cyclone separator, Electrostatic precipitators, Impingement separators, Scrubbers.

Gas constant. By combining Boyle's and Charles's laws, we arrive at a general equation of the form $pv = kT$, where p is the pressure, v the volume, and T the temperature of the gas, while k is a constant depending on the amount of gas used, and the units employed for expressing p and v. When one gram molecule of gas is considered, k may be replaced by R, and the equation becomes $pv = RT$. R is called the gas constant. $R = 0·08204$ litre-atmos. per degree, or $8·31432/(g.\ mole)^4 \times 10^7$ ergs per degree, or 1·987 cal per mole per degree.

Gas laws. The laws which describe the behaviour of gases are Boyle's law, Charles's law, Gay-Lussac's law of gaseous volumes, and Avogadro's hypothesis.

Gas mantle oxide. A mixture of 99 parts of thoria, ThO_2, and 1 part of ceria, CeO_2. In the manufacture of incandescent mantles the cellulose fabric is impregnated with the appropriate mixture of thorium and cerium nitrates. On drying and igniting a skeleton remains which constitutes the mantle. The best light emission from the mantle is obtained with the two oxides in the above proportions.

Gas oil. The petroleum fraction intermediate between kerosine and light lubricating oils. Its main uses are in the manufacture of gas for enriching water gas, as a wash oil for the extraction of benzole from coal gas, and as a burner fuel. Special types are used as diesel fuels.

Gasoline. The term is used in the U.S.A. to denote motor spirit (petrol), but in Britain it normally denotes the petroleum fraction of distillation range 30°-100°, i.e. a stabilized primary flash distillate, which is the total distillate from the primary atmospheric column in a refinery processing crude petroleum. This is subsequently separated into gas and gasoline, the latter being blended into motor spirit.

Gas purifiers. Coal gas for domestic use must be free from hydrogen sulphide, and purifier boxes

GASTRIN GEL

are used to remove this gas. They are of two sorts; water lute and dry lute, and are constructed usually of cast-iron plates bolted together to give a square or rectangular box.

The materials used for purification are: (1) Natural oxide of iron (bog iron ore). (2) Weldon mud. (3) Colloidal ferric hydrate prepared from the residues after extraction of alumina from bauxite.

Gastrin. A hormone of the gastro-intestinal tract: at physiological concentrations it stimulates gastric acid secretion, but it is inhibitory at high concentrations. Gastrin is a heptadecapeptide, which has been isolated in pure form from hog antrum and also obtained by synthesis. The biological activity seems to reside in the carboxyl-terminal tetrapeptide group.

studied chemistry in Paris. He became professor of chemistry at the École Polytechnique in 1806 and in 1832 professor at the Jardin des Plantes. He and Thenard devised a method of preparing potassium and sodium by a chemical process; these elements were used to effect reductions, e.g. boric acid to boron. Gay-Lussac discovered cyanogen, first prepared ethyl iodide, and determined many vapour densities. He died in 1850.

Gay-Lussac's law. Gay-Lussac (1808) stated that when gases combine they do so in volumes which bear a simple ratio to each other, and to that of the product if it is also a gas. Thus, one volume of nitrogen combines with three volumes of hydrogen to yield two volumes of ammonia. The law is only approximately true, e.g. the ratio of the combining volumes of hydrogen and oxygen in

$$Tyr.Gly.Pro.Tyr.Met.(Glu)_5.Ala.Tyr.Gly.Try.Met.Asp.PheNH_2$$

Gate agitator. A paddle agitator (q.v.) having a paddle in the shape of a farm gate.

Gattermann-Koch reaction. Formylation (q.v.) of an aromatic hydrocarbon to yield the corresponding aldehyde can be accomplished by treatment with carbon monoxide, hydrogen chloride and aluminium chloride; at atmospheric pressure cuprous chloride is also required. The reaction resembles a Friedel-Crafts acylation since formyl chloride, HCOCl, is probably involved.

Gattermann's reaction. This is a variation of the Sandmeyer reaction (q.v.); copper powder and hydrogen halide are allowed to react with the diazonium salt solution and halogen is introduced into the aromatic nucleus in place of an amino group.

Gattermann synthesis. A method for the synthesis of aromatic hydroxyaldehydes. For example, aluminium chloride is used to bring about the condensation of phenol with a mixture of gaseous hydrochloric acid and hydrocyanic acid; an aldimine hydrochloride is formed and on hydrolysis gives p-hydroxybenzaldehyde:

$$C_6H_5OH + HCN + HCl$$
$$\longrightarrow p\text{-}C_6H_4(OH)CH:NH\cdot HCl$$
$$\downarrow$$
$$p\text{-}C_6H_4(OH)CHO + NH_4Cl$$

Gaultherin, $C_{18}H_{26}O_{12}$. The parent glycoside of methyl salicylate, it is widely distributed in plants. It is of interest as being a glycoside of the disaccharide, primeverose.

$$C_5H_9O_4\cdot O\cdot C_6H_{10}O_4\cdot O\cdot C_6H_4\cdot CO_2CH_3$$

Methyl salicylate is also found combined with vicianose as violutin. See Salicylic acid.

Gay-Lussac, Joseph Louis. Born in 1778 and

water is not exactly 2:1, but 2·0027:1. The law holds strictly only for ideal gases.

A quite different law, Charles's law (q.v.), is also sometimes known as Gay-Lussac's law.

Geber. See Jabir.

Gegenion. German for counter-ion (q.v.).

Geiger counter. This is a device which is used to detect and measure amounts of radioactivity. It consists of a cylindrical chamber which contains two electrodes, one of which is a fine wire along the axis of the cylinder. The chamber is filled with gas at a low pressure and the incident radiation causes ionization of the gas. If the chamber is polarized with an applied high voltage, the ions produced migrate to the electrodes and the resulting current is detected and amplified.

Geissler tube. This consists of a glass tube containing a gas at a low pressure, and a metal contact at either end sealed through the glass. On applying a suitably high electrical potential to the two electrodes, the gas glows with its own characteristic luminosity.

Gel. Hydrophilic colloids are capable under certain conditions, such as lowering of temperature, of partially coagulating to a mass of intertwining filaments which may enclose the whole of the dispersion medium to produce a pseudo-solid but easily deformable mass or jelly. Such gels may, in some instances, preserve a rigidity when they contain as little as 1% of disperse phase, and generally appear to be heterogeneous under the microscope. Gels are sometimes classified as hydrogels, alcogels, etc., according to whether the dispersion medium is water, alcohol, etc.

Inorganic gelatinous precipitates have much the same type of structure as coherent gels, and

260

can often be made to form true gels on careful choice of conditions. Gels are sometimes divided into elastic and rigid gels. Gelatin is an example of the first type, silica gel of the second, but this classification is not strict, as even silica has a certain amount of elasticity, as is proved by the vibrations produced on tapping a test-tube full of silica gel. Gelatin gel may be converted back to the sol on heating and is thus a reversible gel; silica will not liquefy to a sol on any simple treatment, and is said to be irreversible. See Colloids.

Gelatin. A protein, belonging to the sclero-protein class. It occurs in bones and in fibrous tissue in the form of its anhydride, collagen, which is converted into gelatin on boiling with dilute acids. Gelatin swells in cold water, but is insoluble in it. It dissolves in hot water to give a very viscous solution, and a solution containing 1% or more solidifies to a jelly on cooling. It is particularly rich in glycine and lysine. It is manufactured from bone and from hides, and is used in cooking and photography amongst other industries. It is the principal constituent of glue. See also Photographic gelatin.

Gelatin hardeners (see also Aldehyde hardeners, Diacetyl, Mucochloric acid).

(a) *Inorganic compounds.* Compounds such as chrome alum and potash alum have been known as photographic hardeners for a long time. In fact many polyvalent metal cations can act as hardeners, generally at a pH below 7·0. They can, therefore, be incorporated in acid fixing and stop baths. The cross-links likely to be formed are those between carboxy anions in the gelatin and hydrated polyvalent metal cations. In the case of chromium hardeners cross-links may also involve complexes with gelatin amino groups.

(b) *Organic compounds.* Many organic hardeners are most effective at a pH greater than 7·0. The most widely used organic hardener is formalin. The reaction between formaldehyde and amino groups in the polypeptide chains is complex.

Guanidino and amide groups present in gelatin may also take part in cross-linking reactions with formalin. Formalin hardening can be made more effective by addition of phenols, presumably involving the intermediate formation of poly(hydroxymethyl) phenols. Polyfunctional compounds with a wide range of groups such as isocyanato, alkanesulphonoxy, epoxy, maleimido, ethyleneimino and vinylsulphonyl are hardeners.

Gelatin hardening process. Photographic materials containing gelatin as the medium can be hardened both during manufacture and during processing. The hardening reaction involves the formation of chemical bonds between the hardener and at least two gelatin polypeptide chains. The resulting cross-linked gelatin layer is rigid and can be handled and processed at high temperatures and humidity without the occurrence of softening or sticking. In addition, it has reduced swell in aqueous solutions (excessive swelling leads to reticulation) and improved mechanical properties (against abrasion) particularly during processing.

Hardeners used during manufacture must not adversely affect the photographic properties of the material, and the hardening action should not continue with keeping. Depending upon the hardener used, such groups as amino, guanidino and carboxy groups in the gelatin molecule are involved in the cross-linking reaction. See also Gelatin hardeners.

Gelation. This term is used to denote the partial coagulation of a lyophilic sol which results in the formation of a gel.

Gel filtration. A valuable fractionation method based on separation of molecules according to size, and originally using cross-linked dextran gels (see Sephadex). Small molecules diffuse into the pores of the gel, while large molecules are excluded and accordingly are not retained by a column of the gel when a solution of the mixed substances is allowed to flow through. Many modifications of the method are possible, e.g. combination with ion-exchange chromatography as in the use of 'DEAE-Sephadex' (diethylaminoethyl-Sephadex). Gel filtration is applicable to studies of drug-protein binding, and to the estimation of approximate molecular weights of macromolecules.

Gelignite. A form of gelatin dynamite, consisting of nitroglycerin gelatinized with collodion cotton and mixed with wood meal and potassium nitrate.

Gem-. A prefix indicating that a pair of atoms or groups are attached to the *same* atom, e.g. gem-dimethyl, etc.: its use is trivial and unnecessary when naming an organic compound systematically.

Genetic code. The relationship between the sequence of amino-acids in a protein and the sequence of nucleotides in a nucleic acid controlling the protein synthesis. A sequence of three adjacent nucleotides ('codon') is supposed to determine each particular amino-acid. Several codons may 'code' for the same amino-acid, and are then described as 'degenerate'. The genetic code, expressed as nucleotide sequences, is regarded as the basic source of hereditary information.

Genins. Where a glycoside is composed of a carbohydrate group combined with a compound related in structure to the sterols, the non-carbohydrate portion of the molecule is called a 'genin'. Genins are therefore obtained from the vegetable heart poisons related to digitalis, the toad venoms and the saponins.

Genth, Frederick Augustus (1820-1893). Genth was born at Wachtersbach bei Hanau, and after studying at Heidelberg, Giessen, and Marburg, went to America in 1848. From 1872 onwards he was professor of chemistry and mineralogy at the University of Pennsylvania. He discovered 24 new minerals, discovered and investigated the cobaltammine compounds, and was President of the American Chemical Society in 1880.

Gentian. The dried root of *Gentiana lutea*. The galenical preparations of gentian, the compound infusion, and the compound tincture are used in medicine for their bitter, appetite-stimulating properties. It contains various glycosides and enzymes.

Gentianose, $C_{18}H_{32}O_{16}$. The trisaccharide found in the roots of many species of gentian is 6-β-D-glucopyranosido - α - D - glucopyranosido - β - D-fructofuranoside. It crystallizes in plates, m.p. 209°-211°, $[\alpha]_D$ +33°. It is non-reducing. Emulsin splits it to glucose and sucrose; invertase or dilute acids split it to gentiobiose and fructose.

Gentian violet. See Methyl violet.

Gentiobiose, $C_{12}H_{22}O_{11}$. The sugar of amygdalin and a number of other glycosides, 6-[β-D-glucopyranosido]-D-glucose. It crystallizes in microscopic prisms, m.p. 190°-195°, $[\alpha]_D$ +9·6°.

Geometrical isomerism. See Isomerism.

Geons. See Freons.

Geranial. See Citral-a.

Geraniol, $C_{10}H_{18}O$. A terpene alcohol of the constitution:

CH₃

CH₂OH

H₃C   CH₃

Found in a very large number of essential oils, especially in palmarosa oil, also known as Turkish geranium oil, which is obtained from the grass *Cymbopogon Martinii*. It can be isolated by the separation of its crystalline derivative with calcium chloride. It can also be manufactured from turpentine. It is a colourless oil, smelling of roses, and is unstable in air and on keeping;

b.p. 229°-230°/757 mm, d^{15} 0·883, n_D^{20} 1·4766. It forms a characteristic diphenylurethane, m.p. 82°. It forms citral-a on oxidation. By treatment with gaseous hydrochloric acid and other agents geraniol is converted into limonene.

Gerhardt, Charles Frédéric (1816-1856). A pupil of Liebig, Gerhardt became in 1838 lecture assistant to Dumas in Paris. He was professor of chemistry at Montpellier from 1841 till 1848, when he returned to Paris to open with Laurent a private chemical laboratory. Here his theory of types took form. In 1855 he became professor of chemistry and pharmacy at his native town of Strasburg. His blunt and boorish manner prevented him from enjoying the recognition his work deserved. See 'Charles Gerhardt, Sa Vie', by his son, Charles Gerhardt (Paris, 1900).

Germanite. One of the few minerals containing germanium as an essential constituent, found in the Tsumeb mine in S.W. Africa. A complex copper sulphide containing 6-10% Ge as well as As, Fe, Zn, and Pb.

Germanium, Ge. At.no. 32, At.wt. 72·59. Germanium was discovered in 1886 by Winkler in the mineral argyrodite. It was found to correspond in its general physical and chemical properties with the Group IV element ekasilicon predicted by Mendeléeff. The element usually occurs in nature as the sulphide, notable sources being South African germanite (6·2% Ge), the spelter residues from certain American zinc ores, and the flue dusts obtained by burning certain types of coal. The metal is usually prepared by first isolating the chloride by distillation with hydrochloric acid. Germanium tetrachloride volatilizes with the hydrochloric acid. The chloride is then hydrolysed with water and the resulting oxide is reduced to metal in a stream of hydrogen at about 600°.

The element is a dark grey substance, crystallizing with a modified diamond structure, $a=5·6575$ Å. It is brittle; d 5·323, m.p. 937·4°, b.p. 2830°. It is stable in air at room temperature, but oxidizes superficially on moderate heating. It also combines with chlorine on heating. In its compounds germanium exhibits oxidation states of two and four. Germanium metal is a semiconductor and is used in transistors. It forms alloys which expand slightly on cooling and are used in small scale precision castings.

Germanium chloroform, GeHCl₃. A mobile liquid of b.p. 75°, m.p. −71°, d^0 1·93, obtained by the action of hydrogen chloride on GeCl₂ at 30°. This reaction is reversed by heating to 140°. Germanium chloroform is rapidly hydrolysed by water, and is also attacked by oxygen, one of the products being the oxychloride GeOCl₂.

Germanium halides. Germanium forms both di- and tetra-halides.

Germanium tetrafluoride, GeF_4, m.p. $-15°$, sublimes $-35°$. Obtained by heating barium fluorogermanate, $BaGeF_6$. Fluorogermanates M_2GeF_6 are obtained by dissolving germanium dioxide in hydrofluoric acid.

Germanous fluoride. GeF_2. A white powder made by the action of germanium on the tetrafluoride at $100°$-$300°$. It dissolves in water to give a strongly reducing solution, m.p. $110°$.

The remaining tetrahalides are made by interaction of germanium and the appropriate halogen. $GeCl_4$, m.p. $-49.5°$, b.p. $86.5°$; $GeBr_4$, m.p. $26.1°$, b.p. $186.5°$; GeI_4, m.p. $144°$, b.p. $348°$. $GeCl_4$ and $GeBr_4$ are colourless, GeI_4 is red. All the halides are hydrolysed by water.

The germanous halides are colourless or pale yellow solids prepared by heating the tetrahalides with germanium. They are hydrolysed by water and oxidized by air; $GeCl_2$, sublimes; $GeBr_2$, m.p. $122°$.

Germanium hydrides, Germanes. Three hydrides of germanium have been isolated from the product of the interaction of dilute hydrochloric acid on magnesium germanide. Their formulae are: GeH_4 (m.p. $-165°$, b.p. $-88.5°$), Ge_2H_6 (m.p. $-109°$, b.p. $29°$), and Ge_3H_8 (m.p. $-105.6°$, b.p. $110.5°$). The action of an electrical discharge on GeH_4 gives two isomers of Ge_4H_{10} and higher hydrides up to Ge_9H_{20}. Monogermane, GeH_4, may also be prepared by reduction of germanium tetrachloride with lithium aluminium hydride. The constitutions of these hydrides are similar to those of the saturated aliphatic hydrocarbons; they are, however, oxidized at lower temperatures ($150°$-$300°$). They are unattacked by water, in which they are only slightly soluble. Monogermane is unattacked by 33% sodium hydroxide, but digermane, Ge_2H_6, evolves hydrogen. There are no known volatile germanium hydrides corresponding to ethylene and acetylene, although a yellow polymer with the formula $(GeH_2)_x$ is formed by decomposing calcium germanide, $CaGe$, with dilute hydrochloric acid. Germanium hydrides have potentialities as sources of very pure germanium.

Germanium oxides.

Germanous oxide, GeO, is formed as a yellow to black powder by the action of water on germanous chloride or germanium chloroform. It is almost insoluble in water but gives a faintly acidic solution and forms salts, germanites. It is a strong reducing agent and is readily oxidized.

Germanium dioxide, GeO_2, Obtained by heating germanium strongly in air or by hydrolysis of the tetrachloride. There are two forms with the cristobalite (SiO_2) and rutile (TiO_2) lattices. Is an acidic oxide and forms germanates

M_2GeO_3 and M_2GeO_4 analogous to silicates in which the germanium is four co-ordinate. Also forms complexes $M_2[Ge(OH)_6]$ in which the germanium is six co-ordinate.

Germanium sulphides.

Germanium disulphide, GeS_2, is prepared by heating GeO_2 with sulphur or by the action of hydrogen sulphide on a strongly acidic solution of GeO_2. It forms white crystals, m.p. $800°$. It is fairly soluble in water but the solutions are hydrolysed. It is soluble in alkali sulphide solutions to form thiogermanates.

Germanous sulphide, GeS. Prepared by reducing the disulphide with hydrogen, m.p. $625°$; sublimes at $430°$.

Geronic acid, $C_9H_{16}O_3$. B.p. $275°$-$280°/740mm$, d_4 1.0221. It is soluble in alcohol and ether

$$CH_3 \cdot CO \cdot CH_2 \cdot CH_2 \cdot CH_2 \cdot \underset{\underset{CH_3}{|}}{\overset{\overset{CH_3}{|}}{C}} \cdot COOH$$

and is obtained by treating vitamin A or carotene with ozone and decomposing the ozonides so formed.

g factor. The gyromagnetic ratio. The proportionality factor in the relation between the magnetic moment μ and the number of unpaired electrons. $\mu = g\sqrt{S(S+1)}$.

Ghosh, Sir Jnan Chandra (1894-1959). Educated in Calcutta and at University College, London, Ghosh in 1921 became professor and head of the chemistry department at the University of Dacca. In 1939 he was made director of the Indian Institute of Science, Bangalore. He made notable contributions to physical chemistry, especially to the theory of electrolytes and to reaction mechanisms. See *Nature*, 1959, **183**, 645.

Giauque, William Francis (1895-   ). Born in Ontario, Giauque studied at the University of California where he became professor of chemistry in 1934. He was given the Nobel Prize for chemistry in 1949 for his work in chemical thermodynamics, in particular at temperatures near to absolute zero.

Gibberellic acid, $C_{19}H_{22}O_6$. This is one of several

gibberellins, which were first discovered as metabolic products of the soil-borne fungus, *Gibber-*

ella fujikuroi, which causes a disease of rice seedlings manifested in the tall growth of infected plants. When gibberellic acid was isolated it was shown to have remarkable effects on other plants. With wheat, peas, and other plants there is a marked increase in height of shoots and substantial dry weight increase. It is used for spraying seedless grapes immediately after flowering, when a much heavier crop of grapes is produced. Another effect is to break the dormancy period of seeds, and a potentially important use is in improving the malting of barley.

Gibberellic acid is made commercially by a fermentation process using *Gibberella fujikuroi,* and isolated as white crystals, m.p. 223°-235°. It is soluble in water up to 0·5%, is unstable in water, but stable dry.

The gibberellins have been shown to be natural plant hormones, and have been identified in minute amounts in beans.

Gibbs free energy. See Free energy.

Gibbs, Josiah Willard (1839-1903). Born at New Haven, Connecticut, Gibbs studied at Yale College, Paris, Berlin, and Heidelberg. In 1871 he became professor of mathematical physics at Yale College. His writings deal with thermodynamics, multiple algebra, vector analysis, the electromagnetic theory of light, and statistical mechanics, and of these his work on 'The equilibrium of heterogeneous substances' is generally regarded as most important. In it he enunciated principles which form the foundation of modern physical chemistry. He was awarded the Copley Medal of the Royal Society in 1901.

Gibbs' adsorption equation. This is a relationship between the surface tension (γ) of a solution and the amount of solute adsorbed per cm^2 at the surface (Γ). An approximate form, valid only for dilute solutions of a single non-ionic solute, is often used, namely,

$$\Gamma = (c/RT)(d\gamma/dc)$$

(c being the concentration of solute per cm^3 and R the gas constant). Qualitatively the equation shows that solutes which lower the surface tension are positively adsorbed at the surface (e.g. amyl alcohol in water), whereas solutes which raise the surface tension are negatively adsorbed (e.g. salts). Direct tests of the equation have been carried out by several methods and confirm its validity within the rather large experimental errors inherent in determining Γ.

Gibbs-Helmholtz equation. Most chemical reactions are studied under conditions of constant temperature and pressure. If necessary, reactions may be carried out at constant volume using as reaction vessel a bomb calorimeter. The Gibbs-Helmholtz equation gives the relationship between the heat and free energy changes occurring

during the reaction. For a process at constant volume,

$$\Delta A = \Delta E + T\left(\frac{dA}{dt}\right)_v = \Delta E - T\Delta S$$

ΔA is the change in Helmholtz free energy of the system and is equal and opposite to the maximum work available for the process, and ΔE is the change in internal energy. $T\Delta S$ is the heat absorbed by the system when the process is conducted reversibly.

Under conditions of constant pressure, the Gibbs-Helmholtz equation is

$$\Delta G = \Delta H - T\Delta S$$

where ΔG is the Gibbs free energy change and ΔH is the enthalpy change. Using this equation, it is possible to calculate heat changes for a reaction from the temperature dependence of ΔG. See Free energy.

Gibbsite, $Al(OH)_3$. A monoclinic form of aluminium hydroxide. Sp.gr. 2·3-2·4, hardness about 3. It is a common constituent of bauxite and laterite. It can be obtained by rapid hydrolysis of an aluminate solution or reaction with carbon dioxide at 100°.

Gilsonite. A natural high m.p. bitumen, m.p. 160°-170°. It has a high dielectric strength and very low water absorption.

Ginger. The dried rhizome of *Zingiber officinale,* which is obtained from Jamaica, Africa, and South-east Asia. It contains an essential oil and a pungent oily substance known as 'gingerol'. Ginger is a carminative, and is used with purgatives to prevent griping. It is warming and stimulating to the stomach, and is frequently added to medicines as a flavouring agent. Powdered ginger is one of the constituents of Gregory powder.

Girard's reagents. Quaternary ammonium salts of the type $Me_3NCH_2CONHNH_2^{\oplus}X^{\ominus}$ which form water-soluble compounds with aldehydes and ketones, and are therefore separable from other neutral compounds; the aldehyde or ketone may be subsequently regenerated after separation.

Gitalin, $C_{35}H_{56}O_{12}$. M.p. 155°, $[\alpha]_D -25.2°$. It consists of 2 digitoxose + gitaligenin. Glycoside from foxglove.

Gitonin, $C_{49}H_{80}O_{23}$. M.p. 272°, $[\alpha]_D -50.7°$. It consists of 3 galactose + L-xylose + gitogenin.

Gitoxin, $C_{41}H_{66}O_{15}$. M.p. 285°, $[\alpha]_D +3.5°$. It consists of 3 digitoxose + gitoxigenin. Glycoside from foxglove.

Gladstone, John Hall (1827-1902). Born at Hackney, London, Gladstone studied chemistry at University College, and afterwards at Giessen, under Liebig. In 1874 he was appointed Fullerian professor of chemistry at the Royal Institution. His most important scientific work lay in the sphere of physical chemistry. He emphasized the importance of the spectroscope in chemical research. Of private means, he also took an active part in religious and public work. See *J. Chem. Soc.*, 1905, 591.

Glass. A hard, brittle, amorphous material which is usually transparent or translucent, and resistant to chemical attack. The common lime-soda glass used for bottles and jars is a super-cooled mixture of sodium and calcium silicates, prepared by fusing a mixture of sand, soda-ash, and lime. Numerous special varieties of glass are now made, in which the silica is partly or (infrequently) wholly replaced by another acidic oxide, such as boron trioxide or phosphorus pentoxide, and the sodium is replaced by potassium (potash glass), lithium, an alkaline earth metal, or lead. 'Crown glass' contains potash or barium oxide as the basic constituent; 'flint glass', used largely for optical purposes, contains lead oxide. When glass is heated to the softening point for a prolonged period the constituents begin to crystallize and the glass 'devitrifies', or becomes opaque and more brittle. Coloured glasses are obtained by adding small quantities of certain metallic oxides (or occasionally other compounds) to the melt. Glass can be toughened by rapid cooling of the surface or by chemical treatment of the surface.

Glass electrode. A surface of glass in contact with a solution containing, say, hydrogen ions, develops a potential depending on the concentration of these ions. A glass electrode is a means whereby the potential may be measured. It usually consists of a thin-walled glass bulb immersed in the solution. Electrical contact with the inner wall of the bulb is established by a platinum wire dipping in a solution of an electrolyte which fills the bulb. The thin glass serves as a suitable conductor between the outer and inner walls of the bulb, and hence allows the potential of an electrode in the outer solution to be measured against that of the platinum wire in the inner solution. As the potential depends chiefly on the hydrogen ions and little on the other ions present in solution the glass electrode is widely used to determine pH.

Glauber, Johann Rudolf. Born at Karlstadt, Bavaria, in 1604, and died in 1667. He discovered sodium sulphate, still known as Glauber's salt, and introduced it into medicine.

Glauberite. Anhydrous sodium calcium sulphate, $Na_2SO_4 \cdot CaSO_4$, associated with naturally occurring deposits of sodium sulphate and related salts in Spain, Russia, Canada and the

U.S.A. Monoclinic yellow to grey crystals, sp.gr. 2·8, hardness 2·5-3.

Glauber's salt. See Sodium sulphate.

Glauconite. A green hydrated silicate of iron, aluminium, potassium, etc., of variable composition. It occurs in grains in a variety of sedimentary rocks and is a characteristic constituent of the greensand associated with the English chalk. An earthy material with a similar composition is Green Earth (*q.v.*) or Terra Verte.

Gliadin. A protein, belonging to the prolamine class, present in the seeds of wheat and rye. It is a constituent of gluten flour and of bread.

Gliotoxin, $C_{13}H_{14}N_2O_4S_2$. Colourless monoclinic crystals, m.p. 221° (decomp.). Slightly

soluble in alcohol, almost insoluble in water and acids, unstable in alkalis; $[\alpha]_D^{25} - 290°$ in alcohol. It is an antibiotic, produced by a number of species of *Penicillium* and by *Aspergillus fumigatus*. It is active against a wide range of bacteria and fungi, but is not used clinically owing to its high toxicity.

Globin. A protein, belonging to the histone class. Combined with haem it forms the respiratory pigment haemoglobin. Globins obtained from different sources are not identical, and the difference between the haemoglobins of various animals lies in the globin portion of the molecule.

Globulins. A widely distributed class of proteins, insoluble in water and coagulated by heating. They are soluble in dilute salt solutions, but precipitated by half saturation with ammonium sulphate (a distinction from albumins). They include such proteins as myosin from muscle, fibrinogen from blood, and edestin from hemp. If blood serum is dialysed against distilled water, the salts are removed and a precipitate of globulins, 'euglobulins', appears. If the filtrate from this is half saturated with ammonium sulphate, a further protein precipitate is thrown down. This is called the 'pseudo-globulin' fraction, and differs from the typical globulins in being soluble in water. Pseudo-globulins are found also in milk and other animal tissues.

Glow discharge. When an electrical potential is applied to a gas at low pressure, the gas acts as a conductor, and becomes luminous. The appearance of the discharge has certain characteristic features. Thus at about 0·1 mm in helium there is a narrow dark space next to the cathode (the Aston dark space), with a thin glowing layer of gas next to it (the cathode glow), which is followed by a wider dark space (the Crookes or cathode dark space), then a glowing area (the negative glow), which is separated by the Faraday dark space from a longer area of glowing gas (the positive column), which stretches as far as the anode. The exact dimensions of the various dark spaces and glows vary with the potential, the gas pressure, and the nature of the gas. At pressures even lower than 0·1 mm in helium, the discharge consists only of a negative glow and the Crookes's dark space.

Glucagon. A crystalline polypeptide hormone isolated from the pancreas. It comprises a single chain of 29 amino-acid residues. Its effect is opposite to that of insulin: it causes increased phosphorylase activity, mobilizes liver glycogen and thus leads to an increase in blood glucose concentration.

Glucans. The name given to polymers of D-glucopyranose; β-glucans being polymers of β-D-glucopyranose. Included are cellulose, lichenin, and other materials that are constituents of cell walls.

Glucinium. A former name for beryllium.

Gluconic acid, $C_6H_{12}O_7$. Colourless crystals,

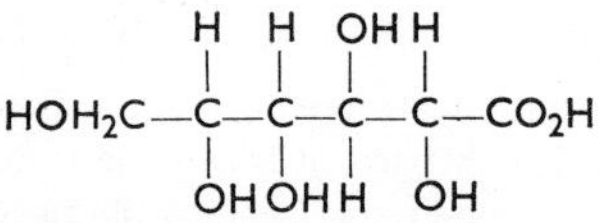

$$HOH_2C-\overset{\displaystyle H}{\underset{\displaystyle OH}{C}}-\overset{\displaystyle H}{\underset{\displaystyle OH}{C}}-\overset{\displaystyle OH}{\underset{\displaystyle H}{C}}-\overset{\displaystyle H}{\underset{\displaystyle OH}{C}}-CO_2H$$

soluble in water and alcohol, m.p. 112°. D-Gluconic acid has initial rotation $[\alpha]_D^{20} - 6·9$, but exists in water as an equilibrium mixture with its lactones with $[\alpha]_D^{20} + 7·5°$. The δ-lactone has m.p. 150°-152° and initial $[\alpha]_D^{20} + 68·0°$ and hydrolyses rapidly to the equilibrium mixture. Glucono-γ-lactone has m.p. 133°-135°, and initial $[\alpha]_D^{20} + 68·0°$ and hydrolyses slowly. Gluconic acid is made by the oxidation of glucose by halogens, by electrolysis, by various moulds, or by bacteria of the *Acetobacter* group.

Glucoproteins, Glycoproteins, Mucoproteins. A class of conjugated proteins containing carbohydrate groups, these groups consisting of a hexosamine, sulphuric acid, acetic acid, and glucuronic acid in molecular proportions. The glucoproteins include the mucins, which are found in connective tissue and in the secretions of the salivary and certain other glands, and the mucoids found, amongst other places, in white of egg. Aqueous solutions of glucoproteins are extremely viscous.

Glucosamine,   chitosamine,   2-aminoglucose,

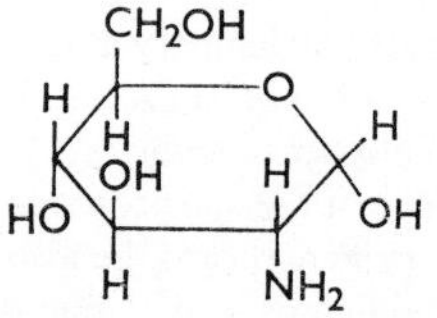

$C_6H_{13}NO_5$. D-Glucosamine can be obtained by the hydrolysis of lobster shells or mould mycelium by hydrochloric acid. It crystallizes in needles from alcohol, m.p. 110°, with decomposition. Soluble in water. Its hydrochloride exists in two crystalline isomeric forms, and has $[\alpha]_D + 72·5°$ in equilibriated solution.

D-Glucose, Dextrose, $C_6H_{12}O_6$. The most common hexose sugar. It is present in many plants, and is the sugar of the blood. It is a constituent of starch, cellulose, glycogen, sucrose, and many glycosides, from all of which it can be obtained by hydrolysis with acids or enzymes.

Like all hexoses it can exist in a number of forms. These are:

(1) aldehyde:

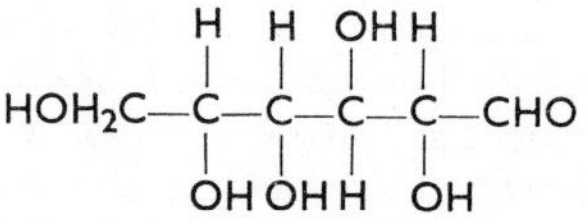

$$HOH_2C-\overset{\displaystyle H}{\underset{\displaystyle OH}{C}}-\overset{\displaystyle H}{\underset{\displaystyle OH}{C}}-\overset{\displaystyle OH}{\underset{\displaystyle H}{C}}-\overset{\displaystyle H}{\underset{\displaystyle OH}{C}}-CHO$$

It exists in this form only in solution, though stable derivatives of the aldehyde structure are known. The optical antipode of D-glucose in which the positions of every H and OH are transposed is L-glucose.

(2) α- and β-glucopyranose:

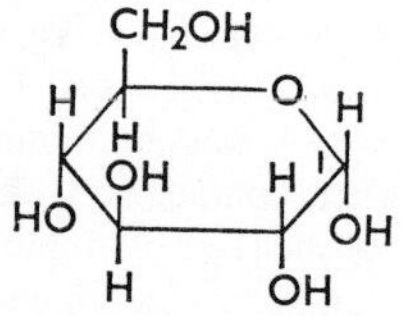

Carbon atom 1 in this formula is asymmetric and two stereoisomers therefore exist, depending on whether the OH group is written below (α) or above (β) the plane of carbon atoms. Both forms crystallize either as the monohydrate or anhydrous.

(3) α- and β-glucofuranose:

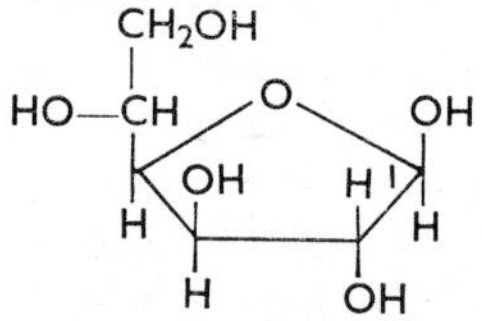

These are unstable and known only in solution. The ethyl glucosides can be obtained crystalline and other derivatives are known.

Ordinary glucose is α-glucopyranose mono-hydrate. It has m.p. 80°-85° and $[\alpha]_D$ +113·4°. In solution it gives a mixture with the β form with $[\alpha]_D^{20}$ +52·5°. It is manufactured from starch by hydrolysis with mineral acids, purification, and crystallization, and is widely used in the confectionery and other food industries. It is about 70% as sweet as sucrose.

Glucosidase. See Emulsin and Maltase.

Glucosides. See Glycosides.

Glucuronic acid, $C_6H_{10}O_7$. An oxidation product of glucose in which the primary alcohol group is oxidized to carboxyl:

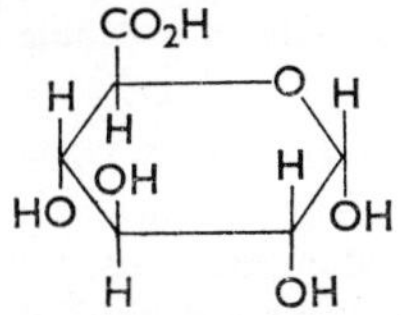

It contains the pyranose ring, and exists in α and β forms. The final rotation is $[\alpha]_D$ +36°. The animal organism has the power of combining toxic substances with glucuronic acid to form compounds of glucosidic type, and thus to excrete them in the urine. It is an important constituent of hemicelluloses and plant gums.

Glucuronidase. This is the enzyme responsible for splitting glucopyranouronides, and hence is responsible for the formation and splitting of the conjugates that glucuronic acid forms with many substances in the mammalian body. It occurs in many tissues. Its optimum pH is 4·5. It has been prepared commercially from certain bacteria.

Glue. A mixture of peptones, or nitrogenous substances of animal origin, which is closely related to the proteins and is probably built up by condensation of amino-acids. Glue is generally prepared from waste skins and cuttings from tanyards, together with bones, skins, tendons, horn-piths, etc. from slaughter-houses. The raw material is treated with milk of lime to remove hair, fat, and other undesirable constituents, and then washed with acid (generally hydrochloric) and water. It is heated with water to about 60° in large open vats ('boiling' process). The waste material is filtered off, and the glue solution concentrated at about the same temperature, decolorized with charcoal or sulphur dioxide and allowed to set in pans. 'Bone glue' is prepared in a similar way from bone cartilage, previously freed from calcium phosphate by treatment with acid. 'Fish glue' is obtained from fish refuse.

Glutaconic acid, $C_5H_6O_4$. Exists in *cis*- and *trans*-forms; both are colourless crystalline solids. *Trans*-glutaconic acid is the stable form; m.p. 138°. Soluble in water, alcohol, and ether. Prepared by treating ethyl β-hydroxyglutarate, dissolved in pyridine, with thionyl chloride at 0°;

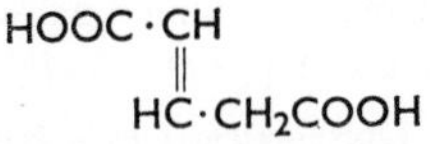

$$HOOC \cdot CH$$
$$\|$$
$$HC \cdot CH_2COOH$$

the ethyl glutaconate so formed is hydrolysed by heating with acid. Forms a hydroxyanhydride when refluxed with acetic anhydride. Alkyl glutaconic acids show tautomerism as well as *cis-trans* isomerism. *cis*-Glutaconic acid has m.p. 136°. Soluble

$$HC \cdot COOH$$
$$\|$$
$$HC \cdot CH_2COOH$$

in water and alcohol, insoluble in chloroform. Prepared by heating the *trans*-acid with acetic anhydride, pouring the product into cold water and evaporating the solution rapidly. This form is stable only as a solid or in solution in ether. When melted or dissolved in water it changes to the *trans* form. Forms the hydroxyanhydride when warmed to 40° with acetic anhydride.

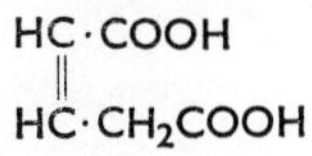

This hydroxy-anhydride (6-hydroxy-α-pyrone) is easily recognized by its colour

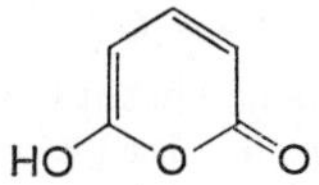

reaction with ferric chloride, the initially formed intense green colour rapidly becoming brown.

Glutamic acid, α-**Aminoglutaric acid,** $C_5H_9NO_4$.

$$HO_2C \cdot CH_2 \cdot CH_2 \cdot CH(NH_2) \cdot CO_2H.$$

Rhombic crystals, m.p. 211°-213°, with decomposition. Soluble up to 1% in water, less soluble in alcohol. The naturally occurring substance is dextrorotatory, $[\alpha]_D^{25}$ +11·5°. Glutamic acid is one of the acidic amino-acids and is present in large quantities among the products of protein hydrolysis. It can be produced from wheat gluten or beet sugar molasses by hydrolysis, but is now usually manufactured by the fermentation of a carbohydrate in the presence of ammonium salts. Its monosodium salt has a meaty flavour and is used as a condiment.

Glutamine, $C_5H_{10}N_2O_3$,

$$H_2NOC \cdot CH_2 \cdot CH_2 \cdot CH(NH_2) \cdot CO_2H.$$

Crystallizes in needles; m.p. 184°-185°. Soluble in water, sparingly soluble in alcohol, $[\alpha]_D^{19}$ +8°. It is the monoamide of glutamic acid, and is widely distributed in plants, especially in seedlings of the *cruciferae* and *caryophyllaceae*, and in the roots of the beet, the carrot, and the radish. It plays a similar role to that of its homologue asparagine in the nitrogen metabolism of plants.

Glutaric acid, $C_5H_8O_4$.

$$HOOCCH_2CH_2CH_2COOH.$$

Crystallizes in colourless plates or needles; m.p. 97°-98°, b.p. 302°-304°. Very soluble in water, alcohol, and ether. Prepared by treating 1,3-dichloropropane with sodium cyanide and heating the product with sodium hydroxide. Forms an anhydride on heating at 230°-280°.

Glutathione, Glutamylcysteinylglycine,
$C_{10}H_{17}N_3O_6S$. A tripeptide, m.p. 190°-192°, with

$$CO \cdot CH_2 \cdot CH_2 \cdot CH \cdot COOH$$
$$| \qquad\qquad\qquad |$$
$$NH \qquad\qquad NH_2$$
$$|$$
$$CH \cdot CO \cdot NH \cdot CH_2 \cdot COOH$$
$$|$$
$$CH_2 \cdot SH$$

decomposition. Very soluble in water, the aqueous solution being unstable on heating, $[\alpha]_{Hg}^{28} - 9 \cdot 4°$. It can be prepared from yeast, and has also been synthesized from its constituent amino-acids. Glutathione is present also in animal tissues, where it acts as an oxygen carrier. The formula given represents the reduced form of glutathione, and may be represented as $G \cdot SH$; it reacts with oxygen:

$$2G \cdot SH + O \rightarrow G \cdot S \cdot S \cdot G + H_2O$$

Glutelin. A protein present in wheat, in gluten flour, and in bread. It is a typical member of the glutelin class of proteins.

Glutelins. A class of proteins found in the seeds of cereals, resembling the prolamines in being insoluble in water and soluble in acids and alkalis, but differing in that they are insoluble in all concentrations of alcohol. Typical glutelins are wheat glutelin and oryzenin from rice.

Gluten. A mixture of proteins present in wheat flour, obtained as an extremely sticky yellowish mass by making a dough and then washing out the starch. This can be made into a powder by dehydrating with acetone. It consists almost entirely of two proteins, gliadin and glutelin, present in about equal quantities, the exact proportions varying with different varieties of wheat.

Glyceraldehyde, Glyceric aldehyde, $C_3H_6O_3$, occurs in optically active forms.

$$OHC \cdot CH(OH) \cdot CH_2OH.$$

D-Glyceraldehyde is a colourless syrup, $[\alpha]_D + 13 \cdot 5°$. May be prepared by mild oxidation of glycerol or by hydrolysis of glyceraldehyde acetal (prepared by oxidation of acrolein acetol). L-Glyceraldehyde, $[\alpha]_D - 14°$ falling to $-7°$. The optically active forms polymerize more readily than the DL-form. DL-Glyceraldehyde forms colourless crystals having the formula $(C_3H_6O_3)_2$, m.p. 138·5°, sparingly soluble in water, soluble in alcohol. Converted to methylglyoxal by warm dilute sulphuric acid.

Glyceric acid, $C_3H_6O_4$,

$$HO_2C \cdot CH(OH) \cdot CH_2OH.$$

An uncrystallizable syrup; it occurs in optically active forms. DL-Glyceric acid is miscible with water and alcohol, but is insoluble in ether. Prepared by oxidation of glycerin with nitric acid. Solutions of the acid give an intense yellow colour with ferric chloride. The optically active forms may be prepared from the DL-acid by fermenting away one of the forms by means of suitable moulds or bacteria.

Glyceric aldehyde. See Glyceraldehyde.

Glycerides. Esters of glycerol. They are classified as mono-, di- and tri-glycerides according to the number of acid radicals combined with the three hydroxyl groups. The tri-glycerides occur naturally in animal and vegetable fats and oils. See Fats.

Glycerol, Glycerin, 1,2,3-Trihydroxypropane, $C_3H_8O_3$. Normally obtained as a colourless, odourless, viscous liquid with a very sweet taste. It may be crystallized at low temperatures from propyl or butyl alcohols

$$CH_2OH$$
$$|$$
$$CHOH$$
$$|$$
$$CH_2OH$$

or liquid ammonia; d^{15} 1·2641, m.p. 20°, b.p. 290° (slight decomposition); 182°/20 mm. Miscible with water and alcohol; slightly soluble in ether; insoluble in chloroform. It absorbs up to 50% of its weight of water vapour. It occurs in combination with various fatty acids in all animal and vegetable fats and oils.

Commercially glycerin is obtained as a by-product in the manufacture of soap, and by various synthetic routes. In soap manufacture the liquor left after soap removal contains either about 45% or 4-8% glycerin, depending on whether water or caustic soda has been used for the fat hydrolysis. In the former case little treatment is required and crude glycerin is obtained after evaporation of the water; in the latter, in addition to other impurities, the solution contains 5-15% sodium chloride which must be removed in special salting evaporators. Crude glycerin is purified by distillation. The various synthetic routes start with propylene. One proceeds via allyl chloride, dichlorohydrin, epichlorohydrin to glycerin, another via allyl alcohol which is oxidized by hydrogen peroxide to glycerin. Some glycerin is also obtained by fermentation of sugars. It is a good solvent for many organic and inorganic compounds. It reacts with hydrochloric acid to form chlorohydrins, and with nitric acid to give nitroglycerin. When heated with sulphuric acid or potassium hydrogen sulphate, acrolein is formed. It is oxidized to a variety of products including glyceraldehyde, dihydroxyacetone, glyceric acid, and oxalic acid. It reduces Fehling's solution only slightly on boiling. It will unite with one, two, or three acid radicals to give glycerides. Glycerol is used in the manufacture of synthetic resins and ester gums, as a moistening agent for tobacco, in the manufacture of explosives and cellulose films, and has many other uses.

Glycerol dichlorohydrins, $C_3H_6Cl_2O$. *Glycerol α-dichlorohydrin, sym-dichloroisopropyl alcohol,* $CH_2Cl—CH(OH)—CH_2Cl$ is a colourless liquid with an ethereal odour; d^{17} 1·3506, b.p. 174°-175°. Soluble in water and ether. Prepared by passing dry hydrogen chloride into glycerin containing 2% acetic acid at 100°-110° until no more is absorbed. The mixture is treated with sodium carbonate to neutralize excess acid and the chlorhydrin distilled. Reduced by sodium to isopropyl alcohol; oxidized by chromic acid to β-dichloroacetone. Converted to α-epichlorohydrin by potassium hydroxide. Used as a solvent for cellulose nitrate and resins.

Glycerol β-dichlorohydrin, 2,3-*dichloropropyl alcohol,* $CH_2Cl—CHCl—CH_2OH$, is a colourless liquid, d^{20} 1·3534, b.p. 182°. Slightly soluble in water; miscible with alcohol, ether, and benzene. Prepared by the chlorination of allyl alcohol. Oxidized by nitric acid to 1,2-dichloropropionic acid. Reacts with sodium hydroxide to give epichlorohydrin.

Glycerol monochlorohydrins, $C_3H_7ClO_2$. *Glycerol α-monochlorohydrin,* 3-*chloropropylene glycol,* $CH_2Cl—CH(OH)—CH_2OH$ is a colourless, rather viscous liquid having a sweet taste; d^0 1·338, b.p. 139°/18 mm. Miscible with water, alcohol, and ether. Prepared by passing dry hydrogen chloride into glycerin containing 2% acetic acid heated to 105°-110°. The reaction is complete when the theoretical increase in weight has occurred; the product is distilled under reduced pressure. Reacts with nitric acid to give a dinitrate which is used in the manufacture of low-freezing dynamites.

Glycerol β-monochlorohydrin, 2-*chlorotrimethylene glycol* $CH_2OH—CHCl—CH_2OH$, is a colourless liquid; d^{20} 1·324, b.p. 146°/18 mm. Miscible with water and alcohol. It is obtained in small amounts in the preparation of the α-chlorohydrin. May be prepared by the action of dilute chlorine water on allyl alcohol.

Glycerophosphoric acid, 3-phosphoglyceric acid. Thought to be an intermediate in the photosynthetic fixation of carbon dioxide in chlorophyll-containing plants. Reduced nicotinamide-adenine dinucleotide phosphate (NADPH) reduces the carbon dioxide, the intermediate being phosphorylated by adenosine triphosphate (ATP). Lecithins (*q.v.*) are fatty acid esters of glycerophosphoric acid derivatives. Commercially glycerophosphoric acid,

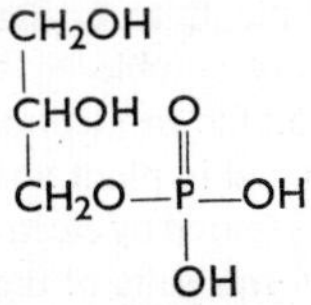

$$CH_2OH$$
$$|$$
$$CHOH \quad O$$
$$| \qquad ||$$
$$CH_2O—P—OH$$
$$|$$
$$OH$$

obtainable as approx. 25-50% solutions, is used to prepare the medicinal glycerophosphate salts, e.g. the calcium salt.

Glyceryl is the name given to the group:

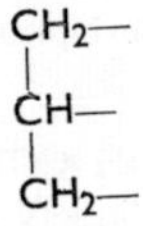

$$CH_2—$$
$$|$$
$$CH—$$
$$|$$
$$CH_2—$$

Glycin. See Aminophenol developers.

Glycine, Aminoacetic acid, $H_2N \cdot CH_2 \cdot COOH$. Crystallizes in colourless prisms; m.p. 260°, with decomposition, turning brown at 228°. Very soluble in water, sparingly soluble in alcohol. It has a sweet taste. Glycine is the simplest of the amino-acids and is a hydrolysis product of proteins. It can be made synthetically by the action of ammonia on chloroacetic acid and by several other methods, and from proteins, such as gelatin, by hydrolysis with acids. It can conveniently be purified via the copper salt. Glycine can be synthesized in the animal body. When given by mouth it has a marked specific dynamic effect, increasing the rate of metabolism by sometimes as much as 50 per cent.

Glycocholic acid, Cholylglycine, $C_{26}H_{43}NO_6$. M.p.154°-155°, with decomposition, $[\alpha]_D^{13} +24·3°$ in water. It occurs as its sodium salt in the bile. On hydrolysis it gives glycine and cholic acid. See Bile salts.

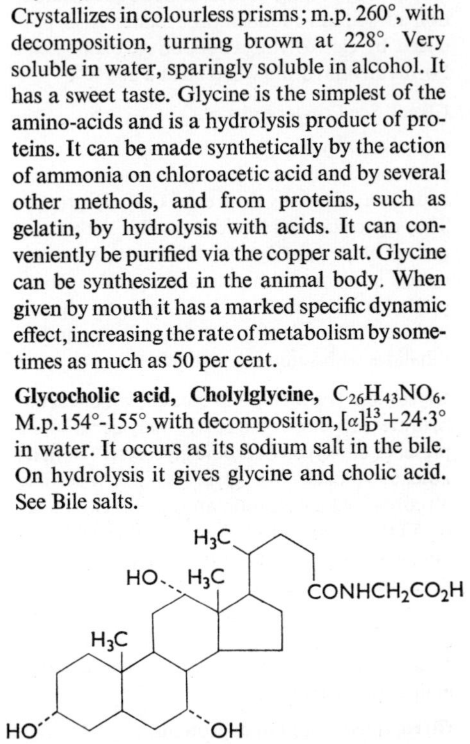

Glycocyamine, Guanidinoacetic acid, $C_3H_7N_3O_2$.

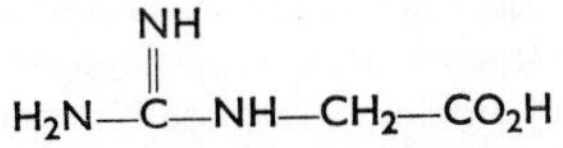

$$NH$$
$$||$$
$$H_2N—C—NH—CH_2—CO_2H$$

Crystallizes in plates, turning brown at 240° and slowly charring. It can be prepared from glycine and urea. In the body it is the precursor of creatine, and is made from glycine and arginine.

Glycogen, $(C_6H_{10}O_5)_x$. The reserve carbohydrate of the animal cell. The molecule is built up of a large number of short chains with 12, or sometimes 18, α-glucose units joined by 1-4 links, the chains being cross-linked (as in amylopectin) by α-1-6 glucoside links. The molecular weight varies, but is often about 4 million. It is a white amorphous powder with no reducing properties, and gives a red colour with iodine. It usually differs from starch in being relatively soluble in hot water, and in not forming viscous solutions. Insoluble glycogens are also found. It is broken down in the digestive system by glucosidases to glucose, but in the cells it is broken down to and built up from glucose-1-phosphate by means of phosphorylases.

Glycollic acid, $CH_2OH \cdot COOH$. Forms colourless crystals which liquefy in the presence of moisture; m.p. 80°. Soluble in water and acetone. Occurs in the juice of the sugar cane and beets. Prepared by boiling a concentrated aqueous solution of sodium monochloroacetate. Also produced by electrolytic reduction of oxalic acid. Forms an anhydride when heated at 100°.

Glycol. See Ethylene glycol.

Glycols. Dihydric alcohols derived from aliphatic hydrocarbons by replacement of two hydrogen atoms by hydroxyl (—OH) groups. They are colourless liquids, miscible with water and alcohol. 1,2-Glycols are obtained by oxidation of olefins with potassium permanganate or lead tetra-acetate; by heating olefin chlorohydrins with weak alkalis or by heating paraffin dihalides with sodium hydroxide.

Glycolysis. The metabolic breakdown of carbohydrates in living organisms: it may occur in the presence of oxygen ('aerobic glycolysis') or in its absence ('anaerobic glycolysis'). Anaerobic glycolysis of glucose ultimately yields two moles of ATP per mole of glucose, together with lactate, which can undergo further energy-yielding degradation in the presence of oxygen. Aerobic glycolysis yields pyruvate, which in turn may give rise to acetyl-coenzyme A and may undergo a variety of other metabolic transformations, e.g. amination to alanine.

Glycoproteins. See Glucoproteins.

Glycosidases. Enzymes which split off glucose (glucosidases) or other sugars from glycosides. α-Glycosidases are relatively uncommon; the most important is maltase. β-Glycosidases are very widely distributed, especially in plants, e.g. emulsin. See Pigman, 'Advances in Enzymology', Vol. 4.

Glycosides. Sugar derivatives in which the hydroxyl group attached to carbon 1 is substituted by an alcoholic, phenolic, or other group. The term glucoside is now used for those glycosides which contain glucose as the sugar, while glycoside refers to all compounds whatever the constituent sugar. The non-sugar portion of the molecule is termed the aglycone. The simplest glucoside is methylglucoside, $C_6H_{11}O_5 \cdot O \cdot CH_3$. As the 1 carbon atom is asymmetric there are two isomerides distinguished as α and β. The natural glucosides nearly all belong to the β-series and are hydrolysed by β-glucosidases. The glycosides of other sugars—pentose, methylpentose, or biose, or triose—in general also belong to the β-series, but require specific enzymes to effect their hydrolysis; these generally accompany them in the plants. Glycosides as a class are colourless, crystalline, bitter substances. Many hundreds have been described, some of general, others of very restricted occurrence. Various functions have been ascribed to them. Probably most substances in plants are at some stage combined with sugar.

Glycylglycine, $C_4H_8N_2O_3$, Crystallizes in leaflets,

$$NH_2 \cdot CH_2 \cdot CO \cdot NH \cdot CH_2 \cdot CO_2H$$

decomposing at 260°-262°, soluble in hot water, sparingly soluble in alcohol. The simplest of the dipeptides, it is formed by the action of glycyl chloride on glycine or by hydrolysing diketopiperazine with hydrochloric acid.

Glyoxal. Crystallizes in yellow prisms; its vapour is green and burns with a violet flame; d^{20} 1·14, m.p. 15°, b.p. 51°. Soluble in water and organic solvents. Readily polymerizes on standing in the presence of moisture; the aqueous solution contains the monomolecular form and reacts as a weak acid. It can be manufactured by oxidation of ethylene glycol with air using a copper oxide catalyst. Used to harden photographic gelatin. See Aldehyde hardeners.

$$\begin{array}{c} CHO \\ | \\ CHO \end{array}$$

Glyoxalase. The enzyme that catalyses the formation of lactic acid from methylglyoxal and water. It is present in many animal tissues, and needs glutathione to activate it.

Glyoxaline, see Imidazole.

Glyoxylate cycle. A sequence of metabolic reactions supplementing the Krebs cycle. It has not been demonstrated in mammalian tissue, but is important in certain micro-organisms and in plant seedlings. The cycle involves (i) a reverse aldol type cleavage of isocitrate to succinate and glyoxylate; (ii) formation of malate from glyoxylate and acetyl-coenzyme A.

Glyoxyldiureide. See Allantoin.

Glyoxylic acid. Forms a thick syrup, rather difficult to crystallize; m.p. 98°, very soluble in water, sparingly soluble in alcohol. Widely distributed in plant and animal tissues. Prepared by electrolytic reduction of oxalic acid. Forms salts of the type $(HO)_2CHCOOM$. Also reacts as an aldehyde. Condenses with urea to give allantoin. Reduced to glycollic acid. Gives a blue colour with sulphuric acid.

$$\begin{array}{c} CHO \\ | \\ COOH \end{array}$$

Glyptals. See Alkyd resins.

Gmelin, Leopold (1788-1853). Son of Johann

Friedrich Gmelin, the author of the 'Geschichte der Chemie,' Leopold studied medicine and chemistry at Göttingen, Tübingen, and Vienna. In 1817 he was appointed professor of chemistry and medicine at Heidelberg. With Kraut, he published the 'Handbuch der anorganische Chemie'. His most notable practical achievement was the discovery of potassium ferricyanide.

Gmelin's reaction. See Bile pigments.

Goitrin, C_5H_7NOS. 5-Vinyl-2-thio-oxazolidone, m.p. 50°, $[\alpha]_D -70°$ (c, 2 in methanol). An antithyroid compound found in the seeds of *Brassica* spp.

Gold, Au. At.wt. 197·2, At.no. 79; m.p. 1063°, b.p. 2660°, d 19·3. Gold, by reason of its occurrence in the free state, and of its marked colour and brilliance, was probably one of the first metals known to man. It usually occurs native, alloyed with silver and sometimes traces of copper and platinum. The richest gold fields are in Africa, in the Transvaal Rand, and in Australia. In North America the fields extend from Mexico to Alaska.

Native gold occurs either in the rock as nuggets or as grains in the alluvial sand. From the auriferous gravel the gold is obtained by washing and amalgamation with mercury on copper plates. The tailings from stamp-mills, poor quality auriferous quartz and finely divided ores are treated by the cyanide process. The gold dissolves in potassium cyanide in the presence of oxygen, the potassium cyanoaurate (I) being later reduced by zinc, and the gold cupelled.

The gold bullion is refined, and small quantities of silver or copper are removed by chlorine or by oxidation.

Considerable quantities of gold are obtained, in the form of 'Doré bullion' (74·5% Ag, 0·5% Cu, 25% Au), by refining the anode slime from the electrolytic purification of copper. The gold from this can be obtained by electrolytic removal of the silver and copper and purified either electrolytically or by cupellation.

Gold is a bright yellow metal. The structure is face-centred cubic, $a = 4·0783$ Å. It is a good conductor of heat and electricity. It is the most ductile metal, and may be beaten into leaves 0·00009 mm thick. The ordinary leaf is 0·0001 mm thick. At ordinary temperatures gold leaf transmits green light, and at 316° it transmits red light. At 550° the metal crystallizes and minute gaps are formed, which make it appear transparent.

Gold is not attacked by oxygen, or by any single acid except selenic. It is soluble in solutions of chlorine, bromine, or iodine, and therefore in aqua regia.

The compounds of gold are all easily converted to the metal. Two series of salts are known, the tripositive auric compounds, ion Au^{+++}, and monopositive aurous compounds, ion Au^+.

Gold bromides. *Aurous bromide*, AuBr, is formed by gently heating auric bromide. *Auric bromide*, $AuBr_3$, which is dimeric, is formed by the direct combination of gold and bromine in aqueous solution. With hydrobromic acid, bromoauric acid, $HAuBr_4$, is formed.

Gold chlorides. *Aurous chloride*, AuCl. Aurous chloride is obtained either by passing chlorine over gold at 173°, or by heating auric chloride to the same temperature. The chloride is decomposed by water with the formation of auric chloride and free gold.

Gold trichloride, Auric chloride, $AuCl_3$. Gold dissolves in aqua regia to form a bright yellow solution, which on evaporation deposits deliquescent yellow crystals of chloroauric acid, $HAuCl_4, 4H_2O$. On heating to 120° these lose hydrochloric acid to form auric chloride, $AuCl_3$. At 175° auric chloride decomposes, giving aurous chloride and chlorine; at still higher temperatures decomposition into gold and chlorine occurs. Chloroauric acid reacts with potassium chloride to give potassium chloroaurate, $KAuCl_4, 2H_2O$. Auric chloride is dimeric with bridging chlorine atoms. Each gold atom has a square-planar co-ordination.

Gold, colloidal. This is obtained by reducing gold chloride solutions with hydrazine, formaldehyde, etc. The solutions have different colours depending on particle size, passing from blue to red, and finally to yellow as the size is diminished. Electron microscopy shows that colloidal gold particles are crystalline. The precipitate obtained by adding a mixture of stannous and stannic chlorides to gold chloride solution, known as Purple of Cassius, is a colloidal form of tin oxide with adsorbed colloidal gold. This is used in the manufacture of a fine ruby glass.

Gold cyanides. *Aurous cyanide*, AuCN, is formed by the action of HCN on auric hydroxide; with excess potassium cyanide, potassium cyanoaurate (I), $KAu(CN)_2$, is formed.

Auric cyanide, $Au(CN)_3$, is made by the action of a very strong acid such as H_2SiF_6 on potassium cyanoaurate (III), $KAu(CN)_4$. $KAu(CN)_4$ is made by mixing hot solutions of auric chloride and potassium cyanide. The gold cyanides are used in the extraction of gold.

Gold fluoride, *Auric fluoride*, AuF_3. Prepared by the action of bromine trifluoride on gold and the heating of the resulting addition compound $BrF_3 \cdot AuF_3$. It is very readily hydrolysed by moisture. By dissolving a mixture of potassium fluoride and gold in bromine trifluoride, potassium fluoroaurate (III) $KAuF_4$, is formed.

Gold hydroxides and oxides. *Aurous oxide*, Au_2O, can be made by precipitating $KAuBr_2$ with alkali. It can be dried at 200° but decomposes at higher temperatures.

Auric hydroxide, AuO(OH). By heating an auric chloride solution with magnesia and by treating the resulting precipitate with nitric acid, the hydroxide is formed. The colour varies between brown and olive green, depending on the conditions of preparation. At 140° the hydroxide loses water and gives *auric oxide*, Au_2O_3, which decomposes on further heating to give gold and oxygen. Auric hydroxide is soluble in excess of alkali to give anionic species such as the $[Au(OH)_4]^-$ aq. ion.

Gold iodides. *Aurous iodide*, AuI, results from the direct combination of the elements; it is only slightly soluble in water. *Auric iodide*, AuI_3, is obtained by adding potassium iodide to auric chloride. It is rather unstable but gives iodoaurates (III), $MAuI_4$, with metal iodides.

Gold number. In order to compare the efficiencies of different protective colloids, Zsigmondy proposed to use the colour change of a gold sol from red to blue on coagulation by electrolytes. The conditions were defined thus: the gold number of a protective colloid is that quantity (in mg) which, when added to 10 ml. of a red gold sol containing 0·05-0·06 g per litre, just prevented the colour change on the addition of 1 ml of 10% sodium chloride solution. The smaller the gold number, the more efficient is the protective colloid. The gold numbers of a few common colloids are given below:

Gelatin and glue	.	0·005-0·01
Sodium caseinate	.	0·01
Haemoglobin .	.	0·03-0·07
Silica sol . .	.	∞
Albumin . .	.	0·1-0·2
Sodium oleate .	.	0·4-1·0
Starch . .	.	*ca.* 25

Gold, organometallic compounds. Compounds formed by the action of Grignard reagents on the trihalides. The derivatives R_2AuX (where R = alkyl or aryl, X = halogen) are the most stable and are dimeric with halogen bridges. Many other derivatives are known; the cyanides are tetrameric. Gold(I) derivatives of the type R_3PAuR' are known.

Gold sensitization. The photographic sensitivity of silver halide emulsions can be increased by treatment with gold salts. It is probable that this results in the formation of sensitivity specks incorporating gold on the surface of the silver

halide grains. Sulphur sensitizers are often added at the same time.

Gold, standard. Pure gold is too soft for use as ornaments or for coinage, and is alloyed with copper or silver, or both. The fineness is expressed either in parts per thousand, or in carats. Pure gold is 24 carat fine, and the five standard alloys of 22, 18, 15, 12 and 9, i.e. parts of gold in 24 of alloy, are legalized. The presence of small quantities of bismuth or lead renders the metal brittle.

Gold sulphides. *Aurous sulphide*, Au_2S is formed as a grey precipitate by passing hydrogen sulphide into a solution of potassium cyanoaurate (I), $KAu(CN)_2$, in the presence of hydrochloric acid. *Auric sulphide*, Au_2S_3, is formed as a black precipitate by the action of hydrogen sulphide on dry $LiAuCl_4$ at $-10°$. Both sulphides give the metal on heating.

Goldschmidt, Victor Moritz (1888-1947). Born at Zürich and educated at the University of Oslo, Goldschmidt became Professor of the Oslo Mineralogical Institute in 1914. In 1927 he became also professor of mineralogy at Göttingen. Virtually the founder of the science of geochemistry through his work on the distribution of the elements, he was also a most distinguished petrologist, crystallographer, and analytical chemist. See *J. Chem. Soc.*, 1949, 2108.

Goldschmidt process. The preparation of sodium formate by pressurizing carbon monoxide and sodium hydroxide at approx. 200°. It is of value as a route to sodium oxalate by the further pyrolysis of sodium formate.

$$CO + NaOH \rightarrow HCO_2Na \xrightarrow{375°} (CO_2Na)_2$$

Goldschmidt reaction. The use of aluminium powder for the reduction of metal oxides or sulphates.

Gomberg, Moses (1866-1947). Born at Elizabetgrad, Russia, Gomberg went to the United States about 1885. He studied at the Universities of Michigan, Munich, and Heidelberg. In 1904 he became professor and in 1927 chairman of the Department of Chemistry of the University of Michigan. The discoverer of stable carbon free radicals, he published many papers, chiefly on triphenylmethyl and its derivatives. He was awarded the Nichols (1914), the Willard Gibbs (1925), and the Chandler Medals (1927), and was President of the American Chemical Society in 1931. See *J. Amer. Chem. Soc.*, 1947, **69**, 2921.

Gonadotropic hormones. Hormones influencing the activity of the gonads, i.e. sex organs. The term is not applied to the steroid sex hormones but to a variety of peptide hormones, produced in the anterior lobe of the pituitary gland and elsewhere. Three main types are distinguished by their effects:—

Follicle-stimulating hormone (FSH), promoting the development of the follicular cells in the ovary and the germinal cells in the testes.

Interstitial cell-stimulating hormone (ICSH), also luteinizing hormone (LH), promoting respectively steroid hormone production in interstitial cells, and the formation of the corpus luteum.

Luteotropic hormone (LTH), stimulating the production of progesterone in the corpus luteum. This hormone is also a lactotropic hormone (prolactin, lactotropin), stimulating the secretion of milk by the mammary gland.

Hormones of the gonadotropin type mostly have molecular weights between 20,000 and 30,000, but chorionic gonadotropin (*q.v.*) is a higher glycoprotein.

Gouy balance. A balance for the determination of magnetic susceptibility. The sample is weighed in and out of a magnetic field and the susceptibility is calculated from the difference in weights.

Graebe, Carl (1841-1927). Professor of chemistry in Geneva. With Liebermann he synthesized alizarin from anthraquinone in 1869.

Graham, Thomas (1805-1869). A native of Glasgow and a graduate of Glasgow University, Graham devoted his whole life to science. In 1830 he was appointed professor of chemistry in the Andersonian University (now the University of Strathclyde), Glasgow. Elected F.R.S. in 1836, he was appointed professor at University College, London in 1837. In 1854 Graham became Master of the Mint. His main work was upon the molecular diffusion of gases; the publication of his 'Elements of Chemistry' in 1841 gained for him a world-wide reputation. See Life, by Dr. Angus Smith (1884).

Graham's law of diffusion. This law states that the rate (r) of diffusion of a gas is inversely proportional to the square root of its density (d), i.e. $r = k \sqrt{\dfrac{1}{d}}$, where k is a constant.

Graham's salt. Polymeric sodium metaphosphate. See Hexametaphosphates.

Grainer. A type of evaporator used in the salt industry consisting of a large shallow pan. The temperature of the brine is kept somewhat below the atmospheric boiling point, heating being by steam coils in the pan or by external heaters. Because evaporation occurs at a still air-liquid interface, large, hard, saucer-shaped crystals are formed, suitable for the requirements of the fishing industry. The crystals fall to the bottom of the pan and are removed by rakes.

Gram atom. The quantity of an element numerically equal to the atomic weight expressed in grams. Thus, the atomic weight of chlorine is 35·5. One gram atom of chlorine weighs 35·5 g.

Gram equivalent. The quantity of a substance equal numerically to the equivalent weight expressed in grams. Thus, the equivalent weight of oxygen is 16/2 or 8. One gram equivalent of oxygen weighs 8 g.

Gramicidin. A substance, insoluble in water, soluble in alcohol, produced by the soil bacterium, *B. brevis*, which is highly bactericidal *in vitro* and *in vivo* against Gram-positive bacteria. Gramicidin S or Soviet gramicidin has been obtained from another strain of *B. brevis* from Russian soil. Unlike gramicidin it is equally effective against both Gram-positive and Gram-negative bacteria. Both gramicidin and gramicidin S have been obtained crystalline and shown to be polypeptides. Gramicidin S is a cyclic dekapeptide with the structure α-L-valyl-L-ornithyl-L-leucyl-D-phenylalanyl-L-propyl-, twice repeated in a cycle.

Gram molecular volume. The volume occupied by the gram molecule of an element or compound in the gaseous state. By Avogadro's hypothesis, the gram molecular volume is the same for all gases under the same conditions of temperature and pressure, and is equal to 22·4 litres at N.T.P.

Gram molecule. The quantity of a compound, or element, equal numerically to the molecular weight expressed in grams. Thus, the molecule of oxygen, O_2, has a molecular weight of $2 \times 16 = 32$. One gram molecule of oxygen weighs 32 g. The word 'mole' is now often used for gram molecule.

Granite. An acid igneous rock with varieties differing widely in colour and grain size, consisting of a granular aggregate of quartz, feldspar, and mica and containing about 65-70% SiO_2. The feldspar (36-68%) is usually a potash feldspar (i.e. orthoclase), the mica (5-18%) is usually of two kinds, white (muscovite) and black (biotite). In some varieties tourmaline may be present. Sp.gr. 2·6-2·8. Extensively used as a building stone and road metal.

Granulation. A general term for any process for producing granules. Granulation is frequently carried out by compacting a fine material and then crushing it, and thus employs techniques of both size enlargement and size reduction.

Graphite. An allotropic form of carbon, also known as plumbago and black lead, which occurs in crystalline forms, and more commonly in apparently amorphous masses of flakes or granules which really consist of very minute hexagonal crystals. The structure consists of parallel sheets, in each of which the carbon atoms form a hexagonal net (see accompanying figure). These sheets are superposed in such a way that only one-half of the atoms in each fall vertically above atoms in the sheet below, and the cell dimension c is accordingly twice the perpendicular distance between adjacent layers. Each carbon atom has three equidistant neighbours in its own layer at a distance of 1·42 Å, the distance found for C—C in aromatic rings. The distance between successive layers of carbon atoms is 3·40 Å, and the weak forces indicated by this large separation account for the easy cleavage parallel to the layers. Colour steel-grey,

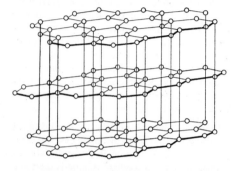

streak black; sp.gr. 2·2. One cleavage, parallel to the layers. High thermal and electrical conductivity. Occurs in Cumberland, Ceylon, United States, Czechoslovakia, Italy, Rumania, and elsewhere. It is used for making lead pencils, electrodes, crucibles, and refractory articles, and as a lubricant.

Considerable quantities of graphite are required as a moderator and reflector in the nuclear energy field. Natural graphite is too impure for this purpose and reactor grade graphite is made by heating to a temperature of about 2800° a high-purity petroleum coke with a pitch binder.

Graphite compounds. Graphite can absorb various substances between the layers of carbon atoms. With strong oxidizing agents 'graphite oxide' is formed; this has a carbon to oxygen ratio of from 3·5:1 to 2·2:1. Water and alcohol can now be absorbed in the separated layers and complete oxidation gives mellitic acid, $C_6(COOH)_6$.

Graphite absorbs molten potassium to form the so-called *alloys*. Two distinct phases, KC_8 (bronze-coloured) and KC_{16} (steel-blue) are known.

Treatment with strong acids in the presence of oxidizing agents gives 'graphite salts'; the sulphate $C_{24}HSO_4 \cdot 2H_2SO_4$ is typical. Graphite will absorb anhydrous chlorides such as ferric chloride. Fluorine (to form $(CF)_n$) and bromine are also taken up; fluorine completely destroys the layer lattice.

Graphitizer. Certain alloy additions (e.g. nickel, copper and silicon) to steel and cast iron favour the graphitic form of carbon in place of Fe_3C. Thus such alloys are generally essential in cast irons but must be used in conjunction with carbide stabilizers in steels for high-temperature service.

Graviton. An elementary particle; the particle which in wave form is a gravitational field.

Greases. Materials which generally consist of a liquid phase, either mineral or vegetable oil, and a metallic soap in a dispersed phase. Calcium, sodium, and aluminium salts are most widely used, but lithium, lead, zinc, and other soaps are made for special purposes. The soaps are made from a variety of fats, oils, and waxes, using stearic, oleic, and other fatty acids; naphthenates are also used.

Green acids. A part of the product of the reaction of sulphuric acid with petroleum. They are mixtures of sulphonic acids and form soaps that are used as emulsifiers, wetting agents, and for other purposes.

Green earth, Terra Verte. Mined at various places in mid-Europe, it is a natural earth similar in composition to the mineral glauconite. Its principal use is as a base for the precipitation of malachite green dyestuff to form the pigment known as Lime Green.

Greenockite. The mineral form of cadmium sulphide, CdS. It forms hexagonal orange-yellow crystals, sp.gr. 4·8, hardness $3-3\frac{1}{2}$. Rare in quantity, but often associated in traces with zinc minerals.

Green verditer. See Malachite.

Green vitriol. See Iron sulphates.

Gregory powder. See Rhubarb.

Grey iron. See Cast irons.

Griess, Johann Peter (1829-1888). Born in Germany, he became chemist to Allsopp & Sons, at Burton-on-Trent. He discovered the aromatic diazo compounds in 1858. See *Chem. and Ind.*, 1958, 616.

Griffin mill. A type of ring-roller mill (*q.v.*).

Grignard, François Auguste Victor (1871-1935). Born and educated at Cherbourg, Grignard proceeded to the University of Lyons, where he proposed to specialize in mathematics. Inspired by Bouveault, he turned his attention to organic chemistry. With the exception of one year at Besançon (1905), and four years as professor at Nancy (1910-14), he spent his entire academic life in the University of Lyons. His discovery of the organo-magnesium compounds gave to organic chemists the 'Grignard reaction'. In 1912 he shared with Sabatier the Nobel Prize for Chemistry. See *J. Chem. Soc.*, 1937, 171.

Grignard reaction. Alkyl and aryl halides, particularly bromides and iodides, react with magnesium in presence of dry ether to form compounds of the type R—Mg—X, where R represents the alkyl or aryl radical and X the halide. These are known as Grignard reagents and are obtained as colourless solids by evaporation of the ether. They are always associated with one or two molecules of ether which are in combination with the magnesium. There is evidence that some Grignard reagents may exist as 1:1 adducts $R_2Mg \cdot MgX_2$. These reagents combine with a large number of types of compounds and the reactions are of great importance in chemical syntheses. It is necessary to carry out the syntheses with rigid exclusion of water and the reagents are generally employed in solution in dry ether or benzene. They react with alkyl and aryl halides to give hydrocarbons and with metal halides to give organometallics. Esters are formed when the reagents combine with orthoformic, formic, or chloroformic esters; carboxylic acids by combination with solid carbon dioxide. Aldehydes give secondary alcohols, while ketones give tertiary alcohols. Amides and nitriles give ketones. Water and dilute acids react to give hydrocarbons. The immediate result of the reaction is often a complex magnesium compound which is decomposed by dilute acids to give the final product. See 'Grignard Reactions of Non-metallic Substances', by Kharasch and Reinmuth.

Grignard reagents. See Grignard reaction.

Grinding. See Crushing and grinding.

Griseofulvin, $C_{17}H_{17}ClO_6$, 7-Chloro-4,6-di-

methoxycoumaran - 3 - one - 2 - spiro - 1' - (2'-methoxy-6'-methylcyclohex-2'-en-4'-one), is a substance of high fungicidal activity, which is non-poisonous to plants and mammals. It is obtained from *Penicillin griseofulvum* and is a colourless solid; m.p. 222°. Insoluble in water, sparingly soluble in many organic solvents.

Grizzlies. These are crude and robust screens used for the classification of very coarse material. They are built of a series of metal bars evenly spaced and arranged on a slope, across which the feed is passed. The direction of the slope, and hence of the flow of material, is usually parallel to the length of the bars. To prevent choking of the interstices the bars are V shaped in section, the broad edges forming the screening surface. Grizzlies may be either stationary or be mechanically vibrated.

Grotthus chain theory. An explanation of the passage of an electric current through a solution, and the chemical changes produced by it in terms of the successive decomposition and recombination of particles of the dissolved substance.

Grotthus-Draper Law. This law, established by Grotthus on theoretical grounds in 1818, and confirmed experimentally by Draper in 1839, states that only light which is absorbed by a substance is effective in inducing a chemical change. It is not true to say that all the light absorbed brings about a chemical change, for some of it may be re-radiated as fluorescence, and some may be dissipated as heat. The light need not necessarily be absorbed directly by the reacting substances, but may be absorbed by an inert substance present in the system, and transferred to the reactants as thermal energy. This process is known as photosensitization (*q.v.*).

Ground state. The lowest energy electronic state of an atom or molecule. The normal state.

Group. A group of elements arranged vertically in the normal form of the Periodic Table. Within a group the elements show distinct chemical resemblances.

Group theory. A mathematical method which considers the effect of a group of operators (e.g. symmetry elements, crystal field) on properties. Used in calculations on spectra, magnetic susceptibility, etc.

Grove, Sir William Robert (1811-1896). A native of Swansea, Grove made numerous investigations on voltaic phenomena and electrolytic decompositions, invented the Grove battery, and was the first to demonstrate the dissociation of water. He was a Fellow of the Royal Society and was awarded a Royal Medal in 1846.

Growth hormone, Somatotropin. A protein hormone isolated from the anterior lobe of the pituitary gland, which stimulates many of the processes of growth. It shows considerable species specificity—the bovine hormone has no effect in man. Human growth hormone has a molecular weight of 27,100.

Gruner's classification of coal. This classification is based on ash-free, sulphur-free, dry coals. There are five classes, varying from the dry coals of long flame (75-80% carbon) to the lean coals, the anthracites of 90-93% carbon. The method of classification is based on the ultimate analysis with a knowledge of the volatile matter, or more particularly the carbon/oxygen ratio.

Guaiacol, $C_7H_8O_2$. Crystallizes in prisms; m.p 32°, b.p. 205°. Sparingly soluble in water, soluble in ordinary organic solvents. It is a constituent of guaiacum resin, and occurs in beechwood tar. It is used medicinally in two forms:
(1) an oily liquid obtained by the fractionation of wood-tar creosote, and (2) colourless crystals prepared synthetically. Guaiacol has a very characteristic odour and a burning taste; its medicinal properties are identical with those of creosote.

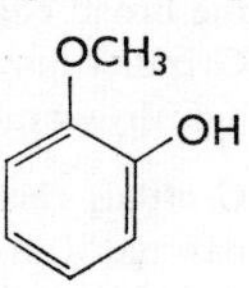

Guaiazulene, S-Guaiazulene, 1,4-Di-methyl-7-isopropyl azulene, $C_{15}H_{18}$. Obtained by the

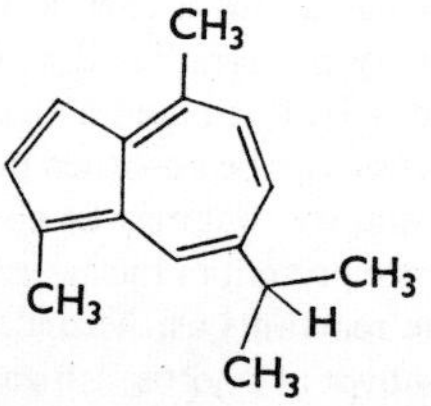

dehydrogenation of guaiol with sulphur. It forms blue plates, m.p. 31·5.° If the dehydrogenation is carried out at a higher temperature using selenium an isomeric product, 2,4-dimethyl-7-isopropylazulene (Se-guaiazulene), is obtained.

Guaiol, $C_{15}H_{26}O$. Is a crystalline alcohol obtained from the wool oil of *Bulnesia sarmienti*,

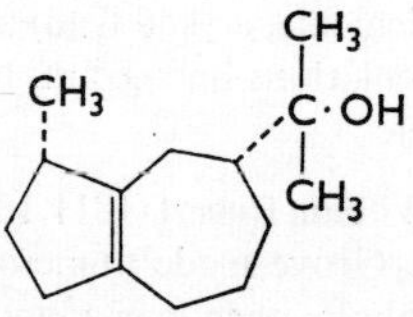

Lorenz, having m.p. 93°, $[\alpha]_D$ −29·8° (in alcohol). It gives a 3,5-dinitrobenzoate, m.p. 137°-137·5°. On heating with sulphur it gives guaiazulene.

Guanese. The enzyme responsible for deaminating guanine to xanthine.

Guanethidine, Ismelin, $C_{10}H_{22}N_4$. Prepared by the interaction of N-amino-ethylazacyclooctane and S-methylisothiourea and conversion of the product to the sulphate. The sulphate is

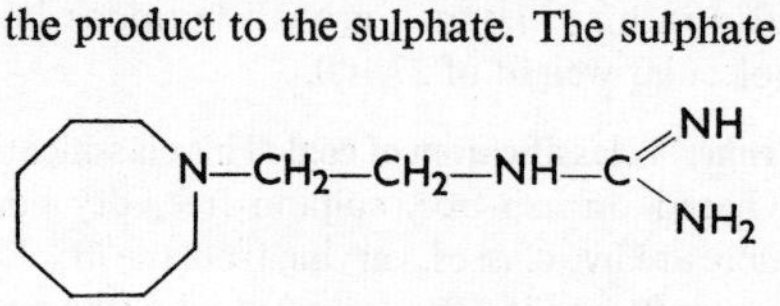

a colourless crystalline powder, m.p. 251°-256° (in a sealed evacuated tube). It is soluble at 20°

in 1·5 parts of water, slightly soluble in alcohol, insoluble in chloroform and ether.

Guanethidine is a sympatholytic agent used in the treatment of hypertension.

Guanidine, Iminourea, CH_5N_3. Deliquescent crystals, soluble in water and alcohol, volatile, and strongly alkaline. Forms many salts, e.g. nitrate, m.p. 214°. It occurs in small quantities in vetch seedlings. It can be prepared by oxidizing guanine or arginine, by the action of hydrochloric acid on biuret, or of ammonia on cyanamide. The most usual method of preparation is by heating ammonium thiocyanate to give guanidine thiocyanate and obtaining the base from this. It is conveniently estimated as the picrate. Guanidine is a muscle poison, affecting the nerve endings. Guanidine nitrate and guanidine picrate have been suggested as constituents of high explosives.

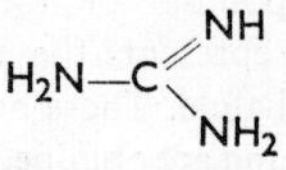

Guanidinoacetic acid. See Glycocyamine.

Guanine, 6-Oxy-2-aminopurine, $C_5H_5N_5O$. An

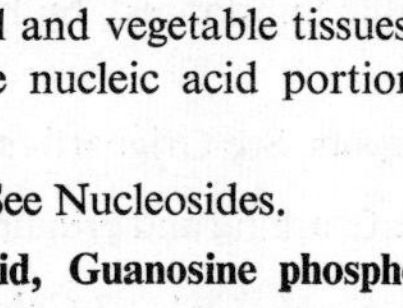

amorphous powder, insoluble in water and alcohol, soluble in acids and alkalis. It is present in all animal and vegetable tissues as a constituent of the nucleic acid portion of nucleoproteins.

Guanosine. See Nucleosides.

Guanylic acid, Guanosine phosphoric acid. A

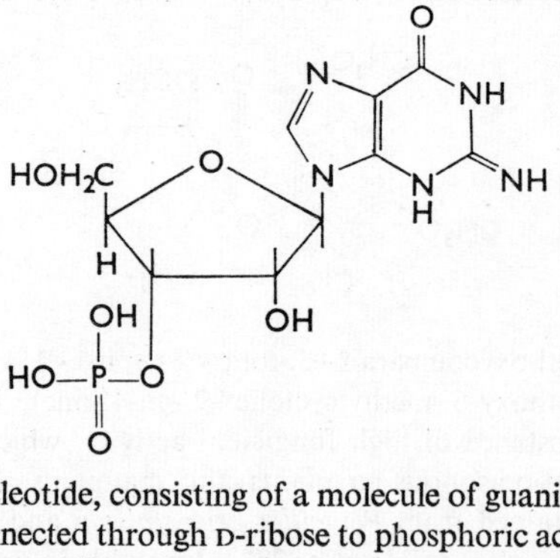

nucleotide, consisting of a molecule of guanine, connected through D-ribose to phosphoric acid. It crystallizes in needles with two molecules of water, m.p. 208°, with decomposition, $[\alpha]_D^{20}$ −7·5°. It is a constituent of nucleic acids, and is found as the free nucleotide in animal glandular tissue.

Guldberg, Cato Maximilian (1836-1902). Guldberg was appointed professor of applied mathematics in the university of his native town of Oslo in 1869. He was associated with his brother-in-law, Peter Waage, in the enunciation of the 'Law of Mass Action'.

Gulose. See Hexose.

Gum acacia, gum arabic. Obtained as an exudate from acacia trees. It is the calcium salt of arabin, a complex polysaccharide built of glucuronic acid, arabinose, rhamnose, and galactose units, with a molecular weight of about 240,000. It is used in pharmacy as an emulsifying and suspending agent and in the manufacture of pills and plasters, in the food industry, as an adhesive, and for many other purposes.

Gum inhibitors. Substances added to gasoline or kerosine to prevent the formation of gum during storage.

Gum tragacanth, Tragacanth. A gum obtained from the genus *Astragalus*. It is a mixture of a neutral polysaccharide with the salt of a complex acid polysaccharide, and on hydrolysis gives chiefly glucuronic acid, arabinose, xylose, and fucose. It swells in water to give a gel of high water content, and is used as a thickening agent in the food and pharmaceutical industries and for other purposes.

Gums. The true plant gums, i.e. gum acacia, gum tragacanth, are the dried exudates from various plants, obtained when the bark is cut or other injury is suffered. They are soluble in water to give very viscous colloidal solutions, sometimes called mucilages (*q.v.*), and are insoluble in organic solvents. They are complex polysaccharides, each containing several different sugar molecules and uronic acid groups.

In the petroleum industry the term gum refers to the dark coloured polymer formed by the oxidation of certain unsaturated compounds of cracked or reformed gasolines.

Guncotton. See Nitrocellulose.

Gunmetal. See Bronze.

Gunpowder. The oldest and best known explosive. Although its origin is unknown, the name of Roger Bacon is associated with its development in the thirteenth century. As a propellant it has been replaced by modern smokeless powders, but it is still an important explosive used in primers, fuses and pyrotechnics. Ordinary black gunpowder consists of about 75% of potassium nitrate, 15% of charcoal and 10% of sulphur. It is granulated during manufacture, grains of different sizes with different burning rates being produced, and these are polished by rotating in closed drums. Gunpowder is relatively insensitive to shock but is very easily ignited and burns with explosive violence. The products of combustion include a considerable amount of solid material (e.g. potassium carbonate and potassium sulphate), which is one reason why gunpowder is unsuitable as a gun propellant.

Gutta-percha. This naturally occurring plastic-like material is a polymer isomeric with natural rubber, having the constitution: poly-trans-1,4-isoprene, as has also another naturally occurring polymer 'balata'. They both exist in two polymorphic (α and β) forms. Originally used as a cable covering and insulant, for belting, and also moulded into tough, chemically-resistant containers, gutta-percha has now been entirely superseded by Polythene. However, it is still used as the tough covering for golf balls. Gutta-percha and balata are obtained from the latex of certain trees occurring in Indonesia and Malaysia (gutta-percha) and in Central America (balata).

Gutzeit's test. A test for the presence of arsenic. The substance suspected of containing arsenic is suitably dissolved, and is then treated with zinc and dilute acid, which leads to formation of arsine, AsH_3, by a process of reduction. The presence of arsine is detected by passing the gas evolved from the zinc and acid over a paper moistened with mercuric chloride solution. A yellow colour, due to the compound $AsH(HgCl)_2$, is first formed. This is transformed successively into brown $As(HgCl)_3$ and to black As_2Hg_3. The yellow or brown stain is compared with standards. Hydrogen sulphide must first be removed from the gas stream by means of lead acetate.

Guyton de Morveau, Louis Bernard (1737-1816). Guyton de Morveau was Avocat-Général in the Parliament of his native city of Dijon. Becoming interested in chemistry he made a systematic study of the subject and commenced to deliver lectures on it at Dijon in 1776. He went later to Paris as a member of the Constituent Assembly set up by the Revolution and assisted in the foundation of the École Polytechnique in 1794. He subsequently became professor of chemistry and director of this institution. His chief service to chemistry lies in his efforts to introduce a logical system of nomenclature.

Gypsum or **Selenite**, $CaSO_4 \cdot 2H_2O$. The monoclinic lattice is of the layer type, in which two sheets of SO_4 groups are bound by Ca^{++} atoms to form a strong double sheet. Successive double sheets are separated by sheets of water molecules. Twinning is common. Sp.gr. = 2.3, hardness = 2, refractive index 1.53. A poor conductor of electricity. Occurs in Northumberland, Cumberland, Nottinghamshire, Staffordshire, Derbyshire, and elsewhere chiefly in the Bunter beds and Keuper marls.

Used in the manufacture of plaster of paris and plaster products, to control the rate of setting of Portland cement, in agriculture, and as a filler. See 'Gypsum and Anhydrite,' A. W. Groves, H.M.S.O., 1958.

Gyratory crusher. This has a crushing head in the form of a vertical upright truncated cone, which is set inside a stationary outer ring. The profile of the ring is such that the clearance between it and the crushing head is considerably greater at the top than at the bottom. The spindle on which the head is mounted has an eccentric bearing, and as it rotates material fed in the top works its way downwards and is crushed between the two surfaces. Gyratory crushers are employed where large quantities of coarse material are to be subjected to size reduction. Maximum capacities can exceed 3,000 tons per hour.

Gyromagnetic ratio. See g factor.

H

Haber, Fritz (1868-1934). Born at Breslau Haber was educated at Berlin, Heidelberg, Charlottenburg, and Karlsruhe. He became professor of chemistry at the Technische Hochschule, Karlsruhe, but in 1911 was appointed professor of physical chemistry and director of the Kaiser Wilhelm Institute, Berlin. He made a study of thermodynamics of gaseous reactions and invented the process for the synthesis of ammonia from nitrogen and hydrogen. Haber was awarded the Nobel Prize for Chemistry in 1918.

Haber process. The process for the direct synthesis of ammonia by combination of nitrogen and hydrogen over a catalyst.

Hadfield, Sir Robert Abbott (1858-1940). Chairman and managing director of Hadfields, Limited and of the Sheffield Gas Company, Hadfield made many important contributions to metallurgy, particularly manganese steel, silicon steel, and special alloy steels. He was the author of numerous books. He was knighted in 1908, elected F.R.S. in 1909 and created a baronet in 1917. See Steel, austenitic. See *J. Chem. Soc.,* 1941, 55.

Haem, $C_{34}H_{32}FeN_4O_4$. The non-protein portion of the haemoglobin molecule. Its structural formula resembles haemin without the chlorine atom; the iron is therefore in the ferrous state. It is obtained by the action of sodium hydrosulphite on haematin, and is reoxidized to haematin on exposure to air.

Haematin, $C_{34}H_{33}FeN_4O_5$. Haematin resembles haem, but the iron is in the ferric state; it bears the same relationship to methaemoglobin as haem does to haemoglobin.

It is formed by oxidizing haemin, and has a similar structural formula, with an OH group replacing the chlorine atom. It forms blue-black crystals decomposing without melting at 200°, insoluble in water, alcohol and ether.

Haematite, Fe_2O_3. This important ore of iron is a blood-red colour in massive formation but forms also black crystals known as specular iron. It is trigonal, hardness 6, sp.gr. 5·2.

Red ochre or reddle is a mixture of haematite, clay, and sometimes other impurities.

Haematite and corundum are isomorphous and are closely related in structure to ilmenite.

Haematoporphyrin. See Porphyrins.

Haematoxylin, $C_{16}H_{14}O_6$. Crystallizes in yellow prisms with three molecules of water, m.p.

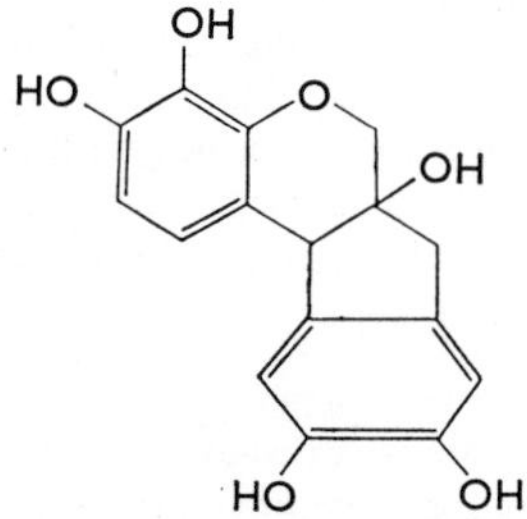

100°-120°. Sparingly soluble in water, soluble in alcohol and ether, also in alkalis giving a purple solution. It is used as a biological stain and can be used as an indicator. It is one of the constituents of the dye logwood.

Haemerythrin. A red iron-containing respiratory pigment found in the plasma and corpuscles of certain annelid worms.

Haemin, $C_{34}H_{32}ClFeN_4O_4$. It is the chloride of

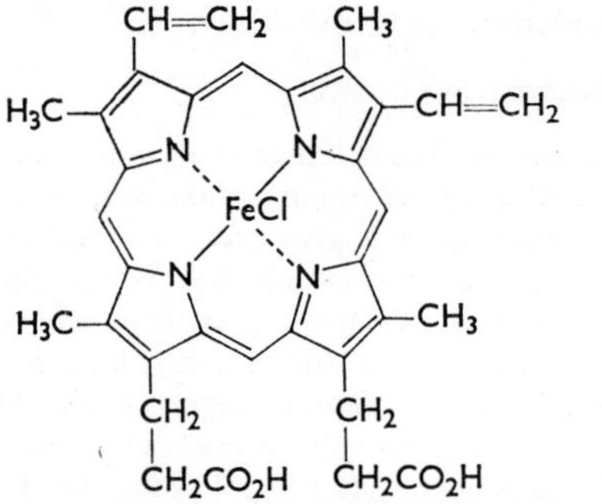

haem, and is readily obtained from blood by drying and extracting with glacial acetic acid and a chloride. It crystallizes in bluish-black microscopic rhombohedra (Teichman's crystals), insoluble in water, alcohol, and ether, soluble in acetic acid. Its isolation serves as a test for blood stains.

Haemochromogens. Compounds of haem with denatured proteins, amino-acids, amines, ammonia, pyridine, and other nitrogenous substances. They all have very similar absorption spectra, and give parahaematins on exposure to atmospheric oxygen. The most familiar haemochromogen is the compound of haem with denatured globin, derived from haemoglobin by treatment with alkali and sodium hydrosulphite.

Haemocyanin. A copper-containing respiratory pigment found in certain crustaceans and molluscs, and obtained crystalline fairly easily. Like haemoglobin, it combines loosely with oxygen; oxyhaemocyanin is blue and the reduced form is colourless. Haemocyanin is not a porphyrin derivative, but is probably a copper proteinate. Haemocyanins from different species differ in their isoelectric points, dissociation curves, molecular weights, and other properties. Their molecular weights are invariably very high, and range from about 400,000 to about 7,000,000.

Haemoglobin. Haemoglobin is the respiratory pigment of the blood of vertebrates. It is also found in some invertebrates, and in the muscles of mammals and birds. It is a conjugated protein consisting of the iron-porphyrin compound haem, combined with the basic protein globin. It has been obtained in a crystalline state, and its molecular weight, as determined by several methods, is about 68,000. It is believed to be built of four haemochromogen units, each containing one molecule of haem and one molecule of globin. It is soluble in water, insoluble in alcohol and ether, and denatured and coagulated by heating. Haemoglobins from different animals have different crystallographic forms, absorption spectra, and dissociation curves. The difference lies in the globin portion of the molecule. The most characteristic and important property of haemoglobin is its ability to combine loosely with oxygen to form oxyhaemoglobin, which readily loses oxygen again on exposure to a vacuum or an atmosphere devoid of oxygen. Haemoglobin combines with oxygen in the lungs, and carries it in the arteries to the tissues, where the oxygen pressure is low, and where it is reduced, returning to the lungs via the veins. Oxyhaemoglobin is scarlet in colour: reduced haemoglobin is of a purplish colour. Haemoglobin also combines very easily with carbon monoxide, forming carboxyhaemoglobin. Haemoglobin also plays a part in regulating the acidity of blood and in the carriage of carbon dioxide; and muscle haemoglobin acts as a respiratory catalyst.

Haemolysis. Haemolysis, or the laking of blood, is the name given to the bursting of the red blood corpuscles. This can be caused by lowering the osmotic pressure of the solution surrounding them, by repeatedly freezing and thawing the blood, and by heating to 60°. The corpuscle membranes can also be destroyed by many reagents which attack them chemically, including acids, alkalis, soaps, saponins, the bile salts, ether, chloroform, and certain snake venoms and pathogenic bacteria, for example the tetanus bacillus.

Hafnium, Hf. At.no. 72, At.wt. 178·6. Hafnium was first characterized in zirconium minerals in 1923 by Coster and von Hevesy by means of its X-ray spectrum. It is invariably found associated with zirconium, from which it is separated by first isolating the zirconium-hafnium mixture from the mineral. Complex fluorides are then formed, and may be separated by fractional crystallization from aqueous solution. The hafnium compound is the more soluble. Alternatively, a process of fractional precipitation of the phosphates is employed. The precipitate is richer in hafnium than the solution. Hafnium and zirconium and their respective compounds are remarkably similar in their chemical properties.

Metallic hafnium has been prepared by decomposing K_2HfF_6 or $HfCl_4$ by heating with sodium. Alternatively, the vapour of HfI_4 may be decomposed in contact with a tungsten filament heated to 1300°. The m.p. of the metal is 2227°. Its density varies from 12·1 to 13·3. It crystallizes with the close-packed hexagonal structure, $a=3·20$, $c=5·07$ Å. The metal is ductile. It is protected from oxidation at room temperature by a superficial coating of oxide, but burns in oxygen at high temperature. It absorbs hydrogen when heated in the gas, and will also combine when heated with the halogens and with nitrogen. It has found a limited application in the manufacture of tungsten filaments, in which it prevents recrystallization of the tungsten. Used in reactor control rods: it has a very large cross-section for neutron capture.

Hafnium compounds. Hafnium compounds are very similar to the corresponding zirconium (IV) compounds. The element is fairly basic in character. Hafnium compounds are more difficult to reduce than are the corresponding zirconium derivatives.

Hafnium oxide (Hafnia), HfO_2. Hafnium oxide is prepared by ignition of hafnium hydroxide, sulphate, or oxalate. It is a white refractory solid (m.p. *ca.* 2800°), which exists in a monoclinic form of density 9·98 and in a tetragonal form of density 10·47. The oxide is closely similar to zirconium dioxide in its chemical behaviour, but is somewhat more basic. On fusion with other metal oxides it forms a series of mixed-metal oxides. No discrete anionic species are known.

Hahn, Otto (1879-   ). Born in Frankfurt am Main, Hahn studied at Munich and Marburg and in 1928 became a director of the Kaiser Wilhelm Institut for Chemistry in Berlin. His work on radioactive elements led in 1939 to his publication of the first recognized fission of the uranium atom into two atoms of medium atomic weight. For this he was awarded the Nobel Prize for chemistry in 1944.

Hair hygrometer. A device for the determination of humidity by measurement of the change in length of a hygroscopic substance such as hair.

Halazone, p-sulphondichloroamidobenzoic **acid, $C_7H_5Cl_2NO_4S$.** A white powder, m.p. 213°, slightly soluble in water to give an unstable solution which readily loses chlorine. It is used in tablets for the sterilization of drinking water.

Haldane gas-analysis apparatus. Used for the analysis of air or mine gases in which there are small quantities of methane and carbon monoxide requiring accurate analysis. The gas is passed into a burette by means of a mercury levelling tube and passed through the different absorption pipettes.

Combustions are carried out by burning the gas and admixed oxygen or air in a chamber in which a platinum coil is glowing brightly. Measurements of changes in volume and amounts of combustion products are determined.

Hales, Stephen (1677–1761). A curate at Teddington. In his 'Statistical Essays' he recorded experiments from which it is clear that he had prepared hydrogen, carbonic acid, carbon monoxide, sulphur dioxide, and marsh gas, without having any clear idea of their nature or composition.

Half-value period, Half life. The time taken for the concentration of a substance to fall to half its initial value. For radioactive elements the half-value period is $0.69 \times 1/\lambda$ where λ is the decay constant. The term is used also for transient free radicals and first-order chemical reactions.

Halibut-liver oil is obtained from the liver of the halibut, *Hippoglossus hippoglossus*. It contains about 100 times as much vitamin A as does cod-liver oil, and is therefore of considerable value in the treatment of vitamin-A deficiency diseases, inasmuch as a medicinal dose of the vitamin

can be administered in a small capsule instead of a relatively large volume of an oil which to many palates is very nauseous.

Halide. A generic name for fluorides, chlorides, bromides, and iodides.

Hall, Charles Martin (1863-1914). Born at Thompson, U.S.A., Hall graduated at Oberlin College. His attention was early attracted to the metal aluminium and the desirability of its cheap production. His researches led to the development of a practical electrolytic process for the isolation of the metal from its naturally occurring compounds. He thus made possible the extensive uses of aluminium today.

Hallachrome, $C_9H_7NO_4$. 5,6-Dihydro-5,6-dioxo-2-indolinecarboxylic acid, a pigment

arising from tyrosine by the action of the enzyme tyrosinase.

Halloysite. A clay mineral $Al_4Si_4O_6(OH)_{16}$; a compact material with a greasy feel and lustre, sp.gr. about 2·1, hardness 1·2, refractive index 1·53.

Hallosyite has the kaolinite type structure and is a member of the group of clay minerals.

Haloform. A generic term for the trihalogen derivatives of methane, i.e. CHF_3, $CHCl_3$, $CHBr_3$, CHI_3.

Halogen. The elements of Group VII of the periodic table, fluorine, chlorine, bromine, iodine, and astatine are called halogens.

Halogenated rubbers. Rubber reacts with halogens and with hydrogen halides, giving, according to the conditions of the reaction, compounds which are formed by addition, substitution, or the two processes simultaneously. The halogen compounds in general swell or dissolve in benzene and its homologues, and in chloroform, carbon tetrachloride, and some other chlorinated solvents, but are insoluble in alcohol and petrol. The technical importance of the bromine, and iodine compounds is limited by their instability as compared with the chlorine compounds. The reaction with bromine and with iodine can be used for the surface hardening of rubber goods, and brominated rubber can be used for attaching rubber to metals. See Chlorinated rubber and Rubber hydrochloride.

Halothane, Fluothane, $CHBrCl \cdot CF_3$. A colourless, mobile, heavy liquid, with an odour resembling chloroform and a sweet, burning taste. It is non-inflammable, d^{20} 1·869-1·874, b.p. 49°-51°. Halothane is a general inhalation anaesthetic administered in oxygen vapour, with an almost complete absence of toxic effects and post-operative sickness.

Hammer mill. This type of mill operates by impact rather than by positive pressure. It consists essentially of a series of hammers hinged between discs mounted on a central horizontal shaft which rotates at a fairly high speed. The flailing of these hammers pulverizes material fed into the mill and the product is discharged through screens which form the lower half of the casing.

Hammett equation. This provides a correlation between the structure and reactivity in the side chain derivatives of aromatic compounds. Its derivation follows from many comparisons between rate constants for various reactions and the equilibrium constants for other reactions, or other functions of molecules which can be measured (e.g. the infra-red carbonyl group stretching frequency, etc.). For example the dissociation constants K_a of a series of para-substituted (nitro, methoxyl, chloro, etc.) benzoic acids may be compared with the rate constant k for the alkaline hydrolysis of para-substituted benzyl chlorides. If log K_a is plotted against log k, the data fall on a straight line. Similar results are obtained for meta-substituted derivatives but not for ortho-substituted derivatives.

The equation

$$\log k = \rho \log K + C$$

expresses this relationship, and when the ring substituent is hydrogen, k_0 is the rate of hydrolysis of benzyl chloride and K_0 is the dissociation constant of benzoic acid. The equation

$$\log \frac{k}{k_0} = \rho\sigma \quad \text{where } \sigma = \log\frac{K}{K_0}$$

may be derived and is known as the Hammett equation. It is usual to maintain the term log K/K_0 as referring to the dissociation of benzoic acids in water at 25°, and to relate other measureable entities to it. The term σ is called the substituent constant since the strength of the benzoic acid depends upon the nature of the substituent. The more positive value of σ infers the more electron attracting nature of the substituent. Negative σ values indicate electron-donating substituents.

The term ρ is a reaction constant and is mathematically evaluated for a particular reaction by plotting log k/k_0 against σ. The slope of the straight lines is ρ, and reflects the sensitivity of the reaction under study to effects of substituents. The value of ρ is obviously affected by temperature, solvent changes, etc.

The equation does not hold without exceptions even for meta and para substituents,

especially when resonance interactions from substituents are possible.

Hammick and Illingworth's rules. A set of empirical rules governing the course of aromatic substitution. If a mono-substituted benzene derivative has the formula C_6H_5XY, where X is attached directly to the nucleus and Y is an atom or group attached to X, then if

(a) Y is in a higher group in the Periodic Table than X, or
(b) Y is in the same group as X but of lower atomic weight, XY is *meta* directing. But if
(c) Y is in a lower group than X, or
(d) X and Y are atoms of the same element, or
(e) XY is just a single atom, XY is *ortho* and *para* directing.

Hydrogen must be considered as a member of group I: in such cases as —CHO the hydrogen must be ignored and only the remaining element considered.

Hantzsch, Arthur Rudolf (1857-1935). Educated at Dresden and Würzburg, Hantzsch was appointed professor at the Polytechnikum in Zürich at the age of 28, and succeeded E. Fischer at Würzburg in 1893. He paid special attention to the stereochemistry of nitrogen compounds, the structure of cyanuric acid, the electrical conductivity of organic compounds, and the structure of acids. See *Proc. Chem. Soc.*, 1959, 1.

Hantzsch synthesis. The formation of pyridine derivatives by the condensation of ethyl acetoacetate with ammonia and an aldehyde. Thus ethyl acetoacetate and aldehyde-ammonia give ethyl dihydrocollidine dicarboxylate:

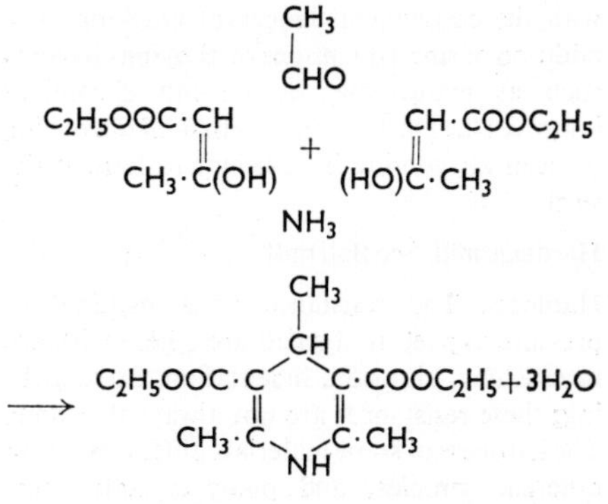

This dihydro compound may be oxidized to the corresponding pyridine derivative by nitrous acid, hydrolysed to the dicarboxylic acid, and converted into collidine (2,4,6-trimethyl-pyridine) by distillation over lime. Acetaldehyde may be replaced by most other aldehydes; thus benzaldehyde gives similarly 2,6-dimethyl-4-phenylpyridine.

Haptens. The specificity of many antigens has been shown to be due to substances of a polysaccharide nature, called haptens, which accompany the proteins of the antigen. Haptens do not produce antibodies if injected into animals, but they react with antibodies produced by injection of the specific antigen. The sugars and carbohydrate acids produced on hydrolysing haptens have in many cases been identified. The existence of haptens of a lipoid nature has also been claimed.

Harcourt, Augustus George Vernon (1834-1919). After studying chemistry at Balliol College, Oxford, Harcourt was, in 1859, elected Lee's reader in chemistry and appointed, in 1872, one of the Metropolitan Gas referees to report on London gas. He introduced the pentane lamp as a standard of illuminating power. He was an excellent manipulator and an inspiring and lucid teacher. See *J. Chem. Soc.*, 1920, 1626.

Harden, Sir Arthur (1865-1940). Born at Manchester, Harden studied at Owens College and at Erlangen. From 1888 to 1897 he was lecturer and demonstrator in chemistry at Owens College, then going to London as chemist to the British Institute of Preventive Medicine, now the Lister Institute, where he became head of the biochemical department and professor of biochemistry in London University. He retired in 1930. He was elected a Fellow of the Royal Society in 1909, and in 1929 was awarded (jointly with v. Euler) the Nobel Prize in chemistry for his work on alcoholic fermentation. See *J. Chem. Soc.*, 1943, 334.

Hardenability. The rate of quenching required to fully harden a steel. A steel of poor hardenability requires a drastic cold water quench, with the consequent danger of cracking. The addition of small quantities of alloying elements such as manganese, nickel and chromium improves the hardenability so that oil quenching or even air cooling is sufficient to harden the steel.

Hardinge mill. See Ball mill.

Hardness. The resistance of a material to pressure applied to a small area, i.e. resistance to crushing, abrasion, indentation, or scratching; these resistances are not always the same. The hardness of some materials differs greatly in different samples, and many crystals show greater hardness in some planes than in others, the hardness being then usually lower in the direction of cleavage.

The hardness of metals and alloys is a measure of their resistance to deformation. The hardness tests, which are simple to carry out, are generally used as a guide to the strength of the material. In the *Vicker's* test a pyramidal diamond is pressed into the metal surface under a known load. A microscope is used to measure the diagonal of the indentation from which the hardness number may be calculated. The *Brinell* method is similar but uses a hardened steel ball, commonly of 10 mm diameter. This method is still much used in industry. It is not satisfactory for very hard alloys as the steel ball deforms. The *Rockwell* tests are commonly used in America. These tests use a hardened steel ball or a conical diamond indenter. In this case the depth of the impression is recorded on a dial gauge. This has the advantage of speed, but a disadvantage of the Rockwell method is that different hardness scales are used for different ranges.

The term hardness is often used as equivalent to refractoriness; thus a hard glaze has a higher melting-point than a soft glaze.

The hardness of water has reference to its behaviour with soap; a soft water readily produces a lather, but a hard water does not. The hardness is said to be temporary when it is removed by boiling the water and permanent if the water is hard after being boiled. Temporary hardness is due to the presence of calcium bicarbonate, permanent hardness to the presence of other soluble calcium and magnesium salts. Hardness is removed by the Permutite process or by the use of detergents.

Hare, Robert (1781-1858). Hare was born at Philadelphia, and from 1818 to 1847 was professor of chemistry at the Medical School of the University of Pennsylvania. He wrote many papers, built the first electric furnace, and invented the oxyhydrogen blowpipe.

Harington, Sir Charles Robert (1897-). Educated at Malvern College and Cambridge University, Harington was appointed lecturer in pathological chemistry, University College, London (1922), reader (1928), and professor (1931). In addition to many papers on chemical and biochemical problems he was associated with Barger in the elucidation of the structure and synthesis of thyroxin (1927). He was elected F.R.S. in 1931. He became Director of the National Institute for Medical Research in 1942.

Harkins, William Draper (1873-1951). Harkins was born at Titusville, Pennsylvania, and educated at Stanford University. After being professor and head of the department of chemistry at the University of Montana he went, in 1912, to the University of Chicago, where he became professor of physical chemistry in 1917, and Andrew MacLeish Distinguished Service Professor in 1935. His numerous contributions to physical chemistry, particularly those on isotopes and atomic structure, gained him the Willard Gibbs Medal in 1928. On retiring he became consultant to Universal Oil Products Co.

Harmaline, $C_{13}H_{14}N_2O$. An alkaloid occurring

with the closely related substances harmine and harmalol in the seeds of *Peganium harmala*. It crystallizes in prisms, m.p. 250°, with decomposition. Sparingly soluble in water, soluble in alcohol. Optically inctive. It causes muscular paralysis.

Hartley, Sir Walter Noel (1846-1913). Hartley was born at Lichfield and proceeded to Edinburgh University with the intention of studying medicine. He decided, however, to devote himself to chemistry and went to Germany to work with Kolbe. In 1879 he was appointed professor of chemistry at the Royal College of Science, Dublin. Retiring from this post in 1911 he received the honour of knighthood. His scientific research was almost entirely connected with spectroscopy. See *J. Chem. Soc.*, 1914, 1207.

Harveyizing. A process for toughening armourplate steel, chrome, nickel chrome, and other similar alloy steels. The steel is skin-carburized by heating in contact with carbon and then heated to a high temperature and quenched very rapidly by spraying with large quantities of water. For an armour-plate steel the composition is about 2% Ni, 1% Cr, and 0·3% C. Carburizing raises the carbon content near the surface to about 2·5% and after the final water-quenching the depth of the hardened surface is from 1-1·5 in.

Hastelloy. See Nickel alloys.

Hatchett, Charles (1765-1847). Hatchett, an English chemist and manufacturer, carried out numerous researches. He discovered the element niobium in the mineral columbite.

Hauy, René-Just (1743-1822). Born at St. Just, Oise, Hauy was, in 1802, appointed professor of mineralogy at the Museum of Natural History. He deduced the fundamental laws of crystallography and was the first to recognize the relationship between the emerald and beryl.

Haworth, Sir William Norman (1883-1950). Born at Chorley, Lancashire, Haworth was educated at the Universities of Manchester and Göttingen. He was appointed reader in chemistry, St. Andrews (1912), professor of organic chemistry, Armstrong College, University of Durham (1920), and professor of chemistry, Birmingham (1925-1948). Haworth established at Birmingham a school of carbohydrate chemistry of international reputation. In particular he will be remembered for his elucidation of the ring structures of the simple sugars and the formulae of many complex carbohydrates. Noteworthy also is his synthesis of ascorbic acid. He was awarded a Nobel Prize in 1937. See *J. Chem. Soc.*, 1951, 2790.

Heat exchanger. Although any plant item in which heat is interchanged between substances could be regarded as a heat exchanger, the term is normally confined to those units where all the heat is transferred from one fluid stream to a second fluid stream, resulting in one being heated and the other being cooled, without change of state in either case.

Heat exchangers account for a large part of chemical plant investment. Shell-and-tube units are by far the most common, but other types are also used. See Shell-and-tube construction.

Heat of atomization. This is defined as the amount of heat required to dissociate 1 g molecule of an element into its atoms.

Heat of combustion. The heat of combustion of a substance is defined as the amount of heat evolved when 1 g molecule of the substance is burned in oxygen at constant volume.

Heat of crystallization. The heat evolved when unit weight of solute crystallizes from an infinite quantity of saturated solution.

Heat of dissociation. This is the amount of heat required to dissociate 1 g molecule of a compound into its elements, or into certain specified smaller molecules.

Heat of formation. This is the heat evolved when 1 g molecule of a compound is formed from its elements under stated conditions of temperature and at constant volume or constant pressure. The standard heat of formation is usually stated for 1 atm. pressure and 25°.

Heat of reaction. Most chemical reactions occur with an energy change which is measured as an enthalpy change. The heat of reaction is the amount of heat (usually in kilocalories) which is absorbed or evolved when the reaction occurs at constant pressure between the amounts of the substances (usually in gram molecules) as indicated by the ordinary chemical equation. The convention now adopted is that for an exothermic reaction (heat evolved) the enthalpy change is negative. For an endothermic reaction (heat absorbed) ΔH is positive. Thus, $C_{(solid)} + \frac{1}{2}O_{(gas)} \rightarrow CO_{(gas)}$, $\Delta H = -26\cdot41$ kcal signifies that when 12·0 g of carbon react with 16 g of oxygen to give 28 g of carbon monoxide, 26·41 kcal of heat are evolved. It is essential to indicate the physical states of the reactants and products since there may be additional heat changes associated with change of state. Heats of reaction are often referred to by special names which indicate the processes occurring, e.g. heats of formation, dilution, combustion, or precipitation.

Heat transfer media. These are fluids used to convey heat from the place where it is being generated to the place where it is required. The heat may be carried as sensible heat, latent heat or both.

Steam is by far the most widely used medium, being cheap, plentiful, non-toxic, non-inflammable and non-corrosive. Since it carries heat mainly as latent heat it is not suitable for temperatures above 200°, owing to the high pressure generated. For higher temperatures up to 400° organic liquids such as the Dowtherms and mineral oils may be used. Mercury and molten salts, such as the eutectic mixture of sodium nitrite, sodium nitrate and potassium nitrate, may be used up to 600°, while above this temperature air and flue gases must be used.

Heavy hydrogen. See Deuterium.

Heavy water, Deuterium oxide D_2O. Water contains a small proportion of the oxide of deuterium and of the mixed oxide HDO. On electrolysis of dilute aqueous solutions of acids or alkalis the hydrogen is liberated preferentially, the residual water ultimately consisting of nearly pure D_2O. The separation factor, which is the ratio of $([D]/[H])_{liq.}/([D]/[H])_{gas}$, depends on the electrodes and on the solution. When heavy water is mixed with a compound of hydrogen an exchange often takes place between atoms of deuterium and hydrogen; consequently heavy water has been used to trace chemical reactions, especially those taking place in the bodies of animals.

Heavy water is used as a moderator in atomic reactors; its function is to slow down and absorb neutrons.

Hehner value. The Hehner value of a fat gives the percentage of fatty acids insoluble in water obtained on saponification of the fat.

Heilbron, Sir Ian (1886-1959). Born and educated in Glasgow, Heilbron was successively professor of organic chemistry at the Royal Technical College, Glasgow, at Liverpool and Manchester Universities, and at Imperial College, London. From 1949-1958 he was director of the Brewing Industry Research Foundation. He worked mainly on the constitution and synthesis of naturally occurring compounds. See *Nature, Lond.*, 1959, **184**, 767.

Heisenberg uncertainty principle. For any particle the uncertainty in position Δx is dependent upon the uncertainty in momentum Δp according to the relation $\Delta p \times \Delta x = h/2\pi$ (h is Planck's constant). According to this principle any particle should possess both wave and particle properties. This has been verified for the elementary particles. It is impossible to know both the position and momentum of a particle.

Helenien, $C_{72}H_{116}O_4$. A pigment occurring in *Tagates* petals. It is an isomer of physalien and consists of lutein combined with two molecules of palmitic acid. It crystallizes in deep red needles, m.p. 92°.

Helianthates. The salts or salt-like compounds of organic bases with the acid form of methyl orange.

Helicorubin. A bright red respiratory catalyst found in the gut of the snail and other molluscs. It contains haem, but differs from haemoglobin in its protein constituent. In a slightly acid medium it combines loosely with oxygen.

Helium, He. At.no. 2, At.wt. 4·003, b.p. −268·94°. First identified spectroscopically in the sun's atmosphere by Janssen but now known to exist to the extent of 0·0005% by volume in the earth's atmosphere. It has been isolated (Ramsay) from uranium minerals where it is a direct product of radioactive decay. The α-particle is the He^{2+} ion. The main source of helium is natural gas and it is extracted by liquefaction of the other gases present. It is used in balloons and dirigibles, as an inert atmosphere for handling and welding active metals and compounds, and in divers' air supplies.

Liquid helium has two forms. Helium II has many very unusual properties. Solid helium can only be obtained by use of high pressures; at ordinary pressure helium is liquid down to absolute zero. It is a monatomic gas, solubility in water at 0° approximately 0·01 ml per ml.

Helium is practically completely inert chemically; it is probably absorbed by metals on sparking but there is no evidence for compound formation. In discharge tubes excited ions of the type He_2^+, HHe^+, and HeH_2^+ are known. Helium may be readily identified and estimated spectroscopically. For further details of this element see 'Helium' by W. H. Keeson.

Helmholtz free energy. See Gibbs-Helmholtz equation.

Helmholtz, Hermann Ludwig Ferdinand (1821-1894). Born at Potsdam, Helmholtz became a surgeon in the army and later assistant at the Berlin Anatomical Museum. He was appointed professor of physiology at Königsberg (1849), at Bonn (1855), and at Heidelberg (1858). In 1871 he became professor of physics at Berlin. His researches covered a wide field including studies in fluid motion and thermodynamics.

He invented the ophthalmoscope. See Chem. Soc. Mem. Lect., 1896.

Hemicelluloses. Hexose and pentose sugars and sugar acids of the uronic type. They have no relation to cellulose. Norman has suggested the alternative name amylo-uronides. They may be divided into a glucose series consisting of glucose, xylose, and glucuronic acid and a galactose series made up of galactose, arabinose, and galacturonic acid. The equivalent uronic acid and pentose (lyxose) of mannose are not found naturally. They are extracted by dilute alkalis, hydrolysed by hot dilute acids. Their purification is a matter of difficulty; it is easier from mature woods than from younger tissues.

Hemihedral forms. Those forms in any crystal system which show the full number of faces required by the symmetry of the system are called holohedral forms. When only half the number of faces found in the holohedral form are present, the form is said to be hemihedral.

Hemimorphite, $(OH)_2Zn_4Si_2O_7 \cdot H_2O$. An important zinc ore; white to yellow, orthorhombic, sp.gr. 3·45, hardness $4\frac{1}{2}$-5. Contains Si_2O_7 units. Often called electric calamine or calamine.

Hempel burette. This is used for gas analysis and consists of a burette in which the gas is measured at constant atmospheric pressure. The burette is connected successively to pipettes containing the various absorbing reagents; these pipettes are of different types according to the nature of the containing liquid.

tivated in India, Egypt, and other tropical countries. The active colouring matter is 2-hydroxy-1,4-naphthaquinone, which is present in about 1% concentration. It is most effective as a dye in acid solution.

Henry, William (1775-1836). Born at Manchester, Henry began to study medicine at Edinburgh University, but his studies were interrupted in order to superintend a chemical business which his father had established. He returned to his studies in 1805, but on graduating did not practise long, preferring chemical research. He investigated the relation between the solubility of a gas and the pressure to which it is subjected.

Henry's law. The mass of gas which is dissolved by a given volume of liquid at a fixed temperature is proportional to the pressure of the gas. This relationship was first put forward by Henry in 1803. The law is only obeyed if no chemical reaction takes place between the gas and the solvent.

Heparin. A preparation obtained from the liver that inhibits the clotting of blood. It is the most most active of all anti-coagulants, 1 mg delaying the clotting of 50 ml of blood for 24 hours. Its chief use is in treating thrombosis, and it is used in blood transfusions, being injected into the donor's vein shortly before bleeding. It is an acetylated sulphuric ester of a complex carbohydrate containing glucosamine and glucuronic acid; the deacetylated molecule has the repeating unit:

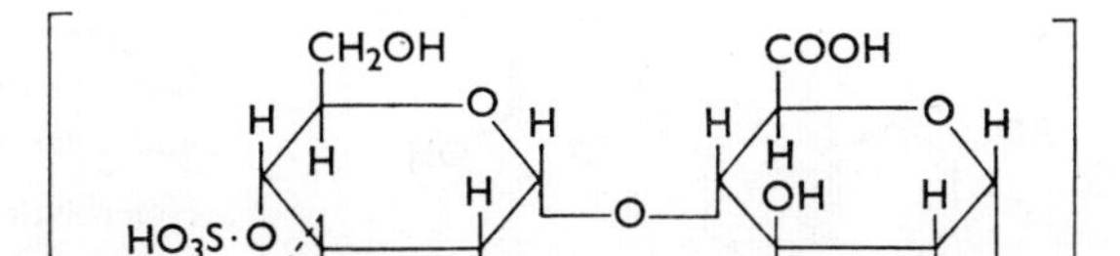

A refinement of this type is the Sodean gas analysis apparatus.

Henderson, George Gerald (1862-1942). Born at Glasgow, Henderson was educated at the Universities of Glasgow and Leipzig. He was appointed professor of chemistry at Glasgow Technical College (1892) and at the University of Glasgow (1919). From the latter chair he retired in 1937. He made numerous investigations upon organic and inorganic problems, including catalysis, and was elected F.R.S. in 1916. See *J. Chem. Soc.*, 1944, 202.

Henderson stove. See Sweating.

Henna. The dried leaves of *Lawsonia alba*, a shrub indigenous to Arabia, but now cul-

Heptachlor, $C_{10}H_5Cl_7$, 1,4,5,6,7,8,8-heptachloro - 3a,4,7,7a - tetrahydro-4,7 - methanoindene. An insecticide similar to chlordane (*q.v.*).

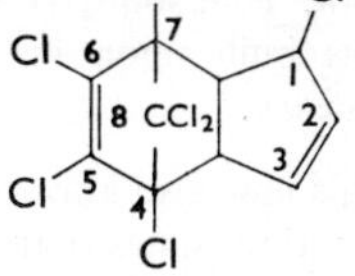

Used to control cotton ball weevil. A white solid, m.p. 95°-96°, soluble in organic solvents.

n-**Heptane,** C_7H_{16}, $CH_3[CH_2]_5CH_3$. A colourless inflammable liquid, d^{20} 0·68378, b.p. 98°. Insoluble in water; miscible with hydrocarbon solvents. Occurs, together with other isomeric hydrocarbons of the paraffin series, in petroleum. Obtained by distillation of petroleum. Eight other paraffin hydrocarbons of the formula C_7H_{16} are possible. Has the general properties of the paraffins. Used with iso-octane in defining the knock-rating of petrols.

Heptose. A carbohydrate with seven carbon atoms.

Heroin. See Diamorphine.

Héroult, Paul Louis Toussaint (1863-1914). Electrochemist and metallurgist, Héroult was born at Thury-Harcourt, Calvados. He carried out pioneer work on the construction of the electric furnace and showed how the metal aluminium could be obtained by the electrolysis of pure bauxite in molten cryolite.

Herschel, Sir John Frederick William (1792-1871). Born at Slough, Bucks, Herschel was educated at Eton and Cambridge. Originally studying for the Bar, he turned his attention towards astronomy in 1816. Although his main researches lie in that field, he was an able chemist and one of the pioneers in the study of optical activity. He was awarded the Copley Medal of the Royal Society in 1821 and knighted in 1831. In 1849 he became Master of the Mint.

Hesperidin, $C_{28}H_{34}O_{15}$. A glycoside obtained from the unripe fruits of *Citrus aurantium*. It is the 7-rhamnoglucoside of 5,7,3'-trihydroxy-4'-methoxyflavanone. It is obtained as small yellow needles, decomposing at 251°, slightly soluble in water and alcohol. See Vitamin P.

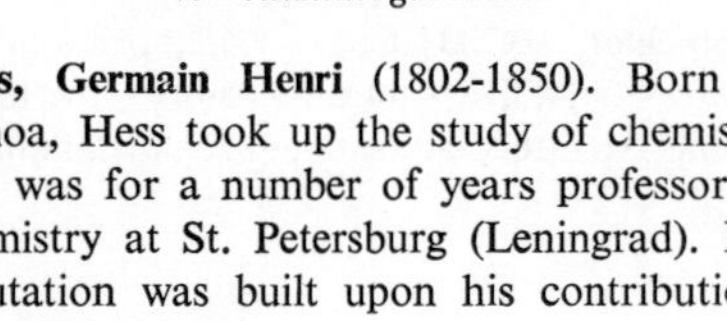

R = Rhamnoglucoside

Hess, Germain Henri (1802-1850). Born at Genoa, Hess took up the study of chemistry and was for a number of years professor of chemistry at St. Petersburg (Leningrad). His reputation was built upon his contributions to thermochemistry.

Hess's law. This law, also known as the law of constant summation, states that no matter how a chemical change is carried out the total heat change for the process is the same, being independent of any intermediate stages. Hess's law is really an application of the first law of thermodynamics to chemical reactions. For example, a molar solution of ammonium chloride may be made by:

(a) Formation of solid ammonium chloride and its subsequent dissolution in water,

$$NH_{3(gas)} + HCl_{(gas)} \rightarrow NH_4Cl_{(solid)}$$
$$\Delta H = -42 \cdot 1 \text{ kcal}$$
$$NH_4Cl_{(solid)} + aq. \rightarrow NH_4Cl_{(aq.)}$$
$$\Delta H = +3 \cdot 9 \text{ kcal}$$

The total heat change is thus $-38 \cdot 2$ kcal.

(b) Ammonium chloride solution may also be made by mixing aqueous solutions of ammonia and hydrochloric acid,

$$NH_{3(gas)} + aq. \rightarrow NH_{3\,(aq.)}$$
$$\Delta H = -8 \cdot 4 \text{ kcal}$$
$$HCl_{(gas)} + aq. \rightarrow HCl_{(aq.)}$$
$$\Delta H = -17 \cdot 3 \text{ kcal}$$
$$HCl_{(aq.)} + NH_{3(aq.)} \rightarrow NH_4Cl_{(aq.)}$$
$$\Delta H = -12 \cdot 3 \text{ kcal}$$

the total heat change being $-38 \cdot 0$ kcal.

By both routes, the enthalpy changes for the overall reaction
$$NH_{3(gas)} + HCl_{(gas)} + aq. \rightarrow NH_4Cl_{(aq.)}$$
are equal within experimental error.

Heteroauxin. See Auxins and 3-Indolylacetic acid.

Heterocyclic. Heterocyclic compounds are compounds which contain a closed ring system in which the atoms are of more than one kind, for example, pyridine, thiophen, and furan.

Heterogeneous catalysis. When the catalyst is in a different phase from the reactants, e.g. a solid catalyst in a reaction between liquids or gases, the process is called heterogeneous catalysis. The reaction may well often take place upon the surface of the catalyst.

Heterogeneous reaction. Reactions which occur between substances in different phases, e.g. between a gas and a solid, or between a liquid and a gas, are termed heterogeneous reactions.

Heterolytic reaction. This occurs when the electrons forming the bond broken are shared *unequally* between the fragments formed, or when two molecules or ions, one with a lone pair of electrons and one with a vacant orbital, react forming a covalent bond.

Heteropoly acids. A group of complex acids (e.g. phosphotungstic acids, tungstomolybdic acids, etc.) having anions which are derived from two different acid-forming oxides. The polyanions contain metal and non-metal atoms in a network held together by oxygen atoms.

HETP. See Theoretical plate.

Hevesy, George von (1885-1966). Born in Budapest, Hevesy studied at Freiburg and worked with Rutherford in Manchester, with Paneth in Vienna and with Bohr in Copenhagen. In 1943 he became professor of organic chemistry at Stockholm. He originated the use of radioactive tracer techniques and for this was awarded the Nobel Prize in chemistry in 1943. With Coster he discovered hafnium in 1922.

Hexachlorobenzene, C_6Cl_6. Forms colourless crystals, m.p. 227°, b.p. 326°. Insoluble in water, soluble in benzene. It is prepared by the drastic chlorination of benzene and some alkyl benzenes. It is also obtained when tetrachloroethylene is passed through an incandescent tube.

Hexachloroethane, C_2Cl_6. Colourless solid, m.p. 187°, sublimes on heating. Insoluble in water; soluble in organic solvents. Prepared by heating carbon tetrachloride with aluminium amalgam. Manufactured by chlorination of *s*-tetrachloroethane in the presence of aluminium chloride. With alkali about 200° it gives oxalic acid, and with antimony pentachloride above 450° it gives carbon tetrachloride. Catalytic reduction gives *s*-tetrachloroethane.

2,5-Hexadione. See Acetonylacetone.

Hexafluorobenzene, C_6F_6. The progenitor of a series of benzene derivatives having fluorine atoms in place of hydrogen. A colourless mobile liquid, b.p. 80°, m.p. 5·2°, n_D^{25} 1·3761, thermally stable at over 500°, which undergoes nucleophilic substitution to give pentafluorophenyl derivatives.

Hexagonal close-packing. One of the two

◯ layer 1
2 layer 2
3 layer 3

simplest ways of packing equal spheres to occupy the minimum volume per sphere, the other being cubic close-packing. Each sphere has twelve equidistant neighbours. Many metals crystallize in one or other of these forms of close-packing.

Hexagonal system. One of the seven crystal systems; it comprises crystals possessing an axis of six-fold or hexagonal symmetry. The crystallographic axes chosen in such crystals are the principal hexagonal axis *z*, and two axes inclined at 60° to one another in a plane perpendicular to the *z* axis. For convenience in indexing the faces of hexagonal crystals a fourth axis, inclined at 60° to the latter axes and in their plane, is also used. Structurally hexagonal crystals are referred to a unit cell having two equal sides *a* and a third side of length *c*.

Examples of hexagonal crystals are: nickel arsenide, graphite, beryl, and numerous metals. See also Crystal symmetry and Crystal structure.

Hexahydrocresols. See Methylcyclohexanol.

Hexahydrophenol. See Cyclohexanol.

Hexalin. See Cyclohexanol.

Hexametaphosphates. Salts derived from Graham's salt $(NaPO_3)_n$, which is obtained when any form of sodium metaphosphate is melted and then allowed to solidify. They are erroneously known as hexametaphosphates but in fact contain polymeric anions, *n* varying from 30 to 90. The sodium salt, which has certain colloidal properties, is known commercially by the trade name of 'Calgon' and is used for water softening, since it prevents soluble calcium salts from reacting with soap. It is made by fusing monosodium phosphate at 760° and rapidly cooling the molten material.

Hexamethylbenzene, $C_{12}H_{18}$. A colourless

crystalline solid, m.p. 164°, b.p. 264°. Insoluble in water, readily soluble in benzene. It can be prepared by the reaction of methyl chloride with benzene, toluene, or preferably pentamethylbenzene in the presence of aluminium chloride. It is oxidized by potassium permanganate to mellitic acid.

Hexamethylenetetramine, Hexamine, $C_6H_{12}N_4$.

Crystallizes in colourless rhombohedra; has a sweetish taste, becoming bitter. Sublimes at about 263° with partial decomposition. Very soluble in water, less soluble in alcohol. Manufactured by adding ammonia to solutions of formaldehyde and concentrating the liquor. Crystallizes from water with one molecule of water of crystallization. This hydrate melts at 15°. It is a weak base (monoacid) and forms salts with acids. Also forms crystalline compounds with metallic salts. It is stable to alkalis but is decomposed by sulphuric acid to formaldehyde and ammonia. It reacts with zinc and hydrochloric acid to give trimethylamine and other products. Hexamine burns with a hot blue flame. It is employed as a urinary antiseptic and is administered together with sodium hydrogen phosphate or one of the benzoates in order that the reaction of the urine may be rendered more acid.

Hexamine. See Hexamethylenetetramine.

Hexanes. There are 5 isomeric hexanes of formula C_6H_{14}, many of which are found in ligroin or petroleum ether, b.p. 60°-80°. n-Hexane, $CH_3[CH_2]_4CH_3$, a colourless liquid, b.p. 69°, which is insoluble in water, is the most important isomer, and is used principally as a solvent.

Hexanitrodiphenylamine, Hexyl,

$$C_6H_2(NO_2)_3 \cdot NH \cdot C_6H_2(NO_2)_3.$$

A yellow crystalline powder which turns brown on exposure to light, and melts with decomposition around 280°. See Aluminized high explosives.

Hexobarbitone, Hexobarbital, $C_{12}H_{16}N_2O_3$.

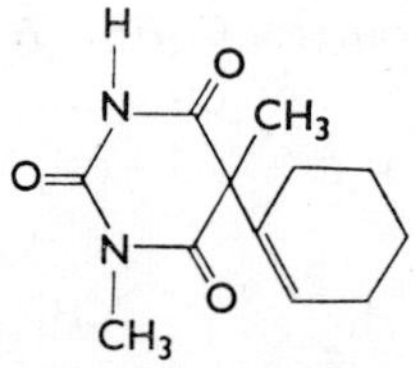

Colourless crystals almost insoluble in water, soluble in alcohol and organic solvents, m.p. 146°; prepared by condensing methylurea with methyl-α-cyano-α-cyclohex-1-enylpropionate and hydrolysing the product. It is a rapidly absorbed hypnotic. The water-soluble sodium salt—hexobarbitone soluble—is injected intravenously to produce general anaesthesia of short duration.

Hexoestrol, $C_{18}H_{22}O_2$. Colourless crystals,

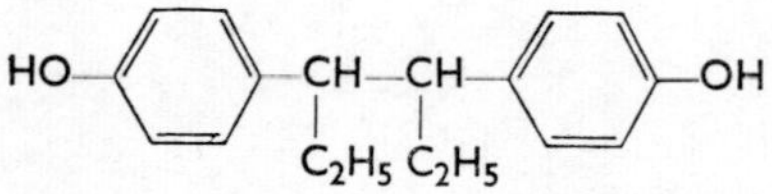

m.p. 185°-188°, almost insoluble in water, soluble in alkalis, alcohol, ether, and acetone. Prepared by catalytic dehydrogenation followed by demethylation of stilboestrol dimethyl ether, or from anethole. It resembles stilboestrol in its oestrogenic activity, but it is better tolerated, less active when taken orally, and more active when injected.

Hexone. Methyl isobutyl ketone.

Hexose. A carbohydrate with six carbon atoms. The hexoses are by far the most important of the simple sugars, and almost all the polysaccharides are built up of hexose units. Three aldohexoses, D-glucose, D-mannose, and D-galactose, are common in plants, either in the free state or as components of polysaccharide

molecules. The configurations of the less important aldohexoses are as follows:

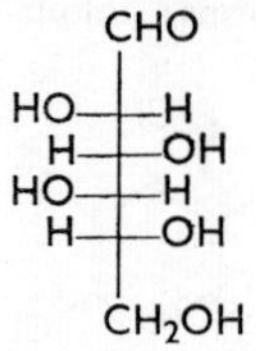

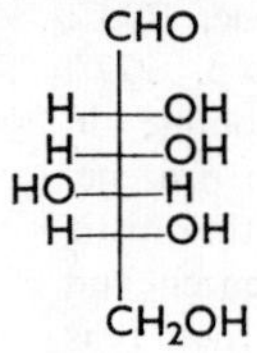

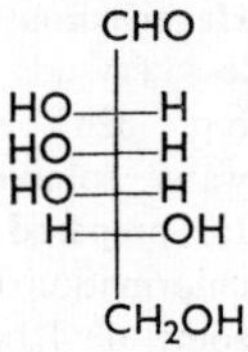

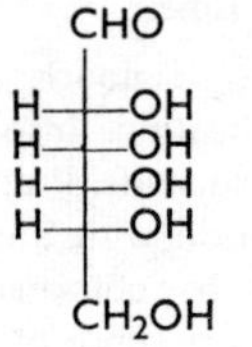

The four ketohexoses are fructose, sorbose, allulose, and tagatose (*q.v.*). See Glucose for example of isomerization between open chain and cyclic structures in a typical hexose molecule.

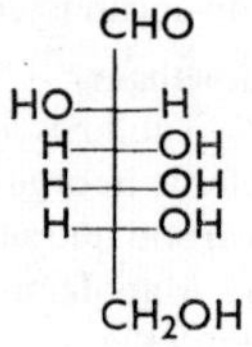

Hexyl. The group C_6H_{13}—. See also Hexanitrodiphenylamine.

Hexylresorcinol, $C_{12}H_{18}O_2$. White needles,

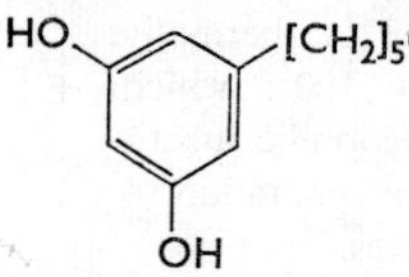

m.p. about 66°, soluble 1 part in 2000 of water, readily soluble in alcohol. It is prepared by condensing hexoic acid with resorcinol and reducing. It is a potent bactericide and is used particularly for treating infections of the urinary tract.

Heyrovsky, Jaroslav (1890-1967). Born in Prague, Heyrovsky studied there and at University College, London, becoming professor of physical chemistry in Prague in 1926 and later director of the Polarographic Research Institute in Prague. He was awarded the Nobel Prize in 1929 for his invention of polarography. See *Nature, Lond.*, 1967, **214**, 953.

Hiduminium. The name applied to a group of light aluminium alloys manufactured by High Duty, Alloys Ltd. 'Hiduminium 23,' '33' and '35' consist of aluminium containing up to 1·5% of manganese. 'Hiduminium RR' alloys contain copper 1·5-3%, nickel 0·5-2%, magnesium 0·05-2%, iron 0·4-2%, silicon 0·5-2%, and titanium 0-0·5%, the remainder being aluminium.

High speed steels. See Steel.

High-spin state. A term used in transition-metal chemistry to denote that the compound has the maximum number of unpaired electrons which is consistent with the electronic configuration and stereochemistry. E.g. iron in K_3FeF_6 has five unpaired electrons. Compare low-spin state.

High-temperature carbonization. When suitable coals are treated in specially constructed ovens or retorts, in the absence of air, and at temperatures from 800°-1300° for periods from 10-24 hours, the more volatile constituents are distilled off and thermal decomposition also occurs. The volatiles are discharged into the hydraulic gas main and a strong compact residue of coke is left in the retort. The equipment commonly in use for high temperature carbonization falls into the categories:

(a) Beehive ovens, originally solely used for the manufacture of metallurgical coke and now almost obsolete.

(b) By-product coke ovens, used for the production of coke with recovery of by-products and utilization of gas as important auxiliaries.

(c) Gasworks retorts in which the gas yield is the important factor. It is necessary, however, that the coke should be utilizable as a fuel in the heating of the retorts, the remainder being available as a domestic fuel.

In any type of oven the properties of the coke (e.g. porosity, strength, size), the amount of raw gas, and analysis of raw gas are dependent on the type of coal used, nature of oven (e.g. width), rate of coking, and flue temperatures.

Hilditch, Thomas Percy (1886-1965). Born in London, Hilditch graduated at University College, London, in 1907. In 1911 he became a research chemist with Joseph Crosfield & Sons and began the association with the chemistry of fats which occupied the rest of his life. He was professor of industrial chemistry at Liverpool from 1926 to 1951 and he and his students are largely responsible for the present knowledge of fat chemistry.

Hillebrand, William Francis (1853-1925). Hillebrand was born in Honolulu, and after early education there, in California, and at Cornell University, he studied at Heidelberg, Strasburg, and Freiberg. In 1880 he became a chemist in the U.S. Geological Survey, and in 1908 was appointed chief chemist of the Bureau of Standards. A prolific writer, Hillebrand exercised a great influence on the development of analytical chemistry, particularly in the field of mineral analysis. He was President of the American Chemical Society in 1906.

Hindered settling. Sedimentation under conditions in which the individual particles are so close together that they interfere with one another's movements and affect the net settling rate of the suspension.

Hinshelwood, Sir Cyril Norman (1897-1967). Born in London, Hinshelwood was educated at Westminster School and Balliol College, Oxford, and was Dr. Lee's professor of chemistry at Oxford from 1937 to 1964. He was president of the Chemical Society, 1946-1948, and of the Royal Society, 1955-1960. He is distinguished for his work on the kinetics of reactions, both chemical and bacteriological, and for this he shared the Nobel Prize for chemistry in 1956.

Hippuric acid, Benzoylglycine, $C_9H_9NO_3$.

Crystallizes in prisms, m.p. 187°, soluble in water and alcohol. It is excreted in small quantities in the urine of mammals as a means of elimination of the toxic benzoic acid which is conjugated with glycine in the kidney.

Hippuricase, Histozyme. The enzyme which converts hippuric acid into benzoic acid and glycine. It is the same as aminoacylase I, the enzyme which acts on N-acylamino acids. It is present in the kidney, liver, pancreas, and other organs and also in *Aspergillus oryzae*.

Hirst, Sir Edmund Langley (1898-1967). Educated at Northgate School, Ipswich, and the University, St. Andrews. Hirst was appointed lecturer in chemistry, Durham (1924), Birmingham (1927), reader in chemistry, Birmingham (1935), professor of organic chemistry, Bristol (1936), Sir William Hall professor of chemistry, Manchester (1944), and Forbes professor of organic chemistry, Edinburgh (1947). His main researches have been upon the carbohydrates and vitamin C. He was elected F.R.S. in 1934.

Hirudin. A substance obtained from the salivary gland of the leech. It is a protein of molecular weight approx. 16,000, which prevents the clotting of blood by acting as a specific inhibitor for thrombin (*q.v.*).

Histamine, 4-Aminoethylglyoxaline, $C_5H_9N_3$.

A base, formed by the bacterial degradation of histidine, and present in ergot and in many animal tissues, where it is liberated in response to injury. If injected it causes a condition of shock with dilatation of the capillaries and a rapid fall in blood pressure. It also causes copious secretion of the gastric juice. It is normally prepared from protein degradation products.

Histidine, α-Amino-β-imidazolpropionic acid,

$$HO_2C \cdot CH \cdot CH_2 \underset{NH_2}{\overset{}{|}}$$

[structure of histidine with imidazole ring]

$C_6H_9N_3O_2$. Crystallizes in colourless plates, m.p. 277°, soluble in 24 parts of water, sparingly soluble in alcohol. The naturally occurring substance is laevorotatory, $[\alpha]_D^{25}$ −38·95°. Histidine is one of the basic amino-acids occurring in the hydrolysis products of proteins, and particularly of the basic proteins, the protamines and histones. It is an essential constituent of the food of animals.

Histones. A class of proteins similar to the protamines, but containing a lower percentage of nitrogen and the basic amino-acids. They are less basic than the protamines, but more so than most proteins. They are usually found in combination with nucleic acid, and are present in the thymus gland of animals, in red blood corpuscles, and in spermatozoa. They are not found in plants.

Histozyme. See Hippuricase.

Hoesch synthesis. A variation of the Gattermann synthesis of hydroxy-aldehydes, this reaction has been widely applied to the synthesis of anthocyanidins. It consists of the condensation of polyhydric phenols with nitriles by the action of hydrochloric acid (with or without zinc chloride as a catalyst). This gives an imine-hydrochloride which on hydrolysis with water gives the hydroxy-ketone.

Hofmann, August Wilhelm von (1818-1892). Born at Giessen, Hofmann entered the university of his native town as a law student in 1836. Under the influence of Liebig, however, he became attracted to the study of chemistry and in 1845 accepted the chair of chemistry at the newly founded College of Chemistry in London. 'A singularly interesting and lucid teacher,' he returned, in 1865, to Germany as professor of chemistry in the University of Berlin and was ennobled in 1888. His extraordinary ability as an investigator did much to hasten the development of organic chemistry and particularly the dye industry. See Mem. Lect., *J. Chem. Soc.*, 1896, 575.

Hofmann conversion of amides. Aliphatic and aromatic amides react with solutions of chlorine or bromine in excess sodium hydroxide to give primary amines containing one carbon atom less than the original amide. The halogen first replaces one of the hydrogen atoms of the amido group to give a chloro- or bromo-amide which reacts with alkali to give an isocyanate; this decomposes to give an amine and carbon dioxide. The reaction is used in the preparation of anthranilic acid.

Hofmann's method (for determining vapour densities). The volume of a given mass of vapour is determined by weighing out the liquid which is to be vaporized in a small stoppered bottle, and introducing it into the vacuum at the top of a barometer tube surrounded by a heating jacket. The liquid vaporizes, and its volume is measured by the depression in the level of the mercury in the barometer tube.

Hofmeister series. See Lyotropic series.

Holdcroft's thermoscopes. Refractory rectangular bars of similar composition to Seger cones and Orton cones and used for the same purpose, i.e. for measuring the effect of heat upon refractories or ceramics when fired in kilns or ovens. In contrast to the use of cones, Holdcroft's thermoscopes are supported horizontally at both ends and the critical point is indicated by the bar sagging in the centre. The temperature range is 600° to 1250°. See Contraction rings.

Holmium. At.no. 67, At.wt. 164·94, d 8·803, m.p. 1461°, b.p. 2600°. Holmium metal has the hexagonal close-packed structure, $a=3·5761$, $c=5·6174$ Å. It is a typical rare-earth element (q.v.).

Holmium compounds. Holmium forms a single series of brownish-yellow salts, the metal having an oxidation state of three. These salts are typical rare-earth compounds (q.v.).

Holohedral forms. See Hemihedral forms.

Homatropine, mandelyltropeine, $C_{16}H_{21}NO_3$. Colourless prisms, m.p. 99°-100°, insoluble in water, soluble in organic solvents. Prepared from tropine and mandelic acid. It is used medicinally as its hydrobromide (m.p. 214°, soluble in 6 parts of water and 60 parts of alcohol) for dilating the pupil of the eye.

[structure of homatropine]

Homo-. Used as a prefix in organic chemistry it indicates a difference of —CH_2— in an other-

[structures of Phthalic acid and Homophthalic acid]

Phthalic acid   Homophthalic acid

wise similar structure. It is applicable to aliphatic, alicyclic and aromatic compounds.

Homocyclic. Homocyclic compounds are compounds which contain a closed ring system in which all the atoms are the same. As the atoms are nearly always carbon atoms, the term carbocyclic is often used. These compounds can be subdivided into aromatic or benzenoid compounds and alicyclic compounds, such as cyclohexane.

Homogeneous catalysis. When the catalyst is in the same phase as the reactants, e.g. a liquid catalyst used to facilitate a reaction between liquids, the process is called homogeneous catalysis.

Homogeneous reaction. Reactions which occur between substances in the same phase, e.g. between gases or between liquids, are termed homogeneous reactions. It should be noted that each solid present in a reactant mixture is regarded as a separate phase, so that a reaction between two solids is not normally a homogeneous reaction.

Homogenizer. A colloid mill of the valve and orifice type.

Homogentisic acid, quinolacetic acid, $C_8H_8O_4$.

Crystallizes in prisms with one molecule of water, m.p. 152°-154°, soluble in water and alcohol. It is excreted in the urine in the rare hereditary disease alkaptonuria. It is very easily oxidized in the air with the formation of dark-coloured products, so that urine in which it is present turns black on standing. It is formed from the amino-acid tyrosine, and is probably an intermediate product in the breakdown of tyrosine in the body.

Homolytic reaction. This occurs when the electrons forming the bond broken are shared equally between the fragments formed, or when species containing odd numbers of electrons (e.g. free radicals) react with each other forming a covalent bond.

Homonuclear molecule. A molecule consisting of identical atoms or groups of atoms is said to be homonuclear, e.g. O_2, N_2, Cl_2, in contrast with a heteronuclear molecule which contains different atoms, e.g. HCl, NO, CO.

Homopolar bond. Another name for a covalent bond.

Homopolar crystal. A crystal in which all the bonds between the atoms are essentially homo-

polar in character. Two important classes of homopolar crystals are the diamond and zinc blende types.

Hooke, Robert (1635-1703). Born at Freshwater, Isle of Wight, Hooke was educated at Westminster School and Oxford, where he assisted Willis and Boyle. In 1662 he became Curator of Experiments to the Royal Society, of which he was elected a Fellow in the following year, and in 1664 was appointed professor of geometry at Gresham College. He also delivered the Cutlerian Lectures. He invented the wheel barometer and made investigations on sound and optics, but from a chemical viewpoint his theories on the nature of combustion form his most interesting work.

Hopcalite. A mixed catalyst which consists, in its simplest form, of a mixture of manganese dioxide and copper oxide. By means of this catalyst it is possible to carry out the selective combustion of carbon monoxide to carbon dioxide in mixtures of carbon monoxide with hydrogen.

Hopkins, Sir Frederick Gowland (1861-1947). Born at Eastbourne and educated in private schools, Hopkins received his first technical training in the laboratory of a consulting chemist. In 1894 he graduated in medicine at the University of London, and in 1899 proceeded to Cambridge for physiological research. In 1914 he was appointed professor of biochemistry there and in 1921 became Sir William Dunn Professor. His brilliant researches included investigations upon uric acid, amino-acids, glutathione and vitamins. He was elected F.R.S. (1905), knighted (1925), awarded the Nobel Prize for Medicine (1929), and created O.M. (1935). See *Biochem. J.*, 1948, **42**, 161.

Hordein. A protein, belonging to the prolamine class, found in the seeds of barley.

Hordenine, *p*-**Hydroxyphenylethyldimethyl-amine,** $C_{10}H_{15}NO$. Crystallizes in colourless

prisms, m.p. 117°, soluble in hot water and alcohol. It is obtained from barley germs, and is slightly toxic with a feeble pressor action.

Hormones. Hormones are compounds secreted directly into the blood stream by certain organs of the body. They are then carried to other organs where they exert a definite physiological action. Thus thyroxine, secreted by the thyroid gland, stimulates the metabolism of the body as a whole, and the hormone of the parathyroids has a regulating effect on the calcium content of the blood. Most of the known hormones are secreted by the endocrine organs, the so-called ductless glands, which appear to have no other function than the manufacture of hormones, but insulin, which is secreted by certain tissues of the pancreas, and the sex hormones, secreted by the testis and ovary, do not fall into this category. For a substance to be classed as a hormone it is essential that the injection of an extract of the organ producing it should restore to the normal condition an animal with the particular organ removed. The hormones fall into no particular chemical group; they vary from the polypeptide insulin to the relatively simple substance adrenaline. Substances resembling the animal hormones are also produced by plants, for example the auxins.

Hornblende. An aluminosilicate of complex composition, $(OH)_2(Ca,Na,K)_2$ $(Mg, Fe, Al)_6$ $(Al_2Si_6)O_{22}$. The crystals are monoclinic with an amphibole type structure and are green or black. Sp.gr. 3·0-3·5, hardness 5-6, refractive index max. 1·68, min. 1·64; m.p. 1180°-1220°. The mineral is moderately magnetic. It is a common constituent of many igneous rocks.

Hot working. Deformation of metals and alloys carried out above the recrystallization temperature. Hardening due to the deformation is counteracted by softening due to recrystallization, so that no increase in hardness results and large reductions in section can be made by processes such as hot rolling or extrusion.

Howard crystallizer. This consists of an inverted cone through which solution flows in an upward direction; it is surrounded by a water jacket. The crystals are kept in suspension until they reach such a size that their rate of fall due to gravity is greater than the upward velocity of the liquid; they then fall to the bottom and are removed at the base of the cone. The advantage of this type of plant is that crystals of any required size may be produced by using a suitable rate of feed to the crystallizer.

HPAN. See Krilium.

Hudson, Claude Silbert (1881-1952). Born at Atlanta, U.S.A., Hudson was educated at Princeton University. After junior teaching appointments, he worked at the Bureau of Chemistry in Washington and at the National Bureau of Standards, later becoming professor of chemistry in the U.S. Public Health Service. A brilliant experimentalist, his work was almost entirely concerned with the chemistry of the carbohydrates, to which he made many notable contributions. See *Nature, Lond.*, 1953, **171**, 371.

Hudson's isorotation rule. For a pair of sugars having the α- and β-constitutions, the molecular rotations may be represented as $(A+B)$ and $(-A+B)$ where A represents the contribution of the 1-carbon atom and B that of the rest of the molecule. The sum of these values, 2B, is characteristic of the sugar structure, and the difference, 2A, is characteristic of the end grouping. Though not strictly accurate this rule is useful on an empirical basis.

Hudson's lactone rule. The sign of a molecular rotation in gamma lactones derived from aldose acids may be predicted by observing the configuration of the gamma (4) carbon atom. Using the planar projection formula, if the hydroxyl in position four is to the right, the lactone is dextrorotatory; if to the left it is laevorotatory. This rule gives reasonably good agreement between theory and observation.

dextrorotatory

Hughes, Edward David (1906-1963). Born in Criccieth, Hughes took a Ph.D in the University of Wales in 1930. He worked for the rest of his life, with the exception of five years as professor of chemistry at Bangor (1943-1948), at University College, London, where he became professor in 1948. His work, much of it in close collaboration with C. K. Ingold, was on the determination of the mechanism of organic reactions.

Humectant. A substance used to preserve the moisture content of materials, e.g. glycerol in confectionery, tobacco, etc.

Hume-Rothery's rule. Alloys of copper and zinc, silver and zinc, silver and cadmium, copper and aluminium, gold and aluminium, manganese and zinc, and many other pairs of metals occur in phases, each phase having a characteristic structure but an indefinite composition between certain limits. Hume-Rothery stated in 1926 that a particular phase is not determined by the chemical properties of the elements concerned or by their oxidation states, but by the relative number of valency electrons and atoms in the structure. The β, γ, and ε phases are characterized by electron:atom ratios of 3:2, 21:13, and 7:4 respectively.

Humic acids. A group of aromatic acids of high molecular weight and unknown structure that are present in soil, and can also be obtained from peat and brown coal. They may be derived from lignins. They are soluble in alkalis and precipitated by acids.

Humidification. The evaporation of a liquid into a gas is known as humidification and the gas is said to become humidified. The terms nearly always, but not invariably, refer to the air-water system.

Humidity. The humidity of moist air may be expressed several ways:

The *absolute humidity* is the mass of water vapour per unit mass of dry air.

The *percentage humidity* is the ratio of the amount of water vapour present per unit mass of dry air to the amount the air could hold if saturated at the same temperature, expressed as a percentage.

The *relative humidity* is the ratio of the partial pressure of the water vapour in the air to the partial pressure of water vapour in the air when saturated at the same temperature. This ratio is usually expressed as a percentage.

The humidities for systems other than air and water are defined in an analogous manner.

Humidity, determination of. The measurement of humidity may be carried out in a number of ways of which the commonest are by determination of the dew-point, by use of a wet-bulb thermometer, or by means of a hair hygrometer. More accurate measurements may be made by determining the thermal conductivity of the air/water-vapour mixture and comparing the result with previous calibrations.

Humin. Humin is the name given to the insoluble dark coloured nitrogenous substance that is formed during the hydrolysis of proteins by acids. Its composition is unknown, but it apparently is formed chiefly from the amino-acid tryptophan.

Humulene, $C_{15}H_{24}$. A sesquiterpene found in oil of hops, b.p. 264°.

Humus. The characteristic organic constituent of the soil. It is a dark coloured amorphous material and is formed by the microbiological decomposition of plant materials, chiefly lignin and proteins. It has a carbon/nitrogen ratio of about 10:1, and occurs in the soil in company with clay, forming the colloidal clay-humus complex.

Hund's rules. These are rules which govern the allocation of electrons to sets of degenerate orbitals. The first rule states that the ground state will have the maximum spin multiplicity, that is, that there will be as many unpaired electrons as is possible in the degenerate orbitals. The second rule states that the ground state will be the one with the maximum orbital angular momentum L.

Hyacinth. See Zircon.

Hyaluronic acid. A polysaccharide of high molecular weight, first isolated from vitreous humour and later from synovial fluid and from a wide range of mesodermal tissues. It is built up of equimolecular amounts of N-acetyl-glucosamine and glucuronic acid.

Hyaluronidase is a mucolytic enzyme obtained from an aqueous extract of mammalian testis by fractional precipitation, dialysis, and freeze-drying. It is a white powder, soluble in water, insoluble in alcohol. It acts by breaking down the cementing substance of the tissue spaces, thus increasing the permeability of the tissues. It is used medicinally to increase the speed of absorption of fluids, and to decrease swelling and pain in intramuscular and subcutaneous injections.

Hybinette process. See Nickel.

Hybridization. The process by which electronic orbitals of differing types but similar energies become combined together to form equivalent orbitals—the number of orbitals being the same before and after hybridization. The commonest types of hybrid orbitals are:

1 s and 1 p give 2 sp orbitals—linear

2 s and 1 p give 3 sp^2 orbitals—trigonal planar

1 s and 3 p give 4 sp^3 orbitals—tetrahedral

1 d, 1 s and 2 p give 4 dsp^2 orbitals—planar

2 d, 1 s, and 3 p give 6 d^2sp^3 orbitals—octahedral

See Electronic configuration.

Hydantoin, $C_3H_4N_2O_2$. Crystallizes in colourless needles, m.p. 220°. Soluble in alcohol, sparingly soluble in water. It can be prepared by the condensation of glycine with potassium cyanate and boiling the hydantoic acid so formed with hydrochloric acid. It is present in beet molasses. Many substituted hydantoins have been prepared.

Hydnocarpic acid, $C_{16}H_{28}O_2$. A fatty acid

$$CH_2-CH_2 \diagdown CH \cdot [CH_2]_{10} \cdot COOH$$
$$CH=CH \diagup$$

occurring as glycerides in chaulmoogra oil and other vegetable oils. It crystallizes in plates, m.p. 59°-60°, soluble in chloroform, sparingly soluble in other organic solvents.

Hydracrylic acid, β-Lactic acid, 2-Hydroxy-propionic acid, $C_3H_6O_3$, $CH_2OH \cdot CH_2COOH$. An uncrystallizable syrup. Soluble in water, alcohol, and ether. Manufactured by treating ethylene cyanohydrin with sodium hydroxide and decomposing the sodium hydracrylate with sulphuric acid. Converted to acrylic acid on heating. Used in the manufacture of acrylic esters.

Hydrargillite. Another name for gibbsite (*q.v.*).

Hydrastine, $C_{21}H_{21}NO_6$. Colourless prisms,

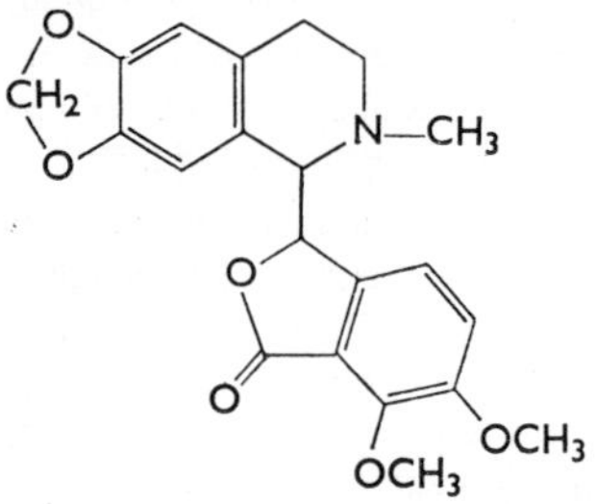

m.p. 132°, insoluble in water, sparingly soluble in alcohol, soluble in ether, chloroform and benzene; $[\alpha]_D^{20}$ $-49 \cdot 8°$ in alcohol. An alkaloid obtained from *Hydrastis canadensis*. It is used medicinally as its hydrochloride which is soluble in water and alcohol. It acts on the central nervous system, causing a slowing of the heart and a rise in blood pressure. It is used to contract the uterus and arrest haemorrhage.

Hydrastinine, $C_{11}H_{13}NO_3$. Colourless needles,

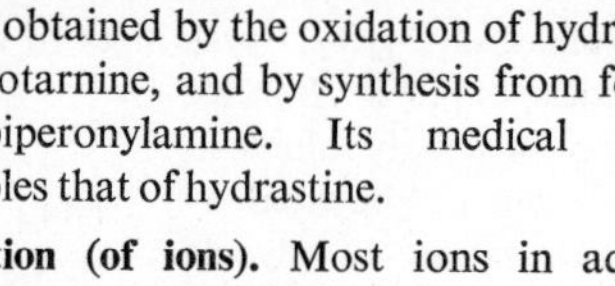

m.p. 116°-117°, soluble in water and alcohol to give a yellow fluorescent solution, and in non-polar solvents to give a colourless solution. It can be obtained by the oxidation of hydrastine, from cotarnine, and by synthesis from formyl-homopiperonylamine. Its medical action resembles that of hydrastine.

Hydration (of ions). Most ions in aqueous solution are associated with one or more molecules of water. The ions are said to be hydrated or solvated. Thus the hydrogen ion is attached to at least one molecule of water and is written H_3O^+— the hydroxonium ion. A recent view of the proton in water is, however, that it exists as the ion $H_9O_4^+$ where the hydroxonium

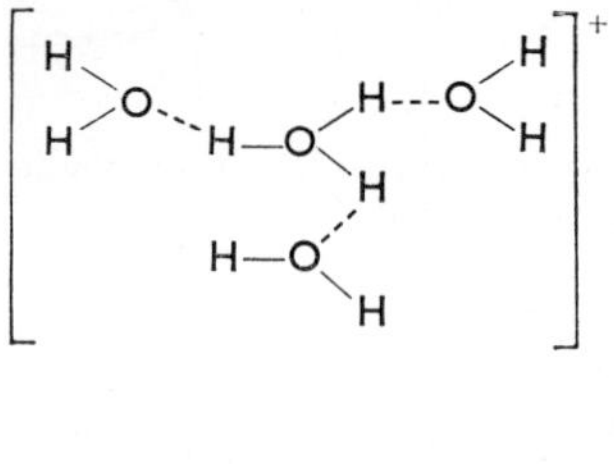

ion is hydrogen bonded to three other water molecules to give the stable entity shown.

Hydration is explained by the attachment of molecules of water to the ion either by electro-static or covalent bonding or both.

Hydraulic cement. A cement, such as Portland cement, which sets or hardens when in contact with or when immersed in water, as distinct from cements which harden on exposure to air or on cooling. Hydraulic cements consist chiefly of tricalcium silicate or tricalcium aluminate, but usually contain a considerable proportion of other (inert) ingredients.

Hydraulic conveying. This is a method of conveying particulate solids by pumping them as a slurry through a pipeline. It is normally used for conveying within a works solids already existing as a slurry, but in some cases it may be economic to transport solids over much longer distances by this means. The method has been used for a variety of materials, among them coal, china clay and wood pulp.

Hydrazine, N_2H_4. A colourless liquid or crystalline solid, m.p. $1 \cdot 8$°, b.p. $113 \cdot 5$°; miscible in all proportions with water, with which it forms a maximum b.p., azeotrope containing $71 \cdot 5\%$ by wt. hydrazine, b.p. $120 \cdot 1$°. Manufactured by the oxidation of ammonia by sodium hypo-chlorite in the presence of glue (Raschig's method); the glue deactivates metallic impurities which would catalyse the undesirable formation of ammonium chloride. A variation of this method utilizes the reaction of aqueous ammo-nia with hypochlorite to produce chloramine, which is further reacted with anhydrous ammonia to give hydrazine. In either case the solution obtained is concentrated by distillation to yield the hydrazine-water azeotrope. This may be sold as such or concentrated by extrac-tive distillation to yield anhydrous hydrazine.

Hydrazine is a weak base, giving salts (e.g. N_2H_4. HCl) with strong acids. It is a very powerful reducing agent, reducing gold, platinum and silver salts in solution to the metals. Anhydrous hydrazine inflames in oxygen and reacts violently with oxidizing agents.

Hydrazine is largely used as a rocket fuel. Smaller quantities are used for removing oxygen from boiler feed-water and in oil-well drilling muds, and for the manufacture of the tobacco herbicide maleic hydrazide.

Hydrazobenzene, $C_{12}H_{12}N_2$. Forms colourless

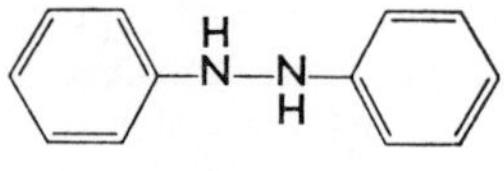

plates, m.p. 131°, insoluble in water, easily soluble in alcohol and ether. In moist air or in alcoholic solution it oxidizes spontaneously to azobenzene. It does not form salts with acids but is converted by them into benzidine by an intramolecular change. It gives two molecules of aniline when treated with a strong reducing agent.

It is prepared by reduction of nitrobenzene with iron and caustic soda. It is also prepared by an electrolytic reduction of nitrobenzene. It is widely used for the preparation of benzidine.

Hydrazoic acid (Azoimide), NH_3. A colourless liquid with a nauseating odour, b.p. 37°, m.p. −80°. Highly poisonous, and explosive in presence of oxygen or oxidizing agents. Generally met with as an aqueous solution, prepared by distilling sodium azide, NaN_3, with dilute acid; sodium azide is conveniently made by passing nitrous oxide over heated sodamide, $NaNH_2$. The salts of hydrazoic acid (azides), particularly lead azide, $Pb(N_3)_2$, are used, on account of their sensitivity to explosion by mechanical shock, in detonators.

Hydrides. There are several distinct types of hydrides.

(a) Salt-like. These are the hydrides of the most electropositive elements (e.g. Na) and contain H^- ions.

(b) Covalent. Formed by most of the non-metals and many transition metals. This class includes such diverse compounds as methane, CH_4, and iron carbonyl hydride, $H_2Fe(CO)_4$. In many compounds of boron the hydrogen atoms act as bridges.

(c) Complexes. These derivatives contain complex anions which may be considered as derived from co-ordination of an H^- ion to a metal or non-metal. Examples are the BH_4^- and ReH_9^{2-} ions.

(d) Transition metal hydrides. These are formed by hydrogen uptake by the metal. The structures of these derivatives are not completely understood. The phases are often non-stoicheiometric.

Hydriodic acid. A solution of hydrogen iodide in water. Such a solution has acidic properties similar to those of hydrochloric and hydrobromic acids, but has, in addition, strong reducing properties. See Hydrogen iodide.

Hydroboration. The addition of B—H bonds across the double bonds of olefins. Thus diborane, B_2H_6, reacts with ethylene to give $B(C_2H_5)_3$. Breakdown of the alkyl borane with acid gives alkanes and with hydrogen peroxide gives alcohols (the orientation is the opposite to that which would result from the direct addition of water across the double bond).

Hydrobromic Acid. An aqueous solution of hydrogen bromide.

Hydrocarbons. This term includes all compounds of carbon and hydrogen only. They are subdivided into aliphatic and cyclic hydrocarbons according to the arrangement of the carbon atoms in the molecule. The aliphatic hydrocarbons are again subdivided into paraffins, olefins, diolefins, etc., according to the number of double bonds in the molecule. The cyclic hydrocarbons are subdivided into aromatic hydrocarbons and cycloparaffins.

Hydrocarbonyls. The metal carbonyl hydrides. The hydrogen generally has acidic properties and the aqueous solutions behave as acids.

Hydrochloric acid. Hydrogen chloride is very soluble in water, a saturated solution containing about 43% of hydrogen chloride. Hydrochloric acid solutions yield on distillation an acid of maximum boiling-point, the composition depending on the pressure. At 50 mm the acid contains 23·2% HCl, at 760 mm 20·24%. The maximum boiling-point acid is a solution and does not correspond to any compound of water and HCl. The relationship between distillation pressure, temperature, and composition of distillate is accurately known, and distillation is used to make up standard HCl solutions. Concentrated hydrochloric acid ($d=1·20$) contains 39% HCl.

Hydrochloric acid is a strong acid. It dissolves many metals with the evolution of hydrogen and formation of chlorides. Chlorides are, mostly, stable salts, those of the weakest bases being readily hydrolysed. Those of silver, mercury (-ous), lead, and thallium are insoluble in water. Hydrochloric acid is manufactured by absorbing hydrogen chloride in water. It is used in the manufacture of other chemicals, in the food industry (e.g. production of glucose and monosodium glutamate), in the metals industry and for oil-well acidizing. It is probably the most corrosive of all acids and must be handled in glass, plastic, or rubber-lined equipment. Among industrial metals only tantalum and certain nickel-molybdenum alloys will resist it.

Hydrochloride. The name given to the salt-like compounds formed by organic bases with hydrochloric acid. In these compounds the basic atom (usually nitrogen) forms a co-ordinate link to the proton leaving a free chloride ion. The hydrochlorides are usually crystalline solids and are often convenient means of isolating bases. Hydrochlorides are also formed by the addition of hydrogen chloride to ionic chlorides, and then contain the HCl_2^- ion.

Hydrocortisone,   17-hydroxycorticosterone, $C_{21}H_{30}O_5$. White crystals, m.p. 217°-220°, relatively insoluble in most solvents. Originally isolated from adrenal glands, hydrocortisone and other related anti-inflammatory steroids are now made from naturally occurring steroids, such as diosgenin or hecogenin, by a number of

chemical steps, the 11-hydroxy group being introduced where necessary by microbiological means. It is also used as its 21-esters for local treatment of inflammatory and allergic conditions.

Hydrocyanic acid. See Hydrogen cyanide.

Hydrofluoric acid. See Hydrogen fluoride.

Hydrofluorosilicic acid, H_2SiF_6. See Fluorosilicates.

Hydroformylation. A particular type of carbonylation reaction. Under the influence of a cobalt catalyst $(HCo(CO)_4)$, an alkene will react with carbon monoxide and hydrogen to produce an aldehyde or a primary alcohol, depending upon conditions. See Oxo reaction.

Hydrogen, H. At.no. 1, At.wt. $1\cdot0080$. A gaseous element (b.p. $-252\cdot8°$), which occurs free in certain natural gases and, in the combined state, is one of the most widespread constituents of the mineral and vegetable kingdom. The element is prepared by the electrolysis of its oxide, H_2O, rendered conducting by dissolving in it a suitable acid, base, or salt. It is evolved at the cathode. Industrially, hydrogen is made by a variety of processes, the most important of which is the steam reforming of hydrocarbons. In this process a hydrocarbon is reacted with steam at a high temperature and pressure (800°-1000°, 30 atm.) over a nickel catalyst to yield a mixture of carbon monoxide and hydrogen. More steam is added and the mixture passed over an iron oxide catalyst at about 420°, when the carbon monoxide partially reduces the steam to hydrogen (the water-gas shift reaction). The carbon dioxide formed is removed by scrubbing with, for example, monoethanolamine solution, and the water-gas shift reaction and scrubbing process carried out twice more. High purity hydrogen results. Hydrogen is also manufactured by the partial oxidation of hydrocarbons and during the catalytic reforming of petroleum fractions.

Hydrogen explodes when mixed with oxygen and sparked or heated; the flammability limits being 4 to 94% hydrogen with oxygen and 4 to 74% with air. It combines with metals of the

alkali and alkaline-earth groups and forms solid salt-like hydrides (e.g. NaH, CaH_2). With numerous non-metals it forms covalent hydrides (e.g. CH_4, NH_3, H_2S, HCl). It also forms interstitial hydrides with transition elements.

With transition metals hydrogen forms covalent hydrides, e.g. $(Ph_3P)_2PtHCl$ or $H_2Fe(CO)_4$; it also forms solid hydrides which are apparently interstitial compounds. In most of its compounds the hydrogen behaves as the electropositive group of the molecule, but complex hydrides and the salt-like hydrides may be considered to be derived from H^- ions.

A combination of high pressure with moderately high temperature will cause hydrogen to attack plain carbon steels. Plants in which hydrogen is encountered under these conditions, e.g. ammonia synthesis plants, have therefore to be constructed of special alloy steels.

Hydrogen is a material of great industrial importance. About two thirds of the total production is utilized for ammonia synthesis, ammonia plants being situated near oil refineries because of this. Much hydrogen is also used in methanol synthesis.

Hydrogenation. A particular form of reduction in which hydrogen is added to a substance by the direct use of gaseous hydrogen. The process is carried out with the aid of a catalyst and proceeds more rapidly at high pressures. The process is of great technical importance. It is used in the manufacture of petrol from coal, of margarine, of detergents, of methyl alcohol, and of many other chemical products.

Hydrogenation of coal. This denotes the process by means of which the hydrogen/carbon ratio of a material such as coal, tar, oil, or spirit is increased and the boiling range of the oil altered. The process consists of treatment at elevated temperatures in the presence of hydrogen under high pressure, usually in the presence of a catalyst.

The atomic ratio of disposable hydrogen/carbon in a typical bituminous coal is about $0\cdot59$, whilst that for a typical motor spirit is about $1\cdot9$. In the hydrogenation of coal the process is carried out in two stages: the hydrogenation of the coal and the hydrogenation of the resulting oils.

The raw coal is cleaned, crushed, and mixed with the catalyst (compounds of tin) and the pasting oil; this oil is obtained partly from products of the first stage, the rest being made up with low-temperature carbonization tar. The paste is then passed through heat exchangers and preheaters, mixed with hydrogen and injected at 250 atmospheres pressure and at 400° to 450° into the converters. After treatment the gases are removed and part of the filtered oil is used for pasting and the rest treated for the recovery of the light oils. The light fraction is further hydrogenated in Stage II, the vapour phase, in which case the procedure is similar to that of the treatment of liquid materials such as tar and oils. Often, however, these latter are given an initial hydrogenation in the liquid phase. The catalyst here may be molybdenum sulphide supported on silica gel, or pelleted molybdenum sulphide, or tungsten sulphide. Temperatures of 450° to 480° are used and combined hydrogenation and controlled degradation take place in this phase. The outgoing products are reduced in pressure to release dissolved gases. The oil product is then distilled and the residue (b.p. > 200°) returned to the converters as recycle oil.

Amongst the liquid materials available for hydrogenation are: high temperature carbonization tar (H/C about 0·7), pitch (H/C about 0·5), low temperature carbonization tar (H/C about 1·1).

Hydrogen bond. When hydrogen is attached to an electronegative element, e.g. O,F, the resultant bond is polarized. If this bond is directed towards another atom, M, with a lone-pair of electrons, a weak bond is formed, known as a hydrogen bond, which may be represented O—H---M. Such bonds cause the association of water and alcohols, and form the basis of ions such as the bifluoride ion, HF_2^-. Hydrogen bonds are formed particularly between hydroxyl and amino groups and oxygen, nitrogen, and halogen atoms; they may be intermolecular or intramolecular. They are important in determining the arrangement of polypeptide and carbohydrate chains in proteins and cellulose, and also in adhesion.

Hydrogen bromide, HBr. A colourless gas, m.p. −88·5°, b.p. −6·7°, which may be obtained directly from the elements using heated charcoal or platinum as catalyst. It is more easily prepared from bromine, red phosphorus, and water, the reaction giving phosphorous and hydrobromic acids, of which only the latter is volatile.

The gas is very soluble in water, 1 vol. dissolving 600 vols. HBr at 0°. The solution is the strong acid, hydrobromic acid, which on distillation forms an acid of maximum boiling point, as does hydrochloric acid. At 760 mm the b.p. is 126° and the solution contains 47·86% HBr. A convenient method of producing hydrobromic acid is to pass sulphur dioxide or hydrogen sulphide through bromine covered by a layer of water.

Hydrogen bromide is used as a brominating and a reducing agent.

Hydrogen chloride, HCl. M.p. −112°, b.p. −85°.

Most hydrogen chloride is produced as a by-product in the chlorination of hydrocarbons and other organic compounds, but it is also manufactured by burning hydrogen and chlorine together and by the action of sulphuric acid on common salt; the last process is economic because of the sodium sulphate produced. The gas is usually absorbed in water to produce hydrochloric acid, which may be sold as such or distilled to produce the anhydrous gas. Hydrogen chloride is a colourless gas with a very irritating acid smell. The vapour density corresponds to the formula HCl. Thermal dissociation is small even at high temperatures (0·4% at 1700°).

The perfectly dry gas is without action on metals such as zinc and iron, although sodium burns in the gas with the formation of sodium chloride and hydrogen. The gas is very soluble in water (see Hydrochloric acid), and two hydrates, $HCl, 2H_2O$ and HCl, H_2O, are known. Hydrogen chloride is used in the production of chlorides and as a condensing agent in organic chemistry. Commercially, large quantities are used in the manufacture of methyl and methylene chloride, ethyl chloride and vinyl chloride.

Hydrogen cyanide, Hydrocyanic acid, Prussic acid, HCN. A colourless liquid, m.p. −13·3°, b.p. 25·7°, d_4^{20} 0·688. Miscible with water and alcohol in all proportions. It burns with a violet flame and has a smell of bitter almonds.

Hydrocyanic acid forms two series of esters, the cyanides $R·C:N$ and the isocyanides $R·N:C$. It is a very weak acid, and its salts are hydrolysed in solution. It is present in many plants in the combined state as amygdalin and other glycosides.

Commercially, hydrogen cyanide is made by reacting together methane, air and ammonia over a platinum catalyst at 1000°, to yield a mixture of the gas with water vapour and small amounts of other products. Other methods include the decomposition of sodium and calcium cyanides with sulphuric acid, the dehydration of formamide, and the recovery from coke-oven gas by absorption in sodium carbonate solution.

Impure hydrocyanic acid polymerizes on keeping, and forms a dark amorphous solid called azulmic acid; the presence of acids prevents polymerization.

It is a very powerful poison, being absorbed with great rapidity and in poisonous doses paralyses the heart's action and the respiration, death occurring with a few minutes.

Due to the widespread use of synthetic fibres and plastics, hydrogen cyanide is now a chemical of great industrial importance, being used for the manufacture of acrylonitrile, adiponitrile and methyl methacrylate. It is also still used as a fumigant.

Hydrogen electrode. A hydrogen electrode consists of a strip of platinum covered with an active layer of platinum black, over which hydrogen is allowed to bubble while it is immersed in a solution containing hydrogen ions. If the concentration of the latter is equal to unit activity and the gas is at 1 atmosphere pressure, the electrode potential is said to be normal and its potential is arbitrarily taken as zero. The electrode serves as the standard for evaluating the electrode potentials of other substances on the 'hydrogen scale,' i.e. with reference to the potential of the normal hydrogen electrode.

Hydrogen fluoride, HF. A colourless and strongly fuming liquid of d 0·988, m.p. $-83·4°$, b.p. 19·5°. Anhydrous hydrogen fluoride is covalent in character and there is considerable association; it is an extremely good solvent for both inorganic salts and covalent organic compounds. Hydrogen fluoride gives an acid, hydrofluoric acid, with water; the system exhibits a maximum boiling point azeotrope containing 36% HF by wt., b.p. 11°. Anhydrous hydrogen fluoride is prepared by heating potassium bifluoride KHF_2, or by treating fluorspar, CaF_2, with sulphuric acid; the latter process is used for its manufacture.

Because both the acid and the anhydrous material attack glass, laboratory apparatus for handling them must be constructed of metal or plastic. Industrially hydrogen fluoride may be handled in mild steel, and hydrofluoric acid in rubber-lined or lead-lined equipment, while monel will withstand both the acid and the anhydrous material.

The principal commercial use of hydrogen fluoride is as a fluorinating agent, especially in the manufacture of chlorofluorohydrocarbons and the processing of uranium. It is also used as an alkylation catalyst in the petroleum industry. Hydrofluoric acid is used in the manufacture of synthetic cryolite, for the cleaning of stainless steel and the etching of glass. It is also used for the removal of silica, both in laboratories and in foundries.

Hydrogen fluoride and hydrofluoric acid are irritant, producing very dangerous wounds on the skin.

The fluorides, which are the salts of hydrofluoric acid, are of two sorts, viz. the normal salts, e.g. NaF, and the acid salts, e.g. KHF_2. The bifluoride ion, HF_2^-, contains a hydrogen bond. In weak aqueous solution the main species present are H_3O^+ and HF_2^-; in stronger solutions anions such as $H_2F_3^-$ and $H_3F_4^-$ are found. The fluorides present notable differences

from the salts of the other halogen acids. Calcium fluoride, for example, is practically insoluble in water, whereas silver fluoride, unlike the other silver halides, is very soluble.

Hydrogen iodide, HI. A gas which liquefies at atmospheric pressure at $-36°$ to a colourless liquid. The latter solidifies at $-53·6°$. The liquid may be coloured violet by traces of iodine or brown by traces of water. The gas is very soluble in water, the saturated solution at 0° having a density of 1·99 and containing 90% of HI. Di-, tri-, and tetrahydrates may be separated by cooling the concentrated aqueous solution. Gaseous HI may be prepared by heating hydrogen and iodine together at 300°, when an equilibrium is established, the attainment of which is accelerated by the presence of spongy platinum, which acts as a catalyst $(2HI \rightleftharpoons H_2 + I_2)$. The gas is usually prepared in the laboratory by the action of water on a mixture of red phosphorus and iodine.

Aqueous hydrogen iodide behaves as a strong acid, and is known as hydriodic acid. It forms a solution of maximum boiling-point 126° at 760 mm pressure, containing 57% of HI. An aqueous solution of density 1·5 is commonly used, especially in organic chemistry, as a reducing agent. Both the gas and its aqueous solution are decomposed by ultra-violet light. A very convenient method of preparing aqueous hydriodic acid is by passing hydrogen sulphide into a suspension of iodine in water. The sulphur which is precipitated may be filtered off and the acid solution concentrated by distillation.

Hydrogen-ion concentration. Hydrogen-ion concentration is measured as the number of gram ions of hydrogen ions present per litre of solution (1 g molecule of hydrogen ion weighs 1 g). Since the concentration of hydrogen ions is often small, e.g. 10^{-5}, the concentration is generally expressed as the logarithm of its reciprocal, which is called a pH value. Thus, if the hydrogen-ion concentration is 10^{-5} g mols. per litre, the pH of the solution is 5. The pH can be determined by means of a glass electrode, or less accurately, by coloured indicators. See Ionization of water.

Hydrogen ions. Hydrogen ions are only formed when the ion can be solvated. Thus a solution of HCl in water contains H_3O^+ and Cl^- ions.

Hydrogenite. A mixture of ferrosilicon and sodium hydroxide which evolves hydrogen with water and has been used as a source of this gas.

Hydrogen overvoltage. In electrolytic processes, in which evolution of hydrogen takes place at a cathode, the potential of the latter is usually more negative than formally required for hydrogen liberation. The cathode, when thus behaving as an irreversible electrode, is said to exhibit an overpotential or overvoltage. The potential difference between the irreversible cathode and the reversible hydrogen electrode in the same solution is termed the hydrogen overvoltage at this particular cathode.

Hydrogen overvoltage depends on the electrode (its material, kind of surface, etc.), and grows logarithmically with the increase of current density. Owing to the negative sign of hydrogen overvoltage the evolution potential of hydrogen is shifted up the electrochemical series enabling therefore the electrodeposition of such metals as Pb, Ni, Zn from the acid solutions on to cathodes of these metals.

Hydrogen peroxide. Pure anhydrous hydrogen peroxide is a clear colourless syrupy liquid, m.p. $-0.9°$, b.p. 150.2, d^{20} 1.4489. When quite pure it is stable in the cold, decomposing at the rate of about 1% a year at 30°, but 1% a week at 66°. Its decomposition is greatly accelerated by alkalis and by very small concentrations of heavy metals, and therefore by dust. It can be stabilized by adding acid or substances that remove heavy metal ions. It blisters the skin and may ignite combustible materials. It is conveniently stored in high purity aluminium.

Hydrogen peroxide is normally used in the form of an aqueous solution, the concentration being expressed by the weight per cent or volume strength, that is, the volume of oxygen in millilitres that 1 ml of the solution will give. Common grades are 3% (10 vols.), 6% (20 vols.) 30% (100 vols.).

Hydrogen peroxide is manufactured by the reduction of 2-ethylanthraquinone using hydrogen and a palladium catalyst to give 2-ethylanthraquinol, followed by direct oxidation to hydrogen peroxide and the quinone. It is also made by the direct liquid-phase oxidation of isopropanol to hydrogen peroxide and acetone, while an older method involves the electrolysis of ammonium hydrogen sulphate followed by the thermal decomposition of the ammonium persulphate formed.

Hydrogen peroxide is a very powerful oxidizing agent, and has the advantage of producing only water as a by-product. It can also act as a reducing agent. It is used for bleaching textiles and other products, in various organic syntheses, and in concentrated form as a propellant. Hydrogen peroxide is dissociated to the H^+ and HO_2^- ions. In the covalent state the molecule has a skew configuration.

Hydrogen persulphides, Sulphanes. Acidification of alkali polysulphide solutions gives a yellow oil which, by distillation, may be separated into its components, H_2S_4, H_2S_5, and H_2S_6, etc. On strong heating these are cracked into H_2S_2

and H_2S_3. All the hydrogen polysulphides are fairly unstable with respect to hydrogen sulphide and sulphur.

Hydrogen selenide, H_2Se. M.p. $-64°$, b.p. $-42°$. Prepared by the action of aluminium selenide on 5M hydrochloric acid. It is a colourless gas, with an abominable odour, causing headache, and scarification of the mucous membranes. It is soluble in water, to yield an acidic solution which will precipitate the selenides of the metals from solutions of their salts.

Hydrogen sulphide, or **Sulphuretted hydrogen,** H_2S. A colourless gas with an unpleasant smell of rotten eggs, and very poisonous; m.p. $-82.9°$, b.p. $-60.8°$, d at b.p. 0.96. It is produced by decaying animal and vegetable matter, and is found in many mineral waters. It is usually prepared by the action of dilute hydrochloric or sulphuric acid upon ferrous sulphide, FeS; 100 vols. of water at 20° dissolve 291 vols. of the gas. It burns in air with a blue flame, forming sulphur dioxide and steam. When passed into aqueous solutions of most of the heavy metals, it forms insoluble sulphides. It was very extensively used as an analytical reagent. It is readily detected by its smell and by its property of blackening alkaline solutions of lead salts.

Hydrogen telluride, H_2Te. Prepared by the action of aluminium telluride on hydrochloric acid. It is a colourless gas, m.p. $-51°$, b.p. $-4°$, d_4^{-20} 2.57, soluble in water and ether, and easily dissociated into its elements. It reacts with solutions of metallic salts to form the tellurides, but these are generally better prepared by heating the elements together in the proper proportions, as most of the tellurides are easily hydrolysed. Hydrogen telluride is toxic.

Hydrolith. See Calcium hydride.

Hydrolysis. In its most general sense, hydrolysis signifies a reaction between any substance and water. It is often restricted, however, to those reactions due directly to the hydrogen and hydroxyl ions of the water. For example, nearly every salt yields a slightly acid or alkaline solution, due to hydrolysis. Thus, sodium acetate yields an alkaline solution, because the acetate ions combine with the hydrogen ions to yield the weak acid acetic acid, and leave a solution containing excess of hydroxyl ions. The reaction may be expressed as follows:

$$Na^+ + CH_3COO^- + H_2O \rightleftharpoons$$
$$Na^+ + OH^- + CH_3COOH$$

Such a reaction may be considered from the standpoint of the law of mass action. The hydrolysis of sodium acetate gives the equation

$$\frac{[OH^-][CH_3COOH]}{[CH_3COO^-][H_2O]} = K_1.$$

But the concentration of water may be considered constant, since it is present in a large excess, hence

$$\frac{[OH^-][CH_3COOH]}{[CH_3COO^-]} = K_2.$$

K_2 is an equilibrium constant. A similar constant may be derived from the equation of any reaction involving hydrolysis, and is termed the hydrolysis constant. Metal ions are often hydrolysed in solution. The ion $M(OH_2)_n^{x+}$ dissociates to the hydroxy species $[M(OH_2)_{n-1}(OH)]^{x-1}$.

Hydrometer. This is a simple device for measuring the density of a liquid, consisting of a cylindrical float whose lower end is conical and weighted and whose upper end terminates in a narrow tube. When placed in a liquid the instrument floats upright with the tube partially immersed, the immersion depending on the liquid density; the latter may be read off from a scale on the tube.

Because of their widespread use for simple process control, hydrometers are frequently calibrated, not in specific gravity, but in some units related to it, which bear (or bore at one time) some relationship to the concentration being so measured. Thus on the Brix scale, used in the sugar industry, n degrees Brix represents a sucrose concentration of $n\%$ by weight in water. Various other scales are in common use, of which the most important are the American Baumé, the Rational Baumé, the Twaddell and the A.P.I.

Hydroperoxides. A class of compounds containing the hydroperoxyl group, HO·O—, the simplest of which is hydrogen peroxide. Organic hydroperoxides are produced by aerial oxidation of many organic compounds, and decompose, frequently with extreme ease, to give alcohols, carbonyl compounds, and other products.

Hydrophilic colloid. Colloidal sols of proteins, carbohydrates, soaps, and other complex organic materials are marked by considerable stability and are not coagulated by small concentrations of electrolyte such as are sufficient to destroy hydrophobic or suspensoid sols such as those of metals or their sulphides. This stability is due to the existence of a sheath of dispersion medium (water) which protects the hydrophilic (water-loving) particles. The essential difference between hydrophilic and hydrophobic colloids is that the former are not coagulated at the isoelectric point.

Hydrophilic sols are characterized by a high viscosity, and often set to gels on cooling; it is possible to prepare them containing a high proportion of the dispersed colloid. They are either soluble monomolecular substances (e.g.

proteins, polymers) or monomolecular substances which aggregate in solution to form colloidal micelles (e.g. soaps, dyes).

Hydrophobic bonding. The association of non-polar molecules or groups in aqueous media, resulting from the tendency of water molecules to exclude non-polar groups.

Hydrophobic colloids. Sols of gold, arsenic etc., are stable owing to the mutual repulsion arising from the like charges on all the colloidal particles. Such sols are not hydrated. On the addition of small concentrations of electrolytes, the charges on the particles become neutralized and coagulation takes place. Such sols are termed hydrophobic (water-hating), and have a viscosity equal to, or only slightly greater than, water. Hydrophobic sols differ from hydrophilic sols in being coagulated at the isoelectric point. It is normally only possible to prepare hydrophobic sols in low concentration. See Colloids, Suspensoids.

Hydroquinone, $C_6H_6O_2$. Colourless hexagonal prisms, m.p. 170·3°, b.p. 285°/730 mm. Readily soluble in alcohol, ether, and hot water, less in cold water. An alkaline solution turns brown in air and reduces Fehling's solution and ammoniacal silver nitrate. With ferric chloride it is oxidized to quinone. It is best prepared from quinone by reduction with sulphur dioxide. It is used as a photographic developer.

Hydrosulphurous acid, Hyposulphurous acid, Dithionous acid, $H_2S_2O_4$. This acid is known only in aqueous solution. It is unstable and is a powerful reducing agent. Its salts are prepared by reducing sulphites. Hydrosulphites contain the

$$\left[\begin{array}{c} O-S-O \\ | \\ O-S-O \end{array}\right]^{2-} \text{ ion.}$$

See Sodium hydrosulphite.

Hydroxonium ion. See Hydration (of ions).

Hydroxy-. A prefix used in organic chemistry to denote that the substance in question contains a hydroxyl (—OH) group.

Hydroxyacetone. See Acetol.

2-Hydroxyethylamine. See Ethanolamines.

Hydroxylamine, NH_2OH. A colourless deliquescent solid, m.p. 33°, which explodes on heating and decomposes slowly, evolving nitrous oxide and nitrogen, at normal temperatures. Usually used as an aqueous solution containing up to 60% of hydroxylamine, which is moderately stable. It is prepared by the hydrolysis of nitroparaffins, by the electrolytic reduction of nitric acid in aqueous hydrochloric acid, or by the reduction of nitric oxide with tin in acid solution; the hydroxylamine is isolated as one of its salts (e.g. NH_2OH, HCl), and is generally marketed in this form. Hydroxylamine is a very weak base, the salts being hydrolysed in solution. It generally acts as a strong reducing agent, but may under certain conditions act as as oxidizing agent, being itself reduced to ammonia. Hydroxylamine and its derivatives form oximes with organic carbonyls (ketones and aldehydes).

Hydroxylaminodisulphates, $HON(SO_3M)_2$. Salts prepared by the action of neutral alkali nitrite solutions on sulphur dioxide or hydrogen sulphide at $0°$ to $-5°$. In acid solution these salts give good yields of hydroxylamine.

Hydroxylation. The introduction of a hydroxyl group into an organic compound. It may be achieved chemically, for example by the action of lead tetraacetate, potassium permanganate, or performic acid on an olefin, or, in particular with steroids, biochemically by the use of appropriate enzymes.

Hydroxyl radical. The univalent group —OH which exists in equilibrium with water vapour and its decomposition products at about $1500°$, prepared by the dissociation of water vapour in an electrical discharge. Hydroxyl radicals recombine fairly rapidly on lowering the temperature. Hydroxyl radicals are also produced in the reaction of ferrous iron with hydrogen peroxide (Fenton's reagent). The hydroxyl ion, OH^-, is one of the ionic dissociation products of water. It combines with protons to form water; substances forming OH^- ions in aqueous solution are bases.

2-Hydroxy-3-naphthoic acid, $C_{11}H_8O_3$. The

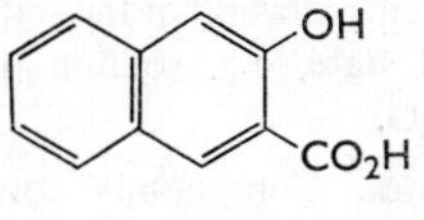

acid crystallizes in leaflets, m.p. $216°$. It is sparingly soluble in hot water, and easily soluble in alcohol and ether. It is prepared by heating sodium β-naphtholate at $250°$ under a pressure of 4 atmospheres of carbon dioxide. The reaction is analogous to that in which salicyclic acid is prepared. Its main outlet is for the preparation of its anilide, Naphtol AS, but it also has a limited application as an end component in a few azo-dyes.

2-Hydroxy-3-naphthoicanilide, $C_{17}H_{13}NO_2$. Forms colourless leaflets, m.p. $243°-244°$. It is

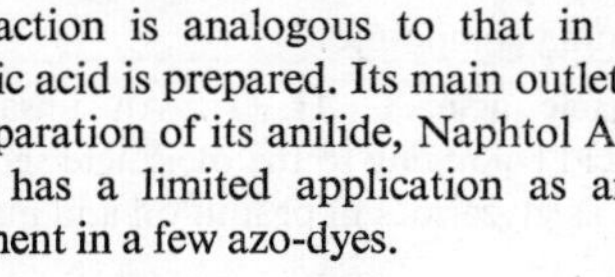

insoluble in water, slightly soluble in alcohol, soluble in nitrobenzene and glacial acetic acid. It readily couples with diazotized aromatic bases after the manner of β-naphthol to give water-insoluble azo compounds.

It is prepared by the action of a condensing agent such as phosphorus trichloride upon a mixture of aniline and 2-hydroxy-3-naphthoic acid in boiling toluene. It is usually known as Naphtol AS, and is a valuable second component for ingrained dyeing. See Azoic dyes.

Hydroxyproline, 5-Hydroxypyrrolidine-2-carboxylic acid, $C_5H_9NO_3$. Crystallizes in platelets,

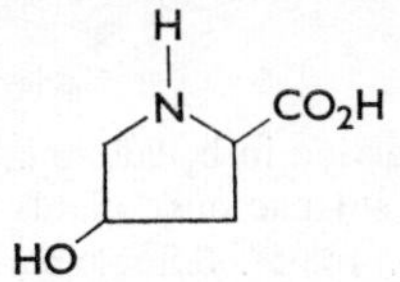

m.p. $270°$. Soluble in water, slightly soluble in alcohol. The laevorotatory form, $[\alpha]_D^{20} -75.2°$, is a constituent of connective-tissue proteins, like collagen and elastin, but not of other proteins.

2-Hydroxypropionic acid. See Hydracrylic acid.

Hydroxyquinol. 1,2,4-trihydroxybenzene, $C_6H_6O_3$. Crystallizes in colourless plates from ether, m.p. $140.5°$; soluble in water and alcohol, insoluble in benzene and chloroform. An aqueous alkaline solution rapidly oxidises and becomes coloured in air. It is obtained with other products by heating hydroquinone with caustic soda solution.

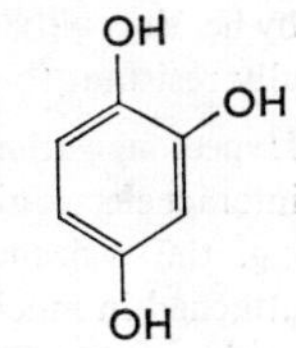

8-Hydroxyquinoline. See Oxine.

Hygroscopic. A term applied to substances which, when exposed to moist air, absorb moisture from it with chemical combination and the formation of either a moist solid or a solution of the solid in water. Examples of hygroscopic materials are magnesium chloride and phosphorus pentoxide. The former readily absorbs water from the air to give an aqueous solution of the salt; the latter combines chemically with the water absorbed, forming phosphoric acid.

Hyoscine, Scopolamine, $C_{17}H_{21}NO_4$. A syrup

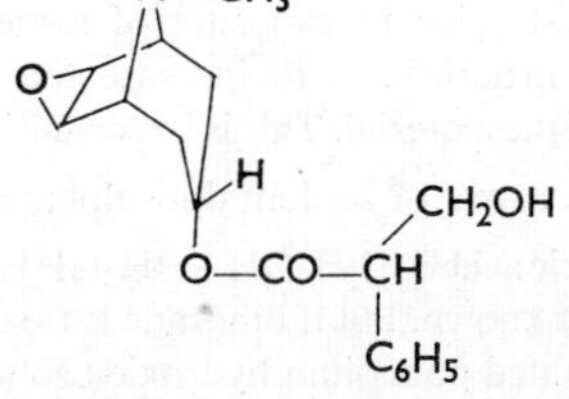

miscible with water and organic solvents, $[\alpha]_D$ $-28°$ in water. It is an intensely poisonous alkaloid obtained from various species of *Datura* and *Scopola*. In its medical action it resembles the closely related compound atropine.

Hyoscyamine, $C_{17}H_{23}NO_3$. A laevorotatory

alkaloid occurring in belladonna, *hyoscyamus*, and other solanaceous plants. Colourless needles, m.p. 108·5°. Soluble in alcohol, less soluble in water, $[\alpha]_D^{15}$ $-22°$ in 50% alcohol. It is easily racemized by alkalis into its optically inactive isomer, atropine. Its physiological action is similar to, but more intense than, atropine.

Hypalon. A trade name for the rubber derived from the chlorosulphonation of polyethylene (to give S; 1·5%; Cl; 27%). It can be vulcanized by heating with, e.g., zinc oxide. It is exceptionally resistant to ozone attack and to ageing.

Hyperconjugation. Alkyl groups appear to interact electronically with unsaturated systems, e.g. the benzene nucleus, to which they are attached in much the same way as do unsaturated groups. The magnitude of this effect, called hyperconjugation, depends on the number of hydrogen atoms attached to the carbon atom immediately adjacent to the unsaturated system. Specifically it indicates C—H conjugation. Considerable controversy exists over the validity of hyperconjugation. It has been postulated to account for the stabilization of aliphatic carbonium ions, and ease of certain elimination reactions.

Hyperons. Elementary particles of mass 2185 times that of the electron; intermediate between a proton and a deuteron. The best established hyperon is the lambda hyperon of zero charge but it is very likely that charged hyperons exist. Hyperons are found in cosmic radiation.

Hypersensitization. The effect of a uniform flash exposure, or of a mercury vapour treatment, just prior to exposure of some photographic materials, is to increase the effective speed of the material. This is hypersensitization.

Hypo. A name for sodium thiosulphate.

Hypoboric acid $H_2[BH_2OH-BH_2OH]$. The free acid is unknown, but if diborane is treated with concentrated potassium hydroxide solution the salt $K_2[BH_2OH-BH_2OH]$ is formed. This is stable to heat up to 500°, is hygroscopic, and is a very strong reducing agent, but immediately decomposes on acidification. See Sub-boric acid.

Hypobromous acid, HBrO. When mercuric oxide is shaken with bromine water, a solution of hypobromous acid is obtained; formed by this means the concentration of HBrO does not exceed 6%. The solution may be distilled in vacuum at low temperatures. It is a straw-coloured liquid, a powerful oxidizing and bleaching agent, and decomposes on warming into bromine and bromic acid.

Hypobromites are obtained by dissolving bromine in cold aqueous caustic soda or potash. Bromide is formed at the same time. These solutions are used as oxidizing agents. Slaked lime absorbs bromine to give a red powder, similar to bleaching powder, probably containing $Ca(OBr)_2$.

Hypochlorous acid, HClO. Solutions of chlorine in water contain free hypochlorous acid, to which they owe their bleaching properties. The acid is known only in solution, and is obtained by shaking chlorine water with yellow precipitated mercuric oxide and distilling. The solution is pale golden-yellow, or colourless when dilute. Hypochlorous acid is very weak; dissociation constant 2×10^{-3}. The concentrated solutions decompose on heating or exposure to sunlight with the evolution of chlorine and oxygen, and the formation of a little chloric acid.

Dilute solutions of the alkalis (e.g. NaOH) absorb chlorine with the formation of chlorides and hypochlorites; with excess of chlorine free hypochlorous acid is produced. Hypochlorous acids and its salts are powerful oxidizing and bleaching agents. Several of the salts are known in the solid state, e.g. sodium hypochlorite, $NaOCl, 6H_2O$.

Hypochromates. Compounds containing the CrO_4^{3-} ion. See Chromites.

Hypofluorites. The name given to covalent compounds containing —OF bonds. Examples are the oxygen fluorides, and CF_3OF. Generally prepared by the action of fluorine on an oxygen-containing compound.

Hypogaeic acid, $C_{16}H_{30}O_2$. An unsaturated fatty acid belonging to the oleic acid series that occurs as glycerides in peanut oil and maize oil, m.p. 33°.

Hypoglycaemic substances. Natural or synthetic drugs which cause a fall in blood glucose concentration. The natural hypoglycaemic hormone, insulin (*q.v.*) is secreted by the pancreas. Synthetic 'oral antidiabetic' drugs, effective when taken by mouth, are available, e.g. chlorpropamide and tolbutamide (*q.v.*). The toxicity of certain plant products is due to hypoglycaemic constituents (e.g. hypoglycins A and B from Jamaican 'Ackee' fruit, *Blighia sapida*).

Hypoglycin A. α-Amino-β-(2-methylenecyclo-propyl)propionic acid, a toxic constituent of the

fruit of *Blighia sapida* ('Ackee') and the cause of Jamaican vomiting sickness. Its ingestion leads to a rapid fall in liver glycogen and in blood sugar concentration, apparently through inhibition of fatty acid oxidation.

Hypoid lubricants. Types of extreme pressure lubricants used for lubricating hypoid gears.

Hypoiodous acid, HIO. This compound is believed to exist in the yellow solution obtained by dissolving iodine in cold dilute alkali. A hypoiodite is probably first formed, then decomposes to iodide and iodate. A dilute solution of the acid may be prepared by shaking iodine with a suspension of freshly prepared mercuric oxide, and filtering. The acid is known only in solution. It has pronounced oxidizing properties, and is in general analogous to hypobromous and hypochlorous acids.

Hyponitrous acid, $H_2N_2O_2$. Sodium hyponitrite, $Na_2N_2O_2$, the sodium salt of this acid, is prepared by the action of sodium amalgam on sodium nitrite solution, or by passing nitric oxide through a solution of sodium in liquid ammonia. Yellow silver hyponitrite, $Ag_2N_2O_2$, is precipitated from the aqueous solution by adding silver nitrate and the colourless crystalline $H_2N_2O_2$ is obtained from $Ag_2N_2O_2$ by the action of a solution of hydrogen chloride in dry ether. The solid is explosive, and the aqueous solution readily decomposes giving nitrous oxide. The alkali metal salts are stable white crystalline solids.

Hypophosphoric acid, $H_4P_2O_6$. M.p. 70°.

Prepared by the action of sodium chlorite on red phosphorus. Stable to aqueous alkali but converted to phosphate on fusing with sodium hydroxide.

Hypophosphorous acid. H_3PO_2. Colourless crystalline solid, mp. 26·5°; its sodium salt, NaH_2PO_2 is formed, with evolution of phosphine, on heating yellow phosphorus with sodium hydroxide

solution. The free acid and its salts (hypophosphites) are powerful reducing agents, precipitating copper hydride, CuH, from solutions of copper salts. Phosphine and hydrogen are liberated when the acid is boiled with sodium hydroxide.

Hypoxanthine, 6-Oxypurine, $C_5H_4N_4O$. Crystallizes in colourless needles, decomposing at 150°. Sparingly soluble in cold water, more soluble in hot. It is a breakdown product of nucleoprotein metabolism, being formed from adenine by the action of the enzyme adenase.

Hypsochromic. See Bathochromic.

Hysteresis. A term applied to certain processes (occurring chiefly in solids) in which the response to an applied variable appears to lag when the variable is changed, with the result that a true reversible position of equilibrium seems never to be reached; in particular, the response curve obtained on increasing the variable differs from that on decreasing the variable. A well-known example is hysteresis of magnetization of iron. The intensity of magnetization induced by a given applied magnetic field is smaller if that field has been reached from lower values than if it follows higher magnetic fields. Hysteresis is also found in the swelling of amorphous bodies (e.g. in the absorption of moisture by textiles), and the adsorption of vapours by porous adsorbents.

I

Ice. The solid form of water. The transition point between liquid and solid water at one atmosphere pressure is defined as 0° on the Centigrade scale. This temperature is lowered by increasing the pressure. By crystallization of water under greatly increased pressure it is possible to obtain at least four forms of solid water which are physically distinct from ordinary ice (Ice I). These rank as distinct phases and their equilibrium relationships have been studied.

The molecules in ice are held together by hydrogen bonds.

Ichthammol. A nearly black viscous liquid containing about 50% of total solids consisting chiefly of the ammonium salts of the sulphonic acids of an oily substance prepared by the destructive distillation of fossil fish deposits. It has slight bacteriostatic properties, and is used in ointments for the treatment of skin diseases and in pessaries for treating cervitis.

Icosahedral. Having the symmetry of an icosahedron, a solid figure with twelve apices; each face is triangular. Icosahedral units are found in many boron derivatives.

Ideal gas. An ideal gas is one which is said to obey exactly the laws of Boyle and Gay-Lussac. In practice, no real gas behaves in this manner, but helium, hydrogen and nitrogen at high temperatures and low pressures behave almost as ideal gases.

Ideal solution. A solution, liquid or solid, in which the thermodynamic activity of each component is proportional to its mole fraction, i.e. each component obeys Raoult's law. Such a solution would be formed from its pure components with zero heat of mixing, zero volume change, and with the ideal entropy of mixing. Only mixtures of closely similar substances, e.g. isotopic elements, form solutions which are precisely ideal, but many mixtures approximate to ideality (e.g. benzene and toluene).

Idose. See Hexose.

Illinium. The former name for the rare-earth metal promethium (q.v.).

Ilmenite, FeO, TiO_2. Black rhombohedral crystals with two molecules in the unit cell; the titanium is in six co-ordination. The crystals are often platy, granular, and weakly magnetic, sp.gr. 4·3, hardness 5·5-6. It is common as an accessory mineral in rocks; workable deposits occur in beach sands, detrital deposits, and in the massive form. It is used in the preparation of titanium oxide for pigments, etc.

Imidazole, $C_3H_4N_2$. Also called glyoxaline or

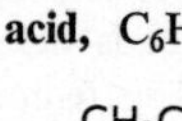

iminazole. The ring is numbered as shown.

Imidazolepyruvic acid, $C_6H_6N_2O_3$. A meta-

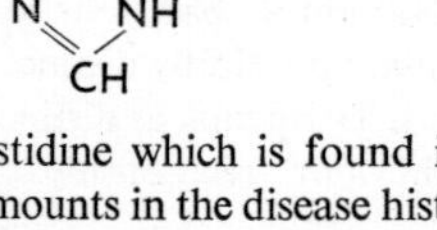

bolite of histidine which is found in urine in abnormal amounts in the disease histidinaemia, ascribed to an inherited enzyme defect or 'inborn error of metabolism'

Imides. In organic chemistry imides are nitrogen-containing ring compounds containing the group

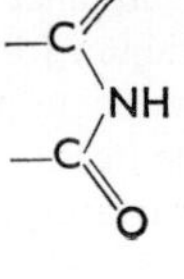

They are formed by heating dibasic acids or their anhydrides with ammonia. The hydrogen atom of the NH group is acidic and can be replaced by a metal. Mild hydrolysis breaks the ring to give the half amide of the acid. See Succinimide and Phthalimide.

In inorganic chemistry the term refers to compounds containing the NH^{2-} ion or the $>NH$ group. These are prepared by the action of heat on amides or by metathetical reactions in liquid ammonia. The heavy metal imides are explosive.

Imino. The name given to the group $>NH$ where the nitrogen atom is part of a ring system or is united by both bonds to a single atom. Such compounds as $R \cdot CO \cdot NHR$ are usually regarded as substituted amides and not as imino compounds.

Imipramine, Tofranil, $C_{19}H_{24}N_2$. A white

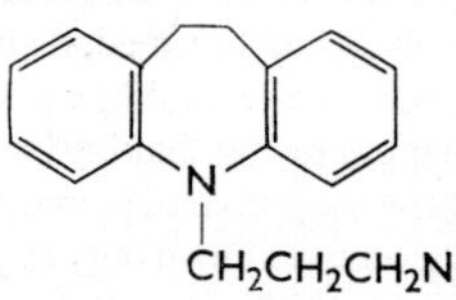

crystalline powder, m.p. 168°-171°. The hydrochloride is soluble at 20° in 2 parts of water and in 1·5 parts of alcohol; readily soluble in chloroform, almost insoluble in ether.

It is used in medicine as an antidepressive, e.g. in the treatment of psychotic depression.

Impact resistance is not a fixed property of a metal or alloy; the result obtained depends upon the size and shape of the test specimen and the nature of the test machine. It gives an approximate measure of the capacity of the substance to withstand shock or impact under the test conditions. The Izod and Charpy are the commonly used tests. These tests are important for body-centred cubic metals and alloys such as steel as these become brittle with falling temperatures. In the Charpy test a standard specimen (10 mm square by 55 mm long) is firmly supported and is suddenly broken by a heavy swinging pendulum (220 ft. lbs. of kinetic energy). The reduced swing of the pendulum is taken as a measure of the energy used in the fracturing of the specimen. Brittle materials such as grey cast irons absorb only a few ft. lbs. of energy while a tough steel may absorb 80 ft. lbs. This test should be carried out over a range of temperatures since a steel which is tough at 25° may be brittle at $-10°$ and so be unsuitable for low temperature equipment. The Izod test is based on similar principles but the specimen size and machine design are slightly different.

Impingement separators, momentum separators. Devices for removing relatively coarse solid or liquid particles from a gas stream. They consist of a chamber or chambers containing a series of vertical baffles on which the gas impinges. It is thus continually forced to change direction, and the particles are thrown out of the gas stream against the baffles, where they collect.

Inconel. See Nickel alloys.

Indamines. Blue and green dyestuffs obtained by the oxidation of 1 molecule of a *p*-diamine with 1 molecule of an aromatic amine or by the interaction of a *p*-nitrosamine with an aromatic amine. A typical indamine is phenylene blue,

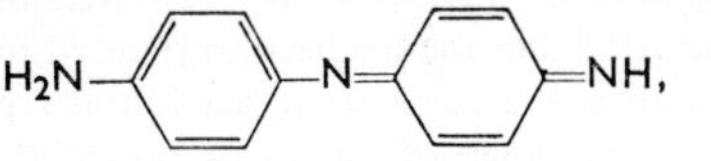

$$H_2N-\bigcirc-N=\bigcirc=NH,$$

which is obtained by the oxidation of *p*-phenylenediamine with aniline hydrochloride. The indamines yield safranines on boiling with aniline hydrochloride solutions. They are not themselves important dyestuffs.

Indanthren red RK (Vat Red 35). A red vat dye having the formula shown below. It is prepared by condensing 1-chloroanthraquinone-2-carboxylic acid with β-naphthylamine in presence of copper powder, and subsequently treating the condensation product with phosphorus pentachloride.

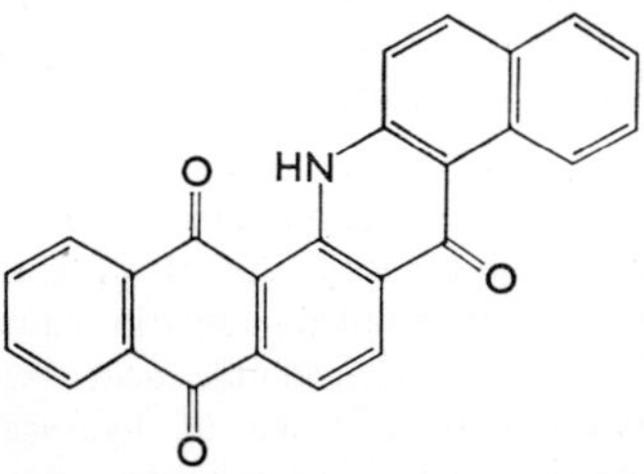

Indanthrone, Indanthren blue RS, Caledon blue RN, (Vat Blue 4). A blue vat dyestuff produced by fusing 2-aminoanthraquinone with caustic potash at 200°-250° and subsequent oxidation in an air current. In practice potassium nitrate or chlorate is added to the melt. Indanthrone has the constitution

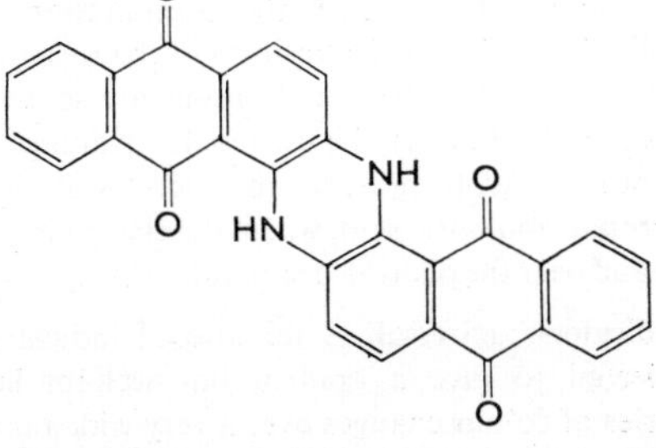

It is a dark blue powder, very slightly soluble in organic solvents, and is very stable. It dyes cotton from an alkaline hydrosulphite vat. The cotton is dyed blue by the dihydro-derivative, which is oxidized to indanthrone on exposure to air. The dyeings are much faster than indigo.

Indene, C_9H_8. A colourless liquid, b.p. 188°, m.p. −2°, obtained from petroleum fractions. It is an acidic hydrocarbon and yields, a sodium salt. The reactions of the 5-membered ring resemble those of cyclopentadiene in forming fulvenes, and cyclopentadienylmetal derivatives.

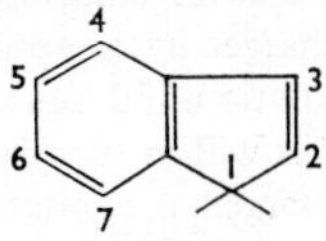

Indene resins. See Coumarone and indene resins.

Indian fire. A mixture of potassium nitrate (24 parts), sulphur (7 parts), and arsenic disulphide (realgar) (2 parts); used in the manufacture of signal lights.

Indican, Indoxyl-β-glucoside, $C_{14}H_{17}NO_6$. A glucoside occurring in woad, from which it is conveniently extracted with acetone. It crystallizes in colourless needles with three molecules

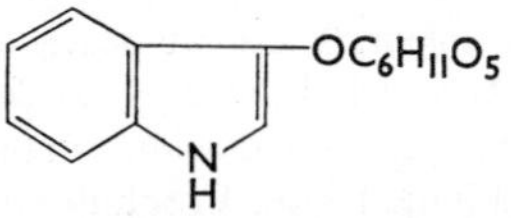

of water; m.p. 57°-58° (176°-178°, anhydrous). It is hydrolysed by dilute acids and by suitable enzymes to indoxyl and glucose. It is the parent substance of natural indigo.

Indican is also the name for the potassium salt of indoxyl sulphuric acid, $C_8H_6KNO_4S$.

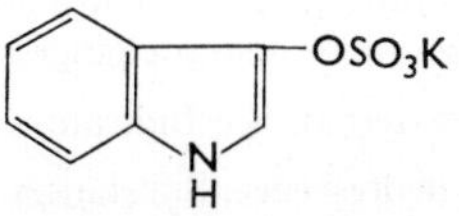

Glistening leaflets, soluble in water, sparingly soluble in alcohol. Indoxyl is toxic, but as indican it is excreted in a form harmless to the body, as one of the ethereal sulphates. The excretion of indican is a measure of the amount of putrefaction occurring in the intestine.

Indicator. In its broadest sense an indicator is a substance which allows the progress of a chemical change to be followed, but it is generally meant to indicate a substance which marks a precise stage in a chemical reaction, usually by a change of colour, or fluorescence of a solution, or by the alteration in the nature of a precipitate. For example, methyl orange, an indicator used in the neutralization of acids with bases, is red when the concentration of hydrogen ions is not less than $10^{-3.1}$ (pH=3·1), and gradually changes through orange to a full yellow colour as the pH increases to 4·4.

Indicators, achromatic. These are substances which give a grey end-point, and generally find application when turbid liquids are being titrated.

Indicators, adsorption. Precipitates have a tendency to adsorb their own ions. Thus if a little chloride is added to a solution of silver nitrate, the silver chloride formed becomes positively charged by the adsorption of silver ions from the solution. If fluorescein is present in the solution, this will in turn be adsorbed by the positively charged precipitate, turning it red or pinkish. As soon as chloride ions are present in excess, all the silver ions adsorbed by the precipitate will be converted into silver chloride, and the precipitate will become negatively charged owing to the adsorption of chloride ions. When this occurs, the fluorescein will go back into solution, in which it has a yellow-green colour, and the precipitate will appear white. Substances such as fluorescein in the above example, which are used to mark the equivalence-point in a precipitation reaction by adsorption or desorption from the precipitate, are called adsorption indicators.

Indicators, colour. These are nearly all organic compounds which behave as weak acids or bases, and have different colours in the undissociated and ionic forms. In solution there is an equilibrium between these forms, the position of which is influenced by the concentration of hydrogen or hydroxyl ions. The hydrogen-ion concentration may thus be estimated from the colour. For a good indicator the colour change must occur between narrow limits of hydrogen-ion concentration. Oxidation-reduction indicators show similar colour changes.

Indicators, external. See Indicators, internal.

Indicators, fluorescence. Substances which indicate changes of hydrogen-ion concentration, etc. by an alteration in the intensity or colour of their fluorescence in daylight or ultra-violet light are termed fluorescence indicators, and find a wide application in the titration of deeply coloured or turbid fluids, such as wine and fruit juice, and many industrial liquids. The fluorescence of acridine, for example, changes from green to violet in the pH range 4·8-5·0.

Indicators, inorganic precipitation. Indicators which function by generally giving a coloured precipitate at the equivalence point. Thus potassium chromate is used as an indicator in the estimation of chloride by titration with silver nitrate; at the end-point there is a red precipitate of silver chromate.

Indicators, internal. Indicators such as methyl orange, which are used in the solution which is being investigated, are termed internal indicators to distinguish them from external indicators, like potassium ferrocyanide, which are kept outside the solution, the condition of which is ascertained by removing an insignificant proportion of it on the tip of a glass rod, and adding it to a drop of the indicator, usually on a white porcelain tile. External indicators are now seldom used.

Indicators, mixed. In order to sharpen the colour change, or restrict the pH range over which it occurs, two or more indicators may be mixed in suitable proportions.

Indicators, oxidation-reduction. These are substances which undergo an oxidation or reduction stage which is thermodynamically reversible and in which either the oxidized or reduced form is strongly coloured. A substance of this type has a definite range of values of potential, over which it exhibits its colour change, the *transition interval* of the indicator. If the potential at the equivalence-point of the redox reaction to be studied lies within this transition interval, then usually the particular substance is suitable as an oxidation-reduction indicator for the reaction.

Indicators, screened. In order to sharpen, or render easily visible, the colour change of an indicator, the indicator solution may be mixed with a solution of a suitable dye, which is itself unchanged in colour during the titration, but acts as an effective colour filter. For example, the colour change in methyl orange is improved considerably by the addition of a small proportion of methylene blue.

Indicators, turbidity. Certain weak organic acids of high molecular weight are insoluble in water but easily soluble in very dilute alkali. The addition of an acid to the alkaline solution causes the flocculation of the insoluble acid over an exceedingly narrow range of hydrogen-ion concentration (the precipitation interval). The commencement of precipitation is generally so well marked (precipitation-, turbidity-, or flocculation-point) that it denotes a definite hydrogen-ion concentration in the solution. The same considerations apply *mutatis mutandis* to the behaviour of the analogous bases towards hydroxyl ions. These indicators are unfortunately of a colloidal nature, and factors which influence the precipitation of colloids also affect the position of the turbidity interval, so that their applications are severely restricted. They may be used with advantage in titrations involving such substances as glycine, veronal, and boric acid, where the change in pH at and near the equivalence-point is slow.

Indicators, universal. A mixture of indicators selected to give a gradual but well-marked series of colour changes over a very wide range of hydrogen-ion concentrations, so that the latter may be rapidly estimated from the particular hue assumed by the indicator in contact with any solution. A typical universal indicator, consisting of a mixture of suitable proportions of methyl orange, methyl red, bromothymol blue, naphtholphthalein, phenolphthalein, and cresolphthalein, changes from red to blue through the spectrum colours in the range pH 3·0 to 11·5.

Indigo (Vat Blue 1), $C_{16}H_{10}N_2O_2$. An important

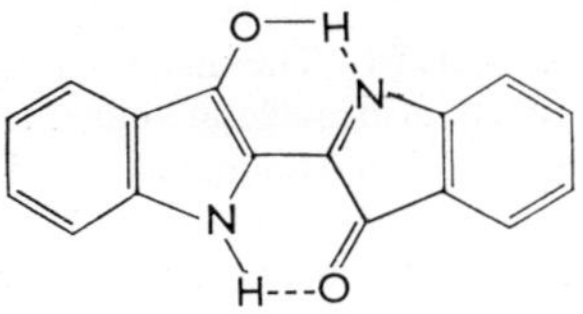

blue vat dyestuff, formerly derived by fermentation of leaves of the plant *indigo fera* to decompose the glucoside indican. It is insoluble in water, slightly soluble in high-boiling solvents, e.g. quinoline, chloronaphthalene. It sublimes on heating with a purple vapour. On treatment with alkaline sodium hydrosulphite solution it dissolves to a golden yellow solution of the alkali salt of indigo white. Reoxidation of the solution with air precipitates indigo.

Indigo is now manufactured from anthranilic acid either (1) by treating with chloroacetic acid to give phenylglycine-*o*-carboxylic acid, which is converted to indigo by treatment with caustic soda, or (2) by treating with formaldehyde, bisulphite, and potassium cyanide, which also results in the formation of phenylglycine-*o*-carboxylic acid. Fusion of the latter with soda-mide gives a better yield of indigo.

Indigo is applied by steeping the material in the alkaline solution of indigo white, which has good affinity for the fibre, and then withdrawing the fibre from the solution and allowing it to oxidize in the air to the insoluble indigo.

Many substituted indigos are also used in dyeing, substitution of the aromatic nucleus by halogen increasing the affinity of the reduced vat solution for the fibre. Thioindigoid dyes, which have sulphur atoms replacing the —NH— groups in the indigo molecule, are also in general use.

Indigo carmine, sodium indigodisulphonate, (Acid Blue 74), $C_{16}H_8N_2Na_2O_8S_2$. A blue

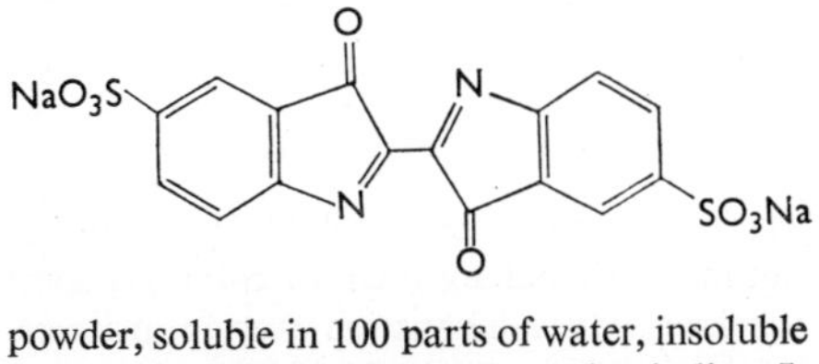

powder, soluble in 100 parts of water, insoluble in alcohol. Obtained by sulphonating indigo. It

has been superseded as a dyestuff, but can be used as an acid-alkali indicator (pH 11·6, blue, to 14·0, yellow) as an oxidation-reduction indicator, and as a colouring matter for foodstuffs (Food Blue 1). Medicinally, under the name of indicarmine, it is injected as a test for kidney efficiency.

Indigosols. Sulphuric acid esters of leuco vat

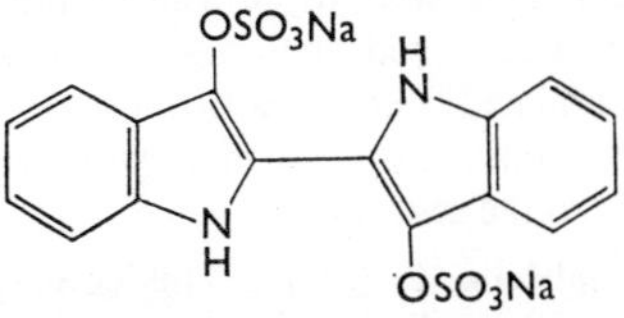

Indigosol O (solubilized indigo)

dyes. This soluble form can be applied directly to fibres, and by chemical oxidation the original vat dye (indigo) is regenerated. Indigo may thus be produced on the fibre without vatting.

Other indigoid and thioindigoid dyes have also been solubilized in the same general way, i.e. from the dry leuco compound by the action of cholorosulphonic acid in presence of pyridine.

Later another solubilization technique extended the range to include anthraquinone dyes —hence the Soledon colours (I.C.I.). Soledon Jade Green XS is the disulphuric ester of leuco dimethoxydibenzanthrone. The dye ultimately produced on the fibre is Caledon Jade Green X.

Indium, In. At.no. 49, At.wt.114·76. A soft white metal, m.p. 156·4°, b.p, 2100°. The element does not occur in nature in the free state, and its compounds are exceedingly rare. It occurs in small amounts in certain specimens of zinc blende. The separation of indium is complex but the metal is eventually precipitated as the hydroxide after removal of most other metals as sulphides. The metal is obtained by electrolysis of the cyanide: it has a tetragonal structure $a=4·594$, $c=4·951$, $d=7·3$ Å. Indium colours the Bunsen flame an intense blue. The metal is stable in oxygen at room temperature, but forms the sesquioxide, In_2O_3, when strongly heated. It combines with chlorine with incandescence to form the chloride $InCl_3$. Indium has a maximum and principal oxidation state of three, but also exhibits an oxidation state of one. The metal dissolves in dilute acids with evolution of hydrogen. Some indium compounds are used for their electrical properties; indium alloys are used in the control rods of nuclear reactors.

Indium halides. Indium forms tripositive, InX_3 (X=F, Cl, Br, I), and monopositive halides, InX (X=Cl, Br, I). The tripositive compounds are prepared by the action of excess of halogen on the metal; the lower oxidation state compounds by reduction of the trihalides with indium. Intermediate halides, e.g. In_2Cl_3

$(In_3^I[In^{III}Cl_6])$ have been reported but are not well characterized.

Indium oxides. The sesquioxide, In_2O_3, is formed when the element is strongly heated in air, or when the hydroxide, $In(OH)_3$, is precipitated from a solution containing tripositive indium by means of ammonia, and ignited. When heated in vacuum at 700° the sesquioxide yields the monoxide, In_2O. The sesquioxide is yellow when hot, red when cold. The monoxide can be sublimed *in vacuo*. Both oxides are fusible only with difficulty. The monoxide is readily oxidized to the sesquioxide.

Indium sulphate, $In_2(SO_4)_3$. This compound is known as the anhydrous salt and also as the hydrate, $In_2(SO_4)_3,6H_2O$. Indium sulphate forms alums $M^I In(SO_4)_2 12H_2O$; solutions of the alums are hydrolysed to the hydroxide at high temperatures.

Indium sulphide, In_2S_3. The sesquisulphide, In_2S_3, is a red solid which melts at $1050° \pm 3°$, and is formed by heating indium in a sealed tube with an excess of sulphur. Treatment of weakly acid solutions of indium salts gives a hydrated sulphide. In_2S_3 is reduced by hydrogen to the monosulphide, In_2S.

Indocarbon blacks (Sulphur blacks 4, 6, 7 and 11). A group of sulphur blacks obtained by the

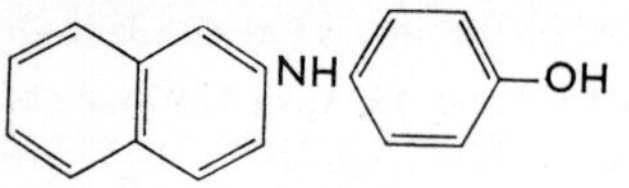

sulphurization of *p*-2-naphthylaminophenol along with optional small amounts of phenol or *p*-dihydroxydiphenylamine.

They are vatted and dyed on cotton in the presence of sodium sulphide as normal sulphur blacks and yield fast dyeings. They can also be applied from a caustic soda/hydrosulphite vat or a caustic soda/hydrosulphite/sodium sulphide vat.

Indole, C_8H_7N. Crystallizes in leaflets; m.p. 52°, b.p. 253°-254°, soluble in hot water, alcohol, and ether. It occurs in coal tar, in various plants, and in faeces, being formed by the action of the intestinal bacteria on tryptophan. It can be prepared by the action of acid on the phenylhydrazone of pyruvic acid to give indole-2-carboxylate which can be decarboxylated to indole.

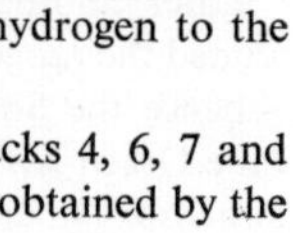

Indolizine (pyrrocoline) ring system. The system

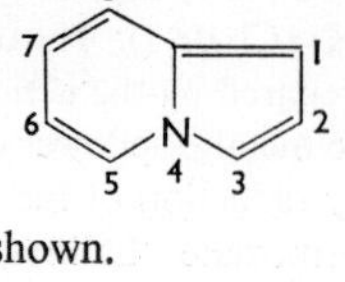

numbered as shown.

3-Indolylacetic acid, $C_{10}H_9NO_2$. Once called

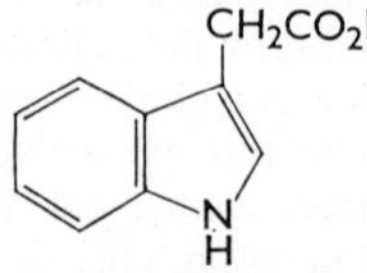

'heteroauxin' this was isolated from urine and from *Rhizopus* cultures, and shown to have auxin properties. It crystallizes in plates, m.p. 164°-165°, and has $[\alpha]_D^{20} - 3·8°$ in alcohol. See Auxins.

Indophenol oxidase. The name given to an enzyme widely distributed in animal and plant tissues. It gives a blue (indophenol) colour with *p*-phenylenediamine and α-naphthol. It has been shown to be identical with cytochrome oxidase (*q.v.*).

Indoxyl, C_8H_7NO. Yellow crystals, m.p. 85°,

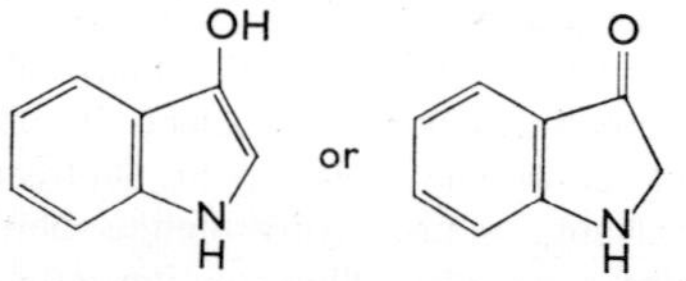

soluble in water and alcohol. It occurs in woad as the glucoside indican, and in mammalian urine, combined with sulphuric acid, as an ester, also called indican. It arises in the body from the bacterial decomposition of tryptophan.

Inductive effect. A substituent effect on an organic compound due to the permanent polarity or polarizability of groups is called an inductive effect. It may be visualized as the inducement of charge either towards or away from a group or atom, with a resulting dipole. Such a hypothesis can account for the increased acidity of trichloroacetic acid over acetic acid.

Indulines. Indulines are important colouring matters obtained by heating aminoazobenzene with a mixture of aniline and aniline hydrochloride. According to the proportions of the ingredients and the conditions, various shades of blue, such as Indamine Blue and Induline Blues 3B and 6B are obtained. These are azines which may be considered as anilidophenylphenosafranines. The structure of Induline 6B (Solvent Blue 7), is

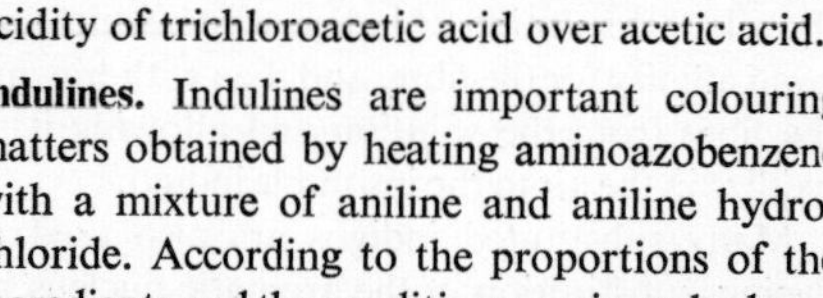

The induline chlorides are soluble in alcohol, but not in water, and are used for colouring spirit varnishes. On sulphonation they form watersoluble indulines which are acid dyes for wool.

Inert gas elements. See Noble gases.

Inert gas formalism. The effective atomic number rule (*q.v.*).

Inert pair effect. The existence of an oxidation state two below the group value for *p* block elements, which is considered to be due to an inert pair of s electrons which take no part in bonding. The effect is shown by e.g., Hg (Hg^0 and Hg^{II}) and Sn (Sn^{II} and Sn^{IV}).

Infrared radiation. Light of frequencies less than about 10^{13} per sec., i.e. of wavelengths greater than about 8000 Å, is called infrared radiation. It is invisible to the human eye, but possesses considerable penetrating power, and photographic plates may be sensitized towards it, so that it finds application in long-distance photography. Interatomic vibrations in molecules cause absorption in the infrared region.

Infrared spectroscopy. As many atomic groupings within molecules show characteristic absorption bands in the infrared region of the spectrum owing to vibrations and rotations, infrared spectroscopy has provided valuable information about molecular structure. The technique has been highly developed and is widely used as a routine tool in analysis and research. A detailed study of the infrared spectrum can provide information of the symmetry of species.

Infusible white precipitate. See Mercurammine compounds.

Infusions. Infusions are dilute solutions containing the water-soluble extractive of vegetable drugs, and are prepared by macerating drugs in distilled water.

Ingold, Sir Christopher Kelk (1893-   ). Born in Sussex, Ingold was educated at University College, Southampton, and at Imperial College, London. He became professor of organic chemistry at Leeds in 1924 and of chemistry at University College, London, in 1930. His researches cover a wide field, but by his work on the structure of organic compounds he has probably contributed more than any other man to change organic chemistry from a collection of isolated facts to an exact science.

Ingrain dyes. To this group belong all those dyestuffs the last stage in the production of which is carried out on the fibre. They can be divided into:

(a) Ice colours, produced, generally on cotton, by impregnating the fibre with the secondary component of an azo-dye, and 'developing' the colour by immersion in an ice-cold bath of a diazonium salt.

(b) Direct cotton dyes containing a free amino group first applied to the fibre and then diazotized and developed with a secondary component.

These two processes, which are complementary, both yield fast insoluble colours.

(c) Aniline black, formed by the oxidation of an aniline salt. It is produced either by oxidizing the fibre impregnated with the salt or by heating the fibre with a solution of aniline containing an oxidizing agent.

Initiators. See Explosives.

Inorganic. Inorganic chemistry is the chemistry of the compounds of all elements other than carbon. Certain simple carbon compounds, such as the carbonates and the cyanides, are usually regarded as inorganic compounds.

Inosinic acid, $C_{10}H_{13}N_4O_8P$. One of the first

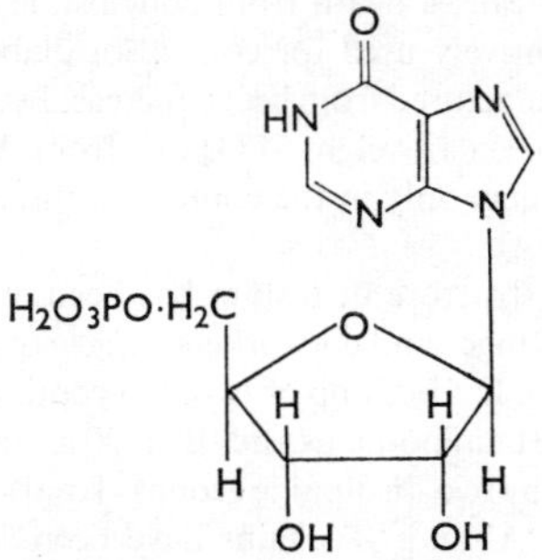

purine nucleotides to be isolated, inosinic acid is the biosynthetic precursor of adenylic acid (AMP) and guanylic acid (guanosine-5'-phosphate). It is hypoxanthine riboside-5-phosphate, and may be prepared from muscle adenylic acid by enzymic deamination.

Inositol. The inositols, $C_6H_{12}O_6$, are hexahydroxycyclohexanes. Nine stereoisomers are possible, four occur naturally, but only one, *meso*- or *i*-inositol (formula shown), is widely distributed. It is present in yeast, in plants as phytic acid, and as a constituent of both plant and animal phosphatides. It has m.p. 225°-226°, and forms a dihydrate, m.p. 218°. It is very soluble in water, insoluble in organic solvents, and has a sweet taste. *i*-Inositol is an

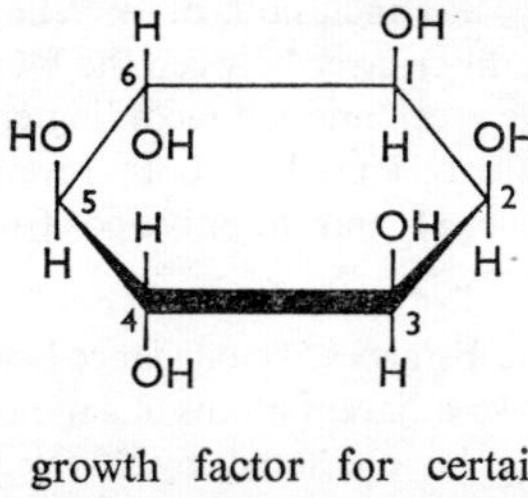

essential growth factor for certain microorganisms and its absence stops the growth of hair in rats and mice, so it is classified in the vitamin B group. It can most easily be obtained from corn steep liquor by precipitation as calcium phytate.

Insulating oil. Highly refined lubricating oil used for cooling and insulating purposes in electrical equipment such as transformers, circuit breakers, etc.

Insulin. The hormone, secreted by the Islets of Langerhans in the pancreas, which maintains the balance of glucose metabolism. The absence of insulin leads to the disease *diabetes mellitus*. Insulin has no action if taken by the mouth, as it is destroyed by intestinal enzymes. When injected, it causes a rapid fall in the blood glucose concentration by promoting oxidation of carbohydrate and storage of glycogen in the muscles. It also inhibits the formation of carbohydrates from lipids. An excessive dose of insulin causes death from convulsions. Insulin is extensively used for control of diabetes and is manufactured from beef pancreas. Beef insulin has molecular weight 5734; that from sheep and pigs differs only in the content of three aminoacids.

The structure of insulin has been elucidated by F. Sanger and co-workers (*Biochem. J.*, 1955, **60**, 541). It is built up of two polypeptide chains, 'A' of 21 amino-acids and 'B' of 30 amino-acids, linked by two disulphide groups. Total syntheses of the 'A' and 'B' chains have been achieved, and the oxidative recombination of naturally derived chains has given insulin in about 50% yield.

Integral tripack material. The name given to colour films and papers in which three separate emulsions are coated on the same support in layers one above the other. Each layer records light from approximately one third the spectrum, i.e. violet-blue, green and red, and colour development (*q.v.*) results in dyes of complementary colour being formed namely, yellow, magenta and cyan respectively. The green- and red-sensitive emulsion layers are sensitized to light of the appropriate wavelengths by the addition of sensitizing dyes to the emulsions, and exposure of these layers by blue light, to which they are naturally sensitive, is prevented by the inclusion of a yellow, blue-absorbing, filter layer between the blue recording and the green and red recording emulsions.

The system is used in both reversal films (transparencies) and negative/positive colour print systems.

Interatomic distances. The distance between the nuclei of two adjacent atoms in a molecule or a crystal can be measured by X-ray analysis, electron diffraction, analysis of spectra, or other physical methods. Interatomic distances can

be considered additive properties of the atomic radii. The interatomic distance can be used to designate the bond order in a compound: e.g.

C—C in aliphatic hydrocarbons	1·54 Å
C—C in graphite	1·42 Å
C—C in benzene	1·39 Å
C—C in ethylene	1·35 Å
C—C in acetylene	1·20 Å

The interatomic distance decreases with increase in bond order.

Intercalation compounds. Derivatives formed by elements or compounds with large lattice spacings in which other molecules are accommodated in the holes in the lattice. The resulting compound may have profoundly altered properties. Thus ferric chloride forms an intercalation compound with graphite, the resulting derivative being stable to water. Intercalation compounds differ from interstitial compounds (*q.v.*) in that they are much less strongly bonded and the lattices are largely unaltered.

Interfacial angles, constancy of. The angle between any particular pair of faces of a particular crystal is constant and is a characteristic of the substance composing the crystal. It does not depend on the size of the crystal.

Interferon. A generic name for substances produced by cells infected with certain viruses and having the property of interfering intracellularly with the replication of the same or other viruses. Commercial production of interferon and its possible use in treating viral diseases (e.g. influenza) are under investigation.

Interhalogen compounds. Compounds formed by the halogen elements with one another. Such compounds are of four types; AB, AB$_3$, AB$_5$, and AB$_7$. The known compounds are ClF, BrF, ClBr, ICl, IBr, ClF$_3$, BrF$_3$, IF$_3$, ICl$_3$, ClF$_5$, BrF$_5$, IF$_5$, and IF$_7$. All these compounds are formed by direct combination of the two halogens. They are readily volatile and exceedingly reactive, especially if the compound in question contains fluorine. No interhalogen compounds are yet known which contain more than two different halogen atoms.

Intermicellar liquid. A synonym for dispersion medium in colloidal systems. See Colloids, Micelle.

Internal compensation. A type of optical activity in which there are two asymmetric centres in the molecule which produce equal and opposite amounts of rotation of the plane of polarization, with the result that the substance is optically inactive.

Internal drum filter. A type of rotary drum filter in which filtration takes place on the inner surface of the drum, this being divided up into a number of segments through which the vacuum is applied. The filter is used for slurries which settle rapidly. It is also known as a Dorrco filter. See Rotary drum filters.

Interstitial compound. Crystalline compounds with a metallic or atomic lattice composed essentially of atoms of an element M, but with atoms or ions of another sort inserted in the interstices between the atoms of M. Palladium hydride is a substance of this type. The essential lattice is that of palladium, but the normal distance between the metal atoms is increased by the presence of hydrogen atoms. Certain other well-known compounds, e.g. the refractory carbides, nitrides, and borides belong to the same class.

Inulin, $(C_6H_{10}O_5)_x$. A fructose polysaccharide, being a chain of some 30 fructofuranose units united by 1:2-junctions. It is present in the underground tubers and rhizomes of the *Compositae*. It is readily hydrolysed by acids. It has $[\alpha]_D -40°$.

Invar. See Nickel alloys.

Invariant system. A system in equilibrium is said to be invariant when it has no degrees of freedom. See Phase rule.

Inversion. See Stereospecific reactions; Walden inversion; Invertase.

Inversion temperature. Most gases are cooled by rapid expansion (the Joule-Thomson effect). Below $-80°$ hydrogen shows this effect, but above this temperature it behaves abnormally and is actually warmed by expansion. This temperature is called the inversion temperature. Helium behaves in a similar manner and has an inversion temperature of $-240°$.

Invertase (Sucrase). The enzyme which hydrolyses sucrose to a mixture of glucose and fructose. The optical rotation changes from positive to negative, and the process is therefore termed inversion. Invertase is present in nearly all yeasts; the amount of it may be considerably increased by allowing the yeast repeatedly to ferment strong sugar solutions. The yeast is allowed to autolyse and the enzyme precipitated by the addition of an equal volume of strong alcohol and later purified by adsorption and elution. Its behaviour has been extensively studied. In particular it inverts sucrose remarkably quickly; the most active preparations are 1200 times as active as the original dry material. Invertase is an article of commerce used in making syrups for the confectionery trade.

Invert sugar. The name given to the mixture of equal parts of glucose and fructose obtained by hydrolysing sucrose. Sucrose is dextrorotatory, $[\alpha]_D = +66·5°$, whereas invert sugar is laevorotatory, $[\alpha]_D = -20·6°$.

Iodates. Salts of iodic acid.

Iodic acid, HIO_3. A colourless solid, crystallizing in the rhombic system, and formed by evaporating iodine with concentrated nitric acid, heating the product to 200°, dissolving the resulting iodine pentoxide in water, and crystallizing. The solid is very soluble in water, and is deliquescent. The aqueous solution is strongly acidic. Iodic acid has strong oxidizing properties (e.g. it will liberate sulphur from hydrogen sulphide and will oxidize sulphurous acid to sulphuric acid). The salts of this acid are known as iodates. They are formed, together with iodides, by dissolving iodine in aqueous alkalis. Addition of an acid to a solution of an iodide containing an iodate results in the liberation of free iodine owing to the reduction of iodate by iodide ion.

Iodine, I. At.no. 53, At.wt.126·9; m.p. 113·5°, b.p. 184·35°, d 4·93. Iodine occurs in small amounts in sea water and in seaweeds. The ashes of the latter, which are known as kelp, are still a source for the small-scale extraction of the element. The major source at present is the mother liquor from the extraction of sodium nitrate from caliche, which occurs in Chile. The mother liquor contains about 6 g of sodium iodate per litre, and the iodine is liberated by treatment with sodium bisulphite or sulphur dioxide. Of considerable commercial importance also are certain American oil-well brines, which contain sodium iodide in sufficient concentration to justify recovery of the element.

Iodine will combine, under certain conditions, with the other halogens to form interhalogen compounds (e.g. ICl, IBr, ICl_3, IF_5, IF_7). It combines with hydrogen when heated with formation of hydrogen iodide. The reaction is reversible. It forms iodides with the metals and non-metals. The products from the former are salt-like, and those from the latter have the characteristics of non-metal halides, notably a ready decomposition by water. Iodine also forms a number of oxides and oxy-acids.

Iodine appears to have some basic properties and forms compounds such as iodine acetate $I(CH_3COO)_3$; IPO_4, and $IONO_3$ which are almost certainly covalent compounds with IO bonds. A co-ordinated positive iodine ion occurs in Ipy_2BF_4 and Ipy_2ClO_4 where the iodine is co-ordinated by pyridine. Anionic iodine occurs in complex ions such as ICl_4^- and IF_6^-.

Iodine is a powerful germicide and as such has many uses in medicine. It and its compounds are used in the treatment of hyperthyroidism and other conditions caused by derangement of the thyroid gland. It is also prescribed for rheumatism. Apart from its medical uses, much iodine is used in the manufacture of photographic chemicals. It is also employed in the manufacture of certain dyes.

Iodine chlorides: *Iodine monochloride*, ICl. A dark-red liquid formed by passing chlorine over iodine. There are two modifications: α, the more stable, has m.p. $27.2°$, β has m.p. $13.9°$. Iodine monochloride boils at $97.4°$, and its vapour density just above the boiling point shows that there is no appreciable dissociation. It can be used as a non-aqueous solvent, and in organic chemistry as an iodinating agent. It is decomposed by water into hydrochloric acid, iodine, and iodic acid, and by alkalis into a mixture of chloride, iodide, and iodate.

Iodine trichloride, ICl_3. A lemon-yellow crystalline solid, $d\ 3.12$, formed by the action of excess of chlorine on iodine or iodine monochloride. The solid sublimes and dissociates into the monochloride and free chlorine. Its dissociation is complete at about $80°$. It is hydrolysed by water to form a mixture of hydrochloric acid, iodine monochloride and iodic acid, HIO_3. With alkalis the decomposition is more complete and the products similar. Owing to this hydrolysis iodine trichloride has strong oxidizing properties in presence of water.

Iodine fluorides. *Iodine trifluoride*, IF_3 is a yellow crystalline solid prepared by interaction of iodine and fluorine in an inert solvent at $-78°$. *Iodine pentafluoride*, IF_5, m.p. $9.4°$, b.p. $100.5°$, is prepared by the action of fluorine on iodine. It has found extensive use as a fairly mild fluorinating agent and also acts as a non-aqueous solvent. *Iodine heptafluoride*, IF_7, b.p. about $4.5°$, is formed by passing iodine pentafluoride and fluorine through a platinum tube at $270°$.

IOF_5 is also known.

Iodine oxides. Iodine forms three oxides, I_2O_4, I_4O_9, and I_2O_5. The lowest oxide I_2O_4 is obtained as a yellow powder by heating iodic acid, HIO_3, with concentrated sulphuric acid and treating the product with water. It appears to have a polymeric structure containing IO and IO_3 groups. I_2O_4 dissolves in hot water to form iodine and iodic acid. The oxide I_4O_9 is formed as a yellow solid on warming iodine gently in ozonized oxygen. Its composition is believed to be $I(IO_3)_3$. It absorbs moisture readily, forming iodic acid and iodine. In common with I_2O_4 it liberates chlorine when heated with hydrochloric acid. When heated at $120°$ it decomposes into the pentoxide (I_2O_5), iodine, and oxygen. I_2O_5 is formed by heating iodic acid at $200°$. It is a white solid, which dissolves in water to form iodic acid, and is thus the only acid-forming

oxide of iodine. It is a strong oxidizing agent and is used in analysis for estimating carbon monoxide in gaseous mixtures by oxidizing the monoxide to carbon dioxide and determining the latter volumetrically.

Iodine value. The iodine value of a fat is the amount of iodine that it will absorb expressed as a percentage of the molecular weight of the fat. Thus triolein, mol.wt. 884, absorbs 6 atoms of iodine, at.wt.127. The iodine values is therefore

$$\frac{6 \times 127}{884} \times 100 = 86.2.$$

Saturated fatty acids absorb no iodine; the iodine value is therefore a measure of the proportion of unsaturated fatty acids present in a fat.

Iodized oil. An addition product of hydriodic acid and poppy-seed oil, containing 39-41% of iodine. It is used in X-ray diagnosis as a contrast medium.

Iodoacetic ester. See Ethyl iodoacetate.

Iodobenzene, C_6H_5I. Colourless liquid, b.p. $188°$. Insoluble in water, miscible in all proportions with organic solvents. The iodine atom is very reactive, and is easily removed by metals. With chlorine an addition compound phenyliodochloride ($C_6H_5ICl_2$) is formed, the iodine being tripositive as in iodine trichloride.

Iodobenzene is prepared by direct iodination of benzene with iodine and nitric acid under reflux or from diazotized aniline and potassium iodide.

Iodoform, Triiodomethane, CHI_3, is a yellow crystalline solid having a powerful and characteristic odour, m.p. $119°$. Insoluble in water; soluble in alcohol, ether, and chloroform. It is volatile in steam. Manufactured by the electrolysis of a solution of an iodide in dilute alcohol or acetone. Fresh iodide and alcohol are run in as fast as the iodoform is deposited. Reacts with potassium hydroxide to give methylene iodide. Decomposed slowly by light and air to carbon dioxide, carbon monoxide, iodine, and water.

It is used in medicine as an antiseptic.

Iodoform reaction. A test used to detect the presence of a $CO \cdot CH_3$ group (or groups which may be converted to this under the reaction conditions). Iodine in alkali converts the acetyl group into iodoform.

$$I_2 + 2NaOH \rightarrow NaI + NaOI + H_2O$$
$$RCOCH_3 + 3NaOI \rightarrow RCOCI_3 + 3NaOH$$
$$RCOCI_3 + NaOH \rightarrow RCO_2Na + HCI_3$$

Iodogorgic acid. See 3,5-Diiodotyrosine.

Iodomethane. See Methyl iodide.

Iodophthalein. The sodium salt of tetra-

iodophenolphthalein $C_{20}H_8I_4Na_2O_4,3H_2O$. Blue-violet crystals, soluble in 7 parts of water, slightly soluble in alcohol. Prepared by iodinating phenolphthalein and used medicinally to render the gall bladder opaque to X-rays.

Ion. An ion is an atom or group of atoms which has gained or lost one or more electrons, and thus carries a negative or a positive charge. Ions are present in solutions of electrolytes in solvents of high dielectric constant. They are generally complexed by the solvent.

Ions also exist in gases which have been subjected to suitable electric disturbances such as a high-tension discharge, or a beam of electrons.

The word is also used to denote a unit in a solid crystal of an electrovalent compound such as sodium chloride in which each sodium atom or ion is electrically attracted by the surrounding chlorine atoms or ions, and each chlorine atom or ion is electrically attracted by the surrounding sodium atoms or ions. The structure of such crystals is termed ionic to indicate that the crystal is not an aggregate of independent molecules.

Ionamine dyes. These dyes wre among the first to be successfully introduced for acetate rayon. They were salts of ω-sulphonic acids of various insoluble aminoazo and aminoanthraquinone compounds, which hydrolysed in the dyeing process with the result that the amino compound was taken up by the fibre. By subsequently diazotizing and developing, deeper shades of improved washing fastness were obtained.

The ionamines are now quite obsolete, as the dyeing process was lengthy and the general fastness properties were only moderate.

Ion exchange. When an ionogenic surface (q.v.) is in contact with water or other ionizing solvent an electrical double layer (q.v.) is set up. The counter-ions are partially free and can readily be exchanged for others of the same sign supplied by soluble electrolytes. Thus the sodium in certain silicates can be replaced by potassium by exhaustively washing the material with a solution of potassium chloride (see Base exchange).

This is one example of the widespread phenomenon of ion exchange. It is exploited particularly with ion-exchange resins. These are synthetic insoluble cross-linked polymers carrying acidic or basic side-groups. They have high exchange capacity and can be used for an almost unlimited number of reactions. They have many applications, including water-treatment, extraction, separation, analysis, and catalysis. Using a 'mixed bed' of anion and cation exchange resins the electrolytes can be removed from a water solution, and very pure water obtained.

Ion exchange equipment. For water treatment, which is the major field of application of ion exchange, fixed beds of resin and cyclic operation are employed. This is because the regeneration period is small compared with the operating period. In the case of chemical processing applications the regeneration period may be much longer than the operating period, and to avoid a large plant and resin inventory more efficient continuous processes with counter-current flow have been devised. These are used for such applications as the recovery of uranium and plutonium from process solutions.

Ion exclusion. The medium inside the pores of an ion-exchange resin is subject to the Donnan membrane equilibrium. It therefore contains a lower concentration than does the external solution of any electrolytes that may be present in the latter. This is 'ion exclusion'. On the other hand, non-electrolytes are not subject to the Donnan effect. Hence, a partial separation of electrolytes from non-electrolytes can be obtained; by using a chromatographic technique complete separation can be effected in favourable cases.

Ionic atmosphere. As a result of the Debye-Hückel theory of interionic attraction, it was shown that in solutions ions of one charge type are surrounded by an atmosphere of ions predominately of the opposite charge type. The effect felt by the central ion is the same in all directions. When an electric field is applied in the solution, however, the central ion moves in one direction whereas the ionic atmosphere moves in the opposite sense giving rise to an asymmetric distribution of ions about the central ion. This effect is important in studies of electrical conductivities of solutions.

Ionic mobility. See Mobility, ionic.

Ionic product. The product of the concentrations of the ions of a substance in solution, which is a constant for weakly ionized substances, because the concentration of undissociated material may be taken to be constant, if it is present in a large excess. See Solubility product.

Ionic radii. The effective radius of an ion in a crystal lattice. Typical ionic radii are:

(figures in Å)

Li^+	0·60	Be^{2+}	0·31	Al^{3+}	0·50
Na^+	0·95	Mg^{2+}	0·65	Sc^{3+}	0·81
K^+	1·33	Ca^{2+}	0·99	Y^{3+}	0·93
Rb^+	1·48	Sr^{2+}	1·13	La^{3+}	1·15
Cs^+	1·69	Ba^{2+}	1·35		
Mn^{2+}	0·80	Cu^+	0·96	Zn^{2+}	0·74
Fe^{2+}	0·75	Ag^+	1·26	Cd^{2+}	0·97
Co^{2+}	0·72	Au^+	1·37	Hg^{2+}	1·10
Ni^{2+}	0·69	Tl^+	1·44		
H^-	2·08	O^{2-}	1·40		
F^-	1·36	S^{2-}	1·84		
Cl^-	1·81	Se^{2-}	1·98		
Br^-	1·95	Te^{2-}	2·21		
I^-	2·16				

Ionium, ^{230}Th. An isotope of thorium.

Ionization chamber. A device for measuring the absolute intensity of an X-ray beam or a beam of ionizing particles, by allowing the rays or particles to ionize the vapour contained in the chamber and measuring the resulting current flowing between suitably placed and charged electrodes. See Counters.

Ionization of water. Pure water has a very low electrical conductivity (specific conductivity about 5×10^{-8}ohm^{-1}cm^{-1}) for it is only very slightly ionized.

The concentration of hydrogen ions, which is equal to that of the hydroxyl ions, is only 10^{-7} g equivalents per litre. The ionic product, $[H^+][OH^-]$ is 10^{-14} at 25°, but increases rapidly with temperature. The pH of pure water is clearly 7. Any solution in which the pH > 7 is thus alkaline (excess of hydroxyl ions), and those with pH < 7 (excess of hydrogen ions) are acid.

Ionization, heat of. The amount of heat required to split one gram molecule of an electrolyte into its ions. For water, the heat required to split one gram molecule (18 grams) into one gram of hydrogen ion and 17 grams of hydroxyl ion is 13,700 calories.

Ionization potential. The energy required to remove an electron from an atom or an ion. Normally measured in electron volts per gram atom.

Ionogenic surface. The charge on a colloidal particle is responsible for its stability and is ionic in nature. If the stabilizing ions on the surface are due to ionization of the wall material of which the particle is formed, the surface is said to be *ionogenic*.

Ionone, $C_{13}H_{20}O$. When pseudoionone (see Citral) is treated with certain reagents such as sodium bisulphate, dilute nitric acid, strong sulphuric acid, or phosphoric acid, a mixture of α- and β-ionone is formed. These products are of commercial importance, being powerful odorants, smelling strongly of violets.

α-Ionone is

It can be separated from β-ionone by distilling the mixed sodium bisulphite compounds in steam when the β-ionone distils, leaving the α-compound, which yields α-ionone by treatment with alkali. α-Ionone has the constants b.p. 123°-124°/11 mm, d^{20} 0·932, n_D^{20} 1·4980. It forms an oxime of m.p. 89°-90°. It has a sweeter smell, more closely resembling that of violets, than the β-compound.

β-Ionone is

It is separated from the α-compound in the manner already described, and has the constants b.p. 140°/18 mm, d^{17} 0·946, n^{17} 1·521. It smells like cedar wood, but has a strong smell of violets in dilute solution. It forms a semi-carbazone of m.p. 148°-149°.

Ion-pair. The Debye-Hückel theory of interionic attraction in solution satisfactorily interprets the behaviour of very dilute electrolyte solutions where long-range interionic effects are important. When the ions are close together, the approximations made in the theory no longer hold and the energy of the mutual attraction of ions is great enough to give rise to the formation of ion-pairs in solution which are capable of withstanding collisions with solvent molecules. This effect is more pronounced in mixed and non-aqueous solvent systems and there is evidence for triple ion pairing in some instances.

Ions (hydration of). See Hydration (of ions).

Ipatieff, Vladimir (1867-1952). Born in Moscow, Ipatieff received his education in military schools, and in 1892 graduated from the Michailow Academy, St. Petersburg. Later he studied chemistry under von Baeyer (Munich) and Vieille (Paris). In 1927 he organized the Institute of High Pressures in Leningrad, but in 1931 he migrated to America, where he became associated with Northwestern University and the Universal Oil Products Company. His investigation of the catalytic chemistry of unsaturated hydrocarbons led to important developments in the oil industry.

Ipecacuanha. The dried root of *Cephaelis ipecacuanha*, a plant indigenous to Brazil. It is used in the form of the powdered drug, a liquid extract, or a tincture. Its medicinal properties are due to alkaloids, of which emetine and cephaeline are the most important. In small doses it is an expectorant, in larger doses an emetic.

Iridates. Deep blue compounds prepared by fusing finely-divided iridium metal with sodium nitrate or sodium peroxide. The nature of these compounds is not known but they appear to contain iridium (VI).

Iridium, Ir. At.no.77, At.wt.193·1. A hard white brittle metal having the face-centred cubic structure ($a = 3·8389$ Å), m.p. 2410°, b.p. 4350°, d 22·65. It is very resistant to chemical attack, and unless very finely divided is quite unaffected by aqua regia. It may be brought into solution by fusion with potassium bisulphate or with oxidizing melts such as potassium nitrate and caustic potash. In its compounds it has oxidation states of -1, 0, 1, 2, 3, 4, 5, and 6. It is mainly used in the form of its alloys with platinum or with osmium (see Osmiridium) for various purposes requiring very hard and incorrodible materials. Iridium compounds are used as catalysts.

Iridium ammines. Tripositive iridium forms very stable ammines of the types [IrA$_4$X$_2$]X, and IrA$_3$X$_3$ (X = halide, NO$_2^-$, NCS$^-$, etc.; A = amine or ammonia). These compounds are very similar to the cobaltammines. Some tetrapositive ammines, e.g. Ir(NH$_3$)$_4$Cl$_2$(NO$_3$)$_2$ can be prepared by oxidation of the corresponding tripositive compounds.

Iridium bromides. IrBr is made by heating the dibromide to 485°. It is a dark brown substance only slightly soluble in water. IrBr$_2$ is brownish-red in colour; it is prepared by heating the hydrated tribromide. Iridium tribromide, IrBr$_3$, is obtained from the hydroxide and aqueous hydrobromic acid. Hydrates with 4 and 1 molecoles of water are known. Complex bromides, e.g. K$_3$IrBr$_6$·4H$_2$O, are known. Hexabromoiridates (IV) M$_2$IrBr$_6$, are deep blue-black salts, prepared from the blue solution made by dissolving Ir(OH)$_4$ in hydrobromic acid.

Iridium carbonyls. Two carbonyls, [Ir(CO$_3$)]$_4$, yellow crystals, subliming at 200°, and [Ir(CO$_4$)]$_2$, greenish-yellow, are prepared by heating the trihalides with carbon monoxide at 100° under 200 atm. pressure. Many carbonyl phosphines and carbonyl halides of iridium are known.

Iridium chlorides. IrCl, IrCl$_2$, IrCl$_3$, and IrCl$_4$ are known. IrCl and IrCl$_2$ are inert insoluble substances formed by the partial dissociation of IrCl$_3$ in an atmosphere of chlorine, over a narrow range of temperature in the neighbourhood of 770°.

The anhydrous trichloride is formed in the dry way by heating (NH$_4$)$_2$IrCl$_6$ in chlorine. It is an olive-green crystalline substance, and is quite insoluble in water, alkalis, or acids. On the other hand, solutions containing IrCl$_3$ can be prepared by wet methods, and from them soluble hydrated chlorides IrCl$_3$·3H$_2$O and IrCl$_3$·1·5H$_2$O can be crystallized. An oxychloride, IrCl$_2$(OH) aq. can be obtained by the action of hydrogen chloride on iridium tetrahydroxide.

The tetrachloride is a brownish-black hygroscopic substance, which is formed when (NH$_4$)$_2$IrCl$_6$ is evaporated with chlorine water, or when the hydrated dioxide dissolves in hydrochloric acid. It is very soluble in water, and is easily reduced to the trichloride.

Iridium chlorides, complex. Potassium chloroiridate (III), K$_3$IrCl$_6$, 3H$_2$O, is easily obtained by gentle reduction of a solution of the chloroiridate (IV), and other chloroiridates (III) may be obtained by double decomposition. They are olive-green crystalline salts, easily soluble in water. Pentahalide complexes. M$_2$IrCl$_5$(H$_2$O) are obtained in a similar manner.

The chloroiridates (IV), M$_2$IrCl$_6$ (where M is a unipositive ion) are deep red or black substances, usually isomorphous with the chloroplatinates (IV). They are formed when the metal is heated in chlorine in presence of an alkali chloride. K$_2$IrCl$_6$ and (NH$_4$)$_2$IrCl$_6$ are only slightly soluble in water.

Iridium fluorides. *Iridium hexafluoride* IrF$_6$, is obtained by interaction of the elements. It is a yellow solid, m.p. 44°, b.p. 53°, which gives a yellow gas. It is rapidly hydrolysed by water.

Iridium tetrafluoride, IrF$_4$. The tetrafluoride is best prepared by the action of iridium hexafluoride on glass at about 100°. It is a yellow solid, m.p. 106°-107°, rapidly hydrolysed by water.

Iridium trifluoride, IrF$_3$, is prepared by reduction of the tetrafluoride with sulphur tetrafluoride. It is a black solid.

Iridium iodides. IrI is a black substance made by heating the tri-iodide. The di-iodide, IrI$_2$, is obtained similarly. Both lower iodides are only slightly soluble in water. Dark brown crystals of the tri-iodide, IrI$_3$, result when the trihydroxide is treated with hydriodic acid; hydrates with 4 and 1 molecules of water are known; it is only very slightly soluble in water.

Iridium oxides. Anhydrous Ir$_2$O$_3$, the sesquioxide, can be made by igniting K$_2$IrCl$_6$ with sodium carbonate. A hydrated sesquioxide, Ir$_2$O$_3$, 5H$_2$O, is precipitated by alkalis (excess being avoided) from solutions containing tri-positive iridium. It is a greenish or black amorphous precipitate, which cannot be completely washed free from alkali, and cannot be dehydrated without decomposition. It is soluble in both acids and alkalis, and the alkaline solutions are oxidized by air, the hydrated dioxide being precipitated.

IrO_2 is formed by the prolonged action of oxygen on the finely-divided metal at about 1000°, and can be obtained by other dry methods, or by dehydration of its hydrate, $IrO_2,2H_2O$ or $Ir(OH)_4$. The latter is formed by precipitation from solutions containing tetra-positive iridium, or by the oxidation with air or hydrogen peroxide of the hydrated sesquioxide or its alkaline solutions. They are both black substances. The hydrated form, when freshly precipitated, is readily soluble in acids, but becomes less so on drying, and the anhydrous dioxide dissolves only very slowly in hydrochloric, and not at all in other acids.

Non-stoicheiometric IrO_3 can be made by igniting iridium with potassium hydroxide and potassium nitrate; it occurs in the iridates (q.v.). Iridium volatilizes in air as the trioxide.

Iridium sulphates. $Ir_2(SO_4)_3,6H_2O$ is obtained by crystallizing, in the complete absence of air, a solution of the sesquioxide in sulphuric acid. It is a yellow crystalline substance, and it, and especially its solution, are very easily oxidized on exposure to air, becoming violet. It forms a series of yellow alums when its solution is mixed with those of alkali sulphates and crystallized; these are rather more stable.

Iridium sulphides. Ir_2S_3 is a brown precipitate formed by the action of hydrogen sulphide on solutions of tripositive iridium. IrS_2 and Ir_3S_8 have been prepared by dry methods. All are attacked by aqua-regia, but not by hydrochloric acid.

Irisin, $(C_6H_{10}O_5)_x$. A polymer of fructose present in the rhizomes of Iris species. The polymerizing unit is a difructose in which the junction is between carbons 2 and 4. It has $[\alpha]_D - 52 \cdot 6°$; the methyl derivative is hydrolysed to tetra- and di-methylfructose in the ratio 1:1.

Iron, Fe. At.no. 26, At.wt.55·85, m.p. 1539°, b.p. 2735°, d 7·87. The metal is body-centred cubic below 950°, $a = 2 \cdot 8664$ Å; face-centred cubic up to 1425°, $a = 3 \cdot 656$ Å, and body-centred cubic to 1425°, $a = 2 \cdot 94$ Å. The metal has pronounced ferromagnetic properties.

It was known in Egypt about 5000 years ago and made its way into Europe about 2000 years later. Meteoric iron contains cobalt and nickel; compounds of iron are found in most clays, sandstones, and granitic rocks. The chief ores are hematite (haematite), Fe_2O_3, brown hematite (hydrated Fe_2O_3), magnetite, Fe_3O_4, siderite or spathic iron ore, $FeCO_3$, iron pyrites, FeS_2, and chalcopyrite, $CuFeS_2$.

Iron is usually prepared from oxide or carbonate ores, from which sulphur, arsenic, etc., have been removed by roasting in air, by reduction with carbon. The ore is mixed with coke and limestone and heated in a blast furnace, the maximum temperature of which is about 1300°. The major acidic impurities are removed as slag (calcium silicate, aluminate, etc.) and the molten crude metal run off into pigs; pig-iron contains from 2 to 4% of carbon with a little phosphorus, sulphur, and silicon. If the silicon content is high the carbon is present almost entirely as graphite; on remelting and casting, such an alloy gives grey cast iron. If the silicon content is low, the carbon is present as cementite, Fe_3C, and gives white cast iron on casting. The sulphur content governs that of manganese, since excessive sulphur forms manganese sulphide, which is appreciably soluble in the slag.

The cast irons are too brittle for many purposes. Wrought iron is made by melting cast iron with scrap-iron in a reverberatory furnace (puddling furnace) lined with Fe_2O_3, which oxidizes carbon, silicon, etc., most of which are then removed by rolling. Cast iron melts at about 1200°. Wrought iron, which is tough, fibrous, and malleable, melts at above 1500°, though it softens at about 1000°. It is not hardened by quenching.

Most iron is now converted into steel by the Bessemer process, Siemens-Martin process, or electrical process. Steel is a mixture of iron with iron carbide, Fe_3C (cementite). Iron will dissolve carbon as well as combine with it and all iron made on the large scale contains some carbon.

Iron that has been in contact with concentrated nitric acid becomes passive owing to the formation of a protective layer of oxide.

See also articles on Cast irons, Cementation process, Cementite, Iron ores, Magnetite, Martensite, Siemens process, Steel, Wrought iron.

Iron acetates. *Ferric acetate* is a complex $(Fe_3Ac_6)Ac_3$. The dihydrate, $Fe(CH_3COO)_3 \cdot 2H_2O$ can only be crystallized with difficulty. Its deep red solutions are hydrolysed on boiling, with precipitation of a basic acetate.

Ferrous acetate, $Fe(CH_3COO)_2$, $4H_2O$, forms pale green crystals, readily soluble in water. The solution oxidizes rather rapidly on exposure to air.

Iron alums. Double salts of ferric sulphate, having the general formula $M_2^1SO_4$, $Fe_2(SO_4)_3$, $24H_2O$ (or $M^1Fe(SO_4)_2$, $12H_2O$). M^1 is an alkali metal, ammonium, or thallium (I), hydroxyl-amine, etc. Ordinary 'iron alum' or 'ferric alum' is ferric ammonium sulphate ($M^1 =$ ammonium); it forms pale amethyst-coloured crystals, readily soluble in water, and is prepared by crystallizing an aqueous solution containing the calculated quantities of ammonium and ferric sulphates.

Iron ammonium sulphate. *Ferrous ammonium sulphate*, $(NH_4)_2SO_4$, $FeSO_4$, $6H_2O$, 'Mohr's salt,' may be obtained as pale green monoclinic crystals from a solution of its constituents. It is frequently used as a standard for potassium permanganate and other volumetric oxidizing agents, being less readily oxidized in air than ferrous sulphate; its use as a primary standard is not to be recommended, as it may be contaminated with isomorphous double-sulphates of zinc or magnesium, which are not removed on recrystallization. Solubility: 20 g at 15°, and 52 g at 70°, in 100 g H_2O.

Iron bromides. *Ferric bromide*, $FeBr_3$, $6H_2O$, is deposited when its solutions, obtained by the usual wet methods, are evaporated over sulphuric acid at ordinary temperatures. It forms dark green needles, m.p. 27°. The *anhydrous salt* is formed when the metal is heated in bromine vapour, as dark red deliquescent crystals. The anhydrous and hydrated salts and the solution all undergo partial dissociation to ferrous bromide and bromine on heating.

Ferrous bromide, $FeBr_2$, may be obtained by the usual methods, and is readily soluble in water. Hydrates with 9, 6, 4, and $2H_2O$ are known.

Iron buff (Pigment Brown 6 and 7), (Hydrated ferric oxide). Incorporated into the weighting of silk for black dyeing and is a component of the highly important Mineral Khaki, still very widely used for dyeing cotton for uniforms, narrow fabrics, etc., for H.M. Forces. The material is impregnated with a mixture of chromic and ferric sulphates, and then passed into a warm sodium carbonate solution. The khaki shade which results has extremely high fastness to light, washing and mud, and can hold its own against similar shades produced entirely from synthetic dyestuffs. It is also widely used for paints and enamels.

Iron carbonate. *Ferrous carbonate*, $FeCO_3$, is precipitated by sodium carbonate from solutions of ferrous salts as a white powder, or it may be obtained crystalline (hexagonal) by heating the solutions in a sealed tube. Complete absence of air is necessary as it oxidizes very readily. It occurs in nature as spathic iron ore, or if crystalline, siderite. It is soluble in water containing

excess of carbon dioxide, but the bicarbonate has not been isolated.

Iron carbonyls. Iron forms three carbonyls, $Fe(CO)_5$, $Fe_2(CO)_9$, and $[Fe(CO)_4]_3$, and also a number of derivatives of these. Iron pentacarbonyl, $Fe(CO)_5$, is formed by the direct union of carbon monoxide with the metal; the reaction is best carried out at 200° and 300 atmospheres. It is a pale-yellow liquid, m.p. $-20°$, b.p. 102°, sp.gr. 1·494 at 0°. On exposure to sunlight it deposits the nonacarbonyl, $Fe_2(CO)_9$, as orange crystals, and this when heated in an inert atmosphere, with a suitable organic solvent yields the tetracarbonyl $[Fe(CO)_4]_3$. This is a dark green crystalline body. These compounds are all typically non-polar substances, soluble in organic solvents, and they all dissociate on heating into carbon monoxide and the metal. Many derivatives of the pentacarbonyl are known, such as $Fe(CO)_4X_2$, where X is a halogen, and $Fe(CO)_4H_2$, which in some respects behaves as a weak acid, the hydrogen being replaceable by metals.

Iron chlorides. *Ferric chloride*, $FeCl_3$. The anhydrous salt is prepared by heating the metal in a stream of chlorine, when it condenses in the cool part of the apparatus as scales which are green by reflected but red by transmitted light. When heated under pressure it melts at 301°, but it sublimes at 280°-285°. Its vapour density corresponds with the formula Fe_2Cl_6 at moderate temperatures, but above 500° dissociation occurs to ferrous chloride and free chlorine. It is very deliquescent and soluble in water, and forms a number of hydrates. The concentrated solutions are partially hydrolysed and brownish-yellow in colour. A number of complex chlorides exist: K_2FeCl_5, H_2O forms red deliquescent crystals, and $(NH_4)_2FeCl_5$, H_2O (garnet cubes) is used medicinally under the name of 'ammonio-chloride of iron.'

Ferrous chloride, $FeCl_2$. The anhydrous salt is formed in white crystalline scales when the metal is heated in dry hydrogen chloride. It volatilizes at red heat, and the vapour density is normal above 1300°, but below this temperature association occurs. In organic solvents the mol. wt. is normal. The salt readily absorbs up to six molecules of ammonia. From its solutions it crystallizes as a rule as the *tetrahydrate*, $FeCl_2$, $4H_2O$, in bluish-green monoclinic crystals. Other hydrates with 6, 2, and 1 H_2O exist. The salt is readily soluble in water. *Double salts* with alkali chlorides are known, e.g. $KFeCl_3 \cdot 2H_2O$.

Iron, complex cyanides. Iron forms many complex cyanides. Of these the best known are the ferro- and ferricyanides (*q.v.*) containing $[Fe(CN)_6]^{4-}$ and $[Fe(CN)_6]^{3-}$ ions. Other complexes in which at least one cyanide group is substituted by another ligand are known. The *nitrosyl pentacyanoferrates (II)* (nitroprussides) contain the ion $[Fe(CN)_5(NO)]^{2-}$. They are prepared by heating potassium ferrocyanide with nitric acid. The sodium salt forms red rhombic prisms and its solution may be used as a sensitive test for sulphides with which it gives a deep violet colour. *Carbonyl pentacyanoferrates* [II] contain the ion $[Fe(CN)_5CO]^{3-}$ and are formed when moist carbon monoxide is passed over ferrocyanides at about 130°. *Monoaquopentacyanoferrates* [III], containing the ion $[Fe(CN)_5H_2O]^{2-}$ result from the action of chlorine on potassium ferrocyanide; on reduction this ion yields the *monoaquopentacyanoferrate* [II] containing the $[Fe(CN)_5(H_2O)]^{3-}$ ion. Nitro, sulphito, and ammine derivatives are known. See Sidgwick 'The Chemical Elements and their Compounds,' p. 1359.

Iron fluorides. *Ferric fluoride*, FeF_3. Anhydrous ferric fluoride may be obtained by the action of hydrogen fluoride on heated ferric oxide or by dehydration of the hydrates in an atmosphere of hydrogen fluoride. It is only slightly soluble in water. The solutions obtained by addition of fluoride ions to ferric solution contain complex ions. From its solutions the salt crystallizes as FeF_3, $4\frac{1}{2}H_2O$, or at higher temperatures as FeF_3, $3H_2O$. It forms complex fluoroferrates (III). Na_3FeF may be obtained as a white, sparingly soluble precipitate from a solution of a ferric salt and sodium fluoride.

Ferrous fluoride, FeF_2, may be obtained in the anhydrous condition as colourless tetragonal crystals by the action of dry hydrogen fluoride on heated iron. It is soluble in water and from the solution may be crystallized as FeF_2, $4H_2O$, in pale-green prisms. A number of *double salts* with fluorides of the alkali metals, e.g. $KFeF_3$, are known.

Iron hydroxides. *Ferric hydroxides.* Naturally-occurring hydrated ferric oxides are known generally as brown haematites; their composition may range from Fe_2O_3, $\frac{1}{2}H_2O$ to Fe_2O_3, $4H_2O$. Among the many varieties are goethite, Fe_2O_3, H_2O (crystalline, rhombic), and limonite, Fe_2O_3, $1\frac{1}{2}H_2O$. Some specimens of the latter are used as pigments, and are known as ochres, umbers, and siennas. The precipitated hydroxide is a voluminous brownish precipitate, whose colour and degree of hydration vary with the conditions. When freshly precipitated it is readily soluble in dilute acids, but on prolonged boiling it approaches the composition Fe_2O_3, H_2O and becomes denser and then dissolves in acids only with difficulty.

All the hydrates appear to fall into two series, the α- and γ-series, of which it may be said as a broad generalization that the former result from

precipitation of a ferric salt and the latter by oxidation. The γ-series are the less stable and are ferromagnetic. α-FeO·OH is identical with goethite, γ-FeO·OH occurs naturally as lepidocrocite. On dehydration at not too high temperatures the α- and γ-hydroxides yield respectively α- and γ-Fe_2O_3.

Colloidal ferric hydroxide may fairly easily be obtained as a deep red hydrosol by partial hydrolysis of ferric chloride solutions followed by dialysis.

Ferrosoferric hydroxide, Fe_3O_4, H_2O or Fe_3O_4, $1\frac{1}{2}H_2O$, may be obtained as a blue-green or black precipitate either by oxidation of ferrous hydroxide or by the action of alkalis on a mixture of a ferrous and a ferric salt. It is only very slowly further oxidized by air.

Ferrous hydroxide, $Fe(OH)_2$, is thrown down by caustic alkalis from solutions of ferrous salts. If prepared in the complete absence of air it is white, but is usually greenish, and on exposure to air it oxidizes rapidly to the blue-green ferrosoferric hydroxide, and at the boiling-point it even reduces water. It has been obtained in the crystalline form (hexagonal prisms) by deposition from hot concentrated alkalis. Its solubility in water is of the order of 10^{-5} mols per litre; it is rather more soluble in caustic alkalis and dissolves readily in dilute acids.

Iron iodide. *Ferrous iodide*, FeI_2, may be obtained as deep red plates by grinding together iron powder and iodine. It is readily soluble in water, and hydrates with 9, 6, 5, 4, and $1H_2O$ are known. The solutions are unstable in air, readily absorbing oxygen with liberation of iodine.

Iron nitrates. *Ferric nitrate*, $Fe(NO_3)_3$, $9H_2O$, forms deliquescent monoclinic crystals which are very soluble in water. A cubic *hexahydrate* also exists. The pure salt is pale amethyst in colour but impure salts are colourless. The solution is brown owing to hydrolysis.

Ferrous nitrate, $Fe(NO_3)_2$, $6H_2O$, may be obtained by cautious evaporation at moderate temperatures of solutions obtained by dissolving the metal in sufficiently dilute nitric acid (sp.gr. 1·035 to 1·115) or by suitable double decompositions. It forms bright green rhombic prisms which are readily soluble in water. Its m.p. is 60·5°, and above this temperature it decomposes. The anhydrous salt is unknown, but an enneahydrate is known at low temperatures.

Iron ores. The chief ores used from the production of iron are:

(1) *Magnetite* mined in large quantities in Sweden, is often magnetised, always ferromagnetic. Pure magnetite is Fe_3O_4. Magnetic separation is employed in separating the ore from foreign matter. The ores contain up to 66% Fe.

(2) *Haematites* approximate to the composition Fe_2O_3; a variety called red haematite occurs in kidney-shaped masses. The haematites are low in sulphur and phosphorus, and contain up to 60% Fe.

(3) *Limonites* or *Brown haematites*, are hydrated oxides of the form $2Fe_2O_3 + 3H_2O$. They occur in Lincolnshire and Northamptonshire.

(4) *Spathic iron ores*, black band or Cleveland ironstones are more or less pure $FeCO_3$. The term clay ironstone is used for impure $FeCO_3$, which may contain up to 15% of clayey matter. These clay-containing ores are often 'self-fluxing,' as they contain sufficient calcium and magnesium carbonate for neutralisation of the acidic oxides present. This effects a great economy in limestone.

Iron oxalates. *Ferric oxalate*, $Fe_2(C_2O_4)_3 . 5H_2O$ is difficult to isolate as it decomposes in sunlight, but the green *oxalatoferrates* (III) such as $K_3Fe(C_2O_4)_3 \cdot 3H_2O$ may be easily crystallized.

Ferrous oxalate, $FeC_2O_4, 2H_2O$, is a yellow precipitate. It dissolves in excess of alkali oxalate, giving a brown solution from which unstable oxalatoferrates (II) such as $K_2Fe(C_2O_4)_2$ may be crystallized.

Iron oxides. *Ferric oxide*, Fe_2O_3, may be obtained by all the usual methods. Various specimens differ rather widely in colour and other properties in accordance with the degree of mechanical sub-division, but there are only two essentially different modifications. Of these the stable α-form is rhombohedral. It occurs in nature, massive as red haematite and crystallized as specular iron-ore. For use as a pigment it is manufactured by ignition of natural ferric hydroxides (ochres), and products obtained under different conditions differ in tint, and are given special names.

Ferric oxide is only soluble in acids with difficulty, and if strongly ignited becomes quite insoluble. At about 1500°, in the absence of oxygen, or at very high temperatures in air, it undergoes dissociation to Fe_3O_4. The finely divided substance has marked catalytic activity, e.g. in the decomposition of potassium chlorate or the combination of sulphur dioxide and oxygen.

The γ-modification crystallizes in cubes and is ferromagnetic. It is formed by the oxidation of Fe_3O_4 or by the dehydration of γ-FeO·OH. When strongly heated it changes over to the stable form.

Ferroso-ferric oxide, (magnetic oxide of iron) Fe_3O_4, occurs in nature as magnetite, and is formed in a number of reactions, e.g. when the metal is heated in steam, or by dissociation of ferric oxide at very high temperatures. It is a black substance, of rather metallic appearance, crystallizes in octahedra, and is ferromagnetic. It has a spinel structure $Fe^{II}Fe^{III}_2O_4$. It dissolves in hydrochloric acid, affording a mixture of ferrous and ferric chlorides.

Ferrous oxide, FeO, may be obtained by reduction of higher oxides, or by ignition (in an inert atmosphere) of such salts as the oxalate or carbonate. Ferrous oxide is normally non-stoicheiometric with a deficiency of iron. At temperatures below 570° it is unstable with respect to Fe_3O_4 and Fe, although the decomposition is slow. It crystallizes in the cubic system (NaCl type), has sp.gr. 5·9, and melts at about 1360°. Its properties depend on the method of preparation, and specimens obtained at low temperatures are extremely oxidizable, and may even be pyrophoric. It dissolves readily in dilute acids.

Iron phosphates. Various phosphates of iron (II) and iron (III) are known. $FePO_4 \cdot 2H_2O$ is soluble in dilute mineral acids but not in acetic acid. Complex phosphates are known. The iron phosphate of medicine is a dark blue powder containing about 50% of $Fe_3(PO_4)_2$, $8H_2O$, together with some ferric phosphate and hydrated ferric oxides.

Iron sulphates. *Ferric sulphate*. Anhydrous ferric sulphate, $Fe_2(SO_4)_3$, may be obtained as a white powder by heating the hydrated salts, or by heating ferric salts with ammonium sulphate. Although readily soluble in water, it dissolves only very slowly, and may appear to be almost insoluble. It decomposes at 530° into ferric oxide and sulphur trioxide. The solution is brown because of hydrolysis. Hydrates with 12, 10, 9, 7, 6, and $3H_2O$ are known, but evaporation usually leads to the deposition of a mixture of an acid and a basic salt.

The *acid sulphate*, $Fe_2(SO_4)_3, H_2SO_4, 8H_2O$, is deposited from solutions containing a sufficient excess of sulphuric acid. It forms complex sulphates, e.g. $NH_4[Fe(SO_4)_2]$ and $K[Fe(SO_4)_2]$, H_2O. These may be obtained by heating their constituents in solution for some hours, when they are deposited as white, sparingly soluble substances.

Ferrous sulphate, $FeSO_4, 7H_2O$, is the best-known ferrous salt, and is sometimes called 'green vitriol' or 'copperas.' Commercially, it is normally obtained from the waste liquor resulting from the pickling of steel in sulphuric acid. The heptahydrate normally crystallizes in the monoclinic system, but a metastable rhombic form also exists. Other hydrates may be obtained having 5 and 1 H_2O, the last-named retaining its water up to rather high temperatures ($> 140°$). It is easily soluble in water. Anhydrous $FeSO_4$, obtained by dehydrating the hydrates, is white and very hygroscopic. It decomposes at red heat, yielding ferric oxide, sulphur trioxide, and sulphur dioxide. The solution is gradually oxidized on exposure to air, a basic ferric sulphate being deposited. Ferrous sulphate forms a series of double salts of the type $M_2^I SO_4$, $FeSO_4$, $6H_2O$ with the sulphates of the alkali group. The best known is ferrous ammonium sulphate, Mohr's salt.

Iron sulphides. *Ferric sulphide*, Fe_2S_3, is unstable and difficult to isolate. It is the first product of the action of hydrogen sulphide on a suspension of ferric hydroxide in water. When moist it soon decomposes to $FeS + FeS_2$, but if dried *in vacuo* over P_2O_5 is much more stable. It is a black substance, which forms soluble *complex sulphides* such as $KFeS_2$ (purple crystals), but is readily hydrolysed by boiling water.

Ferrous sulphide, FeS, is formed as a black hydrated precipitate by the action of alkali sulphides on a solution of a ferrous salt, or it may be precipitated by hydrogen sulphide in the presence of an alkali acetate. It is readily soluble in dilute acids, but not in alkalis. It may be obtained crystalline (hexagonal) by the action of hydrogen sulphide on heated iron, and occurs in nature as troilite. Pure ferrous sulphide is colourless.

In addition to ferrous sulphide, FeS, and ferric sulphide, Fe_2S_3, there are two different disulphides (pyrites and marcasite), FeS_2. The term magnetic pyrites is applied to natural or artificial substances having compositions intermediate between FeS and Fe_2S_3.

Pyrites and marcasite both occur in nature, and both have been obtained artificially. Pyrites is yellow, crystallizes in the cubic system, and has sp. gr. 5·027, whereas marcasite (if pure) is white, rhombic, and has sp. gr. 4·887 (at 25°). Marcasite is converted into pyrites when heated at 450°. The two forms differ in reactivity, pyrites being the more inert to most reagents.

Both of these minerals are used as sources of sulphur dioxide for the manufacture of sulphuric acid.

Iron thiocyanates. *Ferric thiocyanate*, $Fe(NCS)_3$, $6H_2O$, crystallizes in intensely red cubes. Its intense red colour in solution affords a sensitive test for either ferric or thiocyanate ions. There is some doubt as to whether the colour is to be attributed to the un-ionized salt, to complex anions like $[Fe(NCS)_6]^{3-}$, or to both. The colour is destroyed by substances such as fluoride or tartrate which complex ferric ions. *Complex thiocyanates* such as $Na_3Fe(NCS)_6$, $12H_2O$, which forms dark red crystals, may be isolated from the solutions. *Ferrous thiocyanate*, $Fe(NCS)_2 \cdot 3H_2O$, is formed as green crystals by

dissolving iron in thiocyanic acid in the absence of oxygen.

Irone, $C_{14}H_{22}O$. Natural irone, found in orris

α
λ_{max} 229 mμ

β
λ_{max} 294.5 mμ

γ
λ_{max} 226.5 mμ

root, in various species of iris, and also possibly in cassia flowers (*Acacia farnesiana*), is a mixture of three isomeric ketones, the γ-isomer predominating. The α- and γ-isomers have the characteristic fresh violet odour in weak alcoholic solution. The odour of the β-isomer, a conjugated dienone, resembles that of β-ionone. Natural irone is an oil, b.p. 144°/16 mm, d^{20} 0·939, n_D 1·5011, $[\alpha]_D + 33·31°$. Forms a phenylsemicarbazone, m.p. 178°, which is a derivative of the γ-isomer.

Irving-Williams order. The stabilities of series of complexes with different metals fall into the sequence $Mn^{2+} < Fe^{2+} < Co^{2+} < Ni^{2+} < Cu^{2+} > Zn^{2+}$. This is known as the Irving-Williams order and is general for many ligands.

Isatin, $C_8H_5NO_2$.   Yellowish-red   prisms,

m.p. 200°-201°. Sparingly soluble in cold water, readily in hot water or in hot alcohol or benzene. Soluble in alkalis to give a violet solution, which turns pale yellow on warming, owing to hydrolysis to isatinic acid.

First obtained by the oxidation of indigo. It is better prepared by heating α-isatinanilide with dilute mineral acid.

It readily condenses with substances containing a reactive methylene group, e.g. acetoacetic ester. It is used for the preparation of vat dyes by condensation with indoxyl (to give indirubin) or thioindoxyl.

Isoagglutinins. Proteins found in the γ-globulin fraction of serum, which have serological specificity against foreign blood corpuscles. Together with the blood group substances (*q.v.*) of the red blood cells, they are responsible for the incompatibility of certain blood transfusions.

Isoamyl-. The group

Isoamyl alcohol. See Amyl alcohols.

Isobars. Species of the same atomic weight but with different atomic numbers, i.e. having different chemical properties (cf. Isotopes).

Isoborneol, $C_{10}H_{18}O$. This compound is a stereoisomer of borneol formed, together with the latter, by the hydration of camphene or by the reduction of camphor with sodium. $\pm$-Isoborneol is

prepared by the hydration of camphene with a mixture of acetic and sulphuric acids, followed by hydrolysis of the isobornyl acetate so obtained. It is also formed by the catalytic hydrogenation of camphor in the presence of platinum black. The optically active isoborneols have m.p. 214°-217°. Their optical activity varies with the solvent employed, but shows $[\alpha]_D \pm 21\cdot32°$ in toluene solution. It is smoothly oxidized to camphor by air or oxygen in the presence of various catalysts. It can be distinguished from borneol by the *p*-nitrobenzoate, m.p. 129°.

Isobutane, C_4H_{10}. A colourless gas m.p. $-145°$, b.p $-10°$. It occurs in natural gas, and is produced in large amounts in the cracking of petroleum. It is used in refrigeration plant. For chemical properties see Paraffins.

Isobutene. See Butylenes.

Isobutyl-. The group

Isobutyl acetate. See Butyl acetates.

Isobutyl alcohol. See Butyl alcohols.

Isobutylene. See Butylenes.

Isobutylene rubber. See Butyl rubber.

Isobutyryl. The name given to the group

Isocadinene. See Cadinene.

Isocrotonic acid. See Crotonic acids.

Isocyanates. Compounds containing the group $-N{=}C{=}O$. Alkyl isocyanates are prepared from dialkyl sulphates and potassium cyanate. They readily polymerize to isocyanuric esters and are formed as intermediates in the Hofmann decomposition of amides and the Curtius decomposition of azides. Aryl isocyanates are best prepared by the reaction of phosgene and an aromatic amine. They react with alcohols to give urethanes, with ammonia to give phenylurea, and with aniline to give diphenylurea.

The polycondensation of di-isocyanates with polyhydric alcohols gives a wide range of polyurethanes which are used as artificial rubbers and light weight foams, and have other important properties.

Isocyanides. See Carbylamines.

Isodispersion. Many natural substances of high molecular weight form sols in which the dispersed particles, of colloidal dimensions, are all of the same size, and thus are termed isodisperse. Thus haemoglobin forms an isodispersion of particles all of molecular weight 68,000. Helix haemocyanin forms an isodispersion of 'molecular' weight 5,000,000.

Artificially prepared colloidal sols usually possess particles of widely varying size, but approximation to isodispersion can be produced by differential ultra-filtration.

Isoelectric point. As dispersed substances in general are capable of being either positively or negatively charged according to whether positive (including hydrogen) ions or negative (including hydroxyl) ions are predominantly adsorbed, they also possess an isoelectric point at which the net charge on the particles is zero—positive and negative ions being adsorbed to an equal extent. At the isoelectric point the electrophoretic velocity is zero and the substance tends to flocculate. With hydrophilic substances which are protected from coagulation by possession of a sheath of water, the stability is minimum at the isoelectric point (see Colloids, Coagulation, Zwitterion).

Isoelectronic. A term applied to molecules or ions which have the same number of electrons, e.g. CO and N_2.

Isoleucine, 2-Amino-3-methylvaleric acid, $C_6H_{13}NO_2$. Crystallizes in colourless leaves, m.p. 284°, with decomposition. Soluble in water, insoluble in alcohol. The naturally occurring substance is dextrorotatory, $[\alpha]_D^{20}+9\cdot61°$. It

$$\begin{array}{c} CH_3 \\ \\ CH_3 \cdot CH_2 \end{array}\!\!\!>\!\!CH \cdot CH \cdot COOH \\ \qquad\qquad\qquad | \\ \qquad\qquad\quad NH_2$$

is an amino-acid, occurring with leucine as a product of protein hydrolysis.

Isomerases. Enzymes catalysing isomerization. Thus phosphotriose isomerase (once known only as isomerase) catalyses the conversion of 3-phosphoglyceraldehyde to phospho-dihydroxyacetone. Mutases, which catalyse the movement of a radical to another position in a molecule, i.e. the change from glucose-1-phosphate to glucose-6-phosphate, are a special type of isomerase.

Isomerism. Compounds possessing the same percentage composition and the same molecular weight, but differing in at least one of their physical or chemical properties, are said to be isomeric, and each is an isomer, or isomeride, of the others. The isomerism may be of several types.

1. *Structural isomerism*, due to differences in the order in which the atoms are joined together. This is further subdivided into (a) Chain or Nuclear isomerism, due to differences in the arrangement of carbon atoms in the molecule, as in

$$CH_3CH_2CH_2CH_3 \text{ and } CH_3CH\!\!<\!\!\begin{array}{c} CH_3 \\ CH_3 \end{array}$$

(b) Position isomerism, due to differences in the position of some group or atom with regard to the carbon chain or ring, as in $CH_3CH_2CH_2Cl$ and $CH_3CHClCH_3$; and (c) Functional group isomerism or metamerism, due to differences in the type of compound, as in CH_3COCH_3 and CH_3CH_2CHO. Tautomerism, or Dynamic isomerism, is a special case of structural isomerism in which two isomers are directly interconvertible. The reversibility of the change is due to the mobility of a group or atom, which can move from one position to another in the molecule with rearrangement of a double bond. In certain cases it may be due only to a shifting of the double bonds.

The more common types of structure showing tautomerism are the Keto-Enol type,

$$\begin{array}{cc} \overset{\displaystyle H}{\underset{\displaystyle |}{}} \\ >\!\!C\!-\!C\!=\!O \;\rightleftharpoons\; >\!\!C\!=\!C\!-\!OH \\ | \qquad\qquad\qquad | \end{array}$$

as in acetoacetic ester; the Three Carbon type,

$$\begin{array}{cc} H & H \\ | & | \\ >\!\!C\!-\!C\!=\!C\!< \;\rightleftharpoons\; >\!\!C\!=\!C\!-\!C\!< \\ | & | \end{array}$$

as in the substituted glutaconic acids; and the Amido-Amidol type,

$$\begin{array}{c} H \\ | \\ -\!N\!-\!C\!=\!O \;\rightleftharpoons\; -\!N\!=\!C\!-\!OH \\ | \qquad\qquad\qquad | \end{array}$$

as in urea. These isomers are known as tautomers, or tautomerides, and exist in equilibrium in the liquid state or in solution. The speed of conversion of one form to the other varies widely in different cases, and may be so slow that it is possible to isolate both forms in a relatively pure state. There is no interconversion in the solid state. The term Desmotrope has been applied to those tautomers which can be separated from each other. See 'Structure and Mechanism in Organic Chemistry' by Ingold.

2. *Space isomerism or Stereo-isomerism*, due to differences only in the spatial orientation of the atoms in the molecule. This is sub-divided into (a) Optical isomerism due to asymmetry. Such isomers differ only in the direction in which they turn the plane of polarized light. (b) Geometrical, or Cis-Trans isomerism, due to different arrangements of dissimilar atoms or groups attached to two atoms joined by a double bond or forming part of certain ring structures. Thus the isomeric fumaric and maleic acids are represented by the formulae

$$\begin{array}{ccc} H\!-\!C\!-\!COOH & & H\!-\!C\!-\!COOH \\ \| & \text{and} & \| \\ HOOC\!-\!C\!-\!H & & H\!-\!C\!-\!COOH \end{array}$$

respectively. The presence of the double bond restricts the free rotation of the carbon atoms joined by it, and permits the existence of the two forms. Similarly, in certain ring structures which need not contain double bonds, the free rotation of the atoms is restricted and other groups or atoms attached to them may lie above or below the plane of the ring and give rise to geometrical isomers. This isomerism is not confined to the $>\!C\!=\!C\!<$ bond, but exists also in compounds having $>\!C\!=\!N\!-$ or $-\!N\!=\!N\!-$ bonds. In the case of the $>\!C\!=\!C\!<$ double bond or a carbon ring, the isomers are distinguished by the prefixes *cis-* and *trans-* according as two given groups or atoms lie on the same or on opposite sides of the plane of the double bond or ring. In the other cases, the prefixes *syn-* and *anti-* are used; thus the *syn-* aldoximes have the structure

$$\begin{array}{c} R\!-\!C\!-\!H \\ \| \\ N\!-\!OH \end{array}$$

For ketoximes, the group which is *syn* or *anti* to the hydroxyl group must be specified.

Stereoisomers are also found in inorganic complexes, e.g.

$$cis \quad \begin{array}{c} Ph_3P \\ Ph_3P \end{array}\!\!>\!\!Pt\!\!<\!\!\begin{array}{c} Cl \\ Cl \end{array} \quad and \quad trans \quad \begin{array}{c} Ph_3P \\ Cl \end{array}\!\!>\!\!Pt\!\!<\!\!\begin{array}{c} Cl \\ PPh_3 \end{array}$$

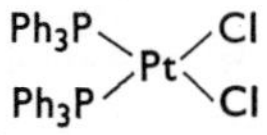

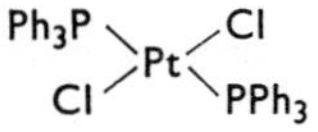

which have square planar co-ordination about the central platinum atom. In addition to these types new types are known: (i) Ionization isomerism, e.g. $[Pt(NH_3)_4Cl_2]Br_2$ and $[Pt(NH_3)_4Br_2]Cl_2$; (ii) Linkage isomerism, e.g. the nitrite ion can co-ordinate through either the oxygen or nitrogen atoms. Since co-ordination numbers in inorganic chemistry vary widely from the limited range adopted by carbon the possibilities for isomerism in inorganic derivatives are greater than in organic chemistry.

See Conformation.

Isomerism, nuclear. The existence of atomic nuclei with the same atomic and mass number but having different nuclear energies and radioactive decay properties. E.g. ^{124}Sb has three isomers, ^{124}Sb, ^{124m}Sb, $^{124m2}Sb$.

Isomerization. The conversion of a compound to an isomer of that compound.

Isomorphism. Commonly any compounds which have the same crystal structure are said to be isomorphous. When a violet crystal of chrome alum is placed in a saturated solution of potash alum it begins to grow, without altering its crystalline form, by the accumulation of colourless potash alum. Moreover, a crystal of chrome alum will always induce crystallization of a super-saturated solution of potash alum, and vice versa. However, many crystals with the same structures will not crystallize on each other.

Isoniazid, Isonicotinic acid hydrazide, $C_6H_7N_3O$. Colourless crystals, soluble in 8 parts of water and 100 parts of alcohol; m.p. 172°. It is prepared by esterifying pyridine-4-carboxylic acid with ethanol, and condensing the ester with hydrazine. It is a bacteristatic agent, active against *Mycobacterium tuberculosis*, and is used in the treatment of tuberculosis. Bacterial resistance to the drug may develop rapidly when it is used alone, but administration with streptomycin or calcium or sodium aminosalicylate decreases the development of resistance.

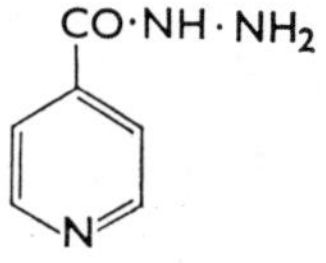

Isonitriles. See Carbylamines.

Isonitrosoketones. Organic compounds containing the group

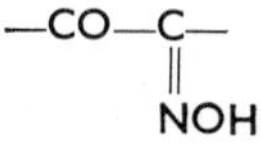

$$-CO-\underset{\underset{NOH}{\|}}{C}-$$

They are monoximes of α-diketones, and are formed by treating ketones with amyl nitrite and hydrochloric acid. They are colourless crystalline solids, soluble in alcohol and ether, but usually sparingly soluble in water. They dissolve in alkalis to give salts having an intense yellow colour. Form α-diketones when treated with sulphuric or nitrous acids. React with hydroxylamine to give dioximes of the diketones.

Iso-octane. See Octanes.

Isoparaffins. Aliphatic hydrocarbons having a branched carbon chain structure. They usually have higher anti-knock value than the corresponding straight chain normal paraffin.

Isopiestic. An adjective applied to solutions of salts, etc. which have the same partial pressure of solvent. The isopiestic method of studying the osmotic properties (activity coefficients, etc.) of solutions is to allow solutions to come to isopiestic equilibrium (by diffusion of vapour from one to another) with a solution of a standard substance in an enclosed vessel at a constant temperature; the concentrations of the isopiestic solutions are then determined. The method is slow but susceptible of high accuracy.

Isopoly acids. Acids which give polymeric anionic species containing one metal only, *cf.* Heteropoly acids.

Isopolymorphism. Substances which have more than one crystalline form isomorphous with the crystalline forms of another substance are said to show isopolymorphism. Thus, the octahedral and rhombic forms of arsenious oxide are respectively isomorphous with the octahedral and rhombic forms of antimony trioxide. These oxides are isodimorphous.

Isoprenaline. Used as the sulphate,

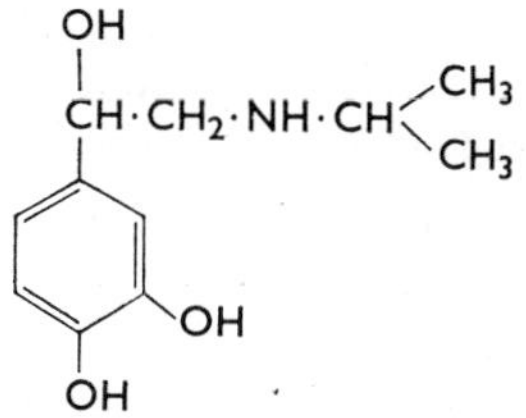

$$\begin{array}{c} OH \\ | \\ CH\cdot CH_2\cdot NH\cdot CH\!\!<\!\!\begin{array}{c} CH_3 \\ CH_3 \end{array} \end{array}$$

$C_{22}H_{36}N_2O_{10}S$, $2H_2O$, and is prepared by condensing isopropylamine with 4-chloroacetocatechol, reducing the product, and converting to the sulphate. It is soluble in 4 parts of water, and almost insoluble in alcohol; m.p. 128°.

Isoprenaline is used in the treatment of asthma, being administered sublingually or by inhalation. Relief is obtained within a few minutes; the drug has a greater effect on the bronchioles than adrenaline.

Isoprene, 2-Methylbutadiene, C_5H_8. A colour-

$$H_2C = C - CH = CH_2$$
$$|$$
$$CH_3$$

less liquid with a penetrating odour, d^{20} 0.6806, b.p. 34°. Insoluble in water; miscible with benzene. It is obtained, together with other products, by the distillation of raw rubber, or by passing the vapour of turpentine oil through a metallic tube heated to redness. Manufactured from methylethyl ketone by treating this with formaldehyde in the presence of potassium hydroxide to give 2-methyl-3-ketobutanol, and reducing this to 2-methylbutylene glycol. The glycol is converted to isoprene when its vapour is passed over a heated acid phosphate. It is also manufactured from acetone and acetylene in an ether solvent in the presence of powdered potassium hydroxide. The resultant acetylenic alcohol is catalytically reduced to 1,1-dimethyl-allyl alcohol which is dehydrated by passing the vapour over alumina. It is converted to a rubber-like polymer by heat or by the action of metallic sodium and other substances. It has been used for the preparation of synthetic rubber-like materials.

Isoprene rule. This proposes that the carbon skeletons of terpenes are built up of isoprene units,

$$C$$
$$|$$
$$C_1 - C_2 - C_3 - C_4$$

so that C_4 of one unit is attached to C_1 of the next. The rare exceptions to this rule can be accommodated by assuming that a methyl group migration occurs at some stage in the biogenesis. Isoprene itself is not the actual precursor, but the closely related compound mevalonic acid (q.v.) is incorporated in high yield into carotenoids, squalene, cholesterol, and other terpenoid compounds.

Isopropanol. See Isopropyl alcohol.

Isopropenyl acetate, $C_5H_8O_2$. A colourless liquid,

$$CH_2 = C(CH_3) \cdot O \cdot CO \cdot CH_3$$

b.p. 96°-97°, d^{20} 0.9173, n_D^{20} 1.4001. Prepared from acetone and keten in the presence of sulphuric acid. The reaction is reversible, hence isopropenyl acetate finds application as an acetylating agent, being more efficient than keten itself. Gives acetates with alcohols and amines, enol acetates with aldehydes and ketones, and acid anhydrides with carboxylic

acids. The substance is heated with isopropenyl acetate and an acid catalyst, so that acetone is continuously removed by distillation.

Isopropenyl acetate gives spinnable fibres on copolymerization with vinyl chloride.

Isopropyl acetate, $C_5H_{10}O_2$. A colourless liquid

$$CH_3COOCH \underset{CH_3}{\overset{CH_3}{<}}$$

with a fragrant odour, d^0 0.9166, b.p. 88.2°. Insoluble in water; miscible with most organic solvents. Manufactured by leading propylene into hot acetic acid containing sulphuric acid, or by heating isopropyl alcohol with acetic and sulphuric acids. It forms a constant-boiling mixture (b.p. 80.1°) with isopropyl alcohol (52.5%). Decomposed by hot alkalis to isopropyl alcohol and an acetate. Used as a solvent for cellulose nitrate and various gums; does not dissolve cellulose acetate.

Isopropyl alcohol, Isopropanol, C_3H_8O. A colourless liquid with a pleasant and characteristic odour; d_{20}^{20} 0.786, b.p. 82.4°. Miscible with water and most organic

$$H_3C \underset{H_3C}{\overset{}{>}} CHOH$$

liquids. Forms an azeotrope, b.p. 80.4°, with water, containing 87.9% alcohol by wt. Manufactured from the propylene present in the gases obtained by the cracking of petroleum. The propylene is absorbed in 85% sulphuric acid and the product diluted with water and distilled. Some isopropyl ether is obtained as a by-product. High purity alcohol for use in essences, perfumes, foodstuffs, etc. is obtained by the catalytic hydrogenation of acetone.

The chemical properties of isopropyl alcohol are those of a typical secondary alcohol. Oxidation with potassium dichromate and sulphuric acid gives acetone.

Much of the isopropyl alcohol produced is used for the manufacture of acetone. It is also used as a solvent for oils, gums, resins, etc., as a chemical intermediate and in various pharmaceutical preparations.

Isopropyl chloride, 2-Chloropropane, C_3H_7Cl. A colourless liquid with a pleasant odour; d^{20} 0.859, b.p. 36.5°. Insoluble in water; miscible with most organic solvents.

$$H_3C \underset{H_3C}{\overset{}{>}} CH \cdot Cl$$

Manufactured by treating isopropyl alcohol with hydrochloric acid in the presence of zinc chloride, or by passing the vapour of the alcohol and hydrochloric acid gas over a heated metallic chloride, such as magnesium chloride. It is used as a fat solvent.

Isopropyl ether, $C_6H_{14}O$. A colourless liquid

$$H_3C \underset{H_3C}{\overset{}{>}} CHOCH \underset{CH_3}{\overset{CH_3}{<}}$$

with a sweet, camphor-like odour; d^{20} 0·725, b.p. 68·4°. Insoluble in water; miscible with most organic solvents. It is produced as a by-product in the manufacture of isopropyl alcohol, and is made by heating this alcohol with sulphuric acid. Like ethyl ether, it forms peroxides when stored for any length of time. It is used as a solvent for dewaxing lubricating oils and for extraction of fats and oils.

Isopropylidene. The name given to the group

Isopropylmethylbenzenes. See Cymenes.

Isopropyl nitrate, $(CH_3)_2 \cdot CH \cdot ONO_2$. A colourless liquid, b.p. 101·5°, m.p. −82°, immiscible with water and petroleum ether but soluble in most organic solvents. It is made by nitration of propylene. It is highly inflammable but relatively insensitive to shock.

Isopulegol. See Isopulegone.

Isopulegone, $C_{10}H_{16}O$. An optically active monocyclic ketone formed by the oxidation of isopulegol with chromic acid, and also possibly accompanying pulegone in pennyroyal oil. (Isopulegol is an alcohol formed by the cyclization of citronellal.) Isopulegone has the following constants: b.p. 101°-102°/ 17 mm, d_4^{20} 0·9208, n_D^{20} 1·4667, $[\alpha]_D$ about +25°. Its semicarbazone has m.p. 175°-176°. Isopulegone is very easily converted into its isomer, pulegone, for example by traces of sodium ethoxide.

Isoquinoline, C_9H_7N. Crystallizes in tablets, m.p. 24°, b.p. 242°, d_4^{20} 1·0986. Odour like that of quinoline, volatile in steam, used for the preparation of Quinoline Red.

Isosbestic point. Examination of spectra, especially of transition metal complex ions, invariably shows a point or points at which extinction coefficients are equal. Such points are referred to as isosbestic points. Many rate studies in solution are made using spectrophotometric techniques; use is made of isosbestic points in such cases to investigate processes such as isomerism, which may take place during these reactions.

Isostructural. Having the same lattice type, e.g. K_2PtCl_6 and Rb_2PtCl_6.

Isotactic polymers. A class of stereospecific polymers of general formula (—CH_2—CHR—)

in which all the substituted carbon atoms have the same stereo-configuration. If such a chain were extended to its maximum length, the substituents (R) would all lie on the same side of the chain. The term was introduced by G. Natta, who first succeeded in preparing isotactic forms of polystyrene and polypropylene, using heterogeneous catalysts of the type developed by K. Ziegler.

Isothiocyanates. Derivatives of the type RNCS in which the bonding is through the nitrogen. See Thiocyanic acid.

Isotones. Atomic nuclei having the same number of neutrons but different mass numbers, e.g. ^{132}Xe and ^{133}Cs.

Isotonic solutions. Solutions having the same osmotic pressure are termed isotonic.

Isotope. The characteristic chemical properties of an atom are due to the number and arrangement of the electrons round the nucleus, which in turn are governed by the resultant positive charge on the nucleus. Hence it is possible to have two atoms of identical chemical properties, but different masses, provided the charge on the nucleus is the same in each case. Elements (or atoms) of the same chemical properties but of different atomic weights are called isotopes. See list of Isotopes on pp. 326-329. In addition to these stable isotopes very many radioactive isotopes of elements are known.

Since the various isotopes of one element differ only in mass, they can be separated by using the very slight difference in physical properties that this mass difference causes. The methods used include fractional distillation, exchange reactions, diffusion, thermal diffusion, electrolysis, and electromagnetic methods.

Isotropic. A substance which has identical properties in all directions in its mass is said to be isotropic. It is applied to substances which crystallize in the cubic system.

Isovaleric acid. See Valeric acids.

Itaconic acid, $C_5H_6O_4$. White crystals, m.p.

162°-164°. Solubility in water: 8 g. in 100 ml at 20°, 73 g in 100 ml at 80°: sparingly soluble in ether, benzene, chloroform. It can be prepared by the fermentation of sugar with the mould *Aspergillus terreus* or by heating citraconic anhydride with water at 150°. Electrolysis of the potassium salt in solution gives allene. Its esters can be polymerized to give plastics.

Izod test. See Impact resistance.

NATURALLY OCCURRING ISOTOPES

* Denotes naturally occurring radioactive isotope

Symbol	Atomic Number (Z)	Mass Number (M)	Relative Abundance (%)	Symbol	Atomic Number (Z)	Mass Number (M)	Relative Abundance (%)
H	1	1	99·98	Sc	21	45	100
D		2	0·02	Ti	22	46	8·0
He	2	3				47	7·8
		4	100			48	73·99
Li	3	6	7·98			49	5·5
		7	92			50	5·3
Be	4	9	100	V	23	50*	0·24
B	5	10	~18·7			51	99·76
		11	~81·3	Cr	24	50	4·31
C	6	12	98·9			52	83·76
		13	1·1			53	9·55
N	7	14	99·635			54	2·38
		15	0·365	Mn	25	55	100
O	8	16	99·76	Fe	26	54	5·8
		17	0·04			56	91·66
		18	0·20			57	2·2
F	9	19	100			58	0·31
Ne	10	20	90·92	Co	27	59	100
		21	0·26	Ni	28	58	67·76
		22	8·82			60	26·16
Na	11	23	100			61	1·25
Mg	12	24	78·70			62	3·66
		25	10·11			64	1·16
		26	11·29	Cu	29	63	69·1
Al	13	27	100			65	30·9
Si	14	28	92·18	Zn	30	64	48·89
		29	4·7			66	27·81
		30	3·1			67	4·11
P	15	31	100			68	18·56
S	16	32	95·0			70	0·62
		33	0·74	Ga	31	69	60·2
		34	4·2			71	39·8
		36	0·016	Ge	32	70	20·55
Cl	17	35	75·53			72	27·37
		37	24·47			73	7·61
Ar	18	36	0·337			74	36·74
		38	0·063			76	7·67
		40	99·600	As	33	75	100
K	19	39	93·10	Se	34	74	0·87
		40*	0·0118			76	9·02
		41	6·91			77	7·58
Ca	20	40	96·97			78	23·52
		42	0·64			80	49·82
		43	0·145			82	9·12
		44	2·06	Br	35	79	50·5
		46	0·0033			81	49·5
		48	0·185				

NATURALLY OCCURRING ISOTOPES (*continued*).

Symbol	Atomic Number (*Z*)	Mass Number (*M*)	Relative Abundance (%)	Symbol	Atomic Number (*Z*)	Mass Number (*M*)	Relative Abundance (%)
Kr	36	78	0·354	In	49	113	4·28
		80	2·27			115*	95·72
		82	11·56	Sn	50	112	0·95
		83	11·55			114	0·65
		84	56·90			115	0·34
		86	17·37			116	14·24
Rb	37	85	72·15			117	7·57
		87*	27·85			118	24·01
Sr	38	84	0·56			119	8·58
		86	9·86			120	32·97
		87	7·02			122	4·71
		88	82·56			124	5·98
Y	39	89	100	Sb	51	121	57·25
Zr	40	90	51·46			123	42·75
		91	11·23	Te	52	120	0·089
		92	17·11			122	2·46
		94	17·40			123	0·87
		96	2·80			124	4·61
Nb	41	93	100			125	6·99
Mo	42	92	15·86			126	18·71
		94	9·12			128	31·79
		95	15·70			130	34·39
		96	16·50	I	53	127	100
		97	9·45	Xe	54	124	0·096
		98	23·75			126	0·090
		100	9·62			128	1·919
Ru	44	96	5·50			129	26·44
		98	1·90			130	4·08
		99	12·70			131	21·18
		100	12·69			132	26·89
		101	17·01			134	10·44
		102	31·63			136	8·87
		104	18·67	Cs	55	133	100
Rh	45	103	100	Ba	56	130	0·101
Pd	46	102	0·8			132	0·097
		104	9·3			134	2·42
		105	22·8			135	6·59
		106	27·2			136	7·81
		108	26·8			137	11·32
		110	13·5			138	71·66
Ag	47	107	51·35	La	57	138*	0·089
		109	48·65			139	99·911
Cd	48	106	1·215	Ce	58	136	0·193
		108	0·875			138	0·250
		110	12·39			140	88·48
		111	12·75			142	11·07
		112	24·07	Pr	59	141	100
		113	12·26	Nd	60	142	27·13
		114	28·86			143	12·20
		116	7·58	(ctd. over)		144*	23·87

NATURALLY OCCURRING ISOTOPES (*continued*).

Symbol	Atomic Number (Z)	Mass Number (M)	Relative Abundance (%)	Symbol	Atomic Number (Z)	Mass Number (M)	Relative Abundance (%)
Nd (ctd.)	60	145	8·30	Ta	73	180	—
		146	17·18			181	99·99
		148	5·72	W	74	178*	$\sim 2\cdot5 \times 10^{-7}$
		150	5·60			180	0·135
Sm	62	144	3·16			182	26·4
		147*	15·07			183	14·4
		148	11·27			184	30·6
		149	13·84			186	28·4
		150	7·47				
		152	26·23	Re	75	185	37·07
		154	22·53			187*	62·93
Eu	63	151	47·77	Os	76	184	0·018
		153	52·23			186	1·59
Gd	64	154	2·15			187	1·64
		155	14·73			188	13·3
		156	20·47			189	16·1
		157	15·58			190	26·4
		158	24·87			192	41·0
		160	21·90	Ir	77	191	38·5
Tb	65	159	100			193	61·5
Dy	66	156	0·0524	Pt	78	190*	0·012
		158	0·0902			192	0·78
		160	2·294			194	32·8
		161	18·88			195	33·7
		162	25·53			196	25·4
		163	24·97			198	7·23
		164	28·18	Au	79	197	100
Ho	67	165	100	Hg	80	196	0·146
Er	68	162	0·136			198	10·02
		164	1·56			199	16·84
		166	33·41			200	23·13
		167	22·94			201	13·22
		168	27·07			202	29·80
		170	14·88			204	6·85
Tm	69	169	100	Tl	81	203	29·5
Yb	70	168	0·140			205	70·5
		170	3·03	Pb	82	204	1·48
		171	14·31			206	23·6
		172	21·82			207	22·6
		173	16·13			208	52·3
		174	31·84	Bi	83	209*	100
		176	12·73	Po	84	210*	—
Lu	71	175	97·40			211*	—
		176*	2·60			212*	—
Hf	72	174*	0·199			214*	—
		176	5·23			215*	—
		177	18·55			216*	—
		178	27·23	At	85	215*	—
		179	13·73			218*	—
		180	35·07				

NATURALLY OCCURRING ISOTOPES (*continued*).

Symbol	Atomic Number (Z)	Mass Number (M)	Relative Abundance (%)	Symbol	Atomic Number (Z)	Mass Number (M)	Relative Abundance (%)
Rn	86	219*	—	Th	90	227*	—
		220*	—			228*	—
		222*	—			232*	—
Fr	87	223*	—	Pa	91	234*	—
Ra	88	226*	—				
		228*	—	U	92	234*	—
Ac	89	227*	—			235*	—
		228*	—			238*	—

J

Jabir ibn Hayyan. Lived about A.D. 720-813 in Baghdad and is supposed to have been the author of a Latin book attributed to Geber which contains an account of chemical experiments. The works of Geber are probably of much later date.

'J-Acid' dyes. See also Direct cotton dyes. The simple monazo-dyes derived from 'J-acid' (2,5-aminonaphthol-7-sulphonic acid), such as

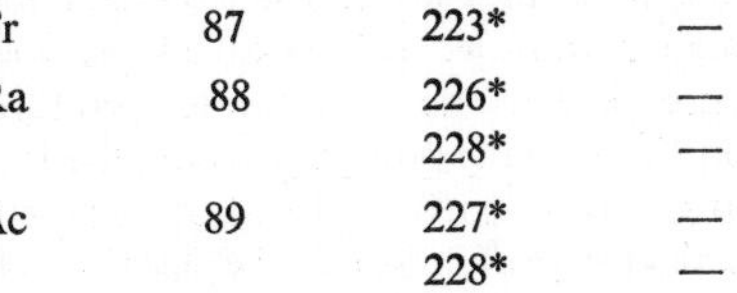

have an affinity for cotton which is not shared by the dyes from other naphtholsulphonic acids. Some complex modifications are faster to acids than are the direct dyes derived from benzidine. In addition to 'J-acid' itself, its N-aryl and N-acyl derivatives are used (Brilliant Benzo Violet 2RL, Brilliant Fast Blue, Rosanthrene O, etc.).

Jade. A semi-precious stone, which consists of two distinct minerals, jadeite, $NaAlSi_2O_6$ a pyroxene, and nephrite, $Ca_2Mg_5(Si_4O_{11})_2(OH)_2$ an amphibole. Both are tough due to interlocking fine fibres. Jade is white to green, greasy and translucent when polished. Jadeite has sp. gr. 3·30-3·35, nephrite sp. gr. 2·90-3·10.

Jahn-Teller effect. The Jahn-Teller theorem states that, when any degenerate electronic state contains a number of electrons such that the degenerate orbitals are not completely filled, the geometry of the species will change so as to produce non-degenerate orbitals. Particularly applied to transition metal compounds where, for example, the d^9 state e.g. Cu(II), generally has a distorted octahedral co-ordination.

Jalapin, $C_{34}H_{62}O_{18}$. The glycosidic resin from Orizaba root which yields on hydrolysis the sug-

ars glucose, rhamnose, and D-fucose, together with jalaponic acid, which is 11-hydroxyhexadecanoic acid. It has m.p. 131°, $[\alpha]_D$ −23°.

Janssen, Pierre Jules Cesar (1824-1907). Born in Paris, Janssen took up the study of mathematics and physics. In 1875 he was appointed Director of the Astrophysical Observatory at Meudon. In 1868, independently with Sir N. Lockyer, Janssen observed a yellow line in the spectrum of the sun's photosphere, the first indication of the element helium.

Jasper. (a) A hardened siliceous clay, often with a striped structure and of various colours; it is used as an ornamental stone and as a gem-stone; (b) a fine, unglazed stoneware invented by Josiah Wedgwood and made by adding barium carbonate to a mixture used for semi-porcelain ware. It can be made of almost any desired colour and can be polished until it feels almost like satin. The copies by Josiah Wedgwood of the famous Portland Vase were in jasper ware.

Jaw crusher. This is a machine in which size reduction of rock or similar material takes place between two jaws set at a narrow angle to each other to form a vertical V. The jaws are constructed of a hard abrasion-resistant material such as manganese steel, one being solidly fixed and the other hinged at its upper or lower end. The movable jaw is given a reciprocating motion by the drive mechanism, and due to the corrugations on their faces material fed into the jaws is subjected to intense localized pressures which bring about breakage. These machines are used for coarse crushing, and the largest can take feed material up to 60 in. in size. Product size can be controlled within limits by adjustment of the clearance between the jaws.

Jig. This is a hydraulic device for the separation of solids of different densities, used for the washing of coal and metallic ores. It consists of a tank with a hopper bottom which is filled with water or some other liquid of suitable specific gravity.

Along the middle of the vessel is a vertical partition extending halfway down, and on one side of it there is a horizontal screen on to which is fed the material to be classified. By the motion of a piston or the application of air pressure on the other side of the partition, liquid is forced through the screen, momentarily lifting the material from it. On the reverse stroke of the piston however, or as the air pressure is released, liquid is fed to the vessel to prevent a backward surge through the screen, so that the particles settle under their own weight. The pulsating action is fairly rapid and the settling periods correspondingly brief, so that classification of material is according to density, rather than a combination of particle size and density as in a simple settling process. The result is that dense material accumulates next to the screen with lighter material on top of it, and the fractions are taken off through gates in the side. Operation is continuous.

jj Coupling. See Russell-Saunders coupling.

Joliot-curium. A name suggested for element 102. See Nobelium.

Joliot, Jean, Frédéric (1900-1958). Trained at the École de Physique, Joliot moved to the Institute de Radium and worked with Irène Curie, whom he later married. They won the Nobel Prize for Chemistry in 1935 for their joint discovery of artificial radioactivity. Later he became head of the Centre National pour la Recherche Scientifique and the (French) High Commission for Atomic Energy. See *Proc. Chem. Soc.*, 1959, 164.

Jones, Sir Ewart Ray Herbert (1911-   ). Educated at the University of Wales where he took a Ph.D. in 1936, Jones was subsequently lecturer and reader at Imperial College, professor of organic chemistry at Manchester, and since 1955 has been Waynflete professor of chemistry at Oxford. He has specialized in the chemistry of natural products and acetylene chemistry.

Jones reductor. A tube containing amalgamated zinc. Used for the reduction of solutions (e.g. ferric to ferrous), prior to estimation.

Joule, James Prescott (1818-1889). Born at Salford, near Manchester, Joule was of independent means, and devoted his life to scientific research. He studied the relations between electrical, mechanical, and chemical effects and deduced the first law of thermodynamics. With Lord Kelvin he discovered the Joule-Thomson effect. His brilliant work was recognized by his election to the Fellowship of the Royal Society, and a Civil List pension. See *Nature*, 1882 (October).

Joule's law. The law states that the internal energy of a gas depends only on its temperature (being independent of its pressure and volume). Like the other gas laws, it is only approximately true. At high pressures it is invalidated by the existence of intermolecular forces.

Joule-Thomson effect (Joule-Kelvin effect). Most gases (except hydrogen and helium) undergo cooling when they are expanded adiabatically through a throttle. This is called the Joule-Thomson effect. The change in temperature is proportional to the drop in pressure; the Joule-Thomson coefficient is the change of temperature per unit change of pressure. The effect, which is used for liquefying air, making solid carbon dioxide, etc., is related to departures from Boyle's law and Joule's law. Hydrogen and helium, which show a warming effect at ordinary temperatures, also show cooling if the experiment is conducted below their inversion temperatures.

J-Sensitization. A property largely confined to the cyanine dyes is that of J-sensitization. Some cyanines, with compact molecular structures, aggregate in solution under conditions conducive to micelle formation, or at higher adsorbed concentrations on the silver halide grain surface. In this orientated aggregate state, the dyes adsorb and sensitize at longer wavelengths than in the monomolecular state. This is in contrast to the behaviour of many dyes of other classes which absorb at shorter wave-lengths in aggregate states. Absorption-bands associated with J-aggregates are characterized by being very narrow, sharp and intense. The related J-sensitization bands have a sharp cut-off at the long wavelength side. It is the latter property which is photographically important. Typical cyanine dyes exhibiting J-sensitization are *bis*-(1-ethyl-2-quinoline)monomethinecyanine (pseudo-cyanine) and *bis*- (3 - ethyl - 2 - benzothiazole) - β - methyltrimethinecyanine (a thiacarbo-cyanine).

Juniper tar oil. See Oil of cade.

Juvenile hormone. A widely distributed insect hormone, not yet chemically defined, which is concerned in larval moulting together with ecdysone (*q.v.*) Hormone activity is also shown by certain simple terpenoids, notably the two *trans*-(Δ^6)-farnesols, their methyl ethers, and farnesal.

K

Kainite. A naturally occurring hydrated double salt of magnesium sulphate and potassium chloride, $MgSO_4$, KCl, $3H_2O$. When pure it forms colourless monoclinic crystals, sp.gr. 2·1, hardness 3. Large beds of kainite of a white, grey, or reddish colour occur in the Stassfurt salt deposits. The mineral is a useful fertilizer, and has been used as a source of potassium salts.

Kaolin. See China clay.

Kaolinite. A white clay mineral with the formula $Al_4Si_4O_{10}(OH)_8$. It has an earthy texture, sp. gr. 2·6, hardness 2-3, m.p. about 1785°. The crystals are triclinic.

Kaolin or china clay is chiefly composed of kaolinite or similar aluminosilicates.

Kapustinskii equation. An empirical relationship which may be used to calculate the lattice energies of crystal salts. The formula is especially useful in those cases where the structure is not precisely known. See Born-Haber cycle.

Karathane. A trade name for 2,4-dinitro-6-(1-

methylheptyl)phenyl crotonate, $C_{18}H_{24}N_2O_6$, a compound which has both acaricidal and fungicidal activity. It is a red-brown oil of high boiling point, insoluble in water but soluble in most organic solvents. It is made by nitration of *o*-caprylphenol. Karathane is used for the control of powdery mildew, and is non-toxic to mammals.

Karrer, Paul (1889-   ). Karrer was born at Moscow and educated at Zürich, where he was an assistant in 1911-12. He then worked with Ehrlich at Frankfurt a.M., returning to Zürich in 1918 as extraordinary professor of organic chemistry. In 1919 he became ordinary professor of chemistry and Director of the Chemical Institute. His work on the carotenoids and flavins and on vitamins A and B_2 gained him the Nobel Prize in Chemistry for 1937 jointly with W. N. Haworth.

Kathaemoglobin. A compound of haematin with denatured globin, formed by treating methaemoglobin with chloroform.

Kayser. A suggested unit of frequency 1 cm^{-1}, similarly the Kilo-Kayser is 1000 cm^{-1}.

K capture. See Radioactivity.

Kekulé, Friedrich August (1829-1896). Born at Darmstadt, Kekulé, originally a student of architecture, fell under the spell of Liebig's lectures at Giessen and, like Hofmann, became a convert to chemistry. After a period spent in study in Paris, Switzerland, and London, he returned, in 1856, to Germany as privatdozent at Heidelberg. Thereafter he became professor of chemistry at Ghent (1858) and Bonn (1867). Although the author and inspirer of a large amount of experimental work, Kekulé's greatest service to chemistry consisted in the development of the theories of molecular structure. See *Mem. Lect., J. Chem. Soc.,* 1898, 97.

Kel-F. A polymeric chlorotrifluoroethylene. Depending upon the degree of polymerization the polymer may be liquid or solid. Used in cases where the material has to be inert to most forms of chemical attack. It is less inert than Teflon but certain forms are thermoplastic and can be moulded.

Kelly filter. A pressure leaf filter having longitudinal leaves set within a horizontal cylindrical vessel, from which they can be withdrawn as a body for cake removal. See Leaf filters.

Kelvin, Lord (William Thomson) (1824-1907). Born at Belfast, Thomson graduated at Cambridge University before proceeding to Paris to work under Regnault. From 1846 until he retired in 1899 he occupied the Chair of Natural Philosophy at Glasgow University. His researches were chiefly in the field of thermodynamics and the compression of gases. He proposed the absolute scale of temperatures, and it was largely due to his investigations that the Atlantic cable was completed. As an inventor of accurate and delicate scientific instruments he was unsurpassed. F.R.S., he was knighted in 1866, raised to the peerage (Baron Kelvin of Largs) in 1892, and created O.M. in 1902.

Kelvin scale. See Absolute temperature.

Kephalin. See Cephalin.

Kerasin, $C_{48}H_{93}NO_8$. A white amorphous

powder, m.p. 180°, with decomposition. Anisotropic. Soluble in hot alcohol, insoluble in water and ether. Laevorotatory. Kerasin is one of the cerebrosides, and is found associated with phrenosin in brain and nervous tissue. On hydrolysis it gives D-galactose, sphingosine, and lignoceric acid.

Lignoceric acid from kerasin has been shown to be a mixture containing C_{22} and C_{26} acids as well as the C_{24} acid indicated in the above formula. Kerasin itself is therefore a mixture.

Keratins. An insoluble group of proteins of the scleroprotein class, found in the skin, hair, nails, horns, hoofs and feathers of animals. Keratins are insoluble in the usual protein solvents and are unattacked by pepsin or trypsin. They can be obtained in crude form by treating any of the above tissues with alcohol, ether and water and removing other proteins by enzymic hydrolysis, the keratins remaining insoluble. Wool keratins have been extensively studied, and methods devised for converting them to soluble forms. The amino-acid composition is marked by high percentages of arginine, glutamic acid and cystine: the sequence has not been determined. Two principal forms, α- and β-keratin, are known. α-Keratin has the α-helix structure first proposed by Pauling and Corey (1950), while β-keratin has an extended configuration. Both structures are complex and incompletely defined.

Kernite, Rasorite. A hydrated sodium borate, $Na_2B_4O_7 \cdot 4H_2O$, which occurs in California and is a major source of boron compounds. It exists as colourless monoclinic crystals, sp.gr. 1·91, hardness 3.

Kerosine. A petroleum fraction of boiling range 150°–300°. Refined grades are used as illuminants and for heating purposes under the popular name of paraffin. Aromatic extracts obtained by solvent refining are used as fuels for internal combustion engines, i.e. tractor vaporizing oil.

Kestose, $C_{18}H_{32}O_{16}$. A trisaccharide which has been found in raw beet sugar, and which is obtained by the action of yeast invertase on sucrose. It is D-glucopyranosyl-D-fructofuranosyl-D-fructofuranoside. It is very soluble in water, not sweet, and non-reducing; m.p. 145°, $[\alpha]_D^{20}$ +27·3°.

Ketals. Ketone acetals of the general formula

$$\begin{array}{c} R \\ \diagdown \\ R' \diagup \end{array} C \begin{array}{c} OR'' \\ \diagup \\ \diagdown OR''' \end{array}$$

They are colourless liquids with characteristic odours, and are prepared by the condensation of ketones with alkyl orthoformates in the presence of alcohols, or by the reaction of acetylenes with alcohols in presence of mercuric oxide and boron trifluoride. In some cases trichloroacetic acid is used as the catalyst. They lose alcohol when heated and form vinyl ethers. Exchange of alcohol groups occurs when the ketals of the lower alcohols are boiled with alcohols of greater molecular weight. See Acetals.

Keten, $CH_2:CO$. A colourless gas, manufactured by passing acetone rapidly through metallic tubes heated at 550°–800°, or by heating acetic acid at 700°–1000°. It is very unstable and dimerizes spontaneously to diketen. Reacts with water to form acetic acid, with alcohols to give acetates, with acetic acid to give acetic anhydride, and with amines to give acetyl derivatives. Used as an acetylating agent, particularly in the manufacture of cellulose acetate.

Ketens. Organic compounds containing the group $>C{=}C{=}O$. They are formed by the action of zinc powder on the acid bromide or chloride of an α-bromo- or α-chloro-fatty acid, or by heating the anhydride of a dibasic acid. Keten itself and other ketens containing the group $-CH{=}C{=}O$ are colourless substances, are polymerized by quinoline and do not form additive compounds with substances containing a $>C{=}O$ or $>C{=}N-$ group. The remaining ketens are highly coloured and form additive compounds with quinoline and with substances containing $>C{=}O$ and $>C{=}N-$ groups. Both types react readily with water to give acids, with alcohols to give esters, and with halogens and halogen acids.

Keto-. A prefix used to denote that the substance in question contains a carbon atom attached to an oxygen atom by a double bond and to two other carbon atoms by single bonds.

Ketols. Organic compounds containing both a keto- and an alcohol group. They are formed by oxidation of glycols or by condensation between two molecules of a ketone. They exhibit the typical properties of both alcohols and ketones.

Ketomalonic acid. See Mesoxalic acid.

Ketones. Organic compounds containing the C·CO·C group. They are classified as aliphatic, aromatic, cyclic, and mixed ketones, the mixed ketones having one aromatic and one aliphatic group attached to the carbonyl group. The cyclic ketones have the carbon of the carbonyl group as part of a ring. They are formed by the dry distillation of the calcium or barium salts of acids, or by passing the vapours of acids over thorium oxide at 400°. Ketones may be obtained by oxidation of secondary alcohols. Aromatic and mixed ketones are usually prepared by Friedel-Crafts reactions. Aliphatic ketones are usually liquids and aromatic ketones solids, they have ethereal or aromatic odours. They are generally insoluble in water but soluble in alcohol or ether. They are reduced to secondary alcohols, but are resistant to oxidation and give mixtures of acids and other products when strongly oxidized. They form oximes with hydroxylamine, hydrazones with hydrazine and substituted hydrazines, and semicarbazones with semicarbazide. Isonitrosoketones are formed by the action of sodium nitrite.

Ketose. A ketose is a sugar containing a potential keto-(CO) group. The presence of the group may be obscured by its inclusion in a ring system. Ketoses are called ketopentoses, ketohexoses, etc., according to the number of carbon atoms they contain.

Ketoximes. Organic substances containing the group $>C{=}NOH$. They are formed by treating ketones with hydroxylamine. They are similar in properties to the aldoximes, but undergo the Beckmann rearrangement when treated with sulphuric acid. They are reduced to primary amines.

Ketyls. Salts of radical anions of ketones, intensely coloured; dimerize readily. Thus reaction between potassium and benzophenone gives an intensely blue solution of $C_6H_5-\overset{\overset{\displaystyle O^{\ominus}}{|}}{C}-C_6H_5$ $K^{\oplus}$ potassium benzophenone ketyl, which is extremely sensitive to oxygen, and on acidification yields benzpinacol.

Kharasch, Morris Selig (1895-1957). Born in the Ukraine, Kharasch emigrated as a boy to America, and took his degree at the University of Chicago, where he spent most of his life, becoming professor in 1930. He worked on many aspects of organic chemistry, but will be remembered in particular for his fundamental work on reactions involving free radicals. See *Proc. Chem. Soc.*, 1958, 361.

Kieserite, $MgSO_4,H_2O$. A mineral, large quantities of which occur in the Stassfurt salt beds. It can be converted to Epsom salt, $MgSO_4,7H_2O$, by dissolving in hot water and crystallizing.

Kieselguhr. See Diatomite.

Kinase. A term used for any enzyme catalysing the transfer of phosphate from ATP to the indicated substrate, e.g. hexokinase (transfer to a hexose). The term 'Phosphokinase' is no longer used.

Kinetic theory of gases. This theory postulates that gases consist of elastic particles having a temperature-dependent, random motion. The properties of gases are derived by applying the laws of probability and of particle dynamics to such a system.

Kinetics, chemical. That branch of chemistry which is concerned with explaining the observed characteristics of chemical reactions (e.g. the effect of pressure, temperature, or concentration of reactants on the velocity of reactions) in terms of the kinetic theory of matter is called chemical kinetics.

Kipping, Frederic Stanley (1863-1949). Educated at Owens College, Manchester, and the University of Munich, Kipping later worked under H. E. Armstrong at the City and Guilds College, before being appointed in 1897 professor of chemistry at University College, Nottingham, from which he retired in 1936. He will chiefly be remembered for his pioneer work on the organic chemistry of silicon. See *Chem. & Ind.*, 1964, 697.

Kipp's apparatus. An apparatus for the production of a gas by the action of a liquid on a solid. It consists of three globes, the top one acts as a reservoir for the liquid and is connected with the bottom globe. The middle globe contains the solid. When gas is drawn off from the middle globe, the liquid in the lower globe rises and reacts with the solid, and when gas is no longer required the back pressure drives the liquid out of contact with the solid and evolution of gas ceases.

Kirchhoff, Gustav Robert (1824-1887). Born at Königsberg, Prussia, Kirchhoff studied under Bunsen at Breslau and Heidelberg. In 1854 he was appointed professor of physics at the University of Heidelberg, and in 1875 he received a similar appointment at Berlin. Working with Bunsen, he discovered the elements caesium and rubidium; he formulated the relationship between heat of reaction and temperature into a law.

Kirchhoff's equation. If Q is the heat evolved when a process (physical or chemical) is carried out at temperature T, the heat which would be evolved if the same process were carried out at a different temperature can be calculated with the aid of Kirchhoff's equation, namely,

$$dQ/dT = C_1 - C_2$$

where C_1 and C_2 are the total heat capacities of the system before and after the process respectively (e.g. reactants and products in a chemical reaction). Kirchhoff's equation is a direct consequence of the first law of thermodynamics: it is invaluable in thermochemistry.

Kish. The term applied to crystalline graphite deposited in iron furnaces on cooling molten iron.

Kjeldahl flask. A round-bottomed flask with a long, wide neck used in the determination of nitrogen by Kjeldahl's method.

Kjeldahl's method for the determination of nitrogen. The principle of the method is the conversion of the nitrogenous substance to ammonium sulphate by boiling with sulphuric acid in the presence of a catalyst, usually copper sulphate. Potassium sulphate is added to raise the boiling-point. The mixture is then made alkaline and the ammonia distilled off into standard acid. The method is particularly suitable for use as a micro method. For details of manipulation see books on analysis or practical biochemistry.

Klaproth, Martin Heinrich (1743-1817). Klaproth was born at Wernigerode, Germany. Although he did not ignore chemistry during the earlier part of his life, it was only after relinquishing his profession of apothecary in 1787 that he devoted himself in earnest to chemical investigations. In 1792 he began to teach chemistry in the Artillery School at Berlin and in 1810 he became the first professor of chemistry at Berlin University. He was one of the first German chemists to uphold Lavoisier's theory of combustion, and carried out a notable series of mineralogical analyses, of which he published detailed results and during which he discovered four elements.

Klaus, Karl Karlovich (1796-1864). Born at Dorpat (Tartu), Esthonia, where he received his early education, Klaus became apprenticed to a pharmacist at St. Petersburg. In 1831 he was appointed assistant in the chemistry department of the University of Dorpat, and in 1852 became professor of pharmacy there. His chemical investigations were on the platinum group of metals. He discovered the element ruthenium.

Kneader. A machine for the mixing of very thick pastes which employs roughly the same action as used in the kneading of dough by hand. It consists usually of a horizontal U-shaped trough carrying two specially shaped mixing blades mounted on parallel horizontal shafts. The bottom of the trough between the blades is ridged so that the clearance between the blades and trough is the same here as elsewhere. The blades revolve slowly and in doing so perform a pulling, folding action which mixes the paste.

Kneaders require to be heavily constructed to withstand the heavy stresses developed and power requirements are high; because of this cooling of the material can be a problem.

Knudsen cell. See Effusion.

Kögl, Fritz (1897-1958). Born in Munich, Kögl studied under Wieland, H. Fischer, and Windaus, and became professor of organic chemistry and biochemistry at Utrecht in 1930. He discovered the auxin activity of 3-indolylacetic acid, elucidated the structure of muscarine, and worked on the chemistry of many natural products. See *Nature*, 1949, **164**, 1609.

Kohlrausch equation. The equation devised to represent the behaviour of strong electrolytes on dilution, viz. $\Lambda_\infty - \Lambda_v = kC^{\frac{1}{2}}$, wherein Λ_∞ is the equivalent conductivity at infinite dilution, Λ_v that at volume v, k is a constant, and C is the concentration of the electrolyte. The equation is only valid at high dilutions.

Kohlraush, Friedrich Wilhelm (1840-1910). Born at Rinteln on the Weser, Kohlraush studied at Göttingen and Erlangen. He was appointed professor of physics at Göttingen (1866), Frankfurt (1870), Darmstadt (1871), Würzburg (1875), and Strasburg (1888). In 1900 he became honorary professor of physics at Berlin. His researches were mainly on electricity and magnetism and on the conductivity of electrolytes.

Kojic acid, 5-Hydroxy-2-hydroxymethyl-γ-pyrone, $C_6H_6O_4$. Crystallizes in needles, m.p. 152°,

soluble in water and alcohol. A product of the action of moulds of the *Aspergillus flavus-oryzae* group on glucose.

Kolbe, Adolphe Wilhelm Hermann (1818-1884). Kolbe was born at Elliehausen, near Göttingen. A pupil of Wöhler, he became assistant to Bunsen, and later worked with Playfair in London. In 1847 he returned to Germany as editor of the 'Dictionary of Chemistry' which had been started by Liebig, whom he succeeded as professor of chemistry at Marburg in 1851. In 1865 he was appointed to the University of Leipzig. A brilliant teacher, his value as a critic was marred by the excessive sharpness and lack of balance of his language. See *J. Chem. Soc.*, 1885, 323.

Kolbe reaction. The preparation of saturated or unsaturated hydrocarbons by the electrolysis of solutions of the alkali salts of aliphatic carboxylic acids. Thus, acetic acid gives ethane,

$$2CH_3CO_2^{\ominus} \rightarrow CH_3—CH_3 + 2CO_2$$

and succinic acid gives ethylene,

$$\begin{array}{c} H_2C—CO_2^{\ominus} \\ | \\ H_2C—CO_2^{\ominus} \end{array} \longrightarrow \begin{array}{c} CH_2 \\ \| \\ CH_2 \end{array} + 2CO_2$$

Kopp, Hermann Franz Moritz (1817-1892). Born at Hanau, Kopp became a pupil of Liebig at Giessen. Together they founded, in 1849, the 'Jahresbericht der Chemie'. In 1863 Kopp became professor of chemistry at Heidelberg. His experimental investigations lay chiefly in the domain of physical chemistry, of which he may, in some respects, be regarded as the founder, but his fame rests mainly on his writings dealing with the history of chemistry. See *Mem. Lect.*, *J. Chem. Soc.*, 1893, 775.

Körner, Wilhelm (Guglielmo) (1839-1925). Born in Cassel, Körner studied at the Polytechnik before proceeding to work with Will, Kopp, Engelbach, and Kekulé. In 1865 he became assistant to Professor Odling at St. Bartholomew's Hospital, and in 1867 was elected to the Chair of Chemistry at Bonn. In 1870 the 'Scuola Superiore di Agricoltura' was founded at Milan, and Körner was appointed to the Chair of Organic Chemistry. His research was chiefly upon the constitution and orientation of aromatic compounds. A member of many learned societies, he was awarded the Davy Medal of the Royal Society. See *J. Chem. Soc,*, 1925, 2975.

Kossel, Albrecht (1853-1927). Born at Rostock, he studied medicine there and at Strasbourg, where he later became assistant in physiological chemistry to Hoppe-Seyler. Later he worked in Berlin and Marburg, and in 1901 became director of the Physiological Institute at Heidelberg. He was the first to show that nucleic acids were built up from purines and pyrimidines, and he worked on protamines, histones and many other compounds of biochemical importance. He was awarded the Nobel Prize for medicine in 1910.

Krebs, Sir Hans Adolf (1900-   ). Born at Hindesheim in Germany, Krebs was educated at several German universities but emigrated to England in 1933, working first at Cambridge. He moved to the University of Sheffield in 1935, where he became professor of biochemistry in 1945. In 1954 he became professor of biochemistry at Oxford. His work has been largely concerned with *in vitro* metabolic processes. In 1932 he proposed the cyclic process of urea production, and in 1937 put forward the tricarboxylic acid cycle (Krebs cycle) as part of the pathway of carbohydrate oxidation. He shared the Nobel Prize for physiology and medicine in 1953.

Krebs' cycle (Citric acid cycle, Tricarboxylic acid cycle). A cyclic sequence of reactions in cell metabolism, by which is achieved the controlled oxidative breakdown of acetyl-coenzyme A (derived from pyruvic acid), fatty acids and amino-acids. The cycle produces carbon dioxide together with reduced coenzymes (CoASH, $NADH_2$, $NADPH_2$, $FADH_2$) which serve as energy sources. For cells growing under aerobic conditions efficient use of the stored energy occurs through the respiratory chain.

Krilium. The trade name of a soil conditioner developed out of experiments to investigate the known effect of dung, and organic matter generally, in improving the structure and aggregate stability of soils. The natural substances were unsatisfactory in several ways, and chemical products, designed to possess aggregate-cementing properties and to persist in soil, were introduced. These include Krilium, a synthetic polyelectrolyte, VAMA, a modified copolymer of vinyl acetate and maleic acid (Krilium 6), and HPAN, the sodium salt of a hydrolysed polyacrylonitrile (Krilium 9).

The solid form of krilium has as active ingredient a copolymer of about equal molar proportions of vinyl acetate and the partial methyl ester of maleic acid. It may be formulated with lime, bentonite, etc. In aqueous form, krilium contains a copolymer of about equal molar proportions of isobutylene and ammonium maleamate.

Krypton, Kr. At.no. 36, At.wt. 83·80, m.p. $-156\cdot7°$, b.p. $-153\cdot3°$, d(liquid) 2·6. One of the noble gases, % atmospheric abundance $1\cdot5 \times 10^{-4}$. It is obtained from liquid air by fractional distillation. It forms a difluoride KrF_2 and probably other compounds on reaction with fluorine under pressure. Oxy-salts are formed on hydrolysis of the fluorides. Also forms clathrates and hydrates. It is used in fluorescent tubes and incandescent lamps. The metre is defined as 1,650,763·73 wavelengths of the orange radiation of ^{86}Kr.

Krystal crystallizer. See Oslo crystallizer.

Kuhn, Richard (1900-   ). Born in Vienna, Kuhn studied chemistry under Willstätter in Munich. In 1926 he became professor at the Technische Hochschule in Zürich and in 1929 professor at the University of Heidelberg and director of the Kaiser Wilhelm Institute for Medical Research. He was awarded the Nobel Prize in chemistry in 1938 for his elucidation of the structure of carotenoids and certain vitamins.

Kundt, August Adolph Eduard Eberhard (1839-1894). Born at Schwerin in Mecklenburg, Kundt studied at Leipzig and Berlin. In 1888 he was appointed professor of experimental physics and Director of the Berlin Physical Institute. His researches were on different branches of physics, particularly on sound, light, and specific heat determinations.

Kunkel, John. Born in 1630, he later entered the laboratory of the Elector of Saxony; he taught chemistry at the University of Wittenburg and was useful in making public the method of preparing phosphorus. He discovered how to make ruby glass by means of purple of Cassius. He died in Stockholm in 1702.

Kurrol salt. A fibrous form of polymeric sodium metaphosphate. It gives a gel with water and is obtained by annealing Graham's salt above 550°. See Hexametaphosphates.

Kyanite. Disthene. Al_2O_3, SiO_2, Trimorphous with andalusite and sillimanite. Crystals are triclinic. There are four molecules in the unit cell. Kyanite is an orthosilicate, as the SiO_4 groups are independent. Sp.gr. 3·56-3·68, hardness 5-7. Pale blue when quite pure, but often grey, yellow or reddish. On heating above 1450° it is converted into mullite, the excess silica being present as a glass. It is used as a refractory, particularly for lining the tanks of glass-melting furnaces.

Kynurenic acid, 4-Hydroxyquinoline-2-carboxylic acid, $C_{10}H_7NO_3$. Crystallizes in needles, m.p. 282°-283°. Insoluble in water, soluble in hot

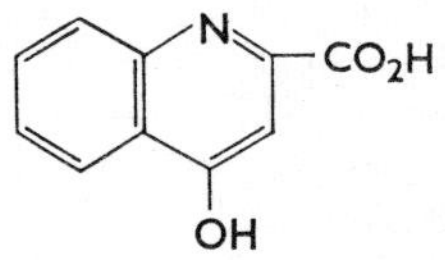

alcohol. It is excreted in the urine of the dog and some other mammals, being formed from the amino-acid tryptophan.

Kynurenine, 3-anthraniloyl-L-alanine, $C_{10}H_{12}N_2O_3$. An intermediate in the metabolic

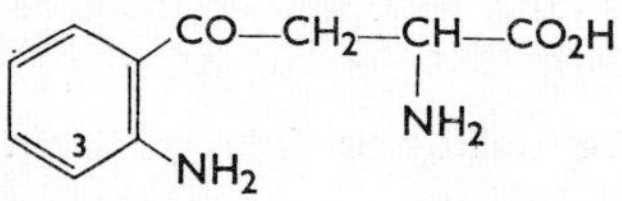

breakdown of tryptophan. This proceeds mainly through cleavage of the indole ring to give formylkynurenine, which is hydrolysed to kynurenine: this undergoes oxidation to 3-hydroxykynurenine, and side-chain cleavage at the carbonyl group gives 3-hydroxyanthranilic acid. This in part, undergoes further ring fission with the formation of acyclic metabolites and of pyridine-carboxylic acids such as quinolinic and nicotinic acid. 3-Hydroxykynurenine is the biogenetic precursor of the ommochromes (*q.v.*), eye pigments of insects and crabs.

L

Lability. The property of a complex or molecule denoting ready replacement of attached groups.

Labradorite. A variety of plagioclase feldspar which varies in composition from 50 to 70 molecular per cent albite with anorthite. The crystals are triclinic, sp.gr. 2·67-2·7, hardness 6. It shrinks greatly when melted; m.p. 1477°. Refrac. index 1·555. Crystals of large size are rare, but often show a brilliant play of colours when viewed at a suitable angle. The fracture is irregular and splinty. It occurs as a primary constituent of some basic igneous rocks. On prolonged weathering it forms kaolin.

Laccase. An enzyme found in various bacteria and mushrooms and also in higher plants and fruits. Effects the oxidation of polyphenols to the respective quinones which subsequently undergo further change. It does not attack tyrosine or monophenols.

Lachesine. Used as the chloride, $C_{20}H_{26}ClNO_3$. This is a white powder, m.p. 212°-216°, soluble in water and alcohol. It is prepared from ethyl iodide, dimethylaminoethanol, and potassium benzilate, and is used as a substitute for atropine for dilating the pupil of the eye.

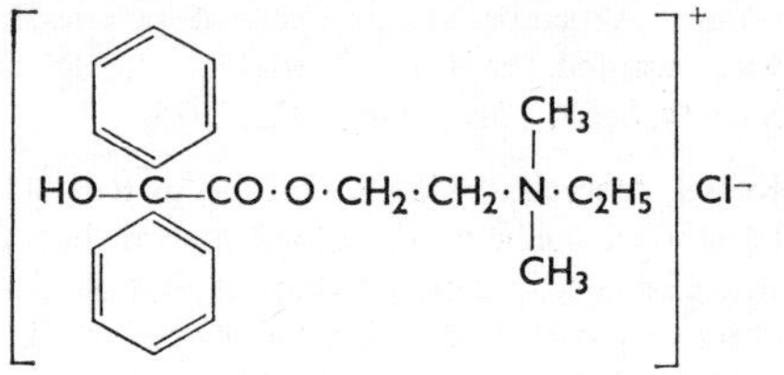

Lactalbumin. A protein, belonging to the albumin class, present in milk. It has a molecular weight of about 17,500, and is very similar in its properties to the albumin of the blood. It contains the essential amino-acid cystine, which is only present in traces in casein, the chief protein of milk.

Lactams. Amino-acids when heated lose water to form lactams. The water is eliminated between the carboxyl group and the amino-group and a cyclic compound is formed. Also obtained by reduction of the imides of dicarboxylic acids or by isomerization of the oximes of cyclic ketones. Rings containing five, six, and eight atoms can be obtained. The lactams are decomposed by heating with alkalis and the amino-acid is formed. They are colourless solids and are extremely poisonous.

Lactic acids, $C_3H_6O_3$. $CH_3·CHOH·COOH$. Lactic acid can be optically active. The acids are colourless syrupy liquids which readily absorb moisture, and are formed by the fermentation of sugars by the *lactobacilli* and some moulds. They are very soluble in water, but sparingly soluble in ether. When slowly distilled they lose water and form lactide. L-Lactic acid, sarcolactic acid, occurs in muscle, being formed by the breakdown of carbohydrate; m.p. 25°-26°; $[\alpha]_D$ +2·67°. D-Lactic acid; m.p. 18°, b.p. 122°/14 mm. Forms an insoluble zinc salt; salts of the active acids are more soluble. Lactic acid is manufactured by the fermentation of pure sugars or of various sugar-containing materials such as starch hydrolysates, and by the hydrolysis of lactonitrile formed by reacting acetaldehyde with hydrogen cyanide. The major use is in the food and beverage industries, where it is used as an acidulant and for the manufacture of a bread additive. It is also used as a chemical intermediate, in textile finishing and in leather tanning.

β-**Lactic acid.** See Hydracrylic acid.

Lactide, $C_6H_8O_4$. Prepared by the slow distilla-

tion of concentrated solutions of the lactic acids. L-Lactide forms colourless rhombic crystals; m.p. 95°, b.p. 150°/25 mm. Sparingly soluble in alcohol and ether. $[\alpha]_D^{18}$ −298° in benzene. Prepared from L-lactic acid. It is partially converted to lactic acid by water. D-Lactide has properties similar to those of L-lactide but its rotation is opposite in sign. DL-Lactide crystallizes in colourless needles, m.p. 124·5°, b.p. 142°/8 mm. Sparingly soluble in alcohol and ether. Obtained from DL-lactic acid.

Lactides. When α-hydroxy-fatty acids are heated they lose water and form lactides. These contain the group

$$CO-O-CH-$$
$$|\qquad\qquad|$$
$$-CH-O-CO$$

and are formed by the interaction between two molecules of the hydroxy-acid whereby a molecule of water is eliminated between the hydroxyl group of one and the carboxyl group of the other. They are decomposed by heating with water to regenerate the original acid.

Lactones. Anhydrides formed by elimination of water between the hydroxyl and carboxyl groups of hydroxy-acids. Since they are ring compounds containing carbon atoms, the ease with which they are formed depends upon the number of atoms in the ring to be formed. The commonest lactones are those of γ- and δ-hydroxy-acids, since these have rings containing five and six atoms respectively. They are usually formed spontaneously in concentrated solutions of the acids, or by heating such solutions with small amounts of sulphuric acid. They are usually crystalline solids which are partially decomposed by water with regeneration of the hydroxy-acid.

Lactose, $C_{12}H_{22}O_{11}$. Milk sugar, first discovered in 1615, occurs in the milk of all animals, but not in plants. Human milk contains 6%, cow's milk, 4%. It is manufactured by the evaporation of whey.

It is glucose-4-β-galactoside. Like glucose it gives rise to two series of isomeric derivatives, the α-lactose of commerce has $[\alpha]_D$ +90°, β-lactose has +35° and the rotation of a solution after standing is +55·3°. Lactose is hydrolysed by the enzyme lactase.

Ladenburg, Albert (1842-1911). Born at Mannheim, Ladenburg was educated at the Polytech-

nic, Karlsruhe, and at Heidelberg University where he worked under Carius. Later he studied under Kekulé (Ghent) and Friedel (Paris). In 1872 he became professor of chemistry at Kiel and in 1889 at Breslau. He investigated the organic compounds of silicon and synthesized the alkaloid coniine. In 1907 he was awarded the Davy Medal of the Royal Society. See 'Chem. Soc. Mem. Lect.' 1913.

Laevorotatory. See Optical activity.

Laevulinic acid, Levulinic acid, Laevulic acid, $C_5H_8O_3CH_3COCH_2CH_2COOH$. Colourless crystals; m.p. 33°-35°, b.p. 245°-246°. Very soluble in water, alcohol, and ether. Prepared by heating cane sugar or starch with concentrated hydrochloric acid. Reduced to γ-valerolactone. Also reacts as a ketone. Used in cotton printing.

Laevulose. An old name for fructose.

Lakes. Insoluble pigments obtained by precipitating sundry natural and artificial colouring matters (dyestuffs, dye-wood extracts, cochineal, and the like) on to suitable bases in the presence of alum, salts of magnesium, zinc, tin, or other metals, and compounds like tannic acid commonly used as mordants in dyeing processes. The preferred bases or substrates are:

(1) alumina, where transparency or richness of colour is desired, as for the manufacture of pigments for use in printing inks.

(2) china clay, where it is desired to make a light soft product with bulk and good suspension properties;

(3) barytes, which is the most important base for pigments used in paint and linoleum manufacture;

(4) blanc fixe, which is usually much more finely divided than the natural crystalline barytes;

(5) green earth and precipitated hydroxide of iron, which are used according to the colour requirement of the product.

Many pigments of excellent quality and excellent fastness to light are made from artificial dyestuffs; but the lakes formerly made from natural dyestuffs, such as madder and the dye-wood extracts, are no longer in demand, either because they are too costly or because the colour fades. The exceptions are crimson lake (an artists' colour) made from cochineal, and logwood extracts (containing haematein as the active principle) used for dyeing wool and silk black in conjunction with iron and chromium salts as mordants.

Lambert's law. This law, proposed by Lambert in 1760, states that layers of equal thickness of a homogeneous material absorb equal proportions of light:

$$I = I_0 e^{-\kappa d},$$

where I is the intensity of the transmitted light, I_0 that of the incident light, d the thickness of the layer, and κ a constant, characteristic of the substance, known as the absorption coefficient; κ also depends on the wavelength of the light employed. When solutions are considered, it is clearly desirable to modify this expression to include the concentration of the absorbing molecules. This modification is embodied in Beer's law (q.v.).

Lamellar compounds. Another name for intercalation compounds.

Laminarin. An extract from brown seaweeds, of which it may comprise up to 30% of the dry matter. It is a white powder with the formula $(C_6H_{10}O_5)_n$, consisting of about 20 β-D-glucopyranose units linked through carbon atoms 1 and 3; branch linkages may also be present. Depending on the source it exists either as a form soluble in cold water (38 g in 100 g at 20°) or as a form soluble in hot but insoluble in cold water.

Laminates. Synthetic resins are used to bond layers of reinforcing agents such as cotton cloth, paper, asbestos fabric, and glass cloth in the production of laminated sheet materials. When amino resins are used to bond the sheets light coloured materials having high track resistance and good tensile strength result. These materials are used for decorative purposes and have sufficient arc resistance for electrical use in saline or dusty conditions. Phenol resin bonded laminates are used industrially in the construction of bearings and gears and for other applications where silent running, strength, and freedom from lubrication are desirable. The materials have high water and acid resistance, but most grades are attacked to a certain extent by alkalis.

Considerable development has taken place in the use of resin bonded glass fibre laminates as structural materials. These laminates can be readily produced without the application of heat or pressure by using polyester or epoxide resins as binders for glass fibre mat or cloth.

Lamp black. A soft black pigment akin to soot, formerly seen in lamp chimneys and obtained by the incomplete combustion of vegetable oils and other organic matter. Now the source of the organic matter is natural gas and petroleum, so that in effect lamp black is generally regarded as

one of the soft grades of carbon black. Used extensively in inks and paints. See Carbon black.

Lande g factor. See g Factor.

Landis, Walter Savage (1881-1944). Born at Pottstown, Pennsylvania, Landis was educated at Lehigh University, studying later at Heidelberg and Aachen. After an academic career at Lehigh from 1902 to 1912 he joined the American Cyanamid Co. as chief technologist, becoming Vice-President in 1922. His work on nitrogen fixation, electric smelting, and heavy chemicals gained him the Chemical Industry Medal in 1936 and the Perkin Medal for 1939.

Landolt, Hans Heinrich (1831-1910). A native of Zürich, Landolt studied chemistry at Zürich, Breslau, Berlin, and Heidelberg. In 1856 he became a dozent at Breslau and in 1867 was appointed professor of chemistry at Bonn. Thereafter he became professor in the newly founded Technische Hochschule at Aix-la-Chapelle (1869) and in the University of Berlin (1891). His contributions to science lie mainly in the fields of refractivity and optical activity. See J. Chem. Soc., 1911, 1653.

Langmuir, Irving (1881-1957). Born in Brooklyn, Langmuir was educated at Columbia University and the University of Göttingen. He was appointed instructor in chemistry at Stevens Institute of Technology (1906) but in 1909 became associated with the Research Laboratories of the General Electric Company. Among his contributions to science are his work on theories of adsorption, the gas-filled lamp and the use of hydrogen in the atomic state for welding. He was awarded the Nobel Prize for Chemistry in 1932. See Proc. Chem. Soc,, 1959, 80.

Langmuir adsorption isotherm. A theoretical equation, derived by Langmuir in 1918 by means of kinetic theory, for the influence of pressure on the adsorption of a gas on a plane solid surface. Many cases of physical adsorption (q.v.) conform to the theory under conditions where the amount of adsorption is less than would correspond to a complete monolayer of gas on the surface of the adsorbent. The equation shows that the fraction, θ, of the surface which carries the adsorbed gas molecules when the pressure is p is given by

$$\theta = \frac{ap}{1+ap}$$

where a is a constant for a given system at a given temperature.

Lanoceric acid, $C_{30}H_{60}O_4$. A saturated dihydroxy-fatty acid occurring combined in wool fat. It crystallizes in leaflets, m.p. 104°-105°, sparingly soluble in ether and benzene.

Lanolin. A crude preparation of cholesterol and

its esters obtained from wool fat. Anhydrous lanolin is extracted from wool by kneading with water to give an emulsion and then centrifuging. It is a pale yellow tenacious substance melting at about 37°. Lanolin itself is anhydrous lanolin mixed with about 30% of water. In medicine it is used either alone or mixed with soft paraffin, lard, or other fat as an ointment base and is a constituent of many toilet creams. It readily penetrates the skin and it is capable of taking up about half its weight of water so that it makes an ideal base for the administration of drugs that are required to be absorbed through the skin.

Lanosterol, Lanostadienol, $C_{30}H_{50}O$. A triter-

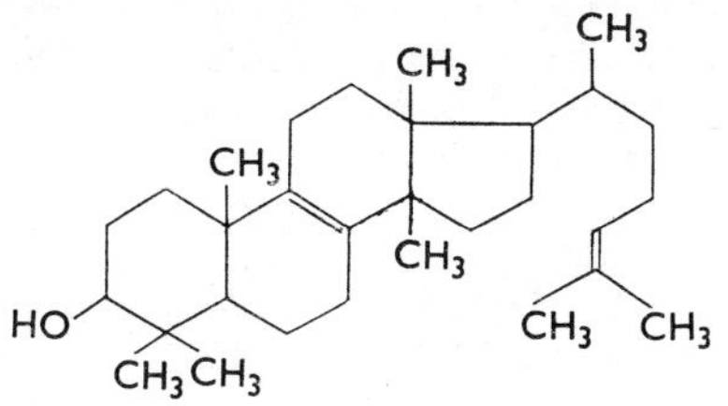

penoid or trimethylsteroid alcohol, found together with cholesterol in the non-saponifiable matter of wool wax. It is 4,4,14-trimethyl-cholesta-5,24-dien-3β-ol and has m.p. 138°-139°, $[\alpha]_D$ +62°; acetate, m.p. 132°-134°.

Lanesterol is the biogenetic parent of cholesterol and of all other commonly occurring sterols: its precursor is squalene (*q.v.*) which affords lanosterol by oxidative cyclisation with rearrangement. (Other modes of cyclisation yield various triterpenoids.)

The relation between lanosterol and cholesterol has been amply confirmed by biosynthetic studies and by chemical syntheses.

Lanthanum. At.no. 57, At.wt. 138·92, *d* 6·174, m.p. 920°, b.p. 3469°. The metal has the hexagonal close-packed structure below 310° ($a =$ 3·770, $c = 12·131$ Å), the cubic close-packed structure from 310° to 868° ($a = 5·303$ Å) and the body-centred cubic structure above 868° ($a =$ 4·26 Å). It is a typical rare-earth element (*q.v.*); the metal oxidises readily in air. It is used in alloys and to a small extent in refractories and for catalysis.

Lanthanum compounds. Lanthanum forms a single series of colourless salts, the metal having an oxidation state of three. These are typical rare-earth compounds (*q.v.*).

Lanthanum nitrate is used as an analytical reagent for acetate groups.

Lanthanides. The elements from lanthanum to lutetium, in which the 4*f* orbitals are being filled, are collectively called lanthanides.

Lanthanide contraction. The phenomenon that the ionic and atomic radii of elements after the lanthanide series are the same as those of the elements in the same groups but occurring before the lanthanides. The phenomenon is due to the steady decrease in radii across the lanthanides and exhibits itself most clearly in the closely similar chemistries of the elements Zr and Hf, Mo and W, etc.

Lanthionine, $C_6H_{12}N_2O_4S$.

$$HO_2C \cdot CH(NH_2) \cdot CH_2 \cdot S \cdot CH_2 \cdot CH(NH_2) \cdot CO_2H$$

β,β'-Thiodialanine an amino-acid isolated from wool hydrolysates. It occurs also in some peptides of bacterial origin, e.g. nisin.

Lapis-lazuli. A deep blue semi-precious stone used by the ancient Egyptians. The powder was used as ultramarine, a pigment now produced artificially. It is a metamorphic rock, the colour being due to the blue feldspathoid lazurite $3(NaAlSiO_4) \cdot Na_2S$.

Lapworth, Arthur (1873-1941). Lapworth was educated at the Mason Science College and the Central Technical College, South Kensington. He was at different times professor of both organic and physical chemistry at Manchester University. He made a life-study of molecular rearrangements in organic compounds. See *Nature*, 1941, **147**, 769.

Laser. A device which produces beams of monochromatic light of very great intensity in which the waves are coherent. The name is derived from Light Amplification by Stimulated Emission of Radiation. The theoretical problems in the construction of lasers were first published by Townes and Schawlow, in 1958, and the first optical laser was built in 1960.

Light emitted from an ordinary source, such as a filament lamp, is not of a single wavelength (non-monochromatic) and neither is it coherently phased, i.e. the wave fronts are out of step with one another. When an atom in its ground state (E_0) absorbs energy (photons) it is excited to a higher energy level (E_1). The energy absorbed may now be spontaneously released either immediately or after some time to yield the ground state of the atom once more. In a laser, however, the excited atom is struck by a photon of exactly the same energy as the one which would be emitted spontaneously. The excited atom is stimulated to emit a photon and return to the ground condition with the result that two photons of precisely the same wavelength are given. The process can now be repeated throughout the system.

An example of a solid laser is the ruby crystal (Al_2O_3 containing about 0·05% chromium). When the chromium atoms absorb light, they are raised to excited states and revert to their ground state by a two-stage process, (a) by yielding some of their energy to the crystal lattice to give a metastable state, and (b) after a few milliseconds in this state by spontaneously emitting photons of wavelength 6,493 Å to return to their original energy level. The laser action takes place when some of the photons emitted from stage (b) stimulate the excited chromium atoms in stage (a) to emit their radiation faster than they normally would and a cascade of photons of wavelength 6,943 Å results. The ruby crystal in the form of a rod several centimetres long and about half a centimetre in diameter has ends which are parallel and optically flat. One end is completely silvered, the other partially silvered. The atoms are excited by a powerful electronic flash tube which is placed close to the crystal. As a result of the silvered ends of the ruby, the photons are reflected back and forward many times along the crystal axis, continuously stimulating emission until a coherent beam of light of very high intensity is emitted through the partly silvered end of the crystal.

Many different types of laser materials are now known. Glasses containing neodymium are used for high-output lasers; gas lasers using helium-neon mixtures or caesium vapour have also been made. The most efficient lasers are those using semi-conductors, with for example gallium arsenide phosphide as the active crystal.

Due to the very high intensity of the laser beams and their coherent nature they may be used in a variety of ways. The beam intensity is such that even a brief flash is sufficient to melt or vapourize very hard materials. A medical application is to 'weld' a torn or injured retina to its support and so prevent its becoming detached. Decayed parts of teeth can be 'removed'. Many advances are possible in the field of telecommunications, and when the efficiency of beam production is increased lasers may be used for cutting and welding processes.

Lassaigne's test. A general test for the presence of nitrogen, halogens, or sulphur in an organic compound, a little of which is heated with a pellet of sodium in a hard-glass test tube; the hot tube is plunged into distilled water and the product ground. The presence of nitrogen is shown by the formation of Prussian blue on heating with a solution of ferrous sulphate containing a trace of ferric salt and hydrochloric acid. With halogen-containing substances sodium halide is formed, detectable with silver nitrate; while the presence of sulphur can be shown with sodium nitroprusside or lead acetate.

Latensification. The treatment of some photographic materials, just after exposure and just before development, with mercury vapour, gold salts, organic acids, ammonia, hydrogen peroxide, sulphur dioxide or bisulphite salts produces an effective increase in photographic

speed. The variety of these chemical treatments implies more than one mechanism for this phenomenon, but changes in the nature, size and environment of the latent image specks are certainly involved. A low-intensity flash, after image-wise exposure, also produces a latensification of the image.

Latent heat. The heat evolved or absorbed in a change in the physical state of a substance, e.g. in its passage from solid to liquid or from liquid to vapour. The heat is generally measured in terms of the number of calories evolved or absorbed per gram or per gram molecule. The heat effect in such changes is reversible. The heat absorbed when one gram of a substance passes from the solid to the liquid state at the melting temperature of the substance in question is called the latent heat of fusion, and that absorbed when one gram of liquid is transformed into vapour is called the latent heat of vaporization; the latter term is employed usually but not always for the change taking place at the boiling point of the liquid at 1 atmosphere pressure.

Latent-image. The change occurring in silver halide grains, which makes them developable after exposure to light, is ascribed to the formation of latent image. The action of light on silver halide is finally to produce silver and halogen. The silver forms at specific low-energy sites on the crystal, often at crystal lattice imperfections, and when the silver specks reach a minimum required size they act as development centres, allowing development of the whole grain to take place. These silver specks are the latent-image specks. In the absence of other acceptors, gelatin takes up the halogen formed from the light reaction. It is the migration of electrons through the crystal lattice which allows formation of latent-image specks at particular sites.

Laterite. A mass of disintegrated rock produced by the weathering of a basic material such as basalt. Its chief constituent is hydrargyllite, $Al_2O_3, 3H_2O$, generally together with some clay and with some free iron oxide. It is one of the most extensive products of rock-decay in the tropics and is the source of much of the red mud in the Amazon and other rivers. It is specially abundant in India, Malaysia, Indonesia, Western Australia, Africa, South America, and China. Laterite differs from clay in the absence of silica and in being a primary deposit (i.e. found *in situ*). The bauxitic fireclays of Ayrshire, Scotland, may be laterites. Its predominant colour is brown; its texture is fine and the particles are apparently amorphous.

Latex. The term refers now to any stable aqueous dispersion of a polymer. Although originally referring to the naturally occurring form of natural rubber, many synthetic rubbers (*q.v.*) such as SBR, Nitrile and Neoprene are produced as latexes, as indeed are other types of synthetic polymers obtained by emulsion polymerization, e.g. polyvinyl chloride and the polyacrylates. Natural rubber latex is the milky juice which exudes from the bark of certain trees when punctured. The most important source is *Hevea brasiliensis*. Latex is an emulsion or suspension containing rubber particles which are round (diameters about 0·5 micron to 2 microns) or pear-shaped (lengths about 1·5 microns to 3 microns). Fresh latex contains about 30%-40% of rubber, about 2% of proteins, and resins, sugar, and mineral matter. Latex coagulates spontaneously on standing for less than 24 hours, and commercially is coagulated by addition of a small quantity of formic or acetic acid. It can be preserved by adding ammonia or a hydrophilic colloid. Latex is concentrated by centrifuging, evaporating, creaming, or filtering, giving a liquid with a rubber content of up to about 80%, depending on the method of concentration.

A latex, whether of natural or synthetic rubber can be used for the direct manufacture of rubber goods by dipping, moulding, spreading, or electro-depositing, and for the manufacture of impregnated textiles, adhesives, and paints. Latexes of non-rubber synthetic polymers are also being increasingly used by the foregoing methods to produce plastic goods. Latex can be vulcanized before coagulation and processing. See Vulcanized latex.

Lattice. The regular three dimensional array of the atoms in a crystal. A crystal lattice is built up from unit cells (*q.v.*).

Lattice energy. The energy released when ions of opposite charge are brought together from infinity to form one gram mole of salt crystal in an ionic lattice. Lattice energies may be derived from the Born-Haber cycle (*q.v.*) and calculated using the Kapustinskii equation.

Laudanum. A tincture of opium containing 1% of morphine.

Laue pattern. The symmetrical array of spots obtained on a photographic plate exposed to a non-homogeneous beam of X-rays after its passage through a crystal. Patterns of this sort were first observed in 1912 by Friedrich and Knipping, working on a suggestion made by Laue. They constitute the earliest, although one of the most difficult, methods of investigating crystal structure by means of X-rays.

Laurent, Auguste (1807-1853). Born at La Folie, near Langres in France, Laurent qualified as a mining engineer but later became tutorial assistant to Dumas in Paris, where he carried out his first chemical investigation. In 1838 he was appointed professor of chemistry at Bordeaux, but returned to Paris in 1845 and three years later was appointed assayer at the Mint. Laurent was distinguished mainly for his experimental and theoretical studies in organic chemistry.

Lauric acid, *n*-**Dodecylic acid,** $C_{12}H_{24}O_2$, $CH_3 \cdot [CH_2]_{10} \cdot COOH$. Crystallizes in needles, m.p. 44°, b.p. 225°/100 mm. A fatty acid occurring as glycerides in milk, spermaceti, laurel oil, coconut oil, palm oil, and other vegetable oils.

Lauryl alcohol, Dodecyl alcohol, $C_{12}H_{26}O$, $CH_3 \cdot [CH_2]_{10} \cdot CH_2OH$. Crystallizes in colourless leaflets; m.p. 24°, b.p. 150°/20 mm. Insoluble in water; soluble in alcohol. Manufactured by reduction of ethyl laurate or glyceryl trilaurate by hydrogen under pressure in the presence of catalysts. Used in manufacture of detergents.

Lautal. A trade name for an aluminium/2% silicon/4% copper alloy resembling duralumin in many respects. It is more resistant to corrosion than aluminium.

Lavoisier, Antoine Laurent (1743-1793). Born in Paris Lavoisier studied chemistry under Rouelle at the Jardin du Roi and in 1765 explained for the first time the setting of plaster of Paris. His experimental researches were not so important as his interpretation of the experiments of other chemists. He took a part in the reform of chemical nomenclature and was precise in his language; he lived at a time when many false theories and surmises prevailed, and he was one of the very few who recognized that suppositions handed down from the past became imposing by the weight of authority they gradually acquire. Lavoisier reasoned from facts only, and his reasoning was reduced to simple operations and was free from prejudices. In this respect he resembled Pasteur. He was able in the space of a few years to give chemistry a strictly scientific character that it had not previously possessed. As a member of the *ferme général* he incurred the hatred of the Convention, was arrested and executed.

Law of constancy of interfacial angles. See Interfacial angles, constancy of.

Law of mass action. See Mass action, law of.

Law of rationality of intercepts. See Rationality of intercepts, law of.

Lawes, Sir John Bennet, Bart. (1814-1900). Lawes is famous for the work he carried out at Rothamsted, his family estate, in association with J. H. Gilbert, on the fixation of nitrogen by plants. He was also the first to make superphosphate and to study the effects of artificial fertilizers on crops. He left Rothamsted in trust to be carried on as an agricultural research station.

Lawrencium. The isotope $^{258}Lw_{102}$ is prepared by bombarding californium with accelerated boron ions. It is the element that completes the $5f$ series of atoms.

Layer lattice. A term applied to crystal structures in which well-defined layers, either simple or composite, of atoms may be distinguished. The forces between the atoms within the layers are stronger than those holding the layers together, leading to good cleavage parallel to the layers. Examples of layer lattices include graphite, boric acid, cadmium iodide and chloride, and molybdenum sulphide.

Lazurite. A blue feldspathoid sodium alumino-silicate of approximate formula $3(NaAlSiO_4)$.-Na_2S. It occurs naturally but is prepared by heating kaolin to red-heat in the absence of air and the presence of sulphur and charcoal. Used as a pigment. See also Ultramarine.

LCAO method. A method of calculation of molecular orbitals based on the concept that the molecular orbitals can be expressed purely in terms of the algebraic sum of the atomic orbitals.

Leaching. The extraction of a soluble material from an insoluble solid by dissolution in a suitable solvent. The soluble material may be either liquid or solid.

On an industrial scale leaching is used for such operations as the extraction of sugar from sugar beet, oil from soya beans and metals from their ores. The type of equipment used depends on the nature of the solid. If it forms a permeable mass the solvent is percolated through beds of the material, otherwise the material is agitated with the solvent and the two then separated. Both types of equipment may be batch or continuous.

Lead, Pb. At. no. 82. The atomic weight of ordinary lead is 207·21; the atomic weight of lead derived from uranium minerals is about 206·1 to 206·6; that of lead derived from thorium minerals is about 208·4. Lead is the ultimate product of the various radioactive-decay series.

It is a silvery-white or greyish metal that has been known from prehistoric times. Sp.gr. 11·33-11·36; m.p. 327·4°, b.p. 1750°. Lead crystallizes with the face-centred cubic structure, $a=4·939$ Å. Sp.ht. at 18° is 0·0299. It is malleable, and may be rolled into sheet or foil and extruded into pipe.

It is usually obtained from the sulphide, PbS, by roasting in a furnace; the roasting takes place in two stages: first the formation of lead sulphate, $PbSO_4$, then a reaction between the sulphide and sulphate to give the metal and sulphur dioxide. Coal or iron is usually added to the sulphide in the furnace. Lead is freed from silver by crystallization or by melting with zinc. It may be refined by electrolysis.

Lead sheets and lead pipes are largely used in industry, and lead is also used in the covering of electric cables. Lead is used on a large scale in the manufacture of lead accumulators, red lead, and white lead. Metallic lead is only superficially oxidized in air and is only soluble in acids in the presence of oxygen owing to the high overpotential of hydrogen on lead. Lead forms two series of salts, lead (II), plumbous; and lead (**IV**), plumbic.

Lead accumulator. An accumulator consists of a number of plates of lead, each alternate plate is connected to one wire and the remaining plates to another wire. The plates are covered with a mixture of oxides of lead and lead sulphate, and are placed in dilute sulphuric acid. When a current is passed through the accumulator, lead dioxide is formed on one set of plates and metallic lead on the other set of plates, and a little extra sulphuric acid is produced. When the accumulator is used to generate electricity the sulphuric acid acts on the lead, the lead oxide, and dioxide, forming lead sulphate and water, and the current of electricity flows until a state of equilibrium is reached.

Lead acetates. The common lead acetate (sugar of lead), $Pb(C_2H_3O_2)_2$, $3H_2O$, forms colourless, monoclinic crystals isomorphous with zinc acetate. Sp.gr. 2·50, m.p. 75°; at 100° it loses acetic acid and water, forming a basic acetate; 100 g of water dissolve 50 g of the salt at 25°. Lead acetate can be obtained anhydrous; it is soluble in alcohol.

Ammonolysis of lead acetate gives two basic lead acetates, $3Pb(CH_3COO)_2 \cdot PbO \cdot H_2O$ and $Pb(CH_3COO)_2 \cdot 2PbO \cdot H_2O$.

Lead tetra-acetate, $Pb(OCOCH_3)_4$, is obtained as an easily hydrolysed colourless crystalline compound from the action of acetic acid and acetic anhydride on red lead, followed by oxidation of the resulting diacetate with chlorine. A powerful oxidizing agent it will convert glycols into the corresponding aldehydes or ketones, and 1,2 dicarboxylic acids into the corresponding Δ^1-alkene.

Lead alloys. The principal alloys of lead are included under the heading 'Tin alloys', other lead alloys are antimonial lead containing from 6% to 8% of antimony, and tellurium lead containing about 0·1% of tellurium. Rose's metal consists of bismuth 50 parts, lead 27 parts, tin 23 parts; it melts at 95°, Wood's metal consists of bismuth 50%, lead 25%, tin 12·5%, cadmium 12·5%; it melts at 70°.

Lead azide, $Pb(N_3)_2$. An initiator prepared in the form of fine white or grey crystals by double decomposition of lead acetate and sodium azide.

It retains its sensitivity when moist, and is more stable than mercury fulminate, and less sensitive to blows. See Explosives.

Lead bromide, $PbBr_2$, m.p. 373°, b.p. 916°. Solubility at 25°, 0·97 g in 100 g water. Lead bromide is readily soluble in hot water and on cooling is precipitated in fine crystals. It forms a trihydrate, $PbBr_2 \cdot 3H_2O$.

Lead carbonate, $PbCO_3$. Occurs as the mineral cerussite, in orthorhombic crystals isomorphous with the carbonates of calcium, strontium, and barium. Density 6·47. It may be prepared by precipitating a cold solution of lead acetate or nitrate with ammonium carbonate.

The most important basic carbonate is white lead; this is a white amorphous solid of indefinite composition but approximating to the formula $2PbCO_3$, $Pb(OH)_2$. White lead is prepared by interaction of lead, air, carbon dioxide, steam, and acetic acid or by electrolytic methods.

Lead chlorides. *Lead chloride,* $PbCl_2$, forms white, silky, rhombic needles, d 5·8, m.p. 298°, b.p. 954°, solubility 1·08 g in 100 g water at 25°. It forms many double chlorides and also basic chlorides.

The mineral matlockite is $PbFCl$; mendipite is $PbCl_2$, $2PbO$. Cassel yellow is a pigment made by fusing lead chloride with lead oxide; it has no definite composition but approximates to $PbCl_2$, $7PbO$.

Lead tetrachloride is a yellow liquid; density 3·18, m.p. −15°. At 105° it decomposes explosively. It is made by the action of concentrated sulphuric acid on ammonium chloroplumbate, $(NH_4)_2PbCl_6$. This salt, and other chloroplumbates, may be precipitated from the yellow solution resulting from solution of lead dioxide in cold hydrochloric acid.

Lead chromates. The normal lead chromate, $PbCrO_4$, is a bright yellow precipitate obtained by mixing solutions of a lead salt and potassium chromate or dichromate. The more basic the compound the more orange is the colour called chrome yellow or chrome orange. Primrose chrome contains a proportion of lead sulphate. Cologne yellow is prepared by heating lead sulphate with a solution of potassium dichromate. See British Standard 282.

Lead fluorides. *Lead (II) fluoride,* PbF_2, m.p. 822°, b.p. 1290°. Prepared by precipitation from soluble lead salts by hydrofluoric acid.

Lead (IV) fluoride, PbF_4, m.p. about 600°. Prepared by the action of fluorine on lead (II) fluoride at 300°. Forms complex fluorides, e.g. K_2PbF_6 and K_3HPbF_8, containing the $PbF_6{}^{2-}$ ion.

Lead hydroxides. Plumbous oxide will take up water but no definite hydroxide has been isolated. The oxide is amphoteric.

Plumbic hydroxide forms a series of salts, the plumbates, M_2PbO_3 and $M_2Pb(OH)_6$. They can be made by fusing lead dioxide with alkalis or by the anodic oxidation of plumbite solutions. The salts are decomposed by water or carbon dioxide but are quite stable thermally.

Lead iodide, PbI_2, consists of golden-yellow hexagonal plates; density 6·16, m.p. 412°. It may be obtained by precipitating a lead salt by a soluble iodide; 100 g of water dissolve 0·04 g of PbI_2 at 0°, and 0·4 g at 100°. There are many compounds of it with other iodides, and various basic lead iodides have been prepared.

Lead nitrate, $Pb(NO_3)_2$. Colourless cubic crystals, usually octahedra; density 4·5; soluble in water; 100 g of water at 25° dissolve 59·6 g of salt. It is prepared by dissolving lead oxide or lead residues in hot dilute nitric acid and allowing the nitrate to crystallize out on cooling; used in calico printing, as a mordant in dyeing, and in the manufacture of chrome yellow.

Basic lead nitrates have been prepared.

Lead oxides. *Lead monoxide,* PbO, the most important lead oxide, exists in two allotropic forms: (a) α-PbO, litharge, d 9·32, tetragonal reddish crystals; (b) β-PbO, massicot, d 9·665, orthorhombic yellow crystals.

Commercially, lead monoxide is made in several ways, all of which involve oxidizing lead either as a liquid or vapour in air and cooling quickly to below 300° to avoid the formation of Pb_3O_4. The colour of the product varies from yellow through grey to reddish brown, depending on the predominant crystal structure and the proportion of free lead. By far the most important use of lead monoxide is in storage batteries, while smaller quantities are used for ceramics, chrome pigments and insecticides.

Lead dioxide or *peroxide*, PbO_2, is a chocolate-coloured solid of density 9·0-9·4. It is converted to the monoxide on heating at 310°. It may be produced from solutions of lead salts by anodic deposition, or from PbO or Pb_3O_4 used anodically. Small quantities are used in the production of high-voltage lightning arrestors and as an oxidizing agent in the dye and chemical industries.

The composition of *red lead* approximates to Pb_3O_4 with rather less oxygen than is denoted by this formula. It is produced by heating lead monoxide in air at 400°-500°. Its major commercial applications are in the manufacture of storage batteries and corrosion-resistant paints, but lesser quantities are used in the manufacture of glass, ceramics and lead dioxide.

Orange lead is a variety of red lead with a specially fine colour; it is used as a pigment.

Lead silicate. Litharge can be fused with silica to form a yellow glassy silicate in which the proportion of PbO varies from 60-90%. Non-vitreous silicates are formed with greater proportions of silica. With high PbO content the glasses are easily attacked by acids, but with lower PbO content this silicate can be made so that it is practically insoluble in dilute acids and may be safely used in glazing pottery and in glass manufacture.

Lead styphnate or **Lead trinitroresorcinate,** $C_6H(NO_2)_3O_2Pb$. An orange yellow crystalline solid, formed by the interaction of lead acetate and magnesium styphnate. More stable than mercury fulminate but less sensitive to impact than mercury fulminate or lead azide. It is used chiefly as an ingredient of detonating compositions.

Lead sulphate, $PbSO_4$. Occurs as the mineral anglesite, in orthorhombic crystals isomorphous with barytes; is a white solid. Hardness about 2·8. Density 6·3-6·39. It is nearly insoluble in water, and can be prepared by adding sulphuric acid to a solution of lead acetate.

Basic lead sulphates are made by shaking lead sulphate and lead hydroxide with water, or by volatilizing galena (lead sulphide) in a current of air. Some of these basic sulphates are useful pigments.

Lead disulphate, $Pb(SO_4)_2$, and lead persulphate, PbS_2O_8, are known.

Lead sulphide, PbS. Occurs naturally as galena. It has m.p. about 1100°, but sublimes at a lower temperature. It may be prepared by precipitating a solution of a lead salt with a soluble sulphide, and is used as a rectifier in electrical components.

Lead tetraethyl, TEL, $Pb(CH_2CH_3)_4$. A poisonous liquid, d_4^{18} 1·659, b.p. 152° at 291 mm, insoluble in water, soluble in ether. It is manufactured by treating an alloy of lead and sodium, whose composition corresponds to the formula NaPb, with liquid ethyl chloride at 40°-60° and 5 atm. The lead tetraethyl formed is steam-distilled from the reaction mixture. The more volatile lead tetramethyl (TML, b.p. 110° at 760 mm Hg) is manufactured similarly.

Mixtures of TEL and TML are used to increase the octane rating of gasolines. Appreciable quantities of ethylene dichloride and ethylene dibromide must be included in order to prevent the deposition of lead compounds in the cylinder.

Lead tetramethyl. See Lead tetraethyl.

Leaf filters. *Pressure leaf filters* have a series of vertical leaves arranged within a horizontal or vertical cylindrical vessel. Each leaf consists of a plate, either with serrated surfaces or formed from heavy wire mesh, on which the filter medium, cloth or fine wire gauze, is supported. Filtration is performed by applying a pressure to the slurry so that a cake is built up on the leaves, filtrate draining away over the plate surfaces to the exit ports. When filtration is complete the cake is removed by applying air or steam pressure, by vibration or by some other means, then discharged. The Kelly, Sweetland and Vallez filters are examples of pressure leaf filters.

Vacuum leaf filters, with the exception of the rotary filter mentioned below, are less common. They are similar except that filtration is brought about by applying a vacuum to the inside of the leaves, which are situated in an open tank. The Moore filter is an example of this type.

The rotary vacuum disc filter (*q.v.*) apart, both pressure and vacuum leaf filters operate batchwise.

Le Bel, Joseph Achille (1847-1930). A nephew of Boussingault, the agricultural chemist, Le Bel was born at Pechelbron, Alsace. He became assistant to Balard and later to Wurtz at the École de Médecine. After the sale of some petroleum property which he inherited Le Bel devoted himself to scientific investigations. He made a number of contributions to organic chemistry but is best known for the theory of the asymmetric carbon atom in optically active compounds.

Leblanc, Nicolas (1742-1806). A French chemist, Leblanc invented, in 1791, the process which bears his name.

Leblanc process. An almost obsolete process for the production of sodium carbonate. Sodium chloride is converted to the sulphate by the action of sulphuric acid, hydrogen chloride appearing as the by-product. The sulphate is reduced to sulphide with coke; the sulphide being immediately converted to carbonate by calcium carbonate. The sodium carbonate is obtained by extraction with water; calcium sulphide is treated for the recovery of sulphur.

Le Chatelier, Henry (1850-1936), professor in Paris, studied the specific heats of gases at high temperatures, electrical conductivity, mass action and other problems of physical chemistry.

Le Chatelier's theorem. This theorem states that when a constraint is applied to a system in equilibrium, the equilibrium tends to change in such a way as to neutralize the effect of the constraint. Thus, when ice at 0° is subjected to pressure, some of the ice melts, for the transformation of ice into water is accompanied by a diminution in volume, and this is just the effect which an increase in pressure would produce on a compressible substance.

Lecithase. Two enzymes exist which are able to

split off the fatty acid groupings from the complex lecithin molecule. The one removes the unsaturated fatty acid, leaving the poisonous lysolecithin, and the other removes the saturated fatty acid group. A third enzyme, a phosphatase, is required to remove the choline phosphate grouping.

Lecithin. A generic name for substances of the type

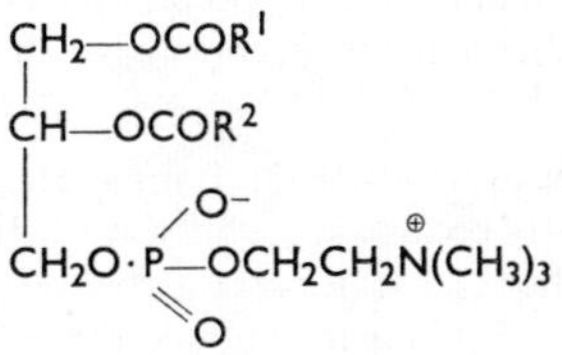

$$CH_2—OCOR^1$$
$$CH—OCOR^2$$
$$CH_2O·P—OCH_2CH_2\overset{\oplus}{N}(CH_3)_3$$

where R^1 and R^2 are fatty acid residues. Usually one acid is saturated and one unsaturated. Lecithins are found in every animal and vegetable cell and are an essential constituent of cells. They are white, waxy substances that darken in the air and are very hygroscopic. They are soluble in alcohol, ether, chloroform, benzene, and many other organic solvents, but insoluble in acetone. They swell up with water to give slimy emulsions or colloidal solutions. They melt at about 60° and decompose to a brown mass at about 110°.

Commercial lecithin is a mixture of phosphatides and glycerides obtained in the manufacture of soya bean oil. It is soluble in mineral oils and fatty acids and can be dispersed in animal and vegetable oils. It gives a thick yellow emulsion with water, and is widely used in the food and other industries.

Lemery, Nicolas (1645-1715). Born in France Lemery practised as a pharmacist. He was a Protestant, and on the Revocation of the Edict of Nantes in 1685 came to London; afterwards he became a Catholic, returned to Paris, and again practised as a pharmacist. He is best known by his book 'Cours de Chimie', originally published in 1675, which passed through many editions and was translated into several languages.

Lepidolite, $LiKAl_2(Al_2Si_2O_{10})(F,OH)_2$. A lithium-potassium mica which forms monoclinic crystals and occurs in small scales or granules of a white, lilac, or pink colour. Sp.gr. 2·5-2·9, hardness, 3-4, refrac. index 1·60, m.p. 925°-945°. Occurs chiefly in pegmatites. It is a raw material for the manufacture of lithium compounds, the commercial mineral containing 3-4% Li_2O.

Leptazol, Pentamethylenetetrazole, $C_6H_{10}N_4$. Colourless crystals, m.p. 57°-60°, soluble in water, alcohol, and ether. Prepared by the reaction between hydrazoic acid and

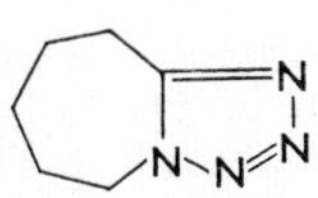

cyclohexanone in benzene solution. It has a stimulatory effect on the nervous system and is used in the treatment of poisoning by hypnotics.

Leuckart reaction. The conversion of ketones and aromatic aldehydes to primary amines by reaction with ammonium formate at a high temperature.

Leucine, α-Aminoisocaproic acid, $C_6H_{13}NO_2$.

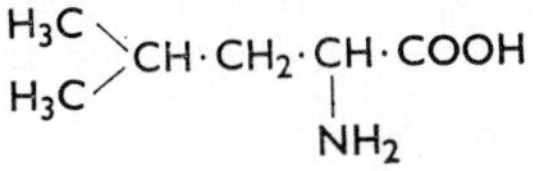

$$\underset{H_3C}{\overset{H_3C}{>}}CH·CH_2·\underset{\underset{NH_2}{|}}{CH}·COOH$$

Crystallizes in colourless plates, m.p. 293°-295°, with decomposition. Soluble up to 2% in water, practically insoluble in alcohol. The naturally occurring substance is laevorotatory in water, $[\alpha]_D^{25} -10·51°$, but dextrorotatory in acid, $[\alpha]_D^{25} +15·20°$ in 6M hydrochloric acid. Leucine is one of the most common of the amino-acids obtained from proteins. It can be obtained by fractional crystallization of hydrolysed proteins.

Leucite. A potassium aluminosilicate, $KAl(SiO_3)_2$, which crystallizes in the cubic system and has a feldspar type structure. Some specimens of leucite are pseudomorphic but form cubic crystals when heated to 600°. Sp.gr. 2·5, hardness, 5-6, m.p. 1320°-1370°, refrac. index 1·508. Leucite occurs chiefly as a primary constituent of recent volcanic rocks; it is brittle and breaks with a conchoidal fracture. It is decomposed by hydrochloric acid.

Leucopterin, $C_6H_5N_5O_3$. A white pigment, obtained from the wings of the common white and

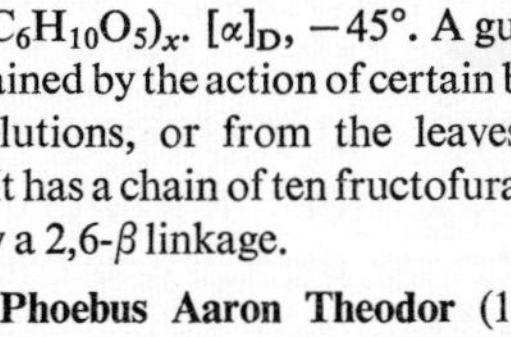

many other butterflies. It gives a yellow sodium salt.

Levan, $(C_6H_{10}O_5)_x$. $[\alpha]_D$, $-45°$. A gummy product obtained by the action of certain bacteria on sugar solutions, or from the leaves of some grasses. It has a chain of ten fructofuranose units joined by a 2,6-β linkage.

Levene, Phoebus Aaron Theodor (1869-1940). Born at St. Petersburg and educated at the Imperial Military Medical Academy, Levene went to the United States in 1892. He supplemented his medical knowledge by studying chemistry at the Universities of Columbia, Berne, Marburg, Berlin, and Munich. In 1905 he joined the staff of the Rockefeller Institute. He published many papers, chiefly on proteins, hexosamines, stereochemistry, and the nucleic acids.

Levulinic acid. See Laevulinic acid.

Lewis, Gilbert Newton (1875-1946). Born at Weymouth, Mass., Lewis was educated at the Universities of Nebraska, Harvard, Leipzig, and Göttingen. He was appointed professor of chemistry at Massachusetts Institute of Technology in 1911, and professor of physical chemistry in the University of California in 1912. In addition to his researches in mathematics and physics, he was noted for his researches in the field of atomic structure and thermodynamics.

Lewis acid. See Acid.

Lewis base. See Base.

Lewisite, 2-Chlorovinyldichloroarsine, $C_2H_2AsCl_3$, $ClCH:CH \cdot AsCl_2$. A pale yellow liquid, m.p. $-13°$, b.p. $190°$. Insoluble in water, soluble in organic solvents. It has a strong smell, resembling that of geraniums. Lewisite has been suggested as a possible agent for chemical warfare, as it has a powerful vesicant action, resembling that of mustard gas, but acting more rapidly. Owing to its arsenic content it is also a systemic poison. It is hydrolysed by water to a solid oxide, m.p. $143°$, and also destroyed by alkalis and by oxidizing agents. It can be manufactured by bubbling acetylene through a mixture of anhydrous arsenic trichloride and aluminium chloride.

Libavius, Andreas. Born in Halle about 1540-1550 he was appointed professor of history and poetry at Jena in 1598. Later he moved to Rothenberg an der Tauber where he taught science. In 1597 he published 'Alchemia'. He has been regarded as the first academic professor of chemistry. He discovered stannic chloride (fuming liquor of Libavius). He died in 1616.

Libby, Willard Frank (1908-   ). Born in Colorado and studying at Berkeley, California, Libby became professor there in 1941. He spent a number of years on work connected with atomic energy. He developed the technique of dating materials with radioactive carbon and was awarded the Nobel Prize in chemistry for this in 1960.

Licanic acid, $C_{18}H_{28}O_3$. White crystals, soluble

$$CH_3 \cdot [CH_2]_3 \cdot [CH:CH]_3 \cdot [CH_2]_4 \cdot CO \cdot$$
$$[CH_2]_2 \cdot COOH$$

in organic solvents. The naturally occurring isomer, α-licanic acid, has m.p. $74°$-$75°$. It is unstable, and is readily isomerized to the β-form, m.p. $99\cdot5°$. It occurs in oiticica and other oils which are used in the protective-coating industry.

Lichenin. The polysaccharide present in the cell walls of many lichens. It is built up in chains of about 80 glucose units. It has 1-3 links as well as 1-4 links, thus accounting for the difference between lichenin and cellulose.

Liebermann's reaction. A colour-test for showing the presence of the —NO or —OH groups. For the detection of an —NO group a small quantity of the substance is dissolved in concentrated sulphuric acid and a crystal of phenol added. A blue-green colour develops on warming, this changes to red on pouring into water, and back to blue with excess of alkali. When the test is used for detecting a phenol, the substance and a crystal of sodium nitrite are dissolved in sulphuric acid and warmed. On dilution and addition of alkali many phenols give distinctive colours.

Liebig, Justus (1803-1873). Born at Darmstadt, Liebig early became acquainted with chemicals in his father's laboratory. Later he was apprenticed to an apothecary but soon gave up this work to study chemistry in Bonn, Erlangen, and Paris. In 1825 Liebig became professor of chemistry in the University of Giessen, and in 1852 he accepted a similar appointment in Munich, having been created a baron in 1845. Liebig was a pioneer in chemical education, and his courses of instruction have served as models elsewhere. In later years he investigated problems in agricultural and physiological chemistry and was editor of the *Annalen*.

Liebig condenser. An apparatus for condensing vapours in small-scale laboratory distillations. It consists of a glass tube, in which condensation occurs, surrounded by a second tube through which cold water is passed.

Liesegang rings. When chemical reaction takes place by double decomposition, one of the reactants in solution diffusing into a gel impregnated with the second reactant, the product, if insoluble, is often deposited, not as a continuous precipitate, but in the form of bands separated by regions of clear gel. These are termed Liesegang rings after their discoverer who first noticed them in the system silver nitrate—potassium dichromate (in gelatin). An excellent Liesegang structure can be produced by placing a layer of $0\cdot880$ ammonia over a gelatin gel containing dilute magnesium chloride.

It is possible to produce Liesegang rings in capillary tubes or porous media without the presence of a gel.

Ligand. A complexing group in co-ordination chemistry. Generally the entity from which electrons are donated. NH_3 is a ligand in $Co(NH_3)_6Cl_3$.

Ligand field theory. An extension of crystal-field theory.

Light oil. The light oil which can be obtained below $195°$ by high temperature distillation of coal tar. It consists mainly of aromatic hydrocarbons.

Lignans. A group of natural products obtained, usually by ethereal or alcoholic extraction, from the wood or exuded resin of the *Coniferae* and other plants, and characterized by the presence in the molecule of the 2,3-dibenzylbutane skeleton:

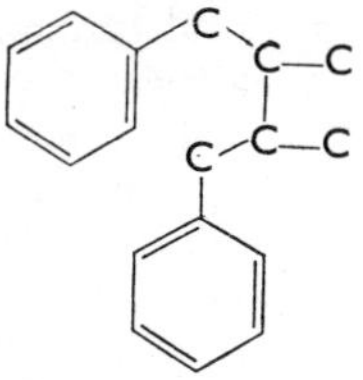

Lignin. A highly polymeric substance occurring with cellulose in lignified plant tissues. It is largely responsible for the strength of wood, which contains 25-30%, and it is extractable from wood pulp by the action of sulphur dioxide and lime-water: it occurs (up to 6%) in sulphite waste liquors from paper mills. The constitution of lignin is not yet fully clarified. It is a complex, cross-linked, highly aromatic structure of molecular weight about 10,000, derived principally from coniferyl alcohol by extensive condensation-polymerization. Lignin is of commercial value as a source of vanillin and other aromatic chemicals.

Lignites, Brown coals. Soft fuels which resemble peats in composition more closely than other types of coal. They occur naturally in beds near the earth's surface; they are consequently comparatively easily worked.

A dry, ashless, brown coal contains 60-75% carbon, 5-6% hydrogen, and 20-33% oxygen. The ash varies over wide limits from 4-12%, and the calorific value is about 7500 Btu/lb for a fuel of about 30-50% moisture.

Lignocaine, Lidocaine, $C_{14}H_{22}N_2O$. Used as the

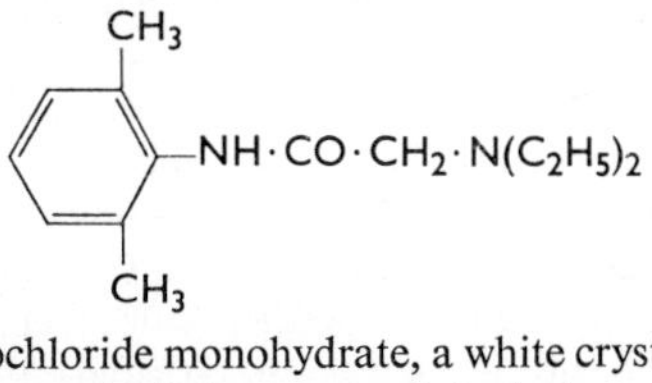

hydrochloride monohydrate, a white crystalline powder, soluble in water and alcohol, m.p. 77°; prepared by the action of chloroacetyl chloride on 2,6-dimethylaniline, treatment of the product with diethylamine, and conversion to the hydrochloride.

Lignocaine is a local anaesthetic; it has a more prolonged and more potent action than procaine, and is mainly used by injection.

Lignoceric acid, $C_{24}H_{48}O_2$. M.p. 84°, d_4^{20} 0·82, n_D^{20} 1·43. It is a fatty acid present free and combined in many oils, fats, and waxes, both vegetable and animal, including sphingomyelin and kerasin.

Ligroin. The distinction between ligroin and petroleum ether is now vague, although strictly ligroin refers to that fraction of refined solvent naphtha with b.p. 80°-130°. It contains aliphatic hydrocarbons and is used as a solvent.

Lime. See Calcium hydroxide and Calcium oxide.

Limestone. The limestones are rocks of sedimentary origin containing the remains of marine organisms or chemically precipitated or transported calcium carbonate. The pure mineral consists of calcium carbonate in the form of calcite, but is rarely found. Commercial limestone contains iron oxide, alumina, magnesia, silica, and sulphur, with a CaO content of 22-56% and a MgO content of up to 21%. It is used as such as a fertilizer and for many other purposes, or is calcined to lime.

Lime sulphur. Known also as *eau grison*, lime sulphur has been used as a fungicide, and in sheep dips against scale insects. It is manufactured by dissolving sulphur in suspensions of calcium hydroxide, and contains calcium polysulphides and thiosulphate. In appearance it is an orange liquid, with a very unpleasant smell. Lime sulphur may not be used in presence of most other materials as it decomposes and liberates hydrogen sulphide.

Lime-water is a saturated solution of calcium hydroxide containing about 0·15% of $Ca(OH)_2$. On heating it becomes turbid as calcium hydroxide is less soluble in hot than in cold water. It absorbs carbon dioxide from the air and may have a film of calcium carbonate on its surface. It is used medicinally as a mild antacid, and in testing for carbon dioxide with which it gives a precipitate which dissolves with excess of the gas.

Limiting density (of a gas). If a mass w g of a gas occupies v litres at 0° and pressure p atmospheres, the quotient w/pv is the density of the gas per unit pressure. Since gases do not obey Boyle's law accurately, w/pv varies with the pressure. The value of this quotient when p approaches zero is called the limiting density of the gas. It represents the density which the gas would possess as an ideal gas, i.e. a gas which obeys the gas laws perfectly.

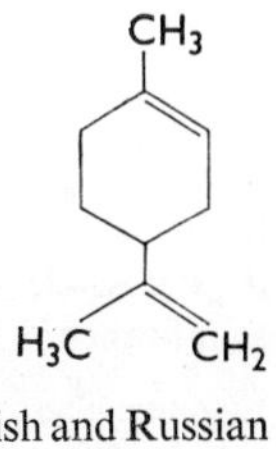

Limonene, $C_{10}H_{16}$. An optically active terpene, very widely distributed. Its racemic form is also of wide occurrence and is known as dipentene. (+)-Limonene occurs in lemon, orange, neroli, bergamot, caraway, and other oils; (−)-limonene in pine-needle, spearmint, and peppermint oils; and dipentene in Swedish and Russian turpentine, citronella oil, and oil of cubebs. It is also obtained by the action of heat on limonene. It is doubtful whether either (+)- or (−)-limonene has been obtained pure, but the following figures were found for highly purified specimens:

(+)-limonene, b.p. 176°-176·4°, d_4^{20} 0·8411, α_D^{20} +126·84°;

(−)-limonene, b.p. 176°-176·4°, d_4^{20} 0·8422 α_D^{20} −122·6°;

(−)- and (+)-limonene form optically active tetrabromides of m.p. 104°-105°.

Dipentene tetrabromide shows m.p. 125°-126°. When heated with sulphur these terpenes yield p-cymene.

Linalool, $C_{10}H_{18}O$.

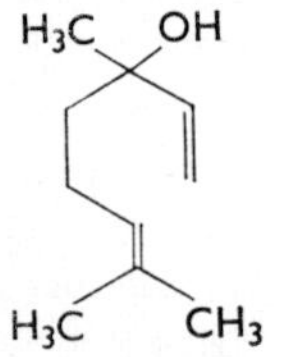

(−)-Linalool is present in oil of linaloe from French Guiana, and also in Mexican oil of linaloe derived from the wood of the plant, the (+)-form being present in Mexican oil of linaloe derived from the seeds. The (−)-form also occurs in many other essential oils, e.g. oil of ylang-ylang and the (+)-form in coriander and orange oils. The oil has to be separated by fractional distillation, and it is therefore questionable whether it has ever been obtained in a pure state. The average constants are b.p.

198°-199°; d^{15} 0·870, $[\alpha]_D$ −20·7° (from lime oil), +19·18° (from orange oil). It forms a phenylurethane of m.p. 63°-65°, and is readily converted into geraniol by acid reagents.

Linamarin, $C_{10}H_{17}NO_6$. Acetonecyanhydrin-β-glucoside, $C_6H_{11}O_5 \cdot O \cdot C(CH_3)_2 \cdot CN$. It is present in young flax plants and in *Phaseolus lunatus* and is probably widely distributed; it is also the glycoside of rubber seeds. It has been synthesized; m.p. 142°-143°. Such glycosides

may be regarded as primary materials for synthesis; in rubber the occurrence of acetone, which it is possible to convert into isoprene, is of significance.

Lindane. The gamma isomer of BHC (*q.v.*).

Linde process. The process for the production of liquid air by compression and then expansion. The cooled air is led back over more compressed air and the process is repeated until liquefaction occurs.

Linderstrøm-Lang, Kaj Ulrik (1896-1959). Born in Copenhagen, Linderstrøm-Lang took a degree in chemical engineering in 1919, and became assistant to S. P. L. Sørensen, whom he succeeded as director of the Carlsberg Laboratory in 1938. He contributed largely to knowledge of the structure of proteins and the behaviour of enzyme systems. See *Nature*, 1959, **184**, 314.

Lindlar catalyst. A 5% palladium on precipitated calcium carbonate catalyst, which has been 'poisoned' with lead, and is useful for the partial hydrogenation of acetylenes to *cis*-alkenes.

Line spectrum. In an atom, the absorption of energy can only lead to one change, the transference of an electron from an orbit of lower to one of higher energy. The reverse of this process, consisting in the return of the electron to the lower orbit, is accompanied by the emission of light of a single, definite frequency, corresponding with the energy liberated in the process. The spectrum of an atom thus consists of a series of definite lines, the light comprising each line having a frequency corresponding with the simple electron transition. This line spectrum is characteristic of an element in the atomic state.

Linkage. Same as Bond (*q.v.*).

Linoleic acid, $C_{18}H_{32}O_2$. *Cis*,9-*cis*,12-octadeca-

dienoic acid. An oil, easily oxidized by air, not distillable without decomposition, except at low pressure (b.p. 204°/1 mm). It occurs widely, in the form of glycerides, in vegetable oils and in mammalian lipids. Cholesterol linoleate is an important constituent of blood. The acid also occurs in lecithins. Together with arachidonic acid it is the most important essential fatty acid (*q.v.*) of diet.

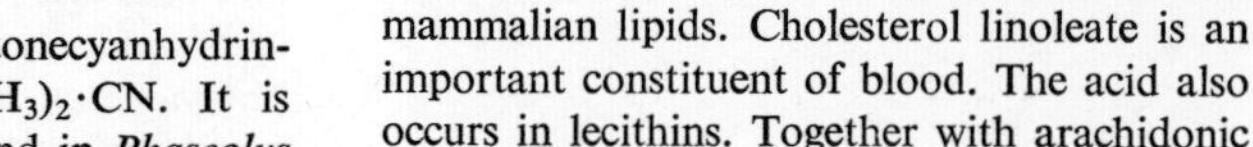

Linolenic acid, $C_{18}H_{30}O_2$, *cis,cis,cis*-9,12,15-

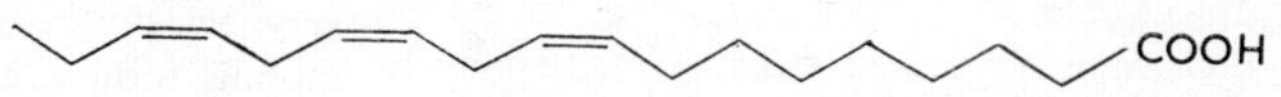

octadecatrienoic acid. An oil, b.p. 230°/17 mm, which occurs widely in glycerides of linseed and other drying oils; the drying effect is due to condensation and polymerization reactions initiated by the action of oxygen on the unsaturated glycerides. Linolenic acid also occurs in lecithin and in serum triglycerides.

γ-Linolenic acid, *cis,cis,cis*-6,9,12-octadeca-trienoic acid has been isolated from the seed oil of *Oenothera biennis* (evening primrose). Both acids can act as 'essential fatty acids', (*q.v.*).

Lipases. Enzymes which act upon the esters of carboxylic acids, including the triglycerides. They are a class of hydrolases. Unlike most enzymes, they are rather non-specific, and act on a variety of carboxylate esters, though at different rates. The reaction is to some extent reversible and under special conditions esters may be synthesized with the aid of a lipase, but *in vivo* the equilibrium is wholly on the side of hydrolysis products. Lipases are widely distributed in plants and animals: high concentrations occur in the liver, the intestinal wall, and the pancreas, from which the enzyme may be isolated by extraction with acetone. The pancreatic lipase selectively hydrolyses the α- or α'-esters in triglycerides, whereas the intestinal lipase also attacks the β-position. See Phospholipases.

Lipid(e)s, Lipin(e)s, Lipoids. The nomenclature of the substances of a fat-like nature is in a very unsatisfactory state. Several conferences have considered the problem and have proposed classifications which do not agree with one another. Bloor's classification, which has not been officially adopted by any body, is one of the most satisfactory. He defines lipids as substances, insoluble in water and soluble in organic solvents, that are related to the fatty acids as esters either actual or potential. He subdivides the lipids into simple lipids, the fats and waxes; compound lipids, the phospholipids and cerebrosides; and derived lipids, the fatty acids, sterols, and alcohols. The terms 'lipins' and 'lipoids' have also been used in much the same sense.

Lipman, Jacob Goodale (1874-1939). Born at Friedrichstadt, Russia, Lipman went to the United States at an early age and was educated at Rutgers College and Cornell University. In 1902 he returned to Rutgers to teach, and became Dean of Agriculture and Director of the New Jersey Agricultural Experiment Station, Rutgers University. His work dealt with soil science, including, in particular, researches on the utilization of nitrogen by plants and the nature of bacteriological action in soils.

Lipoic acid, 6,8-thioctic acid, $C_8H_{14}O_2S_2$.

Lipoic acid acts as a vitamin in that it is required for the growth of certain bacteria, and is a coenzyme for the oxidative decarboxylation of pyruvic acid. It has been isolated from beef liver in optically active form, and the ($\pm$)-form has been prepared as yellow crystals, m.p. 60°, by the oxidation of 6,8-dimercapto-octanoic acid with ferric chloride and oxygen.

Liquefied gas. In the petroleum industry this refers to light hydrocarbons held in the liquid state by pressure to facilitate handling, storage, and transport. It is essentially a mixture of propane and butane, e.g. calor gas.

Liquid crystals. See Crystals, liquid.

Liquid-liquid extraction. This is a method of extracting a desired component from a liquid mixture by bringing the solution into contact with a second liquid, the *solvent*, in which the component is also soluble, and which is immiscible with the first liquid or nearly so. Some of the component enters the solvent, forming an *extract*, while the solution that is left, the *raffinate*, is depleted in the component by this amount. The two phases are separated and the solvent removed from the component by evaporation or distillation. By repeating the process a number of times all of the component may be extracted.

On an industrial scale liquid-liquid extraction is carried out in either *stagewise* or *differential contact equipment*. The former employs a series of *mixer-settler* units in each of which the liquids are first contacted and then allowed to separate. Feed and solvent normally flow counter-current to each other through the system. The characteristic of this method is that the liquid compositions change in a series of steps from stage to stage. In differential contact equipment, consisting of such units as *spray* and *packed towers*, the compositions of the two phases change continuously as they pass through the equipment.

Liquid-liquid extraction is used for such applications as the removal of phenol from aqueous solution with benzene as solvent, and the removal of aromatics from paraffinic and naphthenic hydrocarbons using liquid sulphur dioxide (*Edeleanu process*).

Liquids, structure of. It was originally thought that the molecules in a liquid were arranged in a random manner, i.e. that a liquid was very similar to a gas, except that the molecules were closer together, and therefore the attractive forces were greater. As a result of X-ray and electron diffraction studies, it is now realized that liquids are not perfectly homogeneous like a gas, but some sort of arrangement of the molecules is actually present. Two main views have been put forward in relation to these results. The first attributes a microcrystalline structure to the liquid; an instantaneous picture of the liquid would show a large number of 'cybotactic' groups, in each of which a hundred or more molecules are arranged in an orderly manner, but in the regions between the groups the distribution is quite random. The second view attributes a 'quasi-crystalline' or 'pseudo-crystalline' structure to the liquid. It is supposed that the average distribution of molecules about a particular molecule is the same at any instant. If a number of instantaneous photographs were taken, the molecular distribution about any molecule would appear random, but the statistical average of a number of such pictures would show a definite structure.

Liquidus. The freezing-point of a molten mixture of substances varies with the composition of the mixture. If the freezing-points of the mixtures are plotted as a graph using temperatures as ordinates and composition as abscissae, the line joining the freezing-points is called a liquidus curve. Mixtures generally freeze over a range of temperature. If the temperatures when the last traces of liquid have just solidified (assuming that time has been allowed for equilibrium to set in) are plotted against composition, the resulting graph is called a solidus curve.

Liquorice. The dried root of various species of *Glycyrrhiza*. The extract, also known as Spanish Juice, is used as a demulcent in cough lozenges, while the liquid extract is used in cough mixtures and as a flavouring agent to cover the taste of nauseous medicines. The powdered root and sugar are used as flavouring agents in Compound Liquorice Powder which contains as its active ingredients, senna, fennel, and sulphur.

Litharge. See Lead monoxide.

Lithium, Li. At.no. 3, At.wt. 6·940, m.p. 179°, b.p. 1317°, d 0·54. The most important lithium containing minerals are lepidolite $(Li,K)_2$-$AlSi_3O_9(OH,F)_2$, spodumene $LiAl(SiO_3)_2$, petalite $Li(AlSi_3O_{10})$, and amblygonite $LiAl$-$(F,OH)PO_4$.

After extraction from the ore, the metal is obtained by electrolysis of a fused mixture of lithium and other alkali metal chlorides. Electrolysis of lithium salts results in considerable separation of the two common isotopes ^6Li and ^7Li.

Lithium is a very light, silver-white metal. It crystallizes with the body-centred cubic structure, $a = 3·51$ Å. The metal tarnishes readily in air, although less readily than the other alkali metals. Lithium is a reactive element combining directly with nitrogen, the halogens, hydrogen, etc.

Lithium is a member of the alkali metal group, and in its compounds is unipositive. The small size of the lithium ion gives considerable covalent character to many of its compounds, which in many cases show resemblences to the corresponding lighter alkali-earth derivatives. Lithium

is used in alloys, and its derivatives are used extensively in organic syntheses and as polymerization catalysts.

See *Amer. Chem. Soc. monograph* 'Lithium and its Compounds'.

Lithium aluminium hydride, $LiAlH_4$. Prepared by the action of lithium hydride on aluminium chloride in ether and isolated as a stable solid in dry air at room temperature. Above 125° it decomposes easily into lithium hydride, aluminium and hydrogen. It is soluble in a variety of ethers, but reacts readily with hydroxylic materials and other compounds containing active hydrogen. Uses in inorganic chemistry include preparations of the hydrides of B, Al, Si, Ge, Sn, As and Sb, by reduction of the corresponding metal halides. The selective reduction of a wide variety of organic compounds offers scope for its use in organic chemistry. Carboxylic acids, esters, aldehydes and ketones are reduced to primary amines, and sulphonyl chlorides to mercaptans. (For a comprehensive review see N. G. Gaylord, 'Reduction with Complex Metal Hydrides,' Interscience, London, 1956.)

Lithium aluminium tri-tertiarybutoxy hydride, $LiAl(OBu^t)_3H$. A white solid, which sublimes in vacuum above 250°, but decomposes above 400°. Solubility in tetrahydrofuran and diglyme is high. It is obtained by the reaction of *tert*-butyl alcohol with lithium aluminium hydride, and is used chiefly as a selective reducing agent for converting carboxylic acid chlorides into aldehydes. It is also a stereospecific reducing agent of steroid ketones.

Lithium carbonate, Li_2CO_3. Readily obtained by the addition of excess alkali carbonate solution to one of a lithium salt; lithium carbonate differs from the other alkali carbonates in being only sparingly soluble in water. The carbonate is soluble in the presence of excess carbon dioxide, owing to the formation of lithium bicarbonate, $Li(HCO_3)_2$. It melts at 720°. It is used for manufacturing the hydroxide and other lithium compounds, amongst which are a number that are used in the ceramics industry.

Lithium chloride, $LiCl$. Formed by dissolving the carbonate, oxide, etc., in hydrochloric acid. At low temperatures the dihydrate, $LiCl, 2H_2O$, is obtained. This loses one molecule of water at 19° and becomes anhydrous at 93·5°. The anhydrous crystals are isomorphous with sodium chloride. It is a very hygroscopic substance and can be used to absorb moisture. It is also used in welding aluminium.

Lithium fluoride, LiF. Prepared by the action of hydrofluoric acid on any soluble lithium salt; m.p. 848°. Relatively insoluble in water.

Lithium hydride, LiH. Hydrogen combines

directly with lithium at temperatures greater than 500°. Lithium hydride is a stable, white crystalline material. The fused salt evolves hydrogen from the anode on electrolysis. It is decomposed by water with formation of lithium hydroxide and evolution of hydrogen.

Whilst inert in the massive form, finely divided lithium hydride may ignite in contact with a moist atmosphere. Lithium hydride is used widely as a reducing agent and as a metathetical reagent for the preparation of hydrides. It is also a convenient source of hydrogen.

Lithium hydroxide, LiOH. A strong base made commercially as the monohydrate by the action of lime, either directly on a lithium ore, or on a salt made from the ore. Lithium hydroxide is more similar in solubility to the alkali-earth hydroxides than to the other alkali metal hydroxides. It is used in the manufacture of special greases, in alkaline storage batteries, and for absorbing carbon dioxide in confined spaces.

Lithium organometallic derivatives. Prepared by reaction between lithium and a halocarbon derivative or an organomercurial. Usually spontaneously inflammable in air; soluble in hydrocarbons or non-polar solvents. The molecules are polymeric and are used in organic syntheses and as polymerization agents.

Lithium oxide, Lithia, Li_2O. A white solid which dissolves in water to form lithium hydroxide. It is obtained by burning the metal in oxygen or by heating the carbonate or hydroxide at red heat in a stream of inert gas.

Lithographic printing. See Photolithography.

Lithopone. Also known as Charlton white and Orr's white, was patented by J. B. Orr in 1874. It is made by mixing solutions of barium sulphide and zinc sulphate; the precipitate of barium sulphate (approx. 70%) and zinc sulphide (30%) is washed, dried, calcined, and suddenly cooled in water. It has d 4·3, and is largely used as a pigment owing to its good white colour and excellent body. See British Standard 239.

Litmus. A colouring matter obtained from certain lichens by oxidation in the presence of ammonia. Commercial litmus is sold in small blue cubes of whiting or gypsum with very little colouring matter, and for use as an indicator the cubes are extracted with water and neutralized. The colouring matter is a mixture of compounds, the most important of which, azolitmin, is red in the free state, but its alkaline salts are blue. The pH range is 4·5 to 8·3. Litmus has been largely superseded as an internal indicator by the synthetic dyestuffs, but is still used in the form of litmus paper.

Little, Arthur Dehon (1863-1935). Little was born at Boston, Massachusetts. A pioneer in industrial research and founder of the firm of A. D. Little, Inc., he developed and patented processes of the most diverse character, including pulp- and paper-making, non-inflammable cinematograph films, and artificial silk, and for his work in this field he was awarded the Perkin Medal for 1931.

Liver of sulphur, or **Hepar Sulphuris.** A liver-coloured mass prepared by fusing potassium carbonate with sulphur; it contains potassium sulphide and potassium polysulphides, with some potassium thiosulphate and sulphate. A solution of liver of sulphur is used for mildew and insect pest control.

Lobelia. The dried herb, *Lobelia inflata*, a plant indigenous to North America. It contains several alkaloids, chief among which is lobeline. Lobelia possesses expectorant and emetic properties and is useful against bronchial catarrh and asthma.

Lockyer, Sir Joseph Norman (1836-1920). Born at Rugby, Lockyer became a clerk in the War Office but later was transferred to the Science and Art Department. In 1870 he became lecturer on astronomy at the Royal College of Science, South Kensington, and in the following year Rede lecturer at Cambridge. A pioneer in the spectroscopy of the sun and the stars, he discovered in 1868, independently with Janssen, the presence of helium in the sun's photosphere. He was elected F.R.S. in 1869 and in 1874 gained the Rumford Medal of the Royal Society.

Lomonosov, Mikhail Vasilevitch (1711-1765). The first well-known Russian chemist, Lomonosov was sent from St. Petersburg to study chemistry at Marburg and at Freiburg. In 1741 he returned to St. Petersburg. A man of many interests, his scientific ideas were in many ways in advance of his time and in some ways anticipated the theories of Lavoisier.

Lone-pair. A pair of electrons in a molecule which is not shared by two of the constituent atoms, i.e. does not take part in the bonding. Lone pairs can generally form co-ordinate bonds. They influence the stereochemistry of the molecule.

Long-tube vertical (L.T.V.) evaporators. The characteristic feature of these units is the calandria, or heating element, which consists of a bundle of vertical tubes 1-2 in. in diameter and 20-30 ft. long. The evaporators fall into two categories:

In the *climbing film evaporator* the solution is fed near its boiling point to the bottom of the tubes. Vaporization commences a short distance up and the passage of a high velocity stream of vapour causes the liquid to be carried up the sides of the tubes in a thin film. The mixture of liquid and vapour that emerges is separated in a vessel at the top.

The *falling film evaporator* is similar to the other type except that liquid is fed to the top of the tubes and falls in a film down the walls. Separation of liquid and vapour may either take place in a vessel at the bottom or at the top.

L.T.V. evaporators are widely used because the evaporation per unit area is high, making for low capital cost. Because of low liquid residence times they are suitable for heat-sensitive materials such as fruit juices, particularly the falling film version. They are unsuitable for liquids which deposit solids or cause scaling.

Lorentz, Hendrik Anton (1853-1928). Born at Arnheim, Lorentz studied at Leyden where, in 1878, he was appointed professor of theoretical physics. In 1923 he became Director of Research at the Teyler Institute, Haarlem. His main researches were in the fields of electricity, magnetism, and light, but he made a study of certain properties of liquids, particularly refractivity. With Ludwig Valentin Lorenz (1829-1891), professor of physics at the Copenhagen Military High School, he introduced the Lorentz-Lorenz expression for specific refractive power. He was awarded the Nobel Prize for Physics in 1902.

Loschmidt's number. The number of molecules per unit volume of an ideal gas at 0° and 760 mm pressure; equal to $2\cdot687 \times 10^{19}$ per cm^2.

Lowry, Thomas Martin (1874-1936). Born at Low Moor, Bradford, Yorks, Lowry was educated at Kingswood School, Bath, and the Central Technical College, South Kensington. From 1896 to 1913 he was assistant to Professor H. E. Armstrong. After a period as lecturer in chemistry at the Westminster Training College and Guy's Hospital Medical School he was appointed to the Chair of Physical Chemistry, Cambridge. He devoted his life to the study of optical rotatory power, introducing the term 'mutarotation' in description of the behaviour of nitro-*d*-camphor. In 1914 he was elected F.R.S. and during the first world war created C.B.E. See *J. Chem. Soc.*, 1937, 701.

Low-spin state. A term used in transition-metal chemistry to denote that the compound has the minimum number of unpaired electrons which is consistent with the electronic configuration and stereochemistry. E.g. iron in $K_3Fe(CN)_6$ has one unpaired electron. Compare High-spin state.

Low-temperature carbonization. When coal is heated in a closed retort, the three main products are coke, gas, and oils; by increasing the temperature of carbonization the yield of coke is reduced and that of gas increased. The quality of the gas and the quantity of tar are decreased by secondary changes at high temperatures. The temperature of carbonization is the main factor in determining the yield and quality of the by-products, and the process of low-temperature carbonization has been evolved to bring about: (1) a residue of smokeless fuel, which will be strong, easily ignitable, and will burn freely; (2) a rich gas; and (3) a high yield of good quality oils.

As coal is a very bad conductor of heat, high temperatures are needed to raise the middle of the charge to the carbonizing temperature. Around 600° is the most convenient temperature within the carbonization chamber. The liquid and gaseous products are much more aliphatic than those from high-temperature carbonization, in which the temperature has caused severe cracking and reforming of the primary products. Low-temperature carbonization oils are therefore comparable with petroleum oils, though containing a higher proportion of phenols.

Two main types of plant are used, (1) externally, (2) internally heated.

(1) The retort is of small diameter or thickness so that the layer of coal is thin and the heat can penetrate through the oven wall to the centre of the charge. The layer of coal is at rest. See Coalite process.

(2) Typical of such processes are the Lurgi 'Spülgas' process and the British 'Rexco' process. The British National Coal Board have an experimental process in which carbonization of a fluidized bed of fine coal takes place in an atmosphere of hot combustion gases.

LS coupling. An alternative name for Russell-Saunders coupling.

LSD. Lysergic acid diethylamide. An halucinogen.

Lubricating grease. A semi-solid lubricant composed of a dispersion of soap in mineral oil.

Lubricating oil. Any oil used for lubricating purposes. It may consist of either petroleum or fatty oils or mixtures of these two types, with or without additives. For special applications, for instance aircraft gas turbine oils, synthetic oils may be used.

Luciferins. Substances responsible for bioluminescence i.e. substrates of luciferases. An example is the luciferin from the American firefly, *Photinus pyralis*, shown to be D-2-(6-hydroxy-2-benzothiazolyl)-Δ^2-thiazoline-4-carboxylic acid.

Lully, Raymund (1235-1315). Of Spanish descent, Lully was born at Palma, Majorca. After some years at the court at Aragon he devoted himself to study and was eventually stoned to death in 1315 at Tunis, where he was engaged in converting the heathen, though a tradition asserts that he survived for some years after that date. He attributed great powers to the philosopher's stone, saying 'I would change the sea to gold if it were of mercury', but many of the writings bearing his name are of doubtful authenticity.

Luminous paints are compounded from solid materials (such as calcium sulphide) which, by use of suitable methods of preparation and by addition of traces of heavy metals, can be made to exhibit phosphorescence.

Lumsden's method (for determining vapour densities). This is a modification of Victor Meyer's method whereby, instead of measuring the volume of air displaced by a given mass of vaporized liquid, the volume is kept constant and the increase in pressure is determined.

Lurgi process. See Low-temperature carbonization.

Lutein, $C_{40}H_{56}O_2$. It has the normal carotenoid structure (see Carotene), with the rings:

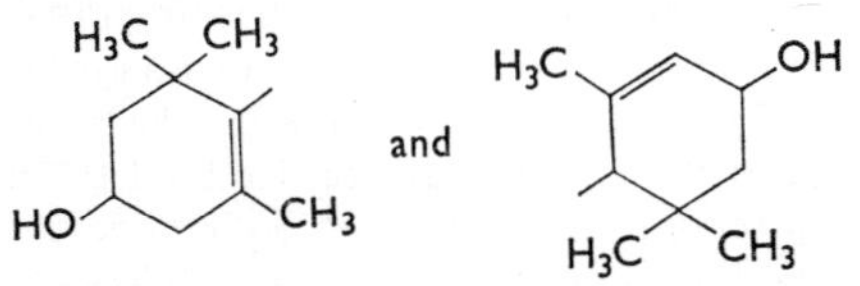

The most common of the xanthophyll pigments, it is present in all green leaves, in blossoms and in various animal sources. It crystallizes in violet prisms with one molecule of methanol; m.p. 193°, soluble in chloroform, benzene, ether, sparingly soluble in alcohol giving yellow solutions; $[\alpha]_{Cd}^{20} +160°$ in chloroform. It is related to α-carotene in the same way as zeaxanthin is to β-carotene.

Luteose. A polysaccharide of high molecular weight which together with malonic acid is obtained on alkaline hydrolysis of luteic acid. This substance is produced in considerable quantity by *Penicillium luteum* when growing on a synthetic medium containing any hexose or pentose sugar. It is believed that the first stage in the growth of most fungi is the synthesis of a complex polysaccharide.

Lutetium, Lu. At.no. 71. At.wt. 175·0, d 9·842, m.p. 1652°, b.p. 3327°. The metal has the hexagonal close-packed structure ($a=3·505$, $c=5·5486$ Å). Lutetium is a typical rare-earth element ($q.v.$).

Lutetium compounds. Lutetium forms a single series of tripositive compounds. These are typical rare-earth compounds ($q.v.$).

Lutidine. The lutidines are dimethylpyridines,

C_7H_9N. The best known is 2,6-lutidine, which is isolated from the basic fraction of coal tar. It is

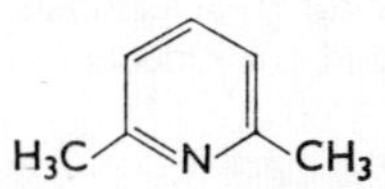

an oily liquid, b.p. 144°, n_D^{20} 1·4979, d_4^{20} 0·9252, miscible with water and most organic solvents.

Lycopene, $C_{40}H_{56}$. The red carotenoid pigment of tomatoes, rose hips, and many other berries. It crystallizes in prisms from petroleum ether, m.p. 175°. Soluble in chloroform and carbon disulphide, sparingly soluble in alcohol, insoluble in water.

It has the normal carotenoid structure (see Carotene) with the opened rings:

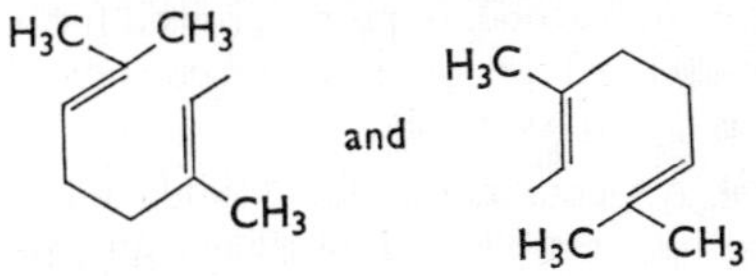

Lyddite. See Picric acid.

Lyman series. See Balmer series.

Lyophilic. Substances are termed lyophilic when their dispersed particles display a marked stability due to solvation. See Colloids, Hydrophilic, Hydrophobic, Organosol.

Lyophobic. Substances are said to be lyophobic when their dispersed particles are unsolvated and hence easily cogulated. See Colloids, Hydrophilic, Hydrophobic.

Lyotropic series. Although hydrophilic sols are not affected by small concentrations of electrolytes, they may be 'salted out' by the addition of certain salts which possess strong dehydrating properties. Citrates, tartrates, and sulphates are very efficient in this connexion; iodides and thiocyanates tend to disperse rather than coagulate. Thus silk or cellulose will peptise to colloidal sols in strong thiocyanate solutions but are reprecipitated by the addition of sulphates to the sols. The arrangement of the different anions in order of their salting-out efficiency is termed the lyotropic or Hofmeister series. This also has a connexion with the coagulating power of salts on hydrophobic sols. See Colloids, Hydrophilic, Hydrophobic, 'Salting out'.

Lysalbic acid. See Protective colloid.

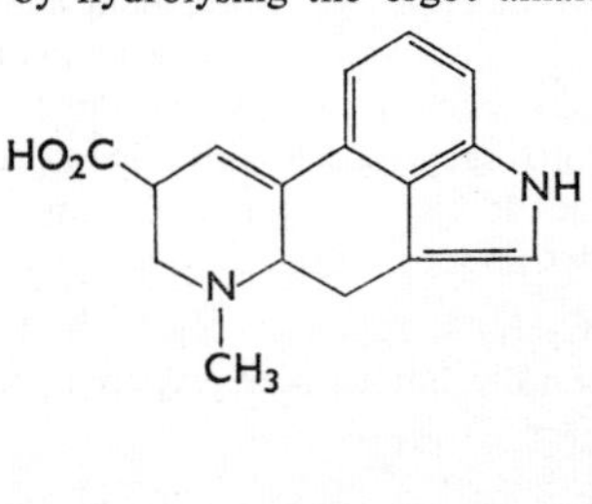

Lysergic acid, $C_{16}H_{16}N_2O_2$. The product obtained by hydrolysing the ergot alkaloids. It is a crystalline solid, m.p. 238° (decomp.), $[\alpha]_D^{20} +40°$ in pyridine. It gives the characteristic blue Keller test for ergot alkaloids. It is reduced with sodium and amyl alcohol to the dihydro compound.

The optically inactive form has been synthesized.

Lysine, α,ϵ-Diaminocaproic acid, $C_6H_{14}N_2O_2$, $H_2N\cdot CH_2\cdot [CH_2]_3\cdot CH(NH_2)\cdot COOH$. Crystallizes in colourless needles, m.p. 224°, with decomposition, $[\alpha]_D^{20} +14\cdot6°$, very soluble in water, insoluble in alcohol. L-(+)-Lysine is one of the basic amino-acids occurring in particularly large quantities in the protamine and histone classes of proteins. It is an essential amino-acid, which cannot be synthesized by the body and must be present in the food for proper growth. It can be manufactured by various fermentation processes or by synthesis.

Lysol. A saponaceous solution containing 50% of isomeric cresols. It is miscible in all proportions with water. Dilute solutions are used as antiseptics and disinfectants in surgical practice.

Lysolecithin. A generic name for monoacylglycerylphosphorylcholines, usually arising by the action of enzymes (phosphatidases, phospholipases) on lecithin. The pancreatic enzyme,

CH₂OCO·R
|
HOCH O
| ‖
CH₂OP—O—CH₂CH₂N⊕(CH₃)₃
|
O⊖

phosphatidase A, appears to hydrolyse specifically the fatty acid ester group at the 2-position in the glycerol moiety. A similar enzyme occurs in the venoms of snakes, bees and wasps. Lysolecithin occurs in small amounts in many tissues, but at higher concentrations is a powerful cytotoxic agent.

Lysomes. Particles, occurring in living cells, which contain hydrolytic enzymes capable of destroying many of the cell constituents. The intact lysosome membrane is effectively impermeable to the enzymes and their potential substrates: injury to it leads to the autolytic phenomena typical of dead, damaged or atrophying cells.

Lysozyme. A substance which can be obtained from nasal mucosa, egg white, plant latex, and certain animal tissues that has the ability to dissolve certain bacteria. It is an enzyme that acts by hydrolysing glycoside links in mucopolysaccharides. It has been obtained crystalline, and has mol.wt. about 17,000.

Lyxose, $C_5H_{10}O_5$. A pentose sugar that does not occur naturally, but has been prepared by degra-

dation of galactose. D-Lyxose exists as hygroscopic colourless crystals, very soluble in water,

slightly soluble in alcohol; m.p. 106°-107°, $[\alpha]_D^{20} +5\cdot5°$, mutarotating to $-14°$. The DL form has m.p. 95°.

M

Maceral. A word coined by Stopes to cover all petrological units seen in microscopic sections of coal as distinct from the visible units seen in hand specimens.

Macleod, John James Rickard (1876-1935). Macleod was born at Dunkeld, Scotland, and educated at Aberdeen, Leipzig, and Cambridge. He was professor of physiology at Western Reserve University, Cleveland, Ohio, from 1903 until 1918, when he went to Toronto in a similar capacity. While there he was awarded the Nobel Prize in Physiology and Medicine for 1923 in conjunction with F. G. Banting for the discovery of insulin, and in the same year was elected a Fellow of the Royal Society, London. In 1927 he returned to Aberdeen as professor of physiology.

Macleod's equation. This equation states that $\gamma = K(D-d)^4$, where γ is the surface tension, D the density of the liquid and d the density of the vapour.

Macquer, Peter Joseph. Born in Paris in 1718; he investigated the nature of Prussian blue, wrote an excellent text-book of chemistry, published a dictionary of chemistry, and paid special attention to the chemistry of dyeing. He died in 1784. See Thomson's 'History,' I, 295.

Macrolides. Compounds with antibiotic activity

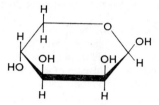
Desosamine

made by *Streptomyces* species and characterized by having a macrocyclic ring. Many macrolides contain one or more unusual sugars in the molecule, including an amino sugar, usually desosamine. Others are polyenes. The macro-lides, which include erythromycin, oleando-mycin and carbomycin (magnamycin), are most active against Gram-positive bacteria.

Macromolecule. The name used for giant molecules of very high molecular weight (usually greater than 10,000). Examples of this type of molecule are proteins and some poly-mers. The term macromolecular is also used to describe structures such as that of diamond, which may be regarded as being one large molecule.

Macroscopic coal constituents. When a hand specimen of bituminous coal is examined by eye it will be seen to contain up to four distinct blended constituents, which vary according to their brightness or dullness, texture, thickness, fracture, friability, or striation.

Stopes called these the four banded con-stituents; fusain, durain, clarain, and vitrain, but these names are only strictly applicable, by definition, to the visible macroscopic con-stituents of British bituminous coals. They are related to the macerals of coal; the macroscopic constituents are the rock types, containing the macerals as sub-units.

Maddrell's salt. A fibrous insoluble form of polymeric sodium metaphosphate. It is obtained by heating $Na_2H_2P_4O_7$ to 230°-300°.

Magenta. See Fuchsin.

Magnalium. The name used for a group of aluminium-magnesium alloys, which originally contained 70-95% of aluminium with 30-5% of magnesium.

Magnesia. See Magnesium oxide.

Magnesioferrite, MgO, Fe_2O_3. One of the spinel minerals. The crystals are octahedra and often covered with small rhombic crystals of ferric oxide; m.p. 1770°, sp.gr. 4·65. Strongly mag-netic. Chiefly important as a constituent of black magnesite bricks in which it acts as a binding agent for the more refractory periclase crystals.

Magnesite. A natural form of magnesium carbonate, $MgCO_3$, which occurs in crystalline and compact varieties. The former consists of white or discoloured aggregates showing cleav-age surfaces, sp.gr. 3·0, hardness 4; individual crystals (which are usually rhombohedral, sometimes hexagonal) are uncommon. The compact variety resembles chalk in appearance and is sometimes described as 'amorphous'; sp.gr. 2·9-3·0. Magnesite is used as a source of magnesium compounds and in the manufacture of refractories.

Magnesium, Mg. At.no. 12, At.wt. 24·32, m.p. 650°, b.p. 1107°, d 1·77. Magnesium crystallizes with the close-packed hexagonal

structure, $a=3·202$, $c=5·199$ Å. Magnesium occurs in a large number of minerals. The following are the most common: dolomite, $(Ca,Mg)CO_3$; carnallite, $MgCl_2,KCl,6H_2O$; kainite, $MgSO_4, 3Na_2SO_4$; and magnesite, $MgCO_3$; schönite, $MgSO_4, K_2SO_4, 6H_2O$. Magnesium compounds are obtained from sea water by precipitation as magnesium hydroxide, from certain brines, and from its ores.

The metal is obtained by the electrolysis of fused carnallite in an iron crucible, which serves as anode, with a carbon cathode. The chlorine is led off and the metal floats to the surface, being protected by a current of coal gas. The semi-fused metal is pressed into wire, which is then rolled into ribbon.

Recently, reduction of MgO with carbon or ferrosilicon in the electric arc (electrothermal process) has been developed. The gaseous Mg is rapidly cooled, and is over 99·9% pure.

The metal is silvery-white in colour, and very light. It may be obtained in a crystalline state by vacuum sublimation at 550°. Although the finely-divided metal readily burns in air or oxygen, with formation of MgO and Mg_3N_2, the massive metal ignites only at high tempera-tures.

Magnesium reduces sodium and potassium oxides on heating. Magnesium powder, mixed with powdered potassium chlorate or barium peroxide, burns explosively when ignited, producing a blinding white flash. The mixture is used in photography, in signalling, and in star shells.

The metal is stable in dry air, but soon becomes covered with oxide in moist air. Powdered magnesium decomposes hot water. The metal is readily soluble in dilute acids, but not in alkalis.

Magnesium alloys. These are used mainly on account of their light weight. They are by no means confined to the aircraft industry. The various alloys are suitable for casting, forging, extrusion and deep pressing. *Electron* is a trade name for a series of alloys containing 6-10% aluminium and up to 3% zinc. Another alloy MCZ contains 2·5% cerium and 0·7% zir-conium.

Magnesium carbides. Both magnesium carbides may be prepared from the metal and acetylene. MgC_2, obtained at 500°, is decomposed by water to give acetylene. Mg_2C_3, obtained from acetylene at 600°, or from methane at 700°, is hydrolysed by water to propyne.

Magnesium carbonate, $MgCO_3$. Occurs naturally as magnesite and in dolomite, $(Ca,Mg)CO_3$. Crystals of magnesium carbonate are rhombo-hedral and are isomorphous with calcite. Only basic carbonates are precipitated by addition of alkaline carbonate to magnesium salt solutions. Suspensions of the basic salts in water dissolve in the presence of excess carbon dioxide with the formation of a bicarbonate, $Mg(HCO_3)_2$. On heating the solution to 50°, crystals of $MgCO_3, 3H_2O$ separate. A mono- and a penta-hydrate are also known.

Two magnesium carbonates differing in density are used in medicine, the light variety being about five times more bulky than the heavy variety. Both are basic carbonates, insoluble in water, with the approximate formula, $(MgCO_3)_3, Mg(OH)_2, 4H_2O$. They are used as antacids and mild laxatives, and are suitable for administering to children.

Magnesium chloride, $MgCl_2$. Obtained from carnallite, $KCl, MgCl_2, 6H_2O$. Carnallite fuses at 176° with the deposition of practically all the potassium chloride; fused magnesium chloride remains. On cooling, the rest of the potassium chloride deposits as carnallite, and pure magnesium chloride hexahydrate is obtained. The anhydrous chloride is obtained by heating the hexahydrate in hydrogen chloride. It has m.p. 708°, b.p. 1412°; solubility of the hexahydrate 54·1 g in 100 g water at 20°. The hexahydrate crystals are very hygroscopic and are used in lubricating cotton thread in spinning. Several other hydrates are known, viz. with $12H_2O$, $8H_2O$ (α and β), $6H_2O$, and $4H_2O$. The crystalline hydrates on heating above 186° undergo hydrolysis, with the formation of magnesium oxychloride, Mg_2OCl_2; on strongly heating in air this evolves chlorine and leaves the oxide. Magnesium oxychlorides are used in making cements; see Sorel's cement.

Magnesium halides. Magnesium fluoride, MgF_2, is only slightly soluble in water and may be precipitated from solution; m.p. 1225°, b.p. 2227°. The other halides are very similar to the chloride (*q.v.*). They are best prepared from the free elements. $MgBr_2$, m.p. 700°; MgI_2, m.p. *ca.* 700°.

Magnesium hydroxide, $Mg(OH)_2$. Formed by the hydration of the oxide, or, more readily, by precipitation of a solution of a magnesium salt with caustic soda. Magnesium hydroxide is slightly soluble in water (0·1 g per litre), the solution possessing an alkaline reaction. A crystalline variety occurs naturally as brucite.

Magnesium nitrate, $Mg(NO_3)_2$. A very stable salt which forms hydrates with 9, 6, and $2H_2O$. It is anhydrous above 130°, but as the hydrates give basic salts on heating, the anhydrous salt must be obtained by dehydration in a stream of nitric acid vapour. Solubility of hexahydrate, 75·1 g per 100 g water at 25°.

Magnesium nitride, Mg_3N_2. Metallic magnesium absorbs nitrogen above 300° to form the nitride. This process is used to remove nitrogen. With water the nitride is hydrolysed to the hydroxide and ammonia.

Magnesium, organic derivatives. The best known of these are the aryl and alkyl halides, the Grignard reagents. Dialkyl and diaryl derivatives are also known.

Magnesium oxide, Magnesia, MgO. Magnesium oxide is formed, as a white, infusible powder (m.p. 2640°), by the combustion of the metal in oxygen, or by the ignition of the hydroxide, carbonate, or nitrate. It occurs as the mineral periclase, forming colourless crystals with the sodium chloride structure. Both the physical and chemical properties depend on the mode of formation. The oxide prepared from the basic carbonate precipitated at 100° is much denser than that from the same substance precipitated at 0°. Whereas a sample of oxide prepared by ignition at 900° is completely hydrated in several days, ignition to 1500° will prevent complete hydration over a period of years. The oxide is readily soluble in dilute acids.

Magnesium oxide is largely used as a refractory owing to its high temperature resistance. It is also used for heat insulation. For medicinal purposes it is made in a light and a heavy form by igniting the corresponding carbonates. It is used in stomach powders as an antacid.

Magnesium perchlorate, $Mg(ClO_4)_2$. This substance, sometimes called anhydrone, is used to absorb water vapour.

Magnesium phosphates. Simple *magnesium phosphate* $Mg_3(PO_4)_2 \cdot 8H_2O$ is precipitated from alkaline solutions of magnesium salts by sodium phosphate. *Magnesium ammonium phosphate*, $MgNH_4PO_4$, is precipitated from solutions containing ammonium salts; it is used in the estimation of magnesium and phosphates.

Magnesium silicate. An insoluble white powder which is slowly decomposed by acids forming a soluble magnesium salt and insoluble silica which has strong adsorptive properties. It is administered to reduce the acidity of the stomach, and to remove toxins by adsorption on the liberated silica. Its neutralizing action is slow, and persists for some time, and as it is not an alkali there is no danger of alkalization.

Magnesium sulphate, $MgSO_4$. Magnesium sulphate is most readily prepared by dissolving dolomite or magnesite in dilute sulphuric acid; on crystallization $MgSO_4, 7H_2O$ (Epsom salt) is obtained; solubility 35·8 g in 100 g water at 20°. The sulphate occurs naturally as kieserite or reichardite, $MgSO_4, H_2O$. On heating to 200° the hydrates lose water to give the anhydrous sulphate. Magnesium sulphate, $MgSO_4$, $7H_2O$, is used as a purgative, as a dressing for cotton goods, and in dyeing with aniline colours.

Magneson, *p* - **Nitrobenzeneazoresorcinol,**

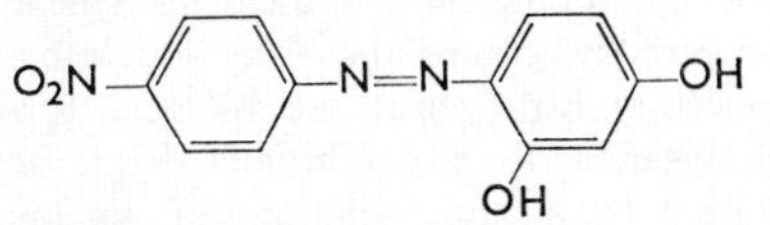

$C_{12}H_9N_3O_4$. A brownish-red powder, soluble in sodium hydroxide. It is used for the detection and estimation of magnesium, with which it forms a blue lake in alkaline solutions.

Magnetic moment. The magnetic moment is related to the magnetic susceptibility by the relation $\mu = 2.84\sqrt{\chi_m(T-\theta)}$. Where χ is the paramagnetic susceptibility per mole, T is the temperature, and θ is a constant (called the Curie temperature).

Magnetic polarization of light. See Verdet's constant.

Magnetic quantum number. See Electronic configuration.

Magnetic resonance. See Nuclear magnetic resonance.

Magnetic separators. These machines employ a magnetic field to separate a strongly magnetic material from a weakly or non-magnetic one. Their applications fall into two categories:

(a) The removal of *tramp iron*. This consists of stray pieces of iron and steel which, if not removed, could cause blockage or damage in process equipment, e.g. crushers. Equipment for this purpose takes a variety of forms, but in all of them a moving stream is subjected to some form of magnetic field which retains the magnetic material and allows the other to pass on.

(b) The *concentration* of magnetic material and the *purification* of non-magnetic material. Separators used for this purpose operate on crushed material of particle size 0·1 in. or less, and may take a dry feed or a slurry. They usually consist of a horizontal rotating drum containing a stationary electromagnet or permanent magnet whose field extends over an arc of the surface only, and on to this drum the material is fed. The magnetic constituents of the feed cling to it until they pass out of the magnetic field, when they fall off. The magnetic and non-magnetic constituents are thus discharged at different points and a separation is thereby effected.

Magnetic susceptibility. Atoms or molecules may have a permanent magnetic moment or an induced moment due to the influence of a magnetic field. In general, the extent of magnetization of any substance is a function of the field in which that substance is placed. The magnetic

susceptibility per unit volume, κ, is defined as the intensity of magnetization induced (I) divided by the field strength (H)

$$\kappa = I/H.$$

The molar magnetic susceptibility χ_m is given by the expression

$$\chi_m = \frac{M}{\rho} \cdot \kappa$$

where M is the molecular weight and ρ the density of the substance. Magnetic susceptibilities are usually determined using a Gouy balance but nuclear magnetic resonance methods may also be used. For a paramagnetic substance $1/\chi$ is proportional to the absolute temperature (Curie-Weiss law).

See Figgis and Lewis, 'Progress in Inorganic Chemistry,' Vol. 6, p. 37; 'Techniques in Inorganic Chemistry,' Vol. 4, p. 137.

Magnetite, Fe_3O_4. A mineral form of black magnetic iron oxide which occurs in massive form in Cornwall, Devon, and elsewhere in the British Isles and also in Norway, Sweden, Siberia, and Canada. The crystals are cubic and strongly magnetic. They break with a sub-conchoidal fracture. Sp.gr. 4·9-5·2, hardness 5-6. Magnetite may be regarded as an iron spinel, $FeFeO_2$; m.p. 1538°, but as magnetite is readily decomposed at 530° its true m.p. is uncertain.

It is an iron ore, a flux, and a pigment for glazes. It is occasionally used as a refractory material for lining the furnaces in which malleable iron is made.

Malachite. Native green hydrated carbonate of copper often used as a decorative stone as it takes a high polish. An artificial form (produced by adding sodium carbonate to a solution of copper sulphate) is known as *Green Verditer* and used as an artists' colour. The native form has a refractive index of 1·9, whilst the artificial form is below 1·6, a difference which enables the materials to be distinguished in paintings.

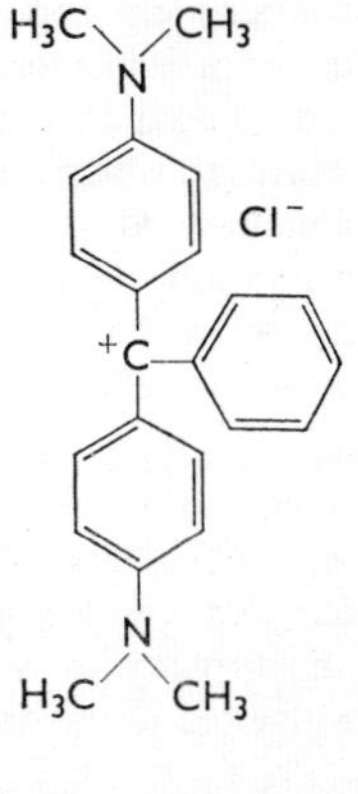

Malachite green (Basic Green 4). The term sometimes means the powdered mineral malachite or the artificial form known as Green Verditer. It properly refers to a di-aminotriphenylmethane dyestuff prepared by condensing benzaldehyde, dimethylaniline, and hydrochloric acid. The leucobase of the dye, which is liberated with alkali, can be oxidized with lead peroxide and hydrochloric acid at 0°, or converted into the oxalate by treatment with oxalic acid. It dyes tannin-mordanted cotton a bluish-green, and is also used for colouring silk, wool, leather, paper, foods, oils, etc.

Malathion. $C_{10}H_{19}O_6PS_2$, O,O-dimethyl-S-1,2-di(ethoxycarbonyl)ethyl phosphorothiolothionate. An organophosphorus insecticide which is

$$(CH_3O)_2\overset{\overset{S}{\uparrow}}{P}\cdot S\cdot CH\cdot COOC_2H_5$$
$$|$$
$$CH_2\cdot COOC_2H_5$$

safe enough for ordinary garden use. The technical material is a yellow to brown oil with an unpleasant garlic-like odour, and the pure material boils at 156-7°/7 mm. Malathion is slightly soluble in water, is miscible with organic solvents other than petroleum oils, and is unstable under alkaline or strongly acid conditions. It is manufactured by the condensation of O,O-dimethylphosphorothiolothionic acid and diethyl maleate in the presence of hydroquinone (as anti-polymerization agent). Malathion is effective against thrips, aphids, and house flies, and gives partial control against scale insects and red spider mite. It should be used with care, but it is one of the least toxic organophosphorus insecticides; rats receiving 1000 p.p.m. in their food for long periods gained weight normally.

Maleamic acid, $C_4H_5NO_3$. The half amide of maleic acid; m.p. 172°-173° (decomp.). Its

$$CH\cdot CONH_2 \quad \text{or} \quad CH\overset{\diagup NH_2}{\underset{\diagdown O}{-C-OH}}$$
$$||$$
$$CH\cdot COOH \qquad\qquad CH-CO$$

ammonium salt, which is made by treating maleic anhydride with ammonia, is used to make Krilium (q.v.).

Male fern. The dried rhizome and the bases of fronds of *Dryopteris Filix-mas*. The oily extract, prepared from it by extraction with ether, contains chlorophyll and about 25% of an active principle termed 'filicin'. Extract of male fern is used almost entirely for expelling tapeworms to which it acts as a poison. The drug is administered in capsules following a period of starvation and purgative, and then, after several hours another purgative is given and the dead worms expelled.

Maleic acid, $C_4H_4O_4$. Crystallizes in colourless prisms, m.p. 130°. Very soluble in water and alcohol. Manufactured by treating maleic anhydride with water. It is converted to the anhydride by heating at 140°.

$$H\cdot C-COOH$$
$$||$$
$$H\cdot C-COOH$$

By prolonged heating at 150°, it is converted to fumaric acid. It is also converted to fumaric acid by heating with water under pressure to 200°. Maleic and fumaric acids are geometrical isomers, and differ only in the arrangement of their carboxyl groups about the double bond. Reduced by hydrogen to succinic acid. Reacts with bromine to give dibromosuccinic acid. Oxidized by alkaline solutions of potassium permanganate to mesotartaric acid. When heated with solutions of sodium hydroxide at 100°, sodium($\pm$)-malate is formed. Used in the preparation of ($\pm$)-malic acid.

Maleic anhydride, $C_4H_2O_3$. A colourless crystalline substance, m.p. 52·6°, b.p. 200°. Soluble in acetone and chloroform; sparingly soluble in petroleum ether. Manufactured by the oxidation of benzene by air at 400°-450° over a vanadium catalyst; furfural, crotonaldehyde and butylenes may also be used as starting materials. Reacts with hot water to give maleic acid. Reduced by hydrogen in presence of catalysts to succinic anhydride. Reacts with conjugated diolefins to give derivatives of Δ^4-tetrahydrophthalic anhydride. Forms resinous substances with terpenes. Its principal use is in the production of polyester resins for glass-fibre-reinforced plastics. It is also employed in the manufacture of alkyd resins for varnishes, drying oils, certain agricultural chemicals and fumaric acid.

$$HC-CO$$
$$|| \qquad\quad \diagdown O$$
$$HC-CO \diagup$$

Maleic hydrazide, $C_4H_4N_2O_2$. A plant growth regulator, prepared by condensation of maleic anhydride with aqueous hydrazine sulphate, maleic hydrazide forms colourless crystals, m.p. 296°-298°, slightly soluble in water and ethanol. Its alkali metal salts are water soluble. It is toxic to grasses, and is used to retard the growth of some plants. Hedges treated with it, for example, require to be cut less frequently.

Malic acid, Hydroxysuccinic acid, $C_4H_6O_5$. (−)-Malic acid crystallizes in colourless needles, m.p. 100°. Very soluble in water and alcohol; sparingly soluble in ether. It occurs in many acid fruits, such as grapes, apples, and gooseberries. It can be prepared by microbiological processes using various moulds or from (+)-bromosuccinic acid by the action of sodium hydroxide. The crystals readily absorb water vapour. Forms complexes with many inorganic salts; these possess optical rotations much greater than that of malic acid. Forms (+)-chlorosuccinic acid when treated with phosphorus pentachloride. This is an example of the Walden

$$H_2CCOOH$$
$$|$$
$$HOCHCOOH$$

inversion. Malic acid is converted to fumaric acid at 140°, and to maleic anhydride at 180°. (+)-Malic acid, m.p. 100°; prepared from (+)-chlorosuccinic acid by the action of moist silver oxide. ($\pm$)-Malic acid, m.p. 133°, is manufactured by heating fumaric or maleic acids with sodium hydroxide solution at 100°.

Malleability. The property which enables a body to be extended in all directions by hammering or rolling. The degree of malleability is gauged by the thinness of leaf or foil which it is possible to produce.

Malleable cast iron. See Cast irons.

Malonic acid, $C_3H_4O_4$. Forms colourless triclinic crystals; above 94° these pass to a monoclinic form; m.p. 135.6°. Soluble in water, alcohol, and ether. Occurs in the mixed calcium salts obtained during the processing of sugar beet. Prepared by heating a solution of sodium cyanoacetate with sodium hydroxide until no more ammonia is evolved. It is isolated either as the free acid or as the sparingly soluble calcium salt. Decomposes above 140° to give acetic acid. Forms crystalline acid and neutral salts. Reacts with aldehydes in presence of primary and secondary bases to give unsaturated substituted acids; some of these very readily lose carbon dioxide to give $\alpha\beta$-unsaturated fatty acids. Its esters are used in organic syntheses.

Malonic ester, Diethyl malonate, $C_7H_{12}O_4$. A

$$H_2C\begin{array}{c}COOCH_2CH_3\\COOCH_2CH_3\end{array}$$

colourless liquid with a faint aromatic odour, d^{18} 1·068, b.p. 197°-198°. Insoluble in water; miscible with organic solvents. Manufactured by treating sodium monochloroacetate with sodium cyanide in alkaline solution at 60°. The resulting sodium cyanoacetate is heated with alcohol and sulphuric acid and the malonic ester extracted with benzene. It is converted to malonic acid and alcohol by boiling with water or dilute alkalis. Like acetoacetic ester, it reacts with sodium alkoxides or metallic sodium—a sodium atom displacing one of the hydrogen atoms of the $CH_2<$ group. This sodium derivative reacts with halogen compounds to give substituted malonic esters of the type

$$RCH\begin{array}{c}COOC_2H_5\\COOC_2H_5\end{array}$$

These also react with sodium, which replaces the remaining hydrogen atom of the original $CH_2<$ group, and by causing these to react with halogen compounds, disubstituted malonic esters are formed. The substituted malonic esters

are hydrolysed by alkali to the acids which are readily decarboxylated to substituted acetic

$$RR'C\begin{array}{c}COOC_2H_5\\COOC_2H_5\end{array}$$

acids. Malonic ester and the esters of the substituted malonic acids react with urea to give barbituric and substituted barbituric acids, which are important drugs.

Malonyl-coenzyme A. This highly reactive natural thioester, usually formed by enzymic carboxylation of acetyl-coenzyme A, is the chain-extending agent in the principal mode of biosynthesis of fatty acids. The terminal (alkyl) group is normally furnished by acetyl-coenzyme A, which then reacts with malonyl-coenzyme A (in association with an 'acyl carrier protein') to give an acetoacetyl-coenzyme A-protein complex. Reduction gives butyryl-coenzyme A which then undergoes a further cycle of reactions involving malonyl-coenzyme A. The process continues to about the C_{16} and C_{18} stage, and the free acids then dissociate from the protein and from coenzyme A.

Malt. Barley grain which has been allowed to germinate and then heated to destroy vitality and dried. The extract prepared from it by digestion with warm water and evaporation of the solution *in vacuo* contains a large proportion of maltose resulting from the action between the diastase and starch in the grain. It is used as a food adjunct in debility and as a vehicle for the administration of cod-liver oil in tuberculosis, in convalescence, and for growing children. It is also widely used for the production of alcoholic beverages.

Maltase. Strictly maltase is the enzyme found in malt that is specific in splitting maltose into two molecules of glucose. Maltases found in the digestive systems of animals and in yeast that can also split off glucose from other α-glucosides should be called α-glucosidases.

Maltol, 3-Hydroxy-2-methyl-4-pyrone, Lariscinic acid, $C_5H_6O_3$. M.p. 161°-162°. A very weak acid, soluble in water and some organic solvents. It occurs naturally in the bark of larch trees, and has been isolated from various wood oils, from roasted malt, and as a breakdown product of streptomycin. It has been recommended for use as a flavouring agent.

Maltose, $C_{12}H_{22}O_{11}$. A disaccharide which is present free in small quantities in barley grains and some other plants, but is more commonly produced by the action of amylase on starch or glycogen. It is 4-[α-D-glucopyranosido]-D-glucopyranose, and the β-form crystallizes as the monohydrate in colourless needles, m.p. 102°-103°, $[\alpha]_D^{20}$ +112° (initial), +136° (final).

Mandelic acid, $C_8H_8O_3$. Colourless rhombic

prisms, ($\pm$)- m.p. 118°, (+)- or (−)- m.p. 133°, $[\alpha]_D \pm 156°$. Readily soluble in alcohol and ether. Occurs combined in the glucoside amygdalin. Prepared by hydrolysis of mandelonitrile (benzaldehyde cyanohydrin); may be resolved by crystallization with cinchonine. It is administered in large doses in the treatment of urinary infections, and passes unchanged into the urine, which it renders bactericidal.

Manganates (VI). Salts derived from the hypothetical manganic acid, H_2MnO_4. They are formed when manganese compounds are fused with alkali in air, or better in the presence of an oxidizing agent such as potassium nitrate or chlorate. They are also formed in solution by careful reduction of permanganates in presence of alkali. *Potassium manganate (VI),* K_2MnO_4, may be obtained by evaporation of solutions obtained in these ways, as dark green rhombic crystals isomorphous with potassium sulphate, but which are usually contaminated with excess alkali and manganese dioxide. In a similar way, *sodium manganate (VI),* Na_2MnO_4, $10H_2O$, isomorphous with the sulphate, may be obtained, and the insoluble *barium manganate (VI),* $BaMnO_4$, can be precipitated. They are only stable in strongly alkaline solution; dilution or neutralization of the solution causes disproportionation to permanganate and hydrated manganese dioxide.

Manganates (V), e.g. barium manganate, $Ba_3(MnO_4)_2$, are isomorphous with phosphates. They are blue in colour and are obtained by electrolytic reduction of permanganate or by fusing manganese dioxide in potassium hydroxide.

Manganates (IV). See Manganites.

Manganese, Mn. At.no. 25, at.wt. 54·93. A soft grey metal, m.p. 1244°, b.p. 2087°, d 7·21. Manganese metal has several forms; those stable at low temperatures have structures which do not correspond to those adopted by other metals. The α- and β- forms are cubic, $a = 8·903$ and $a = 6·29$ Å respectively; γ-Mn, stable 1100° to 1137° is cubic close-packed and δ-Mn, stable to the m.p., body-centred cubic. Manganese occurs in nature chiefly as the ore pyrolusite (MnO_2), but also as the carbonate, and higher oxides (Mn_2O_3 and Mn_3O_4).

On the large scale, alloys of manganese and iron are manufactured by reducing a mixture of the oxides with carbon in a blast furnace. On a small scale, manganese is made by reducing the oxide by carbon or powdered aluminium at a high temperature. However reduction with carbon gives interstitial carbides, and pure manganese is only obtained by electrolytic reduction of a manganese (II) solution.

Metallic manganese is a reactive substance. It combines with oxygen on heating in air and reacts slowly with water. It combines with the halogens, nitrogen, phosphorus, silicon, sulphur and carbon, particularly on heating. In its compounds manganese shows oxidation states of −1, 0, 1, 2, 3, 4, 5, 6 and 7.

Manganese acetates. *Manganese (II) acetate,* $Mn(CH_3CO_2)_2$, $4H_2O$, forms pale red monoclinic crystals, readily soluble in water. *Manganese (III) acetate,* $Mn(CH_3CO_2)_3$, $2H_2O$, is formed by oxidation of manganese (II) acetate with potassium permanganate in presence of glacial acetic acid. It is a reddish-brown crystalline substance, fairly stable in dry air, and soluble in water with partial hydrolysis. It is a useful starting-point for the preparation of tripositive manganese compounds.

Manganese alloys. An alloy steel containing about 12% of manganese and 1·2% carbon is very hard and tough and is used for rock crushers, railway points, and such purposes. Manganin contains about 80 to 86% copper, about 10 to 15% manganese, and from 2 to 5% of nickel. Ferromanganese is about 50% of iron and 50% of manganese; speigeleisen contains less than 20% of manganese, the remainder being iron.

Manganese alums. Prepared by electrolytic oxidation of solutions of manganese (II) sulphate and an alkali sulphate in 25% sulphuric acid. The caesium alum, Cs_2SO_4, $Mn_2(SO_4)_3$, $24H_2O$, is most easily obtained; the rubidium, potassium, and ammonium salts are more soluble and can only be crystallized at low temperatures. They form red octahedra which are decomposed by water.

Manganese blue. Barium manganate (V), usually precipitated on a barium sulphate base.

Manganese borates. The substances obtained by precipitation are of indefinite composition, but definite compounds such as $Mn(BO_2)_2$, $Mn_3(BO_3)_2$, MnB_4O_7, and MnB_6O_{10} may be obtained in the dry way, but are more or less hydrolysed by water. Various manganous borate preparations are used as driers for linseed oil. Their mode of operation is probably catalytic oxidation, and other manganese (II) salts (e.g. the sulphate) have a similar effect.

Manganese bromide. *Manganous bromide,*

$MnBr_2$, crystallizes at ordinary temperatures as the tetrahydrate, α-$MnBr_2$, $4H_2O$, which forms pink-coloured rhombic prisms. Below 13° a hexahydrate is formed, and a β-tetrahydrate, which is always metastable, and a dihydrate, also exist. The anhydrous salt may be obtained by heating the hydrates in a stream of hydrobromic acid. Manganese (II) bromide is very soluble in water. At 18°, 100 g of saturated solution contain 59·1 g of $MnBr_2$.

Manganese bronze. This is technically a brass; see Brass. Also used as the name of a pigment. See Mineral colours.

Manganese carbonate, $MnCO_3$. Precipitated from manganese (II) solution by the use of sodium bicarbonate saturated with carbon dioxide; if precipitated at a high temperature forms red octahedra. The precipitates obtained under ordinary conditions are hydrated basic carbonates of rather indefinite composition. They are all rapidly oxidized in air. Manganese carbonate occurs as the mineral rhodochrosite, crystallizing in the rhombohedral system, isomorphous with calcite.

Manganese carbonyl, Dimanganese decacarbonyl, $Mn_2(CO)_{10}$. Prepared by the action of carbon monoxide under pressure on a manganese (II) salt in the presence of a strong reducing agent. Golden yellow crystals with the structure $(OC)_5Mn-Mn(CO)_5$ with a metal-metal bond. Typical metal carbonyl, gives $NaMn^{-1}(CO)_5$ with sodium.

Manganese chloride. *Manganous chloride*, $MnCl_2$, crystallizes at the ordinary temperature as the α-tetrahydrate, $MnCl_2$, $4H_2O$, in rhombic prisms. Below $-2°$ a hexahydrate, and above 58° a dihydrate, are formed. There is also a β-tetrahydrate which crystallizes from supersaturated solutions, and is always metastable. The transition-point $4H_2O$-$2H_2O$ has been used as a thermometric fixed point ($58·098° \pm ·005°$). The anhydrous salt may be obtained by the action of hydrogen chloride on the heated metal, or by heating the hydrates in a stream of hydrogen chloride. It is a pink deliquescent substance, m.p. 650°. Manganous chloride is very soluble in water: 100 g dissolve at 25° 77·2 g, and at 100° 116 g of $MnCl_2$.

Manganese chlorides, complex. Dipositive complexes of the types $M(MnCl_3)$, $M_2(MnCl_4)$, and $M_4(MnCl_6)$ are known. They are not very stable and are dissociated in water.

Potassium pentachloromanganate (III), K_2MnCl_5, is formed as dark red crystals by addition of KCl to the brown solution of MnO_2 in cold hydrochloric acid. It is moderately soluble and fairly stable in concentrated hydrochloric acid, but is decomposed by water.

Other salts of this series are $(NH_4)_2MnCl_5$, H_2O, Rb_2MnCl_5, and Cs_2MnCl_5; the last two are very sparingly soluble.

The chloromanganates (IV), derived from the hypothetical $MnCl_4$, may best be obtained by the action of fuming hydrochloric acid and an alkali chloride on permanganates. K_2MnCl_6, Rb_2MnCl_6, and $(NH_4)_2MnCl_6$ have been isolated in this way as deep red crystals which slowly decompose with evolution of chlorine. They are instantly decomposed by water.

Manganese cyanides, complex. Simple cyanides of manganese are not known, and the precipitates obtained by addition of an alkali cyanide to a manganese (II) salt always contain alkali metal. They are soluble in excess of alkali cyanide, and from the solution cyanomanganates (II) can be crystallized. The potassium salt, $K_4Mn(CN)_6$, forms violet crystals which give a yellow solution in water, from which, on dilution or addition of a manganese (II) salt, a green precipitate of $KMn(CN)_3$ is obtained. The solution gives characteristically coloured precipitates with salts of heavy metals, and the free acid, $H_4Mn(CN)_6$, has been isolated in colourless crystals by the action of hydrogen sulphide on the lead salt, followed by evaporation *in vacuo*. Its solution soon undergoes hydrolysis, with precipitation of manganese (II) hydroxide.

Solutions of cyanomanganates (II) may be oxidized (even by air) to cyanomanganates (III) such as $K_3Mn(CN)_6$, which forms orange-red crystals isomorphous with the cyanoferrate (III). In solution it is slowly hydrolysed. Heavy-metal cyanomanganates (III) may be obtained as characteristically coloured precipitates.

Reduction of $K_4Mn(CN)_6$ with aluminium in alkaline solution gives $K_5Mn(CN)_6$ containing monopositive manganese. Reduction with potassium in liquid ammonia gives $K_5Mn(CN)_6$ and $K_6Mn(CN)_6 \cdot 2NH_3$, the latter substance containing zero-positive manganese.

Manganese fluorides. *Manganous fluoride*, MnF_2, is formed in solution when the hydroxide or carbonate dissolves in hydrofluoric acid, and crystallizes as the tetrahydrate, MnF_2, $4H_2O$. The anhydrous salt is formed by heating the complex NH_4MnF_3, which is precipitated from solutions of manganese (II) salts by excess of ammonium fluoride. It is not very soluble in water; 100 g dissolves 1·05 g of MnF_2 at 20°, and less at higher temperatures, but it dissolves easily in mineral acids. The aqueous solution is hydrolysed on boiling with precipitation of a basic fluoride.

Manganese trifluoride, $MnF_3, 2H_2O$, is obtained in ruby-red crystals by evaporation of a solution of manganese (III) oxide or hydroxide in hydrofluoric acid. The anhydrous trifluoride is obtained by the action of dilute fluorine on manganese (II) iodide. It is hydrolysed in solution.

Manganese tetrafluoride, MnF_4, results from the action of fluorine on the metal at high temperatures. It is a volatile solid, rapidly hydrolysed by moisture.

Manganese fluorides, complex. Complex manganese (II) fluorides, $MMnF_3$ (M = Na, K, and Rb) are precipitated from aqueous hydrofluoric acid solutions.

Fluoromanganates (III) are prepared by electrolytic oxidation of manganese (II) salts or by the mutual oxidation and reduction of permanganate (VII) and manganese (II) compounds; both processes are carried out in the presence of excess of hydrofluoric acid and an alkali fluoride. The best known are $(NH_4)_2MnF_5$, Na_2MnF_5, and $K_2MnF_5 \cdot H_2O$; they are red crystalline salts, easily hydrolysed in solution. Hexafluoromanganates (III), e.g. K_3MnF_6, are prepared by fusion in alkali hydrogen fluorides.

Hexafluoromanganates (IV) are prepared by electrolytic oxidation of a manganese (II) or manganese (III) solution and by the action of bromine trifluoride, e.g.

$$2KF + Mn(IO)_3 + BrF_3 \rightarrow K_2MnF_6.$$

They are yellow crystalline compounds, strong oxidizing agents, readily hydrolysed by moisture.

Manganese hydroxides. *Manganous hydroxide*, $Mn(OH)_2$, occurs in nature as pyrochroïte, and can be obtained crystalline in the laboratory by deposition from caustic potash at rather high temperatures, when it forms hexagonal prisms. As ordinarily prepared, by precipitation with caustic alkalis in absence of air, it is a white amorphous substance, which very rapidly turns brown on exposure to air, being oxidized to hydrated Mn_2O_3. It dissolves readily in acids and in ammonium salts, and is very slightly soluble in water (about 10^{-5} mol/litre).

Manganic hydroxide, Mn_2O_3, xH_2O or $MnO \cdot OH$, is precipitated when solutions of manganic salts are hydrolysed, or when alkaline solutions of manganese (II) salts are exposed to air. Its colour varies according to the method of preparation from yellowish-brown to dark brown, and it often resembles precipitated ferric hydroxide in appearance. The degree of hydration of the precipitate is somewhat indefinite, but after drying at 100° it has the composition $MnO \cdot OH$ and a hydroxide of this composition occurs in nature as manganite. With acids it reacts as does manganic oxide, but more readily, and in particular orthophosphoric, hydrofluoric, hydrocyanic, and oxalic acids

dissolve it, forming complex manganese (III) salts.

Hydrated manganese dioxide, MnO_2, xH_2O or MnO_2, H_2O, is formed as a brown or black precipitate by a variety of reactions, such as the disproportionation of manganese (III) compounds, alkaline oxidation of manganese (II) compounds, and reduction in neutral solution of permanganates. Its water content is indefinite, but often approximates to MnO_2, H_2O, though it is doubtful whether this formula represents a true compound. It cannot be completely dehydrated without losing oxygen. It behaves as a very feeble acid, forming manganites, and as usually precipitated it contains traces of alkali which cannot be removed by washing.

Manganese iodide. The only known iodide is *manganous iodide*, MnI_2. The anhydrous salt may be obtained by the action of iodine on finely divided manganese under ether, as a rose-red deliquescent mass which decomposes when heated in air. From solutions obtained by the usual wet methods a tetrahydrate, MnI_2, $4H_2O$, is obtained as deliquescent pink crystals. Other hydrates with 1,2,6, and $9H_2O$ are known. Manganous iodide is very soluble in water, and the solution is partially hydrolysed on evaporation, depositing a basic iodide, MnI_2, MnO, $6H_2O$, as colourless crystals.

Manganese nitrate. The only known nitrate is *manganous nitrate*, $Mn(NO_3)_2$. As obtained by the usual wet methods it forms colourless monoclinic crystals, $Mn(NO_3)_2$, $6H_2O$, which melt in their water of crystallization at 25·8°. Hydrates with 4, 2, and 1 molecules of water are also known. On evaporation of a solution, decomposition occurs, hydrated manganese dioxide being deposited. The anhydrous salt cannot be obtained by ordinary methods, but has been prepared by dissolving manganese metal in liquid dinitrogen tetroxide. Manganous nitrate is very soluble, dissolving in its own weight of water at 0°.

Manganese oxalates. *Manganous oxalate*, MnC_2O_4, $3H_2O$, may be obtained as a white powder by precipitation or by the action of oxalic acid on a hot solution of potassium permanganate. A dihydrate is also known, and the anhydrous salt is formed at 110°. Solutions of higher oxides or hydroxides of manganese in oxalic acid contain either manganese(III) oxalate, $Mn_2(C_2O_4)_3$ or a complex derived from it. From these solutions oxalatomanganates(III) such as $K_3[Mn(C_2O_4)_3]$,$3H_2O$ (red needles isomorphous with the oxalatoferrate (III) and green crystals of $Na[Mn(H_2O)_2(C_2O_4)_2]$ have been isolated.

Manganese oxides. MnO, Mn_3O_4, Mn_2O_3,

MnO_2, and Mn_2O_7 are all known. In addition, a number of intermediate oxides have been described. A trioxide, MnO_3, was for long supposed to exist, but it has been shown to be merely an impure form of permanganic acid.

Manganous oxide, MnO, is formed when the hydroxide or carbonate is heated in the absence of air, or by the reduction of the higher oxides by heating in hydrogen or carbon monoxide. Its colour varies from grey to green according to the method of preparation. By heating at high temperatures it may be obtained crystalline in octahedra, sp.gr. 5·09. The crystal structure is of the sodium chloride type. It is very easily oxidized, and can only be reduced to the metal with great difficulty. It dissolves readily in acids forming manganese (II) salts.

Trimanganese tetroxide, Mn_3O_4, occurs in nature as haussmannite. It is the most stable oxide, in that oxy-salts or other oxides are all converted to Mn_3O_4 on ignition in air above 940°. As ordinarily prepared it is a brown amorphous powder, but it becomes crystalline on strong ignition. Two forms exist: tetragonal (haussmannite) and octahedral (isomorphous with magnetite). It has a distorted spinel structure.

Manganic oxide, Mn_2O_3, occurs in nature as braunite, and is most easily obtained in the laboratory by heating MnO_2 in air above 530° but below 940°, at which temperature it begins to lose oxygen, forming Mn_3O_4. It is a brown or black powder, which with acids may form a manganese (III) salt (e.g. cold conc. H_2SO_4), or a manganese (II) salt and MnO_2, xH_2O (e.g. dil. H_2SO_4, HNO_3), or may be reduced, forming a manganese (II) salt (e.g. warm hydrochloric acid gives chlorine and $MnCl_2$).

Manganese dioxide, MnO_2, is found in nature as pyrolusite and polianite. Pyrolusite is isomorphous with stannic oxide, tetragonal. It cannot be obtained artificially by dehydration of the precipitated oxide, but can be prepared by cautious ignition of manganous nitrate as a black amorphous powder. When heated in air it begins to lose oxygen at 530°. With cold hydrochloric acid it gives a brown solution containing higher chlorides, but on warming, chlorine is evolved and $MnCl_2$ formed. With sulphuric acid at ordinary temperatures it yields manganese (III) sulphate and oxygen, but at higher temperatures more oxygen is liberated and manganese (II) sulphate is formed. With sulphurous acid the chief product is manganese (II) dithionate. Finely divided manganese dioxide is a powerful catalyst in many reactions: e.g. the decomposition of potassium chlorate, hydrogen peroxide, and various per-acids, and the oxidation of hydrogen and carbon monoxide. It is used for imparting an amethyst tint to glass, or in smaller amounts to neutralize the yellow tint produced by iron, and also as depolarizer in dry cells of the Leclanché type. A specific oxidizing agent which will not attack alkenes, it will convert allylic and benzylic alcohols into the corresponding aldehydes; certain methylamines are oxidized to formylamines.

Manganese heptoxide, or permanganic anhydride, Mn_2O_7, is formed when potassium permanganate dissolves in cold sulphuric acid containing a little water; it separates out as dark oily drops. With moist air it gives violet fumes of permanganic acid, but is fairly stable in dry air in the cold, although it may explode on warming. It violently attacks organic matter, and a little water causes violent decomposition, liberating ozonized oxygen, but if dropped into excess of water it forms a violet solution of permanganic acid.

Manganese phosphates. Various manganese phosphates, e.g. $Mn_3(PO_4)_2 \cdot 7H_2O$ and $MnHPO_4 \cdot 3H_2O$, may be obtained from aqueous solution. Complex phosphates, e.g. $NH_4MnPO_4 \cdot H_2O$, are also formed from solution. The latter compound may be used for the estimation of manganese; it is ignited to $Mn_2P_2O_7$. Phosphates of tripositive manganese are also known; $MnPO_4 \cdot 2H_2O$ is precipitated after interaction of $KMnO_4$ and $MnSO_4$ in the presence of phosphoric acid. Anionic phosphate complexes are also known.

Manganese sulphates, $MnSO_4$, $Mn_2(SO_4)_3$, and $Mn(SO_4)_2$ are all known.

Manganous sulphate, $MnSO_4$, usually crystallizes as the pentahydrate $MnSO_4$, $5H_2O$, triclinic, isomorphous with $CuSO_4$, $5H_2O$. Below 9° a heptahydrate, and at higher temperatures tetra-, di-, and mono-hydrates are stable. The anhydrous salt may be obtained by dehydrating the hydrates; a temperature above 250° being necessary to expel the last molecule of water, and the anhydrous salt may be heated to its m.p. (700°) without decomposition. It is readily soluble in water—100 g dissolve 53·2 g at 0° and 62·8 g at 20°. Above 27° the monohydrate is the stable solid phase and the solubility decreases with rising temperature.

Manganic sulphate, $Mn_2(SO_4)_3$, may be obtained in solution by heating precipitated manganese dioxide with sulphuric acid to 110°, or by electrolytic oxidation of solutions of manganese (II) sulphate in the presence of an excess of sulphuric acid. It has been isolated as a green deliquescent mass, which with a little water forms a violet solution, but is decomposed on dilution. It forms a series of alums and double salts of the type $M^IMn(SO_4)_2$.

Manganese disulphate, $Mn(SO_4)_2$, is formed by oxidation of solutions of manganese (II) sulphate in sulphuric acid, either by means of lead dioxide at 50° or electrolytically. A deep brown solution is obtained which on cooling deposits black crystals of $Mn(SO_4)_2$. These are stable in the presence of 50% H_2SO_4; water or more dilute acid causes hydrolysis. Above 80° it decomposes to $Mn_2(SO_4)_3$ and oxygen.

Manganese sulphides. MnS, Mn_3S_4, and MnS_2 are known.

Manganous sulphide, MnS, when prepared in the dry way, forms dark green or black cubes or octahedra. In the wet way it is precipitated from alkaline solution in various forms, a pink and a green form being the best known, although other varieties have been described. The exact conditions which lead to the precipitation of the green form have been much investigated, but are not yet fully understood; the pink form is usually precipitated and then usually changes to the green on boiling or sometimes on standing. The reverse change never occurs, so that the green is the stable form. Manganese (II) sulphide has a relatively high solubility, of the order of 10^{-4} mol/litre, and so cannot be precipitated in presence of even the weakest acids. It is very easily oxidized and after drying *in vacuo* may be pyrophoric.

Mn_3S_4 and MnS_2 may be obtained by dry methods; they are decomposed by water.

Manganic salts. Generally maganese (III) salts.

Manganin. An alloy used for electrical resistance wire, particularly for accurate standards for resistance measurement. Typical samples contain copper 53%, manganese 1·7%, nickel 2·5%, zinc 39%, tin 2·7%, aluminium 0·2%; or Cu 70%, Mn 25%, Ni 5%; or Cu 82-86%, Mn 4-15%, Ni 2-12%.

Manganites. Mixed oxides containing manganese (IV). A number of minerals are manganites with varying amounts of manganese. Generally prepared by dry methods, manganites of indefinite compositions are obtained whenever hydrated manganese dioxide is precipitated in the presence of alkali or alkaline earth cations. A hydrated calcium manganite plays an important intermediate part in the Weldon process for manufacturing chlorine.

Manganous salts. Generally manganese (II) salts.

Mannans. Polysaccharides made up of a chain of mannose units. The best-known is mannan A from the endosperm of the ivory nut which is used for making buttons, etc. It consists of a chain of some 80 mannopyranose units joined through carbons 1 and 4. The mannan of salep which differs in being fairly soluble in water is assigned a chain length of 60 units. Mannans are produced by many micro-organisms. Thus the outer cell wall of yeasts contain mannan as well as glucan, chitin, and protein. The yeast *Hansenula holstii* makes a gum which is chemically a phosphorylated mannan. Other micro-organisms produce other mannans of various degrees of complexity.

Mannich reaction. The replacement of active hydrogen atoms in organic compounds (e.g. an hydrogen of a ketone or a hydrogen on the aromatic ring of a phenol) by aminomethyl or substituted aminomethyl groups. This process is also called aminomethylation, and may be accomplished by reacting 37% formaldehyde with the desired amine, e.g. $(CH_3)_2NH$, and the compound RH with active hydrogen atom(s).

$$(CH_3)_2NH + CH_2O + RH \rightarrow$$
$$R \cdot CH_2 \cdot N(CH_3)_2 + H_2O$$

Several variations on this reaction are known. See F. F. Blicke, 'Organic Reactions,' Vol. I (1942).

D-**Mannitol**, $C_6H_{14}O_6$. Mannitol, the alcohol

$$CH_2(OH) \cdot \overset{H}{\underset{OH}{C}} \cdot \overset{H}{\underset{OH}{C}} \cdot \overset{OH}{\underset{H}{C}} \cdot \overset{OH}{\underset{H}{C}} \cdot CH_2(OH)$$

corresponding to mannose, is widely distributed in plants and fungi. It is a white crystalline powder with a sweet taste, solubility 13 g in 100 g water at 14°, 197 g in 100 g at 100°, m.p. 166°, d^{13} 1·52, $[\alpha]_D^{25}$ −49°. It can be made from glucose by electrolytic reduction or isolated from natural sources, e.g. seaweed or manna ash.

D-**Mannose**, $C_6H_{12}O_6$. Obtained by hydrolysis of mannans, a convenient source being the

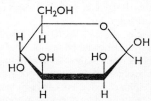

vegetable ivory nut. The β-pyranose form forms rhombic crystals, m.p. 132°, $[\alpha]_D$ −16·3° changing to +14·6° in water. The phenyl hydrazone is sparingly soluble in water; it has m.p. 199°.

Manometers. These instruments are used for measuring the difference in pressure between two points in a liquid or gas. In its simplest form a manometer consists of an upright transparent U-shaped tube, partly filled with a liquid immiscible with the other fluid. The two limbs are connected to the two points where the pressures are to be compared, and the difference in liquid level gives the pressure difference directly. Inverted manometers, their upper part filled with gas, are sometimes used with liquids.

Where small pressure differences are being measured readings may be 'magnified' by the use of an inclined manometer. Alternatively, two immiscible liquids may be used in the same manometer, which then behaves as if it contained a liquid of density equal to the difference in density between the two.

Marcasite, FeS_2. A fairly common mineral, orthorhombic, hardness 6, sp.gr. 4·8. A pale brass-yellow colour with a metallic lustre; it sometimes occurs as twinned octahedra called cockscomb pyrites, or spear pyrites.

Marcet, Alexander (1770-1822). A Swiss physician and chemist, Marcet was appointed lecturer in chemistry at Guy's Hospital, London. In addition to numerous physiological researches he studied certain chemical problems, particularly the properties of carbon disulphide, and the salt content of many samples of sea water.

Margaric acid, *n*-heptadecanoic acid, $CH_3 \cdot [CH_2]_{15} \cdot COOH$. M.p. 61·3°, b.p. 363·3°. Like all other fatty acids with an odd number of carbon atoms it only occurs naturally to a small extent. It is not present in margarine.

Marggraf, Andreas Sigismund (1709-1782). Born in Berlin, Marggraf was famous as an analyst. He was the first to distinguish between lime and alumina, and between potash and soda. He worked on phosphoric acid and showed the similarity between gypsum, heavy-spar, and potassium sulphate. See Thomson's 'History,' I, p. 271.

Marignac, Jean Charles Galissard de. (1817-1894). Born in Geneva, Marignac went to Paris in 1833 and studied chemistry there until 1839; he studied under Liebig at Giessen in 1840 and 1841 and then took a post in the porcelain manufactory at Sèvres, after which he returned to Geneva and became professor of chemistry and mineralogy. He worked successfully on the rare earths and discovered gadolinia and samaria. See Chem. Soc. Memorial Lectures, 1893-1900.

Markownikoff's rule. The rule states that in the addition of hydrogen halides to an ethylenic double bond, the halogen attaches itself to the carbon atom united to the smaller number of hydrogen atoms. The rule may generally be relied on to predict the major product of such an addition; in some cases some of the alternative compound is formed. The rule usually breaks down for hydrogen bromide addition reactions if traces of peroxides are present. For a theoretical discussion of the rule see 'Structure and Mechanism in Organic Chemistry,' by Ingold.

Marsh gas, See Methane.

Marsh's test for arsenic. The principle of this test is that if an arsenic compound is added to a vessel in which nascent hydrogen is being liberated (by the action of sulphuric acid on zinc, by electrolysis, or by other methods), arsine is given off. This is decomposed by passing through a hot tube, and gives a brown mirror of metallic arsenic beyond the heated portion. By comparison with standard mirrors, made using a known quantity of arsenic, a quantitative estimation may be made. The stain is soluble in sodium hypochlorite, a distinction from antimony which otherwise behaves similarly.

Martempering. A heat treatment process for steels which minimizes the dangers of cracking during cooling to martensite. It consists of quenching the steel into a hot quenching bath at about 350°, i.e. just above the Ms temperature. The steel is then allowed to cool slowly in air to room temperature. The martensite forming during this slow cooling is not so liable to cause cracking as is the rapid formation of martensite during quenching right down to room temperature. The Ms temperature is that at which austenite solid solution starts to transform to martensite during cooling. The transformation is complete at Mf; commonly between 150° and 0°. See also Austempering.

Martensite. An acicular or needle-like phase formed in steels which have been cooled from the austenite range faster than a certain critical rate. It is formed by a transformation involving lattice shear. It has no definite carbon content, the carbon being held in supersaturated solid solution. It is the principal constituent of hardened steels, the actual hardness being dependent on the carbon content and increasing as the carbon content increases.

Martensitic transformation. Similar structures to martensite have now been found in other alloy systems, e.g. copper-aluminium. Transformations of this type involving lattice shear and no diffusion are known as martensitic transformations.

Martin, Archer John Porter (1910-   ). The inventor jointly with R. L. M. Synge of paper chromatography and with A. T. James of vapour phase chromatography, Martin has introduced two analytical methods which have made possible a vast increase in chemical knowledge, in particular of the structure of proteins. Born in London and trained in Cambridge, Martin has also worked at the Wool Industries Research Association, at Boots Pure Drug Co., at the Lister Institute and the National Institute for Medical Research. He shared the Nobel Prize for Chemistry in 1952.

Martius yellow, Manchester yellow (Acid Yellow 24). This nitro-dye is the sodium,

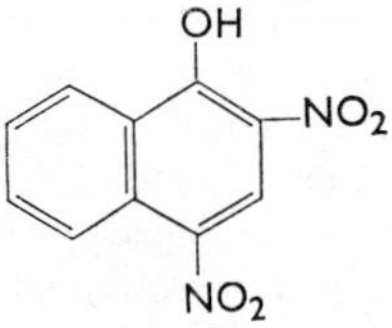

calcium, or ammonium salt of 2,4-dinitro-1-naphthol; it is prepared by the nitration of 1-naphthol-2,4-disulphonic acid. It was formerly largely used for the dyeing of wool.

Maser. A device involving the laser principle but using microwave radiation.

Mass action, Law of. Guldberg and Waage (1864) stated that the rate at which a substance reacts is proportional to its active mass (concentration), and hence the velocity of a chemical reaction is proportional to the products of the concentrations of the reactants. Thus, in the reaction

$$A+B \rightleftharpoons C+D,$$

the velocity of the forward reaction is

$$V_f = k_1[A][B],$$

where k_1 is a constant, and the square brackets denote concentrations. Similarly, for the backward reaction,

$$V_b = k_2[C][D].$$

At equilibrium, $V_f = V_b$,

or $k_1[A][B] = k_2[C][D],$

hence $\dfrac{k_1}{k_2} = \dfrac{[C][D]}{[A][B]} = K.$

The constants k_1 and k_2 are called velocity constants, and K is called the equilibrium constant.

Mass defect. That part of the mass of the constituent particles of a nucleus which is apparent as binding energy rather than as mass. See Atomic energy.

Massicot. See Lead monoxide.

Mass number. The total number of particles (protons and neutrons) in the nucleus.

Mass spectrograph. This is a refined modification of the parabola method of positive-ray analysis, by means of which the masses of ions were compared to an accuracy of about 1 part in 20,000. By its aid Aston provided most of the early information concerning isotopes.

In the modern mass-spectrometer the relative abundance of isotopes or other ionized radicals is determined by measuring the positive ion currents arriving at a fixed electrometer with various controlled magnetic fields and accelerating potentials.

Mass spectrum. The records obtained by means of the mass spectrograph are termed mass spectra. The individual lines in the mass spectrum of an element are due to its isotopes.

Mastics. Preparations of bitumen of various grades used as adhesives and water-proofing compounds.

Masurium. A former name for technetium.

Matlockite. See Lead chlorides.

Matricaria ester, $C_{11}H_{10}O_2$. The methyl ester of deca-2,8-diene-4,6-diynoic acid

$$CH_3 \cdot CH : CH \cdot C \vdots C \cdot C \vdots C \cdot CH : CH \cdot COOCH_3.$$

The *cis*-2 : *cis*-8- and *cis*-2 : *trans*-8-isomers both occur in *Matricaria inodora* (scented bindweed), while the *trans*-2 : *trans*-8-isomer is produced by the mould *Polyporus anthracophilus*.

Matte. The name given to the indefinite mixture of artificial sulphides produced by a smelting operation.

Mauveine, Perkin's Mauve. The first synthetic dye to be prepared (Perkin, 1856). It is

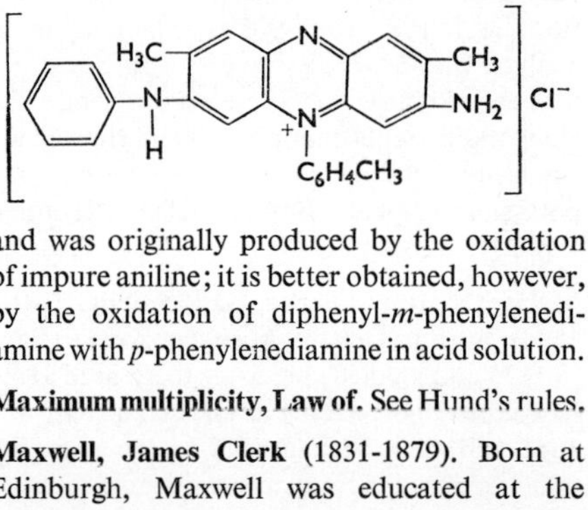

and was originally produced by the oxidation of impure aniline; it is better obtained, however, by the oxidation of diphenyl-*m*-phenylenediamine with *p*-phenylenediamine in acid solution.

Maximum multiplicity, Law of. See Hund's rules.

Maxwell, James Clerk (1831-1879). Born at Edinburgh, Maxwell was educated at the Academy there and at the Universities of Edinburgh and Cambridge. He was professor of natural philosophy, Aberdeen (1856-1860), and professor of physics and astronomy, King's College, London (1860-1868). In 1871, after three years' retirement, he was appointed the first professor of experimental physics at Cambridge. His main researches were in the field of electricity, where he put the ideas of Faraday on a mathematical basis. He also developed the kinetic theory of gases. In 1860 he was awarded the Rumford Medal, and later was elected F.R.S.

Mayow, John. Born in Cornwall in 1645 and practised as a physician. He was one of the first to recognize that a constituent of the air was concerned in combustion, the calcination of metals, and respiration. He found, or had learned, that the same constituent was contained in saltpetre. He died in 1679.

MCPA, 2-methyl-4-chlorophenoxyacetic acid, $C_9H_9ClO_3$, trade name 'Methoxone.' Made by

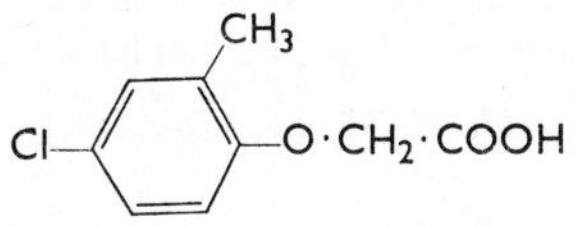

chlorination of *o*-cresol followed by reaction with chloroacetic acid. It is, in the pure state, a white crystalline solid, m.p. 118°-119°. As usually obtained, however, crude MCPA contains both 4- and 6-chloroisomers, there being about 60-65% of the former, and is a light brown solid. Both isomers are insoluble in water. MCPA was developed as a selective weedkiller following research work on the effect of auxin on soil. It was found that extracts containing auxins when applied to plants in very low concentrations caused severe damage to broadleaved species such as charlock but not to grasses and cereals. When the natural plant hormone heteroauxin was identified as β-indolylacetic acid, chemical compounds were synthesized having even greater selectivity. Low-volume spraying of corn fields with MCPA is common farming practice; the sodium salt is sufficiently soluble but amine salts and potassium salt sprays are also available. Crops such as cabbage, turnips, lettuce, peas and tomatoes are very susceptible to damage by spray drift.

MCPB, 4-(4-chloro-2-methylphenoxy)-butyric acid. A compound in itself harmless to plants,

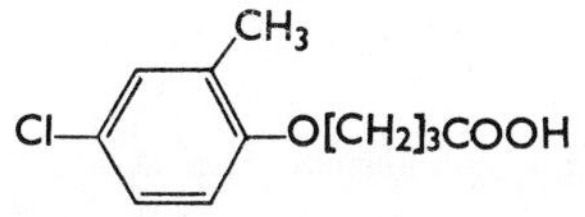

but when absorbed and translocated in the cells it is converted to a powerful herbicide, and results in the death of the plant. Since this conversion is possible in cells of certain plants but not in others, the compound acts as a selective weedkiller. Legumes such as clovers, lucerne, and peas cannot readily effect the conversion, so that a promising means is offered for controlling weeds in legumes and undersown cereal crops. The technical material (90%) is insoluble in water, and soluble in alcohol. It has low mammalian toxicity. Other butyric acid derivatives used commercially are 2,4-D_B and 2,4,5-T_B, the butyric acid analogues of 2,4-D and 2,4,5-T (*q.v.*)

Mean free path. The average distance traversed by a molecule between one collision and the next is called the mean free path of the molecule.

At N.T.P., hydrogen molecules have a mean free path of 1.8×10^{-6} cm, nitrogen molecules 9.5×10^{-6} cm, and carbon dioxide 6.3×10^{-6} cm.

Mechanism of a reaction. The manner in which a reaction proceeds is termed the mechanism of the reaction, and may be expressed in a series of chemical equations. Thus, the mechanism of the reaction between hydrogen and bromine which yields hydrogen bromide may be represented by the following equations:

$$Br_2 = 2Br$$
$$Br + H_2 = HBr + H$$
$$H + Br_2 = HBr + Br$$
$$H + HBr = H_2 + Br$$
$$Br + Br = Br_2.$$

Medicinal paraffin oil. A highly refined mineral oil obtained from petroleum by repeated refining with oleum followed by alcoholic caustic soda and passage through decolorizing earth and filtration as required. The product must be completely water-white, odourless, and tasteless. It is also known as liquid paraffin.

Meehanite. A range of controlled quality, fine-grain, grey cast irons.

Meerschaum, Sepiolite, $Mg_3Si_3O_6(OH)_4$. Occurs in white or grey nodular masses associated with magnesite and serpentine. It has sp.gr. about 2, hardness 2-2½. It is mostly obtained from Turkey; it is easily carved and chiefly used for making pipe bowls and cigar holders.

Meisenheimer, Jakob (1876-1934). Born at Griesheim of peasant stock, Meisenheimer was educated at the Universities of Heidelberg and Munich. In 1909 he was appointed professor of chemistry and Director of the Landwirtschaftliche Hochschule, Berlin. In 1918 he became professor of chemistry at Greifswald; in 1922 he was appointed Director of the Chemistry Institute, University of Tübingen. His scientific investigations covered a wide field, but most notable were his brilliant researches on the stereochemistry of nitrogen. See *J. Chem. Soc.*, 1935, 1355.

Melamine, $C_3H_6N_6$. Crystallizes in colourless

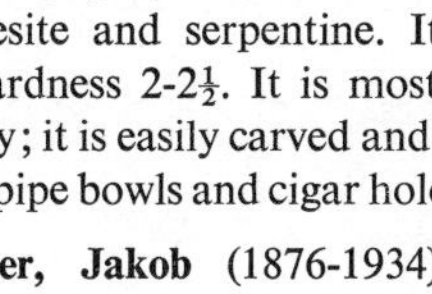

monoclinic prisms, m.p. 354°. Solubility 0·5% in cold water, 5% in hot water. Sparingly soluble in alcohol, insoluble in ether and inert solvents. It is manufactured by heating dicyandiamide, $H_2N \cdot C(NH) \cdot NH \cdot CN$ either alone or in the presence of ammonia or other alkalis, in various organic solvents. Melamine is an important material in the plastics industry. Condensed with formaldehyde and other substances it gives products that are remarkably stable to heat and light.

Melanin. The name melanin has been applied loosely to almost any black pigment found in body tissues or formed from tissues by any biochemical operations. It is the name given to the dark pigment of hair, of the retina and of the skin of dark races, and of the layer of protective sunburn in fair races. One type of melanin is believed to be a polymer of indole-5,6-quinone, formed by the action of the enzyme tyrosinase on tyrosine, which combines with protein to produce the dark pigment. Other polyhydroxyphenyl compounds can be oxidized to pigmented polymers, also called melanins. Some melanins contain appreciable amounts of sulphur.

Melanotropin. The melanocyte-stimulating hormone, also called MSH or intermedin. It is a polypeptide of known structure secreted by the middle lobe of the pituitary gland. It promotes darkening of the skin of fishes and amphibia; its significance in mammals is not clear.

Melatonin, N-acetyl-5-methoxytryptamine, $C_{13}H_{16}N_2O_2$. A hormone occurring in the pineal

(epiphyseal) gland, which has a blanching effect on the skin of amphibia. It acts by causing contraction of melanophores, thus opposing the effect of melanotropin.

Meldola, Raphael (1849-1915). Born in London, Meldola was educated at the Royal College of Chemistry. About 1876 he joined the Atlas Colour Works, where he carried out important researches on dyestuffs, including the discovery of the first oxazine dyestuff, 'Meldola's blue.' In 1885 he became professor of chemistry at Finsbury Technical College and retained this position until his death. In 1913 he was awarded the Davy Medal of the Royal Society, of which he had been a Fellow since 1886. He was President of the Chemical Society (1905-7), of the Society of Dyers and Colourists (1907-10), of the Society of Chemical Industry (1908-9), and of the Institute of Chemistry (1912-15).

Melibiose, $C_{12}H_{22}O_{11}$. 6-[β-D-galactopyranosido]-D-glucopyranose. The dihydrate of the β-form crystallizes with m.p. 85°, $[\alpha]_D$ +112° (initial), +129·5° (final). Obtained with fructose by the hydrolysis of raffinose.

Melissic acid, $C_{30}H_{60}O_2$, $CH_3 \cdot [CH_2]_{28} \cdot COOH$.

A fatty acid occurring in bees' wax, m.p. 94°, soluble in benzene and hot alcohol.

Melissyl alcohol, Myricyl alcohol, $C_{30}H_{62}O$, $CH_3 \cdot [CH_2]_{28} \cdot CH_2OH$. Colourless crystals, m.p. 87°, soluble in organic solvents. It is present as melissyl palmitate in bees' wax.

Mellitic acid, $C_{12}H_6O_{12}$. Colourless needles,

m.p. 286°-288° (closed tube). Readily soluble in water, alcohol, and ether. When heated it decomposes into pyromellitic anhydride, water, and carbon dioxide.

Occurs as the aluminium salt (honeystone) in some lignite beds. Prepared by oxidation of charcoal with concentrated nitric acid.

It condenses with resorcinol and aminophenols to give phthalein and rhodamine dyestuffs respectively.

Melsens, Louis Henri Frédéric (1814-1886). Melsens was professor of chemistry at the École de Médécine Vétérinaire de l'État, Brussels. An organic chemist, he investigated the action of amalgams upon chlorinated acids.

Melting-point. The temperature at which a solid changes into the liquid state, at a given pressure, is called the melting-point. Pure solids usually melt completely at a definite temperature. They are said to have sharp melting-points. Mixtures usually melt over a range of temperature, and have not, therefore, a sharp or definite melting-point.

Membrane equilibrium. See Donnan equilibrium.

Membrane hydrolysis. When a colloidal electrolyte consisting, e.g. of giant anions and normal cations, is separated by a membrane from pure water, the cations are able to diffuse out but the colloidal anions are retained. For each positive ion which penetrates the membrane, a molecule of water will dissociate to provide a compensating OH^- ion, the corresponding H^+ ion tending to diffuse through the membrane to replace the original cation of the colloidal electrolyte. The liquid inside the dialyser thus becomes acid, that outside the dialyser alkaline. This process is termed membrane hydrolysis. See also Colloids, Colloidal electrolyte, Membrane equilibrium.

Menaphthone,   2-methyl-1,4-naphthaquinone, $C_{11}H_8O_2$. A yellow crystalline powder, m.p. 105°-107°, which decomposes in sunlight. Insoluble in water, soluble in fixed oils. Prepared by the oxidation of 2-methylnaphthalene with

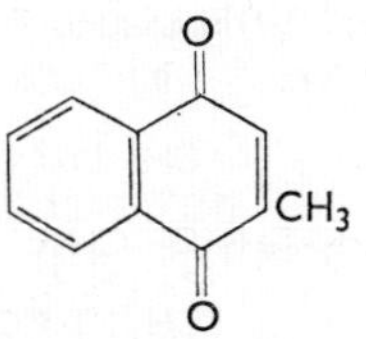

hydrogen peroxide or chromium trioxide. It has vitamin **K** activity and is administered intramuscularly to prevent haemorrhage. It cannot be taken by mouth owing to its irritant action on the gastric mucosa, but its diacetoxy derivative, acetomenthone, can be taken orally.

Menazon, S-(4,6-diamino-1,3,5-triazin-2-yl-methyl) - O,O - dimethylphosphorothiolothio-nate, $C_6H_{12}N_5O_2PS_2$. A white solid, soluble

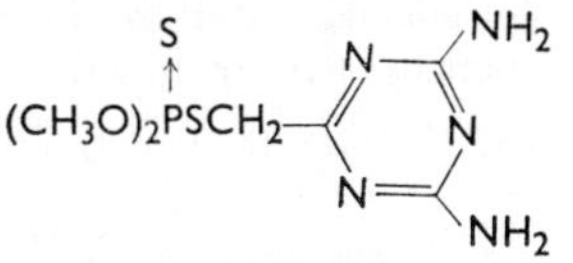

in water, m.p. (decomp.) 160°-162°. It is a systemic aphicide with low mammalian toxicity. See *Chem. & Ind.*, 1961, 630.

Mendel, Lafayette Benedict (1872-1935). Born at Delhi, New York, Mendel studied at Yale, and later at Breslau and Freiburg. Commencing as an assistant in physiological chemistry at the Sheffield Scientific School, Yale, he became assistant professor in 1897, and professor in 1903. From 1921 until his death he was Sterling professor of physiological chemistry in Yale University. In addition to original work on the vitamins, Mendel's researches included investigations on the chemistry of digestion, protein metabolism, and the physiology of growth. He was awarded the Conné Medal in 1934.

Mendeléeff, Dmitri Ivanovich (1834-1907). Mendeléeff's interest in natural science was early stimulated through contact with the exiled Decembrists at Tobolsk in Siberia, his birthplace. Later he studied at the Central Pedagogic Institute, St. Petersburg (Leningrad). After a period in Paris and Heidelberg he returned to St. Petersburg as professor of chemistry at the Technological Institute, and later at the University. In 1893 he was appointed Director of the Bureau of Weights and Measures. He carried out many important investigations into the properties of solutions, but it is with the Periodic Classification of the Elements that his name will always be associated. See Mem. Lect., *J. Chem. Soc.*, 1909, 2077.

Mendelevium, Mv. At.no. 101. An isotope of mendelevium, ²⁵⁶Mv, was produced by bom-

barding ²⁵³Es with α particles. This isotope has a half-life of 90 minutes; ²⁵⁵Mv is also known. As far as can be seen from ion-exchange studies mendelevium behaves as a typical tripositive actinide ion.

Mendipite. See Lead chlorides.

Menshutkin, Nicolai Alexandrovitsch (1842-1907). Born at St. Petersburg, Menshutkin was educated at the Gymnasium and the University there before proceeding to study at Tübingen, Paris, and Marburg. In 1869 he was appointed professor of chemistry at the University of St. Petersburg and, in 1902, he was transferred to the new Polytechnic Institute in the district of Sosnowka. His main researches were on the synthesis and properties of the ureides and studies of velocity of reaction. See *J. Chem. Soc.*, 1911, 1660.

$1-\Delta^{2:8(9)}$-p-**Menthadiene,** $C_{10}H_{16}$. An optically

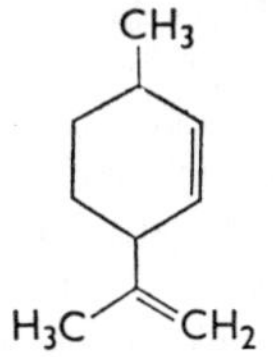

active monocyclic terpene found in chenopodium oil. It forms a crystalline tetrabromide of m.p. 117°.

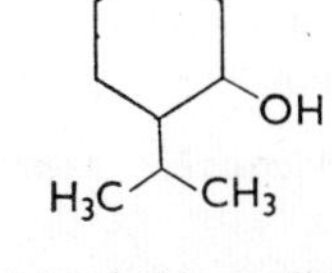

Menthol, $C_{10}H_{20}O$. An optically active monocyclic terpene alcohol; (−)-menthol is a constituent of peppermint oils, which are obtained from various varieties of *Mentha piperita*. In Japanese peppermint oil a small quantity of the isomeric liquid, (+)-neomenthol, is also present. (−)-Menthol is a solid which crystallizes in four different forms. The ordinary α-form consists of broad needles, which are dextrorotatory, whilst when molten or in solution (−)-menthol is laevorotatory. The constants of (−)-menthol are: m.p. 43°, b.p. 216°/760 mm, d_{15}^{15} 0·904, n_D^{20} 1·46096, $[\alpha]_D$ −49·44°. It forms a crystalline phenylurethane of m.p. 112° and a hydrogen phthalate of m.p. 122°. Menthol contains three asymmetric carbon atoms, and can therefore occur theoretically in 4 dextrorotatory, 4 laevorotatory, and 4 racemic forms, most of which have been synthesized and studied. (−)-Menthol and its stereoisomerides are obtainable by chemical reactions from a large number of terpene derivatives, for example, by the reduction of menthone, isomenthone, or piperitone. (−)-Menthol can be converted into p-cymene and can be oxidized to menthone. It is a mild antiseptic and, when applied to the skin, produces a sensation of coldness followed by a feeling of numbness. It is chiefly used externally as an analgesic in rheumatism and neuralgia, for which purpose it is usually dissolved in a mixture of other essential oils to form a liniment. Combined with camphor, eucalyptus oil, and other volatile antiseptics, it is used largely for inhalants or sprays for nasal catarrh and laryngitis.

Menthone, $C_{10}H_{18}O$. An optically active monocyclic ketone; $(-)$-menthone can be obtained by oxidizing $(-)$-menthol, and occurs in Russian peppermint oil. Menthone contains two asymmetric carbon atoms, and can therefore form 4 optically active and 2 racemic modifications, known as $(+)$-, $(-)$-, and $(\pm)$-menthone, and $(+)$-, $(-)$-, and $(\pm)$-isomenthone. The identity of these modifications is still uncertain, but apparently $(-)$-menthone is present in pepperment, geranium, and pennyroyal oils and $(-)$-isomenthone possibly occurs in buchu leaf oil. When $(-)$-menthone is dissolved in strong sulphuric acid, and the mixture cooled, it is partially converted into $(+)$-isomenthone. The following constants of the various isomeric menthones and isomenthones have been recorded: $(-)$-Menthone, m.p. $-7°$, b.p. $204°/750$ mm, $[\alpha]_D$ $-29·60°$; semicarbazone, m.p. $187°$, oxime, m.p. $59°$. $(\pm)$-Menthone, oxime, m.p. $81°-82°$, $(+)$-iso-menthone, b.p. $86°-87°/13$ mm, $[\alpha]_D$ $+91·7°$, $(\pm)$-isoMenthone, b.p. $90°-93°/18$ mm, oxime, m.p. $99°-100°$.

Mepacrine, Atebrin, Quinacrine.

It is prepared as the hydrochloride,
$$C_{23}H_{30}ClN_3O, 2HCl, 2H_2O,$$
which is a bright yellow crystalline powder, soluble in about 40 parts of water. It is prepared synthetically from p-anisidine, acetanilide, β-diethylaminoethyl alcohol and ethylacetoacetate. It is widely used as a substitute for quinine in the treatment of malaria, having a toxic action both on the schizonts and gametocytes of tertian and quartan malaria, but only on the schizonts in sub-tertian malaria. It is no more toxic than quinine and in certain respects

is more reliable. It is also used in the treatment of tapeworm infestations.

Meprobamate, 2,2-Di(carbamoyloxymethyl)pentane, $C_9H_{18}N_2O_4$. A white crystalline powder

soluble in 240 parts of water and in 7 parts of alcohol at 20. It is used medicinally as a tranquilizer.

Meprochol. $[CH_2:C(OCH_3)\cdot CH_2\cdot \overset{+}{N}(CH_3)_3]\overset{-}{B}r$. A white, crystalline, hygroscopic powder, m.p. $173°-174°$, very soluble in water and alcohol, sparingly soluble in ether. It is made by treating trimethyl-(2,3-dibromoallyl)-ammonium bromide with sodium methoxide. It is given by injection as a stimulant in atony of the gut and bladder, especially after operations.

Mepyramine, $C_{17}H_{23}N_3O$. Widely used as its

acid maleate, $C_{21}H_{27}O_5N_3$ (trade name Anthisan), as an antihistamine drug for treating asthma, anaphylaxis, and other allergic conditions. The maleate is a white powder, m.p. $98°-100°$, very soluble in water, alcohol, and chloroform.

Merbromin, $C_{20}H_7Br_2O_5\cdot HgOH\cdot Na_2$. A sodium mercury compound of dibromofluorescein. It is soluble in water, forming a highly fluorescent red solution which is used as a non-irritant antiseptic.

Mercaptals. Acetals in which the oxygen atoms have been replaced by sulphur atoms. They are oily liquids with unpleasant odours; insoluble in water but soluble in alcohol and ether. Formed by treating mercaptans with aldehydes or ketones in the presence of hydrochloric acid or zinc chloride. They are stable compounds and are not decomposed by dilute acids or alkalis. They are oxidized to sulphones.

Mercaptans. Organic compounds containing an —SH group directly united to a carbon atom. They may be regarded as alcohols in which the oxygen atom has been replaced by a sulphur atom. They are liquids with strong and unpleasant odours; insoluble in water but soluble in alcohol. Found in crude petroleum. Prepared by the action of alkyl or aryl halides on potassium hydrogen sulphide or by the reduction of the chlorides of sulphonic acids. They react characteristically with mercuric oxide to give crystalline compounds known as mercaptides. Oxidized by air or mild oxidizing agents to disulphides (—S·S—); nitric acid oxidizes them to sulphonic acids. React with aldehydes and ketones to form mercaptals and mercaptols.

Mercaptobenzthiazole, $C_7H_5NS_2$. A crystalline

powder, m.p. 174°-179°, d 1·42, solubility 0·25 g in 100 g water at 25°. It is prepared by treatment of thiocarbanilide with sulphur, or by heating aniline, carbon disulphide, and nitrobenzene. It is an important rubber accelerator, and on oxidation gives dibenzthiazyl disulphide, also a rubber accelerator.

Mercapturic acids. Derivatives of N-acetyl-cysteine which are excreted in the urine of animals following the ingestion of certain foreign organic compounds, such as alkyl halides and aromatic hydrocarbons. Mercapturic acid conjugation is a general reaction by which reactive or insoluble compounds may be eliminated as inert water-soluble derivatives, e.g. N-acetyl-S-alkylcysteines from bromoalkanes. The formation of mercapturic acids involves reaction with glutathione in the liver.

Mercurammine compounds. The addition of ammonia to an aqueous solution of mercuric chloride gives a compound called infusible white precipitate $H_2N \cdot HgCl$ which has infinite planar zigzag chains. Fusible white precipitate

is formed when ammonia is added to a mercuric chloride solution containing much ammonium chloride. The formula is $Hg(NH_3)_2Cl_2$ and it contains discrete $Hg(NH_3)_2^{2+}$ ions. Millon's base is prepared by the action of aqueous ammonia on the yellow form of mercuric oxide. The formula is $Hg_2NCl \cdot H_2O$ and it contains an infinite, three-dimensional Hg_2N^+ network with water in the holes that remain.

Only mercuric salts form stable ammines; mercurous compounds are rapidly decomposed by ammonia into mercuric compounds and mercury.

Infusible white precipitate is used in the form of an ointment for pruritis and certain skin diseases, and for pediculosis.

Mercuration. The process whereby a ring hydrogen atom of a reactive aromatic compound, e.g. furan, ferrocene, may be directly replaced by an —HgX group, usually by simply mixing the compound with the mercuric salt in a suitable solvent.

Mercury, Hg. At.no. 80, At.wt. 200·61, m.p. −38·87°, b.p. 356·58°, d_0 13·5955. Solid mercury has a rhombohedral structure, a=2·9925 Å, α=70° 44·6′ at −46°. The most important source of mercury is cinnabar, mercuric sulphide, HgS, a red or black mineral found in Spain, Italy, and to a smaller extent in Peru, California, Mexico, China, and Japan. In the extraction of the metal the cinnabar is roasted in a current of air, free mercury and sulphur dioxide being formed.

Mercury is a liquid metal with a silver-white colour. The vapour density corresponds to the monatomic formula Hg. It is not very readily oxidized, slow oxidation taking place at 300°. The metal is unattacked by dilute hydrochloric and sulphuric acids, but dissolves in dilute nitric and hot concentrated sulphuric acids. It is insoluble in alkalis.

Mercury forms two series of compounds, the mercurous compounds, Hg_2X_2, and the mercuric compounds, HgX_2. The metal and its compounds are generally exceedingly poisonous. Mercury is used in reactions and in forming electrical connections. Its compounds are used extensively in syntheses.

Mercury amalgams. Mercury dissolves many metals, forming amalgams, which, when more than a certain amount of metal is present, are solid. Those of potassium and sodium are definite compounds, e.g. $NaHg_2$, KHg_2. Gold, silver, copper, lead, etc., are dissolved by the mercury. Copper and cadmium amalgams are used to some extent as dental stoppings. Cadmium amalgam is used as the cathode in the Weston standard cell.

Mercury carbonates. *Mercurous carbonate*, Hg_2CO_3, can be made as a white precipitate by treating a solution of mercurous nitrate with potassium carbonate or bicarbonate. It turns yellow on keeping and is decomposed by hot water.

Mercuric carbonate, $HgCO_3$, is formed by the action of carbon dioxide on an aqueous suspension of mercuric oxide. An unstable bicarbonate and some basic carbonates are also known.

Mercury chlorides, *Mercuric chloride*, $HgCl_2$; m.p. 280°, b.p. 302°, d 5·41. Mercuric chloride is formed directly from the elements, the reaction taking place in the cold with dry chlorine. It is also formed by dissolving mercury or mercurous chloride in aqua regia. It crystallizes from solution in sparingly soluble, colourless rhombic needles. In aqueous solutions the salt is unionized. Mercuric chloride dissolves in concentrated hydrochloric acid; the solution contains complex ions, $HgCl_4^{2-}$ and $HgCl_3^-$. It is readily soluble in alcohol and ether. The aqueous solutions are readily reduced, and a white precipitate of mercurous chloride is thrown down.

Mercuric chloride, or corrosive sublimate, is a powerful antiseptic even in very dilute solution. It is very poisonous.

Mercurous chloride, Hg_2Cl_2, is prepared by precipitating a solution of mercurous nitrate with hydrochloric acid, or by subliming mercuric chloride with mercury. It is only sparingly soluble in water (0.4 mg per litre at $20°$).

During recent years it has found use in agriculture as an insecticide. It is also used, under the name of calomel, in small doses as a purgative.

Mercury fulminate, $Hg(ONC)_2$. Normally prepared as greyish crystals by dissolving mercury in concentrated nitric acid and pouring the warm solution into alcohol. When dry it is very sensitive to impact and friction, and is used in detonators and cap compositions; it is safe when stored under water. It has certain disadvantages as an initiator, mainly because of instability in hot climates.

Mercury iodides. *Mercuric iodide*, HgI_2, is formed directly from the elements, and by the precipitation of mercuric chloride solution with the calculated amount of potassium iodide. At ordinary temperatures mercuric iodide is a scarlet crystalline substance; on heating to $126°$ a yellow crystalline form is produced. The reverse change occurs on cooling. It is not very soluble in water (0.06 g per litre at $25°$), but dissolves more readily in alcohol. The salt is readily soluble in solutions of mercuric chloride or potassium iodide to give complexes. A solution of potassium iodomercurate (II) containing excess caustic potash is used as a test for ammonia (Nessler's reagent). With traces of ammonia a brown colour, with larger amounts a precipitate of indefinite composition, is formed.

Mercurous iodide, Hg_2I_2, is obtained by precipitation from a solution of a mercurous salt. It varies from yellow to green in colour and is relatively unstable with respect to mercury and mercuric iodide.

Mercury nitrates. *Mercuric nitrate*, $Hg(NO_3)_2$. This is formed by dissolving mercury in excess concentrated nitric acid; hydrates with 8, 2, 1, and $\frac{1}{2}$ molecules of water are known. Mercuric nitrate is decomposed by water or by heating and the oxynitrate $Hg(NO_3)_2 \cdot 2HgO$ is formed; further heating converts this to the oxide.

Mercurous nitrate, $Hg_2(NO_3)_2$ is formed by the action of cold dilute nitric acid on mercury, and the dihydrate crystallizes from the solution on standing. With water the crystals give a white precipitate of a basic nitrate, which is readily soluble in a little nitric acid.

Mercury organometallic derivatives. Many mercury compounds of the types RHgX and R_2Hg are known; they may be prepared from Grignard reagents and mercuric compounds HgX_2. Mercuric acetate mercurates aromatic derivatives to aryl-$HgOOCCH_3$ species. Mercuric halides add across the double bond of olefins to give $XHg—CH_2—CH_2X$ derivatives. Organomercury compounds are used extensively in the preparation of organometallic derivatives of other metals.

Mercury oxides. *Mercuric oxide*, HgO. Prepared by the addition of caustic alkali to a solution of mercuric nitrate; precipitated from cold solutions as a yellow, from hot as an orange, powder. By heating the nitrate alone or mixed with mercury to a moderate temperature, the crystalline red oxide is formed; the red oxide is also formed by heating mercury to $350°$ in oxygen. On heating strongly mercuric oxide decomposes into mercury and oxygen.

Mercurous oxide, Hg_2O. This is formed by oxidizing mercury with potassium permanganate and sodium nitrite or potassium superoxide. It very rapidly decomposes to mercuric oxide and mercury, and cannot be prepared from solution.

Mercury sulphates. *Mercuric sulphate*, $HgSO_4$. Formed by dissolving mercury in excess hot concentrated sulphuric acid, and evaporating to dryness. The white residue may be recrystallized from sulphuric acid, or from a very little water, when colourless crystals of $HgSO_4$, H_2O are produced. It is readily hydrolysed by water to a basic salt, $HgSO_4$, $2HgO$, called turpeth mineral.

Mercurous sulphate, Hg_2SO_4. Formed by warming an excess of mercury with concentrated sulphuric acid, and deposited as a crystalline powder on cooling. It is also prepared by precipitating mercurous nitrate with sulphuric acid. Mercurous sulphate is not very soluble in water (0.6 g per litre at $25°$), and is readily hydrolysed to a basic salt, Hg_2SO_4, Hg_2O, H_2O.

Mercury (Mercuric) sulphide, HgS. Occurs native as cinnabar. It is formed by triturating mercury and sulphur with a little caustic potash solution; the black sulphide produced initially slowly becomes red and crystalline. Mercuric sulphide is precipitated by the addition of hydrogen sulphide to a mercuric salt solution. The black form produced initially becomes red on sublimation. Mercuric sulphide is insoluble in dilute hydrochloric or nitric acids, but dissolves in aqua regia, or in concentrated solutions of potassium or sodium sulphide. In the second case thio-salts are formed, e.g. $K_2HgS_2, 5H_2O$. See Vermilion.

Merocyanine dyes. Also called neutrocyanines, this class of dyes is of considerable importance in providing spectral sensitizers for the photographic industry. The general

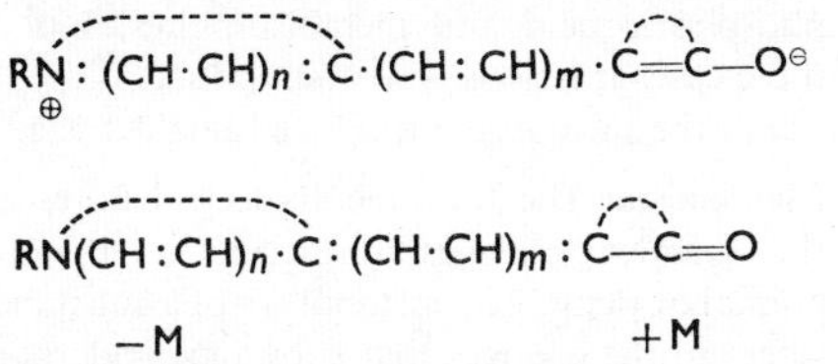

$$\overbrace{RN}^{\oplus} : (CH \cdot CH)_n : \overset{\frown}{C} \cdot (CH : CH)_m \cdot \overset{\frown}{C} = C - O^{\ominus}$$

$$\overbrace{RN}(CH : CH)_n \cdot \overset{\frown}{C} : (CH \cdot CH)_m : \overset{\frown}{C} - C = O$$

$$\qquad -M \qquad\qquad\qquad\qquad +M$$

formula depicts them as electrically neutral molecules, with two extreme structures, one non-ionic and the other zwitterionic. The conjugation is of the extended amide type. They are composed of a 'basic' ($-M$) nitrogen-containing heterocyclic ring system linked through a polymethine chain to an acidic ($+M$) ketomethylene heterocyclic ring system. Heterocyclic nuclei, which may form part of these molecules, include benzoxazole, benzothiazole, pyridine and quinoline as ($-M$) ring systems, and thiohydantoin, rhodanine, oxazol-5-one and thiobarbituric acid derivatives as ($+M$) ring systems. Like the cyanines, they absorb and sensitize at longer wavelengths as the conjugated polymethine chain lengthens (m increases) between the nitrogen atom and the oxygen atom. The colours of these dyes are solvent-sensitive.

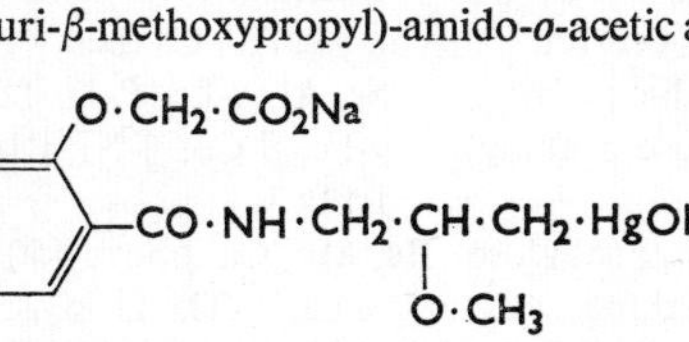

A typical dimethinemerocyanine

Mersalyl. The sodium salt of salicyl-(γ-hydroxy-mercuri-β-methoxypropyl)-amido-o-acetic acid,

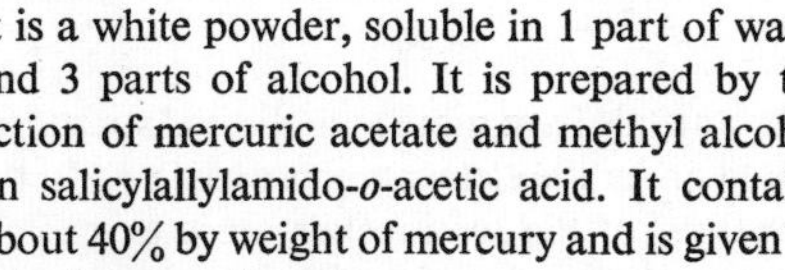

It is a white powder, soluble in 1 part of water and 3 parts of alcohol. It is prepared by the action of mercuric acetate and methyl alcohol on salicylallylamido-o-acetic acid. It contains about 40% by weight of mercury and is given by injection as a diuretic.

Mesaconic acid, Methylfumaric acid, $C_5H_6O_4$.

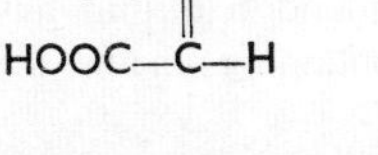

$$H_3C - \underset{\parallel}{C} - COOH$$
$$HOOC - C - H$$

A colourless, crystalline solid, m.p. 240·5°. Sparingly soluble in cold water; insoluble in ether. Prepared by dissolving citraconic acid in ether, adding a solution of bromine in chloroform and exposing the mixture to ultraviolet light. Forms two series of mono-esters owing to the unsymmetrical molecule.

Mescaline, β-(3,4,5-trimethoxyphenyl)-ethylamine, $C_{11}H_{17}NO_3$. An alkaloid obtained from *Lophophora williamsii*. It is a central nervous

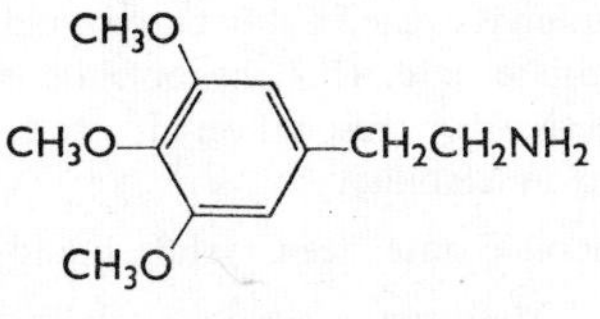

system depressant, but its most interesting effect is that it causes visual hallucinations.

Mescaline is the hallucinatory principle of 'Peyote.' Hallucinations are often in colour, and in some subjects even music is seen in colour.

Mesitylene, 1,3,5 trimethylbenzene. C_9H_{12}. A

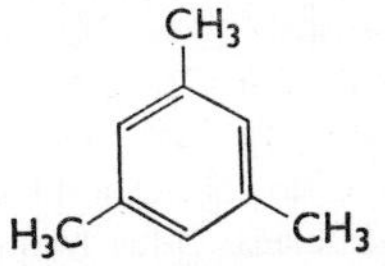

colourless liquid, d^{20} 0·8634, b.p. 165°. It occurs in crude petroleum. Prepared by adding concentrated sulphuric acid to cooled acetone, and then heating the mixture after it has stood for 24 hours. The mesitylene is distilled in steam, washed with sodium hydroxide solution and distilled.

Mesityl oxide, Isopropylidene acetone, $C_6H_{10}O$.

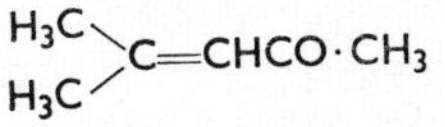

$$\overset{H_3C}{\underset{H_3C}{>}} C = CHCO \cdot CH_3$$

A colourless liquid with a strong peppermint-like odour, d^{20} 0·8653, b.p. 129°. Insoluble in water; miscible with alcohol, acetone, and benzene. Prepared by distilling diacetone alcohol in the presence of a trace of iodine. Converted to phorone by heating in acetone with dehydrating agents such as sulphuric acid. It is a solvent for cellulose acetate and ethylcellulose.

Meso-ionic. Wilson Baker and W. D. Ollis define a compound as meso-ionic if it is a five- or six-membered heterocycle which cannot be represented satisfactorily by any one covalent or polar structure, and possesses a sextet of electrons in association with all the atoms comprising the ring. See Syndones and Nitron.

Mesomerism. A phenomenon encountered in

molecules which may be formulated (in the conventional manner) in two or more ways that have the same spatial arrangement of the atoms and nearly the same potential energy (as, for example, in the Kekulé and Dewar formulations of benzene). In such cases the actual distribution of the electrons which go to make up the bonds is a weighted mean of the distributions corresponding to the various possible formulae. There is, however, no tautomerism or oscillation between the various forms. The electron distribution is evened out to correspond with an intermediate state. This phenomenon is termed mesomerism or resonance. It leads to an increase in stability.

Mesomorphic state. See Crystals, liquid.

Meson, Mesotron. Mesons are subatomic particles with either a positive, negative, or zero charge, which can most conveniently be detected by means of photographic emulsions. Mesons found in the atmosphere at sea level have a mass 210 times that of an electron and a mean lifetime of 2×10^{-6} seconds. These are μ mesons and are found, with other mesons, in cosmic ray studies. π-Mesons, mass 276 times that of electrons, lifetime $2 \cdot 6 \times 10^{-8}$ seconds, have been found at greater heights. They are currently considered to be part of the bonding mechanism in the atomic nucleus. Other mesons (τ, θ, etc.) have been described; they are all found in cosmic radiation and result from high energy nuclear collisions.

Mesoporphyrin. See Porphyrins.

Mesotartaric acid. See Tartaric acids.

Mesothorium. Isotopes of radium and actinium produced in decay series.

Mesoxalic acid, Dihydroxymalonic acid, Keto-malonic acid. Exists in the free state as

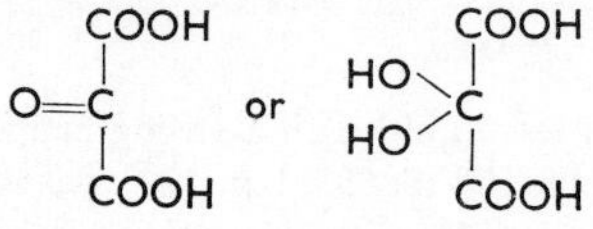

dihydroxymalonic acid, a colourless crystalline substance, m.p. 121°. Soluble in water and alcohol. Prepared by heating alloxan with barium hydroxide or dibromomalonic acid with silver oxide. The calcium and barium salts are sparingly soluble in water. Reacts as a ketone towards hydroxylamine and phenylhydrazine. Forms esters with alcohols. These may be esters of the dihydroxy or of the keto form. The keto-esters react readily with water to give the dihydroxy esters, while these lose water when heated to give the keto esters.

Mesyl. Abbreviation for the methane sulphonyl group, hence mesylate.

Meta. In the formula for meta-cresol, commonly written m-cresol, shown herewith, the CH_3 and OH groups groups are said to be in the meta position to each other. This nomenclature is used only for disubstituted derivatives of benzene. The same prefix is found in meta-phosphoric acid and metabisulphites, but in these cases it is always written in full.

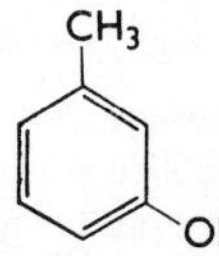

For the substance 'meta,' see Metaldehyde.

Metabolism. The term metabolism denotes all the chemical changes that occur in a living animal or plant. The metabolism of a substance refers to the changes that substance undergoes in an animal or plant. Metabolism is often subdivided into anabolism, which refers to those changes involving breakdown of foodstuffs and their rebuilding to form body tissues, and catabolism, which refers to the breakdown of tissues.

Metal. A general term characterizing certain elements, e.g. gold, silver, copper, mercury, sodium, which have a characteristic lustrous appearance, which are good conductors of heat and electricity, and enter chemical reactions as positive ions, or cations. There are certain elements, such, for example, as tellurium, which have the physical properties of a metal and the chemical properties of a non-metal. The distinction between the two groups is not sharp. The typical metallic structures are the body-centred cubic, the face-centred cubic (cubic close-packed), and the close-packed hexagonal structures. The following table of examples shows the widespread occurrence of these structures.

Structure	*Metal*
Body-centred cubic	Li, Na, K, Rb, Cs, Ba, β-Zr, V, Nb, Ta, α-Cr, Mo, α-W, α-Fe.
Face-centred cubic (cubic close-packing)	Cu, Ag, Au, Ca (below 450°), Sr, Al, β-La, β-Tl, Th, Pb, γ-Fe, β-Co, β-Ni, Rh, Pd, Ir, Pt.
Hexagonal close-packing	Be, Mg, Ca (above 450°), Y, α-La, α-Tl, Ti, α-Zr, Hf, β-Cr, Re, α-Co, α-Ni, Ru, Os.

A few metals have more complicated structures (noted under the elements concerned) whilst the structures of the semi-metals are intermediate between those of true metals and homopolar compounds. For example, germanium and grey tin have the diamond structure; arsenic, antimony, and bismuth have layer structures, and selenium and tellurium have hexagonal structures containing chains in which each atom has only two neighbours (compare the twelve equidistant neighbours in close-packed structures). Equally, certain alloys and compounds have all the properties of a metallic element.

Metalation. The removal of relatively acidic proton from a compound and replacement by a metal atom, such as lithium, sodium or potassium (see also Mercuration). In the process a metal atom is usually transferred from one compound to another: e.g. *n*-butyl-lithium reacts with anisole to give butane and *o*-lithio-anisole.

$$\text{OCH}_3 + n\text{C}_4\text{H}_9\text{Li} \longrightarrow \text{OCH}_3\text{Li} + n\text{C}_4\text{H}_{10}$$

Metaldehyde, $(C_2H_4O)_n$, where $n=4$ or 6. A solid crystalline substance, sublimes without melting at 112°-115°; stable when pure; it is readily formed when acetaldehyde is left in the presence of a catalyst at low temperatures. It is insoluble in water, sparingly soluble in alcohol, and soluble in chloroform and benzene. It is not toxic to mammals, but is very toxic to molluscs and hence used for slug control. It is usually applied in bait form. It is also used as a fuel.

Metallic conduction. This differs from electrolytic conduction in that it is not accompanied by decomposition, and is ascribed to the movements of electrons, not of ions. Drude obtained a satisfactory expression for the conductivity of a metal by assuming that the electrons could be regarded as if they were gas molecules obeying the kinetic laws. Only one or two of the electrons of each atom in a metal exist in the energy state known as the 'conduction band,' i.e. in a 'free' condition. See Mott and Jones, 'The Theory of the Properties of Metals and Alloys' (Oxford U.P. 1945).

Metallocenes. The *bis*-cyclopentadienylmetal compounds $(C_5H_5)_2M$, formed by reaction between the cyclopentadienyl anion and suitable derivatives of the transition metals, e.g. M=Fe, ferrocene: M=Co, cobaltocene: M=Ni, nickelocene. The neutral uncharged complexes of the transition elements Ti to Ni are isostructural, m.p. 174°. They vary in colour, Ti, green: Cr, red: Fe, orange: Co, purple: Os, yellow. Only those metallocenes of the iron group (Fe, Ru, Os) are diamagnetic, the others exhibiting varying degrees of paramagnetism, e.g. cobaltocene, one unpaired electron: manganese dicyclopentadienide, five unpaired electrons. Only the iron group metallocenes exhibit aromatic behaviour (see Ferrocene) and are not particularly sensitive to oxidation. Many

metallocenes may be oxidized to cations, e.g. $(C_5H_5)_2Fe^\oplus$, ferricinium: $(C_5H_5)_2Co^\oplus$, cobalticinium.

Metallography. The study of the constitution and structure of alloys and metals, including examination, by microscopical and other physical means, of the effects of various heat and mechanical treatments on the physical and chemical properties.

Metalloids. Elements which have properties intermediate between the metals and non-metals. The classification is somewhat arbitrary but is best made on the basis of the structure of the free element. Elements such as arsenic, antimony, and bismuth are metalloids. Elements which have no metallic properties and yet are solids at room temperature, e.g. boron and silicon, are sometimes included as metalloids.

Metallurgy. The science of extracting and working metals and their alloys by the application of chemical and physical principles.

Metal-metal bonds. A direct bond between two metal atoms, e.g. in $(OC)_5Mn—Mn(CO)_5$. It is generally inferred from a low magnetic susceptibility indicating electron pairing between the two metal atoms, but is ultimately only established by X-ray crystallographic studies.

Metamerism. A term now rarely used, but which has been applied particularly to the isomerism of amines, e.g. *n*-propylamine, methylethylamine, and trimethylamine are metamers. It has been used also for *functional group isomerism*. See Isomerism.

Metaproteins. The most complex of the degradation products of proteins. They are formed from proteins by the action of acids and alkalis at moderate temperatures. They are insoluble in water and neutral salt solutions, and soluble in dilute acids and alkalis.

Metastable state. See Equilibrium, metastable.

Metasystox. A trade name for demeton-methyl, $C_6H_{15}O_3PS_2$, which is a mixture of O,O-dimethyl-2-ethylthioethyl phosphorothionate, (I) and O,O-dimethyl-S-(2-ethylthioethyl) phosphorothiolate (II). The individual isomers are

(I) $\overset{S}{\underset{\uparrow}{(CH_3O)_2P}}OCH_2CH_2SC_2H_5$

(II) $\overset{O}{\underset{\uparrow}{(CH_3O)_2P}}SCH_2CH_2SC_2H_5$

known as demeton-S-methyl and demeton-O-methyl. (II) is more toxic than (I) to mammals but has similar physical properties. The individual boiling points are very close: (I), 74°/0·15 mm and (II) 89°/0·15 mm, and separation by fractionation is therefore difficult. In addition, a certain amount of isomerization may occur on heating.

Demeton-methyl is prepared from 2-hydroxyethyl ethyl sulphide and dimethyl phosphorochloridothionate in the presence of an acid acceptor, and is an oil, insoluble in water, but soluble in organic solvents. It persists in the plant and remains effective for at least two weeks against sucking insects such as aphids, red spider, mangold fly and chrysanthemum leaf miner. Because of this persistence, metasystox must not be used on food crops within three weeks of harvesting. Certain crops such as *Brassicas* and blackcurrants need a longer interval. Animals should be kept from sprayed areas for at least two weeks. Bees, ladybirds and predators which do not suck the sap are unharmed unless hit by the spray.

Metathetical reaction. Typically a reaction between two salts in which anions are exchanged. The driving force is generally the insolubility of one of the products in the reaction medium. An example of this type of reaction is

$$2AgNO_3 + BaCl_2 \xrightarrow{H_2O} 2AgCl + Ba(NO_3)_2$$

Methacrylic acid, α**-Methylacrylic acid.** Crystallizes in colourless prisms, d^{20} 1·0153, m.p. 15°-16°, b.p. 160·5°; 72°/ 14 mm. Soluble in water, alcohol, and ether. Manufactured by treating acetone cyanohydrin with dilute sulphuric acid. It is reduced by hydrogen to isobutyric acid, and reacts with bromine to give 1,2-dibromoisobutyric acid. Polymerizes when distilled or when heated with hydrochloric acid under pressure. Used in the preparation of synthetic resins; the methyl and ethyl esters form important glass-like polymers.

$$CH_2{=}C{-}COOH$$
$$|$$
$$CH_3$$

Methadone, Amidone, $C_{21}H_{27}NO$. Prepared

from 2-chloro-1-dimethylaminopropane by treating with diphenylmethyl cyanide in the presence of sodamide, and converting to a mixture of ketones from which the methadone is separated. It is converted to its hydrochloride, which is a colourless crystalline powder, soluble in 12 parts of water and in alcohol, m.p. 235°. It is a powerful analgesic, which also depresses the cough centre. It is a much less addictive drug than morphine, and is generally administered for the relief of pain.

Methaemoglobin. A compound of haematin and globin, differing from haemoglobin in that the iron in the molecule is in the tripositive state. It is formed from haemoglobin by the action of weak oxidizing agents such as potassium ferricyanide, nitrites, or methylene blue. On reduction with sodium hydrosulphite it gives haemoglobin.

Methane, Marsh gas, CH_4. A colourless, odourless gas, m.p. $-184°$, b.p. $-164°$. Liquid at $-11°$ under pressure. It is the chief constituent of the natural gas emitted from the earth in various parts of the world. Also formed by the decay of vegetable matter in marshy places; it occurs in coal mines, where explosive mixtures of it with air are known as firedamp, and in coal gas. It is manufactured by passing a mixture of one volume of carbon monoxide and three volumes of hydrogen at atmospheric pressure over a nickel catalyst heated to 230°-250°. The gas mixture is obtained from water gas. Methane is chemically fairly inert but reacts explosively with chlorine at ordinary temperatures; at low temperatures methyl chloride is formed. Used in the manufacture of methyl and methylene chlorides.

Methane base, Bis(p-dimethylaminophenyl)-methane, $C_{17}H_{22}N_2$. Forms colourless leaflets,

$$(CH_3)_2N{-}\bigcirc{-}CH_2{-}\bigcirc{-}N(CH_3)_2$$

m.p. 90°-91°, b.p. 390°. Insoluble in water and cold alcohol, soluble in hot alcohol and in ether and benzene. It is not volatile in steam. It forms salts with mineral acids.

It is prepared by adding a slight excess of formaldehyde to an aqueous solution of dimethylaniline hydrochloride at 85°.

When heated with sulphur the $-CH_2$-group is changed into a $-C{:}S$-group; treatment with ammonia then replaces the sulphur by an imino-group (see Auramine). Oxidation with lead peroxide gives Michler's hydrol. Both these reactions are used commercially.

Methanesulphonic acid, CH_3SO_2OH. M.p. 20°, b.p. 167° at 10 mm., obtained by oxidation of dimethyl disulphide or by the catalytic reaction between methane and sulphur trioxide. Readily soluble in water, but almost insoluble in hydrocarbon solvents.

It is used as a catalyst in esterification, dehydration, polymerisation and alkylation reactions. Converted by, e.g., thionyl chloride, to methanesulphonyl chloride (mesyl chloride) which is useful for characterizing alcohols, amines, etc. as methanesulphonyl (mesyl) derivatives.

376

Methanol. See Methyl alcohol.

Methionic acid, Methylenedisulphonic acid, $CH_4O_6S_2$. A colourless, crystalline solid which readily absorbs water vapour; decomposes on distillation. Soluble in water and alcohol. The potassium salt is prepared by heating methylene chloride with an aqueous solution of potassium sulphite under pressure at 150°-160°. The free acid is obtained by decomposing the sparingly soluble barium salt with sulphuric acid. The aryl esters are very stable, but the alkyl esters decompose on heating to give ethers. Has been used to prepare the higher ethers by heating a solution of the acid in the appropriate alcohol. Resembles malonic acid in some of its reactions.

Methionine, 1-Amino-3-methylmercaptobutyric acid, $C_5H_{11}NO_2S$. Crystallizes in hexagonal

$$CH_3 \cdot CH_2 \cdot CH_2 \cdot CH \cdot CO_2H$$
$$| $$
$$NH_2$$

plates, m.p. 283° with decomposition. Soluble in water and alcohol. The naturally occurring substance is laevorotatory, $[\alpha]_D^{25}$ $-6\cdot87°$. Methionine is one of the natural sulphur-containing amino-acids, and is present in small quantities in the hydrolysis products of proteins. It is an essential constituent of the food of mammals and is particularly important in that it and choline are the only compounds in the diet known to take part in methylating reactions.

Methoin, $C_{12}H_{14}N_2O_2$. Colourless plates,

m.p. 137°, insoluble in water, soluble in 13 parts of alcohol, prepared by methylating 5-ethyl-5-phenylhydantoin.

Methoin is an anticonvulsant, acting on the cerebral motor cortex, and used for the treatment of grand mal. It is less effective for petit mal. It is generally given orally.

Methoxone. A trade name for MCPA (q.v.).

Methoxy-. A prefix used in organic chemistry to denote that the substance contains a methoxyl, or CH_3O—, group.

Methyl-. The name given to the group CH_3—, also written Me—. Methyl radicals can be prepared in the free state by the thermal dissociation of many organic compounds, including lead tetramethyl, or by the photolysis of acetone. It is stable at 900°.

6-Methylacetopyranone. See Dehydracetic acid.

Methyl acrylate, $C_4H_6O_2$, $CH_2:CHCOOCH_3$. A colourless liquid, d^{25} 0·952, b.p. 80°, insoluble in water, soluble in organic solvents. It is manufactured (i) by treating ethylene chlorohydrin with sodium cyanide and heating the β-hydroxy-propionitrile so formed with methanol and sulphuric acid, (ii) by the pyrolysis of the acetate derived from methyl lactate, or (iii) by the reaction of acetylene, carbon monoxide, and methanol in the presence of nickel carbonyl. It readily polymerizes to give colourless rubber-like polymethyl acrylate. See Acrylic resins.

Methylal, Methylformal, $C_3H_8O_2$. A colourless liquid with a pleasant odour, d^{15} 0·872, b.p. 42·3°. Soluble in three parts of water; miscible with most organic solvents. It occurs in commercial formalin, and is made by heating polyoxymethylene with methyl alcohol in the presence of ferric chloride, by treating methylene chloride with sodium methoxide, or by treating a mixture of methyl alcohol and formaldehyde with calcium chloride and a little hydrochloric acid. It is a good solvent, and is also used to replace formaldehyde in many reactions.

Methyl alcohol, Methanol, Wood spirit, Wood naphtha, CH_3OH. A colourless liquid with a spirituous odour; it is poisonous, small doses causing blindness, d^{20} 0·7910, b.p. 64·5°. Miscible with water and most organic solvents. Discovered by Boyle in 1661 among the products of the dry distillation of wood. It occurs as esters in various plant oils, such as wintergreen. It is manufactured by reacting together hydrogen and carbon monoxide, the two gases being passed over a catalyst at 200-350 atm. and 300°-400°; carbon dioxide is sometimes used instead of carbon monoxide. Some methyl alcohol is also produced by the partial oxidation of hydrocarbons. It is readily oxidized by air in presence of nickel or platinum to formaldehyde. Reacts with sulphuric acid to give methyl hydrogen sulphate, dimethyl sulphate, and dimethyl ether. Forms methyl chloride with hydrogen chloride in the presence of zinc chloride. When heated with soda-lime it is converted to sodium formate and hydrogen. Reacts with sodium to give sodium methoxide. It is a good solvent for many inorganic salts and organic compounds. May be detected by oxidation to formaldehyde. Used in the manufacture of formaldehyde, methyl chloride, and many other organic compounds, also as a solvent and as a denaturant for ethyl alcohol.

Methylamines. The methylamines may be regarded as compounds of ammonia in which one, two or three of the hydrogen atoms have been replaced by methyl groups. They are manufactured by the vapour phase reaction of methanol and ammonia at 350°-450° under pressure over an alumina catalyst. The product consists of a mixture of all three compounds; the proportion of the two higher amines may be increased, if so desired, by recycling the mono-methylamine or reducing the ammonia/methanol ratio; the proportion of monomethyl-amine may be increased by diluting the reaction mixture with water or trimethylamine.

Monomethylamine, methylamine, CH_5N, CH_3NH_2, is a colourless, inflammable gas with an ammoniacal odour, very soluble in water, m.p. $-92.5°$, b.p. $-6.6°$. It occurs naturally in some plants, in herring brine and in crude bone oil. It may be prepared in the laboratory by heating formalin with ammonium chloride, when it is obtained as the crystalline hydro-chloride. Monomethylamine is largely employed in the manufacture of herbicides, fungicides and surface-active agents.

Dimethylamine, C_2H_7N, is a colourless, inflammable liquid with an ammoniacal odour, miscible with water, m.p. $-96.0°$, b.p. $7.4°$, d_4^0 0.680. It occurs natu-rally in herring brine. It is prepared in the lab-oratory by treating nitrosodimethylaniline with a hot solution of sodium hydroxide. Dimethyl-amine is largely used in the manufacture of other chemicals. These include the solvents, dimethylacetamide and dimethylformamide, the rocket propellant unsymmetrical dimethyl-hydrazine, surface-active agents, herbicides, fungicides, and rubber accelerators.

Trimethylamine, C_3H_9N is a colourless liquid having a strong fishy odour, mis-cible with water, m.p. $-124°$, b.p. 3.5, d^{-5} 0.662. It occurs naturally in plants, herring brine, bone oil and urine. It reacts with hydrogen peroxide to give trimethylamine oxide and with ethylene oxide to give choline; its commercial importance stems chiefly from this latter reaction.

The solutions of all the methylamines in water are alkaline, but the alkalinity decreases with the number of methyl groups.

Methylated spirit. Ethyl alcohol rendered un-drinkable by means of methyl alcohol and other substances. Four varieties are manufactured, but only one is sold to the general public. *Mineralized methylated spirit* is made by adding 90 volumes of ethyl alcohol (95% alcohol) 9.5 volumes of wood naphtha and 0.5 volume of pyridine. To every 100 gallons of this mixture is added 3/8th gallon mineral naphtha and 1/40th oz. methyl violet. This is the ordinary methylated spirit of commerce. *Industrial methylated spirit* consists of 95 volumes of ethyl alcohol (95%

alcohol) and 5 volumes of wood naphtha. This is used in industries requiring a pure alcohol. *Industrial methylated spirit (pyridinized)* has a further addition of 0.5 volume of crude pyridine, and is used in spirit varnishes and lacquers. *Power methylated spirit* is absolute ethyl alcohol, 92 volumes; benzol, 5 volumes; crude pyridine, 0.5 volume, and crude naphtha, 2.5 volumes. It is coloured by the addition of 1/40 oz. Spirit Red III to every 100 gallons, and is used only in alcohol blend fuels for internal combustion engines.

Methylation. The name given to a process by which a methyl group is added to a compound. In aliphatic chemistry this involves substitution of the hydrogen atom of a hydroxyl, amino, or imino group, and produces an ether or a secondary or tertiary amine respectively. In aromatic chemistry it may also mean the substitution of one of the hydrogen atoms of the ring by the methyl group; this is carried out by the Friedel-Crafts reaction. Amines and amino-compounds may be methylated by heating with formaldehyde in formic acid solution, or by heating with methyl iodide or dimethyl sulphate. For methylation of hydroxy-compounds see Ethers.

Methyl cellosolve. See Ethylene glycol mono-methyl ether.

Methyl chloride, Monochloromethane, CH_3Cl. A colourless gas with a pleasant ethereal odour; it burns with a white flame, b.p. $-24°$. Soluble in water; very soluble in alcohol. Manufactured principally by the reaction of methyl alcohol and hydrogen chloride in the presence of a catalyst, either in the vapour or liquid phase. The chlorination of methane is also used, but to a lesser extent. Reacts with chlorine to give methylene chloride, chloro-form, and carbon tetrachloride. Forms methyl alcohol when treated with milk of lime under pressure. The chief use of methyl chloride is in the production of silicones. It is also used in the manufacture of lead tetramethyl (anti-knock additive), butyl rubber and methyl cellulose.

Methylcholanthrene, $C_{21}H_{16}$. A powerful car-cinogenic substance, crystallizing in straw-

yellow crystals from benzene, m.p. 177°. It has been prepared from cholic acid, and has been synthesized.

Methylcyclohexanol, Methylhexalin, Hexa-hydrocresol, $C_7H_{14}O$. The commercial product is a mixture of the three isomers:

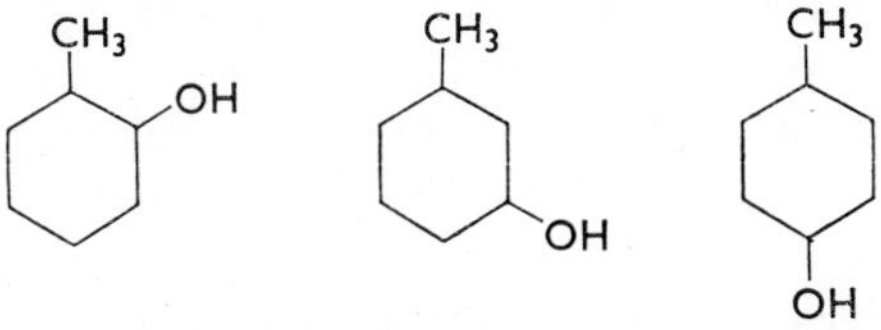

It is a colourless, rather viscous liquid, with a penetrating odour, d^{15} 0·925, boiling range 165°-180°. Soluble to 3% in water; miscible with hydrocarbon solvents. Manufactured by reduction of the cresols from coal tar with hydrogen in the presence of nickel catalysts. Oxidized to methylcyclohexanones. Used as a solvent for fats, oils, gums, and waxes, and in nitrocellulose lacquers. Soaps containing it are important detergents. The esters are used as plasticizers in lacquers. The individual methylcyclohexanols are prepared in a similar manner from the pure cresol, and exist in *cis* and *trans* modifications. They are volatile in steam.

Methylcyclohexanone, $C_7H_{12}O$. The commercial product is a mixture of the three isomers:

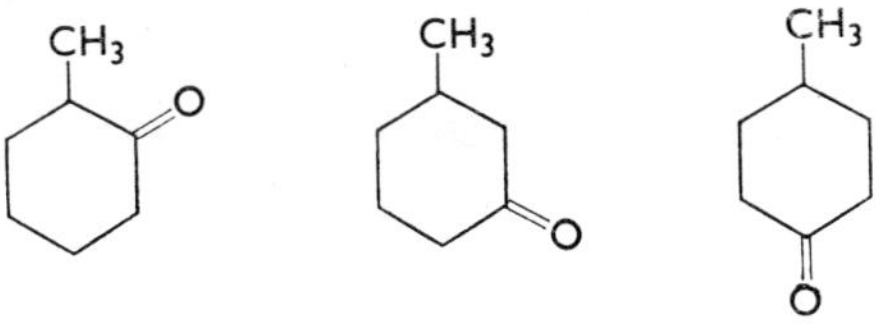

Methylcyclohexanone is a colourless liquid with a penetrating but not unpleasant odour, d^{15} 0·925, boiling range 164°-172°. Soluble to 3% in water; miscible with alcohol and hydrocarbon solvents. Manufactured by passing the vapour of commercial methylcyclohexanol over a heated copper catalyst. Used as solvent for resins and gums in the manufacture of lacquers. The individual methylcyclohexanones may be obtained in a similar manner from the three methylcyclohexanols.

Methyldemeton. The common American name for Metasystox (*q.v.*).

Methyldopa, Aldomet, $C_{10}H_{13}NO_4 \cdot 1\frac{1}{2}H_2O$. The sesquihydrate of $(-)$-β-(3,4-dihydroxyphenyl)-α-methylalanine. A white to yellowish-

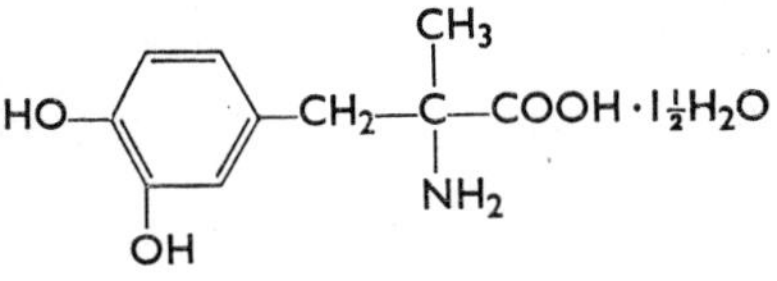

white fine powder which may contain friable lumps. It is soluble at 20° in 100 parts of water, in 400 parts of alcohol and in 0·5 part of dilute hydrochloric acid; practically insoluble in ether.

It is given orally in the treatment of hypertension, as it interferes with the synthesis of noradrenaline.

Methylene. The divalent group $=CH_2$. It is prepared in the free state by the thermal or photochemical dissociation of keten or diazomethane, and is extremely reactive. See Carbenes.

Methylene blue (Basic Blue 8). This is an

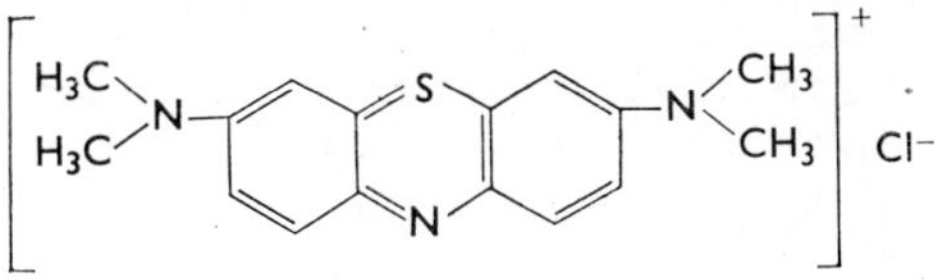

important dyestuff prepared by boiling indamine with dilute acid or a solution of zinc chloride. It is used in dyeing fast fibres and in calico-printing and is of considerable value as a staining material in bacteriological work and microscopy.

In pharmacy it is known as methylthionine chloride and is used for its mildly antiseptic properties.

Methylene chloride. See Dichloromethane.

24-Methylenecholesterol, $C_{28}H_{46}O$. A characteristic sterol of marine invertebrates and also of

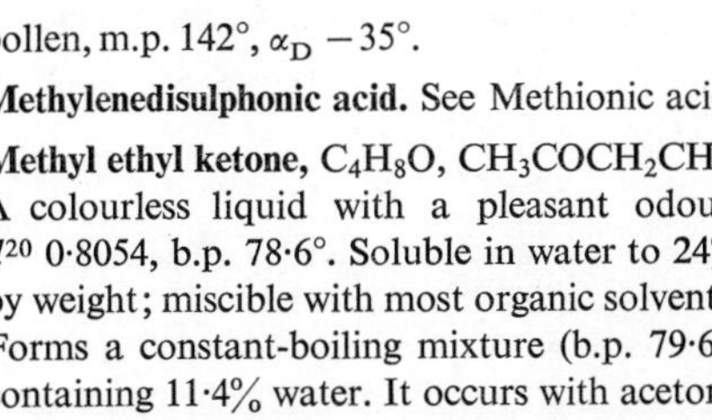

pollen, m.p. 142°, α_D $-35°$.

Methylenedisulphonic acid. See Methionic acid.

Methyl ethyl ketone, C_4H_8O, $CH_3COCH_2CH_3$. A colourless liquid with a pleasant odour, d^{20} 0·8054, b.p. 78·6°. Soluble in water to 24% by weight; miscible with most organic solvents. Forms a constant-boiling mixture (b.p. 79·6°) containing 11·4% water. It occurs with acetone in the products of the destructive distillation of wood. Manufactured by the liquid or vapour phase dehydrogenation of secondary butyl alcohol over a catalyst. Largely used as a solvent, particularly for vinyl and acrylic resins, and for nitrocellulose and cellulose acetate, also for the dewaxing of lubricating oils.

Methylglyoxal, Pyruvic aldehyde, $C_3H_4O_2$, $CH_3 \cdot CO \cdot CHO$. A yellow liquid with a pungent odour. It begins to boil at 72°, and gives a yellow-green vapour. The liquid at room temperatures is dimeric and readily polymerizes to a glassy solid. It has been obtained by the fermentation of sugar by yeast, and may be prepared by the oxidation of acetone by selenium dioxide.

Methylhexalin. See Methylcyclohexanol.

Methyl iodide, Monoiodomethane, CH_3I. A colourless liquid with characteristic odour, b.p. $42 \cdot 8°$, d^{15} $2 \cdot 268$. Insoluble in water; miscible with alcohol and ether. Prepared by heating methyl alcohol and iodine with red phosphorus. Reacts with the hydrogen atoms of hydroxyl and amino-groups to give methoxy- and methyl-amino-compounds and hence used in organic chemistry for methylating these compounds.

Methyl isobutyl ketone, hexone, $C_6H_{12}O$. A colourless liquid,

$$CH_3 \cdot CO \cdot CH_2 \cdot \overset{\displaystyle CH_3}{\underset{\displaystyle CH_3}{CH}}$$

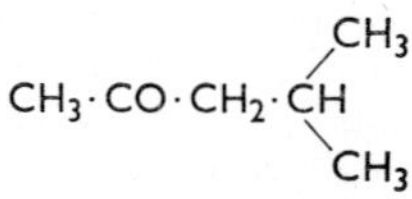

ourless liquid, b.p. $117°$, d_4^{20} $0 \cdot 7978$, n_D^{20} $1 \cdot 3956$. It is manufactured by hydrogenation of mesityl oxide, and is used as a solvent for nitrocellulose and other substances.

Methyl methacrylate, methyl α-methylacrylate,

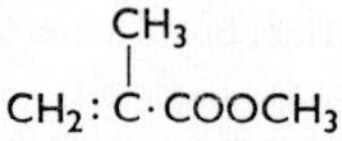

$$\underset{\displaystyle CH_2 : C \cdot COOCH_3}{\overset{\displaystyle CH_3}{|}}$$

$C_5H_8O_2$. A colourless liquid, d^{22} $0 \cdot 945$, b.p. $100 \cdot 3°$. Insoluble in water; miscible with organic solvents. Manufactured by heating acetone cyanohydrin with methyl alcohol and sulphuric acid. It is usually supplied containing dissolved polymerization inhibitor, on removal of which it is readily polymerized to a glass-like polymer. See Acrylic resins.

Methyl orange, 4-dimethylamino-4′-azo-benzene sodium sulphonate, $C_{14}H_{14}N_3NaO_3S$.

Orange crystals prepared by the action of dimethylaniline on diazotized sodium sulphanilate. It is used as an indicator in $0 \cdot 01\%$ aqueous solution, the pH range being $3 \cdot 1$ (red) to $4 \cdot 4$ (yellow).

Methyl oxalate, Dimethyl oxalate, $C_4H_6O_4$. Crystallizes in colourless plates, m.p. $54°$, b.p. $163 \cdot 5°$. Soluble in alcohol; decomposed by hot water. Prepared by boiling anhydrous oxalic acid with absolute methyl alcohol; the ester crystallizes on cooling. Reacts with ammonia to give methyl oxamate and oxamide. When heated with a solution of sodium hydroxide, it is decomposed to oxalic acid and methyl

$$\underset{\displaystyle COOCH_3}{\overset{\displaystyle COOCH_3}{|}}$$

alcohol; this reaction is used to obtain pure methyl alcohol.

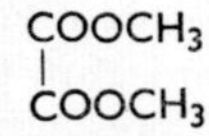

Methyl red, o-carboxybenzeneazodimethyl-aniline, $C_{15}H_{15}N_3O_2$, m.p. $181°$-$182°$. An

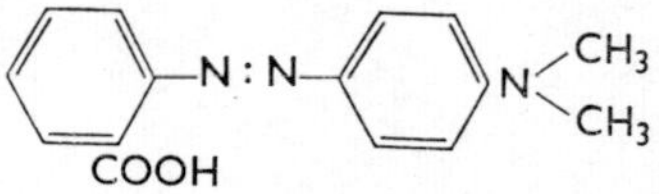

indicator, prepared by the action of dimethyl-aniline on diazotized anthranilic acid. It is used in $0 \cdot 02\%$ solution in 60% alcohol and its pH range is $4 \cdot 4$ (red) to $6 \cdot 0$ (yellow).

Methyl salicylate, $C_8H_8O_3$. A colourless liquid, m.p. $-8 \cdot 6°$, b.p. $223°$, d $1 \cdot 180$-$1 \cdot 185$. It exists in an almost pure state in the essential oils of wintergreen and sweet birch, but is mostly prepared by esterifying salicylic acid. It

has a pleasant characteristic odour and is readily absorbed through the skin. It is used in perfumery and as a flavouring agent in food, drinks, dentifrices, and cosmetics. It has the general medicinal properties of the salicylates, and is applied either alone or with other volatile analgesics for easing the pain of lumbago, rheumatism, and sciatica.

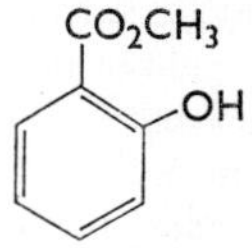

Methylsuccinic acid. See Pyrotartaric acid.

Methylsulphonal. See Sulphonal.

Methyl violet (Basic Violet 1). A violet dye obtained by the oxidation of dimethylaniline with cupric chloride. It consists of a mixture of the hydrochlorides of tetra-, penta-, and hexamethyl-p-rosanilines. The formula given is of the pentamethyl compound:

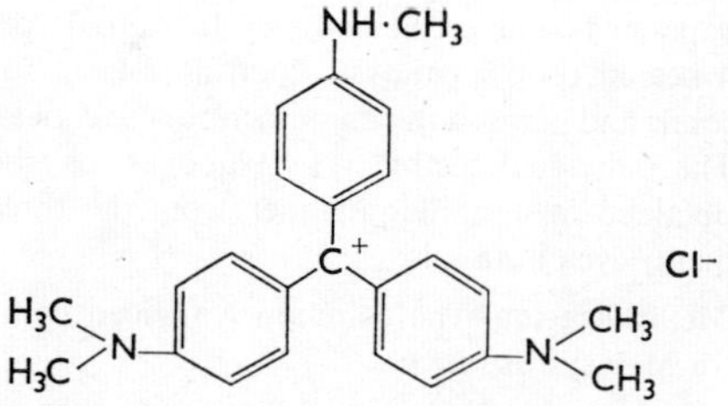

It is used in dyeing jute, for colouring methylated spirits, as a bacteriological stain, and as an indicator, the pH range being $0 \cdot 1$ (yellow) to $3 \cdot 2$ (violet).

Gentian violet is the name that used to be given to a mixture of the hydrochlorides of penta- and hexamethyl-p-rosanilines. The name is now used only in pharmacy, where it usually refers to methyl violet.

Crystal violet is the hydrochloride of hexamethyl-p-rosaniline. It has a powerful antiseptic action on gram-positive organisms and is used medicinally in the treatment of burns and infectious diseases.

Metidium chloride. See Phenanthridine derivatives.

Metol. See Aminophenol developers.

Mevalonic acid, $C_6H_{12}O_4$. D-Mevalonic acid, the 3(R) form of 3,5-dihydroxy-3-methylpentanoic acid, was found to replace acetate as an essential growth factor for *Lactobacillus acidophilus*, and was isolated as the δ-lactone from distillers' dried solubles. The lactone is a hygroscopic crystalline solid, m.p. 28°, very soluble in water and in polar organic solvents. Mevalonic acid benzhydrylamide has m.p. 96°-97°, $[\alpha]_D$ −2° in ethanol.

D-Mevalonic acid is the fundamental intermediate in the biosynthesis of the terpenoids and steroids, together classed as polyisoprenoids. The biogenetic isoprene unit is isopentenyl pyrophosphate which arises by enzymic decarboxylation-dehydration of mevalonic acid pyrophosphate. D-Mevalonic acid is almost quantitatively incorporated into cholesterol synthesized by rat liver homogenates.

Meyer, Julius Lothar (1830-1895). Born at Varel, Oldenburg, Meyer studied medicine at Zürich and Würzburg. After a period spent in physiological research he was appointed, in 1859, a *privatdozent* for physics and chemistry at Breslau, where he published, in 1864, his 'Modern Theories of Chemistry.' Later he became lecturer at the Forestry Academy at Neustadt-Eberswalde, and in 1868 professor of chemistry at the Polytechnic at Karlsruhe. In 1876 Meyer received a similar appointment at Tübingen. From an investigation of the atomic volumes of the elements he formulated the Periodic Law at the same time as Mendeléeff. See Mem. Lect., *J. Chem. Soc.*, 1896, 1403.

Meyer, Victor. Victor Meyer was born in Berlin in 1848 and studied chemistry at Heidelberg in 1865 and afterwards in Baeyer's laboratory in Berlin, then in Stuttgart. He was director of the chemical laboratory at the Zürich Polytechnic from 1872 to 1885 and became professor at Göttingen in 1885 and at Heidelberg in 1889. He studied the chemistry of the aromatic compounds, discovered oximes, and did important work on vapour densities at high temperatures. He coined the term 'stereoisomerism' and worked on that subject. He died in 1897. See 'Chem. Soc. Memorial Lectures, 1893-1900.'

Meyerhof, Otto (1884-1951). One of the greatest of biochemists, Meyerhof was born in Hanover,

and worked at Kiel, Berlin, and Heidelberg. He first studied medicine, but later turned to biochemistry, and carried out some of the fundamental work on the chemistry of muscular contraction. In 1938 he was forced to leave Germany and settled in Pennsylvania. He shared the Nobel Prize for Physiology in 1922. See *Nature*, 1951, **168**, 895.

Mf temperature. See Martempering.

Mica. A group of minerals possessing an excellent basal cleavage enabling the crystals to be split into very thin flexible plates possessing high dielectric strength and low thermal conductivity. Extensively used as an electrical insulator. Ground mica is used to impart lustre to wallpaper and paints, and as a filler. The most important micas are muscovite (potash mica), ideally $KAl_2(AlSi_3)O_{10} \cdot (OH,F)_2$ and phlogopite (amber or magnesia mica), ideally $KMg_3(AlSi_3)O_{10} \cdot (OH,F)_2$. U.S.A., India, U.S.S.R., and Canada supply the bulk of the mica used industrially.

Micelle. Formerly the word was used to mean any type of colloidal particle. Now it is used mainly for aggregation colloids, e.g. soaps and dyes, a micelle being a submicroscopic aggregate of molecules. To a lesser extent micelle is still used also for polyelectrolyte particles. The structure of soap micelles is still controversial. Below a certain concentration soap solutions are not associated; above it they consist almost entirely of micelles; this is called the critical micelle concentration (c.m.c.).

Michaelis constant. An experimentally determined parameter inversely indicative of the affinity of an enzyme for its substrate. For a constant enzyme concentration, the Michaelis constant is that substrate concentration at which the rate of reaction is half its maximum rate. In general, the Michaelis constant is equivalent to the dissociation constant of the enzyme-substrate complex.

Michael reaction. A name originally applied in a restricted sense to the base catalysed addition of active methylene compounds (e.g. malonic ester) to activated unsaturated systems (e.g. $\alpha:\beta$ unsaturated ketones). It is now used in a broader sense to define the conjugate additions of nucleophiles across double bonds conjugated with electron-withdrawing groups such as carbonyl (in $CH_3—CH=CH—COCH_3$), nitrile ($CH_2=CH—CN$) (see Cyanoethylation), nitro, etc.

Michler's hydrol, Bis(p-dimethylaminophenyl)-carbinol, $C_{17}H_{22}N_2O$. Forms colourless prismatic crystals, m.p. 96°. Soluble in alcohol, benzene, and ether. The hydrochloride is soluble in alcohol, but is hydrolysed by water.

It is prepared technically by the oxidation of methane base by lead peroxide and glacial acetic

$(CH_3)_2N$ —⬡— $\overset{OH}{\underset{H}{C}}$ —⬡— $N(CH_3)_2$

acid. It can also be obtained by reduction of Michler's ketone with sodium amalgam in alcohol.

It is used for the preparation of triphenylmethane dyestuffs by condensation with bases, phenols, and many other aromatic compounds.

Michler's ketone, Bis(p-dimethylaminophenyl)-ketone, $C_{17}H_{20}N_2O$. Forms glistening leaflets,

$(CH_3)_2N$ —⬡— $\overset{O}{\overset{\|}{C}}$ —⬡— $N(CH_3)_2$

m.p. 172°. Soluble in alcohol and ether. It is basic and forms salts with mineral acids and is prepared by the action of phosgene on dimethylaniline at 100°.

Reduction with sodium amalgam in alcohol gives Michler's hydrol. Treatment with phosphorus trichloride gives the dichloride. The dichloride is used commercially for the preparation of triphenylmethane dyes by condensation with bases, phenols, and many other aromatic compounds.

Microbalance. A balance capable of detecting and measuring changes in weight of the order of 10^{-6} g or less is termed a microbalance. For ordinary quantitative analysis on the small scale, the microbalances in use generally weigh to about 10 g, and are sensitive to a change of 10^{-6} g. For special purposes balances have been constructed which are sensitive to as little as 10^{-11} g, but the maximum load is correspondingly smaller than that of the ordinary analytical microbalance. Currently, electro-microbalances are coming into use where the displacement is nullified electrically. Such balances are easier to operate and much more robust than conventional microbalances.

Microcosmic salt (Sodium ammonium hydrogen phosphate), $NaNH_4HPO_4$, $4H_2O$. A solid forming colourless monoclinic crystals possessing a saline, ammoniacal taste. Prepared by the action of disodium phosphate on ammonium chloride, or of diammonium phosphate on sodium chloride. The salt is used in qualitative analysis, as it forms 'beads' of characteristic colour on fusion with salts of certain metals.

Micron (μ). One micron $= 10^{-4}$ cm. This term was also proposed by Zsigmondy to describe dispersed particles of such a size as to be visible in the ordinary microscope. See Submicron, Amicron.

Microsomes. A term originally designating a fraction of cell particles which sedimented in the ultracentrifuge between 50,000 and 100,000 **g**. Microsomes are too small to be seen in an optical microscope. Since they are heterogeneous, the term 'microsomal fraction' is now preferred; it includes lysosomes, ribosomes, and possibly other constituent bodies.

Microwave spectroscopy. Microwaves are electromagnetic waves with wavelengths ranging from 1 mm to about 1 m. The microwave beam produced by an oscillator using a Klystron electronic valve is passed through the substance in the gas phase and then picked up in a crystal receiver, and amplified. The resolution of this apparatus is vastly superior to the best infra-red instrument and wavelengths are measured to seven figures. The transitions measured are between levels very close in energy, and information is derived about pure rotational spectra.

Midgley, Thomas (1889-1944). Midgley was born at Beaver Falls, Pennsylvania. He carried out prolonged experiments on detonation in internal-combustion engines, which culminated in the development of lead tetraethyl as an antiknock agent; during this research he invented the Midgley indicator. He also discovered the use of certain organic chlorofluorides as safe refrigerants, and for his work in these two fields was awarded the Nichols Medal in 1923 and the Perkin Medal in 1937. See *Chem. and Eng. News*, 1944, **22**, 1896.

Milk of lime. A suspension of calcium hydroxide in water.

Miller, William Allen (1817-1870). Miller was born at Ipswich, Suffolk. While studying medicine at King's College, London, he came into contact with Daniell and in 1840 spent a short time in Liebig's laboratory at Giessen. In the same year he became a demonstrator in the laboratory at King's College, in 1841 became assistant to Daniell, and in 1845 succeeded him as professor of chemistry. His chief work dealt with spectrum analysis. He was twice President of the Chemical Society (1855-1857, 1865-1867), of which he was an original member.

Millikan, Robert Andrews (1868-1953). Born at Illinois, U.S.A., Millikan was educated at Oberlin College, Columbia University, and the Universities of Berlin and Göttingen. He was appointed professor of physics at the University of Chicago (1910), and at the California Institute of Technology, Pasadena (1921). His brilliant researches on atomic physics, including the determination of the value of *e* (the unit electric charge), brought him much recognition;

he was awarded the Nobel Prize for Physics in 1923.

Millimicron (mμ). One millimicron = 10^{-7} cm.

Millon's base. See Mercurammine compounds.

Mills, William Hobson (1873-1959). Mills studied at Cambridge and Tübingen. From 1902 to 1912 he was Head of the Chemical Department at the Northern Polytechnic Institute, then returned to Cambridge as Fellow and Lecturer of Jesus College and Reader in Stereochemistry in the University. He worked on the cyanine compounds, optical activity, molecular dissymmetry, and stereochemistry. See *Proc. Chem. Soc.*, 1960, 371.

Mineral colours. These are all coloured metallic compounds precipitated within the fibre by special processes. They were formerly widely used on vegetable fibres on account of their high fastness and low cost of application. Included are Prussian blue, chrome yellow (lead chromate), manganese bronze, and iron buff. Many mineral pigments are extensively used for colouring paints, papers, linoleum, lacquers, etc.

Mineral dressing, ore dressing. Concentration of the valuable constituents of a mineral by the application of purely physical processes. Techniques in use include dense media separation, froth flotation, electrostatic and magnetic separation, and jigging.

Minium. Another name for red lead. See Lead oxides, Vermilion.

Minol. See Aluminized high explosives.

Mischmetal. An alloy of impure cerium, containing lanthanum and other rare-earth elements, with 35% of iron. The alloy is prepared by the electrolysis of the fused chlorides of cerium, lanthanum, and other rare-earth metals. This alloy is pyrophoric, i.e. when small particles of the alloy are abraded from the massive metal, by, e.g., rubbing with steel, they oxidize in the air with incandescence. This effect is used in automatic lighters, in which the incandescent particles serve to ignite the vapour of alcohol, petrol, or coal gas. The alloy has also been used in defining the paths of shells and bullets. In this case the friction of the air raises the alloy to incandescence.

Miscibility. A term denoting the extent of mixing. Gases will mix in all proportions and are said to be completely miscible. Two liquids may be completely miscible (or miscible in all proportions) as, e.g. alcohol and water, or only partially miscible, i.e. there is a limit to the extent to which each will dissolve the other, e.g. aniline and water, or almost completely immiscible, e.g. mercury and water. The miscibility

of liquids depends upon the chemical and physical similarity between the liquids, and in particular on their internal pressures. Liquids, with approximately equal internal pressures, are miscible in all proportions.

Mispickel, arsenopyrite, FeAsS. Whitish with a metallic lustre, hardness $5\frac{1}{2}$, sp.gr. 6·0, orthorhombic. A common mineral often associated with tin and tungsten ores and base metal sulphides. It is the main source of arsenic, which is a by-product from the treatment of these ores.

Mitscherlich, Eilhardt (1794-1863). Born at Neuende, Oldenburg, Mitscherlich studied philology at Heidelberg, but later took up chemistry at Göttingen, Berlin, and Stockholm. In 1825 he was appointed professor of chemistry at Berlin. His researches cover a wide field in crystallography, organic, and inorganic chemistry. See *J. Roy. Inst. Chem.*, 1963, **87**, 265.

Mitscherlich's law of isomorphism. In 1819 Mitscherlich put forward the law which states that substances which crystallize in isomorphous forms (i.e. which have identical crystalline forms, and form mixed crystals) have similar chemical compositions. Thus potassium selenate is isomorphous with potassium sulphate, and their formulae are K_2SeO_4 and K_2SO_4 respectively. See also Isomorphism.

Mittasch, Alwyn (1869-1953). A pupil of Ostwald, Mittasch was originally a school teacher, but became attracted to industry. In 1918 he founded the Research Laboratory of the I.G. Farbenindustrie at Oppau, continuing Director until 1933. His private researches were mainly upon problems associated with catalysis, and the metal carbonyls.

Mixed crystals. It often happens that when a solution, containing two substances which crystallize in similar forms, is concentrated, the crystals which deposit are homogeneous, but consist of a mixture of the two substances. Such crystals were formerly called mixed crystals, but are better termed solid solutions.

Mixed metal oxides. Compounds which are formally derived from oxides but contain two or more metal species in an arbitrary ratio. Generally formed by heating mixtures of the appropriate oxy-salts. The structures are determined largely by close packing of the oxide ions and the metal atoms occupy holes between the oxygen atoms. Many compounds formerly thought of as salts—e.g. niobates—are mixed metal oxides.

Mobility, ionic. It was shown by Kohlrausch that the equivalent conductivity at infinite dilution, Λ_∞, of a salt could be expressed as the sum of two independent terms, one due to the cation, the other due to the anion, e.g.

$$\Lambda_\infty = \lambda_+ + \lambda_-$$

λ_+ and λ_- are the equivalent ionic conductivities of the cation and anion. They are not to be confused with the absolute velocities of migration, the ionic mobilities (u), which are the mean velocities of the ions in cm per sec for a potential gradient of 1 V per cm. and which are described by the expressions

$$u_+ = \frac{\lambda_+}{F}; \quad u_- = \frac{\lambda_-}{F}$$

where F is the Faraday.

Mohr's salt. See Iron ammonium sulphate.

Moissan, Ferdinand Frédéric Henri (1852-1907). Apprenticed at first to a pharmacist in his native city, Paris, Moissan began the serious study of chemistry in 1872 under Frémy at the Musée d'Histoire Naturelle. In 1880 he was appointed demonstrator in chemistry at the École Supérieure de Pharmacie where he isolated the element fluorine. After a period as professor at the School of Pharmacy he was appointed professor of chemistry at the University of Paris. His later work included a study of reactions at high temperatures. In 1906 he was awarded the Nobel Prize for Chemistry. See Mem. Lect., *J. Chem. Soc.*, 1912, 477.

Molar fraction. The molar fraction of a compound A in a mixture containing in addition only the compounds B, C, and D, is the number of molecules of A divided by the total number of molecules of A, B, C, and D. In practice, the concentrations of A, B, C, and D are not expressed in actual numbers of molecules, but in fractions or multiples of their gram molecular weights. This does not affect the value of the molar fraction, for the gram molecule of every substance contains the same number of molecules.

Mole. A modern term for gram molecule, i.e. the quantity of a pure substance comprised by 1 g molecular weight of it. One mole of any substance contains 6.023×10^{23} molecules (Avogadro's number).

Molecular conductivity. This is the specific conductance multiplied by the volume in ml containing 1 g molecule of the electrolyte.

Molecular depression constant. See Depression of freezing-point.

Molecular diameters. Very few molecules are spherical, but for the purposes of chemical kinetics this assumption is usually sufficiently accurate. The diameters of some molecules are as follows: H_2 2.38×10^{-8} cm; O_2 3.19×10^{-8} cm; NH_3 3.9×10^{-8} cm; C_6H_6 6.6×10^{-8} cm.

Molecular distillation. This distillation process is carried out at very low pressures, 10^{-2} mmHg or less. Under these conditions the mean free path of the molecules is of the same order as the distance between the surface of the liquid being distilled (*the distilland*) and the surface of the condensate (*distillate*), and they can therefore travel between the two with relatively few collisions. Because of this, distillation can proceed at a fast rate and the risk of thermal decomposition is minimized.

Molecular stills, besides having an unobstructed path for evaporating molecules, must have provision for the continuous renewal of the distilland surface. Were this not done, owing to the absence of convection currents in the distilland and the high evaporation rate, the surface would soon become depleted in the evaporating substance. This is achieved in commercial units by having the distilland in the form of a falling film, by causing it to spread over the surface of a rotor under centrifugal force, or by using wipers.

Molecular distillation is used in the separation and purification of vitamins and other natural products, and for the distillation of high-boiling synthetic organic compounds.

Molecular elevation constant. See Elevation of boiling-point.

Molecular heat. This is the amount of heat required to raise the temperature of 1 g molecule of a substance through 1° C, at either constant pressure or constant volume (specified).

Molecular orbitals. Electronic orbitals which are conceived to surround the group of nuclei forming a molecule. The orbitals may be bonding, anti-bonding, or non-bonding according as to whether the presence of an electron in the orbital tends to hold the molecule together, to cause disruption of the molecule, or to have no effect on the molecule.

Molecular refractivity. See Specific refractivity.

Molecular sieve. Certain zeolites contain regular channels of molecular dimensions throughout their very open crystal structures. These channels are large enough to admit various small molecules such as water, methane, propane, etc., but are not large enough to admit relatively large molecules, e.g. benzene. Consequently they are termed molecular sieves and may be used as preferential sorbents for the smaller species. Zeolites with different pore diameters have been prepared.

Molecular spectrum. See Band spectrum and Continuous spectrum.

Molecular weight. The weight of one molecule referred to the standard of $^{12}C = 12.0000$. It is a ratio (cf. Atomic weight). For stoicheiometric calculations, the molecular weight is expressed in grammes and is known as the gram molecular weight.

Molecule. Defined by Maxwell as 'that small portion of matter which moves about as a whole, so that its parts, if it has any, do not part company during the motion of agitation of the gas.' It is generally accepted to refer to the smallest particle of matter which can exist in a free state (cf. Atom). In the case of ionic substances such as sodium chloride, the molecule is considered as NaCl, although it is known that the solid consists of an orderly arrangement of Na^+ and Cl^- ions.

Molecule, mass of a. The actual mass of a molecule may be obtained by dividing the gram molecular weight by Avogadro's number. Thus, the mass of the oxygen molecule is

$$\frac{32}{6 \cdot 02 \times 10^{23}} = 5 \cdot 32 \times 10^{-23} \text{ g.}$$

Molisch's test. A general test for carbohydrates. The carbohydrate is dissolved in water, alcoholic α-naphthol added, and concentrated sulphuric acid poured down the side of the tube. A deep violet ring is formed at the junction of the liquids. A modification, the 'rapid furfural test,' is used to distinguish between glucose and fructose. A mixture of the sugar, α-naphthol, and concentrated hydrochloric acid is boiled. With fructose and saccharides containing fructose a violet colour is produced immediately the solution boils. With glucose the appearance of the colour is slower.

Molybdates. The salts of molybdic acid; derivatives of the acidic oxide MoO_3. Molybdic acid is formally H_2MoO_4 but there is extensive polymerization of the anions so that poly- or iso-molybdates are very common. In the polymolybdates MoO_6 octahedra share corners. Ammonium molybdate is a paramolybdate and contains the $[Mo_7O_{24}]^{6-}$ ion. Heteromolybdates are formed by incorporation of a hetero atom—almost any atom of the periodic table—into a central hole of the polymolybdate. Thus ammonium phosphomolybdate, a canary-yellow precipitate formed by mixing solutions of ammonium molybdate and a soluble phosphate in the presence of nitric acid, has a central phosphorus atom. The sodium molybdates are used in the ink and dye-lake industries; lead molybdate is used as an opacifier in enamels.

Molybdenite. MoS_2. Occurs naturally in hexagonal crystals with perfect basal cleavage, laminae flexible but not elastic. It is lead-grey and resembles graphite in appearance, but has a much higher sp.gr. (4·7). It is the only important source of molybdenum, and when

purified and finely ground is used in special lubricants.

Molybdenum, Mo. At.no. 42, At.wt. 95·95. A soft, but tough, ductile white metal, resembling platinum; m.p. 2620°, b.p. 4800°, d 10·2. In its compounds it exhibits oxidation states between -2 and $+6$.

Molybdenum crystallizes with the body-centred cubic structure, $a=3\cdot140$ Å. The metal is a moderate conductor of heat and electricity. The chief mineral is molybdenite, MoS_2, a soft, flaky, black material which resembles graphite in appearance. The metal was first isolated in 1782 by Hjelm. It is now obtained commercially by reduction of the trioxide MoO_3 with hydrogen. The oxide is isolated from molybdenite through ammonium molybdate as an intermediate. The metallic powder produced in the reduction is sintered, forged, and rolled into the desired form. The metal is stable in air, but is oxidized rapidly at 600°. It does not combine directly with nitrogen, but is attacked by the halogens. The metal forms carbides very readily, and these are the invariable products of attempts to prepare it by reduction of the oxide with carbon. Boiling hydrochloric acid attacks molybdenum slowly; hot concentrated sulphuric acid does so rapidly, as also do aqua regia and dilute nitric acid; with concentrated nitric acid the metal exhibits passivity.

The main use of molybdenum is as an alloy additive in steels; 0·2-0·5% is used for grain refinement and for the prevention of temper brittleness in chromium and manganese steels; 0·5-2·0% is used for creep resistance. Up to 12% is used in high carbon steels to provide hard carbides for wear resistance in cutting tools.

Molybdenum blue. Reduction of a neutral or weakly acid solution of a molybdate with zinc, sulphur dioxide, hydrogen sulphide, etc., gives a deep blue colloidal liquid. This can be coagulated by addition of an electrolyte to form 'molybdenum blue,' a solid of uncertain composition but undoubtedly containing some molybdenum (V).

Molybdenum bromides. $MoBr_3$, $MoBr_2$, MoO_2Br_2 and $MoOBr_3$ have been described. In their preparation and properties they are very similar to the corresponding chlorides.

Molybdenum carbonyl, $Mo(CO)_6$. A colourless compound prepared by the action of carbon monoxide and a strong reducing agent such as sodium on a molybdenum halide. Sublimes *in vacuo*. Has octahedral co-ordination about the metal. It is used to prepare substituted carbonyls.

Molybdenum chlorides. *Molybdenum oxychlorides*, $MoOCl_4$ and MoO_2Cl_2, are both prepared by the action of chlorine on the dioxide or of thionyl chloride on molybdenum trioxide. A hydrate $MoO_2Cl_2 \cdot H_2O$ may be prepared by heating molybdenum trioxide to 150°-200° in dry halogen chloride. It sublimes easily and may be used in the preparation of other molybdenum compounds; it is easily soluble in water, alcohol, ether and acetone.

Molybdenum hexachloride, $MoCl_6$, is prepared by heating molybdic acid with thionyl chloride.

Molybdenum pentachloride, $MoCl_5$. A dark green solid, m.p. 194°, b.p. 268°. Prepared from the elements. It is very hygroscopic and reacts violently with water to give the oxychloride $MoOCl_3$. Complex oxychlorides, e.g. K_2MoOCl_5, are known.

Molybdenum tetrachloride, $MoCl_4$. A dark brown, easily volatile, powder prepared by heating molybdenum dioxide with a solution of chlorine in carbon tetrachloride in a sealed tube.

Molybdenum trichloride, $MoCl_3$. Dark-red crystals formed by heating the pentachloride to 250° in hydrogen. It is insoluble in water. Complex molybdenum (III) chlorides are obtained by reducing a hexapositive solution. They are brick red and are of the types M_3MoCl_6 and $M_2(MoCl_5 \cdot H_2O)$. An oxychloride $MoOCl \cdot 4 H_2O$ exists in two forms, green and brown.

Molybdenum dichloride, '$MoCl_2$', Mo_6Cl_{12}. A yellow infusible powder obtained by interaction of the elements. It reacts as $(Mo_6Cl_8)Cl_4$.

Molybdenum fluorides. *Molybdenum hexafluoride*, MoF_6. A white crystalline substance, m.p. 17·5°, b.p. 35°. It is immediately hydrolysed by water and adds to alkali fluorides to form adducts, M_2MoF_8.

Molybdenum oxyfluorides, $MoOF_4$ and MoO_2F_2. Made by the action of hydrogen fluoride on $MoOCl_4$ and MoO_2Cl_2 respectively. The former is very hygroscopic and is decomposed by water but the latter is stable in aqueous solution.

Molybdenum penta- and tetrafluoride, MoF_5 and MoF_4, are prepared by the action of fluorine on molybdenum carbonyl or by reducing the hexafluoride with metallic molybdenum. They are separated by distillation *in vacuo*. MoF_5, bright yellow, m.p. 64°, MoF_4, light green. Both fluorides are immediately hydrolysed by water.

Molybdenum trifluoride, MoF_3, is obtained by the reduction of molybdenum pentafluoride by metallic molybdenum. Complexes of the types $MMoF_4 \cdot H_2O$ and M_3MoF_6 are known. An oxyfluoride, $MoOF \cdot 4H_2O$ may be made by treating the chloride with ammonium fluoride.

Molybdenum oxides. *Molybdenum trioxide*, MoO_3. A white powder, the final product of the ignition of the metal or other compounds in air. It melts at 795° to a dark yellow liquid. It is insoluble in water but is soluble in alkalis to form molybdates.

Molybdenum pentoxide. Mo_2O_5. A violet powder obtained by drying the hydrate, $MoO(OH)_3$, which is precipitated from pentapositive molybdenum solutions by ammonia.

Molybdenum dioxide, MoO_2. A dark brown powder obtained by the reduction of the trioxide with hydrogen at 470°. It is insoluble in alkalis and most acids.

Many other oxides of intermediate compositions are known.

Molybdic acids. See Molybdates.

Momentum separators. See Impingement separators.

Monastral Fast Blue B (Pigment Blue 15). A blue pigment first marketed in 1935 by Imperial Chemical Industries. It has a wide variety of uses on account of its high fastness properties for paints, distempers, printing inks, plastics, papers, wallpapers, etc. See Phthalocyanines.

Monazite. A phosphate of the rare earth metals, essentially (Ce, La, Nd, Pr)PO_4 with some thorium silicate (ThO_2 1-18%). Forms yellow-brown monoclinic crystals, sp.gr. 5·2-5·3, hardness $5\frac{1}{2}$. It is the chief source of thorium, cerium, and the rare earths.

Monazite occurs in granites and pegmatites but commercial supplies are mainly obtained from alluvial deposits, especially beach sands in S. India, Brazil, and New South Wales in association with ilmenite, rutile, magnetite, and zircon.

Mond, Ludwig (1839-1909). Born at Cassel in Germany, Mond studied at Marburg and Heidelberg. In 1862 he came to England, where he immediately established himself in industry. In 1867 he became a naturalized British subject. In 1873 he entered into partnership with Sir John Tomlinson Brunner (1842-1919), founding the firm of Brunner, Mond & Co. By his invention of the Mond process for the purification of nickel through the formation of the carbonyl, Mond laid the foundation of the Canadian nickel industry. See 'The Life of Ludwig Mond,' by J. M. Cohen.

Mond process. A process for the extraction of nickel from nickel ores. See Nickel.

Monel. See Nickel alloys.

Monge, Gaspard (1746-1818). Monge was born at Beaune. He was chiefly a mathematician and a physicist, his most important contribution to chemistry being his quantitative experiments on the combustion of hydrogen and oxygen to form water.

Monoacetin. See Acetins.

Monobasic acid. An acid which yields only one series of salts, having only one replaceable hydrogen atom, is termed a monobasic acid, e.g. HCl.

Monochloroethane. See Ethyl chloride.

Monochloroethylene. See Vinyl chloride.

Monochloromethane. See Methyl chloride.

Monoclinic system. One of the crystal systems, which comprises crystals with three unequal crystallographic axes, two of which intersect at an oblique angle, while the third is at right angles to the plane of the other two. The characteristic of this system is the presence of one (and only one) two-fold axis of symmetry and/or one (and only one) plane of symmetry which, if present, is perpendicular to the two-fold axis. Examples of monoclinic crystals include sodium carbonate decahydrate, borax ($Na_2B_4O_7 \cdot 10H_2O$), β-sulphur, potassium chlorate, and oxalic acid. See Crystal symmetry.

Monodentate ligand. A ligand which interacts with the acceptor at only one point, e.g. NH_3.

Monolayers. See Unimolecular films.

Monomer. See Polymerization.

Mono pump. The trade-name of a type of screw pump.

Monosaccharides. Sugars with the formula $C_nH_{2n}O_n$. In the natural sugars n is either 5 or 6.

Monotropy. The existence of two or more crystalline forms of a substance, only one of which is stable. The others are metastable and therefore liable to pass spontaneously into the stable form. In monotropic substances there is no transition temperature (cf. Enantiotropy). The metastable forms are generally prepared by rapidly cooling the vapour or liquid. Phosphorus is the best known example of a monotropic substance, the common white form being metastable with respect to the violet form, to which it slowly changes at elevated temperatures.

Monovinylacetylene, C_4H_4, $CH_2:CH\cdot C:CH$. A colourless gas having a sweet odour, b.p. 5°. Manufactured by the controlled low-temperature polymerization of acetylene in the presence of an aqueous solution of cuprous and ammonium chlorides. Reduced by hydrogen to butadiene and, finally, butane. Reacts with water in the presence of mercuric sulphate to give methyl vinyl ketone. Forms a white silver salt and a yellow copper salt. Forms 2-chlorobutadiene with hydrochloric acid and certain metallic chlorides.

Montanic acid, $C_{27}H_{55}COOH$, octacosanoic acid. Glistening scales, m.p. 89°. A straight-chain, saturated fatty acid, that occurs in many natural waxes.

Montmorillonite. A clay mineral ideally $Al_2Si_4O_{10}(OH)_2 \cdot nH_2O$, but its composition is variable owing to isomorphous substitution. It possesses a three layer lattice structure, high base exchange capacity, and variable moisture content, resulting in a variable basal spacing as shown by X-ray examination, the lattice altering in size at right angles to the layers. Two varieties occur, one swelling greatly in water, the other having marked absorptive properties. Bentonite (*q.v.*) consists mainly of montmorillonite.

Moore filter. A battery of hollow leaves, each consisting of a frame with a covering of a filter medium, is suspended in a tank containing the material to be filtered. Application of a vacuum to the inside of the leaves causes a cake to form on them. When filtration is complete the leaves are removed and air pressure is applied to dislodge the solid.

Moore, Hugh Kelsea (1872-1939). Moore was born at Andover, Massachusetts, and educated at the Massachusetts Institute of Technology. He pursued an industrial career, and from 1903 to 1934 was chief chemist and chemical engineer to the Burgess Sulphite Fibre Co. His work dealt with electrochemical processes, the production of wood pulp, and the construction and operation of evaporators. He was awarded the Perkin Medal, 1925. See *Chem. and Ind.*, 1940, 114.

Mordant dyes. These are dyes of varied constitution. They all possess an acid character, and because of the presence in their molecule of hydroxyl or carboxyl groups are capable of forming lakes with metallic mordants. The methods by which the mordant colours can be affixed to the fibre depend on the nature of the dyestuff and the fibre.

Mordant dyes are mainly used in the dyeing of wool, either by dyeing previously mordanted wool or by mordanting and dyeing in a single bath, or by after-treatment of the dye with a metallic salt. Chromium salts are mainly used for this purpose. The chromium mordant is applied as sodium dichromate in the presence of a reducing acid such as tartaric, oxalic, or formic acid. Typical examples are: Diamond black F, Carmoisine, Logwood, etc.

Morgan, Sir Gilbert Thomas (1872-1940). Educated at the Technical College (Finsbury), the Royal College of Science, and the Universities of London and Birmingham, Morgan was appointed professor of applied chemistry at Finsbury Technical College. Later he became professor of chemistry at the University of Birmingham and, in 1925, Director of the

Chemical Research Laboratory, Teddington (D.S.I.R.). For his original work over a wide field he was elected F.R.S. He was knighted in 1936. See *J. Chem. Soc.*, 1941, 689.

Morley, Edward Williams (1838-1923). Born at Newark, New Jersey, Morley was educated at Williams College, Mass. Although he studied originally for the Church, Morley later devoted himself to chemistry. He was appointed professor of chemistry, Western Reserve University, Cleveland (1868) and Cleveland Medical College (1873). From the latter chair he resigned in 1888 in order to give his time to chemical research. He is noted for the accuracy with which he determined the exact ratio in which hydrogen and oxygen unite by weight. He was awarded the Davy and Willard Gibbs Medals.

Morphine, $C_{17}H_{19}NO_3$. Colourless prisms with one molecule of water; m.p. (anhydrous) 254°, with decomposition. Soluble in 5000 parts of water, 100 parts of ethyl alcohol; $[\alpha]_D^{23} - 130 \cdot 9°$ in methyl alcohol.

Morphine is the principal alkaloid of opium, from which it is obtained by treatment with milk of lime and ammonium chloride. It acts both as a base and as a phenol and reacts to form methyl-morphine (codeine) and diacetylmorphine (diamorphine or heroin). Morphine and its salts,

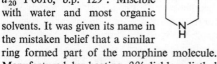

which are more soluble in water than the base, are among the most valuable drugs for the relief of pain. They produce deep sleep, but are habit-forming.

Morpholine, C_4H_9NO. A colourless liquid with a strong ammoniacal odour; d_{20}^{20} 1·0016, b.p. 129°. Miscible with water and most organic solvents. It was given its name in the mistaken belief that a similar ring formed part of the morphine molecule. Manufactured by heating $\beta\beta'$-dichlorodiethyl ether with ammonia, or by heating diethanol-amine with 70% sulphuric acid. It is a moderately strong base, forming soaps with fatty acids. The unstable compounds with volatile inorganic acids are decomposed at relatively low temperatures. Absorbs water and carbon dioxide from the air to give morpholine carbamate, a colourless, crystalline solid. Dilute solutions in water distil with little change in composition. It has a

high solvent power for a very wide range of substances. Used as a solvent and for decreasing corrosion in boilers. Its soaps are used as emulsifying agents.

Morrhuic acid. See Sodium morrhuate.

Morse, Harmon Northrup (1848-1920). Educated at Amherst and Göttingen, Morse was appointed associate professor at Johns Hopkins University in 1876. In 1891 he became professor of chemistry and Director of the Chemical Laboratory. His researches included the exact determinations of the atomic weights of cadmium and zinc and measurements of osmotic pressures.

Mosaic gold. See Tin sulphide.

Mosander, Carl Gustav (1797-1858). One of Berzelius' assistants, Mosander was at one time a Swedish army surgeon and a pharmacist before becoming Curator of the mineral collections at the Stockholm Academy of Sciences and professor of chemistry at the Caroline Institute. An early worker in rare earth chemistry, he first separated lanthana, didymia, erbia, terbia, and yttria. See *Ind. Chemist*, 1958, 420.

Moseley, Henry Gwyn Jeffreys (1887-1915). Born at Weymouth, Moseley was educated at Eton and Trinity College, Oxford. After graduation he became lecturer in physics at the University of Manchester where he was associated with Rutherford. He studied the X-ray spectra of the elements and found that in comparing the corresponding lines in different X-ray spectra there is a shift in passing from one element to the next in the periodic table in accordance with the equation $\sqrt{\dfrac{1}{\lambda}} = a(z - b)$ where λ is the wavelength of the line, a and b are constants and z is the atomic number.

Mössbauer effect. The resonance fluorescence by γ-radiation of an atomic nucleus, returning from an excited state to the ground state. The resonance energy is characteristic of the chemical environment of the nucleus.

Motor spirit. Fuel for internal-combustion engines, with boiling range approximately 0°-200°, popularly designated petrol or gasoline.

Moulding. The making of shapes in suitable materials into which molten metal can be run so that on solidifying its shape corresponds to that of the mould. Moulding, besides being a science, is an art. Moulds are of two kinds: sand or clay moulds, and chill or permanent moulds.

The essential properties of a moulding sand are good refractory nature, a certain degree of porosity in order to allow free passage of gases, and easy removal from the cold casting. A sand mould is composed of two types of sand, the facing sand and the floor or black sand. There are three types of sand moulds. Green sand moulds are made from sand damped sufficiently to hold together when warmed. Dry sand moulds contain added clay and are oven-dried before use. Loam sand moulds require no patterns, being fashioned by hand, and so are plastic in texture. Chill moulds consist entirely of metal, and are used when large numbers of the same type of casting are required. See Plastics moulding.

Ms temperature. See Martempering.

Mucic acid, $C_6H_{10}O_8$. Forms colourless prismatic crystals, m.p. 255° (rapid heating).

$$HOOC-\underset{\underset{OH}{|}}{\overset{\overset{H}{|}}{C}}-\underset{\underset{H}{|}}{\overset{\overset{OH}{|}}{C}}-\underset{\underset{H}{|}}{\overset{\overset{OH}{|}}{C}}-\underset{\underset{OH}{|}}{\overset{\overset{H}{|}}{C}}-COOH$$

Moderately soluble in hot water; insoluble in alcohol. Manufactured by the oxidation of lactose or the galactans from wood with nitric acid. When heated with water it forms a soluble lactone. Converted to furoic acid by heat, and to allomucic acid by heating with pyridine. Distillation of the ammonium salt gives pyrrole. Used in the manufacture of pyrrole.

Mucilages. Plant mucilages differ from gums in that they are the products of normal metabolism. They are slimy, colloidal solutions obtained from seeds, roots, or other parts of the plant by extraction with water. They are polysaccharides, usually containing galactose and galacturonic acid residues and often xylose and arabinose.

In pharmacy the term mucilage is used for the solution of a gum.

Mucins. Complex compounds of amino-sugars, glucuronic acid, and sulphuric acid. Cartilage, tendons, aorta, and sclera contain chondroitin-sulphuric acid, this being a tetrasaccharide made up of two aminogalactose and two glucuronic acid units; the amino-groups are acetylated and the primary alcohol groups esterified with sulphuric acid.

Other mucins yield mucoitinsulphuric acid which is a disaccharide containing glucosamine and glucuronic acid. Mucins form extremely viscous solutions with water, are soluble in dilute alkalis, and insoluble in acetic acid. Gastric mucin, prepared from the linings of pigs stomachs, is used in the treatment of peptic ulcers.

Mucochloric acid, $C_4H_2Cl_2O_3$. More correctly represented by the lactone formula, it is prepared from furfuraldehyde and chlorine in aqueous solution. It forms colourless plates, m.p. 127°, from water. See Aldehyde hardeners.

Mucoids. Glucoproteins, found in white of egg, resembling mucins, but giving solutions that are not so viscous and more soluble in acetic acid.

Mucopeptides. Structural components of the cell walls of Gram-positive and many Gram-negative bacteria. They are insoluble polymers of N-acetylglucosamine and N-acetylmuramic acid, probably involving $\beta(1\rightarrow4)$-glycosidic linkages; small peptide residues, usually composed of D- or L-alanine, D-glutamic acid, and either lysine or α,ϵ-diaminopimelic acid, are attached to the polymer. The antibacterial action of penicillin is ascribed to its inhibition of cell-wall synthesis, possibly by prevention of the interlinking of mucopeptide chains through the peptide residues, or by interference with biosynthesis of one of the essential constituents such as muramic acid.

Mucoproteins. See Glucoproteins.

Muffle furnaces. A gas heated furnace the characteristic feature of which is that the charge does not come into contact with the hot gases. This is effected by putting the charge in a retort or 'box,' whose walls are heated by contact with hot gaseous products of combustion.

Müller, Heinrich Wilhelm Hugo (1833-1915). Born at Tirschenreuth, Bavaria, Müller was educated at Leipzig and Göttingen. In 1854 he came to England as assistant to Warren De La Rue, with whom he carried out numerous researches. He eventually became a director of the firm of Thos. De La Rue & Co., and in connexion with this firm devoted his attention to practical applications of chemistry, with special reference to colours, varnishes, and paper-making. After retiring in 1902 he worked on plant substances. He was President of the Chemical Society in 1885-1887.

Müller, Paul (1899-1965). Born at Olten in Switzerland, Müller read chemistry at the University of Basel. He joined J. R. Geigy S.A. as a research chemist in 1925 and worked there throughout his life. He became interested in pest control and in 1939 discovered the insecticidal properties of DDT. For this he was given the Nobel Prize for medicine in 1948.

Mullite. A mineral aluminium silicate,

$Al_6Si_2O_{13}$. The crystals are orthorhombic, usually seen as 'long laths'. A mixture of mullite and silica is formed by heating kyanite, andalusite or sillimanite. In firebricks which have been heated to 1250° or above, mullite forms a felted mass of lath-like crystals which increase the strength and refractoriness of the brick and are resistant to corrosion.

Multicentre bonds. A bonding molecular orbital formed between three or more atoms containing a pair of electrons. Such bonds are postulated in the boron hydrides.

Multidentate ligand, Polydentate ligand. A ligand which has two or more sites at which it can co-ordinate. Such a ligand can form a bridge or can form a chelate compound. An example is $H_2NCH_2CH_2NH_2$.

Multiple bonding. Bonding between atoms in which there is overlap of orbitals containing more than two electrons in more than one position in space. The electrons may come equally from each atom or be derived from only one of the atoms (co-ordinate bond, back bonding). Generally the primary bond is a σ bond with extra interaction by π bonding.

Multiple effect evaporator. In a simple evaporator, containing only one evaporator unit or *effect*, approximately 1 lb of steam is required to evaporate 1 lb of water. A multiple effect evaporator contains several evaporator units in series, and the steam generated in one effect is fed to the calandria of the next, where it acts as a heating medium and produces further evaporation. The liquid being concentrated progresses from one effect to the next either in the same or the opposite direction to the steam flow. Thus 1 lb of steam is able to evaporate, very approximately, N pounds of water, where N is the number of effects. Since steam is the principal operating cost in evaporation, large economies may be achieved. However, the capital cost of the installation increases with the number of effects, and so there is an economic limit to the number that may be employed for any particular duty. See Evaporator.

Multiple proportions, Law of. This law, proposed by Dalton in 1804, states that when two elements A and B combine to form more than one compound, the weights of B, which combine with a fixed weight of A, are in the proportion of small whole numbers. For example, in nitrous oxide, nitric oxide, and dinitrogen tetroxide, the amounts of nitrogen combined with one part of oxygen are in the proportion 4:2:1. This law is only true to a very limited extent, as very many non-stoicheiometric compounds are known.

Multiplet. The individual lines in a spectrum often consist of two or more closely grouped finer lines, which make up the fine structure of the original line. Each such group, constituting an ordinary line in the spectrum, is termed a multiplet. The finer lines or components are due to the different amounts of energy which the electron possesses by virtue of its spin. The multiplicity is the maximum possible number of such energy values which an atom in a given state can possess by virtue of the electron spin. A multiplet which arises from electronic transitions where there are two such spin states is termed a doublet; where there are three spin states a triplet.

Besides this fine structure due to electronic spin, there are often present still finer lines, known as *hyperfine structure*. These lines are due to slight energy differences arising from the different weights of the isotopes of an element, or from the fact that the nucleus of the atom has the property of spin.

Muntz metal. See Brass.

Muon. A μ-meson. See Meson.

Muramic acid, 3-O-(1′-carboxyethyl)-glucosamine, $C_9H_{17}NO_7$, a uniquely characteristic

component of the cell walls of bacteria, in which it is incorporated in the structural mucopeptides.

Muriatic acid. An old name for hydrochloric acid, still occasionally used in industry. Similarly, potassium chloride is sometimes called 'muriate of potash.'

Muscarine, $C_9H_{21}NO_3$. A base obtained from

certain toadstools. It is stable in alkaline solution, but unstable to acids; $[\alpha]_D^{20} +1.57°$. It is intensely poisonous, having an arresting action on the heart.

Muscovite, $KAl_2(AlSi_3O_{10})(OH)_2$. A variety of white mica which occurs in monoclinic crystals, sp.gr. $=2.8$, hardness 2-2.5. Muscovite is a good electrical insulator below 1100°.

Musk, artificial, $C_{11}H_{13}N_3O_6$. 2,4,6-Trinitro-3-*tert*-butyltoluene, m.p. 97°, yellow crystals which are soluble in most organic solvents. It is used in perfumery.

Muspratt, James (1793-1885). Born at Dublin, Muspratt was apprentice for a time to a wholesale druggist. He served during the Peninsular War in Spain and in 1814 set up in Dublin as a chemical manufacturer. In 1822 he went to Liverpool and later erected plant at St. Helens, Widnes, and Flint. He discovered the value of iron pyrites as a source of sulphur dioxide for sulphuric acid manufacture.

Mustard gas, $\beta\beta'$-**Dichlorodiethyl sulphide, Yperite,** $C_4H_8Cl_2S$. A colourless oily liquid with a faint garlic-like odour; forms prismatic crystals when cooled, m.p. 13°-14°, b.p. 215°-217°, d^{20} 1·2741. Practically insoluble in water; soluble in most organic solvents. Manufactured by treating sulphur monochloride with ethylene at 30°-35°. The product is yellow in colour, and contains colloidal sulphur. It may be purified by distillation under reduced pressure. Reacts with alkalis, and more slowly with water at ordinary temperatures. Decomposed violently by bleaching powder. It is a powerful vesicant and poison, and causes conjunctivitis and temporary blindness. It is an important agent in chemical warfare.

Mustard oil. See Allyl isothiocyanate.

Mutagens. Physical or chemical agents, including ionizing and other radiations, alkylating agents, and deaminating agents, which raise the frequency of mutation greatly above the normal level.

Mutarotation. The phenomenon of spontaneous change of optical activity of an optically active substance when it is dissolved in water, or some other solvent. The optical activity of glucose, for example, falls rapidly when it is freshly dissolved in water, the change being attributed to an isomeric change of the original α-glucose into an equilibrium mixture of the α- and β-forms. These two substances differ in the spatial arrangement of an H— and an OH— group in the molecule. Mutarotation is frequently catalysed by acids or bases, or by both.

Mutases. See Isomerases.

Mycolic acid. See Phthioic acids.

Mycolipenic acid. See Phthioic acids.

Myelin. A sheath-like structure which surrounds the nerve axons in the mammalian nervous system. It is composed of sphingolipids, cholesterol, proteins, polysaccharides and ionic material, linked in an extremely stable membrane which suffers little metabolic change during the life of the animal.

Myleran, 1,4-**dimethanesulphonyloxybutane,** $C_6H_{14}O_6S_2$, $CH_3SO_2O[CH_2]_4OSO_2CH_3$. A cytotoxic alkylating agent used clinically to treat leukaemia.

Myoglobin. The oxhaemoglobin of muscle. It differs from blood haemoglobin in being soluble in concentrated phosphate buffer, and hence can be separated. It has been obtained crystalline, and shown to consist of a single coiled chain of 153 amino-acids and a haem group. The complete amino-acid sequence of sperm whale myoglobin has been determined (Edmundson, 1965). Myoglobin is used by muscle as a rapidly available source of oxygen.

Myosin, See Actomyosin.

Myrcene, $C_{10}H_{16}$. An acyclic monoterpene of the constitutional formula

It is found in many essential oils, e.g. in verbena oil and oil of hops. It has a pleasant smell, does not yield any crystalline derivatives and has the following constants: b.p. 166°-168°/760 mm, d^{15} 0·8013, n_D^{19} 1·4700.

Myricyl alcohol. See Melissyl alcohol.

Myristic acid, n-Tetradecanoic acid, $C_{14}H_{28}O_2$, $CH_3 \cdot [CH_2]_{12} \cdot COOH$. Crystallizes in leaflets, m.p. 58°, b.p. 250·5°/100 mm. A fatty acid occurring as glycerides in milk and in large quantities in certain vegetable oils.

Myrosin. An enzyme of the sulphatase class which is present in black and white mustard seeds and in other *cruciferae*. It hydrolyses the glycoside sinigrin to glucose, allyl isothiocyanate, and potassium hydrogen sulphate. It occurs in special cells wtih finely granular contents which are free from starch, etc. Myrosin is apparently also present in animal tissues.

Myrtenal, $C_{10}H_{14}O$. An unsaturated aldehyde found in false camphor wood oil together with perilla aldehyde, from which it can be separated by decomposing the mixed sodium sulphite compounds with alkali, when (+)-myrtenal is alone regenerated. It is also formed by the oxidation of (+)-myrtenol. Its constants are: b.p. 92°/12·5 mm, d_4^{20} 0·9898, $[\alpha]_D$ +15·682. It forms a semicarbazone of m.p. 230°.

Myrtenol, $C_{10}H_{16}O$. A primary alcohol derived from α-pinene, the (+)-form of which is found in myrtle oil, from which it can be separated by means of the crystalline hydrogen phthalate which it forms with phthalic anhydride. (+)-Myrtenol has b.p. 222°-224°, d^{20} 0·9763, n_D 1·4967, $[\alpha]_D +45·45°$. The hydrogen phthalate has m.p. 114°-115°.

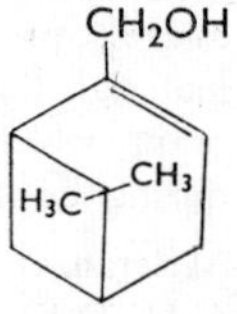

N

NAD. See Nicotinamide-adenine dinucleotide.

NADP. See Nicotinamide-adenine dinucleotide phosphate.

Nalorphine, N-Allylnormorphine, $C_{19}H_{21}NO_3$.

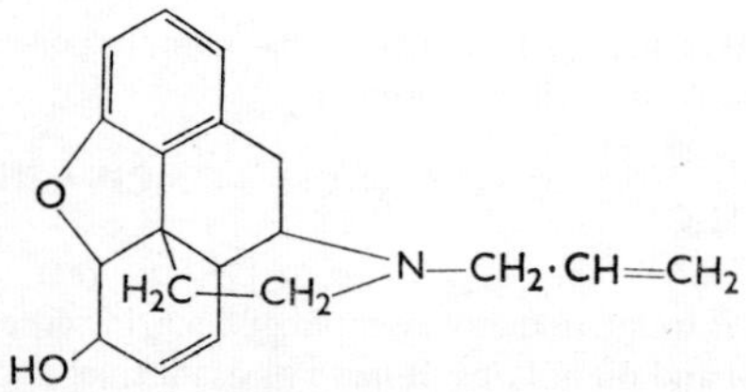

Used as the hydrobromide, a white crystalline powder, m.p. 262°, soluble in alcohol and water; prepared by demethylating morphine, N-allylating, and forming the hydrobromide.

It has few of the actions of morphine, and opposes the actions of analgesics generally. It displaces morphine from enzyme systems in the body, and is used for treating respiratory depression in new-born children.

Napalm. An aluminium soap from coconut oil fatty acids and naphthenic acids used to gel gasoline for incendiary bombs.

Naphtha. A product from coal tar consisting largely of xylenes and higher homologues. It may be divided into 'heavy,' 'solvent,' etc., the difference being largely a matter of density and consequent different distillation analysis.

Petroleum naphtha is the petroleum distillate of nominal boiling range 100°-200°, which is used as a feedstock for reforming processes.

Naphthacene ring system. The system numbered

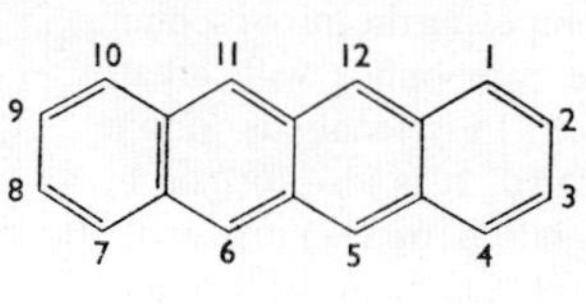

as shown.

Naphthalene, $C_{10}H_8$. A white crystalline solid

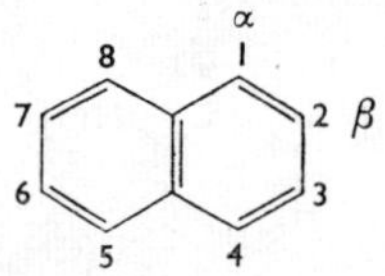

with a penetrating tarry smell; it burns with a very smoky flame. Insoluble in water and light petroleum, soluble in alcohol, ether, and benzene. Very volatile in steam, readily sublimes at low temperatures, m.p. 80°, b.p. 218°, 5·29% soluble in absolute alcohol at 15°, 45·8% soluble in benzene at 15°.

It was discovered in 1820 in coal tar, which contains up to 10% naphthalene; owing to its volatility it is always present in crude coal gas. There are two commercial sources: one is coal tar, from which it is isolated by crystallization or distillation or both; the other is certain petroleum fractions (e.g. resulting from catalytic reforming) rich in methylnaphthalenes, from which naphthalene is obtained by demethylation using hydrogen at 750° and 10-70 atm.

It is a typically aromatic compound and gives additive and substitution reactions more readily than benzene. Can be reduced to a series of compounds containing from 2 to 10 additional hydrogen atoms (e.g. tetralin, decalin), which are liquids of value as solvents. Exhaustive chlorination gives rise to wax-like compounds. It gives rise to two series of monosubstitution products depending upon whether the substituent is in the α- or β-position. Readily nitrates and sulphonates to give valuable dyestuffs intermediates, the substituent entering chiefly into the α position except in the case of sulphonation at a high temperature (150°) which gives a mixture containing 82% of naphthalene-β-sulphonic acid.

Most of the naphthalene produced is utilized in the manufacture of phthalic anhydride, used for plasticizers, alkyd resins and polyesters. It is also used in the manufacture of β-naphthol and insecticides.

Naphthalene sulphonic acids. Naphthalene monosulphonic acids are obtained by direct sulphonation of naphthalene with concentrated sulphuric acid. A mixture of the two possible isomers is always obtained in proportions varying with the temperature of reaction. At temperatures below 40° the product contains 96% of the α-sulphonic acid, at 160°-165° the mixture contains 85% of the β-sulphonic acid. This behaviour must be contrasted with that of nitration which leads almost exclusively to the preparation of the α-nitro-isomer.

Naphthalene-α-sulphonic acid crystallizes with

$2H_2O$, m.p. 90°. It is soluble in water and alcohol. The barium salt is only sparingly soluble in water. It is used for the preparation of α-naphthol by fusion with caustic soda at 270°-320°, and for the preparation of 1,8- and 1,5-nitronaphthalene sulphonic acids.

Naphthalene-β-sulphonic acid crystallizes with $3H_2O$, m.p. 83°. It is very soluble in water. The anhydrous acid melts at 90·5°-91° and is easily soluble in benzene. It forms a soluble sodium salt and much less soluble calcium and barium salts. Its principal use is for the preparation of β-naphthol by fusion with caustic soda at 295°-305°. It is, however, also used for the preparation of nitro-derivatives.

Naphthalene disulphonic acids are prepared by more prolonged sulphonation than in the preparation of the monosulphonic acids. Four isomeric acids are thus obtained in varying proportions. At lower temperatures the mixture contains chiefly the 1,5- and 1,6-acids and at higher temperatures the 2,6- and 2,7-acids predominate. The disulphonic acids are used for the preparation of trisulphonic acids, of nitro-derivatives, and of mono- or di-hydroxy-compounds.

Naphthalene-1,5-disulphonic acid crystallizes with $4H_2O$. It is very soluble in water and gives soluble sodium and barium salts.

Naphthalene-1,6-disulphonic acid crystallises with $4H_2O$. The free acid and its sodium and barium salts are easily soluble in water.

Naphthalene-2,7-disulphonic acid crystallizes in long deliquescent needles. The barium salt is less easily soluble than the sodium salt or the free acid.

Naphthalene-2,6-disulphonic acid is of no commercial interest.

Naphthalene trisulphonic acids can be obtained by more drastic sulphonation of naphthalene or its mono- and disulphonic acids. Only three of the possible isomers are obtained, namely the 1,3,5-, 1,3,6-, and 1,3,7-acids. The position of the substituting groups has thus followed the rule that a second or third sulpho-group never enters the ortho, para, or peri positions to the first or second groups.

The most important of the trisulphonic acids is the 1,3,6-acid which is used for the preparation of H-acid.

Naphthenes. Cyclo-paraffins, saturated hydrocarbons containing at least one closed ring of carbon atoms, e.g. cyclohexane.

Naphthenic acids. Carboxylic acids obtained from crude petroleum. They were first discovered in the naphthene-containing crude oils from Russia and Rumania. These oils are particularly rich in acidic constituents. The acids are obtained by agitating the crude oil with a solu-

tion of sodium hydroxide. The water-soluble sodium salts of the acids are then decomposed with mineral acids. Many belong to a series of general formula $C_nH_{2n-1}COOH$ and are derivatives of cyclopentane, but more complicated alicyclic ring systems have also been found. It has been suggested that the acids are not originally present in the crude oils but are formed from readily oxidizable cycloparaffins during the extraction process. The sodium salts are important detergents and emulsifying agents, while the calcium and barium salts are used in the preparation of coloured lakes for printing inks. The copper salts are used as wood preservatives and insecticides. The lead, cobalt, and manganese salts are used as driers in the paint industry, and the heavy metal salts in general have a wide variety of minor uses, as antifoaming, wetting, and dispersing agents, and stabilizers for vinyl plastics. The acids may be detected by the formation of a green copper salt soluble in petroleum ether.

Naphthine *S.* See Fast printing green.

α-Naphthol, 1-naphthol, $C_{10}H_8O$. Colourless crystalline substance, m.p. 94°, b.p. 278°-280°. Readily soluble in benzene, alcohol, ether, and aqueous caustic alkalis, sparingly soluble in hot water. Has a phenolic odour. Volatile in steam.

Occurs in traces in coal-tar. Usually prepared on the large scale by caustic soda fusion of sodium naphthalene-α-sulphonate but can also be obtained by high-temperature alkaline digestion of α-chloronaphthalene or α-naphthylamine.

Oxidized by acid permanganate or nitric acid to phthalic acid. Gives nitroso-compounds when treated with nitrous acid.

Can be coupled in the 4-position with diazotized bases to give a series of azo dyestuffs; more usually it is first sulphonated to give a valuable series of intermediates for solubilized azo dyestuffs. The nitro-1-naphthols are themselves dyestuffs, e.g. 2,4-dinitro-1-naphthol ('Naphtol Yellow').

Aqueous solutions of α-naphthol and bleaching powder when mixed give first a dark violet coloration followed by a precipitate of the same colour. Gives a picrate with m.p. 189°-190°.

β-Naphthol, 2-naphthol, $C_{10}H_8O$. White crys-

tals, slightly pink when impure, m.p. 122°, b.p. 285°-286°, readily soluble in benzene, ether, alcohol, chloroform, and caustic alkali solutions, only sparingly soluble in hot water. It has a slight phenolic odour and has marked antiseptic properties.

Occurs in traces in high boiling coal-tar fractions. It is prepared commercially by caustic soda fusion of sodium naphthalene-β-sulphonate.

With nitrous acid it gives α-nitroso-β-naphthol. It can also be chlorinated and sulphonated. Oxidized ultimately to phthalic acid on prolonged oxidation.

It couples readily with diazotized bases to give extensive series of azo dyes, and may also couple on the fibre to give 'Ingrained dyeing.' These azo dyes have an hydroxyl group ortho to the azo group which is of special value for after-treatment with co-ordinating metals, e.g. after-chroming with dichromate. It gives rise to important series of dyestuff intermediates obtained by sulphonation and nitration.

Although β-naphthol is employed chiefly for the manufacture of dyes, considerable quantities are used in the manufacture of anti-oxidants.

α-**Naphthylamine,** $C_{10}H_9N$. Colourless crystals, m.p. 50°, b.p. 301°. Insoluble in water, soluble in alcohol and ether. Basic and forms sparingly soluble salts with mineral acids. Prepared by the reduction of α-nitronaphthalene with iron and a trace of hydrochloric acid or by the action of ammonia (or the calcium chloride-ammonia compound) upon α-naphthol at a high temperature and pressure.

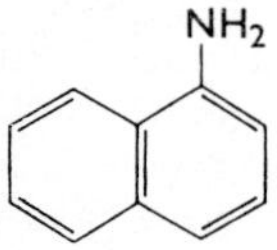

α-Naphthylamine readily diazotizes and couples on to aromatic hydroxylic or basic compounds. It is thus used as a first component in a number of important monoazo dyes. It can also be used as a second component. It sulphonates to give naphthionic acid (α-naphthylamine-4-sulphonic acid). Both α-naphthylamine and β-naphthylamine are carcinogenic compounds.

ingly soluble in cold, easily soluble in hot water, and in alcohol and ether. It is basic and forms a stable hydrochloride and sulphate.

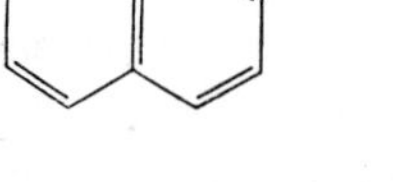

It is prepared by Bucherer's method; β-naphthol is heated with a strong solution of ammonium sulphite and ammonia at 150° for 8 hours. About 6 atmospheres pressure is developed.

It is used as an end component in a few azo-dyes. It is also used for the preparation of sulphonated derivatives. Is a carcinogen.

1-Naphthyl-N-methylcarbamate, $C_{12}H_{11}NO_2$. A

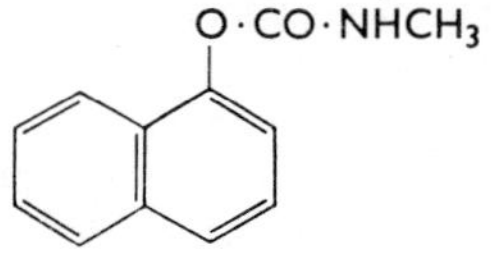

contact insecticide with the trade name 'Sevin', it is a white solid, m.p. 142°, slightly soluble in water and soluble in most organic solvents. It is prepared by reaction of 1-naphthol with methyl isocyanate or with phosgene and an acid acceptor. It is active against many pests and is non-phytotoxic and of low mammalian toxicity. It possesses good residual activity and may be used on fruit, vegetables and other crops.

Naphtol *A.S.* See 2-Hydroxy-3-naphthoic-anilide.

Naphtol blue-black (Acid Black 1). This is a

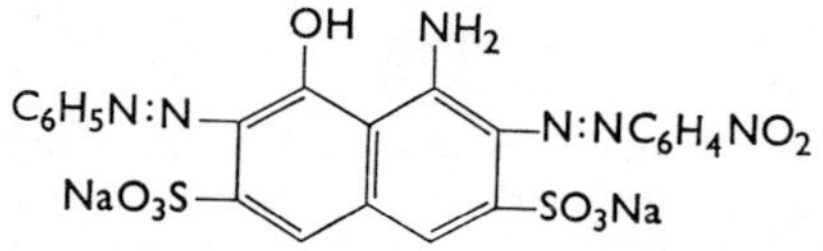

particularly important primary disazo-dye, being widely used for dyeing wool black shades. It is prepared by treating aminonaphthol disulphonic acid H first in acid solution with diazotized *p*-nitraniline and then in alkaline solution with diazotized aniline.

Naphtol green (Acid Green 1). This nitroso-dye

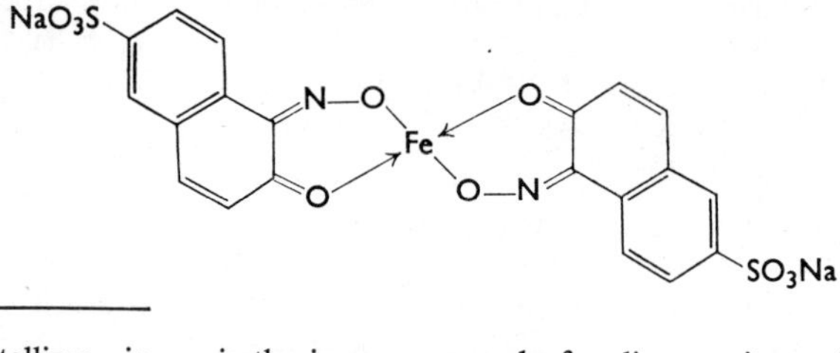

β-**Naphthylamine,** $C_{10}H_9N$. Crystallizes in lustrous leaflets, m.p. 112°, b.p. 294°. It is spar-

is the iron compound of sodium α-nitroso-β-naphthol monosulphonate, formed by the action of nitrous acid on 'Schäffer's Acid,' the product being converted into the complex iron salt. It dyes wool a fast dull green from an acid bath.

Naphtol yellow *S* (Acid Yellow 1). This nitro-

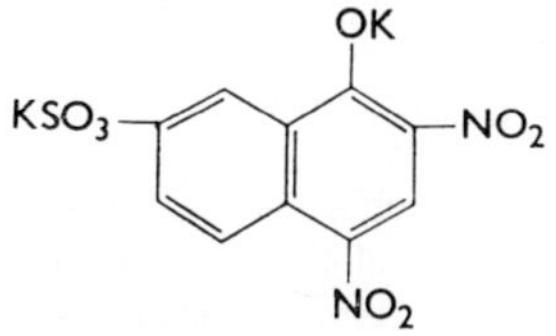

OK

KSO_3 —— —NO$_2$

NO$_2$

dye, the potassium (or sodium) salt of 2,4-dinitro-1-naphthol-7-sulphonic acid (the most important dyestuff of the group) is prepared either by the nitration of 1-naphthol-2,4,7-trisulphonic acid or by the nitration of nitroso-1-naphthol-2,7-disulphonic acid. Naphtol yellow is somewhat faster than the other nitro-dyestuffs. It is used only where fastness to light and washing are of little importance. The dyed materials turn a brownish shade with light. Being non-poisonous it is also used for colouring food (Food Yellow 1).

Naples yellow. A pigment used in oil media and for staining glass and ceramic products. Chemically it is considered to be lead antimonate with some lead oxide approximating to the formula $Pb_3(SbO_4)_2$.

Narcotine, $C_{22}H_{23}NO_7$. Colourless needles,

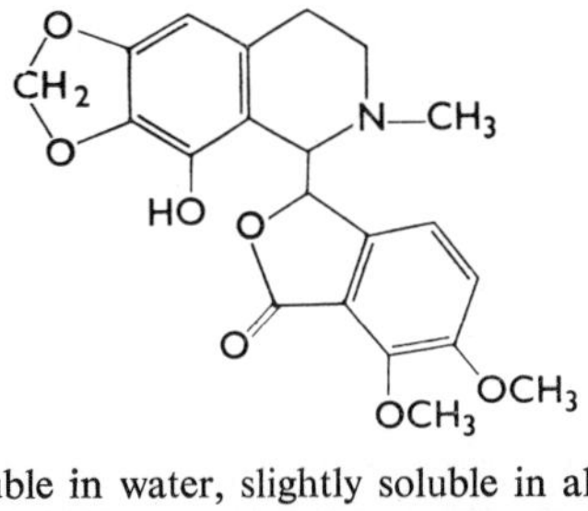

insoluble in water, slightly soluble in alcohol, very soluble in chloroform; laevorotatory. Narcotine is one of the alkaloids of opium, it occurs as the free base in amounts up to 15%. It has a medicinal action resembling that of quinine. It is a constituent of many cough mixtures, as it exerts a suppressive action on the non-productive cough.

Nascent hydrogen. A reactive form of hydrogen obtained *in situ* by electrolysis or by chemical reaction. It is a very powerful reducing agent.

Natural gas. Consists chiefly of the lower members of the paraffin hydrocarbon series. In certain geological formations it issues from the earth under pressure. It acts as an important factor in the production of crude petroleum when produced in association with it. It is also referred to as 'Casinghead gas', and is used extensively as a fuel.

Naval brass. See Brass.

Néel point. The temperature at which magnetic

susceptibility becomes normal. See Anti-ferromagnetism and Ferromagnetism.

Negative adsorption. When adsorption at a surface occurs from a solution, some components may accumulate at higher concentration near the surface than in the bulk, but the others will necessarily be less concentrated there and are said to undergo negative adsorption. According to the Gibbs adsorption equation any solute which raises the interfacial tension of the system will be negatively adsorbed. The negative adsorption of sodium chloride, for example, at the air/water interface has been confirmed by direct experiment.

Negative glow. See Glow discharge.

Nembutal, $C_{11}H_{17}N_2NaO_3$. A trade name for

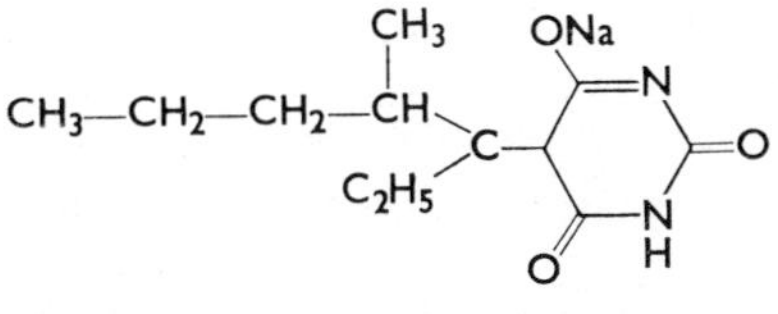

pentobarbital sodium, which is the sodium salt of ethyl-α-methylbutyl barbituric acid. It is a white crystalline powder, very soluble in water and freely soluble in alcohol. It is used as a hypnotic, particularly for its sedative effect before anaesthesia.

Neoarsphenamine, Neosalvarsan,

$$C_{13}H_{13}As_2N_2NaO_4S$$

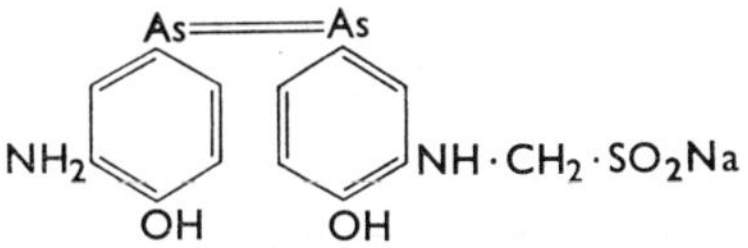

The sodium formaldehyde sulphoxylate compound of arsphenamine. A yellow solid, soluble in water, insoluble in alcohol. The use of this compound has almost entirely replaced that of arsphenamine. It is much less toxic, but slightly less active. It is given intravenously chiefly for syphilis.

Neocinchophen. The ethyl ester of 6-methyl-2-

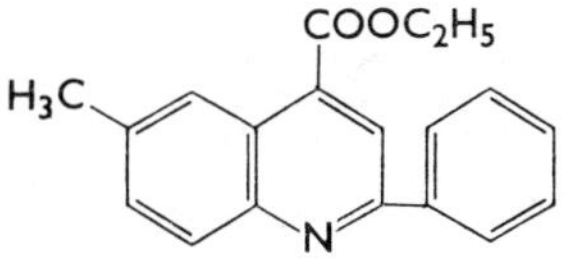

phenylquinoline-4-carboxylic acid, $C_{19}H_{17}NO_2$. A yellowish-white crystalline powder, m.p. 74°. Insoluble in water. It is used medicinally for the same purposes as cinchophen, than which it is less toxic.

Neodymium, Nd. At.no. 60, At.wt. 144·27, *d* 7·004, m.p. 1024°, b.p. 3027°. Neodymium metal has the hexagonal close-packed structure below 868° ($a = 3\cdot6582$, $c = 11\cdot802$ Å) and the body centred cubic structure above 868° ($a = 4\cdot13$ Å). The metal oxidizes readily in air and is a typical rare-earth element (*q.v.*). Neodymium compounds have been used in lasers.

Neodymium compounds. Neodymium (III) compounds are red in colour and are typical rare-earth compounds (*q.v.*). Complex fluorides of neodymium (IV), e.g. Cs_3NdF_7, have been prepared by fluorination of neodymium (III) compounds; $NdCl_2$ and NdI_2 are prepared by reducing the trihalide with metallic neodymium.

Neomycin. An antibiotic produced by *Streptomyces fradiae*, active against staphylococci and some strains of *Pseudomonas* and *Proteus*. It is used for treating skin diseases, and given orally for intestinal infections, but it has severe toxic effects. It is a mixture of several nitrogenous compounds, chemically related to streptomycin.

Neon, Ne. At.no. 10, At.wt. 20·183. Neon is the second most abundant of the rare gases of the atmosphere, in which it occurs to the extent of 0·0018 volume per cent. It was first detected in 1898 by Ramsay and Travers by the fractionation of liquid argon, when it collected in the more volatile fractions. It is now obtained by a combination of fractionation and selective adsorption on activated charcoal, m.p. −248·6°, b.p. −246·0°. The gas is monatomic. The passage of an electrical discharge through neon at low pressure is accompanied by the emission of an orange-red light. This effect is extensively used for illuminated signs. The colour of the discharge may be modified to give a blue or green effect by adding mercury to the neon. The Osglim lamp, which has various technical applications, contains neon or a neon-helium mixture. No chemical compounds of neon are known.

Neopentyl. The name for the group:

$$H_3C-\underset{\underset{\displaystyle CH_3}{|}}{\overset{\overset{\displaystyle CH_3}{|}}{C}}-CH_2-$$

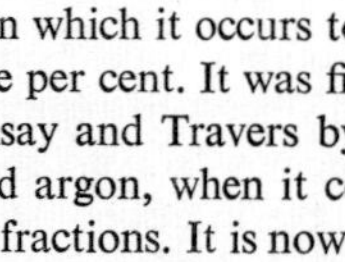

Neophyl. The name for the group:

$$C_6H_5-\underset{\underset{\displaystyle CH_3}{|}}{\overset{\overset{\displaystyle CH_3}{|}}{C}}-CH_2-$$

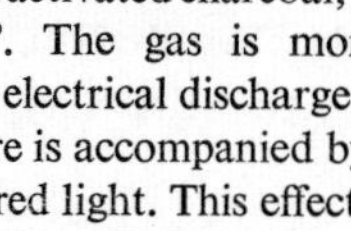

Neoprene. A generic name for the synthetic chloro rubbers obtained by emulsion polymerization of chloroprene (*q.v.*). It has mainly the *trans*-1,4-structure, which accounts for its readiness to crystallize at room temperature. This tendency is controlled by the presence of

sulphur-containing compounds, e.g. thiuram disulphides or by copolymerization with other monomers, e.g. styrene.

By comparison with natural rubber, neoprene has outstanding resistance to oil and ageing, is flame retardant, and has high mechanical strength and abrasion resistance. It has, however, inferior electrical properties due to its greater moisture absorption. It is used in oil resistant products and adhesives, and in the printing field for rollers and plates. It has the property of damping out vibration more than natural rubber and is consequently used extensively in aircraft and motor car production.

Neoprene treated paper has been used as a substitute for cotton filter fabric, giving the paper exceptional wet strength and chemical resistance.

Neoprene can be vulcanized, forming products of high tensile strength without the addition of reinforcing fillers. When stabilized by antioxidants it becomes extremely resistant to degradation.

At low temperatures neoprene loses its flexibility, becoming quite brittle, although this property can be improved by the addition of suitable plasticizers.

Neoretinene. See Rhodopsin.

Neostigmine bromide, $C_{12}H_{19}BrN_2O_2$. A white

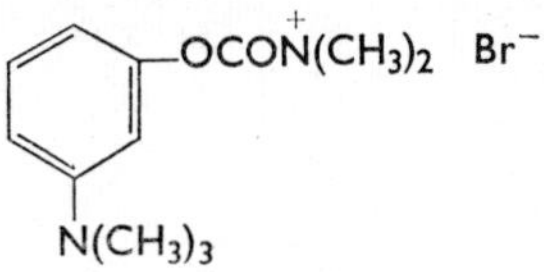

crystalline powder, soluble in water and in alcohol, m.p. 167°, prepared by treating 3-hydroxyphenyltrimethylammonium bromide with dimethylcarbamoyl chloride. Both neostigmine bromide and neostigmine methylsulphate inhibit cholinesterase activity. It thus assists muscular contractions produced by acetylcholine, which is normally destroyed by cholinesterases. It is used to reverse the effect of curarizing drugs, for treating myasthenia gravis, paralytic ileus, and retention of urine following operations.

Nephelauxetic effect. The changes in the spectra of complexes due to the varying degree of covalent character in the metal-ligand bonds. Quantitatively the effect is measured as a ratio of an interelectronic repulsion parameter in a complex compared with the parameter in the free ion.

Nepheline. A feldspathoid mineral occurring in igneous rocks rich in alkali and poor in silica; $(Na,K)(AlSi)_2O_4$ with K_2O not above 7%. The nepheline-containing rock, nepheline syenite, is used as a source of alumina in glass manufacture and as a ceramic flux. Extensive deposits are worked in Ontario.

Nephelometry. A method of quantitative analysis which involves the spectrophotometric estimation of the scattering of light by a colloidal suspension of a precipitate.

Neptunium, Np. At.no. 93, m.p. 640°. All isotopes are radioactive, the most important being ^{237}Np, which has a very long half-life (2·25 × 10^6 years). Its discovery resulted from neutron bombardment of uranium, but traces occur naturally since it is formed by neutron capture by natural uranium. Separation is effected by solvent extraction, ion exchange, or volatility procedures.

The metal is prepared by reducing the trifluoride with barium and appears similar in properties to uranium. It crystallizes in three forms; α-neptunium, stable up to 278°, orthorhombic, $a=4·72$, $b=4·89$, $c=6·66$ Å, d 20·45; β-neptunium, stable 278°-570°, tetragonal, $a=4·90$, $c=3·34$ Å, d 19·36; γ-neptunium, stable 570°-640°, cubic, $a=3·52$ Å, d 18·00.

Neptunium compounds. Similar to uranium compounds. Chief differences are the non-existence of a chloride higher than NpCl$_4$ and the stability of the NpO$_2^+$ ion in aqueous solution. Colours of neptunium salts are: Np^{3+}, blue or purple, Np^{4+}, yellow-green, NpO$_2^+$, green, NpO$_2^{2+}$, pink to red.

Neral. See Citral.

Nernst, Walter (1864-1941). Born at Briesen, West Prussia, Nernst studied at the Universities of Zürich, Berlin, Graz, and Würzburg. He held appointments as professor of physics at Göttingen and at Berlin and Director of the Physik. Techn. Reichsanstalt, Charlottenburg. In 1925 he became Director of the Physical Institute of the University, Berlin. Nernst's brilliant

developed into the Third Law of Thermodynamics.

Nerol, C$_{10}$H$_{18}$O, has the constitutional formula

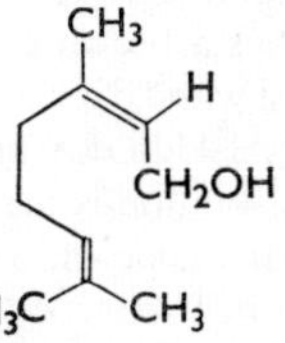

It is a terpenic alcohol and is a constituent of neroli, petit-grain, and bergamot oils and of many other essential oils. It can be separated in the form of its diphenylurethane, m.p. 52°-53°. Nerol has a blander smell than its isomer, geraniol, and is more valuable as a constituent of perfumes. It has the following characteristics, b.p. 225°-226°, d^{15} 0·8813. Nerol resembles geraniol in general properties.

Nerolidol, C$_{15}$H$_{26}$O. A sesquiterpene alcohol,

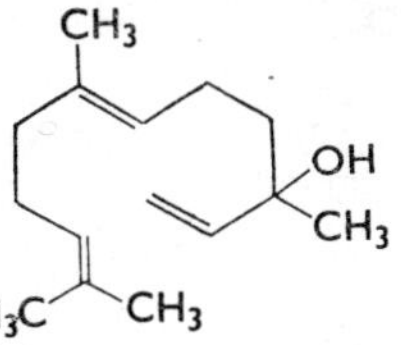

the (+)-form of which is found in neroli oil and in Peru balsam. The corresponding (±)-compound has been obtained synthetically. On oxidation with chromic acid it yields farnesal. (+)-Nerolidol from neroli oil has b.p. 276°, d^{15} 0·8987, n_D^{20} 1·48982, [α]$_D$ +15·5°. (+)-Nerolidol forms a phenylurethane of m.p. 37°-38° but no crystalline derivatives of (±)-nerolidol have been obtained.

Nerve gases. See Fluorophosphoric acids.

Nervone, C$_{48}$H$_{91}$NO$_8$. A cerebroside, crystal-

$$CH_3 \cdot [CH_2]_7 \cdot CH:CH \cdot [CH_2]_{13} \cdot \underset{\underset{\underset{O \cdot CH \cdot [CHOH]_3 \cdot CH \cdot CH_2OH}{|}}{\underset{CH_3 \cdot [CH_2]_{12} \cdot CH_2:CH \cdot CH \cdot CH \cdot CH_2OH}{|}}}{\overset{CO}{\underset{NH}{|}}}$$

researches included contributions to the theory of solutions, work on galvanic cells, and the 'third law' of thermodynamics. He received the Nobel Prize for Chemistry in 1920.

Nernst heat theorem. This states that the internal energy of a system, ΔH, and the corresponding free energy of the system, ΔG, approach each other asymptotically, and become sensibly identical at absolute zero. This theorem was

lizing in needles from alcohol, m.p. 180°, soluble in alcohol, insoluble in water and ether, [α]$_D$ −4·33°, in pyridine. It hydrolyses to D-galactose, sphingosine, and nervonic acid.

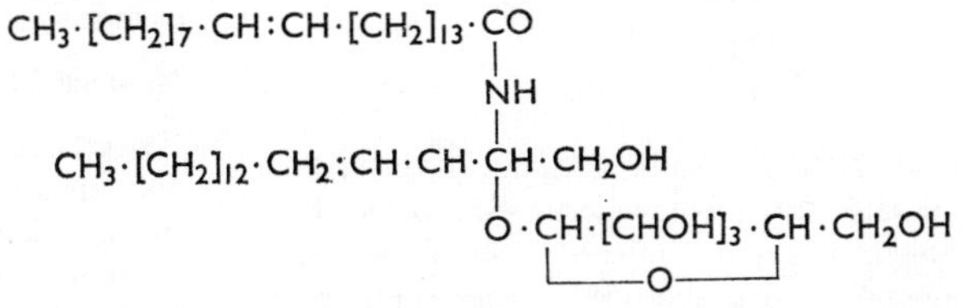

Nervonic acid, cis-14-tetracosanic acid, C$_{24}$H$_{46}$O$_2$,

$$CH_3 \cdot [CH_2]_7 \cdot CH:CH \cdot [CH_2]_{13} \cdot CO_2H$$

A crystalline powder, m.p. 43°, soluble in

alcohol and ether. Obtained on the hydrolysis of nervone.

Nessler's reagent. An alkaline solution of potassium iodomercurate used for detecting ammonia. It gives a brown colour with traces of ammonia, and with larger quantities a brown precipitate of NH_2Hg_2OI. The official British Pharmacopoeia solution is made by dissolving 3·5 g of potassium iodide and 1·25 g of mercuric chloride in 80 ml of water, adding a saturated solution of mercuric chloride till a red precipitate remains, adding 12 g sodium hydroxide and a little more mercuric chloride and making up to 100 ml.

Nessler tubes. Cylinders of thin glass, usually graduated at 50 ml, and used for comparing turbidities and colours of solutions.

Neuraminic acid, $C_9H_{17}NO_8$. An important

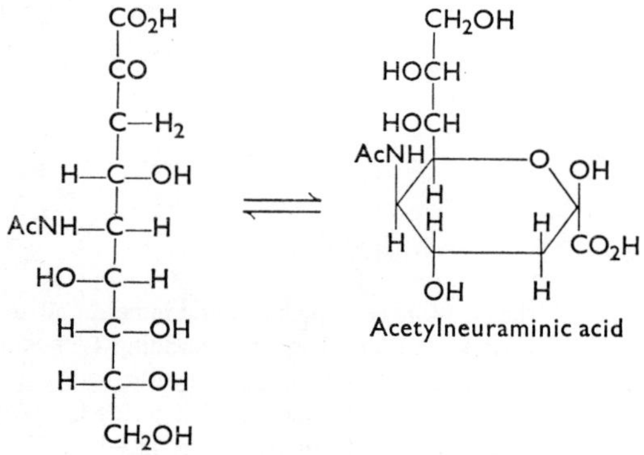

Neutrino. An elementary particle, of mass a fraction of the electron, without charge, and with spin $\frac{1}{2}$, postulated by Pauli to account for the conservation of angular momentum in nuclear transformations. The neutrino has not been directly detected experimentally; it would be expected to pass easily through many kilometres of dense matter.

Neutrocyanines. See Merocyanine dyes.

Neutron. One of the fundamental particles. It has nearly the same mass as a proton but is electrically neutral. It was discovered in 1932 by Chadwick. Neutron diffraction, using the high neutron flux obtainable from an atomic pile, has been used in the determination of molecular structure. A free neutron has a mean life-time of 750 seconds; it decays to give a proton and an electron.

Acetylneuraminic acid

amino sugar, the structure of which represents a condensation product of pyruvic acid with mannosamine. It is widely distributed in animal tissues and secretions, especially in the form of N-acyl derivatives (Sialic acids, *q.v.*).

Neurine, Trimethylvinylammonium hydroxide,

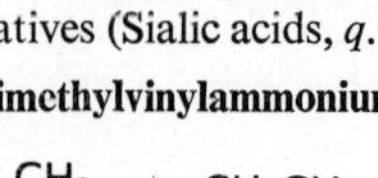

$C_5H_{13}NO$. A liquid forming a crystalline hydrate with three molecules of water. It is present free and combined in brain and other animal and vegetable products and is formed as a product of the putrefaction of lecithin. It can be prepared synthetically from choline and decomposes easily to trimethylamine.

Neutralization, heat of. This is the amount of heat evolved by the neutralization of 1 g equivalent of an acid by 1 g equivalent of a base. For strong acids and strong bases, the heat of neutralization is 13,700 calories, because the only reaction which occurs is the formation of 1 g molecule of water from its ions.

Newlands, John Alexander Reina (1837-1898). Born at Southwark and educated privately, Newlands later studied chemistry under Hofmann. After holding several junior teaching appointments he became chief chemist in a sugar refinery at Victoria Docks. In 1864 he noted a certain periodicity among the chemical elements and announced his law of octaves.

Newlands' Law. See Octaves, law of.

Niacytin. A substance isolated from wheat bran and apparently constituting a 'bound' form of nicotinic acid, rendering this unassimilable by mammals. It is composed of nicotinic acid (5%), glucose (about 50%), xylose, arabinose, and phenolic compounds, principally phenol carboxylic esters.

Nichrome. See Nickel alloys.

Nickel. At.no. 28, At.wt. 58·69. A hard silver-white metal, m.p. 1453°, b.p. 2800°, density 8·90. The metal is not tarnished in air, is attacked by acids except concentrated nitric acid, but is resistant to fused sodium hydroxide. Nickel crystallizes in two forms: α-Ni has the close-packed hexagonal structure, $a=2{\cdot}49$, $c=4{\cdot}08$ Å, and β-Ni has the cubic close-packed structure, $a=3{\cdot}5238$ Å.

The most important nickel ores are found in the Sudbury region of Ontario, Canada. These ores are double sulphides of copper, iron, and nickel, and contain also small amounts of cobalt, selenium, tellurium, silver, and the precious metals (platinum, palladium, gold, etc.). A typical 'rich' ore contains about 2·5% nickel, 4-5% copper, about 30% iron, and 25% silica. The ores are concentrated by flotation and smelted to produce a nickel-copper matte which is treated by one of the following processes:

(a) Orford Process—The matte is treated with nitre cake (sodium sulphate) and coke to produce a mixture of molten sulphides of nickel, copper, and sodium, which on cooling, separates into two layers, the top containing the double sulphides of copper and sodium while the bottom is largely nickel sulphide. The 'tops' and 'bottoms' are separated and the bottoms re-treated to complete the separation. The bottoms are then crushed, ground and leached first with hot water to remove sodium sulphate and then with acid to remove remaining copper and iron, after which they are dried and sintered to produce a crude oxide from which the nickel is extracted.

(b) Since 1949 the Orford process has been gradually superseded by a process in which copper, nickel, and platinum metals are separated by subjecting the matter to controlled cooling, flotation, and magnetic separation. The nickel-rich concentrate is then roasted to oxide. The oxide produced by either of the above processes is treated by either (a) the Mond process or (b) the Electrolytic (Hybinette) process.

(a) Carbonyl process (Mond process).

The oxide is reduced by hydrogen at 400° and the crude nickel converted to nickel carbonyl by reaction with carbon monoxide at 50°. The carbonyl is then heated to 180°, when nickel is deposited in pellet form.

(b) Electrolytic process (Hybinette process).

The oxide is reduced with carbon (coke) to give crude nickel which is cast into anodes. These are placed in a nickel sulphate bath and electrolysed, using thin nickel sheets as cathodes which are withdrawn when of sufficient thickness and cut up for use in alloying or remelted and cast into ingots.

Nickel is used in the form of alloys, as a catalyst in the hydrogenation of fats, and for electroplating.

Nickel accumulator. The nickel accumulator employs the reaction

$$Fe(s)+Ni^{III}+H_2O \rightarrow Fe(OH)_2(s)+Ni(OH)_2$$

The reaction is carried out in an alkaline medium, usually potassium hydroxide with some lithium hydroxide. On charging the ferrous hydroxide is reduced to iron and the nickel hydroxide oxidized to nickel (III) oxide. Its discharge-voltage is only about 1·2 V, and as compared with the lead accumulator it has a rather low current efficiency and is rather more expensive. But it has compensating advantages in lower weight and greater mechanical strength, for the electrode materials are compressed into perforated pockets of nickel-plated steel, and the accumulator can therefore withstand mechanical shocks and high rates of charge or discharge. Many modifications, such as the admixture of other oxides, have been proposed, without affecting the principle of its operation; in particular the partial replacement of iron by cadmium is beneficial.

Nickel alloys. Used for corrosion and scaling resistance. They are expensive and so are confined to specialized applications. *Monel* (67% Ni, 30% Cu, 1·4% Fe, 1% Mn) is a solid solution; it is strong (30 t.s.i.) and tough and has good corrosion resistance under both oxidizing and reducing conditions. It is also resistant to carburizing gases at high temperatures. *K Monel* is a variation containing precipitation-hardening additives which raise the strength to 60 t.s.i. The *Hastelloy* alloys are basically nickel with substantial additions of molybdenum, iron, chromium, tungsten and silicon; the various alloys are resistant to different acids and other chemical engineering corrosive conditions. Many corrosion and heat-resistant alloys are all based on wide variations of the 80% Ni, 20% Cr alloy. *Nichrome* and other equivalent alloys are used in the form of wire and strip for the windings of electrical resistances, furnaces and domestic heaters. *Inconel*, which contains 76% Ni, 15% Cr, 9% Fe, is resistant to acids and alkalis over a wide range of pH values, as well as to high-temperature oxidizing conditions. The *Nimonics* are mainly used for oxidation and creep resistance at very high temperatures such as in jet engines. They contain small additions of other metals which provide the increased strength and creep resistance by a precipitation hardening mechanism. Alloys for permanent magnets such as *Permalloy* contain from 50 to 80% Ni. Alloys such as *Nilo* and *Invar* contain from 36 to 50% Ni, balance Fe; these alloys have controlled low and intermediate coefficients of thermal expansion and so may be used in clocks, thermostats and glass-to-metal seals.

Nickel ammines. Anhydrous salts of nickel, such as the chloride, readily absorb ammonia gas, swelling up to form white voluminous powders with six ammonia molecules per nickel atom.

Salts of the cation $Ni(NH_3)_6^{2+}$ are present in the deep blue solutions obtained by addition of excess of ammonia to solutions of nickel salts, and many of them have been isolated as deep blue or violet crystals. In particular the chloride, bromide, and perchlorate are well known, being only slightly soluble in cold aqueous ammonia.

In addition to the hexammino-salts, a number of lower ammines, and of mixed ammino-hydrates, e.g. $[Ni(NH_3)_4]SO_4, H_2O$ are known.

These compounds are all decomposed by water except in presence of excess of ammonia, and slowly lose ammonia on exposure to air.

Nickel ammonium sulphate,

$$NiSO_4, (NH_4)_2SO_4, 6H_2O.$$

Crystallizes in bluish-green monoclinic prisms from a solution of its component salts. It is not very soluble, 100 g of water dissolving 3·2 g. at 0°, 5·9 g. at 20°, and 14·4 g at 50°. It is used in electroplating.

Nickel arsenide. This compound, NiAs, has given its name to an important crystal structure type. The structure is hexagonal. Many compounds of transition metals with B-sub-group elements crystallize with this structure, for example: CuSn, CrSb, CrSe, NiAs, NiSb, NiBi, PtSn, PtSb. The metal is in octahedral co-ordination but the co-ordination about the non-metal is that of a trigonal biprism.

Nickelates. Nickelates (IV) are obtained by fusing nickel oxide with alkali and an oxidizing agent such as potassium nitrate. They are also obtained by passing oxygen through a nickel tube containing fused alkali. Nickelates (III), $MNiO_2$, are formed by passing oxygen through molten alkali contained in nickel tubes at 650°.

Nickel bromide, $NiBr_2$. The anhydrous salt closely resembles the chloride and may be obtained by similar methods. The hydrate which usually crystallizes from solution is the *trihydrate*, $NiBr_2, 3H_2O$. The *hexahydrate*, $NiBr_2, 6H_2O$, is formed in the cold, but melts in its own water at 28·5°. Below $-2\cdot5°$ an *enneahydrate*, $NiBr_2, 9H_2O$, is formed. 100 g of saturated solution contain at 0° 53·0 g, and at 100° 60·8 g, of $NiBr_2$.

Nickel carbonates. The green precipitates which are thrown down by alkali carbonates from solutions of nickel salts are basic carbonates of somewhat indefinite composition. To prepare the normal carbonate a solution of sodium bicarbonate saturated with carbon dioxide must be employed, and the temperature kept low, when unstable green monoclinic crystals of $NiCO_3, 6H_2O$ are formed. The anhydrous carbonate has been obtained as green rhombo-hedra by the action of calcium carbonate on nickel chloride solution at 150° in a sealed tube.

Nickel carbonyl, $Ni(CO)_4$. A colourless liquid that gives off a toxic vapour; $d\,1\cdot32$, m.p. $-25°$, b.p. 43°. It is prepared by passing carbon monoxide over finely divided nickel at less than 100°. It is used on a large scale in the preparation of nickel by the Mond process, since it is easily decomposed into the metal and carbon monoxide, and as a catalyst in many reactions involving acetylene.

Nickel chloride, $NiCl_2$. The anhydrous chloride sublimes in yellow scales when the metal is heated in chlorine. It can also be obtained by dehydrating the hydrates in an atmosphere of hydrogen chloride. It has the cadmium chloride structure, and its sp.gr. is 3·52. From its solutions the *hexahydrate*, $NiCl_2, 6H_2O$, crystallizes in green deliquescent monoclinic prisms, soluble in alcohol and very soluble in water. 100 g of the saturated solution contain at 0° 35·0 g, at 20° 39·1 g, and at 100° 46·7 g of $NiCl_2$. Hydrates with 7, 4, and 2 H_2O are also known.

Nickel chloride forms a number of double salts with chlorides of the alkali group. Of these nickel ammonium chloride,

$$NiCl_2, NH_4Cl, 6H_2O$$

(green, monoclinic) is the best known.

Nickel complexes. Nickel forms many complexes. Most complexes are light-coloured, paramagnetic, with octahedral co-ordination about the metal, e.g. $[Ni(NH_3)_6]^{2+}$. Red complexes, diamagnetic, have square planar co-ordination. Dark blue or green complexes, e.g. $Ni(Ph_3P)_2Cl_2$, have tetrahedral coordination.

Nickel cyanides. $Ni(CN)_2$ is formed as a green precipitate when an alkali cyanide is added to a solution of a nickel salt. It dissolves in excess of precipitant. A tetrahydrate, $Ni(CN)_2, 4H_2O$, has been obtained in steel-blue leaflets. The cyanide forms complexes with ammonia which have the power of forming clathrate compounds with aromatic hydrocarbons.

Nickel cyanides, complex. Nickel cyanide dissolves in excess of alkali cyanide, and complex salts of the type $M^I_2Ni(CN)_4$ may be crystallized from the solution; $K_2Ni(CN)_4, H_2O$ is the best-known of these. When their solutions are treated with alkali hypobromites the hydrated higher oxide is precipitated, whereas the corresponding cobalt solution is converted to the very stable cobalticyanide. This fact is the basis of an important method for separating nickel from cobalt.

Complex cyanides containing unipositive nickel, such as the red $[K_2Ni(CN)_3]_2$, are formed

400

when the ordinary cyanide solutions are reduced with sodium amalgam. Further reduction gives complexes containing zero-positive nickel, e.g. $K_4Ni(CN)_4$.

Nickel dimethylglyoxime. The normal form in which nickel is weighed in analysis. There is

metal-metal bonding in the solid. The red complex is precipitated from alkaline solution.

Nickel fluoride, NiF_2, $4H_2O$. Obtained in green rhombic octohedra by evaporation of a solution of the hydroxide or carbonate in hydrofluoric acid. The anhydrous salt is yellowish-green, and forms tetragonal crystals having the rutile structure. A number of double salts, such as $(NH_4)NiF_3$ are known. Complex nickel fluorides containing both tri- and tetrapositive nickel, e.g. K_3NiF_6 and K_2NiF_6, are known.

Nickel formate, $Ni(HCOO)_2 \cdot 2H_2O$. A pale green powder, sparingly soluble in water, soluble in acids. It decomposes at about 250°. It is used in the preparation of nickel catalysts for the hydrogenation of oil in the manufacture of soaps and edible fats.

Nickel hydroxide, $Ni(OH)_2$. Obtained as an apple-green precipitate by the action of alkalis on solutions of nickel salts. It can be obtained crystalline by boiling its solution in aqueous ammonia. It is very slightly soluble in water (12·7 mg per litre) and dissolves readily in dilute acids, forming nickel salts, and in ammonia, forming a deep blue solution of an ammino-hydroxide, but it is quite insoluble in caustic alkalis. The ammoniacal solution dissolves silk but not cotton.

Nickel iodide, NiI_2. Crystallizes from solution as the *hexahydrate*, NiI_2, $6H_2O$. It forms bluish-green hygroscopic crystals; 100 g of saturated solution contain at 0° 55·4 g and at 100° 65·3 g of NiI_2. The anhydrous salt is black and is made by direct union of the elements. A monoiodide, NiI, has been made by electrolytic reduction.

Nickel nitrate, $Ni(NO_3)_2$, crystallizes from its solutions at ordinary temperatures as the *hexahydrate*, $Ni(NO_3)_2$, $6H_2O$. This forms green monoclinic crystals which deliquesce in moist air. At 56·7° they melt in their own water; hydrates with 9, 4, and 2 molecules of water are also known. The *anhydrous salt* cannot be obtained by dehydration of the hydrates, but it has been obtained as a yellow powder by the action of liquid N_2O_4 on the metal. Nickel nitrate is very soluble in water: 100 g of satur-

ated solution contain at 0° 44·3 g, at 20° 49·0 g and at 100° 77·1 g of $Ni(NO_3)_2$.

Nickel nitrites, complex. Nickel nitrite, $Ni(NO_2)_2$, may be prepared by interaction of nickel carbonyl and N_2O_4. Stable complex nitrites such as $K_4Ni(NO_2)_6$ (red octahedra) may be crystallized from solutions of their components.

Nickel oxides. NiO is obtained as a green powder by ignition of the hydroxide, nitrate, or carbonate. At higher temperatures it becomes crystalline. It has the rock-salt structure, d 6·8. It dissociates by loss of oxygen above 1000° and is readily reduced to the metal by carbon, hydrogen, or carbon monoxide, the reduction by the latter gas beginning at temperatures as low as 120°. It dissolves easily in mineral acids, forming nickel salts.

The higher oxides are formed as indefinite hydrates by the action of chlorine on suspensions of nickel hydroxide, or by the action of alkaline oxidizing agents such as hypobromites on solutions of nickel salts. They are brown or black precipitates, whose composition may be represented by NiO_x, yH_2O, where $1 < x < 2$. Higher oxides have also been obtained by dry methods; all of these oxides are strong oxidizing agents.

Nickel peroxide, NiO_2, xH_2O, is a quite different substance, and may be regarded as isomeric with the limiting member of the series of oxides referred to above. It is formed by the action of hydrogen peroxide on nickel hydroxide, and is a green substance having the reactions of a true peroxide of dipositive nickel.

Nickel perchlorate, $Ni(ClO_4)_2$. Prepared by dissolving nickel carbonate in perchloric acid. It occurs with 9, 7, 5, 4, and 2 molecules of water and is much used in the study of nickel complexes.

Nickel-silver. The name given to alloys containing 10%-30% Ni, 5%-45% Zn, and the rest copper. These alloys have been widely used in the past for cutlery, tableware, etc., and now such articles as cocks, taps, ornamental castings, are made of them. The actual composition varies for castings of different classes and small amounts of tin, lead, and manganese are often added.

Nickel sulphate, $NiSO_4$. Crystallizes at ordinary temperatures as the heptahydrate $NiSO_4$, $7H_2O$. This forms green rhombic prisms isomorphous with ferrous sulphate heptahydrate, and hence sometimes called nickel vitriol. Crystallization at higher temperatures yields the hexahydrate $NiSO_4$, $6H_2O$, of which there are two modifications: blue, tetragonal pyramids, and green, monoclinic. The blue hexahydrate is the stable solid phase above 31·5°, and the transition to the green form is at 53·3°. Lower hydrates with 5, 4, 2, and $1H_2O$ are known. The monohydrate $NiSO_4, H_2O$ is formed when the other hydrates are heated at 100°, and it is precipitated from solutions of nickel sulphate by concentrated sulphuric acid. As is usual with the sulphates of the vitriol group, the last molecule of water is firmly bound, and cannot be expelled below 280°, at which temperature the anhydrous sulphate, a yellow hygroscopic powder, is obtained.

The anhydrous salt appears insoluble but the hydrates are readily soluble; 100 g of water dissolve at 0° 27·2 g and at 99° 76·7 g of $NiSO_4$.

Double sulphates with the alkali sulphates, of the type $NiSO_4$, $M^I_2SO_4$, $6H_2O$, exist. Of these the best known is nickel ammonium sulphate.

Nickel sulphides. The best-known sulphide of nickel is the monosulphide NiS. When prepared in the dry way it forms a bronze-like mass, insoluble in hydrochloric or sulphuric acid, but soluble in nitric acid. After precipitation it is insoluble in dilute hydrochloric acid, but it cannot be precipitated from acid solutions.

Study of the equilibrium relationships in the nickel-sulphur system indicates that a number of other compounds, Ni_3S_2, Ni_6S_5, and NiS_2, exist.

Nickel vitriol. See Nickel sulphate.

Nicol prism. A calcite crystal, cut in such a way that only one of the refracted rays emerges, the other being returned by total internal reflexion in the direction of the light source. Since the two refracted rays produced when a beam of light enters a calcite crystal are plane polarized in directions which are mutually at right angles, the light emerging from a Nicol prism is plane-polarized.

Nicotinamide-adenine dinucleotide (NAD, NAD⁺). An extremely important and wide-

indicative of the chemical structure, has been approved by the International Union of Biochemistry.

The coenzyme functions as a hydrogen-transfer agent as indicated below:

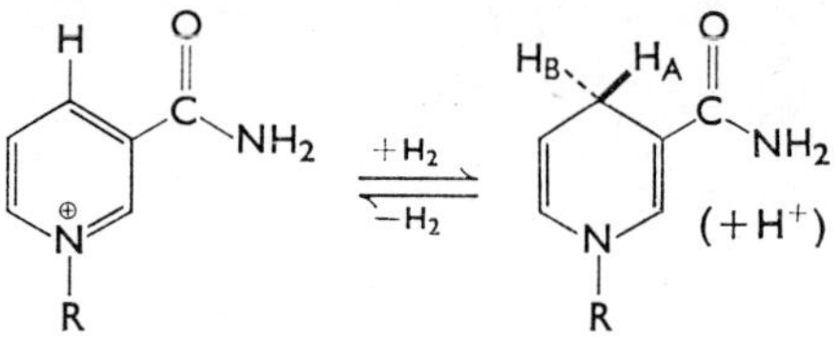

In general, the hydrogen transfer is stereo-specific with respect both to the substrate and to the coenzyme. Certain enzymes activate the 'A' hydrogen in the reduced coenzyme, while others exclusively activate the 'B' hydrogen. The reduced form of the coenzyme may be designated as 'reduced NAD' or as 'NAD $(-H^+)$': in the latter case it is important to write the oxidized form as 'NAD⁺' to emphasize that the reduction involves two electronic equivalents. The form 'NADH₂' is also used.

Nicotinamide-adenine dinucleotide phosphate (NADP, NADP⁺). An important coenzyme of the pyridine nucleotide class. The structure is that of NAD except that the adenosine moiety bears an additional phosphate group at the 2'-position ($R=OPO_3H_2$).

NADP was formerly known by other names, e.g. phospho-cozymase, coenzyme II, code-hydrogenase II, and triphosphopyridine nucleotide (TPN, TPN⁺).

Like NAD, NADP is concerned in hydride-transfer reactions, but the two coenzymes function at different stages in metabolism: NAD—NADH₂ is especially concerned in oxidative phosphorylation, while NADP—NADPH₂ is particularly involved in biosynthesis.

Since the dihydropyridine group in NADH₂

spread coenzyme, formerly known by various names, e.g. cozymase, coenzyme I, codehydrogenase I, and diphosphopyridine nucleotide (DPN, DPN⁺). The present name, which is

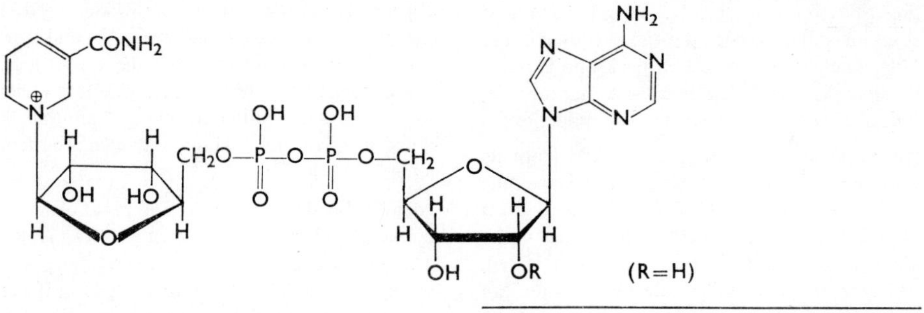

and NADPH₂ has a strong absorption maximum at 340 mμ, whereas the pyridinium group has negligible absorption in this region, enzymic reactions involving the pyridine nucleotides can conveniently be followed spectrophotometrically. This provides a means of assay of enzymes or substrates, and is of wide practical value.

Nicotine, 3 - (1 - methyl - 2 - pyrrolidyl)pyridine, $C_{10}H_{14}N_2$. When pure, nicotine is a colourless liquid, b.p. 247°, $[\alpha]_D - 169°$, but darkens on exposure to air and light. It is soluble in water and most organic solvents. Crude nicotine contains small amounts of other alkaloids, but $(-)$-nicotine is the principal component. It is very poisonous.

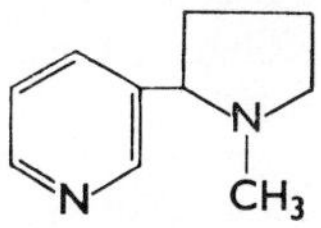

It is used as an insecticide and usually manufactured from tobacco, which contains from 0·5 to 3%.

Nicotinic acid, $C_6H_5NO_2$. Crystallizes in white needles, m.p. 232°, soluble in hot water and alcohol. It can be prepared by oxidizing nicotine with a variety of agents or, more cheaply, from pyridine or quinoline. Nicotinic acid is an essential component of mammalian diet; it is, in fact, the pellagra-preventing factor of vitamin B or a precursor of it. Its amide, nicotinamide, is a constituent of very important coenzymes. See Nicotinamide-adenine dinucleotide.

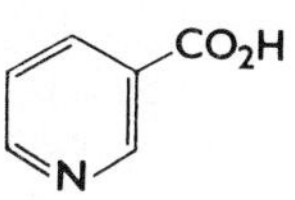

Nicrosilal. An austenitic alloy cast iron containing about 18% Ni and 4% to 6% Si. It is of use in high-temperature work, combining as it does high corrosion, heat, and oxidation resistance. See Ni-Resist, Nomag.

Nieuwland, Julius Arthur (1878-1936). Born at Hansbeke, Belgium, Nieuwland was taken to the United States when three years of age. He was educated at Notre Dame University, Indiana, where he became professor of organic chemistry in 1923. His most important researches were on acetylene, and his preparation of divinylacetylene and monovinylacetylene formed the basis of work leading to the production of the artificial rubber 'Duprene.' He also played an important part in the discovery and development of lewisite.

Ni-Hard. An alloy cast iron containing $4\frac{1}{2}\%$ Ni and $1\frac{1}{2}\%$ Cr. This alloy is finding increasing use in engineering where abrasion resistance, combined with hardness and toughness, is required.

Nikethamide, N-diethylnicotinamide,

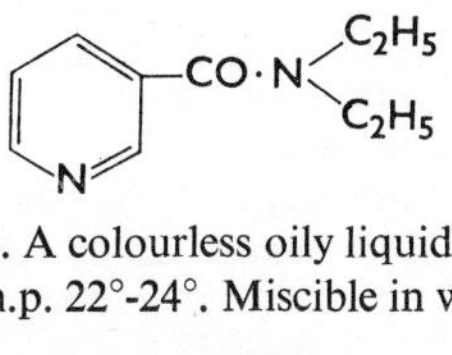

$C_{10}H_{14}N_2O$. A colourless oily liquid or crystalline solid, m.p. 22°-24°. Miscible in water, soluble in organic solvents. It is prepared from nicotinic acid and thionyl chloride, the acid chloride being then treated with diethylamine. Nikethamide is a respiratory stimulant, acting on the medullary centres, and is used in respiratory failure.

Nilo. See Nickel alloys.

Nilson, Fredrik (1840-1899). Born in East Gothland, Nilson studied at the University of Uppsala before engaging in mineralogical research with Sven Otto Petterson. In 1878 Nilson was appointed professor of analytical chemistry at the University of Uppsala and in 1883 was transferred to the Agricultural Academy at Stockholm. By the employment of a potash fertilizer he converted the calcareous moors of the Island of Gothland into land suitable for the growth of sugar beet. See Mem. Lect., *J. Chem. Soc.*, 1900, 1277.

Nimonics. See Nickel alloys.

Ninhydrin, Triketohydrindene hydrate, $C_9H_4O_3 \cdot H_2O$. Light brown crystals, losing water at 125°-130°, m.p. 242° (decomp.). Ninhydrin can be prepared by oxidizing diketohydrindene with selenium dioxide. It gives a blue colour on heating with proteins, peptides, and amino acids and is much used for their detection, particularly as a spray reagent in paper chromatography.

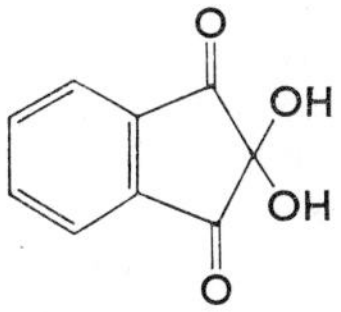

Niobic acid and niobates. The term niobic acid has been applied to the hydrated forms of niobium pentoxide which are formed on hydrolysis of the pentachloride or oxychloride, or by the action of mineral acids on solutions of niobates; the white powders produced in this way contain varying amounts of water, all of which may be driven off by heating to 300°. They are now regarded as gels of niobium pentoxide. When freshly precipitated, the gels are soluble in acids and in alkali solutions, but the solubility decreases on heating or after standing. Numerous niobates, frequently of complex and somewhat indefinite composition, have been described; only those of the alkali metals are soluble in water.

Both orthoniobates, e.g. Na_3NbO_4, and metaniobates, e.g. $NaNbO_3 \cdot 3H_2O$, are known; other polymeric niobates exist. By treatment of niobic acid with hydrogen peroxide, greenish-yellow peroxyniobates are formed. The salt K_3NbO_8 can be precipitated from solution with alcohol. Many niobates are known in the solid state. These are mixed metal oxides (*q.v.*).

Niobium (Columbium), Nb (Cb). At.no. 41,

At.wt. 92·91. A metallic element, occurring in small quantities in numerous minerals, almost invariably as the pentoxide Nb_2O_5. In nature niobium is always associated with the rather less rare element tantalum, to which it shows close similarity in chemical properties. The principal niobium mineral is columbite or niobite, a niobate of iron and manganese, in which the niobium is to some extent replaced by tantalum; specimens rich in tantalum are known as tantalite. This mineral is of frequent occurrence, particularly in Western Australia. The extraction of niobium from its minerals is generally effected by fusion with an alkali, or an alkali carbonate or bisulphite; the product is extracted with water, and the solution of alkali niobate and tantalate decomposed by boiling, when the pentoxides Nb_2O_5 and Ta_2O_5 are precipitated; these are then treated by special methods to remove other elements, particularly titanium.

Metallic niobium is grey, or white when polished, the polished surface becoming slightly yellowish on exposure to air. Some methods of preparation give the metal as a fine black powder. Crystallizes with the body-centred cubic structure $a=3·30$ Å; m.p. 2497°, b.p. 3300°, d 8·57, sp.ht. 0·071. Niobium is said to be less malleable and ductile than tantalum, except in the annealed state. It is harder than wrought iron, and can be welded. From 0·5 to 2·0% niobium is added to steels to provide creep resistance at high temperatures; about 1·0% may be present in stainless steel to prevent weld decay.

Niobium bromides. *Niobium pentabromide*, $NbBr_5$. A red powder or red crystals, m.p. about 150°, volatilizing without decomposition in nitrogen or carbon dioxide at about 270°. Prepared by the action of bromine vapour on gently heated powdered niobium. Readily decomposed by water to niobic acids, and slowly transformed into the oxybromide, $NbOBr_3$, in contact with air. The oxybromide is a yellow solid, very similar to the oxychloride in properties and methods of preparation.

Lower halides $NbBr_4$, $NbBr_3$ and $NbBr_2$, are known. They appear to have polymeric structures.

Niobium carbide, NbC. A grey or brown crystalline solid of great hardness (9-10); sp.gr. 8·2, m.p. 4000°, b.p. 4300°. Produced on heating a mixture of niobium metal and carbon to 1200° in hydrogen.

Niobium chlorides, *Niobium pentachloride*, $NbCl_5$. Yellow needle crystals, sp.gr. 2·73-2·77, m.p. 194°, b.p. 241°, prepared by heating niobium or a mixture of niobium pentoxide and carbon in chlorine; it is difficult to separate from the oxychloride, $NbOCl_3$, which is formed when the pentoxide is used. Niobium pentachloride is hydrolysed by water, giving niobic acids; it is soluble in carbon tetrachloride, chloroform, and alcohol, and very soluble in carbon disulphide. It reacts at a red heat with niobium pentoxide, giving niobium oxychloride, $NbOCl_3$. The oxytrichloride is a white solid forming complex oxychlorides; the pentachloride forms unstable complex chlorides containing the $NbCl_6^-$ ion.

Niobium tetrachloride. $NbCl_4$. Prepared from the metal and the pentachloride. It is a reducing agent which disproportionates above 420°.

Niobium trichloride, $NbCl_3$. A black crystalline solid, resembling iodine in appearance, formed by passing niobium pentachloride vapour through a red-hot tube. It is oxidized on exposure to air, and gives niobium oxychloride, $NbOCl_3$, and carbon monoxide on heating in carbon dioxide.

An intermediate chloride, $Nb_6Cl_{14}·7H_2O$, containing the $[Nb_6Cl_{12}]^{2+}$ ion with metal-metal bonding is also known.

Niobium fluorides. *Niobium pentafluoride*, NbF_5. Colourless, strongly refractive, monoclinic prisms; m.p. 78·9°, b.p. 234·9°, d 3·29. Prepared by the action of fluorine on niobium at 250°, or by the action of anhydrous hydrogen fluoride on niobium pentachloride in a freezing mixture; in either case the product is purified by distillation. The pentafluoride is very hygroscopic and dissolves in water, giving a solution from which niobic acid is precipitated on adding ammonia. Double fluorides (e.g. K_2NbF_7, $KNbF_6$) are very readily formed by niobium pentafluoride and fluorides of other metals.

Niobium trifluoride, NbF_3. A dark blue solid prepared by the action of a hydrogen/hydrogen fluoride mixture on niobium hydride.

Niobium oxyfluorides. $NbOF_3$ and NbO_2F have been reported but are not well characterized. 'Nioboxyfluorides', e.g. Na_3NbOF_6, are well known.

Niobium hydride. A grey or black powder having the approximate composition NbH; prepared by heating niobium in hydrogen, and by other methods. At low temperatures it is a superconductor.

Niobium iodides. *Niobium penta-iodide*, NbI_5, results from the interaction of niobium and iodine.

Niobium tetra-iodide, NbI_4, results by heating NbI_5. It is diamagnetic and the structure shows metal-metal bonding.

Niobium tri-iodide, NbI_3, is obtained by the action of aluminium iodide on niobium pentoxide.

Niobium di-iodide, NbI_2, is prepared as a grey-black powder by reducing the tri-iodide in hydrogen at 300°-400°. It is a strong reducing agent.

Niobium nitrides, NbN and Nb_2N. The nitride NbN forms a grey powder, m.p. 2050°, prepared by heating niobium pentoxide with carbon in nitrogen at 1250°. The nitride, Nb_2N, may be obtained by heating NbN with an equivalent amount of niobium.

Niobium oxides. *Diniobium monoxide*, Nb_2O. An unstable compound prepared by reducing the pentoxide with hydrogen in the presence of moisture.

Niobium monoxide, NbO. A grey metallic powder obtained by heating the dioxide in argon at 1750°.

Niobium dioxide, NbO_2. A bluish-black powder obtained by heating the pentoxide with carbon, or in hydrogen. Unattacked by acids, but oxidized to the pentoxide on heating in air.

Niobium pentoxide, Nb_2O_5. A white powder, becoming yellow on heating; the sp.gr. varies with the method of preparation from 4·37 to 5·02; m.p. 1200°-1250°. Prepared by heating niobium or a lower oxide in oxygen, or by igniting the hydrated oxide precipitated by boiling a solution of an alkali niobate. After ignition the pentoxide resists attack by acids, except hydrofluoric acid. Fused alkalis or alkali carbonates or bisulphates readily react, giving niobates.

Niobium sulphides. The following phases exist in the system niobium/sulphur, Nb_2S, NbS, Nb_2S_3, NbS_4. All may be obtained by heating together the free elements.

Ni-Resist. An austenitic alloy cast iron, containing approximately 14% Ni, 6% Cu, and 2% Cr. It has good corrosion-resisting properties combined with high wear and heat resistance. See also Nicrosilal, Nomag.

Nisin. A mixture of cyclic polypeptides with antibacterial activity produced by some strains of *Streptococcus lactis*. All contain the unusual amino-acids lanthionine, β-methyllanthionine and dehydroalanine. Nisin is used in cheese processing.

Niton. An old name for radon.

Nitrates. The nitrates, salts of nitric acid, are stable compounds which, like the parent acid, are oxidizing agents. All metallic nitrates are soluble in water. Some, such as uranyl nitrate, are readily extracted into organic solvents. Some metallic nitrates, e.g. $Cu(NO_3)_2$ and $Hg(NO_3)_2$ are volatile. On heating, most nitrates decompose, leaving the oxide of the metal and evolving nitrogen dioxide and oxygen; sodium and potassium nitrates, however, give the corresponding nitrites and oxygen, while ammonium nitrate decomposes to nitrous oxide and steam. Nitrates are conveniently identified by the 'brown ring' test; ferrous sulphate is added to the cold solution to be tested, and concentrated sulphuric acid added down the side of the test tube; in the presence of a nitrate a brown or black ring is formed at the junction of the two liquids. This test is unreliable in the presence of bromide or iodide (which also give coloured rings); a sounder test is reduction to ammonia by nascent hydrogen, e.g. from Devarda's alloy and caustic soda. Nitric acid and the nitrates (particularly those of sodium, potassium, calcium, and ammonium) are of great commercial importance; practically all modern explosives contain high proportions of ammonium nitrate or organic nitro-compounds. Nitrates are also employed as fertilizers.

Nitration. See Nitro-compounds.

Nitric acid, HNO_3. A colourless liquid, sp.gr. 1·52, b.p. 86° with partial decomposition; freezes to colourless crystals, m.p. −42°. Miscible in all proportions with water; forms an azeotrope containing 68% by wt. nitric acid, b.p. 120·5°. Hydrates $HNO_3 \cdot H_2O$, $2HNO_3 \cdot 3H_2O$ and $HNO_3 \cdot 3H_2O$ are known.

Nitric acid is today produced almost exclusively from ammonia. A mixture of ammonia and dust-free air containing about 10% by volume of the former is passed into a converter maintained at a temperature of 800°-950°. The converter contains layers of fine platinum-rhodium gauze, and in its passage through them the ammonia is oxidized to a mixture of nitric oxide and water. The gases are cooled, mixed with more air to oxidize the nitric oxide to nitrogen dioxide, and then passed into a cooled absorption column or columns fed with water. An acid containing 50-68% HNO_3 is produced. This is coloured due to the presence of nitrogen oxides; it is bleached by blowing air through it. The equations for the reactions are

$$4NH_3 + O_2 \rightarrow 4NO + 6H_2O$$
$$2NO + O_2 \rightarrow 2NO_2$$
$$3NO_2 + H_2O \rightarrow 2HNO_3 + NO$$

The ammonia conversion is carried out at 1-8 atm. pressure and the absorption process at 3-8 atm. Numerous processes based on the above scheme exist. They differ in the pressures at which the oxidation and absorption processes are carried out, the method of utilizing the considerable heat of reaction, method of cooling the absorption column(s) etc.

Because nitric acid forms an azeotrope with water, if concentrated (95%) acid is required it must be dehydrated by means other than distillation; concentrated sulphuric acid or magnesium nitrate may be used for this purpose.

Chemically, nitric acid is a strong acid, but the majority of its important reactions are due to its oxidising action. Most metals are converted to nitrates with evolution of oxides of nitrogen, the composition of the mixture of oxides formed depending chiefly on the concentration of the acid, the metal used and the temperature of the reaction. Some non-metals (e.g. sulphur, phosphorus, iodine) react to give oxy-acids such as phosphorous or phosphoric acid and iodic acid. Organic substances such as sawdust or alcohol react violently, although the more stable aromatic compounds (benzene, toluene, etc.) are converted to the corresponding nitro-compounds by controllable reactions. Due to its oxidizing properties nitric acid may be handled in stainless steel or aluminium equipment, both metals relying on an oxide film for corrosion resistance.

The bulk of nitric acid produced is utilized in the manufacture of fertilizers, mostly ammonium nitrate. The rest is used for the manufacture of explosives and, to a lesser extent, dyestuffs intermediates and other chemicals. World production of nitric acid in 1964 was approximately 14 million tons.

Nitric oxide. See Nitrogen oxides.

Nitrides. Binary compounds between metals and nitrogen, prepared either by heating the metal in nitrogen or ammonia, or by the action of heat on amides. They are slowly converted to oxides on heating in air and are hydrolysed by water. Nitrides are formed by most elements; those of the transition elements are extremely hard and are interstitial compounds.

Nitriding. A method of surface hardening steel by treating it for several hours in an atmosphere of ammonia gas which dissociates when in contact with the heated steel. The steels must be alloy steels designed specifically for this purpose, the principal alloying elements being Al, Cr, and Mo. The carbon content is within the range 0·2-0·5% according to the core strength required. Heat treatment to give the desired core strength is carried out before nitriding and no quenching or other heat treatment is required after nitriding. The cases produced are thinner (up to 0·5 mm) than in carburized steels, but much harder (1000-1300 Diamond Hardness Number).

Nitrido complexes. Complexes in which an N^{3-} ion is co-ordinately bonded to a metal. The osmiamate ion $[OsO_3N]^-$ is an example.

Nitrile rubber. An emulsion-polymerized co-polymer of butadiene (*ca.* 70%) with structure similar to that of SBR and for that reason requiring a reinforcing filler to develop a high tensile strength. The presence of the nitrile group makes the rubber oil-resistant and so it finds application in sealing rings, gaskets, diaphragms and hose. High acrylonitrile content (*ca.* 40%) makes the copolymer suitable for milling with vinyl chloride polymers to produce a toughened material. See Buna rubbers.

Nitriles. Organic cyanides containing the $-C\equiv N$ group. They are colourless liquids or solids, with peculiar but not unpleasant odours. Solubility in water decreases with increasing molecular weight. Soluble in alcohol and ether. They are formed by heating amides with phosphorus pentoxide or by treating halogen compounds with sodium cyanide. They are decomposed by acids or alkalis to give carboxylic acids containing the same number of carbon atoms as the nitrile. Reduced to primary amines.

Nitrites. Salts of nitrous acid.

Nitroamines. Organic compounds containing both nitro-and amino-groups, usually prepared by partial reduction of poly-nitro-compounds. They have some importance as dyestuffs intermediates. Cyclonite, or cyclotrimethylenetrinitramine, was used as a military explosive in the second world war. Other nitroamines are under investigation as explosives but are not as yet in common use although they have specialized uses where cost is not a critical factor.

m-**Nitroaniline**, $C_6H_6N_2O_2$. Forms yellow needles, m.p. 114°, b.p. 285°. Insoluble in cold water, soluble in hot water, alcohol, and ether.

It is prepared by reduction with sodium sulphide of one of the nitro-groups in *m*-dinitrobenzene.

It is used as a first component in the preparation of azo-dyes.

p-**Nitroaniline**, $C_6H_6N_2O_2$. Forms yellow crystals, m.p. 147°. Insoluble in cold water, readily soluble in hot water and in alcohol. Not volatile in steam.

It is easily prepared in a very pure state by heating *p*-nitrochlorobenzene with concentrated aqueous ammonia in an autoclave at 170°. It is also prepared by alkaline hydrolysis of *p*-nitroacetanilide. A third route is by nitrating and hydrolysing benzylideneaniline.

It is an important dyestuffs intermediate, being used as a first component in azo-dyes and also as a source of *p*-phenylenediamine.

406

o-**Nitroanisole**, $C_7H_7NO_3$. A colourless oil, m.p. 9·4°, b.p. 273°, sp.gr. 1·254 at 20°.

It is prepared by heating *o*-nitrochlorobenzene with sodium methoxide or by methylating *o*-nitrophenol with methyl chloride.

It is reduced to *o*-anisidine by iron and hydrochloric acid.

Nitroanthraquinones. The direct nitration of anthraquinone results chiefly in substitution at the α-positions, 1-nitro- and 1,5- and 1,8-dinitroanthraquinones being obtained. Owing to the difficulty of preparing the pure compounds most anthraquinone derivatives are obtained from the sulphonated anthraquinones.

1-Nitroanthraquinone, m.p. 228°, is prepared by nitrating anthraquinone in sulphuric acid with a slight excess of nitric acid. The nitro-group in this position is very reactive and is easily replaced by chlorine when the gas is passed into a sulphuric acid solution of the nitro-compound. Heating with aqueous pyridine causes replacement by hydroxyl. It is reduced to 1-aminoanthraquinone by treatment with sodium sulphide.

Nitroanthraquinones in which the substituent is in the β(2)- position cannot be obtained by direct methods.

Nitrobenzene, $C_6H_5NO_2$. Colourless highly refractive liquid with characteristic smell, m.p. 5·7°, b.p. 211°, density at 15° 1·209. Insoluble in water, miscible in all proportions with alcohol, ether, and benzene, easily volatile in steam.

It is manufactured by reacting benzene with a mixture of nitric and sulphuric acids. Most of the nitrobenzene produced is used to manufacture aniline, which is obtained from it by reduction. A considerable proportion is used as a raw material in the dyestuffs industry, either as nitrobenzene as such, or as aniline.

Further nitration gives *m*-dinitrobenzene; sulphonation gives *m*-nitrobenzene sulphonic acid. Reduction gives first azoxybenzene, then azobenzene and aniline depending upon the conditions.

Nitrocellulose. Should more correctly be called cellulose nitrate. It is prepared by treating cellulose (usually in the form of cotton waste or paper) with a mixture of nitric and sulphuric acids. Nitrocellulose made from cotton and containing over 13% nitrogen is known as guncotton. Guncotton and colloidon cotton may be represented approximately as cellulose trinitrate and dinitrate respectively, though in fact they consist of the mixed esters. All nitrocelluloses are soluble in acetone, but whereas the lower nitrated forms are soluble in a mixture of alcohol and ether (1:2), those with a nitrogen content of over 12·8% are insoluble. Modern colloidal propellants are based on nitrocellulose in a gelatinized condition. Another use is in the manufacture of blasting gelatin.

Nitrochlorobenzenes, $C_6H_4ClNO_2$. *o*-Nitro-

o-

p-

chlorobenzene forms needle-shaped crystals, m.p. 32·5°, b.p. 245·5° (753 mm).

p-Nitrochlorobenzene forms prisms or leaflets, m.p. 83°, b.p. 238·5° (753 mm).

A mixture of the two mononitrochlorobenzenes is prepared by nitration of chlorobenzene; the mixture can be separated by repeated fractional distillations. Further nitration of the mixture or of either of the mononitro-compounds gives 2,4-dinitrochlorobenzene, m.p. 51°, b.p. 315°.

The nitrochlorobenzenes are valuable dyestuffs intermediates. The presence of the nitrogroups makes the chlorine atom very reactive and easily replaceable. Treatment with ammonia or dilute alkalis substitutes an amino- or hydroxy-group for the chlorine atom and gives rise to a series of nitroanilines and nitrophenols.

Nitro-compounds (aromatic). These form a large group of compounds which contain the nitro-group -NO_2.

Generally speaking the nitro-compounds are prepared by the direct action of nitric acid, the strength of the acid and the temperature of reaction being varied according to the reactivity of the compound and the number of nitrogroups which it is required to introduce. The reaction is greatly facilitated if a mixture of nitric and sulphuric acid is used.

In the nitration of benzene, *m*-dinitro- and sym-trinitrobenzenes are obtained under more vigorous conditions. With naphthalene, α-nitronaphthalene is the first product and further nitration gives a mixture of 1,5- and 1,8-dinitronaphthalenes; 2-nitronaphthalene is never obtained.

The nitro-hydrocarbons are neutral substances but when a nitro-group is introduced into a phenol or amine the acidic properties are greatly increased or the basicity decreased. The presence of a nitro-group also tends to make halogen atoms in the same molecule much more reactive.

On reduction, the nitro-compounds give rise to a series of products, e.g.

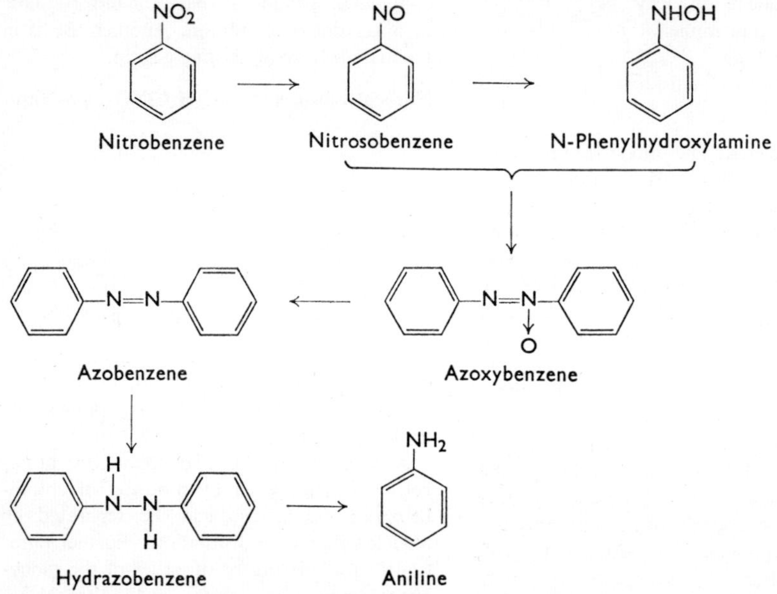

Nitrobenzene   Nitrosobenzene   N-Phenylhydroxylamine

Azobenzene   Azoxybenzene

Hydrazobenzene   Aniline

The most important outlet commercially for the nitro-compounds is the complete reduction to the amines. This is usually done in one stage with iron and a small amount of hydrochloric acid.

Some nitro-compounds are themselves coloured and can be used as dyestuffs, e.g. picric acid. In this case the nitro-group can be considered to be the chromophore.

Nitro-dyes. The salts of the various nitrophenols (or their sulphonic acids). Though many of the nitrophenols, as, for example, p-nitrophenol, are colourless, their salts are coloured. The nitro colours are acid dyestuffs. The nitro-compounds were formerly very largely used for the purpose of dyeing wool and silk. Owing to their fugitive character they are now replaced by the yellow azo-dyes. They all have a more or less pronounced colour; their salts are explosive, and they are poisonous. Typical examples are: Picric acid, Martius yellow (Manchester yellow), Naphtol yellow (q.v.).

Nitrofurantoin, Furadantin, $C_8H_6N_4O_5$. A fine

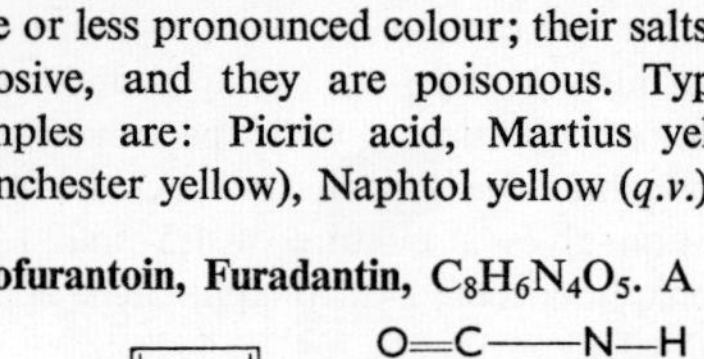

yellow powder or crystals, soluble at 20° in 500 parts of water, in 2,000 parts of alcohol and in

16 parts of dimethylformamide. It is used as a urinary antiseptic when taken orally; active against Gram-negative and Gram-positive organisms that are sulphonamide and penicillin

resistant. It is also used topically as a skin antiseptic.

Nitrogen, N_2. At.no. 7, At.wt. 14·008. A colourless, odourless gas, very slightly lighter than air, condensing to a colourless liquid, b.p. −195·67°, m.p. −209·9°. The gas is slightly soluble in water. The presence in the atmosphere of a gas which does not support combustion (nitrogen) was recognized by Scheele (1772); Lavoisier later named the gas 'azote.' Priestley (1772) regarded nitrogen as air saturated with phlogiston. Atmospheric air normally contains 75·5% of nitrogen by weight (78·06% by volume). The gas obtained on absorbing the oxygen from air (e.g. by passing over heated copper) consists, in the absence of carbon dioxide and water vapour, of nitrogen containing a small proportion of argon and other inert gases, which occur to the extent of about 1·3% by weight (0·94% by volume) in the atmosphere. Nitrogen also occurs in nature as nitrates (e.g. in the Chilean nitrate deposits), ammonia, and ammonium salts, and as proteins (containing about 16% of nitrogen) in animal and vegetable tissues. On a large scale nitrogen is obtained chiefly by fractional distillation of liquid air; in the laboratory it is conveniently prepared by heating a solution of sodium nitrite and ammonium chloride, the gas being freed from traces of nitric oxide and oxygen by passing through acidified potassium dichromate solution and over red-hot copper. The purest nitrogen is obtained by heating barium or sodium azides. Chemically nitrogen is very inert. It does not support combustion. The gas combines with heated alkali or alkaline-earth metals (e.g. Li, Ca), and with certain other elements, giving nitrides (e.g. Li_3N, Ca_3N_2), in which nitrogen is tripositive. Nitrogen combines directly with hydrogen over a catalyst, such as iron or molybdenum, forming ammonia; nitrogen also combines with oxygen, particularly in an electric arc, giving nitric oxide in small quantity. Both these reactions are of considerable commercial importance. Heated calcium carbide absorbs nitrogen, forming calcium cyanamide, $CaCN_2$; this yields ammonia on treatment with steam. Cyanides are formed by the action of nitrogen on a heated mixture of an alkali-metal hydroxide and carbon. *Active nitrogen* is a much more reactive, unstable form of the gas, prepared by the action of a high-tension electric discharge on ordinary nitrogen; it emits a yellow glow. Commercially, nitrogen is used chiefly in the large-scale synthesis of ammonia. It is also used to produce an inert atmosphere in certain chemical and metallurgical processes.

Nitrogen fixation. The use of atmospheric nitrogen in the manufacture of commercially important nitrogen compounds, chiefly nitric acid, ammonia, and ammonium salts. Conversion to ammonia is effected by the Haber process, and nitric acid is obtained by oxidation of ammonia. Bacteria present in the roots of certain plants fix atmospheric nitrogen; so do *Azotobacter*, free-living soil microorganisms, though the latter are inefficient and play only a small part in regulating the soil nitrogen balance.

Nitrogen fluorides. The parent compound is *nitrogen trifluoride*, NF_3, m.p. $-206\cdot7°$, b.p. $-129°$, prepared by the electrolysis of fused ammonium hydrogen fluoride. It is a very inert substance, but the other nitrogen fluorides tend to explode, either spontaneously or in the presence of organic materials. Other nitrogen fluorides are *tetrafluorohydrazine*, F_2NNF_2, prepared by the action of copper on nitrogen trifluoride and *cis-* and *trans-difluorodiazine*, $FN{=}NF$. There is an extensive chemistry of the substituted nitrogen fluorides, e.g. nitrosodifluoroamine, F_2NNO. See Colburn, *Adv. Fluorine Chem.*, 3, 92.

Nitrogen iodide. A black solid, known as 'nitrogen iodide,' and having the formula $NH_3 \cdot NI_3$, is formed on mixing alcoholic solutions of iodine and ammonia. The solid is stable when moist, but when dry explodes on slight mechanical shock. It is a strong oxidizing agent. The true nitrogen tri-iodide, NI_3, is a black powder obtained by passing ammonia gas over the salt $KIBr_2$, and rapidly washing the residue with water.

Nitrogen mustards. The name given to certain poly-(β-chloroethyl)-amines with the general formula

$$R{-}N\begin{array}{l}{\nearrow}CH_2CH_2Cl\\{\searrow}CH_2CH_2Cl\end{array}$$

in which R is an alkyl, alkylamine, or alkyl chloride group. These have vesicant and other properties similar to those of mustard gas, including an action on cells resembling that of X-rays. They have been used in place of radiation therapy in the treatment of leukaemia, Hodgkin's disease, and similar conditions.

Nitrogen oxides, *Nitrous oxide*, N_2O. A colourless gas with a faintly sweet odour and taste, b.p. $-88\cdot5°$, m.p. $-90\cdot8°$. Appreciably soluble in cold water ($1\cdot3$ vols. per vol. of water at 0°), and more soluble in alcohol. Nitrous oxide is prepared commercially and in the laboratory by careful heating of ammonium nitrate. Nitrous oxide is fairly easily decomposed on heating to temperatures above 520°, giving nitrogen and oxygen. Nitrous oxide is an endothermic compound and is decomposed by powerful detonation. The gas is used as a mild anaesthetic for minor operations; it is marketed for this purpose in small steel cylinders. Nitrous oxide is a linear molecule with the structure NNO.

Nitric oxide, NO. A colourless gas, slightly denser than air, giving a blue liquid, m.p. $-164°$, b.p. $-152°$. The gas is practically insoluble in water, a convenient solvent being ferrous sulphate solution, which rapidly absorbs the gas in the cold owing to the formation of the ion $[(H_2O)_5Fe(NO)]^{2+}$, and evolves the nitric oxide again on heating. Nitric oxide is prepared in the laboratory by the action of nitric acid (1 vol. of concentrated acid to 1 vol. of water) on copper turnings; the rather impure product is purified by absorption in ferrous sulphate solution, as described above. Pure nitric oxide is also prepared by the action of mercury on a mixture of nitric and sulphuric acids. On the commercial scale, nitric oxide, an intermediate in the manufacture of nitric acid, is made by the catalytic oxidation of ammonia. Nitric oxide is the most stable oxide of nitrogen, decomposing only above 1000°. Nitric oxide is an odd electron molecule; it combines immediately with oxygen to give nitrogen dioxide. Nitric oxide stored under pressure can disproportionate to nitrous oxide and nitrogen dioxide.

Nitrogen dioxide or *peroxide*, *dinitrogen*

tetroxide, N_2O_4, (NO_2). The solid dioxide exists as pale yellow crystals, m.p. $-11\cdot2°$. The liquid is pale yellow, b.p. $21\cdot15°$, forming a pale yellow vapour containing N_2O_4 molecules. On heating it largely dissociates to NO_2 molecules, the colour of the vapour darkening with rise of temperature. This dissociation is complete at $140°$; further heating causes dissociation to colourless nitric oxide and oxygen. Liquid nitrogen dioxide has good solvent properties and many anhydrous nitrates may be prepared in this solvent. See 'The Chemistry of Dinitrogen Tetroxide' by P. Gray (R.I.C. monograph).

Nitrogen trioxide, or *sesquioxide*, N_2O_3. A dark blue volatile liquid stable only below about $-20°$, prepared by distilling moderately dilute nitric acid with arsenious oxide, the distillate being collected in a freezing mixture. The liquid gives a red vapour in which the trioxide is almost completely dissociated into a mixture of equal volumes of nitric oxide, NO, and nitrogen dioxide, NO_2. It gives nitrites with alkalis.

Nitrogen tri- or *hexoxide*, NO_3. A white solid, not stable above $-140°$, prepared by the action of an electric discharge on a mixture of oxygen and nitrogen dioxide.

Nitrogen pentoxide, N_2O_5. A white, hygroscopic, crystalline solid which sublimes at $32\cdot5°$ and is stable only below $0°$. Prepared by the action of chlorine on silver nitrate, or of phosphorus pentoxide on concentrated nitric acid. Nitrogen pentoxide is very readily decomposed into nitrogen dioxide and oxygen. It dissolves with a hissing noise in water, forming nitric acid, of which the pentoxide is the anhydride. In the solid state N_2O_5 is nitronium nitrate, $NO_2{}^+NO_3{}^-$.

Nitrogen sulphide. See Sulphur nitride.

Nitrogen trichloride, NCl_3. A very dangerously explosive oily liquid, prepared by the action of chlorine on ammonium chloride solution; the related compounds mono- and dichloramine, NH_2Cl, and $NHCl_2$, are formed in the reaction.

Nitroglycerin(e), Glyceryl trinitrate, $C_3H_5N_3O_9$. An oily liquid prepared by treating glycerin with a mixture of nitric and sulphuric acids. When pure it is colourless, odourless, insoluble in water; m.p. $8°$, sp.gr. $1\cdot6$; soluble in various organic solvents. It has a pronounced physiological effect, its vapour giving rise to headaches. It is a very powerful and dangerous explosive and is never used alone due to its sensitivity. Is used in propellants and dynamites.

$$CH_2ONO_2$$
$$|$$
$$CHONO_2$$
$$|$$
$$CH_2ONO_2$$

Nitroguanidine, $H_2N\cdot C(:NH)\cdot NH\cdot NO_2$. A white crystalline powder which is usually manufactured from calcium carbide via calcium cyanamide, dicyandiamide, and guanidine nitrate which is converted to nitroguanidine by the action of conc. H_2SO_4. Soluble in hot water, m.p. $232°$. It is used in some modern propellants to make them cooler and flashless.

Nitron, $C_{20}H_{16}N_3$. Nitron is used, in 10% solu-

$$C_6H_5-N-\!\!\!-N$$

tion in normal acetic acid, as a precipitating reagent for nitrates. After addition to the boiling solution and standing, a precipitate containing $16\cdot79\%$ of NO_3 is formed. Nitron gives precipitates with most uninegative anions, e.g. ClO_4^-, PF_6^-, BF_4^-, and can be used for the determination of boron, rhenium and tungsten.

α-Nitronaphthalene, $C_{10}H_7NO_2$. Long lustrous needles, m.p. $61°$, b.p. $304°$. Insoluble in water, readily soluble in benzene, ether, and hot alcohol. Oxidized by chromic acid or potassium permanganate to 3-nitrophthalic acid; acid reducing agents give α-naphthylamine. Readily nitrated, sulphonated, and chlorinated.

It is prepared by the direct nitration of naphthalene with a mixture of nitric and sulphuric acids. Its chief use is for the preparation of α-naphthylamine and its derivatives.

Nitronium salts. Salts containing the NO_2^+ ion. These salts may be prepared by the action of strong acids on concentrated nitric acid or by reactions involving nitrogen dioxide in bromine trifluoride. The nitronium ion is the active agent in the nitration of aromatic systems in mixtures of nitric acid and sulphuric acid or with nitronium fluoroborate.

Nitroparaffins, $C_nN_{2n+1}NO_2$. Colourless, pleasant smelling but rather toxic liquids, sparingly soluble in water. They may be prepared by the action of silver nitrate on alkyl halides. The lower members are manufactured by the vapour phase reaction of propane with nitric acid at $400°$; a mixture of products results which may be separated by distillation. Nitroparaffins containing an α hydrogen atom dissolve in aqueous alkali giving the salt of the *aci*-nitro compound, e.g.

$$CH_3NO_2 \rightarrow [CH_2\!\!=\!\!NO_2]^-Na^+$$

which on treatment with concentrated mineral acids is hydrolysed to the corresponding aldehyde or ketone. Reduction of nitroparaffins with tin and hydrochloric acid gives the amine.

The lower nitroparaffins are used as propellants for military purposes, as solvents and as chemical intermediates.

p-**Nitrophenetole**, $C_8H_9NO_3$. Forms prismatic crystals, m.p. 58°, b.p. 283°, sp.gr.1·18 at 15°. It is prepared by the ethylation of *p*-nitrophenol with ethyl chloride. It is used for preparing *p*-phenetidine.

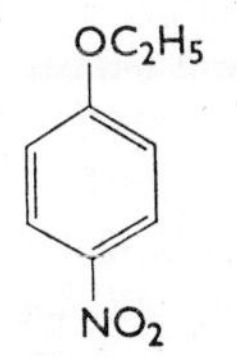

OC₂H₅ / NO₂

o-**Nitrophenol**, $C_6H_5NO_3$. Bright yellow needles, m.p. 45°, b.p. 214°, sparingly soluble in cold water. It gives a deep red solution in alkali; soluble in alcohol.

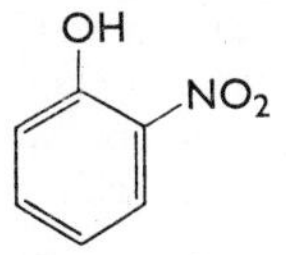

OH / NO₂

Prepared together with *p*-nitrophenol by careful nitration of phenol, from which mixture it is separated by distillation in steam. Sodium sulphide reduces it to *o*-aminophenol.

p-**Nitrophenol**, $C_6H_5NO_3$. Colourless needles, m.p. 114°. Soluble in hot water, very soluble in alcohol.

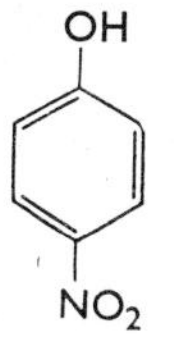

OH / NO₂

Prepared together with *o*-nitrophenol by careful nitration of phenol, from which mixture it remains as an involatile residue after distillation in steam. Reduction with iron and hydrochloric acid gives *p*-aminophenol.

Nitroprussides. See Iron, complex cyanides.

p-**Nitrosodimethylaniline**, $C_8H_{10}N_2O$. The free base forms dark green leaflets, m.p. 85°. On standing it goes browner in colour. It is basic and forms a hydrochloride as intensely yellow needles, soluble in water, but less soluble in dilute hydrochloric acid. It reduces to *p*-aminodimethylaniline and gives dimethylamine with hot sodium hydroxide solution.

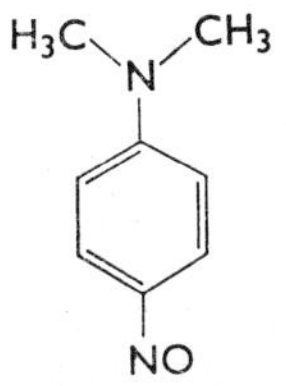

H₃C N CH₃ / NO

It is prepared by the action of nitrous acid upon dimethylaniline at 0°.

It is used for the preparation of indamines by condensation with dialkylanilines, and for the preparation of azines and oxazines by condensation with *m*-diamines and phenols.

Nitroso-dyes (Quinone-oximes). Nitroso-dyes are the reaction products of nitrous acid and phenols, or hydroxylamine on *p*-quinone. The nitroso-dyes are used in the form of coloured lakes which they give with metals. The lakes are derived from the oxime structures (see nitrosophenol). In practice only the *o*-nitrocompounds of phenols are used as dyestuffs. The *o*-nitrophenols are themselves only slightly coloured, but form coloured complex compounds with metallic salts. The colour can be formed in a fibre previously treated with

the metallic salt and varies with the metal used. The nitroso-colours are polygenetic. They are all used for calico printing, generally on an iron mordant. Typical examples are: Dinitrosoresorcinol (Fast green), Naphtol green B, Fast printing green.

Nitrosomethylurea. A colourless crystalline solid, $NH_2CON(NO)CH_3$ m.p. 123°-124°. Insoluble in water; soluble in alcohol and ether. Prepared by adding sodium nitrite solution to a solution of methylurea nitrate. It is unstable and slowly decomposes at ordinary temperatures. Reacts with cold potassium hydroxide solution to give diazomethane.

Nitrosonium salts. Salts containing the NO^+ ion. Many such salts result from the reaction of nitrosyl chloride with metallic chlorides.

Nitrosonium tetrafluoroborate, $NOBF_4$. A white solid, isomorphous with ammonium tetrafluoroborate. It sublimes at 0·01 mm and 250° without decomposition. It is very hygroscopic; reaction with water gives oxides of nitrogen, but reactions with alcohols give nitrito esters. Aromatic primary amine hydrochlorides give diazonium tetrafluoroborates which may be pyrolysed to give aromatic fluoro derivatives. Secondary aliphatic amines react with it to give nitroso-amines.

p-**Nitrosophenol**, $C_6H_5NO_2$. Forms greyish-

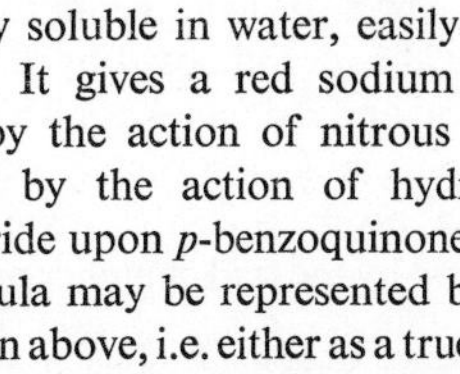

OH / NO   or   O / NOH

brown leaflets, which decompose at 124°. Moderately soluble in water, easily in alcohol and ether. It gives a red sodium salt. It is prepared by the action of nitrous acid upon phenol or by the action of hydroxylamine hydrochloride upon *p*-benzoquinone.

Its formula may be represented by either of those shown above, i.e. either as a true *p*-nitrosophenol or a *p*-benzoquinonemonoxime. The coloured derivatives, e.g. the sodium salt, are probably derived from the quinone form. Direct methylation gives a coloured compound which has been shown to be quinonemethoxime $O:C_6H_4:NOCH_3$; *p*-nitrosoanisole

$$CH_3O \cdot C_6H_4 \cdot NO$$

has been obtained by another route and is colourless.

p-Nitrosophenol condenses with bases to form indophenols, which are much used for the production of sulphur colours. The most important is the indophenol from carbazole which is used for the preparation of Hydron blue.

Nitrososulphuric acid, Nitrosulphuric acid, Nitrosulphonic acid. Alternative and less generally accepted names for nitrosylsulphuric acid.

Nitrosyl. Compounds containing one or more NO groups joined directly to a metal atom are called nitrosyls; a special modification of the covalent link, in which *three* electrons are donated by the nitrogen atom to the metal atom, is probably involved in their structure. Typical nitrosyl compounds are $Fe(NO)_2(CO)_2$, $Co(NO)_2I$, and $Co(NO)(CO)_3$.

Nitrosyl chloride, ClNO. An orange-yellow gas with a pungent odour resembling that of nitrogen dioxide, readily condensing to a red liquid, b.p. $-6\cdot4°$, which freezes to a yellow solid, m.p. $-65°$. Nitrosyl chloride is present in aqua regia, but is prepared in the laboratory by treating nitrosyl sulphuric acid with sodium chloride. Nitrosyl chloride is readily decomposed by water or alkalis, giving nitrous and hydrochloric acids or their salts; it dissociates on heating to high temperatures, giving nitric oxide and chlorine. Many addition compounds with metallic chlorides (e.g. $ZnCl_2,NOCl$) are known. Most metals are attacked by nitrosyl chloride.

Nitrosyl fluoride, FNO. A colourless gas, m.p. $-133°$, b.p. $-60°$, prepared by reaction between fluorine and nitric oxide or between silver fluoride and nitrosyl chloride. It is the parent compound of the nitrosonium salts of complex fluoroacids, e.g. $NO^+BF_4^-$.

Nitrosyl sulphuric acid ('Chamber Crystals'), $NOHSO_4$. A white crystalline solid melting with decomposition at $73°$, conveniently prepared by passing sulphur dioxide into cold fuming nitric acid. The acid is decomposed by water, giving sulphuric acid and red fumes of nitrogen oxides. Nitrosylsulphuric acid probably occurs as an intermediate product in the manufacture of sulphuric acid by the lead chamber process.

m-**Nitrotoluene,** $C_7H_7NO_2$, has m.p. $16°$, b.p. $230°$. Prepared (3-4%) by separation from the mixture of isomers obtained on mononitrating toluene.

o-**Nitrotoluene,** $C_7H_7NO_2$. Colourless liquid, b.p. $220\cdot4°$, d_{15} $1\cdot164$. Volatile in steam, insoluble in water, miscible with most organic solvents.

It is prepared by the direct nitration of toluene as a 50-60% component of the mixture of isomers, from which it has to be separated by fractional distillation and crystallization.

Used for the preparation of *o*-toluidine.

p-**Nitrotoluene,** $C_7H_7NO_2$. Colourless rhombic crystals, m.p. $51°$-$52°$, b.p. $237\cdot7°$.

It is prepared by mono nitrating toluene, as a 40% constituent of the mixture of isomers, from which it can be separated by crystallization. It is reduced to *p*-toluidine with iron and hydrochloric acid.

Nitrourea, $NH_2CONHNO_2$. A colourless crystalline solid, m.p. $158\cdot5°$. Soluble in water, alcohol, and ether. Prepared by adding urea nitrate to concentrated sulphuric acid at $0°$ and pouring the mixture on to ice. It is a strong acid, and forms salts. Not readily oxidized but can be detonated. Used in the preparation of semicarbazide.

Nitrous acid, HNO_2. The pale blue solution obtained by acidifying a solution of a nitrite contains small quantities of nitrous acid; this readily decomposes on warming or shaking giving nitric oxide and nitrogen dioxide or nitric acid, the latter chiefly in dilute solutions. The use of nitrous acid in the diazo reaction is of considerable importance in the dyestuffs industry, and its salts, the nitrites (chiefly sodium nitrite) are commercial products; nitrous acid is liberated by acidifying the nitrite solution in the presence of the compound to be diazotized. Sodium nitrite is manufactured by heating sodium nitrate (Chile saltpetre) with lead, and it is a by-product in the nitrogen fixation industry. Nitrous acid and the nitrites normally act as reducing agents, although they have an oxidizing action on certain substances (e.g. sulphur dioxide, hydrogen sulphide). The nitrites of the alkali metals are comparatively stable in the dry state; they detonate violently on warming with cyanides or thiosulphates. Solutions of nitrites give the 'brown ring' test (see Nitric acid), using *dilute* sulphuric acid. A gaseous mixture of nitric oxide, nitrogen dioxide, and water contains the *cis*- and *trans*-forms of HONO.

Nitryl halides, XNO_2. Nitryl fluoride and chloride are known. The chloride is obtained by the action of nitric acid on chlorosulphonic acid or by the action of nitrosyl chloride on ozone. Fluorination with silver fluoride gives nitryl fluoride, which also results from the action of fluorine on nitrogen dioxide. Both compounds are colourless gases; FNO_2 m.p. $-166°$, b.p. $-72\cdot5°$; $ClNO_2$ m.p. $-145°$, b.p. $-15\cdot9°$. On hydrolysis nitryl chloride gives a nitrite and a hypochlorite. Nitryl compounds are the parent substances of the nitronium salts.

Nitroxylenes, $C_8H_9NO_2$, $C_6H_3(CH_3)_2NO_2$. See Xylidines.

NMR. A widely used abbreviation for nuclear magnetic resonance (*q.v.*).

Nobel, Alfred Bernhard (1833-1896). Born at Stockholm, Nobel was trained as both chemist and engineer. He devoted his life to a study of explosives, and his best-known contribution to chemistry is the invention of dynamite in 1866. From the manufacture of explosives and from the Baku oilfields he built up a large fortune, the bulk of which he left, in trust, for the establishment of the Nobel Prizes. These, five in number, are awarded annually for achievements in Physics, Chemistry, Physiology or Medicine, Literature, and the furthering of Peace.

Nobelium, No. A name proposed for the element of atomic number 102. The element was supposed to have been prepared by bombarding ^{244}Cm with carbon ions, but the experiment could not be repeated. Isotopes $^{254}102$, $^{255}102$, and $^{256}102$ have subsequently been prepared by bombardment of species of lower mass, and have been identified. The name Joliot-curium has also been suggested for this species.

Noble gases. The elements helium, argon, krypton, xenon, and radon.

Nollet, Jean Antoine (1700-1770). Professor of physics in Paris, Nollet noticed, in 1748, the passage of water molecules through a parchment membrane which retained the solute molecules with the subsequent development of osmotic pressure.

Nomag. An austenitic alloy cast iron containing 10-12% Ni and 5-6% Mn. It is machinable, is non-magnetic, and has a very high electrical resistance, but is inferior in corrosion-resisting properties to other austenitic cast irons such as Ni-Resist and Nicrosilal.

Non-aqueous solution. Any solution in which the solvent is not water is a non-aqueous solution. Non-aqueous solvents can have self-ionization in a manner similar to that of water. See Acids.

Non-polar liquid. See Normal liquid.

Non-polar molecule. A molecule is said to be non-polar when it has zero dipole moment. Symmetrical covalent compounds are generally non-polar, for the electrons are symmetrically arranged.

Non-stoicheiometric compounds. Compounds in which the ratios of the number of atoms present do not follow simple integers. Most interstitial compounds are non-stoichiometric and many transition metal oxides form non-stoicheiometric phases.

Nontronite. See Potter's clay.

Nopinene. See β-Pinene.

Nor-. The most common use of the prefix nor- in the name of an organic compound is to indicate the loss of a CH_2 group, thus nornicotine has the formula $C_9H_{12}N_2$, while nicotine is $C_{10}H_{14}N_2$. The same convention is used with steroids. In terpene nomenclature nor- indicates the loss of all the methyl groups from the parent compound. With amino-acids however the use of nor- turns the trivial name of a branched chain compound to the isomeric straight chain compound, thus norvaline is 2-amino-*n*-valeric acid.

Noradrenaline, $C_8H_{10}NO_3$. Administered as

the acid tartrate, which is soluble in water and insoluble in most organic solvents. It is prepared by treating chloroacetylcatechol with ammonia, reducing the product, and resolving the racemic mixture of bases with (+)-tartaric acid. A solution in hydrochloric acid has $[\alpha]_D -45°$ to $-48°$; m.p. 103°. It is liberated in the adrenal medulla with adrenaline and released at the sympathetic nerve endings. Its actions are similar to those of adrenaline, except that it reduces the flow of blood in muscles and does not increase cardiac output. It is used in cases of peripheral vasomotor collapse, and is administered intravenously.

Norbornadiene, C_7H_8. Bicyclo[2:2:1]hepta-2,5-diene, a slightly coloured liquid, b.p. 90°, which is obtained by a Diels-Alder reaction between cyclopentadiene and acetylene at approximately 150°. At temperatures in excess of 450° it rearranges to cycloheptatriene (tropilidene).

Nordhausen sulphuric acid. See Sulphuric acid, fuming.

Norethisterone, 17-ethinyl-19-nortestosterone,

$C_{20}H_{26}O_2$ (trade name Norlutin). A progestogen and ovulation inhibitor, used as an oral contraceptive. The $\Delta5(10)$-isomer, mestranol (trade name Enovid) has similar physiological effects. Selective hydrogenation of norethisterone gives 17-α-ethyl-19-nortestosterone (trade name Nilevar), a progestational and anabolic agent.

Normalizing. The heating of a steel to a temperature just above its upper critical point (750°-900° depending on its carbon content), keeping it at that temperature for a certain time and then allowing it to cool down in air. Normalizing is carried out to relieve stresses set up by previous operations. The operation is similar to annealing, but owing to the more rapid cooling yields

industries for the U.S. Department of Commerce, and during the 1914-1918 war, as special agent of the same department, compiled the 'Dyestuff Census' and led the campaign to create an American dyestuffs industry. Later Norton was active both as an editor of chemical publications and as a consultant, and in 1929 became research chemist to the American Cyanamid Co. In 1937 he was awarded the Lavoisier Medal of the Société Chimique de France.

Novobiocin. An antimicrobial substance pro-

a finer structure, the pearlite laminations being less distinct. The term is rather a loose one, since thin sections cool quickly, whereas the centres of large masses cool slowly and often show an annealed or semi-annealed structure.

Normal liquid. A liquid in which the molecules have no tendency to associate. The simpler liquid hydrocarbons approximate to this type, while water, acetic acid, and alcohol may be cited as examples of abnormal liquids.

Normal solution. A normal solution of a substance is one which contains 1 g equivalent of the substance in 1 litre of solution. A normal solution must have the equivalent referred to a specific reaction and this is often not done. A normal solution may be indicated by the letter N, thus, N-hydrochloric acid signifies a normal solution of hydrogen chloride. Likewise 0·1 N or 1/10 N signifies a solution containing one-tenth of the g equivalent of the substance dissolved in 1 litre of the solution; 2N signifies two g equivalents per litre of solution.

Normal temperature and pressure (NTP). The arbitrary values are 0° and 760 mm of mercury. Synonymous with standard temperature and pressure (STP).

Northrop, John Howard (1891-   ). Born in New York State, he was trained at Columbia University where he obtained a Ph.D. in 1915. After a period at the Rockefeller Institute he moved in 1924 to the department of bacteriology in the University of California. He shared the Nobel Prize in 1946 for his work in crystallizing proteolytic enzymes.

Norton, Thomas Herbert (1851-1941). Born at Rushford, New York, Norton was educated at Hamilton College, Heidelberg, Berlin, and Paris. In 1906, while U.S. Consul at Chemnitz, he compiled a survey of foreign chemical

duced by the growth of *Streptomyces niveus* or related organisms. It is a white or yellowish white crystalline powder. The sodium salt is soluble at 20° in 5 parts of water, and in 7 parts of alcohol. The calcium salt is also used medicinally. Novobiocin is effective against Grampositive bacteria and is used against microorganisms resistant to the more commonly used antibiotics. See 'Progress in Industrial Microbiology' (Hockenhull), Vol. III, p. 93.

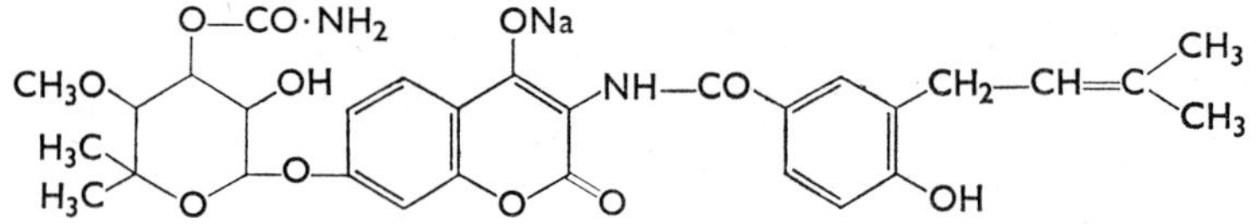

Noyes, Arthur Amos (1866-1936). Born at Newburyport, U.S.A., Noyes was educated at Massachusetts Institute of Technology and at Leipzig. He as appointed professor of theoretical chemistry, M.I.T. (1899), and Director of the Gates Chemical Laboratory, California (1915). He was the author of numerous books and his original work covered a wide field; associated with Blanchard, he studied ionic conductivities. In 1915 he was awarded the Willard Gibbs Medal.

Noyes, William Albert (1857-1941). Noyes was born at Independence, Iowa, and educated at Grinnell College and the Johns Hopkins University. After being professor of chemistry at the University of Tennessee (1883-86) and the Rose Polytechnic Institute (1886-1903) he was appointed first chief chemist of the Bureau of Standards. In 1907 he became professor of chemistry and director of the Chemical Laboratories at the University of Illinois, retiring in 1926. He received the Nichols Medal (with H. C. P. Weber, 1909), the Willard Gibbs Medal (1919), and the Priestley Medal (1935); and was President of the American Chemical Society in 1920. His researches dealt with atomic weights, the camphor compounds, and electronic theories of valency.

NTP. See Normal temperature and pressure.

Nuclear magnetic resonance. A technique for studying nuclear paramagnetism (q.v.). The substance under test is placed in a very strong magnetic field which must be both uniform and steady. This produces a 'splitting' of the nuclear energy levels. The sample is then subjected to an additional, weak, oscillating magnetic field produced by passing r.f. current, at e.g. 30 megacycles frequency, through a surrounding coil, and the frequency of this field is slowly 'scanned' over an appropriate range. At certain precise frequencies the nuclear magnets in effect resonate with the field in undergoing transitions between the two principal magnetic energy levels. The resonance is detected in a search coil and is amplified and recorded. The effects being very feeble, the apparatus is highly elaborate and expensive, but the technique has assumed great importance for analysis of molecular structure because the resonance frequencies of a particular element are influenced by the electronic environment in which the atom is situated. Thus three different kinds of hydrogen atom are detected in ethanol, corresponding to those in the CH_3, CH_2, and OH groups. In addition to direct information from the resonance frequencies the nuclei couple together to give fine structure in the n.m.r. spectrum. The extent and nature of the coupling provides further information on molecular structure.

Nuclear paramagnetism. The nuclei of certain species have spin and the total angular momentum is given by

$$\frac{h}{2\pi}\sqrt{I(I+1)}$$

where I is the nuclear spin number (I=0, $\frac{1}{2}$, 1, $\frac{3}{2}$ ...). I=0 corresponds to a nucleus without spin. Since nuclei are also charged they behave as magnetic dipoles and nuclear magnetic resonance techniques can be used to study nuclei with I > 0.

Isotope	Spin No. I	% Abundance
^1H	$\frac{1}{2}$	99·98
^2H	1	0·0156
^{12}C	0	98·9
^{13}C	$\frac{1}{2}$	1·1
^{14}N	1	99·62
^{15}N	$\frac{1}{2}$	0·38
^{19}F	$\frac{1}{2}$	100
^{31}P	$\frac{1}{2}$	100

Nuclear quadrupole moment. The electric quadrupole moment of the nucleus.

Nuclear spin. The hyperfine structure of certain spectra (see Multiplet) has led to the view that the nucleus has a property with the characteristics of spin. The angular momentum of nuclear particles is expressed in units of $(h/2\pi)$. (h = Planck's constant).

Nucleases. Those enzymes which hydrolyse nucleic acids. The process is thought to take place in three stages each requiring a different enzyme. Nucleinase first acts to simplify the polynucleotides to mononucleotides, from which nucleotidase liberates phosphoric acid forming a nucleoside which is finally hydrolysed to a sugar (ribose) and a base by nucleosidase. The nucleases are present in the plasma, the intestinal juice, and the liver, whilst the last-named enzyme is conveniently prepared from the pancreas.

Nucleation. The formation of particles of a fresh phase (e.g. liquid from vapour, crystals from vapour, solution, or melt; vapour from liquid), is liable to be delayed beyond the point where the new phase would be thermodynamically stable; the phenomena of super-cooling, super-saturation and super-heating are examples. Phase-separation does not occur until suitable nuclei are present. They may be either foreign particles (e.g. of dust or dissolved gases) or self-nuclei which form spontaneously at a certain degree of super-saturation (or super-cooling). Nucleation is the process of formation of nuclei.

Nucleic acids. These are essential components of all living cells, as they carry the necessary hereditary information enabling highly specific proteins to be constructed. There are two types of nucleic acid; deoxyribose nucleic acid, DNA, is found in the nuclei of cells; ribose nucleic acid, RNA, is found mainly in the cytoplasm. They are polynucleotides; DNA is built of the nucleotides of the purines adenine and guanine and the pyrimidines cytosine and uracil. The DNA molecule consists of two helical chains coiled round the same axis, each chain consisting of alternate phosphate and sugar groups connected through carbons 3 and 5 of the pentose molecule, and with the bases attached to the pentose. The chains are held together by hydrogen bonds between the bases. Spatial considerations demand that of two linked bases one must be a purine and the other a pyrimidine. It is also assumed that only two specific pairs can bind, adenine with uracil and guanine with cytosine. Thus given a sequence of bases on one chain, that on the other is determined. If the chains are uncoiled and separated any new chain built on one of the originals has a standard sequence.

In RNA the sugar is ribose and thymine replaces uracil. Different varieties of RNA exist with widely different molecular weights. Messenger RNA conveys information in the form of the sequence of bases from DNA to RNA on the ribosomes, where proteins are built up from amino-acids on the RNA template. Each sequence of three bases, called a codon, codes for a specific amino-acid. Thus the order of amino-acids on a protein is ultimately based on the order of nucleotides on the DNA molecule. See Nucleoproteins.

Nucleide. A distinct species of atom, which is completely characterized by the constitution of its nucleus, i.e. the numbers of protons and neutrons, and by its mode of radioactive decay.

Nucleons. Particles of mass number 1, or protons and neutrons.

Nucleophilic reagents. Groups which act by donating or sharing their electrons. Examples are the hydroxyl anion, halide ions, and OR^- and SR^- groups.

Nucleophilic substitution describes a reaction proceeding in the broadest sense according to the equation:

$$R—X + :N \rightarrow R—N + X^{\ominus} \qquad (1)$$

where R may be an alkyl, aryl, metal or metalloid group, and X and N may be a wide variety of both inorganic and organic anions: in addition N may be an uncharged compound with an unshared electron pair, e.g. amines, water. The mechanisms of these reactions have been investigated very extensively, and may proceed in two ways: S_n2 *reactions* (substitution nucleophilic bimolecular) proceed according to step (1) since the rate-determining step of the reaction involves two particles, i.e. the kinetics are second order: in general S_n2 reactions involve a Walden inversion. S_n1 reactions (substitution nucleophilic unimolecular) are dependent upon a preliminary cleavage of the R—X bond, step (2), in determining the rate

$$R—X \rightarrow R^{\oplus} + X^{\ominus} \qquad (2)$$

of the reaction: this is slow compared to step (3)

$$R^{\oplus} + N \rightarrow R—N^{\oplus} \qquad (3)$$

These reactions follow first-order kinetics and proceed with racemisation if the reaction site is an optically active centre. For alkyl halides nucleophilic substitution proceeds easily: primary halides favour S_n2 mechanisms and tertiary halides favour S_n1 mechanisms. Aryl halides undergo nucleophilic substitution with difficulty and sometimes involve aryne intermediates (*q.v.*). See C. A. Bunton, 'Nucleophilic substitution at a saturated carbon atom,' Elsevier 1963.

Nucleoproteins. A group of substances consisting of proteins, usually of the basic histone or protamine type, conjugated with nucleic acids. The protein may form a third coaxial chain with the two nucleic acid chains in the molecule. Nucleoproteins are present in the nuclei of all cells and are of the most fundamental importance in the formation of living matter. Chromosomes are largely nucleoproteins; and some simple plant viruses have been obtained as crystalline water-soluble substances and shown to be pure nucleoproteins. Nucleoproteins are most readily obtained from glands, such as the thymus or pancreas, or from fish roes. See Nucleic acids.

Nucleosides. Glycosides of heterocyclic bases, in particular of purines and pyrimidines. They are crystalline substances, sparingly soluble in water. The nucleosides forming part of the molecule of ribose nucleic acid are the 9-β-D-ribofuranosides of adenine and guanine (adenosine and guanosine), and the 3-β-D-ribofuranosides of cytosine and uracil (cytidine and uridine). In deoxynucleic acid the sugar is deoxyribose and the uracil is replaced by thymine. The formula of adenosine is:

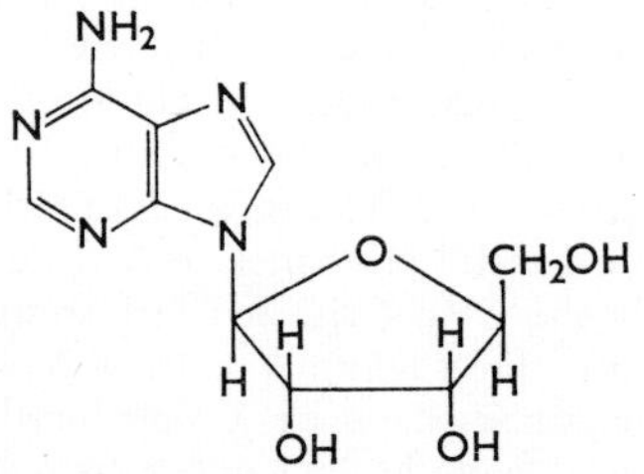

The formula of deoxycytidine is:

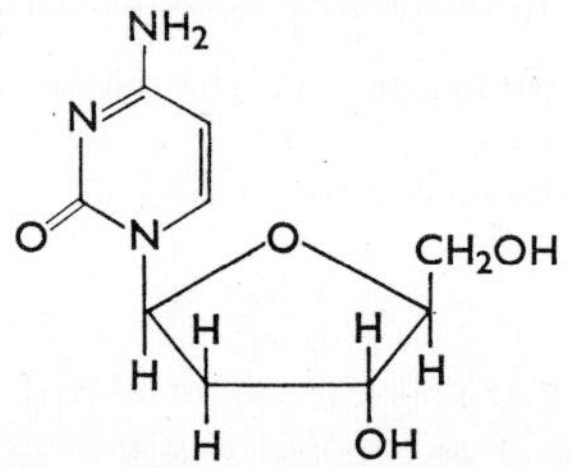

Nucleotides. Originally applied to the phosphate esters of compounds of pentose sugars with purine or pyrimidine bases obtained as breakdown products of nucleic acids, the term is now used for phosphates of glycerides of all heterocyclic bases, and thus to such substances as adenosine triphosphate, nicotinamide-adenine dinucleotide and other coenzymes.

Nucleus, atomic. The nucleus of an atom is the small but massive internal core of the atom, which contains all the positive charge in the atom. The weight and any radioactive properties are associated with the nucleus; the chemical properties and the u.v. and visible spectra are properties of the planetary electrons.

Nujol. A trade name for a heavy medicinal paraffin oil. Extensively used as a mulling agent in spectroscopy.

Nux vomica consists of the dried ripe seeds of *Strychnos nux vomica*, a tree indigenous to India and the Malay Archipelago. It owes its medicinal properties to the alkaloids strychnine and brucine. It is a powerful tonic, stimulating the heart and respiratory organs and increasing nervous energy.

Nylon. The generic term used to describe a class of synthetic fibres and plastics which have the polyamide structure. Such materials are manufactured either by the condensation polymerization of α, ω-aminomonocarboxylic acids, or of aliphatic diamines with aliphatic dicarboxylic acids. A number of different nylons are now well established for the production of textile fibres, monofilaments, injection moulding materials, and extrusion materials. The different polyamides are identified by reference being made to the carbon numbers of the component di-acid, di-amine, or amino-acid monomers. Thus nylon 6 is produced from ω-aminocaproic acid (6 carbons); nylon 6·6 has hexamethylenediamine (6 carbons) and adipic acid (6 carbons) as its component monomers; while nylon 6·10 is derived from hexamethylenediamine and sebacic acid (10 carbons). Additional to these simple nylons, both copolymers and plasticized products are now in use. The nylons are thermoplastic materials, characterized by their high melting points (185°-265°), insolubility in normal organic solvents, outstanding toughness, and impact resistance. Monofilaments and films show considerable increase in mechanical strength following orientation by cold drawing.

Nystatin. A polyene antifungal substance produced by *Streptomyces noursei*. Its structure has not been elucidated. It is obtained as a hygroscopic yellow to light brown powder only sparingly soluble in most solvents. It is used systematically for treating alimentary moniliasis and fungal infections of the respiratory tract, and topically for fungal skin infections.

O

Obsidian. An acid extrusive igneous rock, glassy in texture.

Occlusion. A term used either to denote retention of a gas or of solids by a metal, or the absorption of an electrolyte by a precipitate. The term is not precise in its meaning. In the case of a gas and a metal, it includes adsorption in the ordinary sense, and also penetration of the metal lattice by atoms or molecules of the gas with formation of an interstitial compound (e.g. in the occlusion of hydrogen by palladium). In connexion with the contamination of metals by solids, the term is applied chiefly to the retention of small amounts of slag, etc., by a metal, which is probably a mechanical process.

Ochre. The ochres are earthy pigments, yellow to brownish red in colour. The more yellow varieties are the mineral limonite, mixed with clay, and may contain 15-65% Fe_2O_3. Yellow ochres are mined in France and South Africa. The redder varieties are akin to haematite and are found widely spread. The distinction between ochres and raw siennas is indefinite, both being regarded as natural earth containing hydrated ferric oxide.

Synthetic yellow ochres are chemically prepared hydrated ferric oxide; reds are obtained by calcining the yellow varieties. See British Standard 312.

Ocimene, $C_{10}H_{16}$. An acyclic monoterpene of constitutional formula

$$CH_2{:}CH \cdot C(CH_3){:}CH \cdot CH_2 \cdot CH{:}C(CH_3) \cdot CH_3$$

It is found in the oil obtained from the leaves of *Ocimum basilicum*, grown in Java, and probably in various other essential oils; b.p. 81°/30 mm, d^{21} 0·799, n_D^{18} 1·4857. On heating ocimene is isomerized to allo-ocimene.

$$(CH_3)_2C{:}CH \cdot CH{:}CH \cdot C(CH_3){:}CH \cdot CH_3$$

Octahedral co-ordination. Regular co-ordination

of six ligands. The ligands approach the metal from the corners of an octahedron. Sulphur hexafluoride has octahedral co-ordination about the sulphur.

Octane number. This is a measure of the anti-knock value of an internal combustion engine fuel. It is measured by matching in a standard engine against a blend of 2,2,4-trimethylpentane (iso-octane) and normal heptane; the percentage of iso-octane in the blend equivalent in knocking tendency to the fuel under test being designated the octane number.

Octanes, C_8H_{18}. Hydrocarbons of the paraffin series. There are eighteen possible paraffin hydrocarbons of this formula. They occur in petroleum and have boiling-points between 99° and 125°. The most important isomer is 2,2,4-trimethylpentane, $(CH_3)_3C \cdot CH_2 \cdot CH(CH_3)_2$, usually called iso-octane. This is produced in large quantities by various methods from the butane-butylene fraction of the gas from the cracking of petroleum. It is a colourless liquid, d_4^{20} 0·6918, b.p. 99·3°. It has marked anti-knock properties and is used as a standard for determining the 'knock-rating' of petrols. Another isomer, 2-methylheptane, is sometimes, and more correctly, also called iso-octane. It has d_4^{20} 0·6980, b.p. 117·2°.

Octanol-2. See Capryl alcohol.

Octant rule. This relates the sign and the amplitude of Cotton effect (*q.v.*) curves with the geometry and substitution of cyclohexanone derivatives and has been applied especially to steroids. It may also be extended to other cyclic ketones.

Octaves, law of. Newlands (1863-1864) found that when the elements are arranged in order of increasing atomic weights, the first element is similar to the eighth, the second to the ninth, the third to the tenth, and so on. He termed this relationship the 'law of octaves'. See Periodic law.

Octet. A term used in connexion with atomic structure to denote a group of eight extra-nuclear electrons. Such a group of eight has a peculiar stability, and forms the outer electron shell in all the noble gases except helium. The conception of the octet as a particularly stable structure is also important in determining the valency of the elements, in that when atoms combine by the process of sharing or donating their electrons they tend to do so in such ratios that each atom has a completed octet. Sodium, for example, which has one electron in its outer shell will lose this electron—forming Na^+ with an octet of electrons—to chlorine which gains an electron so that the Cl^- ion also has an octet of electrons.

Octyl alcohols. Compounds with the formula $C_8H_{17}OH$. See Capryl alcohol.

Odling, William (1829-1921). A Londoner by birth, Odling was intended for the medical profession, but instead became lecturer in chemistry at Guy's Hospital. In 1863 he became professor of chemistry at St. Bartholomew's Hospital, in 1868 Fullerian professor of chemistry at the Royal Institution, and in 1872 Waynflete professor of chemistry in Oxford University, retiring in 1912. He supported the views of Laurent and Gerhardt, advocated the adoption of the atomic weight $O = 16$ instead of $O = 8$, gave O_3 as the formula for ozone, and put forward a classification of the silicates. See *J. Roy. Inst. Chem.*, 1957, **81**, 728.

Oenanthic acid. *n*-Heptanoic acid, $C_7H_{14}O_2$. An oily liquid, m.p. −9°, b.p. 115-6°/11 mm., d_4^{15} 0·92099. It can be prepared by the oxidation of heptanal, and has growth inhibiting properties against micro-organisms. Its presence has been reported in certain natural oils and waxes.

β-Oestradiol, $C_{18}H_{24}O_2$. Colourless crystals, m.p. 174°, $[\alpha]_D^{20} + 75°$ to $+ 82°$ in dioxan. Oestradiol was first prepared by the reduction of

oestrone, and later was found in the urine of pregnant mares and the ovaries of pigs. It is more

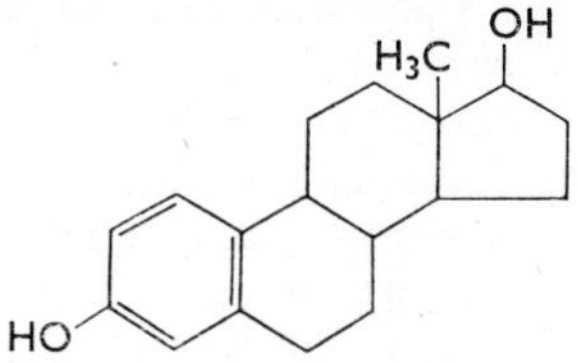

active physiologically than oestrone and seems to be the true female follicular sex hormone.

Oestriol, $C_{18}H_{24}O_3$. Colourless crystals,

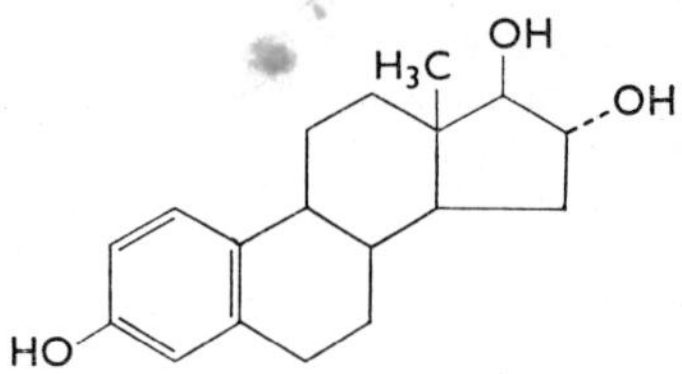

m.p. 283°, soluble in alcohol, insoluble in water, $[\alpha]_D + 34·4°$ in pyridine. It is a substance present in the urine of pregnant women and formed from oestrone by treatment with potassium bisulphate. It possesses female sex hormone activity, but is not nearly so active as oestrone.

Oestrogens. These are the follicular female sex hormones, which are formed in the ovaries under the stimulation of the gonadotropic hormone of the pituitary gland. They are responsible for inducing oestrous, promoting the growth of the uterus, the vagina, and the mammary glands, and developing the secondary sexual characteristics. During pregnancy large quantities are excreted, particularly by the mare, which in one pregnancy may excrete as much as 25 g of pure hormone. They are found also in the urine of male members of the equine species. Oestradiol is the most potent of the naturally occurring oestrogens, and is probably the true hormone, of which oestrone, oestriol, equilin, and equilinin (*q.v.*) are metabolic products. Stilboestrol and hexoestrol (*q.v.*) are synthetic products with oestrogenic activity that are much used medicinally, as they can be administered by mouth and are much cheaper than the naturally occurring oestrogens.

Oestrone, $C_{18}H_{22}O_2$. Colourless crystals,

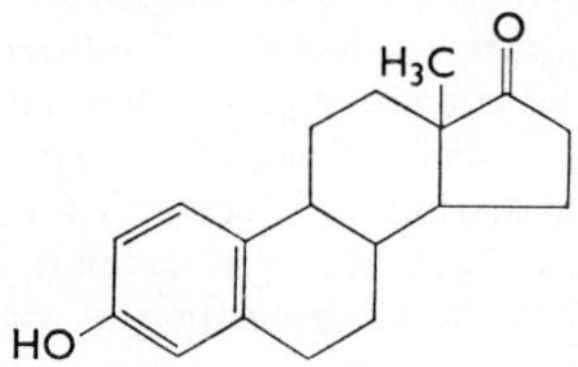

m.p. 258°, $[\alpha]_D^{20} + 158°$ to $+ 161°$ in dioxan. Insoluble in water, slightly soluble in alcohol, soluble in ether and chloroform. It has all the actions of the female sex hormones, but is poorly absorbed, and has been replaced by other oestrogens in clinical use.

Oil of anise. Commonly called oil of aniseed, it is obtained by steam distillation from star anise fruits, *Illicium verum*. It consists chiefly of anethole (*q.v.*) and is used as a carminative and as an ingredient of cough lozenges and cough mixtures, where its warm taste and mild expectorant action relieve tickling cough. It is also employed as a flavouring agent.

Oil of cade, Juniper tar oil. A brownish-black oil obtained by the destructive distillation of the branches of *Juniperus oxycedrus*. It has an empyreumatic odour, and is used in ointment form as a stimulating antiseptic against certain kinds of eczema and other skin diseases. It is also combined in a soap to be used for toilet purposes for persons with unhealthy skins.

Oil of cajeput. The volatile oil distilled from the leaves of *Melaleuca leucadendron*. It contains over 50% of cineole, and is used internally as a carminative and intestinal antiseptic. Externally applied it is a stimulant and a mild counter-irritant.

Oil of camphor. Two fractions of the natural oil of camphor are used medicinally: (1) light oil of camphor is an almost colourless fraction containing a small amount of camphor, about 30% of cineole, and the remainder terpenes; and (2) dark oil of camphor consists very largely of safrole. Both are used externally in the preparation of liniments.

Oil of caraway. Obtained by distillation from the ripe fruits of *Carum carvi*. It contains about 60% of carvone, and is used to relieve flatulent colic.

Oil of cinnamon. The volatile oil distilled from the bark of *Cinnamonum zeylanicum*. The chief constituent of this oil is cinnamic aldehyde, $C_6H_5 \cdot CH:CH \cdot CHO$, which occurs to the extent of upwards of 50%, but the delicate aroma which renders this oil more valuable than oil of cassia, which contains up to 90% of cinnamic aldehyde, is due to other constituents. In the United States the rectified oil of cassia is known as oil of cinnamon. Oil of cinnamon is carminative and antiseptic.

Oil of cloves. The volatile oil distilled from cloves consisting largely of eugenol. It has antiseptic properties, and is added to many preparations as a preservative to prevent putrefaction. Like many essential oils, it has carminative properties.

Oil of coriander. The volatile oil distilled from the ripe fruits of *Coriandrum sativum*. Its chief constituent is the alcohol, coriandrol, $C_{10}H_{17}OH$, which is present to the extent of 65-80%. It is aromatic, stimulative, and carminative.

Oil of dill. A volatile oil steam-distilled from the ripe fruits of *Anethum graveolens*. It contains about 50% of carvone (*q.v.*), to which it owes its medicinal properties. It is a carminative, and dill water is especially useful for relieving griping flatulence in infants.

Oil of peppermint. The oil distilled from the fresh flowering tops of *Mentha piperita* containing about 50% of menthol, together with menthyl esters and the ketone, menthone (*q.v.*). It is an aromatic carminative, and relieves flatulence and colic. Externally it acts as a mild analgesic; it has also mild antiseptic properties. A dilute solution of peppermint oil is used as a vehicle for mixtures.

Oil of wintergreen. See Methyl salicylate.

Oil soluble resins. Alkyd resins modified with drying-oils of drying-oil fatty acids. They are soluble in drying-oil and hydrocarbon thinners, are light-stable, and hence are suitable for protection of paints, varnishes, and enamels.

Oleandomycin, $C_{35}H_{61}NO_{12}$. A useful antibiotic

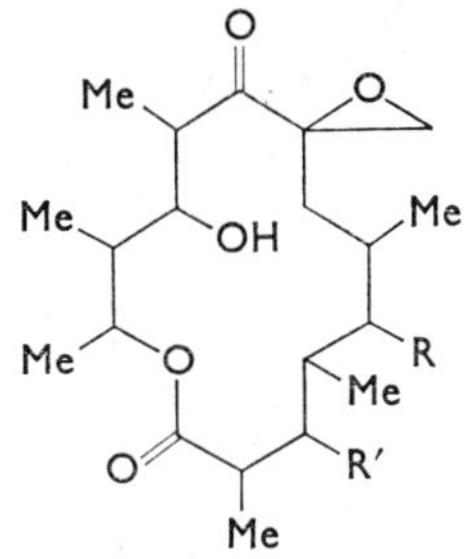

R = desosamine residue
(cf. erythromycin)

R′ = L-oleandrose residue:

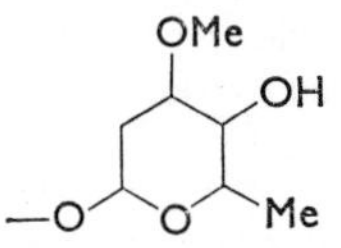

of the macrolide class, produced by certain *Streptomyces* spp., and active against most Gram-positive and some Gram-negative bacteria, as well as *Rickettsiae* and viruses. Oleandomycin is of value for patients who are sensitive to the more generally used antibiotics. It is sold as the phosphate, a white crystalline powder, soluble in water and alcohol.

Oleandrin, $C_{30}H_{46}O_9$. M.p. 249°. It is composed of digitalose and digitaligenin.

Olefin complexes. Co-ordination compounds in

which an olefin is bonded to a metal. The bonding is generally considered to be by overlap of the π bonding orbital of the olefin with a suitable orbital of the metal and by back bonding from a suitable orbital of the metal into a π^* anti-bonding orbital of the olefin. The olefin is thus bonded sideways on to the metal. Examples of olefin complexes are:

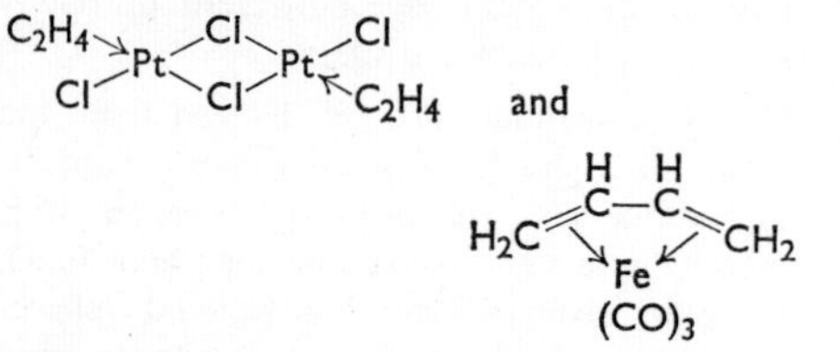

Olefins, Alkenes. Aliphatic hydrocarbons of the general formula C_nH_{2n} containing one double bond; they are isomeric with the cycloparaffins. In physical properties they closely resemble the paraffins; the lower members are gases, the intermediate ones liquids, while the higher members are waxy solids. They are insoluble in water but soluble in chloroform and benzene. They burn with a smoky, luminous flame. They occur in crude petroleum and in the gases from the cracking of petroleum. Olefins are more reactive than paraffins, adding groups across the double bond. Reduced to paraffins by hydrogen in presence of nickel catalysts. React with halogens to give dihalides and with halogen acids to give alkyl halides. Dilute chlorine or bromine solutions in water react to give chloro- or bromohydrins. They dissolve in concentrated sulphuric acid to give alkylsulphonic acids and dialkyl sulphates, and are oxidized by potassium permanganate or lead tetra-acetate to glycols. They polymerize when heated in the presence of zinc chloride or sulphuric acid. May be prepared by heating aliphatic alcohols with sulphuric acid or by passing the alcohol vapour over heated alumina. They are used as fuels and are the starting materials for the preparation of alcohols, glycols, and other substances.

Oleic acid, $C_{18}H_{34}O_2$. A colourless liquid,

$$CH_3 \cdot [CH_2]_7 \cdot CH : CH \cdot [CH_2]_7 \cdot COOH.$$

d_4^{20} 0·89. It is dimorphous, the stable form freezing to a white crystalline solid at 16°, and the unstable form at 12°; b.p. 286°/100 mm. Soluble in alcohol and ether, insoluble in water. It has the *cis* configuration. Oleic acid occurs naturally in larger quantities than any other fatty acid, being present as glycerides in most fats and oils. It forms one third of the total fatty acids of cow's milk. It can be isolated from olive oil or lard by saponification, acidulation and fractional distillation. A crude grade is manufactured from inedible tallow, and is used in the production of lubricants, detergents, resins, and other products.

Oleum. See Sulphuric acid, fuming.

Oligomer. A polymer composed from only a small number of monomeric units, hence oligomerisation.

Olivine. A general term for an isomorphous series of abundant rock-forming minerals (Mg, Fe)$_2$SiO$_4$, occurring in basic and ultrabasic igneous rocks. The high magnesium variety is used in the manufacture of neutral refractory bricks. These minerals contain discrete SiO$_4$ tetrahedra.

Ommochromes. A group of eye pigments found

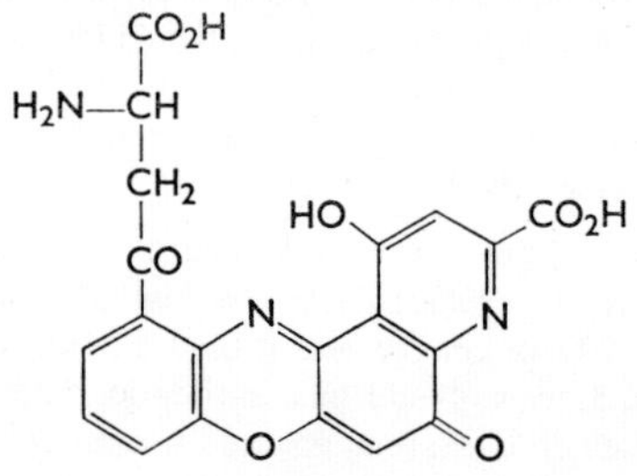

Xanthommatine

in insects and crabs, and derived biosynthetically from tryptophan. Xanthommatine, the simplest and commonest member, arises (and has been synthesized) from two molecules of 3-hydroxykynurenine (see Kynurenine). As pigments of the eyes of the fruit fly (*Drosophila*), ommochromes provided one of the earliest demonstrations of the genetic control of biochemical reactions. Mutants were obtained in which one or other of the reactions in the biosynthesis was blocked; the absence of the pigment was apparent from the paleness of the eyes.

'Onium compounds. Groups of organic compounds of the type $R_x A^+$ which are analogous to ammonium compounds. Examples of the ions present are phosphonium $R_4P^\oplus$, oxonium $R_3O^\oplus$, sulphonium $R_3S^\oplus$, iodonium $R_2I^\oplus$.

Onnes, Heike Kammerlingh (1853-1926). Onnes was educated at the Burger-school and the University of his native Groningen. In 1871 he went to Heidelberg to work with Bunsen and in 1882 was appointed professor of experimental physics at Leyden. His investigations were on the properties of substances at low temperatures and culminated in the liquefaction of helium. In 1913 he was awarded a Nobel Prize. See Mem. Lect., *J. Chem. Soc.*, 1927, 1193.

Onyx. A form of silica similar to chalcedony and agate, with concentric zones of white and brown or grey. It is used as a gemstone.

Oöporphyrin. See Porphyrins.

Opal. A compact amorphous form of hydrated silica containing up to 10% of combined water, which occurs in cavities in certain volcanic and weathered sedimentary rocks. It is used as a gemstone. It is also a constituent of the geyserite or siliceous sinter deposited from hot springs, and of diatomite.

Open circuit grinding. See Closed circuit grinding.

Opium. The dried latex which exudes from the unripe capsules of *Papaver somniferum* after the outer skin has been cut with a knife. It contains a large number of alkaloids, chief among which are morphine, codeine, and narcotine. Opium is used chiefly as a narcotic, and while this action is principally due to the morphine, it is modified by the other alkaloids.

Ophthalmic acid, γ-glutamyl-α-amino-n-butyryl-glycine, is a tripeptide analogous to glutathione, found in the eye lens.

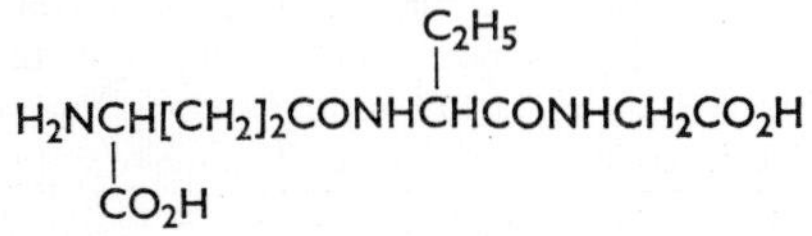

$$H_2NCH[CH_2]_2CONHCHCONHCH_2CO_2H$$

with C_2H_5 above the central CH and CO_2H below the H_2NCH carbon.

Oppenauer oxidation. The oxidation of secondary alcohols to ketones using aluminium *tert*-butoxide.

Opsin. See Rhodopsin.

Optical activity. The property possessed by certain substances of rotating the plane of polarization of polarized light. The property is exhibited by certain solids and liquids (e.g. tartaric acid and some tertiary alcohols), and may also be observed in solutions of such substances, and in the vapour phase. It is associated with asymmetry either of a molecule, an ion, or a crystal lattice. Molecules may be asymmetric due to having four different groups joined to one carbon atom, or from restricted rotation about a central bond.

Optically active substances are termed dextro-rotatory or laevorotatory according to whether the plane of polarization of the light is rotated to the right or to the left with respect to the direction of incidence of the light. The prefixes d- and l- were once used to indicate which optical isomer was which, but now the correct prefixes are (+)- for dextrorotatory, and (−)- for laevorotatory compounds, with (±)- for racemic compounds. With carbohydrates and amino-acids the prefixes D- and L- are used to indicate configuration, not direction of rotation. The convention has been made that the configuration of D-glyceric aldehyde shall be represented by formula I and L-glyceric aldehyde by formula II.

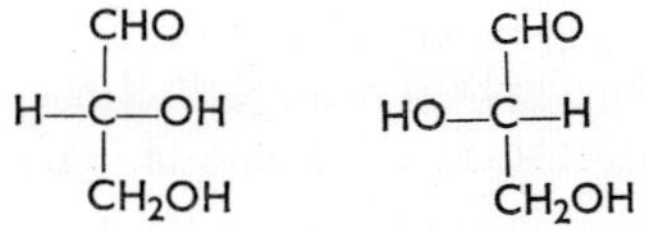

$$\begin{array}{cc} CHO & CHO \\ H-C-OH & HO-C-H \\ CH_2OH & CH_2OH \\ I & II \end{array}$$

When the formulae of other sugars are written in this way those which have the configuration

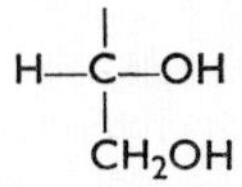

$$\begin{array}{c} H-C-OH \\ CH_2OH \end{array}$$

are given the prefix D-, while L- is used for those with the configuration

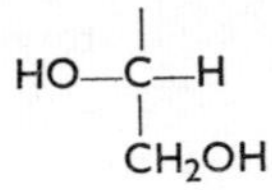

$$\begin{array}{c} HO-C-H \\ CH_2OH \end{array}$$

The same nomenclature has been adopted for amino-acids, the configurational family to which the α-carbon atom belongs being denoted by the prefixes D- and L-. See also R, S convention, Asymmetry.

Optical electrons. In general, only the outermost electrons in an atom are concerned in producing the emission or absorption of light. Such electrons are termed optical electrons.

Optical exaltation. An abnormal increase in the refractivity of an organic compound, over and above the additive amount to be expected from the bonds present, due to the presence of a system of conjugated double bonds.

Optical rotatory dispersion, ORD. A description of the changes in optical rotation of an optically active molecule, organic or inorganic, with the wavelength of the light. The variation of specific rotation with wavelength increases as an absorption band is approached, and the rotation may pass through a maximum or minimum when the absorption band is crossed. This is the so-called Cotton effect (*q.v.*). The effect is particularly sensitive to structural features of many molecules and is used in structural and stereochemical studies. See C. Djerassi. 'Optical Rotatory Dispersion' McGraw-Hill Inc., N.Y., 1960.

Orange IV (Acid Orange 5). An aminoazo-dye (sulphanilic acid with diphenylamine) which was used mainly in wool-cotton union dyeing from a neutral dyebath, but is now of little interest.

Orange lead. See Lead oxides.

Orbital. Loosely used to describe the geometrical figure which describes the most probable location of an electron. More rigorously the allowed energy level for electrons. See Electronic configuration.

Orbital angular momentum (L). The total

angular momentum of a set of electrons in a shell. For filled and empty shells, L is zero.

Orcinol, $C_7H_8O_2$. Crystallizes in prisms from

water with one molecule of water and in anhydrous leaflets from chloroform; m.p. (anhydrous) 107°-108°, b.p. 287°-290°. Soluble in water, alcohol, and ether. It is a constituent of many lichens, from which it can be extracted with alkali.

γ-Orcinol is 2,4-dihydroxytoluene, but β-orcinol is 2,6-dihydroxy-1,4-xylene, $C_8H_{10}O_2$.

Order of reaction. A term used in chemical kinetics referring to the mathematical dependence of the rate of a reaction on the concentration of reactants. For example, if a substance A reacts with another B and the rate is found experimentally to be directly proportional to the concentration of A, the reaction is said to be first order with respect to A. If it is also proportional to the concentration of B, the overall reaction is said to be second order. The order is thus the power to which concentration terms are raised in the mathematical expression for the rate of reaction. In some cases the rate may be of zero order (i.e. independent of concentration) or of fractional or non-integral order with respect to particular reactants. The order of a reaction does not necessarily indicate the actual molecularity of the reaction mechanism because many reactions proceed in steps.

Ore dressing. See Mineral dressing.

Orford process. A process for the extraction of nickel from nickel ores. See Nickel.

Organic. Until the early part of the nineteenth century chemical substances of animal or plant origin were designated as 'organic' and held to differ fundamentally from 'inorganic' substances of mineral origin in that a 'vital force' was required for their production. The 'vital force' theory was discredited in 1828 by Wöhler but the term 'organic' has remained. Organic chemistry is now the study of the compounds of carbon, whether they be isolated from natural sources or synthesized in the laboratory. Most, but not all, organic compounds contain hydrogen as well as carbon, while other common elements are oxygen, nitrogen, the halogens, sulphur, and phosphorus. These and other elements are usually bound to carbon by covalent bonds as distinct from the ionic links typical of inorganic compounds. A few very simple carbon compounds, e.g. metallic carbonates, are considered as inorganic, and the large class of organometallic compounds is of interest to both inorganic and organic chemists.

Organoboranes. Compounds containing at least one direct carbon to boron bond. The commonest classes are the trialkylboranes R_3B and the dialkylboranes R_2BH. Recently developed as extremely useful organic synthetic reagents, they are decomposed by aqueous acid to alkanes and by alkaline peroxide to alcohols: the latter reaction provides a convenient method, via the technique of hydroboration, for the effective *cis*-hydration of alkenes in an anti-Markownikoff direction. Acid hydrolysis of the hydroboration product of internal acetylenes provides a convenient synthesis of *cis*-alkenes.

Methods of producing B—C bonds include nucleophilic displacement at a boron atom in BX_3 (X=halogens or $B(OR)_3$) by, e.g. a Grignard reagent, and a *pseudo*-Friedel-Crafts reaction with an aromatic hydrocarbon, BX_3, and $AlCl_3$. See also Carboranes.

Organochlorine insecticides. This group of compounds, which includes aldrin, dieldrin, chlordane, BHC and DDT, contains some highly active insecticides which, until quite recently, have been very widely used. Traces of them, however, find their way into the bodies of animals and insects and are stored, principally in the fat. As the result of this the animals may become poisonous to their predators. The application of organochlorine insecticides is now restricted in most countries.

Organometallic compounds. Organic or inorganic compounds in which one or more carbon atoms are linked to one or more metal atoms.

The chemistry of these compounds represents the common interests of inorganic and organic chemists. It is usual to exclude the carbonates, carbides, and many cyanides, although many metal isonitrile and metal carbonyl complexes are considered to be organometallic. Most metals form organometallic compounds; many are unstable and spontaneously inflammable in air whilst others are resistant to boiling acids. Consequently a broad spectrum of reactivity includes Grignard reagents, organo-aluminium compounds (e.g. Ziegler catalysts) and cyclopentadienylides (sandwich compounds, metallocenes), and reflects the degree of ionic character of the metal-carbon bond.

Organometalloids. Compounds containing a direct bond between one or more carbon atoms and one or more metalloid atoms.

Organophosphorus compounds. The most important application of organophosphorus compounds is in the field of pesticides. Most of these pesticidal organophosphorus compounds are esters of acids containing phosphorus, e.g. dialkylhydrogenphosphorothiolothionates, $(RO)_2P(S)SH$ (R = methyl, ethyl), dialkylphosphorochloridothionates, $(RO)_2P(S)Cl$, and *bis*(dimethylamino)phosphorochloridate

$$(CH_3)_2N \diagdown \\ \qquad\qquad P(O)Cl \\ (CH_3)_2N \diagup$$

Among the best known organophosphorus pesticides are malathion, parathion, schradan, and dimefox (*q.v.*).

Organosol. Colloidal dispersions in organic dispersion media are termed, in general, organosols and in some instances specific terms such as alcosol, benzosol, etc., are used to indicate that the dispersion medium is alcohol or benzene. These terms are used in contrast to the more usual hydrosols in which water is the dispersion medium. Examples of organosols are nitrocellulose, collodions, and rubber solutions in toluene or naphtha.

Orifice meter. This important instrument is extensively used for measuring the flow of liquids and gases in pipes. A thin plate carries a sharp-edged circular hole of diameter perhaps 1/4 to 3/4 that of the pipe in which it is to be used, and is installed between two flanges with the hole central. In order to pass through the orifice the fluid stream must contract, and as a result the velocity of the fluid at the orifice and just beyond is considerably greater than in the rest of the pipe. Energy considerations require that the increase in kinetic energy be accompanied by a decrease in pressure, and if a manometer is connected between a point upstream of the plate and one immediately downstream of it, the pressure difference gives a measure of the flow rate.

Orifice meters are widely used because they are simple and cheap to manufacture and install, and their design is so well standardized they do not require calibration. Their principal disadvantages are that a high proportion of the pressure change is not recoverable (i.e. they cause a high pressure loss), their accuracy is sensitive to the presence of adjacent upstream pipe fittings, e.g. valves, bends, and any one instrument can only cover a limited flow range.

Orlon. A brand name for polyacrylonitrile fibre. The synthetic fibre can be produced by either wet or dry spinning. The yarn so formed is usually drawn to give great improvement in chemical resistance, strength, and other fibre properties. Polyacrylonitrile fibres are outstanding for their resistance to outdoor exposure, low water absorption, wet and dry strength, and fatigue resistance. The yarns resemble silk in appearance and feel, but possess the bulking and thermal insulation properties of wool.

Ornithine, αδ-Diaminovaleric acid, $C_5H_{12}N_2O_2$.

$$NH_2 \cdot CH_2 \cdot CH_2 \cdot CH_2 \cdot CH \cdot COOH \\ \qquad\qquad\qquad\qquad\quad | \\ \qquad\qquad\qquad\qquad NH_2$$

Soluble in water and alcohol, m.p. 140°, $[\alpha]_D^{25}$ +11·5°. An amino-acid occurring occasionally among the hydrolysis products of proteins, being probably formed by the breakdown of arginine. It is formed from arginine by the action of the enzyme arginase and takes part in the cycle of events leading to the production of urea.

L-**Ornithuric acid** (N,N/-dibenzoyl-L-ornithine). A urinary metabolite of benzoic acid or its metabolic precursors in domestic fowls. Conjugation of aromatic acids with ornithine in fowls is apparently the counterpart of glycine conjugation in mammals.

Orotic acid, uracil-4-carboxylic acid, $C_5H_4N_2O_4$.

Colourless crystals, m.p. 345°, slightly soluble in hot water. First isolated from milk, orotic acid has been shown to be capable of being used by rats for the synthesis of pyrimidines.

Orpiment. A naturally occurring mineral form of arsenic trisulphide, As_2S_3.

Orsat gas-analysis apparatus. This type of gas analysis apparatus is usually portable, and consists of a measuring burette affixed to which is a levelling bottle containing water by means of which the gas is drawn into the apparatus and transferred in turn to the various absorption pipettes containing the respective reagents.

The apparatus is used normally for flue gas analysis and consists of three pipettes containing:

(1) Strong caustic potash solution which absorbs carbon dioxide.

(2) Alkaline pyrogallol solution which absorbs oxygen.

(3) Acid cuprous chloride which absorbs carbon monoxide.

The apparatus can be adapted for the estimation of hydrogen, methane or other combustible gases by including another tube for explosion purposes in which a spark can be passed by means of an induction coil worked by a small battery. A fraction of the gas after removal of the absorbable constituents is made up to 100 ml with air or oxygen and exploded and the amount of carbon dioxide formed in the explosion determined.

Ortho. In the case of disubstituted derivatives of benzene the prefix ortho has a precise structural significance. Thus in the accompanying formula for orthocresol, commonly written *o*-cresol, the CH_3 and OH groups are said to be in the ortho position to each other. The prefix is also found in orthophosphates, orthocarbonates, orthoformates, and orthosilicates, which are derivatives of $PO(OH)_3$, the hypothetical $C(OH)_4$, $HC(OH)_3$, and $Si(OH)_4$ respectively; in these the word 'ortho' is always written in full.

Orthocaine, methyl-3-amino-4-hydroxybenzoate, $C_8H_9NO_3$. A white crystalline powder, m.p. 141°- 143°. Slightly soluble in water, soluble in 7 parts of alcohol. It may be prepared from *p*-hydroxybenzoic acid. It is a local anaesthetic used chiefly as a dusting powder for the relief of painful skin conditions.

Orthochromatic sensitization. The extension of sensitivity of photographic silver halide emulsions by sensitizing dyes to include the green region of the spectrum is known as orthochromatic sensitization. Whereas blue and green images are recorded on such a material, red images are not. Spectral sensitizers for ortho materials absorb green light, and pass on the energy to the silver halide crystals. Examples of such dyes are erythrosin, Orthochrome T, Pinaflavol and thiacarbocyanine.

Orthochrome T, $C_{25}H_{27}IN_2$. A 2,4'-cyanine,

related to Ethyl Red, which is a strong photographic sensitizer for the yellow and green spectral regions. This magenta dye can be prepared by the action of alkali on a hot solution of the ethiodides of 6-methylquinoline and 6-methylquinaldine.

Orthoclase. A monoclinic feldspar, $K(AlSi_3)O_8$. Sp.gr. 2·6, hardness 6, m.p. 1200°. The best commercial orthoclase melts at about 1280°.

Orthoformic ester, ethyl orthoformate. A
$$HC(OC_2H_5)_3$$
colourless liquid, b.p. 145°-147°; d^4 0·8964. It is insoluble in water, but soluble in ether. Prepared by the action of chloroform on sodium ethoxide. It reacts with aldehydes to give acetals,

and with Grignard reagents to give aldehydes. Used in organic syntheses.

Ortho-hydrogen. The hydrogen molecule can exist in two forms, which may be pictured as due to differences in the direction of spin of the nuclei of the two atoms. When both spin in the same direction we have *para-hydrogen*; when the spins are symmetrical, or in opposite directions, we have *ortho-hydrogen*. Ordinary hydrogen is a mixture of the two forms; at normal temperatures the composition being 25% para and 75% ortho. Almost pure para-hydrogen has been prepared by cooling ordinary hydrogen to a very low temperature in contact with charcoal, which acted as a catalyst. The two forms have identical chemical properties, but slightly different physical properties.

Orthorhombic system. One of the crystal systems comprising crystals with three crystallographic axes which are at right angles, but which are all of different lengths. This is also known as the rhombic system. Crystals of this system possess a two-fold axis of symmetry which is either the intersection of two planes of symmetry or is perpendicular to two other two-fold axes. The maximum symmetry of the system consists of three mutually perpendicular planes of symmetry, the lines of intersection of these planes being three two-fold axes. Typical examples are: α-sulphur, potassium nitrate, and iodine.

Orton cones. The Orton cone is an American modification of the Seger cone (*q.v.*), and is made up in the following series:

(1) The soft series: temperature range 585°- 905°.
(2) Low temperature series: temperature range 890°-1145°.
(3) Intermediate series: temperature range 1125°-1530°.
(4) High temperature series: temperature range 1580°-2015°.

The manner of use is similar to that with Seger cones and Holdcroft's thermoscopes, (*q.v.*). See also Contraction rings.

Osazones. Organic compounds containing the grouping

They are formed by treating α-diketones, α-hydroxyaldehydes, hydroxyketones, aminoaldehydes, or aminoketones with phenylhydrazine. The substance is dissolved in water or dilute acetic acid, the phenylhydrazine added and the mixture warmed. The osazone crystallizes out on cooling the solution. Various nitro- or bromo-phenylhydrazines are also used and their osazones often crystallize more readily than the simple phenylosazones. They are crystalline solids sparingly soluble in water but soluble in alcohol. Sugars are identified by their osazones which have characteristic melting-points, formation times, or crystal appearance.

Oslo crystallizer, Krystal crystallizer. Originally developed in Norway, this is now the most important type of industrial crystallizer. It consists of a vertical cylindrical vessel into which a super-saturated solution of the material being crystal-lized is introduced through a central dip pipe extending almost to the bottom. In the vessel there is a mass of small crystals maintained in a fluid-ized state (i.e. in suspension) by the upward flow of liquid. During its passage through the bed the solution deposits some of its excess solid, the crystals gradually growing in size, and leaves the vessel in a saturated or slightly super-saturated state. When a crystal grows to such a size that the liquid velocity is no longer sufficient to support it, it falls to the bottom, and from here product crystals are taken off through a valve. Continuous nucleation and attrition provide fresh seed crystals.

Supersaturation of the inlet solution may be produced in two ways:

(a) If the substance being crystallized has a solubility which is strongly temperature dependent, hot saturated solution is added to the liquor leaving the crystallizer and the resulting mixture is passed through a cooler and back into the crystallizer.

(b) If the solubility does not increase much with temperature the solution leaving the crystallizer body is passed through a heater which raises it to its boiling point. It then enters a vessel under slightly lower pressure where some of the liquid *flashes* off, i.e. evaporates, producing a supersaturated solution which is recycled to the crystallizer body. Both types of crystallizer are continuous.

Oslo crystallisers produce evenly-sized, well-shaped crystals and are well-adapted to large-scale production. Many inorganic salts and some organic compounds are handled by them.

Osmates. Osmates (VIII) with $[OsO_4(OH)_2]^{2-}$ ions are obtained by the action of OsO_4 on a solution of an alkaline hydroxide. Reduction with alcohol gives pink $[OsO_2(OH)_4]^{2-}$ ions containing osmium (VI). Many substitution products of the osmate (VI) ion are known in which the OH groups are replaced by halide, oxalate, etc.

Osmiamic acid, $HOsO_3N$. Prepared in solution from its salts, but decomposes on concentration. The alkali osmiamates are formed by the action of ammonia on a cold alkaline solution of osmium tetroxide; they are orange-yellow crystalline bodies. Other salts may be prepared by double decomposition.

Osmic acid. A name often but incorrectly given to osmium tetroxide and its solution in water. This solution contains free OsO_4. In alkaline solution $[OsO_4(OH)_2]^{2-}$ ions are present.

Osmiridium. The name given to native or synthetic alloys of osmium and iridium. The native alloy occurs as very hard metallic granules having a sp.gr. of from 19·3 to 21·1. It contains from 50% to 80% Ir, 15% to 40% Os with, as a rule, a few per cent of Ru and Rh and small amounts of other metals (Pt, Cu, Fe, Ni). It is used for special purposes in which a very hard and incorrodible material is required, such as the tips of fountain pen nibs and sparking points.

Osmium, Os. At.no. 76, At.wt. 190·2. Osmium is a very hard, brittle, bluish-white metal, $d=22·61$, m.p. 3050°, b.p. 5500°. It has the hexagonal close-packed structure, $a=2·733, c=4·319$Å.

Osmium is rather more easily oxidized than most of the platinum metals, although its alloy with iridium, osmiridium, is very resistant. Osmium is oxidized quite readily by air at temperatures above 200°, forming the volatile tetroxide, and is readily dissolved by aqua regia and even by fuming nitric acid. In its compounds it exhibits oxidation states of 0, 1, 2, 3, 4, 5, 6, 7, and 8. When finely divided the metal has great catalytic powers and its use as a hydrogenating catalyst has been proposed. It is also used for the manufacture of electric light filaments, and the tetroxide is used as a stain in microscopic work.

Osmium bromides. $OsBr_4$, $OsBr_3$, Os_2Br_7, have been prepared by interaction of the elements; Os_2Br_9 results from the action of hydrobromic acid on OsO_4. Brown, tripositive complex bromides, M_3OsBr_6, are prepared by electrolytic reduction of M_2OsBr_6 salts in hydrobromic acid solution. The hexabromo-osmates (IV), M_2OsBr_6, are prepared by dissolving osmium dioxide in hydrobromic acid and precipitating with alkali bromides.

Osmium carbonyls. Osmium forms two carbonyls, $Os(CO)_5$, m.p. $-15°$, and $Os_3(CO)_{12}$, yellow crystals, m.p. 224°, sublimes 130°, by the action of carbon monoxide on an osmium halide in the presence of copper or silver. Carbonyl halides of the types $Os(CO)_3X_2$, $Os(CO)_4X_2$ and $(Os(CO)_4X)_2$ are known.

Osmium chlorides. $OsCl_2$ is formed by the decomposition of the trichloride at 500° under reduced pressure. It is a dark-brown powder, little

425

affected by water, although on prolonged boiling it forms a yellow solution.

$OsCl_3$ in the anhydrous state is best obtained by the ignition of $(NH_4)_2OsCl_6$ in chlorine at 350°. It forms brownish-black hygroscopic crystals, readily soluble in water. $OsCl_3, 3H_2O$ has been obtained by wet methods as dark-green crystals.

$OsCl_4$ is formed by direct union of the elements at about 700°. It is a black sublimate which gives a yellow vapour. It is slowly hydrolysed by water. $OsOCl_4$ results from the action of an oxygen-chlorine mixture on the metal. It gives Cs_2OsOCl_6 with caesium chloride.

Osmium chlorides, complex. There are two series: the chloro-osmates (III), $M^I_3OsCl_6$, and the chloro-osmates (IV), $M^I_2OsCl_6$. Both may be obtained by the reduction, under suitable conditions, of OsO_4 with HCl in presence of an alkali chloride. Both $K_3OsCl_6,3H_2O$ and $(NH_4)_3OsCl_6,3H_2O$ are dark red crystals, readily soluble in water. K_2OsCl_6 forms red octahedra, and is isomorphous with K_2PtCl_6.

Osmium fluorides. *Osmium heptafluoride,* OsF_7, results from the action of fluorine under pressure at high temperatures.

Osmium hexafluoride, OsF_6, is a pale green crystalline solid obtained by the action of fluorine on the metal; m.p. 32·1°, b.p. 45·9°. It is stable in dried glass.

Osmium pentafluoride, OsF_5, is a blue compound prepared by the reduction of OsF_6 with tungsten carbonyl; m.p. 70°, b.p. 226°.

Osmium tetrafluoride, OsF_4, is a yellow solid, m.p. 230°, prepared in the same reaction as the pentafluoride.

In addition to the binary fluorides, oxyfluorides OsO_3F_2, $OsOF_5$ and $OsOF_4$ are known.

Osmium fluorides, complex. *Hexafluoro-osmates* (V), $MOsF_6$. Prepared by the action of bromine trifluoride on a mixture of equivalent proportions of alkali halide and osmium tetrabromide. They are white, crystalline solids, stable in dry air but blackening in moist air. *Hexafluoro-osmates (IV),* M_2OsF_6. Obtained by dissolving hexafluoro-osmates (V) in water and adding alkali. Oxygen is evolved and pale yellow crystals of hexafluoro-osmates (IV) separate.

Osmium iodides. Iodides OsI_3, OsI_2, and OsI can be prepared by interaction of the elements. Complex iodides, M_2OsI_6, are obtained by the action of hydrogen iodide on $K_2Os(NO_2)_5$.

Osmium nitrido derivatives. These are closely related to osmiamic acid. Nitrido osmiamates $[OsN(H_2O)X_4]^-$, $[OsN(H_2O)(OH)_2X_2]^-$ $(OsNX_5)^{2-}$, (X=halide or other ligand) are formed by reaction of a complex ion with potassium osmiamate. The action of ammonia

on OsX_6^{2-} species gives $[Os_2N(NH_3)_8X_2]X_3$ species.

Osmium oxides. *Osmium tetroxide,* OsO_4. Prepared by oxidation of the metal or its compounds with nitric acid, m.p. 40·6°, b.p. 131·2°. Very volatile, has a tetrahedral molecule, forms yellow crystals, the vapour is very poisonous. With alkalis gives unstable complex ions of the types $[OsO_4(OH)_2]^{2-}$ and $[OsO_4(OH)(H_2O)]^-$. Used in organic chemistry to effect the oxidation of olefinic double bonds to *cis* diols and, in the presence of pyridine, to oxidize aromatic hydrocarbons.

Osmium (VII) oxide, Os_2O_7, is not known, but salts containing the $[OsO_6]^{5-}$ and $[OsO_5]^{3-}$ ions result from the action of KO_2 and alkali metal oxide on the metal osmate.

Osmium (VI) oxide, OsO_3, is not known. Osmyl complexes contain the trans $[OsO_2X_4]^{2-}$ groupings where X may be a variety of complexing agents.

Osmium (IV) oxide, OsO_2. A black or dark brown solid made by heating the metal with OsO_4. No anionic species are known.

Osmium sulphide, OsS_2. Prepared by combination of the elements at 600°. It is a black solid having the pyrites structure. It is insoluble in alkalis and in non-oxidizing acids.

Osmocyanides. The best-known compounds of dipositive osmium. $K_4Os(CN)_6, 3H_2O$ is obtained by the action of KCN on alkaline solutions of the tetroxide, or by fusion of various osmium compounds with KCN. It forms yellow crystals, and its solution gives characteristically coloured precipitates with various heavy metal salts. The free acid $H_4Os(CN)_6$ can be isolated as white crystals.

Osmosis. The process of spontaneous flow of liquids through a membrane. This effect is usually observed across a membrane such as a piece of parchment or a plant or animal membrane, and when there is a difference in the chemical potential of the solutions on the two sides of the membrane. Thus, if a membrane separates two liquids, one of which is the pure solvent and the other a solution, some of the solvent will pass through the membrane from the pure solvent into the solution.

Osmotic coefficient. A parameter, introduced by Bjerrum, to represent the degree of non-ideality of any non-ideal solution. It is chiefly used in representing data obtained from the so-called colligative properties of solutions, i.e. osmotic pressure, elevation of the b.p., depression of the f.p., and reduced partial pressure. The property observed in all these phenomena is, in effect, the thermodynamic activity a_1 of the solvent in the solution. Now in ideal solutions a_1 is equal to the mole fraction of solvent N_1. In non-ideal solutions they are deemed to be related by the equation $a_1 = N_1 g$, which serves as the definition of the osmotic coefficient g. It can be shown that $(1 - g)$ is a convenient measure of the degree of departure of that solution from ideality. The coefficient g is therefore an alternative parameter to the activity coefficient, to which it is mathematically related.

Osmotic pressure. The osmotic pressure of a solution is the excess hydrostatic pressure which must be applied to it to counter-balance the process of osmosis. Thus a solution under this excess pressure can come to osmotic equilibrium with the same solvent on the other side of a membrane permeable only to the solvent. In dilute solutions non-electrolytes exert an osmotic pressure equal to the pressure they would exert if they existed as gases under the same conditions of molecular concentration and temperature.

Ostwald, Carl Wilhelm Wolfgang (1883-1943). Wolfgang Ostwald was born at Riga, Russia, and educated at Leipzig. After working as a research assistant at the Physiological Institute of the University of California from 1904 to 1906 he returned to Leipzig, where he pursued an academic career, becoming ordinary professor of colloid chemistry in 1935. He wrote several books on colloid chemistry and edited the *Kolloid-Zeitschrift* and the *Kolloid Beihefte*.

Ostwald, Wilhelm Friedrich (1853-1932). Ostwald received his early education at the University of Dorpat. In 1881 he was appointed professor of chemistry in the Polytechnic of his native town, Riga, and in 1887 professor of physical chemistry in the University of Leipzig. He was awarded the Nobel Prize in 1909. An inspiring teacher, Ostwald laid the foundations of many sections of physical chemistry. He discovered the 'Ostwald process' for the preparation of nitric acid by the oxidation of ammonia. See Mem. Lect., *J. Chem. Soc.*, 1933, 316.

Ostwald ripening. Ostwald ripening is the name given to a process of crystal growth. Thus if a mixture of coarse and fine crystals of a substance is in contact with a solvent for the material, the coarse crystals grow at the expense of the fine crystals which ultimately disappear. This phenomenon is due to the higher energy content of the smaller crystals dependent on the work involved in breaking the crystal lattice. By solution, this excess energy is released in the form of heat and more material becomes available for recrystallization on to the larger crystal seed. The process is used in analysis and photography to obtain crystals with the desired characteristics.

O'Sullivan, Cornelius (1841-1907). Born at Bandon, Co. Cork, O'Sullivan studied in London at the Royal School of Mines and the Royal College of Chemistry. In 1869 he became assistant brewer and chemist to Messrs. Bass, with whom he remained for the rest of his career, eventually becoming chief brewer. His more important papers deal with the chemistry of starch and of the carbohydrates. He was awarded the Longstaff Medal of the Chemical Society in 1884, and in 1885 was elected a Fellow of the Royal Society.

Ouabain, G-Strophanthin. The glycoside prepared from *Strophanthus gratus*. It is made up of rhamnose and ouabagenin. It acts on the heart in a similar way to digitalis.

Ovalbumin, Egg albumin. The chief protein constituent of white of egg. It can be prepared by precipitating the globulins from egg white by half saturation with ammonium sulphate and then precipitating the ovalbumin by adding acetic acid. It crystallizes in fine needles, soluble in water. The molecule contains phosphorus and a polysaccharide. It has a molecular weight of about 44,000.

Over-voltage, Over-potential. The excess potential, over and above the reversible electrode potential, that must be applied to an electrode for electrolysis to occur at a given rate. For example, while evolution of hydrogen occurs practically at the reversible potential on a platinized platinum electrode, no hydrogen is evolved from a mercury electrode until an over-voltage of about 1 volt (more negative) is reached. Over-voltage is of great practical importance in electroplating, electro-analysis, electro-reduction, polarography, etc. The theory of the phenomenon is at present incomplete.

Oxalacetic acid, $C_4H_4O_5$. The keto form of this acid, $HOOC \cdot CO \cdot CH_2 \cdot COOH$ has not been isolated, though salts and esters of it have been obtained as colourless crystals. Two enol forms are known

$$\begin{array}{ccc} HOOC \cdot C \cdot OH & & HOOC \cdot C \cdot OH \\ \| & and & \| \\ H \cdot C \cdot COOH & & HOOC \cdot C \cdot H \end{array}$$

Trans, m.p. 184°, and *cis*, m.p. 152°. Soluble in water and alcohol. The diethyl ester, called oxalacetic ester, is a valuable starting material for many syntheses.

Oxalates. Salts or esters of oxalic acid.

Oxalic acid. Crystallizes from water in large colourless prisms containing two molecules of water of crystallization. It is poisonous, causing paralysis of the nervous system; m.p. 101·5° (hydrate), 189·5° (anhydrous).

$$\begin{array}{c} COOH \\ | \\ COOH \end{array}$$

Soluble in water and alcohol; sparingly soluble in ether (solubility increases in presence of hydrochloric acid). It occurs as the free acid in beet leaves, and as potassium hydrogen oxalate in wood sorrel and rhubarb. Commercially, oxalic acid is made from sodium formate. This is obtained by heating anhydrous sodium hydroxide with carbon monoxide in an autoclave at 150°-200° and 7-10 atm. When reaction is complete the pressure is reduced and the temperature raised to 400°. Hydrogen is evolved and sodium oxalate formed; from the sodium salt the acid is readily liberated by sulphuric acid. Oxalic acid is also obtained as a by-product in the manufacture of citric acid and by the oxidation of carbohydrates with nitric acid in presence of vanadium pentoxide.

The anhydrous acid sublimes at about 157°. When heated with sulphuric acid it is decomposed to carbon monoxide, carbon dioxide, and water. Gives formic acid when heated with glycerin. Forms both acid and neutral salts. The normal potassium and ammonium salts are soluble in water; the corresponding acid salts are less soluble and the salts of other metals are only sparingly soluble. The calcium salt is very insoluble. Oxalic acid is used for metal cleaning and as a chemical intermediate. Because of its bleaching action it is widely employed for textile finishing and cleaning, and is also used for whitening leather.

Oxalic ester. See Diethyl oxalate.

Oxamide. A colourless crystalline solid, insoluble in water and alcohol, prepared by mixing ethyl oxalate with concentrated ammonia. When heated it decomposes. Reacts with hot water to give ammonium oxalate. Forms dicyanogen when heated with phosphorus pentoxide.

$$\begin{matrix} CONH_2 \\ | \\ CONH_2 \end{matrix}$$

Oxanthrol (1) is tautomeric with anthrahydroquinone(2); both forms may be isolated

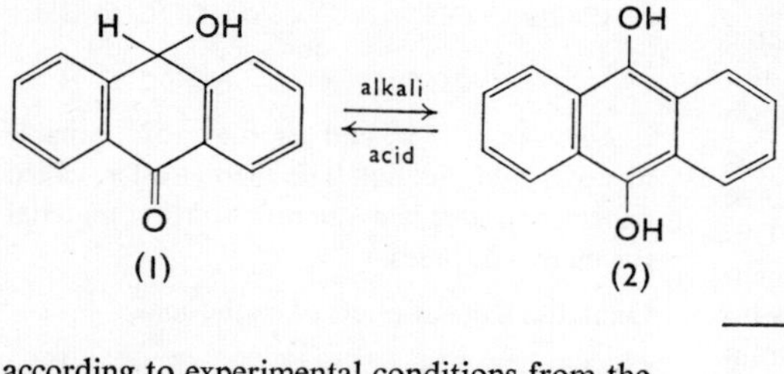

Oxazole ring. The ring is numbered as shown.

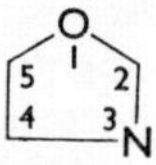

Oxetones. Derivatives of 1,6-dioxaspiro-[4,4]-nonane. Prepared by condensation of two

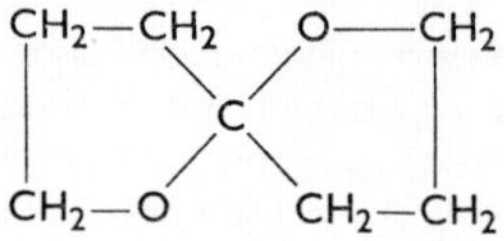

molecules of a γ-lactone in the presence of sodium or sodium methoxide followed by decarboxylation of the product, or by hydrogenation of derivatives of 2-furylpropanol.

Oxetones are sensitive to acids and with hydrochloric or hydrobromic acids give γγ-dihaloketones. They have been shown to inhibit the growth of neoplasms.

Oxidases. Dehydrogenating enzymes that can transfer hydrogen directly to molecular oxygen.

Oxidation. Any process whereby the proportion of the electronegative constituent in a compound is increased, as, for example, in the conversion of Cu_2O to CuO, or of $FeCl_2$ to $FeCl_3$. Oxidation consists of the removal of an electron or electrons.

Oxidation-reduction potential, Redox potential. If an unattackable electrode is immersed in a reversible oxidation-reduction system a potential difference is set up at the electrode. This is called the oxidation-reduction potential and in combination with another suitable electrode can be measured by a potentiometer. It is a measure of the tendency of the system to undergo oxidation or reduction. Oxidation potentials are expressed relative to the hydrogen

(1)   (2)

according to experimental conditions from the zinc dust and alkali reduction of anthraquinone. Oxanthrol is a greenish-yellow compound, decomposing at 205°, which dissolves in alkali giving a blood-red solution; on shaking in air the solution is rapidly decolourized and yellow anthraquinone separates, leaving an alkaline solution of hydrogen peroxide.

electrode as zero. $E = \dfrac{RT}{nF} \ln K$ for the reaction,

where E is the potential and K is the equilibrium constant.

Oxidation state. The formal electronic state of an element in a compound when considered as the number of electrons less or more than in the free atom. Thus in Na^+Cl^- the sodium and chlorine have oxidation states $+1$ and -1 respectively. Bonds formed by co-ordination are considered not to affect the oxidation state. Thus $[Co(NH_3)_6]^{3+}$ contains Co(III) and $Fe(CO)_5$ contains Fe(0). When bonds are formed between like atoms fractional oxidation states are not invoked, e.g. in $H_3C—CH_3$ and $(OC)_5Mn—Mn(CO)_5$.

Oxidative phosphorylation. The process occurring in the respiratory chain by which ATP is formed through a series of coupled reactions utilizing the reduced coenzymes produced in the Krebs cycle. Oxidative phosphorylation takes place in the mitochondria. Certain substances block the formation of ATP without interfering with the electron-transport processes. This effect is known as the uncoupling of oxidative phosphorylation: it is produced by 2,4-dinitrophenol, by dicoumarol and by thyroxine.

Oxide. A compound of oxygen with another element. Oxides are divided into acidic oxides, which react with bases to form salts (e.g. SO_2, P_2O_5); basic oxides, which react with acids to form salts (e.g. CuO, CaO), and amphoteric oxides, which exhibit both basic and acidic properties (e.g. Al_2O_3). There are in addition a few oxides which are sometimes classed as neutral oxides (e.g. CO, NO), and also peroxides, which are metallic derivatives of hydrogen peroxide.

In many cases substances commonly regarded as oxides do in fact contain considerable amounts of combined water, the complete removal of which markedly affects the properties of the substance. Some oxides, e.g. ZnO, change colour on heating. Others, for example CdO, show a colour dependent to a large extent on the manner of preparation; in such oxides the proportion of metal to oxygen is slightly non-stoicheiometric.

Oximes. Organic compounds containing the group $=N·OH$ united directly to a carbon atom. See Aldoximes and Ketoximes.

Oxine, 8-Hydroxyquinoline, C_9H_7NO. Crystallizes in light brown needles from alcohol, m.p. $75°-76°$. Soluble in alcohol, practically insoluble in water, soluble in acids and alkalis. It forms insoluble derivatives when its phenolic hydrogen atom is replaced by metals. The solubilities of the derivatives vary under different conditions and hence oxine is widely used in analysis. It can be used for estimating magnesium, aluminium, zinc, and many other metals. Many oxinates are extracted and the metal is estimated spectrophotometrically.

Potassium 8-hydroxyquinoline sulphonate, which is a light yellow crystalline powder soluble in water, is used as an antiseptic under the trade name of Chinosol; its antiseptic action depends on its property of forming complexes with metals essential to the growth of bacteria and so removing them from solution.

Oxonium. A positive ion containing a central oxygen atom. The hydroxonium ion, H_3O^+, exists in aqueous solutions of acid, and solid salts containing this ion may be prepared. The trimethyloxonium, Me_3O^+, and triphenyloxonium, Ph_3O^+, ions and their derivatives are also known.

Oxo reaction. A reaction which involves the addition of water gas (H_2+CO) to an olefin under high pressure (125-200 atm.) at $90°-200°$ in the presence of a catalyst. The latter may be mixtures of oxides of cobalt, thorium and copper on kieselguhr, or dicobalt octacarbonyl. The products are aldehydes which may be further hydrogenated using the same catalysts to primary alcohols. A modification using carbon monoxide and water instead of water gas yields carboxylic acids. See Carbonylation, Hydroformylation.

Oxyanions. Anions which may be considered as being formed by co-ordination of oxide ions, O^{2-}, to metal or non-metal cations, e.g. the sulphate ion SO_4^{2-} is built up from S^{6+} and $4O^{2-}$ ions. Oxyanions are the normal species in water as complex fluoro-anions are the normal species in anhydrous hydrogen fluoride.

Oxyazo dyes. These form a group of azo dyestuffs characterized by the presence of a hydroxyl group in the molecule. The soluble oxyazo compounds are the sodium salts of the various sulphonic acids, and are prepared by combining sulphonic acids of phenols and naphthols with diazo salts. Typical examples are: Orange II, Crystal Ponceau, Fast red A. See Azo-dyes.

Oxycyanogen, $(OCN)_2$. A free pseudohalogen, which is formed in solution by the action of oxidizing agents on potassium cyanate. It is also prepared by the action of cyanogen bromide on silver oxide. Its solutions are very unstable.

Oxygen, O. At.no. 8, At.wt. 16·0000. An almost colourless, odourless gas; slightly soluble in water, 100 volumes of water at $0°$ dissolving nearly 5 volumes of oxygen at normal pressure; it can be condensed to a bluish liquid boiling at $-183°$ at 760 mm; m.p. $-218·9°$; the solid is pale blue in colour. Liquid and molecular oxygen is paramagnetic.

Oxygen is the most abundant element in the earth's crust. It is contained in the air, in water, in limestone, sandstone, and all other rocks. It was discovered independently by Scheele about

1772, and by Priestley in 1774, but Scheele did not publish his discovery until 1777.

Oxygen is manufactured on a large-scale by the distillation of liquid air. On a small scale oxygen is conveniently made by heating potassium chlorate mixed with manganese dioxide, the latter acting as a catalyst.

Metallic silver and some other metals absorb oxygen at about 500° and emit it on cooling. Oxygen combines with most of the elements to form oxides, some of which are acidic, some basic. The molecule of oxygen consists of two atoms; a modification in which the molecule consists of three atoms is ozone.

Formerly used mainly in the welding and cutting of metals, oxygen is now a chemical of growing importance, chiefly due to its adoption in steel-making. It is also used in the manufacture of acetylene, ammonia, methanol and other chemicals. It is essential to most forms of life.

Oxygen fluorides. *Oxygen difluoride*, OF_2, is prepared by passing fluorine through dilute cooled sodium hydroxide solution. It has m.p. $-224°$, b.p. $-145°$. It is only slowly hydrolysed by water at ambient temperature, and is a strong oxidizing agent when sparked. Other oxygen fluorides, O_2F_2, O_4F_2, O_5F_2 and O_6F_2, are prepared by passing an electric discharge through a mixture of oxygen, ozone, and fluorine.

Oxyhaemoglobin. See Haemoglobin.

Oxytetracycline. See Tetracyclines.

Oxytocin. A cyclic peptide hormone secreted by

CyS.Tyr.Ileu.Glu(NH₂).Asp(NH₂).CyS.Pro.Leu.Gly.NH₂

the posterior lobe of the pituitary gland. It stimulates contraction of the smooth muscle of the uterus. Also, during lactation, it promotes the ejection of milk. Oxytocin was the first peptide hormone to be synthesized. It is used in obstetrical and veterinary practice.

Ozokerite. A naturally occurring wax which on refining yields a hard white microcrystalline wax known as ceresin.

Ozone, O_3. An allotropic form of oxygen which, in the pure state, is a gas with a pale blue colour condensing to a dark blue liquid (b.p. $-112·4°$; m.p. $-249·7°$; crit. temp. $-5°$). Ozone mixed with oxygen is prepared by passing oxygen through an ozonizer, which consists either of two co-axial tubes or of a series of plates between which an electrical brush discharge is passing. Ozone is decomposed rapidly at temperatures above 100°, or at room temperature in the presence of certain catalysts (e.g. MnO_2). It has

very strong oxidizing properties, and is used in a diluted form for sterilizing water, for purifying air, and for carrying out certain oxidation reactions in organic chemistry. The molecule of ozone is bent.

Ozonides. Products of the action of ozone on various classes of unsaturated organic compounds. They have the structure shown. Ozonides are prepared by passing ozonized air or oxygen into the unsaturated compound dissolved in a suitable solvent. Most ozonides are thick oils with an unpleasant choking smell and are explosive. They are decomposed readily,

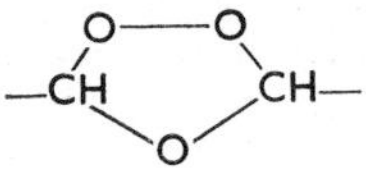

some by water, others by acetic acid or reducing agents. From an analysis of the decomposition products the position of the double bond in the original unsaturated compound can usually be determined. Inorganic ozonides, such as potassium ozonide, KO_3, also exist. These contain the O_3^- ion.

Ozonizer. Apparatus for the preparation of ozone by passing oxygen through an electrical discharge.

P

Packed column, packed tower. This is one of the two principal types of plant used for gas-liquid contacting. It consists of a long vertical column filled with a packing material over which the liquid flowing down the column, solvent in the case of gas absorption or reflux in the case of distillation, can spread itself, thus providing a large area for contact between phases. For efficient operation this liquid must be spread evenly over the top of the packing, this being done by a *distributor*. The greater the packed height of the column the greater the path length over which transfer of material between phases can occur, and thus the degree of separation or absorption that such a unit can achieve is directly related to this height.

Packed columns are widely used for gas absorption and for small-scale industrial distillation operations. They provide a low resistance to the flow of gas or vapour, are simple in construction and can be readily made from corrosion-resistant materials. Distribution of liquid is a problem in large diameter units. Packed columns are also used for liquid-liquid extraction. See also Packings.

Packing fraction. The mass of atoms might be expected to be a simple sum of the masses of the elemental particles making up the atoms, but some of this mass is converted to energy ($E = mc^2$) which is used to hold the nucleus together.

The packing fraction is defined as the mass defect divided by the mass number. The mass defect is the difference between the actual atomic mass and the mass number (the total mass of the individual protons and neutrons considered to make up the nucleus). The lightest and heaviest elements have a positive packing fraction, and the intermediate elements have a negative packing fraction. See Atomic energy.

Packings, column packings, tower packings. Wood, metal and plastic grids are used in absorption and cooling towers. *Raschig rings*, cylinders of metal, ceramic or glass with length equal to diameter, are used for packings in both distillation and absorption columns. *Saddles*, ceramic pieces in the shape of a saddle, are more efficient than Raschig rings, though more expensive. *High efficiency packings* are used in distillation columns for difficult separations where it is necessary to obtain a large number of theoretical plates in a comparatively small packed height. They generally consist of metal in the form of gauze or wire mesh. See Theoretical plate.

Paddle agitator. A large, flat blade with plane vertical is attached to a vertical drive shaft, the whole revolving comparatively slowly in the vessel whose contents are to be stirred. The shape of the blade depends on the particular duty being performed, e.g. an *anchor paddle*, so called because of its shape, has a profile which is the same as that of the vessel, and tends to dislodge any material adhering to the walls or bottom. Paddle agitators tend to impart a swirling motion to a liquid. They are useful for solid-liquid suspensions and can handle pastes and viscous materials.

Palau. A gold platinum alloy used in chemical ware.

Palladium, At.no. 46, At.wt. 106·4. A white metal resembling silver in appearance and platinum in its mechanical properties. It has the face-centred cubic structure $a = 3·8902$ Å, d 12·02, m.p. 1552°, b.p. 3560°. It is the least noble of the platinum metals, being dissolved by conc. nitric acid or by hot sulphuric acid. At a dull red-heat it is oxidized superficially, or completely if finely divided, to PdO, which, however, decomposes at higher temperatures. Its most important property is its catalytic activity. The compact metal enables hydrogen to be oxidized by air at

280°, and the finely divided forms ('spongy palladium' and 'palladium black') are still more active and in their presence hydrogen is converted to water at room temperatures.

In its compounds palladium shows oxidation states of 0, 1, 2, 3, and 4.

Its principal uses are applications of its catalytic activity or of its power of absorbing hydrogen. The salts are used in photography, and alloys with gold have been used as substitutes for platinum.

Palladium ammines. Dipositive palladium forms a number of stable ammines, which are analogous to those of dipositive platinum and have the co-ordination number four. The chief types are $[PdA_4]X_2$ and $[PdA_2X_2]$, in which A is ammonia or a substituted ammonia or other such molecule, and X a univalent acidic radical. From the observed isomerism and from crystal structure determinations 4-covalent palladium compounds have planar co-ordination.

Palladium and hydrogen. Palladium, on exposure to hydrogen, takes up several hundred times its volume of the gas. This is true of the compact metal; the finely divided forms absorb the gas more rapidly and to an even greater extent. The product may be regarded as an alloy: its appearance is but little different from that of the original metal, but its electrical conductivity is much diminished and its mechanical properties are affected. The hydrogen in this condition has an enhanced chemical activity and can perform many reduction reactions. The amount of hydrogen absorbed depends greatly on the previous history of the metal and the presence of impurities ('poisons'); it varies in a rather complicated manner with temperature and pressure. The hydrogen forms an interstitial compound with the metallic palladium.

Palladium black. A very finely divided precipitate obtained by the action of reducing agents on solutions of palladium salts. Its behaviour is that of the metal in a very fine state of subdivision, but it always contains some oxygen. It is a very powerful catalyst for hydrogenations and has been used instead of nickel for this purpose, as the reactions take place at lower temperatures.

Palladium bromides. *Palladous bromide*, $PdBr_2$, is a brown substance, made from the elements in the presence of nitric acid. It is insoluble in water but forms *bromopalladates* (II), M_2PdBr_4, in hydrobromic acid solutions. *Hexabromopalladates* (IV), M_2PdBr_6, are formed by the action of bromine on bromopalladates (II). They are black in colour.

Palladium chloride. Anhydrous $PdCl_2$ may be obtained by heating the metal in chlorine, or by carefully dehydrating $PdCl_2$, $2H_2O$, which is obtained by crystallization of the solution formed by the action of hydrochloric acid and chlorine on the metal. The dihydrate is a brown hygroscopic mass; the anhydrous salt forms dark-red crystals which decompose at about 150° in an inert atmosphere, but can be sublimed at low red-heat in a current of chlorine.

Palladium chlorides, complex. Three series of complex chlorides exist, having the general formulae M_2PdCl_4, M_2PdCl_5, and M_2PdCl_6, where M is a unipositive metal.

The tetrachloropalladates (II), of which K_2PdCl_4 is the best known, are readily obtained as brownish-yellow crystals by crystallizing solutions of their component chlorides.

The hexachloropalladates (IV) are formed by the action of chlorine on solutions of the chloropalladates (II). The potassium salt, K_2PdCl_6, is the best known; it is a dark-red substance, isomorphous with K_2PtCl_6, and, like it, sparingly soluble in water.

Palladium cyanides. *Palladous cyanide*, $Pd(CN)_2$, is obtained as a yellow precipitate when mercuric cyanide is added to a solution of palladium (II) chloride. It dissolves in solutions of alkali cyanide to give complexes $M_2Pd(CN)_4$. Reduction of $K_2Pd(CN)_4$ with potassium in liquid ammonia gives the zeropositive compound $K_4Pd(CN)_4$.

Palladium fluorides. *Palladium trifluoride*, PdF_3, is a black substance prepared by the action of bromine trifluoride on palladous chloride. It has the structure $Pd^{2+}[Pd^{IV}F_6]^{2-}$. Complex fluoropalladates (IV), M_2PdF_6, are formed by the action of bromine trifluoride on chloropalladates (II). All these fluorides are immediately hydrolysed by water.

Palladium oxides. PdO is the only oxide which is known in the anhydrous condition. It is formed by careful ignition of the nitrate, by prolonged heating of the finely divided metal in oxygen at about 800°, or in a hydrated form by hydrolysis of palladous salts, either on boiling with excess of water or by addition of sodium carbonate. It dissolves easily in dilute acids.

A hydrated sesquioxide, Pd_2O_3, xH_2O, has been obtained as an unstable brown precipitate by electrolytic oxidation of palladous solutions. The hydrated dioxide PdO_2, xH_2O is formed by the same method or by precipitation from solutions containing tetrapositive palladium. Both are very unstable, and cannot be dehydrated without decomposition.

Palladium, spongy. A finely-divided form of the metal obtained by reduction in the dry way, e.g. by heating an amminochloride in hydrogen.

Palladium sulphides. Pd_4S, $Pd_{14}S_5$, $Pd_{11}S_5$, PdS, and PdS_2 are known. They are best obtained by dry methods, although PdS is precipitated by hydrogen sulphide from solutions of palladium compounds. They are all inert insoluble substances. PdS_2 forms soluble double sulphides such as Na_2PdS_3 with sulphides of the alkali metals.

Palladous iodide, PdI_2. A black powder obtained by precipitation. It is insoluble in water but dissolves in excess of iodide solution, forming iodopalladates (II) such as K_2PdI_4. No higher iodide is known.

Palladous nitrate, $Pd(NO_3)_2$. Formed when the metal dissolves in nitric acid. It is a brownish-yellow crystalline salt, very deliquescent and readily soluble in water, forming an unstable solution which is very easily hydrolysed, precipitating PdO.

Palladous sulphate, $PdSO_4$, $2H_2O$. Obtained as reddish deliquescent crystals by the usual wet methods. It is readily soluble in water, the solution being hydrolysed on dilution and a basic salt precipitated.

Palmitic acid, *n*-hexadecanoic acid, $C_{16}H_{32}O_2$, $CH_3 \cdot [CH_2]_{14} \cdot COOH$. Crystallizes in needles, m.p. 63·1°, b.p. 351°. Soluble in ether, slightly soluble in alcohol, insoluble in water. Palmitic acid is one of the most widespread fatty acids and occurs as glycerides in most animal and vegetable fats and oils and as esters of alcohols other than glycerol in various waxes. The best sources of it are Japan wax and palm oil. It forms 40% of the total fatty acids of cows' milk. A solid mixture of palmitic and stearic acids, 'stearine', is used for making candles, and the sodium and potassium salts of palmitic and stearic acids are the soaps. Palmitic acid can be obtained by hydrolysing natural fats with superheated steam when it is the first fatty acid to distil over.

Palygorskite. See Fuller's earth.

Pamaquin (trade name **Plasmoquin**), $C_{42}H_{45}N_3O_7$ is the salt of 6-methoxy-8-(ω-diethylamino-α-methylbutyl)aminoquinoline

with pamoic acid (*q.v.*). It is a yellow granular powder, insoluble in water, readily soluble in alcohol. It is a synthetic antimalarial, used either alone, or better in association with quinine or mepacrine. Unlike quinine it acts more powerfully on the gametocytes than the schizonts of the malaria parasite.

Pamoic acid, Embonic acid, $C_{23}H_{16}O_6$. 2,2'-Dihydroxy - 1,1' - dinaphthylmethane - 3,3' -dicarboxylic acid. It is used to form salts with

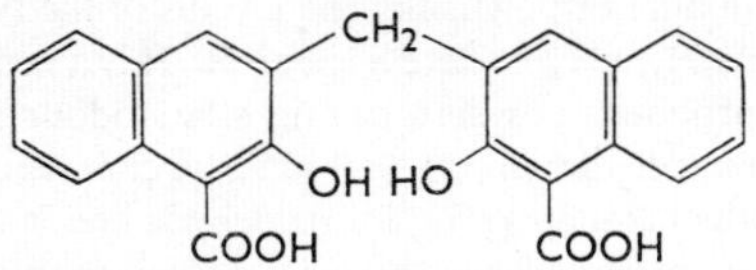

organic bases used in medicine where insolubility in water and lack of absorption from the alimentary canal are required.

Panchromatic sensitization. The extension of sensitivity of photographic silver halide emulsions by sensitizing dyes to the whole of the visible spectrum is known as panchromatic sensitization. The effect is achieved by employing mixtures of green and red sensitizers. One of the earliest commercially available pan materials incorporated quinoline red and cyanine as green and red sensitizers respectively. The first adequately sensitized pan plate for general use, with pinacyanol and pinachrome as sensitizers, was marketed in 1906 by Wratten and Wainwright.

Pan crusher. See Edge runner mill.

Paneth, Friedrich Adolf (1887-1958). Born in Vienna and educated at the Universities of Vienna, Munich, and Glasgow, Paneth held chairs at Prague, Hamburg, Berlin, Koenigsberg, and Durham, and worked also at Imperial College, London, and as head of the chemistry section of the atomic energy team at Montreal from 1943-1945. He was finally director of the Max-Planck Institute for Chemistry at Mainz. He worked for much of his life with radioactive isotopes, using these as tracers for dating rocks, meteorites, etc. See *Proc. Chem. Soc.*, 1959, 103.

Pantothenic acid, $C_9H_{17}NO_5$. Has been

obtained as a viscous oil, $[\alpha]_D^{25} +37\cdot5°$. The calcium and sodium salts are crystalline. Pantothenic acid is a growth factor for certain microorganisms and acts as a vitamin in that it will cure a dermatitis in chicks. It is present in many natural products and can be prepared by condensing β,β-dimethyl-α-hydroxybutyrolactone with β-alanine.

Papain. A typical plant proteinase. The commercial product is the dried latex from the papaya tree. Its activity depends on its SH group

content. It acts at temperatures as high as 50°-60°, and its optimum pH range is 4 to 7.

Papaverine, $C_{20}H_{21}NO_4$. One of the alkaloids of

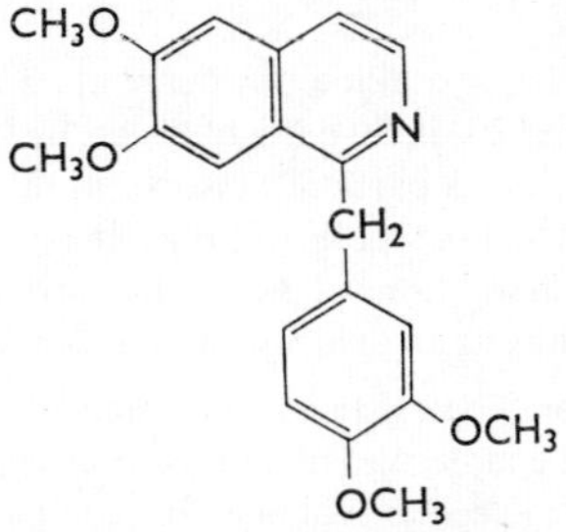

opium. It crystallizes in prisms from alcohol-ether and in needles from chloroform-petroleum ether, m.p. 147°. Insoluble in water, soluble in hot alcohol. Optically inactive, it forms crystalline salts with acids. The hydrochloride has little analgesic action, and is used for treating coronary spasm and various types of colic.

Paper. Paper is prepared by the dehydration of an interwoven mat of hydrated cellulose fibres. Nearly any type of fibrous cellulose material can be used in its preparation. The properties of the resulting paper depend largely on the degree of hydration and sub-division of the fibres. In order to make paper less porous and, to some degree, water-repellent, it has to be sized.

Para. In the accompanying formula for para-cresol, commonly written *p*-cresol, the CH_3 and OH groups are said to be in the para position to each other. This use of the prefix is confined to disubstituted benzene derivatives; in such cases as para-hydrogen and para-formaldehyde the prefix has no uniform structural significance and is always written in full.

Parabanic acid, Oxalylurea, $C_3H_2N_2O_3$. Crystallizes in needles or prisms, which partially sublime at 100° and decompose at 243°. Soluble in water. It can also be crystallized with one molecule of water, which it loses at 150°-160°. It can be prepared from urea and oxalyl chloride. Its salts are unstable.

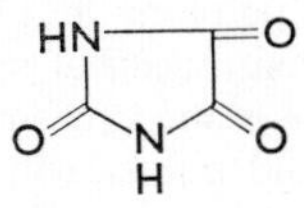

Paracelsus, Philippus Aureolus Theophrastus Paracelsus Bombastus von Hohenheim. Born at Etzel in Switzerland in 1493; he wandered from one country to another practising as a surgeon or a quack; he was a vain, impudent charlatan, but he insisted that chemistry ought to be used not to make gold but medicines and other useful substances. He died at Salzburg in 1540.

Paracetamol, 4-acetamidophenol, $C_8H_9NO_2$.

HO—⬡—NHCOCH₃

Is a white crystalline powder, m.p. 169°-172°. Soluble at 20° in 70 parts of water, in 7 parts of alcohol, in 13 parts of acetone, in 40 parts of glycerol and in 9 parts of propylene glycol, also soluble in solutions of the alkali hydroxides. It is used orally as an analgesic and antipyretic.

Parachor. The existence of attractive forces between the molecules of a liquid prevents the use of the molecular volume for comparing the dimensions of molecules. To allow for these forces Sugden employed instead the parachor $p = \gamma^{\frac{1}{4}}\left(\dfrac{M}{D-d}\right)$, where γ is the surface tension, M the molecular weight, and D and d the densities of the liquid and vapour respectively. The parachor is a measure of the molecular volume, and was once widely used to determine the constitution of organic and inorganic compounds.

Paracyanogen, $(CN)_x$. The white or brown polymer formed when cyanogen is heated to 400°. It has the structure:

Paraffin. See Kerosine.

Paraffinic crude oil. A crude oil which on distillation yields a residue containing a proportion of paraffin wax in distinction to those crudes which yield an asphaltic residue.

Paraffins, Alkanes. Aliphatic hydrocarbons of the general formula C_nH_{2n+2}. The first four members are gases, the higher members are liquids and those above $C_{16}H_{34}$ are waxy solids. They are insoluble in water but soluble in chloroform and benzene. They form the chief constituents of petroleum. They are remarkably resistant to chemical action and only chlorine and bromine will react with any ease. These give chloro- and bromo-substituted paraffins respectively. They are formed by the reduction of olefins or by treating alkyl iodides with sodium in ethereal solution.

Paraffin wax. Wax of a crystalline structure obtained from certain petroleum crudes and shale oil, and consisting essentially of hydrocarbons of molecular formula about $C_{20}H_{42}$ and upwards. When refined it is almost tasteless and odourless and very inert chemically, and is used in the manufacture of candles, polishes, ointments, and for waterproofing paper and textiles.

Pharmaceutical hard paraffin is a grade with m.p. 50°-57°, insoluble in water, acetone, and cold alcohol; soluble in benzene, chloroform, and ether.

Paraformaldehyde, Paraform, Trioxymethylene. A mixture of polymethylene glycols of the type $(CH_2O)_n$, xH_2O where n is 6 to 50. It is a white, amorphous powder having the odour of formaldehyde; m.p. 120°-130°. The commercial product contains 95% formaldehyde and is obtained in white flocculent masses when solutions of formaldehyde are evaporated or allowed to stand. When heated it is converted to formaldehyde. Used as a convenient solid substitute for formaldehyde.

Parahaematins. Compounds of haematin with denatured proteins and certain nitrogenous bases. They resemble the haemochromogens, but the iron atom is in the tripositive state.

Para-hydrogen. See Ortho-hydrogen.

Paraldehyde, $(C_2H_4O)_3$. A colourless, mobile liquid, m.p. 12·5°, b.p. 124°, slightly soluble in water with the formula:—

It is formed when acetaldehyde is allowed to stand in the presence of a catalyst at moderate temperatures. It is used to some extent as a soporific.

Paramagnetism. The property possessed by a substance of producing a greater concentration of lines of magnetic force within itself than in the surrounding magnetic field when it is placed in such a field. Paramagnetism is associated with the presence of unpaired electrons in an ion or molecule. The results of measurements of magnetic susceptibilities have been of great use in the theory of valency.

Para-oxon, diethyl-p-nitrophenylphosphate,

$C_{10}H_{14}NO_6P$. Para-oxon is the trade name for the oxygen analogue of parathion ($q.v.$). It is a red-yellow oil of high b.p., which may be prepared from diethyl phosphorochloridate and sodium p-nitrophenate. It is very poisonous and has high insecticidal activity; it has been regarded as being too toxic towards mammals for general use.

Paraquat, 1,1′-dimethyl-4,4′-bipyridylium dimethylsulphate or dichloride. Both salts are white crystalline solids, m.p. 175-180°, very soluble in water, the methylsulphate being deliquescent, and are prepared by quaternization of 4,4′-bipyridyl with dimethyl sulphate or

$$H_3C-N^+ \text{(ring)} \text{(ring)} N^+-CH_3 \quad Cl_2^- \quad \text{or}$$
$$(CH_3OSO_3)_2^-$$

methyl chloride. Paraquat is a contact herbicide which is rendered inactive on contact with the soil, and hence is used for weed control before emergence of the crop. It is also used to control grass weeds in leguminous crops, and also in certain countries to control dodder (*Cuscuta trifolii*) in lucerne. See W. R. Boon, *Chem. and Ind.*, 1965, 782. See also Diquat.

Parathion,   Diethyl-*p*-nitrophenylphosphoro-thionate, $C_{10}H_{14}NO_5PS$. An insecticide which,

$$NO_2-\text{(ring)}-OP(OC_2H_5)_2$$
with S above P

when pure, is a colourless, almost odourless oil, m.p. 6°, b.p. 157°-162°/0·6 mm. The technical product is dark brown, with a garlic-like odour, of about 90% purity. Parathion is slightly soluble in water and petroleum oils, and soluble in most other organic solvents, and is manufactured by reaction of diethyl phosphorochloridothionate, $(C_2H_5O)_2P(S)Cl$, with sodium *p*-nitrophenate. Sprays are effective as contact and stomach poisons against many species, particularly aphids and capsids, and are very active against red spider mite. Parathion has high mammalian toxicity, with cumulative effect. Special precautions are necessary to prevent inhalation and skin contamination.

Parathormone. The hormone secreted by the parathyroid gland, which controls calcium metabolism. It acts to cause an increase in calcium ions in the blood, and its production is in turn subject to feedback control by the blood calcium ion concentration. Parathormone also promotes the excretion of phosphate via the kidney.

Paregoric. A tincture of opium containing 0·5% of morphine, together with benzoic acid, camphor, and oil of anise. It is an ingredient of some cough mixtures.

Paris green. See Emerald green.

Parkerizing. A trade name for a process for phosphate coating (*q.v.*).

Parkes's process. A method employed for de-silverizing lead. Zinc is added to molten argentiferous lead and the mixture allowed to cool until a skin of zinc-silver alloy is formed. This is re-moved and the silver recovered by distillation of the zinc. The process can be repeated until the remaining lead contains only 0·0005% silver.

Parr, Samuel Wilson (1857-1931). Parr was born at Granville, Illinois, and was educated at the University of Illinois and at Cornell University. He became an instructor at Illinois College (1885-1886) and then professor of general science (1886-1891). In 1891 he returned to the University of Illinois as professor of applied chemistry. His chief researches were devoted to improvements in calorimeters and to the study of coal. He was President of the American Chemical Society in 1928.

Partial condenser. This type of condenser is sometimes used on distillation columns where the overhead product is a mixture of vapours and condensation therefore occurs over a temperature range. The vapour is partially condensed by heat exchange with another process stream, and the remainder is condensed in a *final condenser* using cooling water. The advantage of this arrangement is that some of the heat in the vapour stream is utilized, and at the same time the vapour itself is enriched in the more volatile components. The partial condenser is sometimes called a *dephlegmator*.

Partial pressure. In a mixture of gases or vapours, each constituent can be regarded as making a contribution to the total pressure equal to the pressure which the same amount of the constituent would exert if it were alone present in an evacuated vessel of the same volume as that which contains the gaseous mixture. This is called the partial pressure of the constituent. See also Total pressure.

Parting. The process of separating gold from silver. There are three chief methods employed:

(i) The mixture is treated with strong sulphuric acid which gives silver sulphate but leaves the gold unattacked. The silver is recovered from solution by precipitation with copper or zinc.

(ii) Strong nitric acid does not attack gold but gives a solution of silver nitrate. Addition of sodium chloride gives silver chloride which is reduced to the metal by hydrogen evolved when zinc and sulphuric acid are in contact with the silver chloride.

(iii) The passage of chlorine into the fused alloy covered with borax gives a preferential formation of silver chloride; the process being carried on until orange vapours appear which are evidence of the gold being attacked. The amount of silver must be small for the successful operation of this method.

Partition law. This states that when a heterogeneous system of two or more phases is in equilibrium, the ratio of the concentrations (or strictly activities) of the same molecular species in the phases is constant at constant temperature. The constant ratio between any two phases is known as the partition coefficient. The law is also known as the distribution law.

Paschen series. See Balmer series.

Passivity. Metals such as iron, cobalt, nickel, chromium, and bismuth, when brought into contact with certain oxidizing agents such as conc. nitric acid, chromic acid, hydrogen peroxide, do not dissolve but become passive, and exhibit different properties from those of the untreated materials. Iron made passive by dipping in strong nitric acid does not precipitate copper from copper sulphate. The passivity is induced by formation of a surface film of oxide.

Pasteur, Louis. Born at Dôle, in the Jura, in 1822; he studied chemistry and crystallography under Balard and Dumas. In 1848 he discovered laevorotatory tartaric acid and its salts, and became deputy professor at Strasburg. In 1854 he became professor at Lille, and in 1857 at the École Normale, Paris. In 1860 he began to investigate the spontaneous generation of life, and after prolonged experiments proved that living matter always came from living matter, spores, seeds, and so on, almost always present in the air or on the earth. He studied for several years the nature of fermentation and the diseases of wine and beer, the disease then prevalent in silk-worms, and the nature of anthrax. He discovered how to cure anthrax, and was the first to understand the modern methods of inoculation and antiseptic hygiene. Finally, he undertook an investigation of hydrophobia, and after prolonged study, learned how to cure this disease in animals and human beings. He died in 1895.

Pasteur effect. It was first noticed by Pasteur with yeast, and has since been shown to be true also for other cells, that a cell that can break down sugar both in the presence (to carbon dioxide and water) and in the absence of oxygen (to carbon dioxide and alcohol) will break down more sugar in the absence of oxygen than in its presence. This is known as the Pasteur effect.

Pasteurization. There are two officially recognized methods of pasteurizing milk in Britain, the 'holder' method in which milk is heated at 145°-150°F for 30 minutes and immediately cooled to 55°F or below, and the High-Temperature Short-Time (H.T.S.T.) method in which the milk is retained at not less that 162°F for at least 15 seconds and then cooled. Milk is tested for efficiency of pasteurization by seeing if it still contains phosphatase. The term pasteurization is

loosely used to describe any form of heat treatment of milk other than complete sterilization.

Patina. Bronze, iron, and other metals are sometimes given an attractive and corrosion-resisting surface by forming a thin layer of oxide as the result of warming the metal. These oxide films are called patinas.

Pattinson, Hugh Lee (1796-1858). Inventor of the process that bears his name, Pattinson was born in Northumberland, and was employed at a local lead factory. He also discovered a process for making magnesia from dolomite, and was the founder of the Washington Chemical Company. See *Chem. and Ind.*, 1958, 1498.

Pattinson's process. An obsolete process for the recovery of silver from commercial lead. When molten argentiferous lead cools, crystals of pure lead are deposited first. These are removed by perforated iron ladles. The process is continued until the remaining silver-lead eutectic solidifies *en masse*, when it contains about $2\frac{1}{2}\%$ silver. Thus the process, which is carried out in iron pots, is similar to a fractional crystallization. It yields lead containing about 0·0001% silver and the eutectic lead-silver alloy. The silver is recovered from the latter by cupellation.

Patulin, clavacin, claviformin, $C_7H_6O_4$. White

crystals, m.p. 110°, soluble in water and organic solvents. An antibiotic substance produced by *Penicillium patulum* and other moulds. It is bacteriostatic *in vitro* to many micro-organisms, but is also toxic to higher animals.

Pauli, Wolfgang (1900-1958). Born in Vienna, Pauli is famous for his reasoning in theoretical physics, including the exclusion principle, which states that two electrons cannot occupy the same orbital at the same time, or that no two electrons in an atom may have identical sets of quantum numbers. Pauli was also the first to propose the existence of the neutrino. See *Proc. Chem. Soc.*, 1959, 281.

Pauli exclusion principle. See Exclusion principle.

Pauling, Linus (1901-   ). Born in Portland, Oregon, Pauling studied at the California Institute of Technology and later became professor of chemistry there. He is chiefly famous for his development of the theory of the chemical bond and for the idea of resonance. He was awarded the Nobel Prize for chemistry in 1954, has received the Davy Medal of the Royal Society, the Nichols Medal of the American Chemical Society and many other awards.

Pearl ash. See Potassium carbonate.

Pearlite. The name given to a eutectoid of ferrite and cementite, so called because many specimens of mild steel, after etching, exhibit a play of colours resembling mother-of-pearl. As the carbon content of a mild steel increases the pearlite in the slowly cooled specimen increases up to 0·89% carbon, and hence pearlite contains 0·89% carbon or 13·35% Fe_3C. 'Divorced' pearlite is the term given to the pearlitic structure of a steel that has been subjected to prolonged annealing below the critical temperature. This causes a coalescing of the iron carbide particles into larger groups which appear embedded in the ferrite matrix. A 'divorced' pearlite structure, while undesirable for machining, is advantageous in steels that have to withstand repeated deformation.

The appearance of pearlite under the microscope varies with the treatment but is generally laminar.

Peat. A naturally occurring fuel found in bogs and containing about 90% water; the remaining 10% is combustible and contains in the dry ashless state about 60% carbon, 5% hydrogen, and about 34% oxygen, and has a calorific value in this state of about 9000 Btu/lb. Though some of the water can be pressed out, the residual material is in a form of a gel and must be air dried, or furnace dried, before use.

The peat deposits vary in colour from light brown to black and possess a spongy texture.

Pebble mill. A tube mill which utilizes flint or ceramic pebbles as the grinding medium. See Ball mill.

Pectin. Defined (American National Formulary) as a purified carbohydrate product obtained from the dilute acid extract of the inner portion of the rind of citrus fruits or from apple pomace. It is a mixture, the most important constituent of which is methyl pectate, which is the methyl ester of pectic acid, a high molecular weight polymer of D-galacturonic acid, which has the formula:

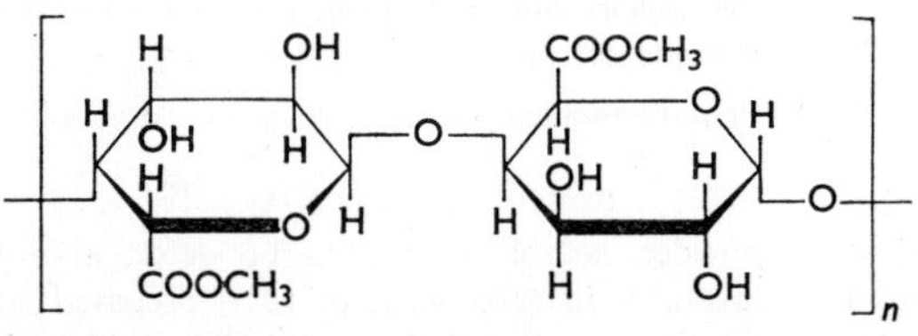

plant products, and confers on jams their typical gelling property. Pectin is manufactured as a white powder, soluble in water, and used to assist the setting of jams and jellies, and for numerous other purposes. Low methoxyl pectins, with under 7% methoxyl, give firmer gels than pectins proper.

Pegmatites. The last portions to solidify in the formation of plutonic rocks. They are commonly associated with granites and are variable in composition, normally containing coarse grained and sometimes very large crystals of typical granite minerals. Some pegmatites, which have an important content of minerals of the rarer elements, are of commercial value, e.g. beryl, spodumene, amblygonite, pollucite, cassiterite, rare-earth silicates, columbite, tantalite, wolframite, and pitchblende.

Pelargonic acid, nonanoic acid, $C_9H_{18}O_2$, $CH_3 \cdot [CH_2]_7 \cdot COOH$. An oily liquid, with a rancid odour, m.p. 12·5°, b.p. 253°-254°, $d_4^{12·5}$ 0·9109, n_D 1·43057. It can be prepared by the oxidation of oleic acid or undecane. It has been found, with other fatty acids with odd numbers of carbon atoms, in small amounts in human hair.

Pelargonin. The anthocyan glycoside of the scarlet geranium, dahlia, gladiola and many other plants. It is the 3,5-diglucoside of pelargonidin. Other anthocyans which contain pelargonidin are (1) callistiphin from red carnations and the purple red aster which is a 3-β-glucoside, (2) monardaein or salvianin from scarlet *Salvia splendens*, etc., which is a 3,5-diglucoside carrying in addition p-hydroxy-cinnamic acid and malonic acid.

Pelargonin-3-biosides are of widespread occurrence, e.g. in the nasturtium, scarlet runner bean, gloxinia. See Anthocyanins.

Penetration. A method of expressing the hardness of a solid by the depth to which a loaded needle penetrates under standard conditions of load, time, temperature, etc. This method is used to compare one sample of a solid with another, sometimes after subjecting to a standardized heat treatment.

Pectin also contains araban and galactan. It is present in fruits, root vegetables, and other

Penetrometer. An instrument for carrying out penetration tests for the determination of the hardness of certain solids such as asphaltic bitumen or paraffin wax.

Penicillin. The penicillins are a group of bactericidal antibiotics containing the basic ring structure of penicillanic acid:

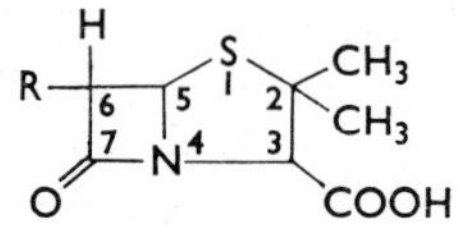

The first and the still most widely used penicillin is benzylpenicillin (penicillin G, $R = C_6H_5 \cdot CH_2 \cdot CO \cdot NH-$), which is made by growing suitable strains of *Penicillium chrysogenum* on a carbohydrate medium, extracting the brew and crystallizing as the sodium or potassium salt. This and all other penicillins are white crystalline powders, very soluble in water. Benzylpenicillin is very unstable, being destroyed by heat, alkalis, alcohol, oxidizing agents, heavy metals, and the enzyme penicillinase, produced by certain bacteria. It is inactivated by gastric juice and must be injected when treating other than surface infections. It is very active against many Gram-positive pathogenic bacteria.

The action of penicillin can be prolonged by using sparingly soluble salts such as procaine penicillin, and benzathine penicillin (N,N'-dibenzylethylenediaminedi(benzylpenicillin). These are generally injected intramuscularly to form a depot. Phenoxymethylpenicillin (penicillin V, $R = C_6H_5 \cdot O \cdot CH_2 \cdot CO \cdot NH-$) is similarly made by fermentation and has the advantage that it is more stable to acids and can be taken orally.

Many semi-synthetic penicillins are made from 6-aminopenicillanic acid (6-APA, $R = NH_2$) which itself is made by the action on benzylpenicillin of the enzyme penicillin amidase which is contained in numerous micro-organisms. The 6-APA is coupled chemically with appropriate compounds to give penicillins with special properties. Thus phenethicillin (trade name Broxil), α-phenoxyethylpenicillin ($R = C_6H_5 \cdot O \cdot CH_2 \cdot CH_2 \cdot CO \cdot NH-$), and propicillin (trade names Brocillin and Ultrapen), ($R = C_6H_5 \cdot O \cdot [CH_2]_3 \cdot CO \cdot NH-$) have the advantage of increased acid stability.

Ampicillin (trade name Penbritin), $D(-)$-α-aminophenylpenicillin

$$(R = C_6H_5 \cdot CH \cdot (NH_2) \cdot CO \cdot NH-)$$

was the first broad-spectrum penicillin, active not only against Gram-positive but also against many Gram-negative bacteria. This is stable to acids but attacked by penicillinase.

Methicillin (trade name Celbenin), 2,6-dimethoxyphenylpenicillin, is not attacked by *staphylococci*, but is unstable to acids. It is used

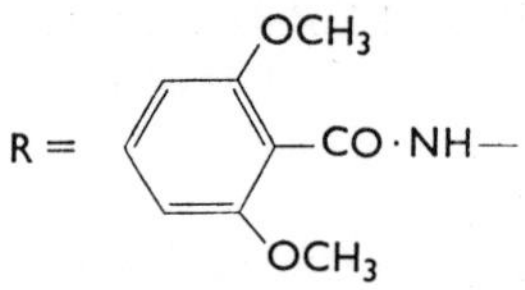

to treat resistent *staphylococci* by intramuscular injection.

Cloxacillin (trade name of sodium salt,

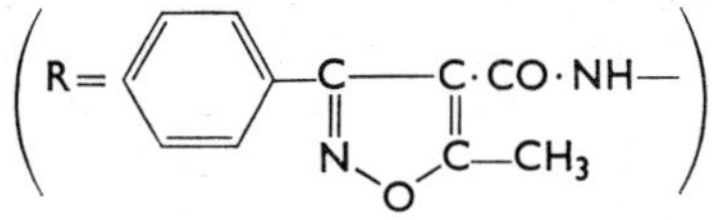

Orbenin), 3-*o*-chlorophenyl-5-methylisooxazolyl penicillin, is stable both to acids and to staphylococcal penicillinase, and is highly active against Gram-positive organisms. The penicillins have been shown to owe their bactericidal activity to stopping bacterial cell wall formation. See also Cephalosporin C, Mucopeptides.

Penicillinase. An enzyme produced by some bacteria, which inactivates penicillin by hydrolysing the β-lactam ring and forming an inactive penicilloic acid:

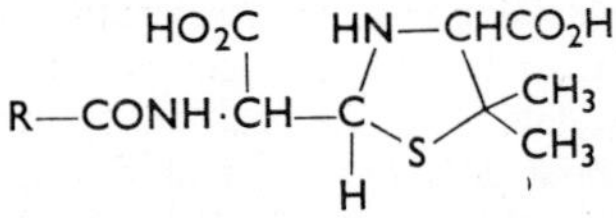

Pentaerythritol, $C_5H_{12}O_4$. A colourless crystalline compound, m.p. 260°, soluble in water and

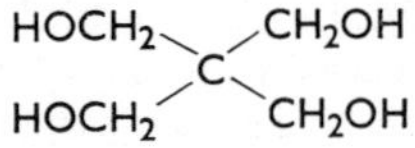

alcohol. It is made by reacting acetaldehyde and formaldehyde in the presence of alkali. It is used in alkyd resin production and in the manufacture of its tetranitrate.

Pentaerythritol tetranitrate, (PETN or penthrite), $C(CH_2 \cdot O \cdot NO_2)_4$. Short prismatic needles, insoluble in water, sparingly soluble in organic solvents (except acetone); m.p. 138°-140°. It is made by nitrating pentaerythritol, and is a very stable and extremely powerful and violent explosive. It is too sensitive for most purposes without a desensitizer such as wax. Mixed with TNT it forms pentolite.

Pentafluorosulphur compounds. See Sulphur fluoride derivatives.

Pentamethonium iodide. A white crystalline

$$(CH_3)_3 \overset{+}{N}[CH_2]_5 \overset{+}{N}(CH_3)_3, \, 2I^-.$$

powder, soluble in 4 parts of water, almost insoluble in acetone, m.p. 302°, prepared by treating pentamethylene di-iodide with trimethylamine.

Pentamethonium is a ganglionic blocking agent, an action which results in a lowering of blood pressure. The drug is used in treating hypertension, and for decreasing bleeding during operations.

Pentamidine. This is used as its 2-hydroxyethane-1-sulphonate, $C_{19}H_{24}N_4O_2 \cdot 2C_2H_6O_4S$, a white

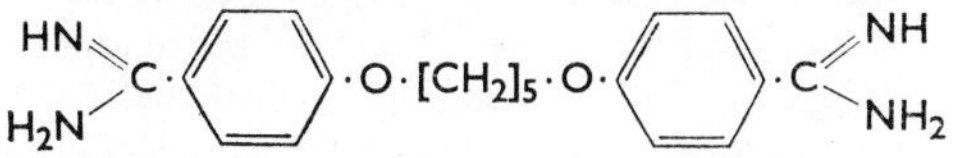

crystalline powder, soluble in 10 parts of water, slightly soluble in alcohol; m.p. 190°, which is made by saturating an alcoholic solution of 1,5-di(p-cyanophenoxy)pentane with hydrogen chloride, treating with sodium hydroxide, and then with ammonium 2-hydroxyethane-1-sulphonate. It is used both as a prophylactic and in the treatment of trypanosomiasis; it is particularly useful in the early stages of the disease as it does not readily penetrate the cerebrospinal fluid.

Pentanes, C_5H_{12}. Three hydrocarbons of the paraffin series of this formula are possible. They occur in the low boiling fractions of petroleum from which they are prepared. They are inflammable liquids. $CH_3 \cdot CH_2 \cdot CH_2 \cdot CH_2 \cdot CH_3$, n-Pentane, b.p. 38°, is used as a standard illuminant in photometry.

Pentathionic acid. See Polythionic acids.

Pentolite. A mixture of pentaerythritol tetranitrate and TNT.

Penton. A trade name for a chlorinated polyether derived from 3,3-bis(chloromethyl)-1-oxacyclobutane. Its repeat unit is:

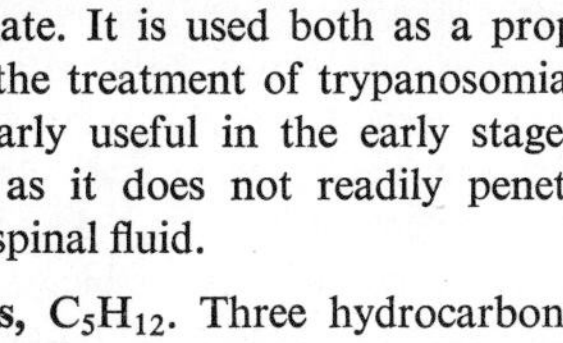

where $n = 250,000$ to $350,000$. It has been used as a plastics material resistant to chemical attack at temperatures up to 120°.

Pentosans. Hemicelluloses which give pentoses on hydrolysis. The most widely distributed are xylan and araban.

Pentose. A carbohydrate with five carbon atoms. Of the aldopentoses, both stereoisomers of arabinose occur naturally, and the D-forms of xylose and ribose; lyxose does not occur naturally. There are four (two pairs of stereoisomers) possible ketopentoses.

Peonin. The anthocyanin of the peony. The 3,5-diglucoside of 3′-methylcyanidin (peonidin).

Pepsin, Pepsinogen. Pepsin is the protein-digesting enzyme of the gastric juice and is secreted by the gastric cells in great quantities.

As formed it is completely inactive and requires acidification to convert pepsinogen into pepsin. Both enzymes have been prepared by Northrop in crystalline form, pepsinogen in fine needles, pepsin in doubly-pointed hexagonal prisms. Pepsin is of the albumin class, the estimated molecular weight is about 38,000. Pepsin has greatest activity in acid solution at pH 2, and is much more specific than was formerly believed, splitting links between the α-carboxyl group of a dicarboxylic amino-acid and the α-amino radical of an aromatic amino-acid.

Peptidase. On Bergmann's nomenclature all the proteolytic enzymes of the digestive tract are called peptidases. Proteins are digested first by the endopeptidases pepsin, trypsin, and chymotrypsin, which break specific links which may be far from the ends of the chains, forming much smaller units, which are then attacked stepwise at both ends of the chains by the exopeptidases. These are carboxypeptidase, formed by the pancreas, which removes terminal units with free carboxyl groups, aminopeptidase, from the intestinal secretions, which splits off units with free amino groups, and dipeptidase, also from the intestine, which splits dipeptides into amino-acids.

Peptides. Substances composed of two or more amino-acids, and designated as di-, tri-, oligo-, poly-peptides, etc., according to the number of amino-acids linked by the peptide bond —CO·NH—. The simplest peptide is glycyl-glycine, $H_2N \cdot CH_2 \cdot CO \cdot NH \cdot CH_2 \cdot CO_2H$.

Naturally occurring peptides possessing important physiological activity include glutathione, gastrin and angiotensin; several pituitary hormones (e.g. oxytocin, vasopressin); and a number of antibiotics (e.g. bacitracin, polymyxin). Peptides also arise, and are frequently studied, as partial hydrolysis products of proteins. Methods for peptide synthesis are very highly developed.

Peptization. This term, originally proposed by Graham, is sometimes used in a general way to imply the converse of coagulation, i.e. dispersion, especially when the process results in the formation of a colloidal sol. Peptization is, however, generally restricted to a chemical means of dispersion in which the colloidal particles are stabilized by the adsorption of charged ions. An example of peptization is the formation of silver iodide sols by shaking the neutral precipitate with a small excess of either potassium iodide or silver nitrate; with the former reagent the resultant sol is negative, with the latter, positive. Peptization often occurs in analysis; thus on passing hydrogen sulphide through a suspension of arsenic sulphide in water the precipitate is peptized to a clear yellow sol. See Colloids.

Peptones. Low molecular weight degradation products of proteins which can diffuse slowly through parchment membranes. They are soluble in water, acids, alkalis, and salt solutions, and are not precipitated by full saturation with ammonium sulphate. They are formed from proteins by enzymic action.

Per-acids may be regarded as derivatives of hydrogen peroxide, the molecules of which contain one or more directly linked pairs of oxygen atoms, —O—O—. The persulphuric acids and their salts are of some importance. Permanganic, perchloric, and periodic acids are not per-acids in the true sense, the prefix 'per-' being incorrectly used in these cases. In many peroxy derivatives of the transition metals the O—O group is bonded symmetrically

$$M \leftarrow \begin{matrix} O \\ | \\ O \end{matrix}$$ to the metal. Many peroxy derivatives are

used in analysis since the compounds are highly coloured. See Perchromic acids, Perborates, Percarbonates.

Organic per-acids are prepared by the action of hydrogen peroxide or an inorganic per-acid on carboxylic acids or anhydrides, or by the action of sodium methoxide on an acyl peroxide or by electrolytic oxidation. The more stable per-acids, such as perbenzoic, monoperphthalic, convert olefins to epoxides, which on hydrolysis give *trans*-glycols. Peracetic and performic acids with olefins give the monoester of the glycol.

Perborates, Perborax. By treating a cold solution of borax with sodium peroxide or hydrogen peroxide and caustic soda, sodium perborate $NaBO_2, 3H_2O, H_2O_2$ is formed. This is not a true per-acid, but a borate containing H_2O_2 of crystallization. The compound ('perborax') is stable in the dry state, only slightly soluble in water, and the solution possesses bleaching and antiseptic properties. A crystalline compound of the same composition is obtained by electrolysis of a solution of borax and sodium carbonate. Perborax is used as a bleaching agent and as an antiseptic.

Percarbonates. Salts of the percarbonic acids, H_2CO_4 and $H_2C_2O_6$; neither of the acids can be isolated. If sodium hydroperoxide reacts with carbon dioxide, or normal carbonates are treated with hydrogen peroxide, $Na_2CO_4 \cdot H_2O_2$ and $Na_2C_2O_6 \cdot H_2O_2$, peroxyhydrated peroxycarbonates, result. These compounds, which have been used in washing powders, are more stable than the true percarbonates, and may be further stabilized by the addition of substances such as magnesium silicate or waterglass. Recent work has suggested that most percarbonates are

normal carbonates with hydrogen peroxide of crystallization.

Perchloric acid, $HClO_4$. Obtained by distilling potassium perchlorate with concentrated sulphuric acid. The distillate, perchloric acid, is a colourless, or slightly yellow, strongly fuming liquid. The preparation is best carried out at reduced pressure. Purification by distillation at low pressure (11 mm) gives a white crystalline distillate of the monohydrate $HClO_4, H_2O$. This hydrate on distillation gives the anhydrous acid and a maximum boiling-point acid containing $71 \cdot 6\%$ of $HClO_4$. The anhydrous acid is somewhat unstable and explodes violently on warming to 92°. The oily aqueous acid of maximum boiling-point is quite stable. The aqueous acid dissolves metals such as iron or zinc with the evolution of hydrogen. The acid is a less powerful oxidizing agent than chloric acid. Perchloric acid is not a true per-acid since it does not contain peroxy groups. It is very liable to explode when in contact with organic compounds.

Potassium perchlorate is obtained by heating the chlorate to 480°. It is relatively insoluble and is precipitated in one method of estimating potassium. Technically the sodium salt is obtained by the prolonged electrolysis of concentrated sodium chloride solutions at 80° at high current density. It is used to some extent in the manufacture of detonators and explosives. Silver perchlorate is very soluble in water, ether, and benzene.

Perchloryl fluoride, $FClO_3$. A stable non-corrosive gas, b.p. $-47 \cdot 5°$, prepared by interaction of sodium perchlorate and fluorosulphuric acid. It is used as an oxidizing agent.

Perewskites. An alternative spelling of perovskites (*q.v.*).

Perfluoroalkyl derivatives. Organic derivatives in which all the hydrogen atoms, except those in the functional groups, have been replaced by fluorine. Thus C_6F_6 is perfluorobenzene; C_6F_5COOH is perfluorobenzoic acid.

Peri. A prefix sometimes used to denote the positional relationship between groups occupying the 1, 8 positions on the naphthalene ring. As a special case the two groups may be part of a third ring. 1-Naphthylamine-8-sulphonic acid is sometimes referred to as Peri Acid.

Perillaldehyde, $C_{12}H_{14}O$. A monocyclic aldehyde the (−)-form of which is present in perilla oil and in oil from the fruit of *Siler trilobum* and the (+)-form in false camphorwood oil from *Hernandia peltata*. It can be isolated as a crystalline compound with sodium bisulphite. For the (−)-form the following constants are recorded: b.p. 104°-105°/10 mm, d^{18} 0·9617, n_D 1·5075, $[\alpha]_D$ − 146°. For the (+)-form $[\alpha]_D$ +135·6° has been recorded. It forms a semicarbazone, m.p. 199°-200°, and an oxime, m.p. 102°.

Period. A group of elements arranged horizontally in the normal form of the Periodic Table, a period being elements from an alkali metal to a noble gas. The periods are (a) the very short period H, He, (b) two short periods Li—Ne and

Periodic precipitates. An alternative name for Liesegang rings.

Periodic table. A table in which the elements are arranged in order of atomic numbers, the arrangement being such as to emphasize the chemical relationships between the elements and to emphasize the relationships between elements with similar electronic configurations. The heaviest element at present known is 104, the unnamed relation of zirconium.

THE PERIODIC TABLE

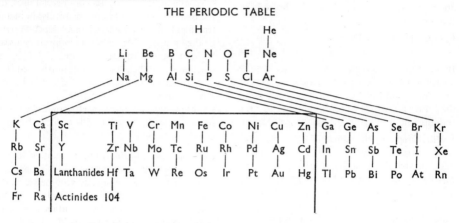

Lanthanides: La, Ce, Pr, Nd, Pm, Sm, Eu, Gd, Tb, Dy, Ho, Er, Tm, Yb, Lu.
Actinides: Ac, Th, Pa, U, Np, Pu, Am, Cm, Bk, Cf, Es, Fm, Md, 102, Lw.

Na—Ar, (c) two long periods containing transition elements K—Kr and Rb—Xe, (d) a very long period containing the rare-earth elements, Cs—Rn, (e) an unfinished period Fr—.

Periodic acids. The simplest of the periodic acids is the crystalline substance H_5IO_6, one method of preparing which is by the low-temperature electrolysis of a concentrated solution of iodic acid in a divided cell. The acid is readily soluble in water, and is a strong oxidizing agent, although it is not a true per-acid in the sense of containing the —O—O— group. Its composition is probably $IO(OH)_5$. It loses water when heated to 100° and forms a second per-acid HIO_4 (i.e. $IO_3(OH)$). The acid H_5IO_6 is known in the form of acid and normal salts, e.g. $Ag_2H_3IO_6$ and Ag_5IO_6. A number of partially dehydrated periodic acids, such as H_3IO_5, are also known, and these may also form both normal and acid salts.

Periodic law. Mendeléef (1869), independently of Newlands, put forward the law that 'the properties of the elements are periodic functions of the atomic weights,' i.e. by arranging the elements in order of increasing atomic weights, elements having similar properties occur at fixed intervals. This principle, with the modification that atomic numbers are used instead of atomic weights, forms the basis of the Periodic table.

Peritectic. A particular type of solid-liquid phase equilibrium system, occurring commonly with binary alloys, where the two components form limited ranges of solid solution in one another (but are completely miscible in the liquid state). A peritectic system differs from a eutectic system in having no minimum in the freezing point-composition curve.

Perkin, Sir William Henry (1838-1907). Born in London, Perkin became in 1853 a student of Hofmann at the Royal College of Chemistry. His enthusiasm for chemistry led to the establishment of a small laboratory in his father's house, and there in 1856 he discovered the first synthetic dye, mauveine. In the following year he opened a factory for its commercial preparation. His scientific investigations continued with the synthesis of coumarin and other important substances, while he introduced into organic chemistry the Perkin reaction. Later his work involved a study of magnetic rotatory power. He was elected F.R.S. in 1866 and knighted in 1906. See *J. Chem. Soc.*, 1908, 2214.

Perkin, William Henry, jr. (1860-1929). Perkin jr. was born at Sudbury and received his early chemical training at the Royal College of Science. For five years he worked in Germany under Wislicenus and Baeyer, and in 1886 was appointed professor of chemistry at the Heriot-Watt College, Edinburgh. Elected F.R.S. in 1890, he succeeded Schorlemmer at Manchester two years later, and in 1912 was appointed professor at Oxford. His chemical insight and experimental skill made him one of the foremost synthetic organic chemists of his time.

Perkin reaction. A condensation between aromatic aldehydes and the sodium salts of fatty acids or their aromatic derivatives. The original reaction between benzaldehyde and sodium acetate in the presence of acetic anhydride leads to sodium cinnamate:

$$C_6H_5CHO + H_3C \cdot COONa \rightarrow$$
$$C_6H_5CH : CHCOONa$$

In general, condensation takes place at the α-carbon atom, leading to simple cinnamic acids or to their α-substituted derivatives. When possible, the anhydride corresponding to the sodium salt should be the condensing agent.

Perlite. Originally the name of a glassy volcanic rock, but recently applied to a light-weight product produced on a considerable scale by rapidly heating to their softening point crushed and graded perlites and similar glassy highly siliceous volcanic materials containing 2-6% of water. The particles 'pop' with the evolution of the water as steam, yielding a product with a bulk density ranging from 7-15 lb per cubic foot. It is used as a light-weight aggregate in heat and sound insulating plasters and as a loose fill.

Permalloy. A nickel-iron alloy containing 78·5% Ni, with low carbon and sulphur. Characterized by a very high permeability in low magnetic fields and a hysteresis loss of about one-fifteenth of that of pure iron. It is extensively used in submarine cables where high permeability in low magnetic fields is essential. After it has been finally heat-treated it must not be stressed or its magnetic properties are seriously impaired. The best properties are obtained by heating to 900°, cooling slowly, reheating to 600° and finally cooling in air. *Mumetal* is similar in properties to permalloy but contains some manganese and copper.

Perminvar is a variety of permalloy, having a constant magnetic permeability for variable magnetic fields of low intensity. The composition is 45-60% Ni, 30-25% Fe, 25-15% Co.

Permanganates. The salts of permanganic acid are usually readily soluble in water and crystallize well. In crystalline form and solubility they resemble the perchlorates. They are of an intense violet colour, the crystals usually appearing black. They are very powerful oxidizing agents, being easily reduced in acid solution to manganese (II) salts, in neutral solution to manganese dioxide or manganates (IV), and in alkaline solution to manganates (VI). Potassium permanganate, $KMnO_4$, is the most important permanganate. It is manufactured by roasting pyrolusite with caustic potash in the presence of air at 300°. The green solution of the manganate (VI) which results on extraction with water may be treated with carbon dioxide, which causes disproportionation to permanganate and manganese dioxide, or may be oxidized electrolytically. It forms rhombic prisms and is not very soluble in water: 100 g dissolve at 20° 6·5 g and at 75° 32·3 g. Its commercial uses, in the manufacture of various chemicals, in metal treatment and as a bactericide, all depend on its oxidizing properties, as do its laboratory uses. Sodium permanganate, $NaMnO_4$, $3H_2O$, is much more soluble. A crude solution is used as a disinfectant under the name of Condy's Fluid. Silver permanganate, $AgMnO_4$, is not very soluble and is even more reactive than the other permanganates; its solution is reduced by gaseous hydrogen.

Permanganate titrations. On account of its intense colour and easy purification, potassium permanganate is an important volumetric oxidizing agent which requires no indicator even in 0·01 M-solution. When used, as in most estimations, in presence of sulphuric acid, it is reduced to manganese (II) sulphate, so that its equivalent weight is 31·60. As distilled water may contain traces of reducing matter, solutions are not made up by weight, but are standardized after having been boiled (or left to stand for some days) and then filtered. The best standards are sodium oxalate and pure (electrolytic) iron; crystallized oxalic acid and ferrous ammonium sulphate are also frequently used but are less reliable. It is important to test the sulphuric acid for reducing matter. The solution may be used for the direct titration of ferrous iron, hydrogen peroxide, ferrocyanide, and oxalate; in the last case the solution must be hot (80°); suitable back titrations enable it to be used for the estimation of a great variety of oxidizing and reducing agents. In the titration of ferrous iron, the presence of chloride interferes owing to induced oxidation of the latter, but the disadvantage can be overcome by titrating in presence of an excess of manganese (II) sulphate. In some estimations permanganate is used in almost neutral solution, when hydrated manganese dioxide (or a manganate (IV)) is formed and the equivalent weight is 52·68. An important instance of this procedure is the determination of dipositive manganese (the Volhard method); the titration is carried out in the presence of a zinc salt and suspended zinc oxide.

Permanganic acid, $HMnO_4$. Obtained in solution by dissolving manganese heptoxide in water, or by double decomposition between barium permanganate and sulphuric acid, or by electrolysis of solutions of permanganates with a porous partition. It is a strong monobasic acid and in dilute solution (less than 1%) is fairly stable. The solution can be concentrated up to about 20%, but the concentrated solutions are very unstable and soon decompose to hydrated manganese dioxide and oxygen.

Permonosulphuric acid (Caro's acid), H_2SO_5, $HO \cdot SO_2 \cdot O \cdot OH$. A powerful oxidizing agent obtained by the action of hydrogen peroxide on concentrated sulphuric acid, or by the action of 40% sulphuric acid on potassium persulphate in the cold. The pure acid can be obtained in the form of white crystals of m.p. about 45° by the action of the calculated quantity of 100% hydrogen peroxide on chlorosulphonic acid. It rapidly liberates iodine from potassium iodide.

Permutite process. The process of softening hard water by passage through a natural or artificial zeolite. The sodium in the zeolite is replaced by doubly charged ions from the water and the zeolite may be recharged by treatment with brine. Calcium and magnesium ions are thus removed from solution.

Perniobic acids and perniobates. A yellow perniobic acid, $HNbO_4$, xH_2O, has been obtained by treating potassium perniobate with dilute sulphuric acid and dialysing the resulting solution; a similar product is formed on treating niobic acid with 30% hydrogen peroxide. The amorphous solid loses oxygen at 100°, and gives hydrogen peroxide on treatment with dilute acid. Perniobates of the alkali metals, having the general formula M_3NbO_8, and forming stable white powders, are formed on treating the niobates with hydrogen peroxide and a solution of the alkali hydroxide; the solid product is precipitated on adding alcohol.

Perovskite. The name given to a group of compounds of formula MNX_3, in which M and N are positive ions and X is either fluorine or oxygen. The lattices are based on a simple cubic structure with M at the corners of a cube, N at the body centre, and X at the face centres. M is co-ordinated by 12X atoms; N is co-ordinated by 6X atoms. Examples are $KNiF_3$, $BaTiO_3$, and $KNbO_3$. Many perovskites show distortions from the idealised cubic structure.

Peroxidases. Enzymes that occur in plants and catalyse the transfer of peroxide oxygen to oxidizable substances. The best source is horseradish, the peroxidase from which has been shown to be a haematin compound. The enzymes give a characteristic blue colour with guaiacum. See 'Peroxidase' by B. C. Saunders, R.I.C. Monograph, No. 1, 1957.

Peroxides. Oxides, the molecules of which contain linked pairs of oxygen atoms (see Peracids) or which contain O_2^{2-} ions; they give hydrogen peroxide on treatment with dilute acids; BaO_2 and NaO_2 are typical peroxides. The dioxides MnO_2, PbO_2, NO_2, etc., are frequently, but incorrectly, termed 'peroxides'.

Peroxychromates. An acidified chromate (VI) solution treated with hydrogen peroxide gives a blue coloration which can be extracted into ether. Adducts of the formula $BCr^{VI}(O)(O_2)_2$ are formed with bases. The formation of the blue colour is the basis of the test used for the detection of chromate, or, after formation and distillation of chromyl chloride, of chloride. Other peroxychromates are also known. Red salts $M_3Cr^V(O_2)_4$ are formed by the action of H_2O_2 on alkaline chromate solutions and violet salts $M[Cr^{VI}(O)_2(O_2)_2H]$ by the action of H_2O_2 on a weakly acidic solution of a chromate. The action of excess of aqueous ammonia on other peroxychromates gives $Cr^{IV}(O_2)_2 \cdot 3NH_3$. All peroxychromates are liable to be explosive.

Peroxymolybdates. If acid solutions of molybdates are treated with hydrogen peroxide they turn yellow or orange. Two series of salts, M_2MoO_6, yellow and M_2MoO_8, red are known. The latter are explosive.

Peroxytantalates. A solution of a tantalate gives peroxytantalates with hydrogen peroxide. The salt $K_3TaO_8 \cdot \frac{1}{2}H_2O$ and the acid $HTaO_4$ have been isolated.

Peroxytitanates. The addition of hydrogen peroxide to a solution of titanium (IV) sulphate gives an orange colour due to the peroxy ion $TiO_2(SO_4)_2^{2-}$. The salt $K_4TiO_8 \cdot 6H_2O$ is known.

Peroxyvanadates. Salts of peroxyvanadic acid, HVO_4, may be obtained by the action of hydrogen peroxide on vanadates. The salts are yellow or deep orange in colour; the free acid itself cannot be isolated.

Perspex. A brand name for cast polymethyl methacrylate sheet. See Acrylic resins.

Persulphuric acid (Perdisulphuric acid), $H_2S_2O_8$. $HO \cdot SO_2 \cdot O \cdot O \cdot SO_2 \cdot OH$. A dibasic acid obtained by the electrolysis of a solution of potassium sulphate in dilute sulphuric acid at high current density. White crystals of potassium persulphate are formed. A dilute solution of the free acid is obtained by the action of sulphuric acid on barium persulphate. The free acid is obtainable in solid form by the action of chlorosulphonic acid on Caro's acid and melts with decomposition at about 60°. The solid persulphates are fairly stable. The persulphates are strong oxidizing agents and decompose on heating, with formation of oxygen. They give no precipitate with barium chloride.

Perylene ring system. The system is numbered as shown.

Petalite, (Li, Na) (AlSi$_4$)O$_{10}$. A lithium aluminium silicate containing from 2-4·5% Li$_2$O. The chief sources are Rhodesia and S.W. Africa and of recent years considerable amounts have been treated for the extraction of lithium and its compounds. Colour white to grey, occasionally greenish or reddish, sp.gr. 2·4, hardness 6-6½.

Pethidine, C$_{15}$H$_{21}$NO$_2$. Its hydrochloride, which

is obtained as colourless crystals, m.p. 187°-189°, soluble in water, less soluble in alcohol, is used as an analgesic and sedative, particularly in childbirth. It can satisfactorily replace morphine in a number of conditions.

Petit, Alexis Thérèse (1791-1820). Professor of physics at the Lycée Bonaparte. See Dulong.

Petrol. A trade name originally held by one of the companies marketing motor spirit, and now popularly used to mean motor spirit or aviation spirit.

Petrolatum. An unctuous salve-like residuum from non-asphaltic petroleum. It is available commercially under a wide variety of names and in various degrees of purity, i.e. petroleum jelly, soft paraffin, mineral jelly, paraffinum molle, etc. Two varieties, white and yellow, are used in pharmacy, the white variety being bleached. Both melt between 38° and 56°, are insoluble in water and alcohol, soluble in ether and benzene. They are poorly absorbed by the skin and are used as a basis for medicaments.

Petroleum. A naturally occurring material, consisting essentially of hydrocarbons, solid, liquid, and gas, with smaller proportions of sulphur, nitrogen, and oxygen compounds.

Petroleum coke. The solid material obtained as a by-product in the thermal cracking of petroleum. Certain grades are used in the manufacture of electrodes and special steels.

Petroleum ether, light petroleum. Lower aliphatic hydrocarbons of high volatility and a narrow distillation range. It is made in a number of grades; the two most common having distillation ranges 40°-60° and 60°-80°.

Petroleum jelly. See Petrolatum.

Pettersson, Sven Otto (1848-1941). Pettersson was professor of chemistry at the University of Stockholm from 1881 till 1907. Along with Nilson he carried out researches on the elements titanium and germanium.

Pewter. See Tin alloys.

Pfeffer, Wilhelm (1845-1920). Privatdozent at Bonn and professor of botany at the Universities of Tübingen and Leipzig, Pfeffer is noted for his work on osmotic pressure.

pH. See Hydrogen-ion concentration.

pH-meter. An instrument for measuring the pH of solutions, suspensions, tissues, etc., generally with the aid of a glass electrode. The apparatus consists essentially of an electrometer-valve potentiometer, with provision of an adjustment for backing off the asymmetry potential of the electrode. Two types of pH-meter are available: the 'null' type is the more accurate, the 'direct reading' type the more rapid. pH-meters are widely used in research, analysis and process-control; portable, bench, recording, and controlling models are made.

Phaeophorbide. See Chlorophyll.

Phaeophytin. See Chlorophyll.

Phalloidin, C$_{35}$H$_{46}$N$_8$O$_{10}$S. One of a group of very toxic cyclic peptides, occurring in the mushroom *Amanita phalloides*, the death-cap fungus. The structures of phalloidin, and the related compounds phalloin and phallacidin, were elucidated by Th. Wieland. See Amanitins.

Pharaoh's Serpents' eggs. Pillules of mercuric thiocyanate, Hg(CNS)$_2$, with gum as a binding agent. When ignited they burn freely and evolve a very voluminous, snake-like ash.

Pharbitin, C$_{26}$H$_{48}$O$_{13}$. The glycoside of the seeds of *Pharbitis nil* consists of glucose, rhamnose, and ipurolic acid (3,11-dihydroxymyristic acid). It has m.p. 156°, $[\alpha]_D$ −46·6°.

Phase. A phase may be defined as any portion of a system which is homogeneous and divided from any other homogeneous portion of the system by a boundary. For example in a closed vessel containing ice, water, and water vapour, there are three phases: the solid phase, ice; the liquid phase, water; and the gaseous phase, water vapour.

Phase diagram. A diagram showing the conditions of equilibrium between various phases. In one-component systems a pressure-temperature diagram is used, in two-component systems a composition-temperature (pressure constant) diagram or a composition-pressure (temperature constant) diagram is used, etc.

Phase rule. The phase rule states that in a system at equilibrium, if the number of phases is P, the number of degrees of freedom is F, and the number of components is C, then $P+F=C+2$.

Phellandral, 4-Isopropyl-1-cyclohexene-1-aldehyde, $C_{10}H_{16}O$. A terpenic aldehyde, the (−)-form of which is found in water fennel oil and in the oils from *Eucalyptus hemiphloia, E. polybractea,* and *E. Bakeri.* It is easily isolated in the form of a slightly soluble crystalline compound with sodium bisulphite. The constants are: b.p. 90°/5 mm, d^{20} 0·9412, n_D^{20} 1·4912.

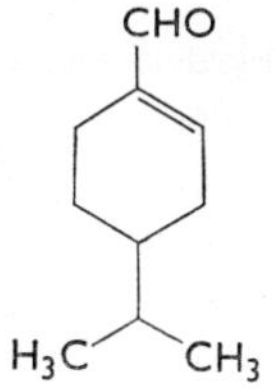

CHO

H_3C　　CH_3

It forms a semicarbazone of m.p. 202°-204° and an oxime of m.p. 87°.

α-Phellandrene, 5-Isopropyl-2-methyl-1,3-cyclohexadiene, $C_{10}H_{16}$. A monoclinic terpene, which is optically active. (+)-α-Phellandrene occurs in bitter fennel oil, ginger-grass oil, and Ceylon and Seychelles cinnamon oil, and (−)-α-phellandrene in various eucalyptus oils. It is a colourless oil, which tends to decompose when distilled at atmospheric pressure. A purified form of (−)-α-phellandrene had the constants b.p. 58°-59°/16 mm, d_4^{20} 0·8324, n_D^{20} 1·4724, $[\alpha]_D^{20}$ −177·4°. It forms a nitrosyl chloride which can be resolved into two isomers, one of m.p. 113°-114° and the other of m.p. 105°-106°.

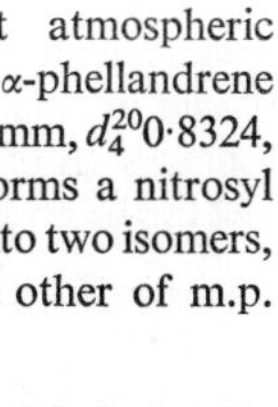

CH₃

H_3C　　CH_3

β-Phellandrene, 3-Isopropyl-6-methylenecyclohexene, $C_{10}H_{16}$. An optically active monocyclic terpene, isomeric with α-phellandrene. (+)-β-Phellandrene occurs in water-fennel oil, lemon oil, and the oil from *Bupleurum fruticosum,* and (−)-β-phellandrene in Japanese peppermint oil and in the oil from *Pinus contorta.*

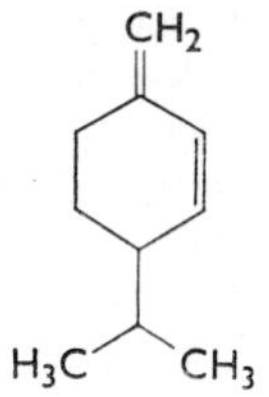

CH_2

H_3C　　CH_3

(+)-β-Phellandrene has the constants: b.p. 171°-172°, d^{20} 0·8520, n_D^{20} 1·4788, $[\alpha]_D$ +65·2°. It is unstable and polymerizes if distilled. It yields a crystalline nitrosite which can be resolved into two isomers melting at 102° and 97°-98° respectively.

Phenacaine, Holocaine. The hydrochloride of *p*-phenetidylphenacetin, $C_{18}H_{22}N_2O_2, HCl, H_2O$.

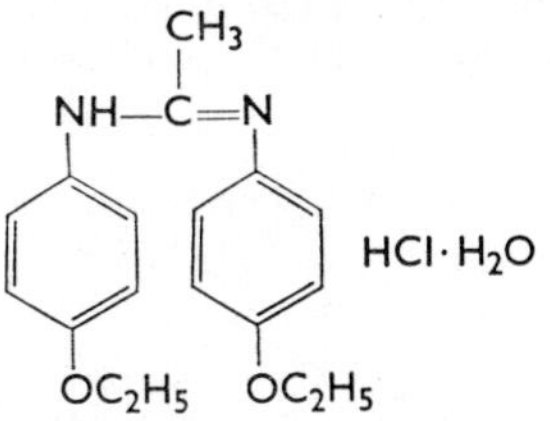

CH_3
$NH-C=N$
$HCl \cdot H_2O$
OC_2H_5　OC_2H_5

Its constitution is entirely different from that of the majority of cocaine substitutes which are mostly benzoyl or substituted benzoyl esters of amino-alcohols. Phenacaine possesses local anaesthetic properties, but it is not suitable for hypodermic use. It is employed almost entirely in ophthalmic practice in the form of a 1% aqueous solution.

Phenacetin, aceto-*p*-phenetidide, $C_{10}H_{13}NO_2$.

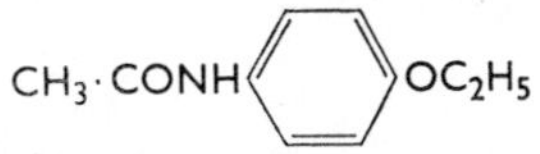

$CH_3 \cdot CONH \langle\ \rangle OC_2H_5$

White crystals, m.p. 137°-138°, soluble in 1700 parts of water and 21 parts of alcohol. Prepared from phenol, via *p*-nitrophenol, *p*-nitrophenetole, and *p*-phenetidine. It is used medicinally as an analgesic and antipyretic.

Phenanthrene ring system. The system is numbered as shown.

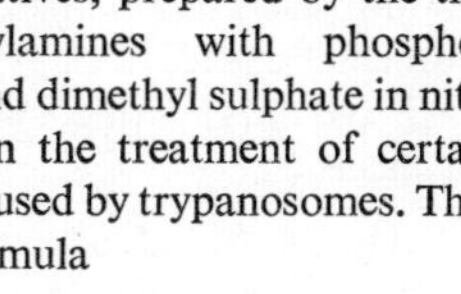

Phenanthridine derivatives. Various phenanthridine derivatives, prepared by the treatment of acyl-*o*-xenylamines with phosphorus oxychloride and dimethyl sulphate in nitrobenzene, are used in the treatment of certain tropical diseases caused by trypanosomes. They have the general formula

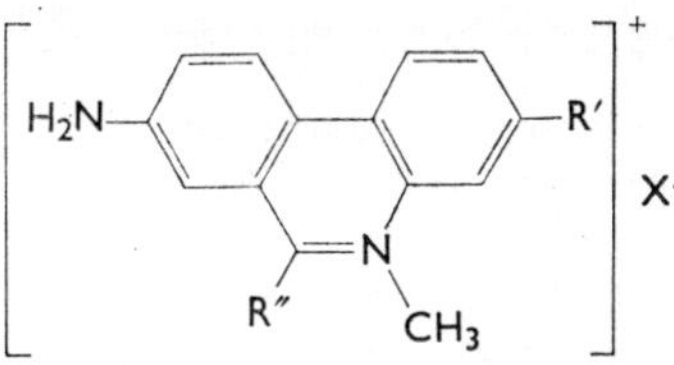

In phenidium chloride (phenanthridinium 897), $R'=H$, $R''=p—C_6H_4NH_2$, and $X=Cl$.

In metidium chloride (phenanthridinium 1508), $R'=H$, $R''=m—C_6H_4NH_2$, and $X=Cl$.

In dimidium bromide (phenanthridinium 1553), R′=NH₂, R″=C₆H₅, and X=Br.

o-Phenanthroline, 1,10-phenanthroline,
C₁₂H₈N₂. Made by heating o-phenylene-

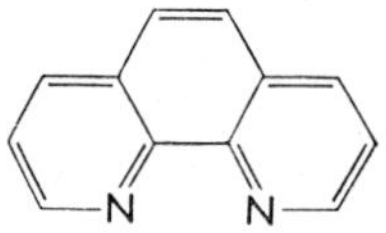

diamine with glycerol, nitrobenzene, and conc. sulphuric acid. It exists as a monohydrate m.p. 94°, or anhydrous m.p. 117°. Slightly soluble in water, soluble in many organic solvents, it is used as a complexing reagent in the estimation of ferrous iron.

Phenazone, antipyrin, 1-phenyl-2,3-dimethyl-5-pyrazolone, C₁₁H₁₂N₂O. White crystals, m.p.

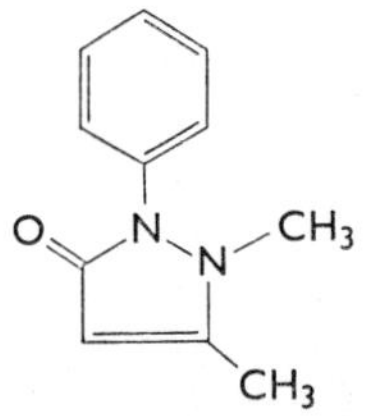

114°, b.p. 319°. Very soluble in water and alcohol. Prepared by condensing phenylhydrazine with ethylacetoacetate and methylating with methyl iodide. It is an analgesic and antipyretic. It is more rapid in action than phenacetin, but more toxic.

p-Phenetidine, C₈H₁₁NO. A colourless oil, m.p. 2°-4°, b.p. 254°, sp.gr. 1·0613 at 15°. Insoluble in water, only slightly volatile in steam. Its hydrochloride has m.p. 234°, and is easily soluble in water.

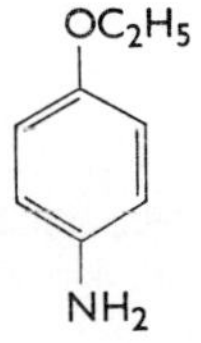

It is usually prepared by the reduction of p-nitrophenetole with iron and hydrochloric acid.

It is used as a dyestuffs intermediate. Its acetyl derivative is phenacetin.

Phenetole, C₈H₁₀O. A colourless, aromatic liquid, b.p. 172°. Insoluble in water, miscible with alcohol and ether.

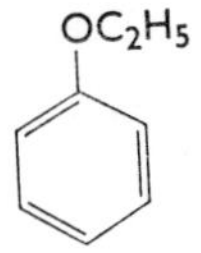

It is prepared by heating potassium phenate with ethyl iodide, or by adding ethyl alcohol to a mixture of phenol and phosphorus pentoxide at 200°.

Phenidium chloride. See Phenanthridine derivatives.

Phenindamine, C₁₉H₁₉N. Used as the acid tartrate, which is a white powder, soluble in 100

parts of water, insoluble in alcohol. It is an antihistamine drug, but it does not produce depres-

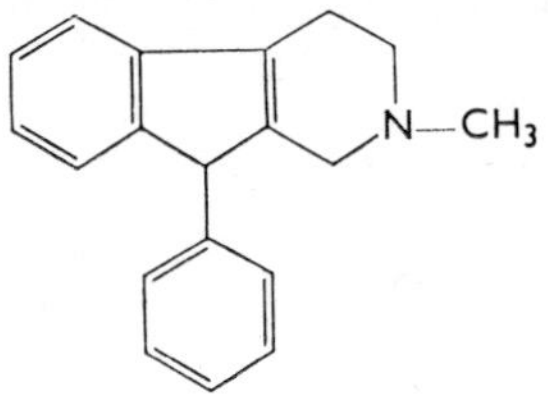

sion on administration. It is used for treating itching and other skin conditions, and has been used for treating parkinsonism.

Phenindione, 2-Phenylindane-1,3-dione,

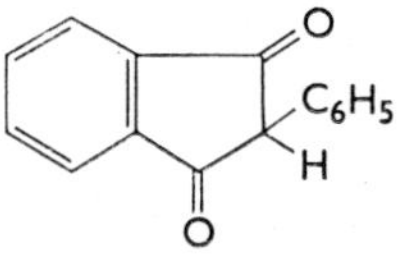

C₁₅H₁₀O₂. A white crystalline powder, m.p. 150°, slightly soluble in water, soluble in benzene; prepared by cyclization of diphenylpyruvic acid in the presence of sulphuric acid. It is a synthetic anticoagulant which can be used orally for the treatment of thrombosis and in surgery.

Pheniodol, C₁₅H₁₂I₂O₃. A creamy-white powder,

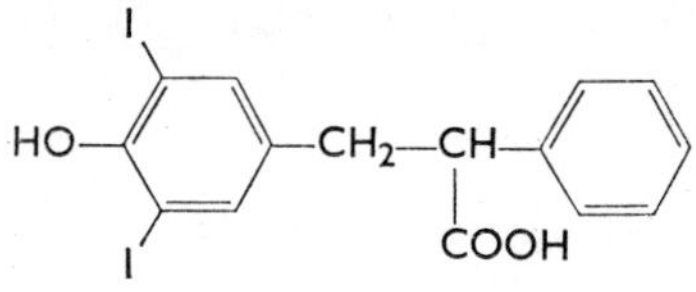

m.p. 160°-162°, almost insoluble in water, soluble in alcohol and alkalis. It has largely replaced iodophthalein as a contrast medium in radiography of the biliary tract, as it is less toxic and can be given in large doses by mouth.

Phenobarbitone, phenylethylbarbituric acid, C₁₂H₁₂N₂O₃. White crystals, m.p. 174°, soluble in 1000 parts of water and 15 of alcohol. Prepared by condensing the ethyl ester of phenylethylmalonic acid with urea. It is a more active hypnotic than barbitone. It and its sodium salt—soluble phenobarbitone—are used as sedatives in insomnia and epilepsy.

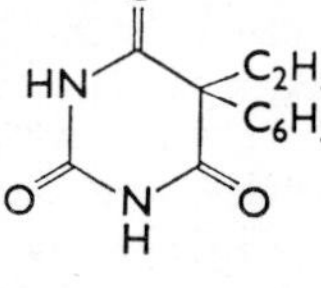

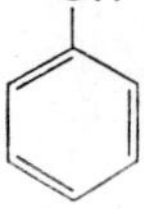

Phenol, C₆H₆O. Long colourless prismatic crystals, m.p. 43°, b.p. 183°, d^{15} 1·066. Soluble in 15 parts of water at room temperature; larger amounts of phenol in water give a two-phase system of phenol solution floating on a lower layer of wet phenol. Miscible with water in all proportions at 84°. Soluble in alcohol, ether, and benzene. Volatile in steam.

It occurs in the coal-tar fraction distilling at 190°-230° and a little is still obtained from this source. Most phenol is, however, obtained synthetically by one of the following processes: fusion of sodium benzenesulphonate with caustic soda to give sodium phenate; hydrolysis of chlorobenzene by dilute caustic soda at 400° and 300 atm. to give sodium phenate (Dow process); catalytic vapour-phase reaction of steam and chlorobenzene at 500° (Raschig process); direct oxidation of cumene (isopropylbenzene) to the hydroperoxide, followed by acid cleavage to acetone and phenol; catalytic liquid-phase oxidation of toluene to benzoic acid and then phenol. Where the phenate is formed, phenol is liberated by acidification.

Phenol is acidic and forms metallic salts. It is readily halogenated, sulphonated, and nitrated. It is of great commercial importance and is used in quantity for the manufacture of phenolic and epoxy resins, caprolactam and non-ionic detergents. It is the starting material for making both precursors of Nylon 66. It is also used in the manufacture of various dyes, explosives, pharmaceuticals and perfumes.

Phenol coefficient. See Rideal-Walker test.

Phenol-formaldehyde resins. Phenols and formaldehyde readily condense under both acid and alkaline conditions to give curable resins. Following Baekeland's pioneer work, moulded plastics of the Bakelite type were the major products of the plastics industry during the first half of this century; their production has now been outstripped by several other groups of plastics. Two important types of phenolic resin are extensively used. The novolak resin, produced under acid conditions from phenol and insufficient formaldehyde to allow complete resinification, is widely used for the manufacture of general purpose phenolic moulding materials. A resol type resin (a fully thermocurable material), manufactured by phenol-formaldehyde condensation under alkaline conditions, is used for the production of heavily reinforced moulding materials, paper, cloth, and asbestos based laminates, and for stovable lacquers and hot-setting adhesives. There is limited production of a third type of resin, the cast phenolic resin (q.v.).

Phenolphthalein, $C_{20}H_{14}O_4$. Colourless crystals, m.p. 254°. Prepared by heating phthalic anhydride and phenol in the presence of sulphuric acid. Extensively used as an indicator in 0·04% solution in alcohol, the pH range being 8·3 (colourless) to 10·4 (red). The disodium salt (carboxylate and one phenyl group) is red but

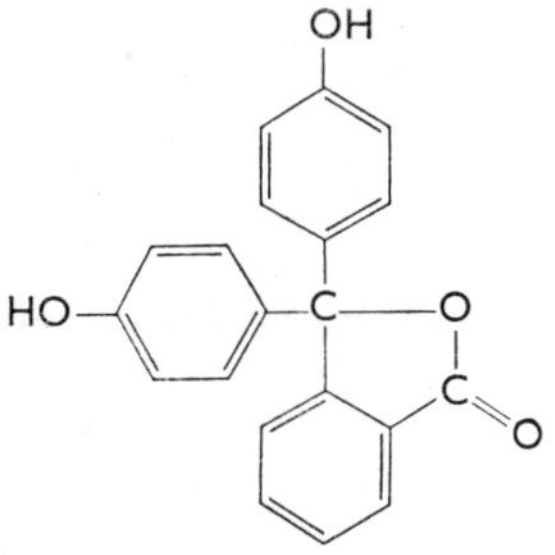

Colourless
form

the trisodium salt is colourless. It is used medicinally as a purgative.

Phenol red, Phenolsulphonphthalein, $C_{19}H_{14}O_5S$.

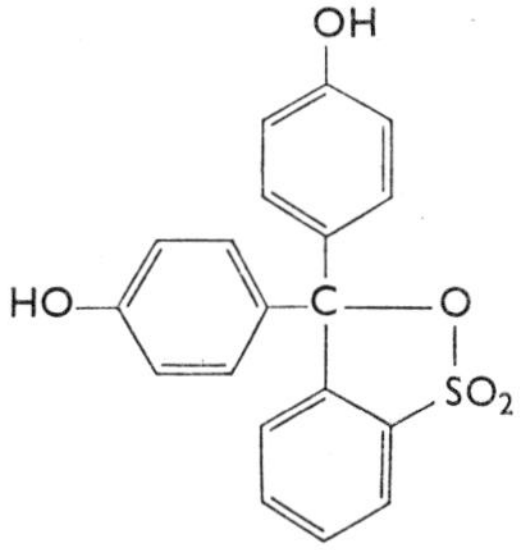

Prepared by heating phenol with o-sulphobenzoic anhydride, and used as an indicator in 0·04% aqueous solution. Its pH range is 6·7 (yellow) to 8·3 (red).

It is used as a test for renal function; a neutralized aqueous solution containing 6 milligrams is injected intravenously and the urine is drawn off with a catheter into a vessel containing a solution of sodium hydroxide. A red colour indicates when elimination begins and 50% of that injected should be recovered during the first hour, the amount being determined colorimetrically by comparison with standard solutions.

Phenols. Compounds containing at least one hydroxyl group attached directly to a carbon atom of a benzene ring. They have a slight acidic nature, and are soluble in caustic alkalis forming metallic salts, the phenates. Their solubility in water increases with the number of hydroxyl groups. Polyhydric phenols have a strong reducing action.

Phenosafranine, $C_{18}H_{15}ClN_4$. A red dye, which

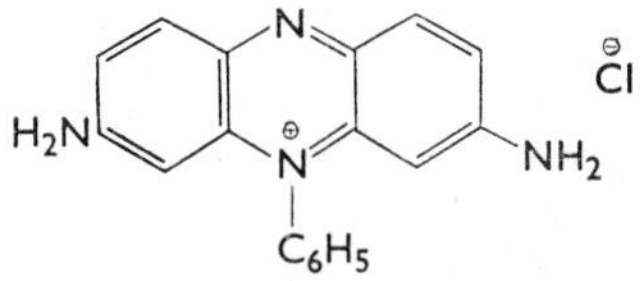

crystallizes in lustrous golden plates from water. It is prepared by the oxidation with potassium dichromate of a mixture of aniline with p-phenylenediamine or 4,4′-diaminodiphenylamine. It is a powerful photographic desensitizer. See Desensitization.

Phenothiazine, $C_{12}H_9NS$. Colourless or light yellow crystals which darken to olive-green on exposure to light; m.p. 183°-197°, insoluble in water, slightly soluble in alcohol, soluble in

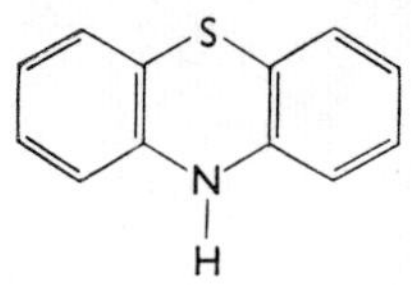

acetone. It is made by heating diphenylamine with sulphur, and is used as an anthelmintic in veterinary practice, but is poisonous to man.

Phenoxyacetic acid herbicides. See 2,4-D; MCPA.

Phenoxyethanol, Ethylene glycol monophenyl ether, $C_6H_5O \cdot CH_2 \cdot CH_2OH$. A colourless, viscous liquid, b.p. 117°/7 mm, d_{20}^{20} 1·109, n_D^{22} 1·535. Slightly soluble in water, miscible with alcohol. Made by heating sodium phenoxide with ethylene chlorohydrin. It is an antiseptic which is particularly effective against *Pseudomonas pyocyaneus*, and certain other organisms, and is used in the local treatment of infected wounds.

Phenoxy resin. A thermoplastic epoxy resin showing some similarity to the polycarbonates. Its structure may be represented as follows:

$$+O \cdot C_6H_4 \cdot C(CH_3)_2 \cdot C_6H_4 \cdot O \cdot CH_2 \cdot CH(OH) \cdot CH_2 +_n$$

where n is about 100.

Phentolamine, $C_{17}H_{19}N_3O$. Used as the hydrochloride or methanesulphonate. The hydrochloride is a white powder, m.p. 238°, soluble in

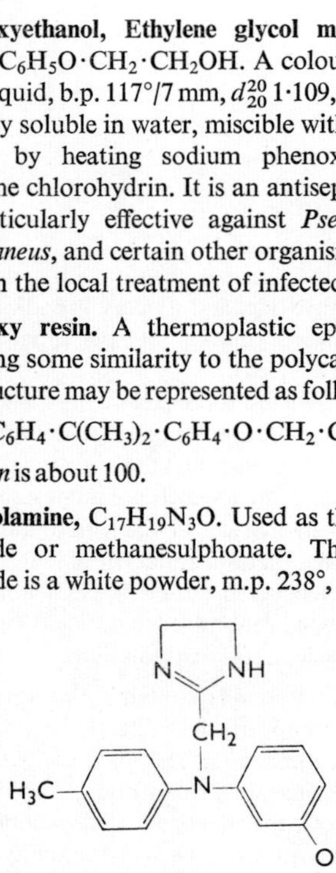

100 parts of water and in 60 parts of alcohol.

The drug reverses the pressor effects of adrenaline, causing a fall in blood pressure. Its use is thus in the treatment of hypertension.

Phenyl. The group C_6H_5- or Ph. Prepared with difficulty in the free state by the photolysis of aromatic ketones. The radical appears to occur as an intermediate in many organic reactions in solution.

Phenylalanine, α-Amino-β-phenylpropionic acid, $C_9H_{11}NO_2$. Crystallizes in colourless leaves,

m.p. 283°. Soluble in water up to 3%. The naturally occurring substance is laevorotatory,

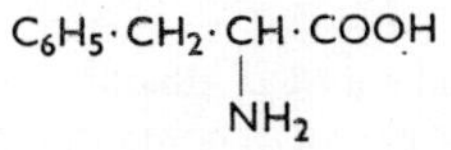

$$C_6H_5 \cdot CH_2 \cdot CH \cdot COOH$$
$$|$$
$$NH_2$$

$[\alpha]_D^{20}$ −35·1°. It is one of the essential amino-acids that must be present in the food of animals.

***m*-Phenylenediamine,** $C_6H_8N_2$. Colourless rhombic crystals, m.p. 63°, b.p. 287°, very soluble in water, alcohol, and ether. Turns brown in air.

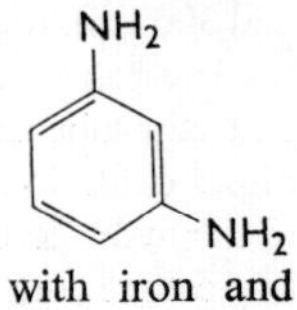

Prepared by a one-stage reduction of *m*-dinitrobenzene with iron and hydrochloric acid.

Basic, forms a stable water-soluble dihydrochloride. Diazotization gives brown azo-dyes (Bismarck brown) owing to the coupling of the partially diazotized base with the excess of diamine. Is also used as an end component of many azo-dyes, readily coupling with one or two molecules of diazo compound.

***o*-Phenylenediamine,** $C_6H_8N_2$. Brown-yellow crystals, m.p. 103°-104°, b.p. 256°-258°, soluble in organic solvents but only slightly in water. Its solutions reduce silver ions and it has long been used as a photographic developer. It is also used as a dye-precursor, for the synthesis of phenazine derivatives, and for characterizing (*inter alia*) α-diketones.

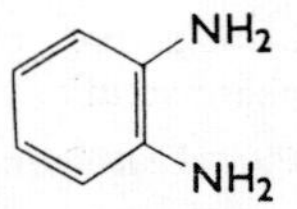

***p*-Phenylenediamine,** $C_6H_8N_2$. White crystals, m.p. 147°, b.p. 267°, which darken rapidly in air. Prepared by reducing *p*-nitroaniline or aminoazobenzene. Oxidizing agents convert it to quinone derivatives, hence it cannot be diazotised with nitric acid.

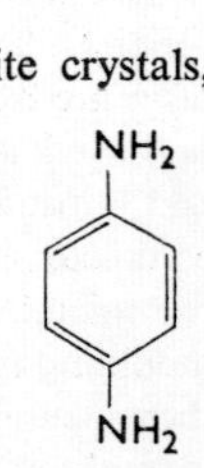

It is used for hair dyeing, as a rubber accelerator and as a photographic developer.

Certain of its derivatives are extensively used as developers in colour photography. These have the formula:

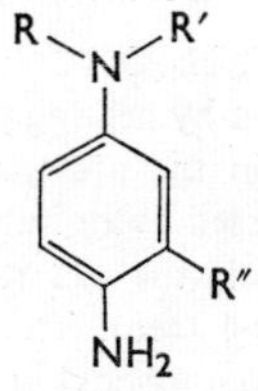

where R and R′ are alkyl or substituted alkyl and R″ is hydrogen, alkyl, or substituted alkyl.

N-Phenylglycine, $C_8H_9NO_2$. Forms white

crystals, m.p. 127°, fairly soluble in water. The alkali-metal salts are easily soluble, the calcium salt sparingly soluble.

It can be prepared in three ways:

1. By the condensation of aniline with chloroacetic acid.

2. By heating aniline, caustic soda, formaldehyde, and potassium cyanide.

3. By heating aniline, lime, and trichloroethylene.

It is an important intermediate in the indigo industry. When phenylglycine is fused with sodamide a good yield of indoxyl is obtained. The indoxyl is easily oxidized to indigo.

N-Phenylglycine-o-carboxylic acid, $C_9H_9NO_4$.

The acid forms a sandy powder, m.p. 207°, with decomposition. Fairly soluble in hot water, alcohol, ether, and glacial acetic acid, insoluble in benzene.

It is prepared by the action of chloroacetic acid upon anthranilic acid. It can also be prepared by the action of potassium cyanide and formaldehyde on anthranilic acid, followed by hydrolysis with caustic soda of the nitrile of anthranilic acid first produced.

It is used for the preparation of indigo into which it is readily converted on alkaline fusion.

Phenylhdyrazine, $C_6H_8N_2$. A colourless, refractive oil, b.p. 240°-241°, with slight decomposition. When pure it sets to a crystalline mass at 19°. It

is conveniently purified by crystallization from ether or by distillation *in vacuo*. It rapidly becomes brown when exposed to air. Sparingly soluble in water, volatile in steam. It forms a stable hydrochloride which can be crystallized unchanged from hot water. It is very poisonous.

It is prepared commercially by treating benzene diazonium chloride with sodium sulphite and then reducing the mixture with zinc dust and acetic acid. It can also be prepared by reduction of benzene diazonium chloride with stannous chloride.

Phenylhydrazine is a strong reducing agent; it reduces Fehling's solution in the cold and reduces aromatic nitro compounds to the amines. It is a valuable reagent in organic chemistry for the identification of compounds containing ketonic groups, hydrazones being obtained. Compounds containing the grouping —CHOH—CO—, e.g. glucose, fructose, etc., react with two molecules of phenylhydrazine to give osazones.

Phenylhydrazine condenses with acetoacetic ester to give a pyrazolone derivative which on methylation gives phenazone. The sulphonic acid similarly gives rise to the tartrazine dyestuffs.

Phenylhydrazine-p-sulphonic acid, $C_6H_8N_2O_3S$. Forms lustrous, colourless needles, with $\frac{1}{2}H_2O$. Sparingly soluble in cold water, much more so in hot water.

It is prepared by reducing diazotized sulphanilic acid with an excess of sodium sulphite.

It is a typical hydrazine in its reactions with ketones, and with acetoacetic ester. The latter reaction gives rise to the tartrazine dyestuffs, and is much used commercially.

Phenylhydrazones. Compounds containing the group

which are formed by treating aldehydes or ketones with phenylhydrazine in acetic acid solution. They are crystalline solids having definite melting-points and are usually sparingly soluble. Decomposed by heating with hydrochloric acid to regenerate the aldehyde or ketone. React with sodium ethoxide to give hydrocarbons, and with zinc chloride to give derivatives of indole. They may be used for the identification of aldehydes and ketones, but are now less important for this purpose than 2,4-dinitrophenylhydrazones.

Phenyl isocyanate, C_6H_5NCO. A pungent

lachrymatory almost colourless liquid; m.p. −33°, b.p. 162°, $d^{19\cdot6}$ 1·0956, n_D^{20} 1·535. Used as a dehydrating agent and for characterisation of alcohols. Prepared from aniline and phosgene in the presence of hydrogen chloride.

Phenylmercuric acetate, $C_8H_8HgO_2$. A powerful fungicide and selective herbicide. Prepared

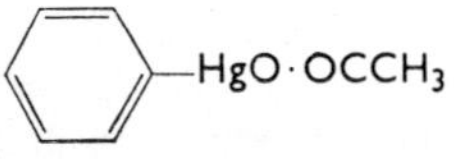

from benzene and mercuric acetate in glacial acetic acid, it is a white crystalline substance, m.p. 149°-153°, sparingly soluble in water but soluble in organic solvents. It has high mammalian toxicity, and being also slightly volatile at room temperatures, great care must be exercised in handling it.

1-Phenylpyrazolid-3-one, Phenidone, $C_9H_{10}N_2O$. A colourless crystalline solid, m.p. 121°, soluble in alkaline solutions and most organic solvents. Made by reacting phenylhydrazine with ethyl acrylate to obtain the hydrazide which cyclizes to the product. Its major commercial importance is as a photographic developing agent, being used particularly in conjunction with hydroquinone.

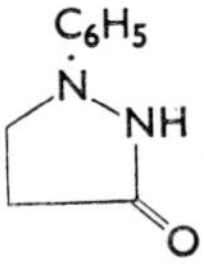

Phenytoin, 5,5-Diphenylhydantoin,

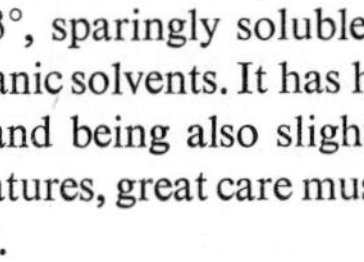

$C_{15}H_{12}N_2O_2$. It is used as its sodium salt, 'soluble phenytoin' or 'phenytoin sodium', which is a white hygroscopic powder, soluble in water and alcohol, and is unstable, readily absorbing carbon dioxide and liberating phenytoin. Made by treating α-bromodiphenylacetylurea with alcoholic ammonia. It has a mild hypnotic and strong anticonvulsant action, and is used in the treatment of epilepsy.

Pheromones. This term, coined by Karlson (1959), defines substances which are secreted externally by one individual and which elicit a specific response from other individuals of the same species. Examples are: insect sex attractants such as bombykol (hexadeca-10-*trans*,12-*cis*-dien-1-ol) from the silk moth; trail markers of ants; and 'Queen substance' of the honey bee (9-oxodec-2-*trans*-enoic acid).

Philosopher's stone. See Transmutation.

Phlogopite. See Mica.

Phloridzin, $C_{21}H_{24}O_{10}$. This glycoside present in the root bark of the apple, pear, cherry, plum, has many unusual properties, and is not a normal β-glucoside. It is not hydrolysed by emulsin. The constitution is

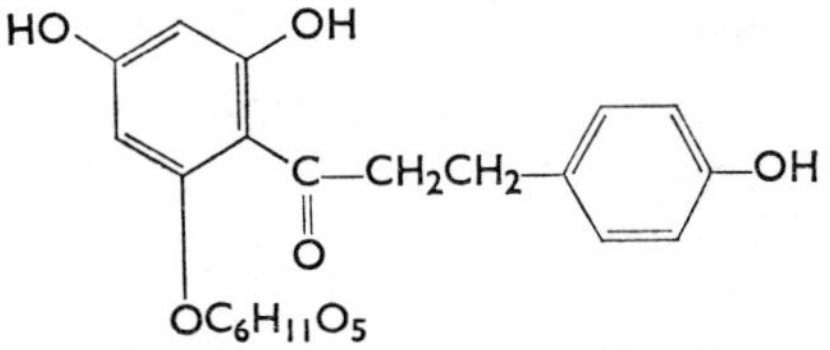

Phloroglucinol, $C_6H_6O_3$. Colourless crystals,

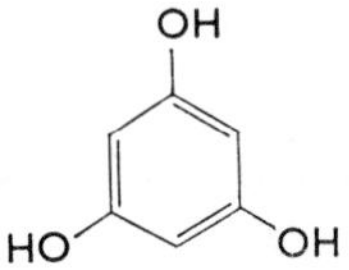

dihydrate from water. Water of crystallization lost at 100°. Anhydrous compound, m.p. 200°-219°, depending upon rate of heating. Readily soluble in water, alcohol, and ether. The aqueous solution gives a blue-violet colour with ferric chloride, reduces Fehling's solution, and absorbs oxygen, but less readily than pyrogallol.

It occurs in many natural glycosides. It can be prepared by fusing resorcinol with caustic soda, and manufactured from trinitrotoluene via trinitrobenzoic acid and triaminobenzene.

It reacts chemically as if it were either 1,3,5-trihydroxybenzene or the triketone of hexahydrobenzene. The trialkyl derivative of the hydroxy-form or the trioxime of the keto-form can be obtained from phloroglucinol by reacting in a suitable manner. In certain cases derivatives of the two forms are interchangeable.

Phorone,   Di-isopropylideneacetone, $C_9H_{14}O$.

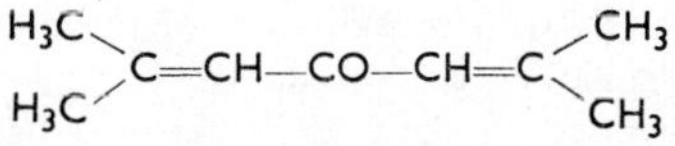

Occurs as a yellow liquid having a camphor-like odour, m.p. 28°, b.p. 198·5°. Insoluble in water; soluble in alcohol, acetone, and benzene. It is formed when acetone is saturated with hydrogen chloride and allowed to stand. Resembles camphor in many of its properties and is a solvent for cellulose nitrate.

Phosdrin, dimethylmethyl-2-crotonylphosphate,

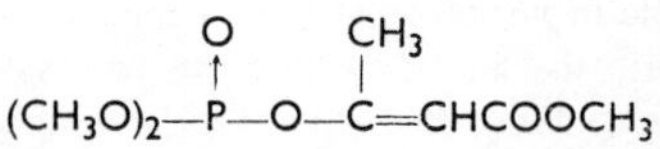

$C_7H_{13}O_6P$. A trade name for a highly active systemic insecticide; both *cis* and *trans* isomers are active. It can be made by reacting trimethyl phosphite with methyl 2-chloroacetoacetate. It is a liquid, b.p. 325°, miscible with water, but very rapidly hydrolysed in solution. This rapid decomposition enables it to be used as a close-to-harvest treatment without danger of harmful residues in the crop.

Phosgene. See Carbonyl chloride.

Phosphagen, Phosphocreatine, Creatine phosphate. A compound present in vertebrate

$$HN:C \begin{array}{c} NH \cdot P {\overset{OH}{\underset{OH}{\diagdown}}} = O \\ N—CH_2 \cdot COOH \\ | \\ CH_3 \end{array}$$

muscle that breaks down on contraction to creatine and phosphoric acid, and is resynthesized during the recovery process. The name phosphagen is sometimes also applied to arginine phosphate, which replaces creatine phosphate in invertebrate muscle.

Phosphatase. A group of enzymes of outstanding importance. They hydrolyse the many different combinations of phosphoric acid with organic substances, for example the sugar phosphates. Such compounds are constantly being formed and destroyed as intermediates in a large number of cell processes, for example, alcoholic fermentation, muscle metabolism to lactic acid, bone formation, and others. The enzymes also act synthetically, and they function independently of the living cell. Active extracts of the enzymes are obtained by autolysis of yeast juice, or of tissue. The group is subdivided into acid and alkaline phosphatases which act in solutions of the indicated pH, and into mono- and di-esterases which hydrolyse the appropriate esters. It includes enzymes which hydrolyse pyrophosphates as well as those acting on orthophosphates. All these have relatively low specificity. There are also highly specific phosphatases acting for example on sugar phosphates.

Phosphate coatings. Commonly applied to steels and other alloys in order to give improved corrosion resistance. The coatings are applied by spraying or dipping, using a mixed phosphate solution. Such coatings provide an excellent keying surface for painting. They also improve the retention of lubricants on the surface. The process is used for all types of articles from typewriter and camera parts to complete motor-car body shells.

Phosphate esters. The phosphate esters of commerce are compounds of orthophosphoric acid and alkyl or aryl alcohols. The most important is tricresyl phosphate (TCP), $(CH_3C_6H_4O)_3PO$, which is manufactured by the action of phosphorus oxychloride on technical cresol. The latter consists of a mixture of the *o*-, *m*- and *p*-isomers (or sometimes just the *m*- and *p*-isomers) and the tricresyl phosphate produced is therefore also a mixture of isomers. It is important as a plasticizer, particularly for vinyl chloride and cellulose plastics, since it renders them non-flammable. It is also used as a hydraulic fluid.

Other phosphate esters, particularly dimethylphenyl phosphate, dimethylxylyl phosphate, cresyldiphenyl phosphate and trimethyl phosphate, are used as gasoline additives. They are manufactured in a similar manner to tricresyl phosphate.

Phosphates. Salts of phosphoric acid.

Phosphatidases. See Phospholipases.

Phosphatides, Phospholipin(e)s, Phospholipid(e)s. A group of substances of a fatty nature which are essential components of all animal and vegetable cells. They contain phosphorus and nitrogen and on hydrolysis give fatty acids, phosphoric acid, and basic substances such as choline. They are soluble in the usual fat solvents with the exception of acetone. They are amphoteric and have many precipitation reactions in common with the proteins. Included in the phosphatides are lecithin, cephalin, and sphingomyelin.

Phosphides. Compounds of metals with phosphorus, e.g. Ca_3P_2, AlP. The phosphides are prepared by heating the metals with phosphorus, by reducing the corresponding phosphates with carbon in an electric furnace, or by treating a solution of a salt of the metal with phosphine or yellow phosphorus. Some yield phosphine on treatment with water or dilute acids. Calcium phosphide, Ca_3P_2, manufactured by passing phosphorus vapour over heated quicklime, is used in 'Holmes's signals', which ignite when thrown into the sea owing to the formation of phosphine.

Phosphinates. Alkyl derivatives of hypophos-

phorous acid H^+ $\begin{bmatrix} H \\ HPO \\ O \end{bmatrix}^-$; e.g. $\begin{array}{c} H \\ HPOR \\ O \end{array}$

is an alkyl phosphinate; $\begin{array}{c} HPOR \\ O \\ R \end{array}$ is a dialkyl phosphinate.

Phosphine. See Phosphorus hydrides.

Phosphinites. Derivatives of an acid such as

$\begin{array}{c} H \\ R\,PO \\ R \end{array}$; a dialkyl phosphinous acid.

Phosphites. Derivatives of phosphorous acid. Organic phosphites are obtained from the reaction of alcohols, thiols, or phenols with phosphorus trichloride. Depending on the relative proportions of the reagents, one or two chlorine atoms may be substituted. In the presence of bases all three chlorine atoms are replaced and tertiary phosphites, $(RO)_3P$, formed.

Mono- and dihalophosphites, $(RO)_2PCl$ and $(RO)PCl_2$, on hydrolysis give secondary and primary phosphites respectively. The former are colourless neutral liquids which can be distilled in a vacuum, whereas the latter are syrups with acidic properties and cannot be distilled.

Halophosphites and phosphites are used as intermediates in organic synthesis. Tertiary phosphites have been used as antioxidants in lubricating oils. See 'Organophosphorus Compounds', by Kosolapoff.

Phospholipases. Enzymes effecting the cleavage of phosphatides either at the carboxylate or at the phosphate ester linkages. Phospholipase A, present in bee and snake venoms, is a carboxylic ester hydrolase which produces lysolecithin (*q.v.*). Phospholipases C and D are phosphoric diester hydrolases which attack the phosphate ester linkage. The phospholipases have also been known as phosphatidases and as lecithinases.

Phospholipid(e)s, Phospholipin(e)s. See Phosphatides.

Phosphomolybdates. Salts of phosphomolybdic acids, e.g. $H_3PMo_{12}O_{40}$, with complex polyanions of structure similar to the phosphotungstates. The yellow precipitate obtained from solutions of phosphates by the addition of ammonium molybdate is used for the qualitative identification of phosphate. It may also be used, for the spectrophotometric estimation of molybdenum or phosphorus.

Phosphonites. Derivatives such as $\begin{array}{c}R\ POR\\ O\\ R\end{array}$; a dialkyl alkylphosphonite.

Phosphonitrilic derivatives (PNX_2). A group of polymers. The simplest compounds, the chlorides, are formed by heating phosphorus pentachloride with ammonium chloride at 150°. Various

polymers are known; most compounds have cyclic structures as shown but some linear polymers are known. On heating the chlorides to 300° they are converted to materials possessing some rubber-like properties. The chlorine atoms may be substituted by many other groups.

Phosphonium salts. White crystalline salts analogous to the ammonium halides, e.g. PH_4I. Formed by the action of dry hydrogen halides on phosphine, which functions as a weak base. Phosphonium salts are readily dissociated into phosphine and the hydrogen halide, phosphonium chloride not being stable at normal pressures and temperatures. Organo-phosphonium salts, e.g. $(C_6H_5)_3PH^+BF_4^-$, are much more stable than the unsubstituted derivatives; the stability increases with increasing substitution of hydrogen by alkyl or aryl groups.

Phosphoproteins. A class of proteins, rich in phosphorus and readily yielding phosphoric acid on alkaline hydrolysis. It includes casein from milk and vitellin from egg yolk.

Phosphoranes. Organic derivatives of pentacovalent phosphorus, R_5P, the best known being pentaphenylphosphorane, $(C_6H_5)_5P$; also included in this class are the alkylidene phosphoranes, e.g. $\begin{array}{c}R\\ \diagdown\\ \diagup\\ R'\end{array}C{=}PR_3''$ where R'' is usually phenyl, which are important synthetic intermediates in the Wittig synthesis.

Phosphor bronze. See Bronze.

Phosphorescence. Some substances absorb light and as a result are induced to emit radiations themselves; when the emission occurs only during irradiation, the process is termed fluorescence, but when it continues after the removal of the source of light, it is termed phosphorescence, and may be regarded as fluorescence in which the atoms or molecules of the absorbing substance are capable of metastable states.

Phosphoric acids. A number of phosphoric acids are known, the most important being *ortho-*, *meta-*, and *pyro-phosphoric* acids, H_3PO_4, $(HPO_3)_n$, and $H_4P_2O_7$, respectively. Pure ortho-phosphoric acid is best prepared on a small scale by heating yellow phosphorus with nitric acid. The ortho-acid forms colourless crystals melting at about 40°, readily soluble in water giving an odourless solution with a sharp taste; this solution has been used in the manufacture of soft drinks. On heating to about 220° the ortho-acid is converted to pyro-phosphoric acid; this is prepared in a pure state as colourless crystals, m.p. 61°, by warming solid orthophosphoric acid with phosphorus oxychloride, evaporating the solution, and cooling. Metaphosphoric acid is prepared as a sticky syrup by heating either the ortho- or the pyro-acid to 320°; on stronger heating followed by cooling a 'glass' is formed. In aqueous solution meta- and pyro-phosphoric acids are converted to orthophosphoric acid, the change being accelerated by heating.

The phosphates form a large and important group of compounds. Ortho-phosphoric acid is tribasic with the structure $OP(OH)_3$ and gives series of salts such as Na_3PO_4, Na_2HPO_4, and NaH_2PO_4. The alkali metal salts (except those of lithium) are soluble in water; because of hydrolysis the tertiary salts (Na_3PO_4) are alkaline in solution, and the primary salts (NaH_2PO_4) are acid. The secondary salts (Na_2HPO_4) are practically neutral, and the ordinary 'sodium phosphate' of commerce, obtained by neutralizing the acid with sodium hydroxide, is Na_2HPO_4, $12H_2O$. The ortho-phosphates of other metals are insoluble in water, but soluble in dilute mineral acids. Many different metaphosphates are known, e.g. glass-like $NaPO_3$ prepared by heating micro-cosmic salt ($NaNH_4HPO_4$), Maddrell's salt, Graham's salt; these contain tetrahedral PO_4 groups which share two oxygens with neigh-bouring groups and have different degrees of polymerisation.

Pyrophosphoric acid has the formula

$$(HO)_2P(O) \cdot O \cdot P(O)(OH)_2$$

and although it contains four replaceable hydrogen atoms, only salts containing two or four metal atoms per molecule, e.g. $Na_4P_2O_7$, $Na_2H_2P_2O_7$, are common; these salts, are prepared by heating Na_2HPO_4 and NaH_2PO_4, respectively.

Solutions of phosphates, in the presence of excess of nitric acid, give a yellow crystalline precipitate with ammonium molybdate. The precipitate is soluble in ammonia; with ortho-phosphates it forms in the cold, but with meta- and pyrophosphates heating is necessary. Arsenates also give the test on heating. Ortho-phosphates are determined gravimetrically by precipitation as $MgNH_4PO_4$, $6H_2O$, formed by adding magnesium chloride to a strongly ammoniacal solution of the phosphate; the precipitate may be ignited and weighed as $Mg_2P_2O_7$.

Phosphates, particularly 'superphosphates' (*q.v.*), are of importance commercially as fertilizers.

Phosphors. Substances which can be made to exhibit phosphorescence. Used particularly in colour television.

Phosphorous acids. Phosphorous acid, H_3PO_3 is obtained in solution by the action of cold water on phosphorus trioxide, or of water on phos-phorus trichloride; it may be obtained from the solutions as a colourless crystalline solid, m.p. 70·1°, which readily decomposes on heating, forming phosphine and orthophosphoric acid. Phosphorous acid

is dibasic and two series of phosphites, e.g. NaH_2PO_3 and Na_2HPO_3, are formed. The acid and its salts are reducing agents; silver nitrate solution gives first a white precipitate of silver phosphite, which later darkens owing to reduction to metallic silver. Various derivatives of phosphorous acid containing P—O—P bonds are known,

e.g. diphosphorous or pyrophosphorous acid.

Phosphorus, P. At.no. 15, At.wt. 30·979. A non-metallic element existing in several allotropic forms. The most reactive form, 'white' or 'yellow' phosphorus, is a soft translucent white or yellowish-white, waxy solid, which shows a crystalline structure on fracture; d 1·857; m.p. 44·2° (the liquid readily supercools), b.p. 280·5°. Yellow phosphorus is almost insoluble in water, but soluble in carbon disulphide (in which it exists as P_4 molecules), olive oil, benzene, and other organic solvents. In the air yellow phos-phorus is phosphorescent, owing to slow oxid-ation, and it readily catches fire on slight warm-ing; it is therefore kept under water. Yellow phosphorus is highly poisonous. On standing the yellow form is slowly transformed into 'red' phosphorus, which is comparatively unreactive and non-poisonous; the change is accelerated by heating to 250° in presence of a catalyst, such as a trace of iodine. Red or violet phosphorus is a violet-red powder, sp.gr. 2·106, which vaporizes on strong heating, and on condensation gives the yellow form. It does not ignite in air below about 240°, and is insoluble in carbon disulphide. The other principal allotrope is black phosphorus, obtained from yellow phosphorus under a pres-sure of 35,000 atm. or by heating yellow phos-phorus at 220°-370° in the presence of mercury. Other supposed allotropes are probably violet phosphorus in various states of division.

Phosphorus is an essential constituent of living tissues, occurring particularly in bones as cal-cium phosphate; lecithins, which are esters of phosphoric acid, play a part in metabolic pro-cesses, and phosphorus is a necessary constituent of foods. Plants absorb phosphorus compounds from the soil, and fertilizers containing phos-phates are much used. In nature phosphorus occurs chiefly as phosphate minerals; rock phosphate and apatite are those chiefly used in phosphorus production. Elementary phos-phorus is obtained directly from phosphate rock by fusing it with sand and coke in an electric arc furnace. After dust removal the phosphorus vapour evolved is condensed to the yellow form by spraying water into it, and is subsequently stored as a liquid under water.

In its compounds phosphorus is either tri- or pentapositive but, owing to the formation of P—P bonds, compounds may appear to have other oxidation states. Elementary phosphorus is easily oxidized; strong nitric acid converts the yellow and red forms to phosphoric and phosphorous acids, respectively. Caustic alkalis attack the yellow form, but not the red form, giving phosphorus hydrides.

Most of the phosphorus produced is converted to the various phosphoric acids and their derivatives. It is, however, also used for making matches (the red form only), for producing organic phosphorus compounds and as an alloying agent for metals, e.g. phosphor bronze.

Phosphorus halides. Phosphorus forms halides of the types PX_3 (X=F, Cl, Br, I), PX_5, (X=F, Cl, Br), oxyhalides POX_3 (X=F, Cl, Br), and thiophosphoryl halides PSX_3 (X=F, Cl, Br). Tetrahalides, P_2F_4, P_2Cl_4, and P_2I_4, with a phosphorus–phosphorus bond are also known. The trihalides have pyramidal structures; PF_5 has a trigonal bipyramidal structure, whilst the other pentahalides are ionic, $PCl_4^+ PCl_6^-$ and $PBr_4^+ Br^-$ respectively. Many of these halides contain two different halogens. The fluorides are colourless gases (b.p. $PF_3 -101\cdot5°$, $PF_5 -75°$) prepared by the action of arsenic trifluoride on the corresponding phosphorus chlorides; PF_5 is also formed by the action of fluorine on phosphorus. Phosphorus trichloride is a colourless liquid, b.p. $74\cdot7°$, prepared by passing chlorine over phosphorus; excess of chlorine gives the pentachloride, a white easily-sublimed solid, which is also formed on dropping the trichloride into an atmosphere of chlorine. The tribromide (colourless liquid, b.p. $175\cdot3°$) and pentabromide (yellow crystals) are similarly prepared. The iodides, PI_3 and P_2I_4, are obtained on evaporating a solution of phosphorus and iodine in carbon disulphide. All phosphorus halides are rapidly hydrolysed by water, the hydrogen halides being evolved; the trihalides give phosphorous acid as a final product, and the pentahalides give phosphoric acid; PCl_5 gives the oxychloride $POCl_3$ as an intermediate product.

The phosphorus halides are of considerable value in organic chemistry as halogenating agents; in general, substances containing a hydroxyl group react readily with phosphorus halides, the hydroxyl group being replaced by a halogen atom. Phosphorus oxychloride, manufactured by treating a mixture of phosphorus trichloride and phosphorus pentoxide with chlorine, is of considerable commercial importance. It is used for making tricresyl phosphate,

a plasticizer, and cresyl diphenyl phosphate, a petrol additive, as well as other organic compounds.

Phosphorus hydrides. The principal hydride of phosphorus is phosphine, PH_3, a colourless gas, b.p. $-87\cdot7°$, m.p. $-133\cdot5°$, slightly soluble in water; as normally prepared the gas is spontaneously inflammable in air and has a strong fishy odour. It is formed by the action of water on calcium phosphide, Ca_3P_2, or by heating yellow phosphorus with caustic alkali solution; the latter method also gives much hydrogen. A purer gas which is not spontaneously inflammable is prepared by warming phosphonium iodide with caustic alkali solution. Phosphine is decomposed to its elements by heating to 450° in the absence of oxygen; combustion of the gas in air or oxygen gives white fumes of phosphorus oxides. It reacts with solutions of many metallic salts, precipitating the corresponding phosphides. Phosphine also resembles its analogue, ammonia, in forming phosphonium salts, and in forming complexes with many metallic salts. The alkylphosphines, in which the hydrogen atoms are replaced by alkyl groups, also give complexes. The spontaneous inflammability of impure phosphine is due to the presence of traces of diphosphine, P_2H_4, a liquid of b.p. 52°, which may be condensed out in a freezing mixture. Phosphine has been used for fumigating crops against insects and rodents. Yellow solid hydrides of phosphorus have been described, but they probably consist of mixtures of phosphine and yellow phosphorus.

Phosphorus oxides. *Phosphorus trioxide* (phosphorous oxide), P_4O_6. A white waxy crystalline solid, possessing an odour of garlic, m.p. $23\cdot8°$, b.p. $175\cdot8°$; it is soluble in carbon disulphide, benzene, etc. Phosphorus trioxide is prepared by burning phosphorus in a limited supply of air, the product being condensed in a cooled tube. In air it oxidizes readily at normal temperatures, and inflames at about 70°, giving the pentoxide; it also catches fire in chlorine, a mixture of phosphorus oxychlorides being formed. The trioxide dissolves slowly in cold water or alkalis, giving phosphorous acid, H_3PO_3, or one of its salts; with hot water a violent reaction occurs, with formation of phosphine and phosphoric acid, H_3PO_4. The molecule contains a tetrahedron of phosphorus atoms with an oxygen at the centre of each edge.

Phosphorus dioxide, PO_2. A white crystalline solid which sublimes at 180° in a vacuum, and is generally prepared by heating the trioxide in a sealed tube; the dioxide sublimes on to a cooled portion of the tube, leaving a residue of red phosphorus. The vapour density at high temperatures indicates the formula P_8O_{16}. With water a mixture of phosphorous and phosphoric acids is formed (compare nitrogen dioxide).

Phosphorus pentoxide (*Phosphoric oxide* or *anhydride*), P_4O_{10}. A voluminous white powder, subliming at 350°, prepared by burning phosphorus in an adequate supply of air or oxygen; unlike the trioxide it is not readily soluble in organic solvents, and is odourless. Phosphorus pentoxide exhibits an exceedingly strong affinity for water, with which it combines initially to form metaphosphoric acid, $(HPO_3)_n$; it is therefore much used as an efficient drying agent for gases. The pentoxide also withdraws the elements of water from certain oxy-acids and other compounds containing oxygen and hydrogen (e.g. nitric acid on heating with phosphorus pentoxide gives nitrogen pentoxide, N_2O_5; acetamide, CH_3CONH_2, gives acetonitrile, CH_3CN). With excess of water the pentoxide gives metaphosphoric acid, which is converted successively to pyro- and orthophosphoric acids, on standing or on boiling. The structure is very similar to that of phosphorus trioxide but with an extra oxygen coordinated to each phosphorus atom.

Phosphorus sulphides. The sulphides P_4S_{10}, P_4S_7, P_4S_5, and P_4S_3 are yellow solids prepared by heating red phosphorus with sulphur in suitable proportions. The sulphide P_4S_3 is used in the manufacture of safety matches. Phosphorus pentasulphide, P_4S_{10}, is used in the preparation of organic sulphur derivatives.

Phosphorylase. The enzymes which catalyze the breakdown or synthesis of certain polysaccharides plus phosphate, to or from glucose-1-phosphate are called phosphorylases. They are widely distributed in plant and animal tissues. The enzyme from most animal tissues synthesizes a polysaccharide resembling glycogen, but muscle phosphorylase, like plant phosphorylases, synthesizes an amylose, which gives an X-ray diffraction pattern similar to that of the natural plant product. A phosphorylase producing a synthetic amylopectin has been isolated from potato juice. The phosphorylases are proteins with adenylic acid as the probable prosthetic group.

Phosphoryl halides. Phosphorus oxyhalides. See Phosphorus halides.

Phosphotungstic acids. A group of complex acids, such as $H_3PW_{12}O_{40}$, the salts of which have many molecules of water of crystallization. The structures of the anions are built up by the sharing of oxygens of WO_6 octahedra with other octahedra and with a central PO_4 tetrahedron.

Phosvitin. A polyphosphorylated protein isolated from egg yolk.

Photochemistry. The science dealing with chemical reactions brought about by the action of light. The first principle of photochemistry states that only light which is absorbed by the system can possibly produce chemical effects; any light which passes through the material or is scattered is necessarily ineffective. Consequently, it is essential to determine the absorption spectrum of the substances concerned and to identify the spectral regions responsible for the reaction. The second principle is that absorption of light is a quantum process. The primary step in a photochemical reaction is therefore the absorption of a quantum of light energy by a particular atom, molecule or ion which is thereby raised to an 'excited state' containing an excess quantum of energy equal to hv, (where h is Planck's constant and v is the frequency of the light absorbed). Only electronic excitation can bring about chemical reaction and therefore radiation in the far infra-red region is ineffective. Photochemical reactions are generally noticed with visible or ultra-violet radiation, the latter being the more powerful. The following table indicates the energy quanta of the light in different spectral regions, expressed in kilocalories per mole.

Region	Far u.v.	Near u.v.	Blue	Red	Near i.r.
Wave length (Å)	1000	3000	4000	7000	10,000
Energy (kcal/mole)	284	95	71	41	28

Radiation in the far ultra-violet is therefore powerful enough to break any chemical bond: e.g. oxygen gas is dissociated into oxygen atoms, the photochemical reaction being written

$$O_2(g) + hv \rightarrow 2O$$

However, not all photochemical reactions involve actual dissociation of molecules into atoms; many proceed by way of electronically excited molecules. An excited molecule may return to its ground state within about 10^{-4} sec while emitting its absorbed energy as fluorescence or passing it on to neighbouring molecules as thermal energy; in these cases no photochemical reaction is produced. In some cases, however, the excited molecule is capable of undergoing reaction, the light supplying the activation energy needed to induce reaction.

455

After the primary step in a photochemical reaction, the secondary processes may be quite complicated—for example, when atoms and free radicals are formed. Consequently the 'quantum yield', i.e. the number of molecules which are caused to react for a single quantum of light absorbed, is only exceptionally equal to exactly unity. For example, the quantum yield of the decomposition of methyl iodide by ultraviolet light is only about 10^{-2} because some of the free radicals formed re-combine. On the other hand, the quantum yield of the reaction of $H_2 + Cl_2$ is 10^4 to 10^6 (and the mixture may explode) because this is a chain reaction.

The absorbed light in this case acts as catalyst for a spontaneous reaction, but in other cases it may supply energy to make possible a reaction which, without light, would be thermodynamically impossible. In some cases, such a reaction reverses itself by thermal reaction (e.g. if left in the dark) and, hence, during irradiation a *photostationary state* is reached.

The light producing a photochemical reaction is most commonly absorbed by one of the reactants, but many examples are known where energy absorbed by another species is passed to the reactants; this is the phenomenon of *photosensitization*.

Photoconduction. Certain substances, notably selenium, are poor conductors of electricity in the dark, but are much better conductors when exposed to light. This phenomenon, known as photoconduction, is due to the liberation of electrons under the influence of light and is the basis of some commercial photocopying processes.

Photodissociation. When a molecule absorbs a quantum of radiation it may dissociate into smaller molecules, or into atoms. Thus, acetone absorbs light and is split up into methyl radicals and carbon monoxide:

$$(CH_3)_2CO \rightarrow 2CH_3 + CO.$$

Such a dissociation, induced by light, is called photodissociation.

Photo-electric cells. When certain elements, particularly the alkali metals, are exposed to light of a suitable wavelength, electrons are emitted, the intensity of the emission being proportional to the intensity of the incident light. This process, known as the photo-electric effect, can be made the basis of an instrument for measuring light intensity. Such a photo-electric cell consists essentially of an evacuated glass bulb coated over a part of the inner surface with a suitable substance, e.g. caesium, and provided with an insulated electrode mounted in the middle of the bulb. The strength of the current flowing between the caesium and the insulated electrode

over the evacuated space in the bulb is a measure of the intensity of the incident radiation.

Photographic developers. Developers used in photography are reducing agents which can either be inorganic or organic compounds. Not all reducing agents can be used as developers, as many show no discrimination in activity between exposed and unexposed halide grains while others are not energetic enough to reduce the exposed crystals. Many useful developers are vinylogues (commonly aromatic) of hydrogen peroxide, hydroxylamine, hydrazine and its alkyl and aryl derivatives.

Photographic fog. Fog is the term used to describe the density (usually unwanted) which results from the development of silver halide grains which have not been exposed to light.

Photographic gelatin. Specially selected gelatins are still the essential media for photographic silver halide emulsions. No attempts to date to replace photographic gelatin by synthetic media have been entirely successful. It has several desirable photographic properties, in addition to that of being a protective colloid for the emulsion grains. It enhances emulsion sensitivity by providing sulphur sensitizers and allowing Ostwald ripening to occur during the digestion process. It also has restraining, stabilizing and anti-fogging properties. Gelatin permits free access to the grains by aqueous processing solutions. It can also be cross-linked by inorganic or organic hardeners to improve its handling characteristics, or reacted with, for example, acid chlorides or anhydrides to provide derivatives with novel properties.

Photo-lithography. The mechanical printing process involving the use of a photographically-prepared printing plate, on which the image areas are oleophilic (non-aqueous, ink receptive) and the non-image areas are hydrophilic (water receptive, ink repellant). The plate is generally made of grained aluminium or zinc, on which is coated the light-sensitive material. Before the current pre-coated materials were available, plates were coated for example with a dichromated colloid, on a mechanical whirler. After exposure the plate was inked, and then developed in water to wash off the unhardened unexposed areas.

Photoluminescence. A general term applied to the emission of light as a result of an initial light absorption. It embraces the phenomena of fluorescence and phosphorescence (*q.v.*).

Photolysis. The decomposition or reaction of a substance or substances on exposure to light. Thus the light-induced chlorination of methane involves the photolysis of chlorine molecules to chlorine atoms. The wavelength of light required to produce photolysis depends on the energy of the bond to be broken but is generally in the range 2000-8000 Å.

Photon. A quantum of light energy. For light of frequency v the energy contained in one photon is hv (h being Planck's constant).

Photosensitization. A process in which a photochemical reaction is induced to occur by the presence of a substance (the photosensitizer) which absorbs the light but itself is substantially

exposed to light of a suitable wavelength. The original colour returns in the dark, and the reversion is accelerated by heating. The phenomenon was first noticed in tetrachloro-α-ketonaphthalene, which is normally white, but which reddens on illumination. Some inorganic compounds are phototropic, notably a large series of mercury complexes, some of which show very marked and rapid changes.

Phrenosin, Cerebron, $C_{48}H_{93}NO_9$. A white

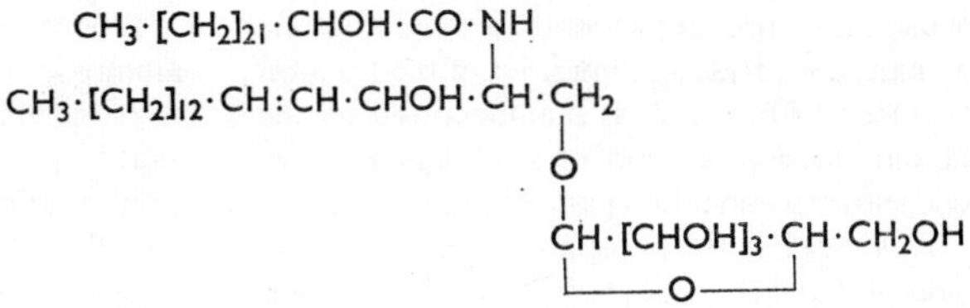

$$CH_3 \cdot [CH_2]_{21} \cdot CHOH \cdot CO \cdot NH$$
$$CH_3 \cdot [CH_2]_{12} \cdot CH:CH \cdot CHOH \cdot CH \cdot CH_2$$
$$O$$
$$CH \cdot [CHOH]_3 \cdot CH \cdot CH_2OH$$
$$\underline{\qquad O \qquad}$$

unchanged at the end of the reaction, the absorbed light energy being passed on to the main reactants. E.g. when hydrogen is exposed to light of wavelength 2536 Å, no absorption of the light occurs, and the hydrogen remains completely unaffected. If mercury vapour is added to the hydrogen, the mercury atoms absorb the radiation, and thus become rich in energy. When such an excited mercury atom collides with a hydrogen molecule, it can transfer some of its energy to the hydrogen, and cause it to dissociate into atoms:

$$Hg^* + H_2 = Hg + 2H$$

The hydrogen has apparently been made sensitive to the light which it does not absorb.

Photostationary state. In chemistry, a stationary state is identical with a state of equilibrium under specified conditions. In a photochemical reaction, a stationary state obtains when the rate of removal of the reactants by light is just balanced by the rate of recombination or reaction of the products to yield the original reactants. This condition is referred to as a photostationary state.

Photosynthesis. Synthesis brought about by the action of light, for example the formation of hydrogen chloride by exposing a mixture of hydrogen and chlorine to sunlight. The most important photosynthetic reaction is that by which green plants incorporate carbon dioxide, and thereby build up first sucrose and then the carbon compounds from which all living matter is made. Plant photosynthesis is effected by a complex cycle of reactions. See M. Calvin, *J. Chem. Soc.*, 1956, 1895.

Phototropy. A term introduced by Marckwald (1899) to denote the reversible change of colour which certain organic substances undergo when

powder, m.p. about 212°, soluble in hot alcohol, insoluble in cold alcohol and ether, $[\alpha]_D^{20} +3.7°$. Phrenosin is one of the cerebrosides, and is present in brain and nervous tissue. On hydrolysis it gives D-galactose, sphingosine, and phrenosinic acid.

Phrenosinic acid, Cerebronic acid. A dull white powder, m.p. 100°-101°, $[\alpha]_D^{22} +3.33°$. It is obtained on hydrolysis of phrenosin, and is α-hydroxylignoceric acid,

$$CH_3 \cdot [CH_2]_{21} \cdot CHOH \cdot COOH.$$

Phthalamide, $C_8H_8N_2O_2$. Colourless crystals; on heating to 200°-210° melts with decomposition into phthalimide and ammonia. Very slightly soluble in water and alcohol, insoluble in ether.

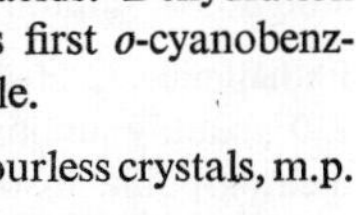

Prepared by stirring phthalimide with cold concentrated ammonia solution. Hydrolysed to phthalic acid with dilute acids. Dehydration with acetic anhydride gives first o-cyanobenzamide and then phthalonitrile.

Phthalic acid, $C_8H_6O_4$. Colourless crystals, m.p. 190°-210°, depending upon rate of heating. At its melting-point it decomposes into water and phthalic anhydride. Readily soluble in hot water, much less so in cold. Soluble in alcohol, sparingly soluble in ether.

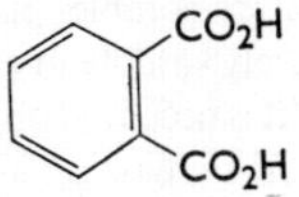

Prepared by oxidation of naphthalene or o-xylene, or by alkaline hydrolysis of phthalic anhydride.

It is a dibasic acid, and forms stable metallic salts. Distillation with soda lime gives benzene. Readily dehydrated to phthalic anhydride. Its reactions are the same as for phthalic anhydride (*q.v.*) in which form it is almost invariably used.

Phthalic anhydride, $C_8H_4O_3$. Long silky needles, m.p. 130°, b.p. 284°. Sparingly soluble in cold water, more readily in hot, being slowly converted into phthalic acid. Soluble in alcohol and ether. Sublimes rapidly below its m.p.; this is the most convenient method of purification.

Prepared by the oxidation of naphthalene with sulphuric acid at 270°-300° in the presence of mercuric sulphate; under these conditions the phthalic anhydride sublimes out of the reaction mixture as formed. It is manufactured by the vapour phase oxidation of naphthalene or *o*-xylene over a vanadium pentoxide catalyst.

Treatment with phosphorus pentachloride gives phthalyl chloride; reduction with zinc and acetic acid gives phthalide. Fusion with urea gives phthalimide.

It is a valuable dyestuffs intermediate. It can be condensed with benzene and aluminium chloride to give anthraquinone. This general reaction is much used for preparing substituted anthraquinones. With phenols and a condensing agent phthalic anhydride gives rise to phthalein dyestuffs, e.g. phenolphthalein, eosin. It also condenses with quinaldine derivatives to give 'quinoline' dyes. However, the chief commercial uses of phthalic anhydride are in the manufacture of dialkyl phthalate plasticizers and alkyd resins.

Phthalic esters. Because of their low vapour pressures and chemical stability, various esters of phthalic acid such as diethyl (b.p. 298°), dibutyl (b.p. 340°) and di-*n*-octyl (b.p. 248°) are used as plasticizers. The dimethyl and dibutyl esters are also used as insect repellants. They are all manufactured by reacting phthalic anhydride with the alcohol in the presence of catalytic amounts of sulphuric acid.

Phthalimide, $C_8H_5NO_2$. Colourless plates, m.p. 230°, readily sublimes at its melting-point. Insoluble in water, soluble in alcohol, barely soluble in ether.

It is prepared on the large scale by passing ammonia into molten phthalic anhydride. Also obtained by melting together urea and phthalic anhydride.

Phthalimide dissolves in alkalis to give at first N-metal derivatives, but on warming the solution the ring opens, and salts of phthalamic acid are obtained. Reduced to phthalide with zinc and caustic soda solution: prolonged hydrolysis with acids or alkalis gives phthalic acid or its salts. Treatment with concentrated ammonia solution gives phthalamide.

When treated with alkaline hypochlorite solution anthranilic acid is obtained. This reaction, the first stage in the indigo synthesis, is the most important commercial outlet for phthalimide.

Phthalocyanines. An important class of organic colouring matters capable of general application as pigments and of more limited use as dyestuffs. They are characterized by their great fastness and brilliance of shade. The shades are green to blue in colour.

They can be prepared by three general methods:

1. Heating phthalic anhydride with urea (or ammonia) and a metallic salt.
2. Heating *o*-cyanobenzamide with a metallic salt.
3. Heating phthalonitrile with a metal or metallic salt.

Depending upon the metallic compound used, different metallic phthalocyanine derivatives are obtained, e.g. when copper chloride is used copper phthalocyanine (Monastral Fast Blue B) is obtained; when sodium amyloxide is used sodium phthalocyanine is obtained from which the sodium can be removed by acid treatment to give metal-free phthalocyanine (Monastral Fast Blue G). Lead phthalocyanine is a bright green colour.

The parent metal-free phthalocyanine can also be prepared by elimination by acids of the metal from some of the other metallic phthalocyanines, e.g. lead, magnesium, manganese phthalocyanines.

The phthalocyanines must be suitably dispersed to be used as pigments or they can be sulphonated to water-soluble forms for dyeing and for precipitation as lakes. The dispersion is carried out by solution in sulphuric acid, followed by precipitation in water.

The phthalocyanine molecule is remarkably stable to heat and chemical reagents. The metal-free and heavy metal compounds sublime practically unchanged at 550°-580°.

Structurally, the molecule is formed by the union of one atom of the metal with four mole-

cules of phthalonitrile. Copper phthalocyanine is typical, and has the formula $C_{32}H_{16}CuN_8$.

The other phthalocyanines are derived from

the above by replacement of the copper atom by two atoms of a monopositive or by one atom of a dipositive metal.

Phthalonitrile, $C_8H_4N_2$. Colourless needles, m.p. 140°, b.p. 290°. Readily soluble in alcohol and benzene, slightly soluble in hot water. It can be distilled without decomposition at atmospheric pressure. Slowly hydrolysed to phthalic acid by dilute acids and alkalis.

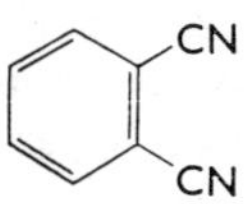

It can be obtained by dehydration of *o*-cyanobenzamide or phthalamide with acetic acid. On a larger scale the dehydration is better carried out by means of phosgene in pyridine solution. Another suitable method is to pass a mixture of ammonia and phthalimide over a catalyst at 350°-450°.

It is an important intermediate for the preparation of phthalocyanine pigments into which it is converted by heating with metallic salts.

Phthalylsulphathiazole, $C_{17}H_{13}N_3O_5S_2$. Prepared by the interaction of sulphathiazole and phthalic anhydride. It is a white crystalline powder almost insoluble in water, readily soluble in aqueous alkali hydroxides and in hydrochloric

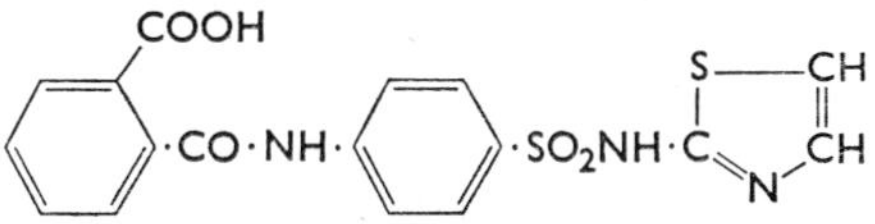

acid. It is used to reduce the bacterial content of the large intestine, e.g. in the acute phase of bacillary dysentery.

Phthiocol, 2-methyl-3-hydroxy-1,4-naphthaquinone, $C_{11}H_8O_3$. Crystallizes in yellow prisms,

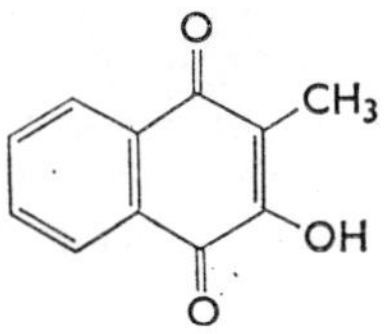

m.p. 173°-174°. Insoluble in water. Soluble in hot alcohol, in ether, and in alkalis, in which it has a deep red colour. Phthiocol is a pigment obtained from tubercle bacilli. It has been synthesized by treating 2-methylnaphthaquinone with bleaching powder and acidifying with sulphuric acid. It can readily be reduced and reoxidized. Phthiocol has, to a lesser degree, the

antihaemorrhagic property of vitamin **K** and may be a breakdown product of one of the **K** vitamins.

Phthioic acids, phthienoic acids. A group of branched-chain fatty acids isolated from mycobacteria. The term is chiefly used for acids ranging from C_{22} to C_{28}, while the term 'mycolic acid' generally refers to hydroxy-acids of higher molecular weight, also found in mycobacteria, and derived by coupling two or more molecules of fatty acid. An example of a phthienoic acid is the physiologically active C_{27}-acid, mycolipenic acid, from virulent strains of tubercle bacilli; it is

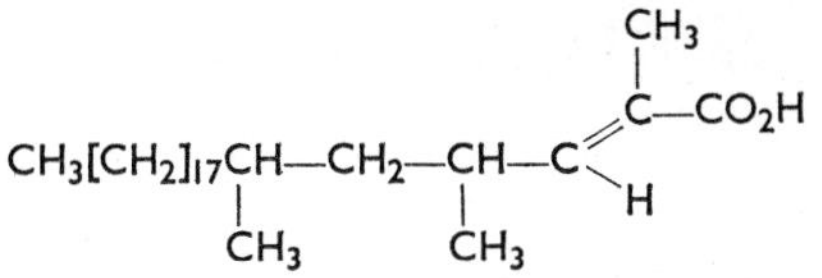

trans-2,4,6-trimethyl-2-tetracosenoic acid.

Phyllins. See Chlorophyll.

Physalaemin. A linear peptide isolated from amphibian skin: the structure has been confirmed by synthesis:

Tyr.Ala.Asp.Pro.Asp.Lys.Phe.Tyr.Gly.Leu.Met.

Physalaemin is one of the most potent of known vasodilators—about three times as active as eledoisin and more than a hundred times as active as bradykinin.

Physalien, $C_{72}H_{116}O_4$. A pigment occurring in *Physalis franchetti* and *Lycium halifolium*. It is zeaxanthin dipalmitate, and crystallizes in dark red long flat rods or prisms, m.p. 99°. Soluble in ether and benzene, almost insoluble in alcohol.

Physical development. Physical development is the term applied in photography to the process in which a soluble silver complex present in the developer solution is reduced by the developing agent to metallic silver which is deposited on the latent image nuclei on the exposed halide grains. Alternatively, the silver can be deposited on minute particles of a heavy metal or other foreign particle dispersed in a suitable carrier.

Physostigmine, Eserine, $C_{15}H_{21}N_3O_2$. A laevorotatory alkaloid obtained from Calabar bean, one of the 'ordeal' poisons from the west coast of Africa. The salicylate and sulphate are employed in ophthalmic practice to contract the pupil of the eye and to overcome the dilatation caused by atropine, homatropine, and cocaine.

It is occasionally administered by hypodermic injection for tetanus and in intestinal obstruction.

Phytanic acid, $C_{20}H_{40}O_2$. 3,7,11,15-Tetramethyl-hexadecanoic acid, a diterpenoid acid found in bovine plasma phospholipids.

$$(CH_3)_2CHCH_2CH_2\cdot[CH_2CH\cdot CH_2CH_2]_2\cdot CH_2CH\cdot CH_2CO_2H$$
$$\underset{CH_3}{\qquad\qquad\qquad\quad}\underset{CH_3}{\qquad\qquad}$$

Phytic acid, $C_6H_6(OPO(OH)_2)_6$. *Meso*-inositol hexaphosphoric acid, a water-soluble syrup, sparingly soluble in organic solvents and strongly acidic. Occurs as its insoluble calcium magnesium salt, phytin, in seeds. It is also found in blood plasma phospholipids and in the erythrocytes of chicken blood.

Phytin. $Ca_5Mg(C_6H_{12}O_{24}P_6\cdot 3H_2O)_2$ (approx.). A trade name for phytic acid calcium magnesium salt. It is widely distributed in plant seeds and is conveniently obtained from corn steep liquor. It is used medicinally as a source of phosphate.

Phytochemistry. The chemistry of compounds associated with plants.

Phytol, $C_{20}H_{40}O$. A diterpenic alcohol obtained

$$CH_3\cdot[CH\cdot CH_2\cdot CH_2\cdot CH_2]_3\cdot C:CH\cdot CH_2OH$$
$$\underset{CH_3}{\qquad\qquad}\underset{CH_3}{\qquad\qquad\qquad}$$

by the action of alkalis on chlorophyll. A colourless oil with the following constants: d_4^{25} 0·8491, n_D^{25} 1·4623, b.p. 202·5°-204°/10 mm. On oxidation it yields a ketone $C_{18}H_{36}O$ of b.p. 174·8°-175·2° at 11 mm, which in turn gives a semicarbazone of m.p. 67°.

Phytosterols. Sterols of plants, e.g. β-sitosterol, campesterol, stigmasterol (all widely distributed), 24-methylenecholesterol (the principal sterol of pollen), yeast sterols such as ergosterol. Cholesterol is not a typical phytosterol, but is not confined to animals as was formerly supposed.

Pi-bonding, π-bonding. Overlap of orbitals such that the actual overlap occurs in two volumes in space for the one bond, e.g. a *p—p* bond

points of overlap

Pickling. The term given to the process of immersing metal sheets, rods, castings, etc., in a bath of either dilute sulphuric or hydrochloric acid for a short period, followed by washing in water. It is carried out to obtain a clean scale-free surface, such as is required on sheet iron before galvanizing.

Picolines, C_6H_7N. The picolines are methyl-pyridines. They are found with pyridine in bone oil and coal tar.

α-Picoline has b.p. 129°, d_4^{15} 0·9497; β-picoline has b.p. 144°, d_4^{25}0·9515; γ-picoline has b.p. 143°, d_4^{15} 0·9571. All are miscible with water and most other solvents. α-Picoline is used in the manufacture of the monomer 2-vinylpyridine,

β-picoline for nicotinic acid, and γ-picoline for isoniazid.

Picramic acid, $C_6H_5N_3O_5$. Crystallizes in red

needles, m.p. 168°-169°. Insoluble in cold water, easily in hot. Soluble in dilute acids and alkalis.

It is prepared by reduction of picric acid with sodium hydrogen sulphide.

It is used for the preparation of azo-dyes, which can be 'after-chromed' by treatment with metallic salts owing to the presence of a hydroxyl group ortho to the amino-group.

Picrates. Derivatives (salts) of picric acid, i.e. $X^{\oplus}[OC_6H_2(NO_2)_3]^{\ominus}$. A convenient method of characterization of basic organic compounds, i.e. amines, involves the preparation of picrates which are usually crystalline solids with sharp melting points. Some picrates, especially of metals, explode on heating. Aromatic hydrocarbons form charge transfer complexes with picric acid, also known as picrates.

Picric acid, Trinitrophenol, $C_6H_2OH\cdot(NO_2)_3$. Bright yellow crystals, prepared usually by the nitration of phenolsulphonic acid; m.p. 122°. Readily soluble in benzene or alcohol, sparingly soluble in water. It is used in the dyeing industry

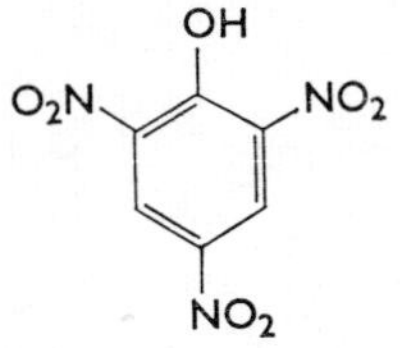

and also as an explosive. Is not very sensitive but attacks metals and can form metallic picrates which are very sensitive to shock. Because of this and other disadvantages, it has largely been replaced by other materials as a high explosive. In the cast form it is known as Lyddite.

Picrolonic acid, $C_{10}H_8N_4O_5$. Crystallizes in fine

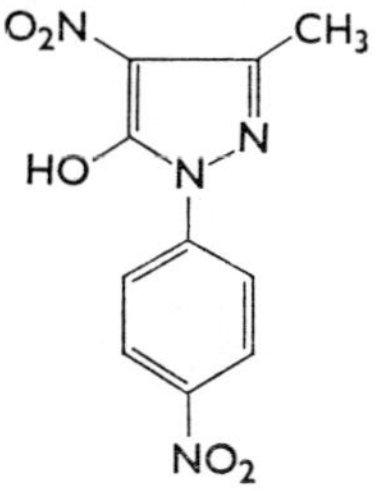

yellow needles, m.p. 116·5°. Slightly soluble in water and alcohol; more soluble in boiling methyl alcohol. Decomposed at temperatures above its melting-point. Its calcium, copper, and lead salts are insoluble in water. Forms crystalline compounds with many organic bases; these compounds are usually sparingly soluble in water or dilute alcohol and have sharply defined melting-points. Used for the isolation and identification of organic bases, and in tests for calcium, copper, and lead.

Pictet, Amé (1857-1937). Pictet was educated in his native city of Geneva, at the Polytechnikum at Dresden, and at Bonn. In 1880 he became an assistant to Graebe at Geneva, and after a short visit to Paris became a Privatdozent in 1882. In 1894 he was appointed extraordinary professor of organic chemistry, in 1899 ordinary professor of pharmaceutical, biological, and toxicological chemistry, and in 1906 he occupied the chair of general chemistry and became director of the laboratories. He retired in 1932. His work dealt with the vegetable alkaloids, with the low-pressure distillation of coal, and with the sugars.

Piezoelectricity. The electric charge developed in anisotropic crystals when subjected to stress.

Pig iron is the product obtained from a blast furnace. The molten metal from the furnace is run into sand moulds. The liquid iron runs from the main channel into channels at right angles termed 'sows', each of which feeds a series of 'pigs'. These pigs are of semicircular section and are 3 to 4 in. wide and about 3 ft. long. The terms pig iron and cast iron are sometimes used for the same material, but 'cast iron' refers to pig iron that has been remelted and cast to a finished shape.

Pilocarpine, $C_{11}H_{16}N_2O_2$. A colourless oil,

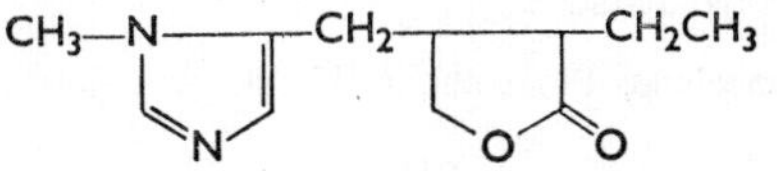

b.p. 260°/5 mm. Soluble in water and alcohol; $[\alpha]_D^{20}$ +100·5°. One of the alkaloids obtained from the leaves of various species of *Jaborandi*. It acts on the nerve endings of the secretory cells causing increased secretion of sweat and saliva, but is now rarely used systemically owing to its depressant action on the heart. Pilocarpine nitrate is used as a miotic in 1% aqueous solution.

Pimaric acid. See Dextropimaric acid.

Pimelic acid, $C_7H_{12}O_4$, HOOC·$[CH_2]_5$·COOH. Colourless prisms, m.p. 105°. Soluble up to 5% in cold water, also soluble in alcohol. It is present in castor oil. It can be prepared from pentamethylene chloride via the nitrile and by the reduction of salicylic acid.

Pinachrome, $C_{27}H_{31}IN_2O_2$. A 2,4'-cyanine

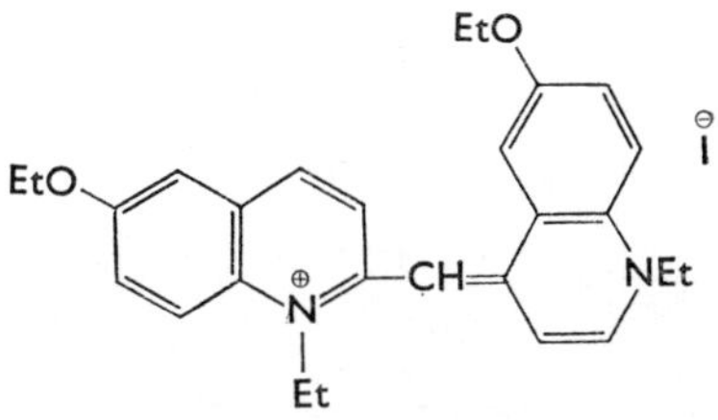

related to Ethyl Red, but with absorption and spectral sensitization bands shifted to longer wavelengths. This violet dye has been used as a green sensitizer for ortho plates, and in combination with a red sensitizer in pan-sensitized plates. It is prepared by the action of alkali on a hot solution of the ethiodides of 6-ethoxyquinoline and 6-ethoxyquinaldine.

Pinacol, Pinacone, $C_6H_{14}O_2$. A colourless,

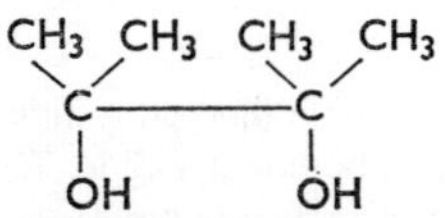

crystalline substance, m.p. 38°, b.p. 175°. Sparingly soluble in cold water; soluble in hot water, alcohol, and ether. Crystallizes from water as a hexahydrate melting at 47°. Prepared by treating a mixture of acetone and benzene with magnesium amalgam. Water is added when the reaction is over, and the benzene layer, on concentration, deposits crystals of pinacol hydrate. When heated with sulphuric acid, it forms pinacolone. Dimethylbutadiene is formed when the vapour of pinacol is passed over alumina at 400°. Used in the manufacture of dimethylbutadiene.

Pinacolone, Pinacolin, $C_6H_{12}O$. A colourless

$$CH_3-\underset{\underset{CH_3}{|}}{\overset{\overset{CH_3}{|}}{C}}-\underset{\overset{||}{O}}{C}-CH_3$$

liquid with a camphor-like odour, d^{16} 0·7999, b.p. 103°-106°/746 mm. Insoluble in water; miscible with alcohol and ether. Prepared by heating pinacol hydrate with sulphuric acid and distilling the mixture. It is reduced to pinacolyl alcohol and oxidized to trimethylacetic acid.

Pinacol-pinacolone rearrangement. When heated with mineral or organic acids, pinacols undergo a molecular rearrangement with loss of water to give ketones known as pinacolones. The change involves the loss of one hydroxyl group, as a neutral water molecule derived from the protonated pinacol, followed by an intramolecular migration of an alkyl group in the carbonium ion thus formed, and loss of a proton from the remaining hydroxyl group to give a ketone.

Pinacols. 1,2-Glycols of the type where R_1, R_2,

$$\underset{\underset{OH}{|}}{\overset{\overset{R_1}{|}}{C}}\underset{\underset{OH}{|}}{\overset{\overset{R_2\ R_3}{|}\ \ \ \overset{R_4}{|}}{C}}$$

etc., are alkyl or aryl radicals. They are formed by reducing aromatic ketones with zinc and dilute acid, or from aliphatic ketones by reduction with magnesium amalgam.

Pinacone. See Pinacol.

Pinacyanol, $C_{25}H_{25}IN_2$. A trimethinecyanine

prepared from quinaldine ethiodide with ethyl orthoformate in boiling pyridine. This blue dye was the first red sensitizer used in a number of early pan-sensitized plates. It can be supersensitized by auramine.

Pinaflavol, $C_{17}H_{21}IN_2$. A purple styryl dye prepared from α-picoline ethiodide and p-dimethylaminobenzaldehyde in ethanol, in the presence of a base such as piperidine. A powerful

sensitizer for the green and yellow spectral regions, especially useful together with a red sensitizer for the preparation of pan-sensitized plates.

Pinakryptol green, isophenosafranine,

$C_{18}H_{15}ClN_4$. A dull green dye isomeric with phenosafranine, prepared by the reductive cyclization of the reaction product from picryl chloride and o-aminodiphenylamine. It is a powerful desensitizer, with little residual stain. See Desensitization.

Pinakryptol yellow, $C_{20}H_{19}ClN_2O_3$. A styryl dye

crystallizing in yellow needles, soluble in water, and prepared from 6-ethoxy-1,2-dimethyl-quinolinium chloride with m-nitrobenzaldehyde in alcohol, in the presence of a base. It is a powerful desensitizer. See Desensitization.

Pinane, $C_{10}H_{18}$. A saturated hydrocarbon produced by the catalytic hydrogenation of α- or β-pinene. It can exist in both *cis*- and *trans*-forms. By reducing (−)-α-pinene with hydrogen and a nickel catalyst at 220°–230° *trans*-(−)-pinane was obtained of b.p. 162°-164°/720 mm, $d^{17·5}$ 0·8519, $n_D^{17·5}$ 1·45952, $[\alpha]_D$ −16·1. By reducing in the presence of platinum black at ordinary temperatures (−)-α-pinene formed *cis*-(−)-pinane, b.p. 164·8°-165·8°/716 mm, d^{20} 0·8562, n_D^{20} 1·4624, $[\alpha]_D$ −18·9°. Pinane is very stable to mineral acids and to oxidizing agents.

α-Pinene, $C_{10}H_{16}$. A dicyclic terpene. The most important of the terpene hydro-carbons. It is found in most essen-tial oils derived from the *Coniferae*, and is the main constituent of tur-pentine oil. As it contains two asymmetric carbon atoms, the hydrocarbon separated from various essential oils varies greatly in optical rotatory power, and it is difficult to obtain pure. The following constants probably relate to almost pure specimens: m.p. $-50°$, b.p. $156°$, d^{15} 0·8620, n_D^{12} 0·14650, $[\alpha]_D$ $\pm 48·85°$. (+)-α-Pinene is found in American, German, Russian, and Swedish turpentine oils, and $(-)$-α-pinene in French turpentine oil and English pine-needle oil. The (+)-form is easily obtained in a pure state by fractionation of Greek turpentine oil, of which it constitutes 95%. Pinene may be sepa-rated from turpentine oil in the form of its crystalline nitrosochloride, $C_{10}H_{16}ClNO$, from which the ($\pm$)-form may be recovered by boiling with aniline in alcoholic solution. When heated under pressure at 250°-270°, α-pinene is con-verted into dipentene. It can be reduced by hydrogen in the presence of a catalyst to form pinane. It is oxidized by air or oxygen, both wet and dry. With moist air it forms sobrerol, $C_{10}H_{18}O_2$, which forms the oxide pinol by the action of weak mineral acids.

By oxidation with permanganate it forms pinonic acid, $C_{10}H_{16}O_3$, a monobasic acid de-rived from cyclobutane. With strong sulphuric acid it forms a mixture of limonene, dipentene, terpinolene, terpinene, camphene, and *p*-cymene. When gaseous hydrogen chloride is passed into turpentine oil a crystalline substance separates, which is known as 'artificial camphor' and can also be formed by passing hydrogen chloride into solutions of oil of turpentine in various solvents. It has the composition $C_{10}H_{17}Cl$, and consists of bornyl chloride, derived from α-pinene by intra-molecular change. α-Pinene reacts with picric acid in benzene solution to form a mixture of bornyl picrate and fenchyl picrate.

β-Pinene, Nopinene, $C_{10}H_{16}$. α-Pinene in nature is usually accompanied by smaller but variable amounts of $(-)$-β-pinene. Natural (+)-β-pinene has only been found in one oil, ex-tracted from the ripe fruits of *Ferula galbaniflua*. β-Pinene yields no crystalline derivatives. It shows the constants: b.p. 162°-163°, d^{15} 0·874, n_D^{15} 0·4872, $[\alpha]_D$ $-22·4°$. On oxidation with potass-ium permanganate it forms nopinic acid, $C_{10}H_{16}O_3$, of m.p. 126°-127°.

Pinitol, $C_7H_{14}O_6$. The methyl ether of D-inositol. It is also known as matezite or sennite; it is found in residues from the manufacture of coniferin, in senna leaves, and Madagascar rubber. It has m.p. 186°, $[\alpha]_D$ $+65·5°$.

Pink salt. See Ammonium chlorostannate.

Pinnaglobulin. A brown respiratory pigment present in the blood of the lamellibranch, *Pinna squamosa*. It resembles haemocyanin, but con-tains manganese in place of copper.

Pinocampheol, $C_{10}H_{18}O$. There are four iso-meric alcohols, pinocam-pheol, *neo*pinocampheol, *iso*pinocampheol and *neoiso*pinocampheol, differ-ing only in the orientation of their methyl and hydroxyl groups. The properties listed below apply to pinocampheol. The ($\pm$)-form is formed by the reduction of ($\pm$)-pino-camphone with sodium in moist ethereal solu-tion, by the reduction of carvopinone and by the reduction of $(-)$-pinocamphone. $(-)$-Pinocam-pheol, which is found in oil of hyssop, is a crystalline solid of m.p. 67°, b.p. 217°, d_{15}^{20} 0·9725, n_D^{20} 1·4877, $[\alpha]_D$ $-72°$ (in benzene); the (+)-form has $[\alpha]_D$ $+72°$ and the constants are otherwise identical with those above. The optically active forms give a phenylurethane with m.p. 77°.

Pinocamphone, $C_{10}H_{16}O$. A dicyclic ketone, the $(-)$-form of which constitutes about 45% of oil of hyssop. The ($\pm$)-form is obtained by reduction of nitrosopinene with zinc dust in acetic acid solution. It forms pinonic acid on oxidation. $(-)$-Pinocam-phone has b.p. 211°, d^{15} 0·964, n_D^{20} 1·4728, $[\alpha]_D$ $-23°$; those of the (+)-form are identical except for the sign of the rotation. Both optically active forms give a semicarbazone with m.p. 227°.

Pinocarveol, $C_{10}H_{16}O$. A dicyclic terpene alco-hol, the $(-)$-form of which is present in the oil of *Euca-lyptus globulus*. It is also formed amongst other pro-ducts by the auto-oxidation of β-pinene. It can be iso-lated as the hydrogen phthalate and also by its compound with boric acid. $(-)$-Pinocarveol has m.p. 7°, b.p. 208°-209°, d^{20} 0·981, n^{20} 1·49961, $[\alpha]_D$ $-61·67$. The ($\pm$)-form has b.p. 215°-218°, d^{18} 0·980, n_D^{18} 1·4988. $(-)$-Pinocarveol forms a phenyl-urethane of m.p. 88°-89°, that from the ($\pm$)-form melting at 95°-96°.

Piperazine, $C_4H_{10}N_2$. The hexahydrate forms colourless crystals, m.p. 44° (104° when anhydrous), b.p. 146°; soluble in water and alcohol. Made by the action of alcoholic ammonia on ethylene chloride, piperazine is used in human and veterinary medicine in the treatment of threadworm and roundworm infestations. It is formulated as the adipate, citrate or phosphate either in tablet or in liquid form for oral administration to both children and adults.

Piperazine citrate, $(C_4H_{10}N_2)_3, 2C_6H_8O_7$, contains a variable amount of water of crystallization. It is a fine, white, granular powder, m.p. ~190°, soluble at 20° in 1·5 parts of water.

Piperidine, $C_5H_{11}N$. A colourless liquid with a characteristic ammoniacal smell; m.p. −9°, b.p. 106°, d_4^{20} 0·8606. Miscible with water. It is present in pepper as the alkaloid piperine from which it can be obtained by heating with alkali. It can also be prepared by the reduction of pyridine, either electrolytically or by other means. Piperidine is a strong base, behaving like the aliphatic amines.

Piperine, $C_{17}H_{19}NO_3$. An alkaloid present in

pepper. It crystallizes in columns, m.p. 129·5°. Insoluble in water, soluble in alcohol. Alcoholic solutions have a burning taste. It hydrolyses to piperic acid and piperidine.

Piperitol, $C_{10}H_{18}O$. An optically active, secondary terpene alcohol. (−)-Piperitol is found in various eucalyptus oils and (+)-piperitol in the oil from a species of *Andropogon*. A somewhat viscous oil of pleasant smell. The constants of the (+)-form were found to be b.p. 165°-170°/200 mm, d_{30}^{30} 0·911, n_D^{30} 1·474, $[\alpha]_D$ +46·0°, and for the (−)-form d^{22} 0·923, n_D^{22} 1·476, $[\alpha]_D$ −34·1°. It yields piperitone on oxidation with chromic acid.

Piperitone, $C_{10}H_{16}O$. An optically active terpene ketone, the (−)-form of which is found in a very large number of eucalyptus oils, and especially in oil from *Eucalyptus dives*. The (+)-form is found in Japanese peppermint oil, and in the oil from Sudan Mahareb grass. When the active forms are dis-

tilled at ordinary pressures they are partially racemized, and they are completely racemized by digestion with an alcoholic solution of potassium hydroxide or by sodium ethoxide.

Piperitone is of considerable technical importance. It is a colourless oil of a pleasant peppermint-like smell. (−)-Piperitone has the following constants: b.p. 109·5°-110·5°/15 mm, d_4^{20} 0·9324, n_D^{20} 1·4848, $[\alpha]_D^{20}$ −51·53°. Piperitone forms a mixture of two semicarbazones. From the racemic form the slightly soluble α-semicarbazone melts at 226°-227°, and the β-semicarbazone at 174°-176°. (+)-Piperitone yields an optically active α semicarbazone of m.p. 193°-194°. Piperitone yields thymol on oxidation with ferric chloride. On reduction with hydrogen in presence of a nickel catalyst it yields menthone. On reduction with sodium in alcoholic solution all forms of piperitone yield racemic menthols and *iso*menthols together with some racemic α-phellandrene.

Piperonal, $C_8H_6O_3$. White crystals, m.p. 37°,

b.p. 263°. Very slightly soluble in water, soluble in alcohol and ether.

Occurs associated with vanillin. Obtained on oxidation of various natural products such as piperine.

It is used extensively in soap perfumery.

Piperonyl butoxide, $C_{19}H_{30}O_5$. An example of an

insecticide synergist, which is often used in conjunction with pyrethrum. It is a pale yellow oil, b.p. 180°/1 mm, soluble in most organic solvents. Alone it has no insecticidal activity, but it enhances not only the insect toxicity, but also the persistency, of pyrethrum. It is non-toxic to mammals.

Pitch, Coal tar pitch. The product left behind when the more volatile portions of coal tar are distilled in intermittent or continuous stills. The physical and chemical characteristics depend upon the rank of the coal from which the tar was obtained and the temperature at which the 'cut' is made between volatile and non-volatile products during distillation (usually from 300° to 350°). In chemical composition and physical properties it resembles bitumen from petroleum deposits, but contains more oxygen and always contains a high proportion of free carbon. It is used as a binding material for road surfaces and fuel briquettes.

Pitchblende. The massive variety of uraninite. It is a heavy black mineral resembling pitch in appearance, and consists largely of uranium oxides, but thorium, cerium, lead, etc., are usually present in variable amounts. Markedly radioactive with a high specific gravity (6·4-9·7) and important as a source of uranium and radium.

Pitchstone. A volcanic glass resembling obsidian and derived from naturally-fused porphyry. It is sometimes used as a flux in coloured pottery.

Pivalic acid, $(CH_3)_3C \cdot COOH$, trimethylacetic acid. It is a colourless solid, m.p. 35·5°, b.p. 163·8°. It is prepared by the carboxylation of isobutylene with carbon monoxide in sulphuric acid or by the oxidation of pinacone with sodium hypobromite, and is an intermediate in the synthesis of various industrial products. It is esterified only with difficulty owing to the steric hindrance of the methyl groups.

Plagioclase. A sub-group of the feldspars consisting of a mixture of sodium and calcium feldspars. The crystals are triclinic; sp.gr. 2·6-2·7, hardness 6.

Planar complexes. Complexes in which the metal atom is surrounded by four ligands in a plane. The hybridization is normally considered as dsp_2. Examples are the $[Pt(NH_3)_4]^{2+}$ and $[PtCl_4]^{2-}$ ions.

Planck's constant, (h). The constant relating the energy and frequency of radiation, $E = hv$. It has the value $6·6256 \times 10^{-27}$ erg sec.

Plane of symmetry. See Symmetry elements.

Planetary electrons. The extranuclear electrons. See Electronic configuration.

Plasmalogens. A group of phospholipids of

A choline plasmalogen

animal tissues, analogous to lecithin and cephalin, and differing from these in that the acyl moiety attached to the α-hydroxyl of glycerol is replaced by a *cis*-1-unsaturated long chain alkyl; i.e. a vinyl ether group. The plasmalogens are termed choline plasmalogens, ethanolamine plasmalogens and serine plasmalogens. On hydrolysis, plasmalogens yield acetals through

attack of the liberated 2-hydroxyl group on the vinyl ether bond. Such artefacts were originally mistaken for a class of natural phospholipids ('acetal phosphatides').

Plaster. A material used to cover and produce a pleasing surface on a wall or other structure. The chief materials are (i) a mixture of lime and sand or of Portland cement and sand, and (ii) several materials consisting essentially of plaster of Paris.

Plaster of Paris. An incompletely hydrated calcium sulphate corresponding to the formula $2CaSO_4$, H_2O, produced by heating gypsum until three-quarters of the water in the latter has been driven off. The remaining water may reversibly be removed by gentle heating, but on moderately strong heating the gypsum becomes 'dead-burnt', and will no longer revert to plaster of Paris on addition of water. The setting of plaster is the result of rehydration due to the added water; it is accompanied by a slight expansion.

Plastic explosives. For special applications it is useful to have an explosive which can be moulded by hand. A number of plastic explosives exist based on cyclonite admixed with an oily or rubbery binder, depending upon the climatic conditions to which the material will be exposed.

Plasticizer. A plasticizer is a substance added to a resin (usually a thermoplastic) in order to alter its elastic and flow properties, without changing the chemical nature of the material. The normal purpose is to reduce the softening point of the plastics composition and to increase its flexibility and impact resistance, usually at the expense of its tensile strength. Plasticizers as a class are chemically stable, non-volatile solvents, typified by esters such as tricresyl phosphate, dioctyl phthalate, dibutyl sebacate, and the polymeric adipate-laurate. Not all polymers can be readily plasticized. Thus, though polyvinyl chloride can be modified by numerous plasticizers to give elastomeric materials, no suitable plasticizer has been found for polystyrene.

Plastics. The term plastics is one of commercial classification, to which no strictly scientific definition can be applied. At best a plastics material can be described as an artificial material, usually of organic origin and polymeric in structure, which at some time during its manufacture has been shaped by flow, and which is not rubber, metal, ceramic, wood, or leather.

The simplest classification of plastics is on the basis of their thermal behaviour. Some plastics can repeatedly be softened by heating and hardened again by chilling. These materials are known as thermoplastics and are typified by Polythene and polyvinyl chloride. Other plastics, in their final moulded state, do not soften on heating, being both infusible and insoluble. These are described as thermoset or thermo-cured and are derived from such important thermosetting materials as phenol-formaldehyde resins or amino-resins.

The further classification of plastics is based either on their chemical derivation or final structure. Some of the important groups are the phenolics, the amino-plastics, the cellulose plastics, the vinyls, the styrene plastics, the acrylics, the polyamides or Nylons, the poly-esters, and the polyurethanes.

Plastics moulding. Plastics moulding consists in shaping materials while in a heat-softened stage and setting them, either by continued heating for thermosetting materials, or by cooling in the case of thermoplastics. Thermosetting materials may be compression moulded, usually in hardened steel moulds using hydraulic presses, or may be transfer moulded in which case they are passed in the softened state from a charging pot through a channel in the mould block to the main mould cavity by the application of suffi-cient pressure. Thermoplastic materials are moulded largely by injection of the hot softened material into a cold die: compression moulding of thermoplastics, using moulds which are alter-nately heated and cooled, may also be carried out. Much thermoplastic is extruded to give con-tinuous lengths of pipe, tube, rod, strip, sheet, film, and material of various other cross-sections. Extrusion blow moulding, where hot extruded material is blown within a mould cavity, is used for the production of plastic containers, especi-ally Polythene bottles. Moulding by vacuum forming of heat-softened thermoplastic sheet is a method of importance for the production of refrigerator liners, display articles, and bubble packs.

Plastoquinones. A family of trisubstituted

benzoquinones, e.g. 2,3-dimethyl-5-polyiso-prenylbenzoquinone. They occur in chloroplasts and play an essential part in photosynthetic processes.

Plate, tray. The vapour-liquid contacting units in an absorption or fractionating column. The term 'plate' tends to be used in Britain, 'tray' in the U.S.A. See Plate column, Bubble-cap plate, Sieve plate.

Plate column, tray column. The plate column, or

tray column as it is known in the U.S.A., is the plant most widely used for vapour-liquid con-tacting, and as such is employed in gas absorp-tion and stripping and for fractional distillation. It consists of a vertical cylindrical column con-taining a series of horizontal *plates* or *trays* spaced up to 3 ft. apart and set one above the other all the way up the column. Liquid flows down the column from plate to plate and vapour passes upwards through holes in them. Vapour-liquid contacting is by bubbles of vapour passing upwards through the pools of liquid on the plates, these pools being maintained by means of *weirs* at the liquid inlet and outlet on the plates. Liquid is carried from one plate to the next usually, but not invariably, by ducts called *downcomers*. There are a number of types of plate in use, but the operation of most of them is similar.

Since the transfer of material between phases takes place on the plates, the degree of gas absorption, or of separation in the case of a distillation column, depends directly on their number. The latter is therefore dependent on the required duty.

Plate columns are always used for large-scale operation; diameters range up to 20 ft. or so and heights in excess of 100 ft. are not uncommon. See also Bubble-cap plate, Sieve plate.

Plate efficiency, tray efficiency. If a plate in a distillation or absorption column were 100% efficient, perfect contacting would occur on it, and the liquid and vapour streams leaving the plate would be in equilibrium with each other. In practice the efficiency of plates is usually less than 100%, with the result that the number required to achieve a given degree of separation or absorption is greater than the theoretical number. The lower the plate efficiency the greater is the ratio of the actual number of plates required to the theoretical number. Plate efficiency is of great importance, since the cost of a column, and therefore of the operation it is performing, is directly related to the plate efficiency.

Platinum, Pt. At.no. 78, At.wt. 195·23. The most abundant and most important member of the group of metals to which it has given its name. It is a very malleable and ductile metal, and is harder than silver. It has m.p. 1769°, b.p. 4000°, d 21·45, and it has the face-centred cubic structure, $a=3·9237$ Å. Chemically it is very noble. It is perfectly stable in air at ordinary temperatures, and is quite unaffected by most reagents. Fluorine and chlorine gases do not attack it below 300°. It is, however, attacked by aqua regia, by fused alkalis, and by cyanide solutions in the presence of air. Hot con-centrated sulphuric acid slowly attacks it, and observations on this point are rather conflicting, presumably because the attack is much inhibited by sulphur dioxide or substances (such as arsenious oxide) which are capable of liberating it. The compact metal has marked catalytic activity, and this is much enhanced when it is present in one of the finely divided forms (see Platinum, spongy; Platinum black). In its compounds it is usually di- or tetra-positive.

Native platinum is usually found in the form of small grains, but occasionally large nuggets and more rarely cubic crystals are found. Some specimens are strongly magnetic, a property which is connected with the presence of iron, although there is no definite parallelism between the iron content and the magnetism, As a rule it contains from 60 to 85% of Pt, with smaller amounts of the other platinum metals and also iron and copper.

Its mechanical, chemical, and catalytic properties make it a very important metal in industry, in the arts, and in scientific work. Alloys with silver (as a rule containing 25% or 33% of platinum) are used in dentistry, and alloys containing about 10% of iridium in jewellery. In the laboratory, crucibles and other apparatus made of platinum (again often alloyed with a little iridium) are much used. On account of its coefficient of expansion it is the most suitable metal for sealing through glass, and for many kinds of electro-chemical work platinum electrodes are indispensable. 'Blackened' platinum electrodes consist of platinum gauze, foil, or wire on which a layer of very finely-divided platinum has been electrolytically deposited, preferably from a solution containing traces of lead. Other laboratory uses are in thermocouples (Pt/Pt-Rh is the most usual combination) and resistance thermometers. In industry, platinum catalysts are of great importance, especially in the contact process for sulphuric acid and in the oxidation of ammonia to nitric acid. For these purposes gauze may be used, or asbestos, or better, some soluble porous material such as dehydrated magnesium sulphate may be impregnated with finely-divided metal. The advantage of a soluble vehicle is that it enables the metal to be easily recovered should it become 'poisoned'.

Platinum alkyls. Platinum forms stable compounds with Pt—C bonds. $PtCl_4$ reacts with Grignard reagents to give $[R_3PtCl]_4$ and $[R_4Pt]_4$ tetramers in which there are methyl groups bridging between three platinum atoms. The Me_3Pt group is very stable.

Platinum ammines. Two well-defined and stable series exist, the platinous ammines which are derived from dipositive platinum and in which the co-ordination number is four, and the platinic ammines in which platinum is tetra-

positive and has the co-ordination number six.

The simpler *platinous ammines* have formulae $(PtA_4)X_2$, $(PtA_3X)X$, PtA_2X_2, $(PtA_2X)_2$; the first and third are the most usual types (A is ammonia or a substituted ammonia, X is a monocharged anionic grouping). These ammines have a planar configuration about the central platinum atom.

Platinic ammines are known for every type from $(PtA_6)X_4$ to $M(PtAX_5)$; they have octahedral co-ordination about the central platinum atom.

Platinum black. A finely-divided and usually impure form of the metal obtained by precipitation from solution with the aid of reducing agents such as aluminium, hydrazine hydrate, or sodium formate. It is a very powerful catalyst.

Platinum bromides. $PtBr_2$ is a brown insoluble substance formed by the decomposition of $PtBr_4$. $PtBr_4$ is formed by the gentle ignition of H_2PtBr_6, but is not obtained pure as it partially dissociates, forming the lower bromides.

Platinum bromides, complex. Bromoplatinous acid, H_2PtBr_4, exists in solution, and some of its salts are known. They resemble the chloroplatinates (II), with which they are isomorphous.

Bromoplatinic acid is formed when a mixture of hydrobromic and nitric acids acts on the metal. It crystallizes as H_2PtBr_6, $9H_2O$ in red monoclinic prisms, m.p. 180°, which are readily soluble in water or alcohol. The bromoplatinates (IV) resemble the chloroplatinates (IV), and are isomorphous with them.

Platinum chlorides. $PtCl_2$ and $PtCl_4$ are known. The substance commonly known as platinum chloride is chloroplatinic acid (see platinum chlorides, complex).

$PtCl_2$ is formed by the partial decomposition of $PtCl_4$ or of one of the chloro acids, or by the action of chlorine on the finely-divided metal at 360°. It is a grey or brown powder, insoluble in water but soluble in hydrochloric acid, owing to the formation of a complex acid. It forms many complexes, e.g. with ammonia and ethylene.

$PtCl_4$ is obtained by heating chloroplatinic acid in a current of chlorine. It is a reddish hygroscopic substance, and forms a series of hydrates with one, two, four and five molecules of water, the tetrahydrate being the most stable under ordinary conditions. Its aqueous solutions have a strongly acid reaction, and may be regarded as containing the acid $H_2[PtCl_4(OH)_2]$, with which the dihydrate may be identified.

Platinum chlorides, complex. The simple chlorides of platinum readily form complex acids of various types.

Tetrachloroplatinous acid, H_2PtCl_4, exists in a solution of $PtCl_2$ in HCl. On attempting to concentrate it, a reddish deliquescent mass of *trichlorohydroxyplatinous acid*, $H_2[PtCl_3(OH)]$, H_2O is obtained. The tetrachloroplatinates (II) are stable, red, crystalline salts, prepared by gentle reduction of the chloroplatinates (IV). They are mostly soluble in water, and the four chlorine atoms are arranged in a plane. Salts of $H_2PtCl_3(OH)$ are not so well known, but the silver and lead salts have been described as brown precipitates.

Chloroplatinic acid, H_2PtCl_6, is formed when the metal dissolves in aqua regia, and on evaporation reddish needles of H_2PtCl_6, $6H_2O$, which melt in their own water at 60°, are obtained. This is probably the best-known platinum compound, and is commonly called platinic chloride. It is a strong acid, and forms a series of stable salts, the chloroplatinates (IV). Of these, the potassium and ammonium salts are anhydrous, and very sparingly soluble in water, a fact which is of importance in analytical chemistry. The caesium and rubidium salts are even less soluble. These all form yellow octahedra. The silver salt also is insoluble, but most of the other chloroplatinates are readily soluble hydrated salts.

A number of *chlorohydroxyplatinic acids*, of general formula $H_2[PtCl_{6-x}(OH)_x]$, are known in solution, and one of them, $H_2PtCl_4(OH)_2$, may be identified with $PtCl_4$, $2H_2O$. They are all strong acids, and many of their salts have been described.

Platinum cyanides, complex. The platinocyanides or cyanoplatinates (II) are an important series of stable salts derived from $H_2Pt(CN)_4$. The free acid may be obtained by decomposition of a heavy-metal salt with hydrogen sulphide, and forms red deliquescent $H_2Pt(CN)_4 \cdot 5H_2O$ readily soluble in water, alcohol, and ether. The alkali metal salts are formed when solutions of platinum compounds are warmed with alkali cyanide, or when the metal dissolves in a cyanide solution. Other salts may be obtained by double decomposition. They are mostly soluble hydrated salts which crystallize well, and are remarkable for the variety of colours they exhibit: they may be red, yellow, purple, blue, or green; often different hydrates of the same salt differ markedly in colour, and they are often dichroic. Many of them exhibit fluorescence; the barium salt, $BaPt(CN)_4, 4H_2O$, is often used as a fluorescent screen in work with radium or X-rays.

Platinum fluorides. *Platinic fluoride*, PtF_4, is a light-brown powder obtained by the action of bromine trifluoride on platinic chloride. It is hydrolysed by water on boiling. Hexafluoroplatinates (IV), M_2PtF_6, are yellow crystalline substances prepared by treating the corresponding chloroplatinates with bromine trifluoride. They are stable to hydrolysis but give chloroplatinates (IV) with hydrochloric acid.

Platinum pentafluoride, PtF_5 and *Platinum hexafluoride*, PtF_6, are volatile substances obtained by allowing fluorine to act on a heated platinum wire. The latter is dark red in colour, m.p. 61·3, b.p. 69·1, and gives a brownish-red vapour. It decomposes slowly in glass apparatus. PtF_6 is a very strong oxidizing agent. It oxidizes oxygen to O_2PtF_6 and xenon to $XePtF_6$ and other products. It is reduced to hexafluoroplatinates (V). Other oxyfluorides known are $PtOF_3$ and $PtOF_4$.

Platinum iodides. The di-iodide and tetraiodide, PtI_2 and PtI_4 are both black insoluble powders which may be obtained by double decomposition. They dissolve in hydriodic acid to form complexes. PtI_4, although not soluble in water, is soluble in alcohol. A tri-iodide, PtI_3, is prepared by thermal decomposition of PtI_4.

Platinum iodides, complex. *Iodoplatinic acid*, H_2PtI_6, $9H_2O$, can be obtained as dark-red monoclinic crystals from a solution of PtI_4 in hydriodic acid. It breaks up on heating, or slowly in solution, into HI and PtI_4. A number of its salts are known; $(NH_4)_2PtI_6$ and K_2PtI_6 are anhydrous and isomorphous with the chlorosalts, but are more soluble than these. They form black crystals, and give a deep red solution which is not very stable and soon deposits PtI_4.

Platinum (II) complexes, M_2PtI_4, are formed when platinum (IV) chloride is treated with iodide solutions. The platinum is reduced and remains in solution.

Platinum metals. The platinum metals are ruthenium, rhodium, palladium, osmium, iridium, and platinum. They were formerly placed in Group VIII of the Periodic Table but are now placed at the ends of the transition series in groups with iron, cobalt, and nickel. Ruthenium, rhodium, and palladium are sometimes distinguished as the 'light platinum metals', the other three being the 'heavy platinum metals'. They occur all together as alloys which are classified according to their composition as 'native platinum' and 'osmiridium'. They are found in the Urals, on the western slopes of the Rockies (British Columbia and California), and in the Republic of Colombia. Many gold, silver, and copper ores, and the nickel ores of Ontario contain small amounts of platinum and palladium. Their chemistry is discussed under the individual metals.

Platinum nitrites, complex. No simple nitrites of platinum are known, but complex nitrites of dipositive platinum, $M_2Pt(NO_2)_4$, and mixed complex nitrites containing halogens of both di- and tetra-positive platinum exist.

Platinum oxides. PtO is formed when the finely divided metal is heated in oxygen at about 430°. On being more strongly heated it decomposes to the metal and PtO_2, which itself decomposes at higher temperatures. The hydrated monoxide PtO, H_2O is precipitated by caustic alkalis from solutions of platinum (II) compounds. It cannot be dehydrated without decomposition, and is very reactive, being easily reduced to the metal and also easily oxidized on exposure to air.

A hydrated brown sesquioxide, Pt_2O_3, xH_2O, is precipitated from a solution of the trichloride by alkalis. It is soluble in excess of alkali and also in concentrated acids. It cannot be dehydrated without decomposition.

The dioxide is the anhydride of hexahydroxyplatinic acid, $H_2Pt(OH)_6$, i.e. PtO_2, $4H_2O$. It may be obtained as a white precipitate by neutralizing with acetic acid solutions of (e.g.) $PtCl_4$ which have been boiled with excess of caustic alkali. It dissolves in alkalis forming salts, several of which are known in the crystalline state, and also in hydrochloric acid, forming chlorohydroxyplatinic acids. Lower hydrates with 3, 2 and $1H_2O$ also exist. Platinum volatilizes in air as the dioxide.

A trioxide, PtO_3, is known. It is a reddish-brown and very unstable substance which has powerful oxidizing properties, and gradually loses oxygen even at ordinary temperatures. It is formed as a rather indefinite compound with alkali, formulated K_2O, $3PtO_3$, by electrolytic oxidation of alkaline solutions of the dioxide. The compound appears as a yellow layer on the anode, and when this is treated with cold dilute acetic acid the trioxide is liberated.

Preparations of platinum oxides obtained by various dry methods are very powerful hydrogenating catalysts, even more active in this respect than platinum black.

Platinum, spongy. The form of the metal obtained by ignition of ammonium chloroplatinate (IV). It is a soft, porous, grey mass, and has great catalytic activity.

Platinum sulphate, $Pt(SO_4)_2$, $4H_2O$. Obtained from the solution which results when the finely-divided metal is heated with sulphuric acid, or when an alternating current is passed between platinum electrodes in sulphuric acid. It forms orange crystals. The solution is easily hydrolysed, depositing a basic salt.

Platinum sulphides, PtS and PtS_2, may be obtained by precipitation with hydrogen sulphide from solutions of di- and tetra-positive platinum respectively. They are both black precipitates. PtS is converted to platinum on heating in air.

PtS_2 is more reactive, and easily oxidizes in air, forming an oxysulphide.

Playfair, Lyon, (1819-1898). Playfair was born at Meerut, Bengal, of Scottish parents, and was educated at St. Andrews and Glasgow. He studied chemistry under Graham, to whom he was subsequently assistant at University College, London, before going to Giessen to study under Liebig. After being chemical manager of the Primrose Calico Printing Works and professor of chemistry at the Royal Institution, Manchester, he became chemist to the Geological Survey. In 1858 he was appointed professor of chemistry in the University of Edinburgh. His chief work was done in connexion with numerous Royal Commissions and Select Committees.

Pleochroism. Crystals which vary in colour according to the direction of observation are said to be pleochroic. Very marked pleochroism is exhibited by crystalline platinocyanides, e.g. $K_2Pt(CN)_4$.

Plioform resins. A trade name for cyclized rubber products made by treatment of rubber with complex tin chlorides. They have excellent electrical properties, are resistant to most acids and alkalis, and are unaffected by oxygen, light, and moisture. They are soluble in hydrocarbons, and used mainly in the production of chemically resistant surface coatings.

Pliolite resins. A trade name applied only to surface coating grades of cyclized rubber products. See Plioform resins.

Plücker, Julius (1801-1868). Born at Elberfeld, Plücker studied at the Universities of Bonn, Heidelberg, and Berlin. He was appointed professor of mathematics, Friedrich Wilhelm's Gymnasium, Berlin (1833), and at Halle (1834), professor of mathematics, and finally professor of physics at Bonn (1836). Plücker discovered the emission of cathode rays when an electric discharge was allowed to take place in a highly evacuated glass tube and, according to Hittorf, was the first to see the lines of the hydrogen spectrum. His main field of research was geometry.

Plumbane, Lead hydride, PbH_4. A colourless unstable gas obtained by the action of acids on a magnesium-lead alloy.

Plumbates. See Lead hydroxides.

Plutonium, Pu. At.no. 94, m.p. 639·5°, estimated b.p. 3800°, d^{18} 19·82. Plutonium is made artificially from uranium in atomic piles by the absorption of slow neutrons and subsequent β decay. It is separated from uranium and fission products by solvent extraction processes. Traces of plutonium are found in nature and undoubtedly result from neutron capture by natural uranium.

The most widely studied isotope, ^{239}Pu, is extremely hazardous to health because of its high α activity and cannot be handled without special precautions. It has a half-life of about 24,400 years. It is a fissile material.

Metallic plutonium crystallizes in six phases; it is similar to uranium in reactivity and methods of preparation.

Plutonium compounds. Plutonium resembles uranium chemically but with plutonium there is much greater instability of the higher oxidation states. Thus Pu(IV) can only be oxidized to Pu(VI) by permanganate or similar strong oxidizing agents. With the exception of fluorine, where PuF_3, PuF_4, and PuF_6 are known, the highest halide compound formed is in the tripositive state. Colours observed for plutonium compounds are: Pu^{3+}, blue; Pu^{4+}, green; Pu^{5+}, red; Pu^{6+}, pink to red.

Polar bond. An electrovalent bond. See Valency, theory of.

Polarimeter. An instrument for measuring the amount by which the plane of polarization of plane-polarized light is rotated in passing through a medium.

Polarization. When a molecule possessing a dipole moment is placed in an electric field the molecules tend to set themselves in a certain direction, much as a compass needle takes up a position in a magnetic field. This orientation effect is called orientation polarization. At the same time the electrons in the molecule are slightly displaced in a direction towards the positive pole of the field. This is called electron polarization. In addition, the nuclei having positive charges are slightly displaced relative to one another. This is atomic polarization, and is usually of a very small magnitude. The total polarization of a molecule is the sum of the orientation, electronic, and atomic polarizations.

The term electrolytic polarization refers to the effects met with in electrolysis due to existence of overpotential and concentration changes in the neighbourhood of the electrode. See Hydrogen overvoltage.

Polarizibility. When an atom or molecule is subjected to an electric field, the electrons are drawn slightly away from the positive nuclei and a dipole is induced. The strength of this dipole, divided by the field strength, is called the polarizibility of the substance. Such *electronic* polarizibility can be determined from measurements of refractive index at wavelengths in the visible region of the spectrum. If far infra-red light is used, an additional effect, *atomic* polarization, is also observed. Polarizibility has the dimensions of volume.

Polar solvent. A solvent, the molecules of which have good solvating power. Generally, the greater the dipole of the molecules of the solvent the better the liquid as a solvent for ionic substances.

Polar molecule. Since different elements have differing electronegativities, the two electrons in a covalent link are not shared equally. This gives a separation of charge over the bond and, if the effects are not cancelled out, over the whole molecule. Such a molecule is known as a polar molecule. Thus in covalent hydrogen chloride $\overset{\delta+}{H}{-}\overset{\delta-}{Cl}$ the pair of electrons is closer to the chlorine than the hydrogen and the molecule has a resultant dipole moment. Lone pairs of electrons also make molecules strongly polar.

Polarography. A highly developed electrochemical method of analysis. It is particularly applicable to dilute solutions of substances which are susceptible to electrolytic reduction at a mercury cathode. A dropping-mercury electrode is used and the current-voltage curve for the solution ('polarogram') is generally recorded. The polarogram shows a 'step' for each reducible substance present in the solution. The step occurs at a characteristic potential and its height is proportional to the concentration of the component. In favourable cases several components can be detected and quantitatively determined from one polarogram. The method is particularly valuable for determining traces of metals, but it is also very useful for other substances. The technique can be adapted for the investigation of complexes in solution and also for work in non-aqueous solvents.

Pollucite, $(Cs,Na)AlSi_2O_6,nH_2O$ (n is usually near $\frac{1}{2}$). A complex caesium aluminium silicate containing 24-36% Cs_2O and up to 1·6% Rb_2O. Colourless, sp.gr. 2·68-2·98, hardness $6\frac{1}{2}$. The crystals are cubic, and it usually occurs massive in pegmatites accompanied by lithium minerals. It is practically the only commercial source of caesium and is obtained mainly from S. Dakota.

Polonium, Po. At.no. 84, At.wt. 210. It has m.p. $\sim$225°, b.p. $\sim$950°. Polonium was originally discovered as a decay product of radium but is now obtained by the neutron irradiation of bismuth. ^{210}Po has a half-life of 138 days, being α active. Polonium is separated from other elements present by chemical means and is purified by electrodeposition on copper, nickel, or a platinum metal. The metal is obtained by vacuum-sublimation of the deposits or by thermal decomposition of the sulphide or dioxide. There are two modifications, α-polonium, cubic, $a=3·345$ Å, d 9·196, and β-polonium, the high temperature form, rhombohedral, $a=3·359$ Å, $\alpha=98°\,13'$, $d\,9·398$. The high activity of the element makes the handling of polonium compounds very hazardous; all experiments are carried out in a glove-box. Polonium has been used as a neutron source and for the elimination of static electricity in certain industries. For a review of the properties of polonium see Bagnall (*Quarterly Reviews*, 1957, **11**, 30).

Polonium compounds. Polonium is a member of the sulphur sub-group and shows many similarities to tellurium. However polonium hydroxide and dioxide are more basic than the corresponding tellurium compounds, and the dihalides are quite stable. The *halides* PoX_4 and PoX_2 are known. The tetrapositive halides are obtained by the action of the metal with the halogen and form complex halides, M_2PoX_6. Both $PoCl_2$, and $PoBr_2$ are obtained by thermal degradation of the tetrahalides. *Polonium dioxide*, PoO_2, is obtained from the elements at 250°, it is basic in character; a monoxide, PoO, and a trioxide, PoO_3 are also known. Lead and mercuric polonides, containing the Po^{2-} ion, have been prepared by interaction of the elements. Most polonium salts are highly coloured, being red or yellow. All polonium compounds are readily hydrolysed and reduced.

Polyacetals. See Polyformaldehyde.

Polycarbonates. A group of thermoplastics, characterized by their toughness, high softening point, and clarity, and very suitable for injection moulding. They are derived from the polycondensation of bisphenols, such as diphenylolpropane, $HO \cdot C_6H_4 \cdot C(CH_3)_2 \cdot C_6H_4 \cdot OH$, with carbonyl chloride. In the example quoted, the structure of the polymer can be represented as:

Polychloroprene. See Neoprene.

Polydentate ligand. See Multidentate ligand.

Polydispersion. In most colloidal sols, the dispersed particles are of very varying size unless some means have been adopted to exclude particles outside certain size limits. Such a sol is said to be polydisperse. Thus gelatin solution is a polydisperse protein dispersion with particles of molecular weight between 10,000 and 70,000. See Colloids, Isodispersion.

Polyelectrolyte. A macromolecular compound containing many ionizable groups within the same molecule. A polyelectrolyte may be purely anionic or cationic, or may be amphoteric, and the individual ionizing groups may be weak or strong acids. Examples: strongly acidic—poly-

styrene sulphonic acid: weakly acidic—polymethacrylic acid, alginic acid: strongly basic—polyvinylpyridinium bromide: weakly basic—polyvinylamine: amphoteric—polyglycine, or any protein. The term is generally used for soluble substances, but ion-exchange resins and fibrous proteins could be considered insoluble polyelectrolytes.

Polyenes. Compounds with many carbon-to-carbon double bonds, e.g. carotenoids, c.f. dienes, trienes.

Polyesters. A number of resins, plastics, and synthetic fibres can be generally described as polyesters, since they are based on resins produced by the condensation of polyhydric alcohols with polybasic acids.

Linear polyesters, e.g. polyethylene terephthalate, are saturated thermoplastic materials that are widely applied in the form of drawn melt-spun fibres (e.g. Terylene, Dacron) and oriented cast film (e.g. Melinex, Mylar).

Unsaturated polyester resins, such as the polycondensate from phthalic anhydride, propylene glycol, and maleic anhydride, will readily copolymerize with minor proportions of styrene and methyl methacrylate under the influence of an organic peroxide catalyst, to give thermoset products. Together with glass fibre reinforcement, such resins are now being used for the production of aircraft parts, sports-car bodies, sailing boats, crash-helmets, corrugated roof lights, wall panels, etc.

Moulding materials based on mixtures of unsaturated polyester resins and partially polymerized polyfunctional unsaturated esters (such as diallyl phthalate) are more usually known as alkyd moulding materials.

Polyethylene. An alternative name for Polythene, generally used in the U.S.A.

Polyformaldehyde. Highly crystalline polymers of formaldehyde, with molecular weights in the range 20,000-100,000, manufactured by the polymerization of very pure anhydrous formaldehyde in the presence of, e.g., triphenylphosphine (20 p.p.m.). The resultant polyoxymethylenes are stabilized by end-group esterification with acetic anhydride and in this form are used commercially as plastics, being also known as acetal resins and polyacetals. Copolymers of formaldehyde and certain cyclic ethers such as ethylene oxide and 1,3-dioxolane are also included in this same group of materials. Polyformaldehyde plastics are gaining increasing acceptance as engineering materials in applications where previously non-ferrous metals such as brass or aluminium might have been used.

Polyhalides. A class of compounds formed by adding halogens and interhalogens to alkali or other halides. Most are readily hydrolysed in water. The formula types of the ions formed are A_n^-, AB_n^-, and $AB_mC_n^-$; examples of compounds of each class being CsI_3, $KICl_2$, and $CsClIBr$.

Polyhalite, $K_2Ca_2Mg(SO_4)_4$. A triclinic mineral (hardness $2\frac{1}{2}$-3, sp.gr. 2·77) found in compact masses in layers associated with deposits of other potassium salts at Stassfurt and in W. Texas and Mexico. It is a valuable source of potash.

Polyiodides. A group of compounds containing the ions I_3^-, I_5^-, I_7^-, and I_9^-, formed by dissolving iodine in solutions of iodides. Such compounds are most familiar in the case of the alkali elements (e.g. KI_3, CsI_5, KI_7), but are also known for other metals and bases. They can often be isolated in the solid state, but dissociate readily with formation of free iodine.

Polyisobutylene. A synthetic resin of the ethenoid class, used as a base for adhesives and sometimes as an additive (10-15%) in Polythene. It varies from a sticky liquid to a rubbery solid according to its molecular weight.

Polyisoprene. Early attempts to polymerize isoprene gave rise to an uncontrolled reaction that yielded polyisoprene containing a random mixture of units of all the four possible isomeric forms and having no worthwhile elastomeric properties. However, the advent of stereoregular polymerization has allowed the production of pure poly-*cis*-1,4-isoprene, which being identical in structure to natural rubber is of great commercial significance.

Polyketides. A term used to denote natural organic compounds regarded as arising from poly-β-ketonic intermediates derived by condensation of acetate units. The concept of the 'acetate hypothesis', accounting for the biosynthesis of a wide range of aliphatic, alicyclic, aromatic and heterocyclic compounds, was due originally to J. N. Collie (1893), but was greatly enlarged by A. J. Birch (1953), who also proved its correctness in a number of examples. Biosynthesis of fatty acids, many aromatic compounds, natural oxygen heterocyclics, tetracycline antibiotics, and other fungal metabolites has been shown to occur via polyketide routes. Mevalonic acid is a special case, arising from only three acetate units.

Polymerization. The term was originally used, by Berzelius, to describe any process in which two or more molecules of the same substance unite, to give a molecule (polymer) with the same percentage composition as the original substance (monomer), but with a molecular weight which is an integral multiple of the original. Now the term includes any process that results in the formation of large molecules (macromolecules), consisting of repeated structural units. These structural units (described as 'mers') are contributed by the reacting monomers, but, constitutionally, need not be identical with them.

Polymerization processes yielding polymers, whose mers are constitutionally identical to the reacting monomers are now classified as *addition polymerizations*. Thus styrene can be converted, by addition polymerization, to polystyrene:

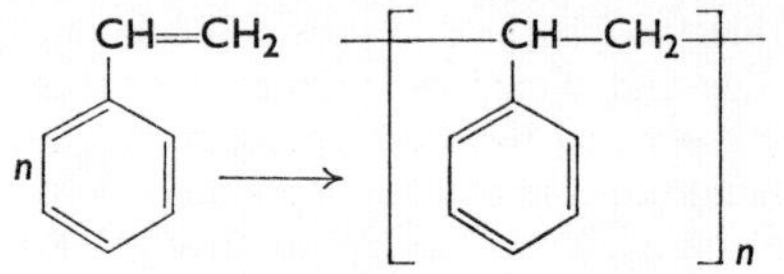

From this it can be seen that the monomer and the polymer differ only in bond distribution, but otherwise are identical.

Such reactions can be initiated by free radicals, derived from compounds (initiators) such as benzoyl peroxide, ammonium persulphate, or azodi-isobutyronitrile; or by reactive ions, derived, for example from boron trifluoride or titanium tetrachloride. The process is also known in the plastics industry as 'vinyl polymerization' since the best known examples are those involving vinyl or related monomers. Addition polymerizations are characterized by their extremely rapid rates, achieved at relatively low temperatures, especially in the case of ionic initiated polymerizations. The kinetics are typical of those expected of chain reactions. Industrially the process is important for the production of many polymers and copolymers used for the manufacture of plastics and synthetic rubbers. It is carried out in a variety of ways.

Mass polymerization describes the method where bulk monomer is converted to polymers, as, for instance, in the production of polymethyl methacrylate sheets (batch process) or the production of general purpose polystyrene (continuous process).

Solution polymerization is where the reaction is completed in the presence of a solvent, such as the solution polymerization of styrene to polystyrene in ethylbenzene solution.

Suspension polymerization, also known as dispersed mass, pearl, or granular polymerization, is a special type of mass conversion, where the monomer, containing dissolved initiator, is polymerized while dispersed in the form of fine droplets in a second non-reactive liquid (usually water).

Emulsion polymerization involves the conversion of an aqueous emulsion of the monomer in the presence of a water soluble initiator to a polymer latex (colloidal dispersion of polymer in water). Both vinyl and styrene polymers and their respective copolymers are produced in

472

large quantities by suspension and emulsion methods.

Condensation polymerization differs from addition polymerization in that the polymer is formed by reaction of monomers, each step in the process resulting in the elimination of some easily removed molecule (often water). For example the polyester polyethylene terephthalate (Terylene) is formed by the condensation polymerization (polycondensation) of ethylene glycol with terephthalic acid:

$$n\text{HO} \cdot [\text{CH}_2]_2 \cdot \text{OH} + n\text{HO} \cdot \text{CO}\langle\bigcirc\rangle\text{CO}_2\text{H}$$

$$\downarrow$$

$$\left[\text{O} \cdot [\text{CH}_2]_2 \cdot \text{O} \cdot \text{CO}\langle\bigcirc\rangle \cdot \text{CO} \right]_n + n\text{H}_2\text{O}$$

Here the empirical compositions of polymer and reacting monomers are different and the structural unit (mer) has no constitutional identity with the monomer components.

The kinetics of this type of polymerization are the same as for simple condensation; for this reason, the use of the term polycondensation is perhaps more appropriate. Unless kinetic evidence suggests otherwise, polymerizations involving the formation of chain polymers from cyclic compounds, following ring scission, are classed as condensation polymerizations. Some important condensation polymers are those derived from phenol, urea, or melamine and formaldehyde; the polyesters; the polyamides (Nylons); the polysiloxanes (silicones).

Polymethylene glycols. Compounds formed by the union of several molecules of formaldehyde with a molecule of water. They are of the type

$$\text{HO}{-}\text{CH}_2\text{OCH}_2\text{O} \ldots \text{CH}_2\text{OH},$$

and are formed in aqueous solutions of formaldehyde. The size of the molecule increases with increasing concentration of formaldehyde. They are readily decomposed by heat to give formaldehyde and show all its reactions.

Polymorphism. If a substance is able to exist in more than one crystalline form, it is said to be polymorphous. The different forms are referred to as polymorphs, and the phenomenon is termed polymorphism. Thus, mercuric iodide crystallizes from organic solvents in yellow, orthorhombic plates, which slowly revert to the more stable red, tetragonal form. Polymorphism of the elements is known as allotropy.

Polymyxins. A group of closely related antibiotics produced by *Bacillus polymyxa*. They are basic peptides, containing L-α,γ-diaminobutyric acid, L-threonine, two other amino-acids, X, and a fatty acid group, R.

They have been isolated as hydrochlorides, very soluble in water, insoluble in ether and acetone. They are active against a wide range of bacteria, particularly Gram-negative ones. Polymyxin B (trade name Aerosporin) is used as its sulphate in the treatment of severe infections incapable of treatment by other drugs, but has toxic side-effects. It is a mixture of polymyxin B_1 (R = 6-methyloctanoyl, X = D-Phe) and polymyxin B_2 (R = 6-methylheptanoyl, X = D-Phe). Polymyxin E (colistin A) (R = 6-methyloctanoyl, X = D-Leu) is used topically or by injection for *Pseudomonas* infections.

Polypeptides. See Peptides.

Polyphosphates. Phosphate anions containing PO_4 units linked by sharing oxygens with other tetrahedra. The polyphosphates may either be in chain forms, e.g. $[P_2O_7]^{4-}$, $[P_3O_{10}]^{5-}$, or in a ring form $[P_3O_9]^{3-}$ and $[P_4O_{12}]^{4-}$, tri and tetra-metaphosphates respectively.

Polypropylene. The first isotactic polymer to be produced on a commercial scale. It was introduced as a thermoplastic moulding material, following the fundamental work of G. Natta on the polymerization of olefins using stereospecific catalysts. Although polypropylene resembles high density Polythene in many respects, it differs in its density (0·90-0·91), higher softening point, and higher brittle point.

Polysaccharides. Carbohydrates derived from monosaccharides by the removal of $n-1$ molecules of water from n molecules of monosaccharides. All the higher carbohydrates are polysaccharides.

Polystyrene. One of the most widely used thermoplastics. It is a member of the ethenoid group of plastics, and is produced by emulsion dispersion, and continuous mass polymerization of its monomer. In bulk, it is a clear glass-like material of low density (1·05) and outstanding moisture resistance. The original use of polystyrene as a very efficient electrical insulator, especially at high frequencies, is still of great technical importance. Apart from special purpose mouldings produced for such applications, oriented polystyrene foil is also available for electrical use.

Much polystyrene is moulded directly as the pure polymer, but substantial quantities of 'toughened' polystyrenes are used. These materials are blends of polystyrene with rubbery copolymers, e.g. styrene-butadiene copolymer.

Although these blends have much improved impact resistance, they cannot be produced with the high optical clarity and surface gloss characteristic of the unmodified polymer. Apart from the wide use of toughened polystyrenes for injection moulding, considerable quantities are converted to sheet, by extrusion, for after-fabrication by vacuum forming. Expanded polystyrene (Styrofoam) is widely applied as a low temperature insulating material, as a buoyancy medium, and in packaging.

Polytetrafluoroethylene. Also known as PTFE and sometimes as CF2 polymer, this unique plastics material is produced from its gaseous monomer by emulsion polymerization under pressure. It is a tough translucent material having the high sp.gr. of 2·20. Its unique character is seen in its high softening temperature (327°) and decomposition point (400°); flexibility at very low temperature ($-80°$); low coefficient of friction (that of wet ice); outstanding abhesive (i.e. non-stick) properties; excellent chemical resistance (being attacked only by such powerful reagents as liquid sodium and fluorine gas); and outstanding electrical insulating properties especially at high frequencies. PTFE is available in the form of powder, aqueous dispersion, sinter-moulded block, tube, rod and tape. It is also sinter-moulded admixed with modifying fillers such as metal powders, chopped glass fibres, and graphite powder. It is used in small but significant amounts for the production of sealing rings, gaskets, and diaphragms in chemical plant; sintered with phosphor-bronze powder to give self-lubricating bearings; applied to processing rollers and mixers to give non-sticking surfaces; and as a high temperature flexible electrical insulating material. The two well established brand names are Fluon and Teflon.

Polythene, Polyethylene. A waxy, translucent, somewhat flexible thermoplastic, made by polymerizing ethylene at high pressures (1000-1200 atm) and elevated temperatures (180°-190°) in the presence of a trace of oxygen. It is one of the lightest plastics (sp.gr. 0·92-0·93). Below 60°, Polythene is insoluble in all solvents and is resistant to the action of most reagents, other than strong oxidizing acids. Above 115°, the polymer changes from a clear solid to a relatively low viscosity melt. Exposure to air, at this temperature and above, gives rise to fairly extensive oxidative degradation, unless anti-oxidants are included with the polymer. Polythene is widely used as an extrusion material, for the production of pipe, tube, sheet, film, for wire and cable covering, and as a general purpose injection moulding material.

Other types of ethylene polymers, generally known as low pressure, high density, or linear Polythenes, are now available. These are produced by polymerization of ethylene at lower pressures (400 atm) in the presence of heterogeneous catalysts. The polymers so produced are characterized by having higher densities (0·94-0·98) higher melting points (c. 130°) and a greater degree of crystallinity (80 % compared with 60 % for normal Polythene). Structurally, low pressure Polythenes show a reduction in the extent of branching of the chain molecules. These polymers have the obvious advantages of greater rigidity and toughness, harder surface, and better heat resistance than normal Polythene.

Polythionic acids, $H_2S_nO_6$, Polythionates. A series of more or less unstable dibasic acids, obtained by the action of iodine solution on sodium sulphite, thiosulphate, and mixtures of these, by the action of hydrogen sulphide on other members of the same series and of hydrogen sulphide on H_2SO_3 at 0°. The best known as alkali salts are: dithionic acid $H_2S_2O_6$, trithionic acid $H_2S_3O_6$, tetrathionic acid $H_2S_4O_6$, pentathionic acid $H_2S_5O_6$, and hexathionic acid $H_2S_6O_6$.

Aqueous solutions of the free acids decompose on concentration, yielding sulphuric acid, sulphur dioxide, and sulphur. Aqueous solutions of their alkali salts decompose slowly. They yield no precipitate with barium chloride solution. Solid barium and alkali salts of various acids of the series have been prepared.

Polyurethanes. A group of synthetic polymeric materials with the urethane group

$$-NH \cdot CO \cdot O-$$

as an integral part of the polymer chain. Polyurethane fibres, plastics, rubbers, lacquers, and adhesives can all be produced by reaction of di- and tri-isocyanates with compounds containing active hydrogen, in particular with glycols. Thus, the important synthetic fibre, Perlon U (a brand name), is formed from the interaction of hexamethylenedi-isocyanate and 1,4 butylene glycol. Both thermoplastic and thermosetting moulding materials are in use, the moulded products from which range from soft elastomers to tough rigid solids. Polyurethane foams, varying widely in both density and flexibility, are being used in many fields. These foams are readily produced by reaction of especially the tolylenedi-isocyanates with certain grades of polyesters and polyethers. Polyurethane adhesives, formed from di-isocyanates such as 2,4-tolylenedi-isocyanate or methylenebis(p-phenyleneisocyanate) and glycols, as for instance polyethylene and polypropylene glycols, can be used to secure the interbonding of dissimilar materials such as glass, metals, rubbers, and plastics.

Polyvinyl acetals. A group of polymeric materials, of limited but important application, obtained by the action of certain aldehydes on either polyvinyl acetate or polyvinyl alcohol. All can be represented by the general formula:

$$-\left[-CH-CH_2-CH-CH_2-\right]-$$

The commercially important products have R as H, CH_3, and C_3H_7. Polyvinyl formal (R is H) is most generally used for the enamel coating of copper wire for coils. Polyvinyl butyral (R is C_3H_7) is used as a base for safety-glass inter-layers, strippable coatings, and pressure sensi-tive adhesives.

Polyvinyl acetate. Produced from its monomer by emulsion polymerization. The latex so ob-tained is used in considerable quantity as a base for emulsion paints, adhesives, and impregnants for fabrics and papers. Polyvinyl acetate is too soft and has too low a distortion temperature to find application as a moulded plastics material, but it is the important intermediate for the production of polyvinyl alcohol and the polyvinyl acetals.

Polyvinyl alcohol. Since vinyl alcohol does not exist, its polymer is obtained by the alcoholysis with methanol of polyvinyl acetate. The polymer is compounded with glycol plasticizers to give thermoplastic compositions that are available in the form of clear films, sheeting, extruded tubing and other sections, and monofilaments. These materials are all distinguished by their elastomeric properties, complete resistance to hydrocarbon solvents, and ready solubility (un-less specially insolubilized) in hot water. Poly-vinyl alcohol solutions are useful as release agents, and as textile sizes, for paper treating, in water based adhesives, and as aqueous suspend-ing agents.

Polyvinyl chloride. This ethenoid polymer is pro-duced as a fine white powder by both emulsion polymerization and suspension polymerization of the gas vinyl chloride when liquefied under nitrogen pressure, The terms PVC and 'vinyl' are commonly used to refer to not only the polymer, but to all materials of which polyvinyl chloride is a constituent. PVC compositions are produced by hot mixing (150°-160°) the polymer with plasticizers, such as tricresyl phos-phate, dibutyl, and dioctyl phthalates, and small proportions of stabilizers (e.g. lead carbonate or calcium stearate), stearate lubricants, and

colours to give materials in a wide range of hardness, from rigid (little or no plasticizer) to very soft (equal proportion of plasticizer to polymer), and in a wide range of colours as well as crystal clear. Unplasticized flexible PVC foils are normally produced from vinyl chloride-acetate copolymers by calendering and stretch-ing.

In amount used, PVC is second to Polythene in plastics materials, advantage being taken of its toughness, good weathering properties, chemical and solvent resistance, non-inflammability, high electrical resistance, colour possibilities, and choice of hardness and flexibility, especially in the lower temperature ranges. PVC plastics are extruded as wire and cable coverings, garden hose, piping, tubing, tubular film, sheet, strip, monofilaments and fibres. Continuous films and sheeting, both unsupported and supported on textiles, can be produced by calendering. Rigid PVC is compression moulded to give large sheets for chemical plant liners and ducting and also to produce unbreakable microgroove gramophone records. Dispersions of vinyl polymer in suitable plasticizers (PVC pastes or plastisols) are widely used for the manufacture of soft flexible toys, gloves, coated wire racks and baskets. Rigid and flexible foams based on PVC have received wide application in many fields.

Polyvinylidene chloride. See Vinylidene chloride polymers.

Polyvinylpyrrolidone (PVP), $(C_6H_9NO)_n$. A

$$\left[\begin{array}{c} CH_2-CH_2 \\ CH_2 \quad C=O \\ N \\ CH-CH_2 \end{array}\right]_n$$

polymer, usually of chain length between 200 and 7000, consisting of a white powder, insoluble in ether, but soluble in water and in many organic solvents. It is made by treating acetylene with formaldehyde, cyclizing to butyrolactone, treating with ammonia, vinylation, and poly-merization with hydrogen peroxide. Polyvinyl-pyrrolidone is used as a 'volume expander' of blood plasma (with suitable salts to achieve iso-tonicity). It is used in the pharmaceutical in-dustry in the production of tablet granules and the spray coating of tablets. It is also widely used as a dispersing agent for pigments, and in brew-ing.

Laboratory uses include the isolation of leucocytes by sedimentation (aided by PVP), and its application as a stationary phase modifier in gas-liquid chromatography.

Ponceau 4G (Acid Orange 12). Prepared from

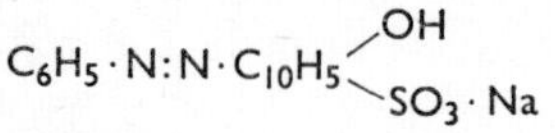

$$C_6H_5 \cdot N : N \cdot C_{10}H_5 \underset{SO_3 \cdot Na}{\overset{OH}{<}}$$

benzene diazonium chloride and β-naphthol monosulphonic acid S ('Schäffer's acid'). It is used chiefly for dyeing non-textiles.

Pope, Sir William Jackson (1870-1939). Born and educated in London, Pope was professor of chemistry at the University of Cambridge from 1908. His numerous investigations included the discovery of the optical activity due to asymmetry of the nitrogen, sulphur, selenium, and tin atoms. He was awarded the Longstaff Medal (Chemical Society), the Davy Medal (Royal Society), and the Messel Medal (Society of Chemical Industry). Elected F.R.S., Pope was in 1919 created K.B.E. See *J. Chem. Soc.*, 1941, 697.

Populin, $C_{20}H_{22}O_8$. Monobenzoylsalicin

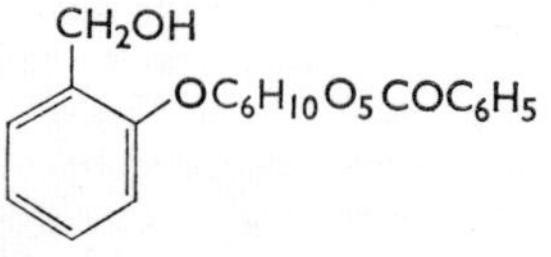

$$\overset{CH_2OH}{\underset{}{\bigcirc}} OC_6H_{10}O_5 COC_6H_5$$

containing the benzoyl group in the sugar nucleus. It is found in the bark of a number of species of poplar. Other benzoyl esters of the sugars are known.

Porphobilinogen, $C_{10}H_{14}N_2O_4$. The immediate

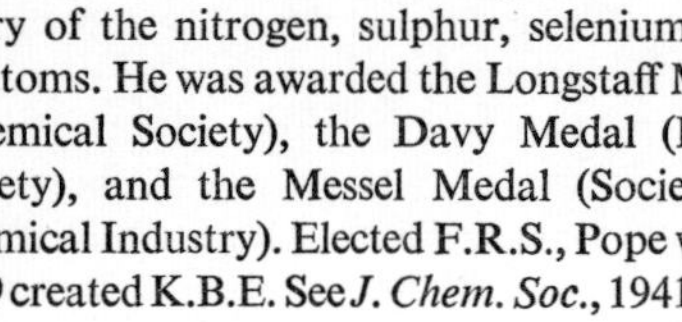

$$HO_2CCH_2CH_2 \underset{\underset{H}{N}}{\overset{CH_2CO_2H}{\diagdown}} CH_2NH_2$$

biogenetic precursor of the porphyrins, itself arising by enzyme-catalysed condensation of two molecules of δ-aminolaevulic acid.

Porphyrins. A group of naturally occurring pigments. Haemoglobin and other animal respiratory pigments and chlorophyll, the respiratory catalyst of plants, are compounds of porphyrins with metals. They are derivatives of the substance porphine which has the formula,

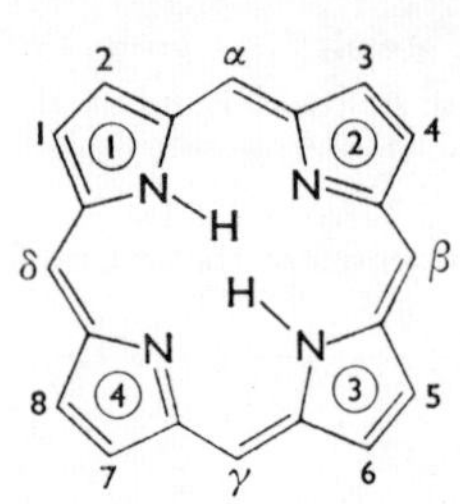

the rings and carbon atoms being numbered and lettered as shown.

The structure of the several porphyrins is most conveniently shown by the accompanying table, which gives the positions of the constituent groups.

Protoporphyrin, $C_{34}H_{34}N_4O_4$, is the porphyrin present in haem, and can be obtained by treating haemin with formic acid and metallic iron. It is identical with oöporphyrin, which occurs in the egg-shells of certain birds.

Mesoporphyrin, $C_{34}H_{38}N_4O_4$, is obtained by treating hæmin with hydriodic acid.

Haematoporphyrin, $C_{34}H_{38}N_4O_6$, is obtained from haemin or haematin by the action of strong acids. It forms deep red crystals, soluble in alcohol, sparingly soluble in ether, insoluble in water.

Aetioporphyrin, $C_{32}H_{38}N_4$, is obtained by heating haematoporphyrin with soda-lime. It forms deep red crystals, soluble in acetone, sparingly soluble in alcohol, insoluble in water.

Coproporphyrin, $C_{36}H_{38}N_4O_8$, is found in the faeces and in normal urine, in the serum of various animals, and in certain yeasts.

Uroporphyrin, $C_{40}H_{38}N_4O_{16}$, is excreted in the urine in the rare congenital disease porphyrinuria.

Rhodoporphyrin, $C_{32}H_{34}N_4O_4$, and pyrroporphyrin, $C_{31}H_{34}N_4O_2$, are obtained by alkaline degradation of chlorophyll; and pyrroaetioporphyrin, $C_{30}H_{34}N_4$, by decarboxylation of these substances.

Porphyrins have also been found in oil shales, in petroleum, in asphalts, and in coal. There is little doubt that these have been derived from chlorophyll and haem, as they resemble the

	1	2	3	4	5	6	7	8
Protoporphyrin	CH_3	C_2H_3	CH_3	C_2H_3	CH_3	C_2H_4COOH	C_2H_4COOH	CH_3
Mesoporphyrin	CH_3	C_2H_5	CH_3	C_2H_5	CH_3	C_2H_4COOH	C_2H_4COOH	CH_3
Haematoporphyrin	CH_3	$CHOH \cdot CH_3$	CH_3	$CHOH \cdot CH_3$	CH_3	C_2H_4COOH	C_2H_4COOH	CH_3
Deuteroporphyrin	CH_3	H	CH_3	H	CH_3	C_2H_4COOH	C_2H_4COOH	CH_3
Aetioporphyrin	CH_3	C_2H_5	CH_3	C_2H_5	CH_3	C_2H_5	C_2H_5	CH_3
Coproporphyrin	CH_3	C_2H_4COOH	CH_3	C_2H_4COOH	CH_3	C_2H_4COOH	C_2H_4COOH	CH_3
Uroporphyrin	CH_3	$C_2H_3(COOH)_2$	CH_3	$C_2H_3(COOH)_2$	CH_3	$C_2H_3(COOH)_2$	$C_2H_3(COOH)_2$	CH_3
Rhodoporphyrin	CH_3	C_2H_5	CH_3	C_2H_5	CH_3	$COOH$	C_2H_4COOH	CH_3
Pyrroporphyrin	CH_3	C_2H_5	CH_3	C_2H_5	CH_3	H	C_2H_4COOH	CH_3
Pyrroaetioporphyrin	CH_3	C_2H_5	CH_3	C_2H_5	CH_3	H	C_2H_5	CH_3

animal and plant porphyrins in the positions of their side chains.

Portland cement. A hydraulic cement which, when set, is supposed to resemble Portland stone. It is made by calcining a mixture of calcium carbonate (chalk or limestone) and some aluminosiliceous material (clay or 'mud') in suitable proportions so as to produce a partially fused clinker, which is afterwards ground to powder. It may also be made from argillaceous limestones and chalk or pure limestone. The precise chemical and mineralogical composition of Portland cement is not known, but it is generally accepted that hardening is due to the successive formation of various hydrates of calcium silicates and aluminates.

Positive displacement pumps. These form one of the two principal classes of pumps. The pumping action is achieved by drawing liquid into the pump body and then displacing it by means of a piston, diaphragm or other moving agent. The characteristic of these machines is that the throughput is a function of pump speed and displacement only, and is not appreciably affected by the pressure against which they are working. This is in contrast with the behaviour of centrifugal pumps, whose capacity decreases markedly as the head against which they are pumping increases.

Positive rays. When an electrical discharge passes through a gas at low pressure, some of the gas molecules become ionized with a positive charge, i.e. lose one or more of their electrons. Such ions pass towards the cathode under the influence of the electric field within the tube, and if a hole is cut in the cathode they will pass through in the form of a beam. Such beams are termed positive rays, or canal rays.

Positive-ray analysis. When a beam of cations (i.e. positive rays) is passed through a magnetic and an electrical field, the various ions are deflected to different extents, depending on their velocities, masses, and charges, and may be detected photographically or in a counter. Positive-ray analysis is used in the mass-spectrometer for the determination of molecular structure.

Positron. The positron is the ultimate indivisible positive charge, or atom of positive electricity. It is the positive counterpart of the electron.

Potash alum. See Alum.

Potassamide, potassium amide, KNH_2. Prepared by dissolving potassium in liquid ammonia or, in a mixture with potassium hydroxide, by dissolving K_2O in liquid ammonia. It is a base in the ammonia system. Potassium first forms a blue solution in liquid ammonia, this is a very strong and useful reducing agent. The blue solution ultimately liberates hydrogen with formation of potassamide.

Potassium, K. At.no. 19, At.wt. 39·100; m.p. 62·3°, b.p. 760°, d 0·87, Crystal structure—body-centred cubic, $a = 5·333$ Å. Potassium is widely distributed; in primary rocks as orthoclase feldspar, $K[AlSi_3O_8]$; in plant life as the oxalate, tartrate, etc.; in animal life in the blood, milk, etc.; and in deposits such as those at Stassfurt. The principal sources of potassium compounds are the Stassfurt and Mulhouse deposits, the New Mexico potash beds, Russian deposits, and the waters of the Dead Sea and of Searles' Lake in California. Potassium salts have also been obtained direct from sea water by solar evaporation.

The metal is obtained by the electrolysis of fused potassium hydroxide in a cell of similar construction to that used for the preparation of sodium. The metal may also be obtained by the reduction of the fluoride or carbonate with carbon or calcium carbide.

Potassium is a very soft, silver-white metal. It is stable in dry air or oxygen, but rapidly becomes corroded in the presence of moisture. It reacts violently with water; the hydrogen evolved burns in air. It exhibits a great affinity for oxygen, extracting it even from the oxides of boron and silicon. It reacts with the chlorides of magnesium and aluminium to give the metal and potassium chloride.

Potassium shows a weak radioactivity, due to the isotope of mass 40.

Potassium acetate, $KC_2H_3O_2$. A colourless deliquescent white powder with a lustrous appearance. Very soluble in water. It occurs in the sap of many plants and trees.

Potassium antimonyl tartrate, Tartar emetic, $K(SbO)C_4H_4O_6$, $\frac{1}{2}H_2O$. Colourless rhombic crystals, soluble up to 6% in cold water, more soluble hot. It is used medicinally as an emetic, and is injected in the treatment of kala-azar, as antimony salts are toxic to the parasite causing it.

Potassium arsenates. Three simple potassium arsenates, K_3AsO_4, K_2HAsO_4, and KH_2AsO_4, are known, and are produced by the appropriate neutralization reactions between arsenic acid and potassium hydroxide. Pyroarsenates and other higher arsenates are also known.

Potassium bicarbonate, $KHCO_3$. Occurs naturally in the mineral calcinite. Is prepared by saturating solutions of potassium carbonate with carbon dioxide. It is less readily soluble than the carbonate, 27·7 g in 100 g H_2O at 0°.

Potassium bisulphate, $KHSO_4$. If a solution of potassium sulphate is treated with an equivalent amount of sulphuric acid, potassium hydrogen sulphate or bisulphate, $KHSO_4$, is formed. This is deposited on crystallization in the anhydrous form.

Potassium bromate, $KBrO_3$. Formed, together with bromide, by dissolving bromine in hot concentrated caustic potash. The salts may be separated by fractional crystallization, the bromate being much less soluble than the bromide (3·01 g in 100 g H_2O at 0°). On heating, the salt decomposes, with the liberation of oxygen and the formation of bromide.

Potassium bromide, KBr. Obtained by neutralizing potassium hydroxide or carbonate with hydrobromic acid, or by dissolving bromine in caustic potash. It has the NaCl lattice. No hydrates are known. It has m.p. 728°, b.p. 1376°, and is readily soluble in water (53·5 g in 100 g at 0°), and in liquid ammonia, forming $KBr,4NH_3$ (m.p. −45°). The compound is used to some extent in photography, and in medicine for its sedative action.

Potassium *tert*-butoxide, $KOC(CH_3)_3$. A white crystalline solid obtained in an alcohol-free form by sublimation (200°/0·1 mm) of the product made by dissolving potassium in tertiary butyl alcohol. It is extremely hygroscopic, but a very powerful organic base. It is readily soluble in toluene, diethyl ether, tetrahydrofuran, and dimethyl sulphoxide. Solutions in the latter solvent increase the rate of many reactions depending upon proton abstraction.

Potassium carbonate, K_2CO_3. Also known as pearl ash, it is a white deliquescent powder, m.p. 901°, which dissolves readily in water to give a strongly alkaline solution, solubility 105 g in 100 g water at 0°. Hydrates with $6H_2O$ and $1\frac{1}{2}H_2O$ exist. It is made by a modification of the Solvay process using alcoholic solutions.

Potassium chlorate, $KClO_3$. Hot lime-water on treatment with chlorine gives calcium chloride and chlorate. The addition of potassium chloride to this solution results in the deposition of potassium chlorate. It may also be obtained from the sodium chlorate produced by electrolysis of sodium chloride solutions. It is readily purified by recrystallization; solubility at 15° is 5·7 g in 100 g H_2O. On heating potassium chlorate to 510°, both potassium chloride and perchlorate are formed; at higher temperatures oxygen is evolved and potassium chloride remains.

Potassium chloride, KCl. The most important potassium salt, occurs naturally as the mineral sylvine, and in a variety of other minerals. Among these are sylvinite (KCl with NaCl), carnallite ($KCl \cdot MgCl_2 \cdot 6H_2O$), kainite ($KCl \cdot MgSO_4 \cdot 3H_2O$) and 'hard salt' (KCl with NaCl and $MgSO_4 \cdot H_2O$). It also occurs in cer-

tain natural brines. The most important deposits of potassium chloride are at Stassfurt in Germany, but U.S.A. sources furnish about 40% of the world's supply. In nearly all cases the potassium chloride is separated by a process of fractional crystallization.

Potassium chloride (sylvine) has d 1·984, m.p. 776°, b.p. 1500°. The crystals have the cubic sodium chloride lattice, a_0 6·276 Å. Potassium chloride is soluble in water (27·6 g in 100 g H_2O at 0°) and in methyl, ethyl, propyl and butyl alcohols.

More than 90% of the potassium chloride produced is used for fertilizers. The rest is used to produce other potassium compounds.

Potassium chromate, K_2CrO_4. Yellow crystals, prepared by heating a source of chromium with potassium carbonate and lime or by electrolysing potassium hydroxide with a ferrochrome electrode. Used in the production of potassium dichromate and as a source of chromate (VI) ion.

Potassium citrate. $K_3C_6H_5O_7$, H_2O. Colourless crystals, very soluble in water, slightly soluble in alcohol. It is used medicinally as a diuretic and to render the urine less acid.

Potassium cyanide, KCN. Obtained by igniting the ferrocyanide alone or with potassium carbonate; m.p. 634·5°. It is usually prepared by Beilby's process; a fused mixture of potassium carbonate with carbon reacts with ammonia gas to give potassium cyanide and water. The fused cyanide is decanted and moulded, and is then sufficiently pure for ordinary purposes. The salt may be further purified by crystallization from anhydrous liquid ammonia. Potassium cyanide is a very poisonous substance; it is very soluble in water (71·6 g in 100 g H_2O at 25°), the solution being strongly hydrolysed. On standing, the aqueous solutions slowly evolve hydrogen cyanide.

Potassium dichromate, $K_2Cr_2O_7$. Orange-red triclinic crystals, m.p. 396°; 100 parts of water dissolve about 10 parts. It is prepared by heating chrome iron ore with potassium carbonate and lime, and acidifying to convert the chromate to dichromate, or by electrolysing potassium hydroxide with a ferrochrome anode. It is used in the preparation of chrome pigments, as a bleaching agent, and as an oxidizing agent in many organic preparations. It is also used in volumetric analysis.

Potassium fluoride, KF. Obtained directly from the elements, or more readily by the neutralization of potassium hydroxide or carbonate with hydrofluoric acid. It has m.p. 846°, d 2·523°, solubility 96·5 g in 100 g water at 25°. The salt crystallizes in the cubic system with the sodium chloride structure. In addition to the anhydrous salt, both a dihydrate and a tetra-hydrate are known.

A number of acid fluorides are known, e.g. KF, HF; KF, 2HF; and KF, 3HF. The melting-point decreases with increasing proportion of hydrofluoric acid. The acid salts are used in the preparation of fluorine by electrolysis.

Potassium hydrogen sulphate. An alternative name for potassium bisulphate.

Potassium hydrogen tartrate, Cream of tartar, $C_4H_5O_6K$. Colourless rhombic prisms, insoluble in cold water, soluble up to 6% in boiling water. It occurs in grape juice and is deposited as argol during fermentation. It is largely used as an in-gredient of baking powders, as it reacts slowly with sodium bicarbonate in the presence of water and carbon dioxide is given off.

Potassium hydroxide, KOH. M.p. 306°. It is prepared on the large scale by the electrolysis of potassium chloride solutions. Very pure hydrox-ide is obtained by action of barium hydroxide on potassium sulphate, or of water on potassium amalgam. Forms a white, translucent, fibrous solid after fusion. Hydrates with 2, $1\frac{1}{2}$, and $1H_2O$ are known. The aqueous solutions are very strongly basic and act as strong electrolytes; solubility 112·8 g in 100 g water at 25°.

Potassium iodate, KIO_3. Formed together with the iodide in the reaction between iodine and hot caustic potash. No hydrates are known, and the salt may be dried by heating to 160°. Several acid iodates are known, e.g. KIO_3, HIO_3, and KIO_3, $2HIO_3$.

Potassium iodide, KI. Most readily prepared by dissolving iodine in hot caustic potash, when both potassium iodide and iodate are formed. It may be separated by fractional crystallization. Potassium iodide is readily soluble in water (56 g of KI in 100 g H_2O at 0°), alcohol, acetone, pyridine, acetonitrile, etc. It crystallizes in the cubic system with the sodium chloride structure. It is also soluble in liquid ammonia (compounds KI, $6NH_3$ and KI, $4NH_3$ are known), and in liquid sulphur dioxide. Aqueous solutions of potassium iodide dissolve iodine with the forma-tion of polyiodides such as KI_3, KI_5 and KI_7. It is used medicinally in the treatment of goitre, syphilis, rheumatism, arteriosclerosis, and other diseases.

Potassium nitrate, KNO_3. Usually prepared by fractional crystallization from a solution of sodium nitrate and potassium chloride. Potas-sium nitrate is soluble in water (13·43 g in 100 g H_2O at 0°), liquid ammonia, and methyl alcohol.

Potassium nitrite, KNO_2, is prepared by reduc-tion of potassium nitrate with lead. It has m.p. 440°. It is used in organic diazotizations.

Potassium oxalate, $C_2O_4K_2,H_2O$. Colourless monoclinic prisms or pyramids, soluble in water (1 in 3). The acid salt, C_2O_4HK, potassium hydrogen oxalate, occurs either anhydrous in monoclinic prisms, or in triclinic crystals with one molecule of water of crystallization. It is less soluble in water (1 in 6 at 60°) and is unstable in solution below 50°, decomposing to give potassium quadroxalate or tetroxalate, $C_2O_4HK, C_2O_4H_2, 2H_2O$, which forms triclinic crystals slightly soluble in cold water (1 in 30) more soluble in hot. Potassium tetroxalate is used under the names of 'salts of sorrel' and 'salts of lemon' for removing inkstains and iron mould. The potassium oxalates can all be prepared by neutralizing oxalic acid with potassium hydroxide or carbonate in the requisite proportions and crystallizing.

Potassium oxides. *Potassium monoxide,* K_2O. Obtained by heating potassium nitrate with the theoretical quantity of potassium *in vacuo.* It reacts violently with water with the formation of the hydroxide, and with liquid ammonia with the formation of the hydroxide and potassamide, KNH_2. The hydrate $K_2O \cdot 3H_2O$, is known.

Potassium peroxide, K_2O_2. Obtained by pass-ing oxygen into a liquid ammonia solution of potassium at $-60°$. Gives hydrogen peroxide with acids. Unstable hydrates K_2O_2, H_2O, and $K_2O_2 \cdot 2H_2O$, are known.

Potassium superoxide, KO_2. Prepared by burning potassium in excess oxygen. It is a yel-low, paramagnetic powder, m.p. 380°. On strong heating, oxygen is evolved and the monoxide re-mains; it reacts with water to form the hydroxide, hydrogen peroxide, and oxygen.

Potassium perchlorate, $KClO_4$. Readily prepared by neutralizing perchloric acid with caustic potash, or by heating potassium chlorate to 510°. Solubility at 0° is 0.75 g per 100 g H_2O. It is still less soluble in aqueous ethyl alcohol, and is used in the separation of potassium from sodium in gravimetric determinations of the former.

It is obtained commercially by reacting con-centrated sodium perchlorate solution (made electrolytically) with potassium chloride solu-tion.

Potassium periodate, KIO_4. Prepared by the oxidation of a potassium iodate solution with chlorine. The salt is not very soluble in water (0·51 g in 100 g H_2O at 25°). Two other periodates are known, $K_4I_2O_9, 9H_2O$ and $K_4I_2O_9$. KIO_4 is used as an oxidizing agent.

Potassium permanganate, $KMnO_4$. See Perman-ganates and Permanganate titrations.

Potassium persulphate, $K_2S_2O_8$. Obtained by double decomposition between ammonium per-sulphate and potassium carbonate, or by the direct electrolysis of potassium sulphate solutions. Aqueous solutions of the salt slowly evolve oxygen with the formation of potassium bisulphate.

Potassium polysulphides. From the system K_2S—S it appears that the sulphides K_2S_2, K_2S_3, K_2S_4, K_2S_5, and K_2S_6 exist. From aqueous alcoholic solutions of KS_2 and S the following compounds have been isolated: $K_2S_2 \cdot 3H_2O$; K_2S_3; $K_2S_4 \cdot 2H_2O$; $K_2S_4 \cdot 4H_2O$; and $K_2S_5 \cdot H_2O$. The compounds are all hygroscopic and readily oxidized in the air. Aqueous solutions deposit sulphur and evolve hydrogen sulphide on the addition of dilute acid.

Potassium sulphate, K_2SO_4. Does not occur free in nature, but in combination with sodium sulphate in glaserite, $3K_2SO_4$, Na_2SO_4; with magnesium sulphate in schönite, K_2SO_4, $MgSO_4$, $4H_2O$; and with calcium sulphate in syngenite, $K_2SO_4 \cdot CaSO_4 \cdot H_2O$. The salt is usually prepared from schönite by the addition of potassium chloride and subsequent fractional crystallization. The sulphate is the first to be deposited (solubility 10·3 g in $100\,g\,H_2O$ at 15°).

May be prepared by neutralizing caustic potash or potassium carbonate with dilute sulphuric acid. Anhydrous rhombic prisms are deposited after evaporation.

Many acid salts, e.g. $K_2SO_4 \cdot 3H_2SO_4$; $K_2SO_4 \cdot H_2SO_4$; $4K_2SO_4 \cdot 3H_2SO_4$; $K_2SO_4 \cdot KHSO_4$; K_2SO_4, $6KHSO_4 \cdot H_2SO \cdot_4$, and KHS_2O_7 are formed from solutions of potassium sulphate in aqueous sulphuric acid.

Potassium sulphide, K_2S. The anhydrous compound is formed by the action of sulphur vapour on potassium in vacuum at 200°-300°. The product is a white powder. It is also obtained by passing hydrogen over the heated sulphate. If a solution of caustic potash is saturated with hydrogen sulphide and evaporated, crystals of the hydrosulphide $2KHS$, H_2O are deposited. Solutions of the hydrosulphide on treatment with an equivalent volume of caustic potash solution, on evaporation, yield crystals of the monosulphide pentahydrate, K_2S, $5H_2O$. The dihydrate $K_2S \cdot 2H_2O$ is also known.

Aqueous solutions of the sulphide are partly hydrolysed, and slowly lose hydrogen sulphide on standing.

Potassium sulphite, K_2SO_3. The anhydrous salt is obtained in fine crystals by the saturation of concentrated caustic potash with sulphur dioxide, and the addition of a further quantity of caustic potash, in an inert atmosphere, followed by rapid drying in a vacuum desiccator.

On saturating a solution of caustic potash (33 g in $100\,g\,H_2O$) with sulphur dioxide at 100°, and cooling to 20°, crystals of potassium pyrosulphite, $K_2S_2O_5$, are deposited.

Potentiometric titration. A titration in which the end-point is determined by observing the changes in potential of a suitable indicating electrode.

Potter's clay. A term used for any clay or earth which can be used for making pottery, either alone or after admixture with non-plastic materials, though the term is usually restricted to the clays used for fine pottery. The composition varies greatly, and is usually of minor importance; the essential properties are sufficient plasticity to enable the desired articles to be shaped readily and sufficient refractoriness to enable the pottery to be burned in a potter's oven or kiln. Other properties, such as smoothness of working during the shaping, the colour of the finished ware, brittleness, porosity of the ware, etc., are also important in some instances. The red colour of terra-cotta flowerpots and some other pottery is due to iron compounds (probably nontronite) in the clay; these decompose on heating and liberate ferric oxide or complexes rich in ferric oxide which are red in colour. Other colours are produced by firing the kiln or oven under reducing conditions, or by adding coloured oxides to the clay.

Powder metallurgy. The production of metal products, or products containing metals as major components, from powders by sintering processes.

Powder of algorath. See Antimony oxychlorides.

Power kerosine. A volatile kerosine of high antiknock value, essentially a blend of aromatic hydrocarbons, used in tractor engines and usually called tractor vaporizing oil (TVO).

Praseodymium, Pr. At.no. 59, At.wt. 140·92, d 6·782, m.p. 935°, b.p. 3127°. Below 798° the metal has the hexagonal close-packed structure ($a = 3·6702$, $c = 11·822$ Å); above 798° the structure is body-centred cubic ($a = 4·13$ Å). It is a typical rare-earth element (q.v.). The metal is readily oxidized in air.

Praseodymium compounds. Praseodymium (III) salts are pale green in colour and are typical rare-earth compounds (q.v.). Praseodymium oxide, Pr_2O_3 and ozone yield black oxides Pr_6O_{11} and PrO_2. Complex fluorides, e.g. $NaPrF_5$ and K_2PrF_6, can be obtained by the action of fluorine on mixtures of alkali fluorides and praseodymium compounds.

Precipitation hardening. The term is used for a phenomenon observed in certain alloys. It is associated with a change in properties with time. Hardening takes place when a supersaturated solution in the solid state tends to decompose with partial precipitation of the solute metal as an intermetallic compound. The first stages of this precipitation result in a pinning of the dislocations with a resultant increase in hardness and decrease in ductility. Duralumin (Al+4% Cu) exhibits age hardening. After quenching from 480° to provide a supersaturated solid solution of Cu in Al, its hardness will increase on standing for four days at room temperature or 1 hour at 100°. This 'artificial' or high-temperature ageing is referred to as precipitation hardening and is common in many alloy systems, in particular steels for high-temperature service.

Precipitation interval. See Indicators, turbidity.

Precipitation point. See Indicators, turbidity.

Predissociation. A term used in spectroscopy in connexion with a type of molecular band spectrum. The bands are diffuse; they have no sharp convergence limit, but merge gradually into a continuum. This is explained by postulating that absorption of light excites the molecule initially into a metastable state, but after a few vibrations the molecule may dissociate.

Prednisolone, $C_{21}H_{28}O_5$. 11β, 17α, 21-Trihydroxypregna - 1, 4 - diene - 3, 20 - dione. Prepared chemically from dihydrocortisone

acetate, or by the action of certain microorganisms on hydrocortisone. It is a white crystalline powder, soluble in alcohol, and insoluble in water. It is also used as the acetate, m.p. 240°.

It is used for the same purposes as cortisone, for treating rheumatoid arthritis, rheumatic fever, etc., but it is effective in smaller doses. It is especially useful in the treatment of asthma.

Pregl, Fritz (1869-1930). Born at Laibach, Pregl studied at Graz, Tübingen, Leipzig, and Berlin. In 1905 he became extraordinary professor of physiological chemistry at Graz, and in 1910 went to Innsbruck as ordinary professor of applied medical chemistry. In 1913 he returned to Graz in a similar capacity and remained there to the end of his career. His introduction of microchemical methods revolutionized analytical chemistry and gained him the Nobel Prize in chemistry in 1923.

Pregnane, 17β-Ethylaetiocholane, $C_{21}H_{36}$. M.p. 83·5°, $[\alpha]_D^{19}$ +20°. It does not occur naturally, but has been obtained synthetically. It is the basic

hydrocarbon skeleton of biologically and clinically important steroids.

Pregnanediol, $C_{21}H_{36}O_2$. Although there are 4

isomeric pregnane-3,20-diols, differing only in orientation of the hydroxyl groups at positions 3 and 20, only the 3(α),20(α)-diol occurs naturally. It accompanies oestrone in the urine of pregnant women but has no physiological activity. It is probably formed by reduction of progesterone and is used in the manufacture of this substance. Plates from alcohol, m.p. 238°, $[\alpha]_D^{20}$ +27°; sparingly soluble in organic solvents.

Premetallised dyes. One of the most important classes of dyestuffs. They are of two types.

(1) 1:1 *complex*, i.e. one dye molecule is combined with one metal atom (usually chromium).

This type was marketed shortly after the first world war as Neolan dyes (Ciba) and Palatine Fast dyes (I.G.): later I.C.I. introduced Ultralan dyes.

They are soluble chromium co-ordination complexes derived from lake-forming monoazo dyes usually having an *o*-hydroxy structure.

These dyes have proved very useful in wool dyeing and are applied in a similar manner to the level dyeing acid dyes. They have also a limited use on other fibres such as silk, Nylon and Acrilan.

(2) 2:1 *complex*, i.e. two molecules of dye are combined with each chromium atom.

These dyes have been introduced since 1950 and include Irgalan, Cibalan, Vialan Fast and Isolan dyes. Their introduction represents one of the major advances in dyestuff technology during this century and involves the solubilizing of the dye by means of groups other than the usual sulphonic acid group.

They have proved successful in dyeing wool by a simple dyeing process giving dyeings of excellent fastness to light and to most wet treatments, in addition to having other very useful features, e.g. ability to dye evenly on wool of varying qualities. They are also proving useful for dyeing silk and many synthetic fibres including Nylon, Perlon, and Acrilan.

Prephenic acid, $C_{10}H_{10}O_6$. An intermediate in

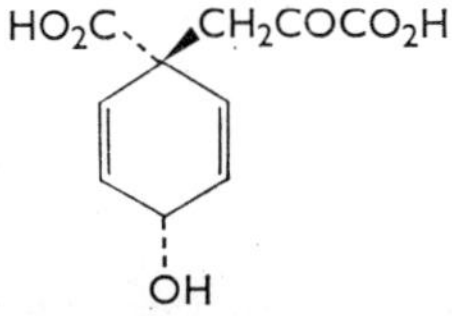

the 'shikimic acid pathway' of aromatic biosynthesis, arising by rearrangement of chorismic acid. It is the precursor of phenylpyruvic acid (which is obtained readily in the laboratory merely on acidification of a solution of prephenic acid), and of *p*-hydroxyphenylpyruvic acid. These in turn yield by transamination phenylalanine and tyrosine.

Pressure distillate. Product of a cracking process

which on distillation and refining yields a cracked gasoline.

Priestley, Joseph. The son of poor parents, he was born in 1733 and elected to the Royal Society in 1766. He became a Unitarian minister in Leeds, and invented soda-water. Appointed librarian to Lord Shelburne in 1772 and remained with him for seven years engaged in the study of various gases. He was the first to prepare sulphur dioxide, ammonia gas, and nitrous oxide. Discovered oxygen in 1774 and published an account of it, not knowing that Scheele had discovered it about two years earlier. Emigrated to America and died there in 1804. See Thorpe's 'Essays'.

Primaquine, $C_{15}H_{21}N_3O$. Used as the diphosphate, which is a red crystalline powder, m.p.

201°, soluble in water, insoluble in alcohol. It is an antimalarial, more active and less toxic than

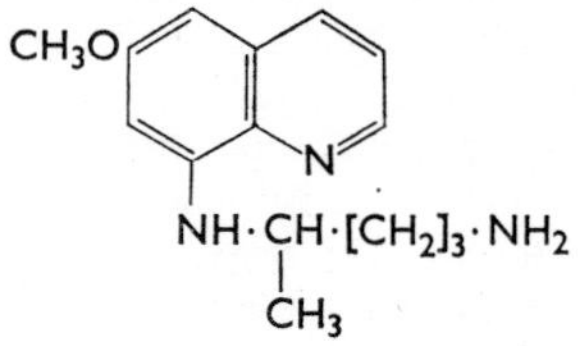

pamaquin, and is used chiefly in treating *Plasmodium vivax* infections.

Primeverose, $C_{11}H_{20}O_{10}$. A disaccharide, glucose-6-β-D-xyloside, only found as a constituent of the glycosides gaultherin, rhamnicosin, primeverin, genticaulin, etc. The crystals melt at 208°; $[\alpha]_D -3\cdot4°$.

Primidone, $C_{12}H_{14}N_2O_2$. It is 5-ethyl-5-phenyl-hexahydropyrimidine-4,6-dione. It is a white

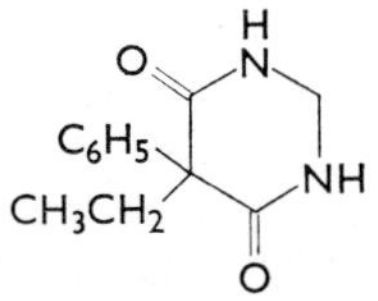

crystalline powder, m.p. 281°, slightly soluble in water, insoluble in organic solvents, prepared by reacting α-ethyl-α-phenylmalonamide with formic acid or formamide. It is an anticonvulsant used in treating grand mal and psychomotor epilepsy, but has several undesirable side-effects.

Primuline (Direct Yellow 59). Primuline base is a

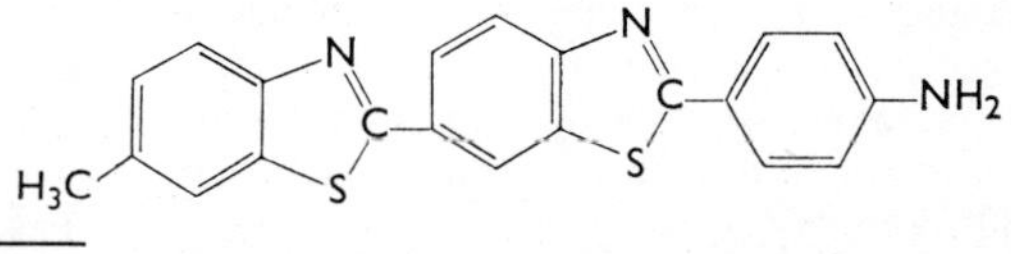

mixture of the dithio-base shown above and a trithio-base formed by condensation of one extra molecule of *p*-toluidine and sulphur.

It is prepared as a 40% constituent of the mixture of bases obtained by heating 2 molecules of *p*-toluidine with 4 atoms of sulphur. The mixture as thus prepared also contains 50% of dehydrothiotoluidine.

Primuline is used as a first component in azo-dyes. The dyes thus produced are direct cotton colours. It can also be sulphonated. The properties of primuline and dehydrothiotoluidine are very similar. The crude mixture of bases is usually used without separation.

The sulphonated compound has itself direct affinity for the fibre. If it is used thus it can be diazotized on the fibre and coupled *in situ* with a secondary component. The 'ingrained dyeing' thus produced has improved wet fastness properties over the direct dyed material.

Principal quantum number. See Electronic configuration.

Procainamide hydrochloride, $C_{13}H_{22}ClN_3O$. A

$$NH_2{-}C_6H_4{-}CONH[CH_2]_2N(C_2H_5)_2\cdot HCl$$

white crystalline powder, very soluble in water and in alcohol, m.p. 167°. It has actions similar to those of procaine, but has greater effects on the heart, decreasing excitability and contractility. It is used to reduce the risk of fibrillation during operations on the chest.

Procaine, ethocaine, diethylaminoethyl-*p*-aminobenzoate. $NH_2\cdot C_6H_4\cdot COOC_2H_4\cdot N(C_2H_5)_2$, $C_{13}H_{20}N_2O_2$. Crystallizes in colourless needles with two molecules of water from aqueous alcohol; m.p. 51° (61° anhydrous). Sparingly soluble inwater. Its hydrochloride (trade name Novocaine) has m.p. 153°-156° and is very soluble in water. It is prepared by the action of diethylaminoethyl chloride on sodium *p*-aminobenzoate. The hydrochloride is a powerful local anaesthetic, particularly when used in conjunction with adrenaline. It is much less toxic than cocaine which it has very largely replaced.

Producer gas or **Air gas.** A mixture of carbon monoxide and nitrogen used for industrial heating purposes; it is prepared by passing air with a little steam through a bed of incandescent coke in a 'producer', or closed furnace, in which the coke rests on a suitable grate. To secure maximum efficiency the producer gas should be burnt while still hot from the producer; if it is allowed to cool before use about 30% of the available heat is lost.

Proflavine, 2,8-diaminoacridine sulphate

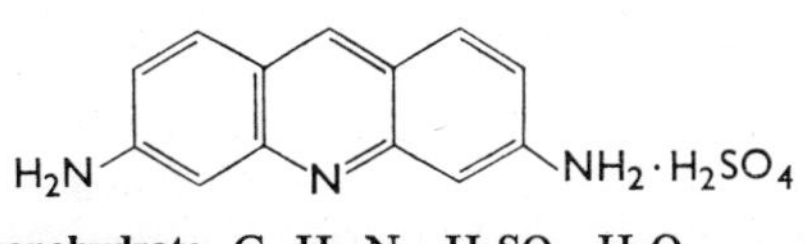

$$H_2N \cdots N \cdots NH_2\cdot H_2SO_4$$

monohydrate, $C_{13}H_{11}N_3$, H_2SO_4, H_2O.
A red crystalline powder, soluble in water and slightly soluble in alcohol. Both proflavine and acriflavine are effective against gram positive and gram negative bacteria, and are used for the treatment of infected wounds, vaginitis, and gonococcal infections.

Progesterone, Progestin, $C_{21}H_{30}O_2$. Colourless crystals, existing in two forms with equal physiological activity, (α) prisms from ether, m.p. 128·5°, (β) needles from petroleum ether, m.p. 121°-122°. Soluble in organic solvents, sparingly soluble in water, $[\alpha]_D$ +192°. Progesterone is the hormone of the corpus luteum. It

governs the growth and development of the uterus during pregnancy.

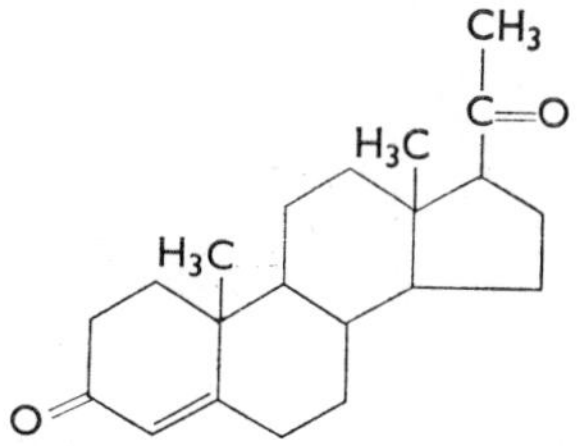

Progesterone can be manufactured from cholesterol, from certain steroid sapogenins, and from stigmasterol. It is given by injection in the treatment of abortion and of certain menstrual disturbances.

Proguanil, $C_{11}H_{16}ClN_5$. Trade name Paludrine. It is obtained as the hydrochloride, m.p. 248°, soluble in 110 parts of water and 40 parts of alcohol, which is prepared by treating *p*-chlorophenyldicyandiamide with isopropylamine hydrochloride. It is used for the prevention and

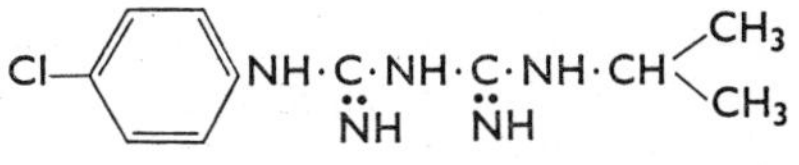

$$Cl{-}C_6H_4{-}NH\cdot C\cdot NH\cdot C\cdot NH\cdot CH\underset{CH_3}{\overset{CH_3}{<}}$$

treatment of malaria. In certain types of malaria it kills the latent tissue parasites, preventing recurrence of attacks on cessation of treatment. It is not the best drug to use in acute malarial infection, as quinine acts more rapidly on the parasites in the red blood cells.

Prolactin. One of the hormones obtained from the anterior lobe of the pituitary gland, the presence of which is necessary for the secretion of milk. It is a protein, with mol.wt. about 33,000.

Prolamines. A class of proteins, formerly called gliadins, found in the seeds of cereals. They resemble the glutelins in being insoluble in water and absolute alcohol, but differ in being soluble in 70% alcohol. They are soluble in dilute acids and alkalis. Typical glutelins are gliadin from wheat, hordein from barley, and zein from maize.

Proline, α-Pyrrolidinecarboxylic acid, $C_5H_9NO_2$. Crystallizes in flat needles, m.p. 220°-222°. Soluble in water and alcohol. The naturally occurring product is laevorotatory, $[\alpha]_D^{20}$ −77·4°. While not strictly an amino-acid, it is commonly included in the list of those obtained by the hydrolysis of proteins.

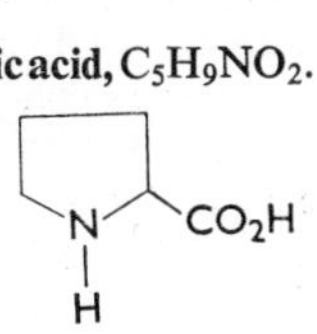

Promazine. See Chlorpromazine.

Prometal. A variety of cast iron specially suitable for the construction of furnace parts.

Promethazine, $C_{17}H_{20}N_2S$. Used as the hydro-chloride, which is a white powder, m.p. 223°,

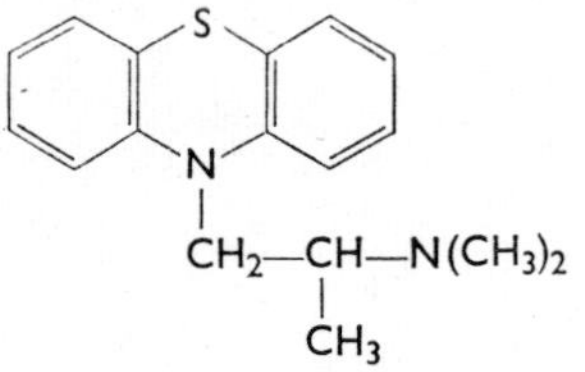

very soluble in water, soluble in alcohol and chloroform. Prepared by condensing pheno-thiazine with 2-chloro-1-dimethylaminopro-pane in the presence of sodamide, and convert-ing to the hydrochloride.

It is a powerful antagonist of histamine, antagonizing its effect on plain muscle of the bronchioles, bladder, intestine, and uterus, and preventing the dilation of capillaries. Prometha-zine is used in the treatment of allergic reactions, such as hay fever and dermatitis, and allergic reactions due to drugs. Side effects include seda-tion, dryness of the mouth, and vomiting.

Promethium, Pm. At.no. 61, At.wt. 145. Prome-thium has only been obtained as a product of the fission of uranium; two isotopes, [147]Pm and [149]Pm, have been identified, having half-lives of 3·7 years and 47 hours respectively.

Element no. 61 was previously called illinium. With such a short life its natural existence would not be possible.

Promethium compounds. Only a very few pro-methium compounds are known, the pro-methium existing in the +3 oxidation state. The salts are rose-pink in colour and are typical rare-earth compounds (q.v.).

Prontosil, Prontosil rubrum. A trade name for sulphamidochrysoidin, 4-sulphonamido-2, 4-di-aminoazobenzene, $C_{12}H_{13}N_5O_2S$. It is a red

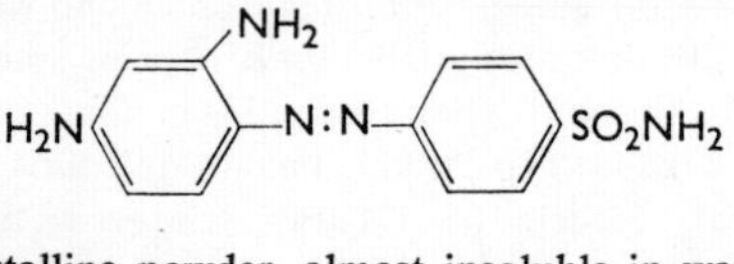

crystalline powder, almost insoluble in water, moderately soluble in alcohol. Prontosil was the first of the sulphonamides to be used medically, and has since been superseded by more effective compounds. It is inactive in vitro and owes its activity in the body to being broken down to sulphanilamide.

Proof spirit. The legal standard used in assessing the strength of alcoholic liquors for Excise pur-poses. It is defined as a solution of ethyl alcohol in water such as shall, at 51°F, weigh exactly 12/13 of an equal volume of distilled water at 51° F. This corresponds to an alcoholic solution containing 49·28% w/w or 57·10% v/v at 60° F

and has a specific gravity of 0·91976 at 15·6° C. Other strengths are described as so many degrees over- or under-proof. Thus 100 volumes of a spirit of 20° over-proof when diluted with 20 volumes of water would give a spirit of proof strength; similarly 100 volumes of a spirit 20° under-proof contains 80 volumes of spirit of proof strength.

Propane, $C_3H_8, CH_3CH_2CH_3$. A colourless in-flammable gas with a peculiar odour. M.p. $-190°$, b.p. $-44·5°$. It occurs in the natural gas from petroleum. Also obtained by reduction of propylene. Has general properties of the par-affins. Used as a refrigerant and as a fuel.

1,3-Propane dithiol, $HS[CH_2]_3SH$, is a liquid, b.p. 170°-171°, with an extremely disagreeable odour. Slightly soluble in water, but volatile in steam, it dissolves readily in most organic sol-vents. It is principally used in organic chemistry for protecting a carbonyl group as a trimethylene

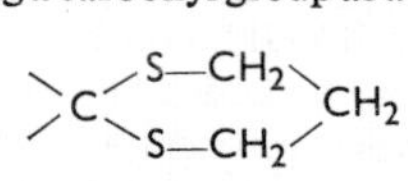

dithioketal whilst transformations are effected at other centres of the molecule.

Propargyl alcohol, 2-propyn-1-ol,

$$HC\!:\!C\cdot CH_2OH.$$

B.p. 112°, n_D^{20} 1·430, d_4^{20} 0·9485, miscible with water and most polar organic solvents, im-miscible with petroleum ether. It is easily polymerized by heat or alkali, and used widely in organic synthesis.

Propathene. A trade name for a range of plastics materials based on isotactic polypropylene and certain of its copolymers.

Propellants. A general description for an explo-sive used to propel a rocket, bullet, shot, or shell. Colloidal propellants, often referred to as cor-dites, are based on nitrocellulose and vary from straightforward gelatinized propellants consist-ing largely of nitrocellulose to mixtures contain-ing nitrocellulose, nitroglycerin and nitroguani-dine. Nitrocellulose propellants, single based propellants, consist essentially of a mixture of nitrocellulose, plasticizer, and stabilizer. The plasticizer may be residual solvent but with the more modern ones a material like dibutyl phthalate is used. The stabilizer employed is usually diphenylamine and its function is to react and remove the acid decomposition pro-ducts which form when nitrocellulose decom-poses. Numerous additives are used to achieve certain ballistic requirements. Dinitrotoluene makes the composition cooler, i.e. burn at a lower temperature, and thereby causes less erosion in the gun barrel. The aim is to achieve steady burning and the complete gelatinization of the nitrocellulose is therefore essential. Usually the nitrocellulose is gelatinized by acetone or ether/alcohol mixture and the other ingredients added and incorporated. Pressing to the desired size and shape and finally drying to a particular volatile matter content (this consisting of a mixture of water and solvent) completes the process. Double based propellants or propellants containing nitrocellulose and nitroglycerin have been used extensively in the United Kingdom and are the basis for a number of rocket motors. In their processing, nitrocellulose is mixed with nitroglycerin and a stabilizer which is often N,N'-diethyl-N,N'-diphenylurea, although the latter is now replaced by the less basic 2-nitrodiphenylamine in more recent compositions. Usually this procedure is accomplished by water mixing in the absence of any solvent although a process using acetone can be employed. The paste formed at this stage is dried, gelatinized on hot rolls and finally pressed to the desired size and shape. Triple based propellants or propellants containing nitroguanidine, nitroglycerin and nitrocellulose are relatively flashless and supply much of the requirements for guns in Britain. They are manufactured by wet-mixing nitrocellulose and nitroglycerin, drying the resultant paste and incorporating this with nitroguanidine and N,N'-diethyl-N,N'-diphenylurea in the presence of acetone. The incorporated dough is pressed and the remaining acetone dried off in stoves at 40°. There are variations in this technique designed to achieve a better finish on the propellant stick. The object in all these methods of manufacture is to obtain a product which has uniform ballistics and is safe to store in any part of the world.

Composite propellants. This class of propellant, consisting of an oxidant, usually inorganic, mixed with an organic fuel which may also act as a binder, can be used in rocket motors. Of the oxidants which have been investigated the most common is ammonium perchlorate. This material is sensitive to friction but when mixed with a plastic or rubbery fuel quickly loses its sensitivity. The fuel is usually rubbery in nature and is frequently cured *in situ*.

Liquid propellants. The best known example is isopropyl nitrate, which has high energy, burns steadily and stores safely but is volatile and has ignition risks similar to those of petrol. Oxidants such as liquid oxygen and concentrated hydrogen peroxide can be used in this propellant field by providing the oxygen to burn kerosine or other hydrocarbon fuel. Nitrogen dioxide is also used as an oxidant and when employed in conjunction with hydrazine derivatives forms a powerful hypergolic (self ignitory) mixture. Much work has been carried out on fluorine compounds as oxidants and on fuels containing hydrides. Such combinations can give very high energies in relation to their weight. Liquids in general have a limited use except in very large motors.

The word 'propellant' is also used for the liquefied gas in a pressurized aerosol container.

Propeller mixer, propeller agitator. One or two marine-type propellers are mounted on a vertical shaft which is rotated in the liquid to be stirred. The propellers produce an axial thrust, and deflection of the liquid stream at the bottom of the tank produces a circulating motion. These mixers have a tendency to produce a vortex, and to avoid this they are usually set off-centre and, or the shaft is inclined. In very large tanks the propeller may be carried on a shaft entering through the side.

Propeller mixers are extensively used for the agitation of thin liquids and the suspension of solids in them. They are reasonably economical in power, can be used over a wide range of speeds and do not become fouled. They are not, however, suitable for viscous liquids.

Propene. See Propylene.

Propionic acid, $C_3H_6O_2$, CH_3CH_2COOH. A colourless liquid with an odour resembling that of acetic acid; m.p. 24°, b.p. 140·7°. Miscible with water and alcohol. Occurs in the products of the distillation of wood. Prepared by the oxidation of propyl alcohol or by the reduction of acrylic acid.

Propyl. The univalent group $-C_3H_7$, which occurs in two isomeric forms: normal propyl, or Pr^n, which is $CH_3 \cdot CH_2 \cdot CH_2-$, and *iso* propyl or Pr^i, which is $(CH_3)_2CH-$. The former radical has been prepared in the free state by the photolysis of di-*n*-propyl ketone. It is less stable thermally than methyl or ethyl.

***n*-Propyl alcohol, *n*-Propanol,** C_3H_8O, $CH_3CH_2CH_2OH$. A colourless liquid with a pleasant odour; d^{20} 0·8035, b.p. 97·4°. Miscible with water, alcohol, ether, and acetone. It occurs in fusel oil and is separated by distillation. Also obtained by the hydrogenation of propylene oxide. Oxidized to propaldehyde and propionic acid. Forms propylene when heated with sulphuric acid. Used as a solvent and for the preparation of esters.

Propylene, Propene, C_3H_6, $CH_3CH=CH_2$. A colourless gas, m.p. $-185·2°$, b.p. $-48°$. Occurs in the gases from the cracking of petroleum. Prepared by passing the vapour of isopropyl alcohol over heated alumina. Reacts with sulphuric acid to give isopropyl ether and isopropyl alcohol; with halogens to give propylene dihalides; with dilute chlorine water to give propylene chlorohydrin, and with hydrogen in the presence of catalysts to give propane.

Used in the manufacture of these compounds and others derived from them.

Propylene chlorohydrins, C_3H_7ClO. Both of the chlorohydrins are formed as colourless liquids by the action of dilute solutions of hypochlorous acid on propylene, or by the action of hydrochloric acid on propylene oxide. The product contains about 90% α-chlorohydrin and 10% β-chlorohydrin.

α-*Propylene chlorohydrin*, 1-chloro-2-hydroxypropane, $CH_2Cl \cdot CHOH \cdot CH_3$, d^{20} 1·111, b.p. 127°. Miscible with water; forms constant-boiling mixture (b.p. 96·4°) containing 46% chlorohydrin. Used in organic syntheses.

β-*Propylene chlorohydrin*, 2-chloropropyl alcohol, $CH_3CHClCH_2OH$; d^{20} 1·103, b.p. 134°.

Both of these chlorohydrins are converted to propylene glycol by heating with solutions of sodium bicarbonate; when heated with solid sodium hydroxide they give propylene oxide.

Propylene dichloride, 1,2-Dichloropropane, $CH_3CHClCH_2Cl$. A colourless liquid with a pleasant odour; d^{20}_{20} 1·159, b.p. 96°. Almost insoluble in water; miscible with alcohol, benzene, and petroleum ether. Manufactured by treating liquid chlorine with an excess of liquid propylene. It is very similar in properties to ethylene dichloride, and is used for similar purposes.

Propylene glycol, 1,2-Dihydroxypropane $CH_3 \cdot CHOH \cdot CH_2OH$. A colourless, almost odourless liquid. It has a sweet taste, but is more acrid than ethylene glycol; d^{20}_{20} 1·038, b.p. 187·4°. Miscible with water and alcohol; only slightly soluble in benzene. Manufactured by heating propylene chlorohydrin with a solution of sodium bicarbonate under pressure. It closely resembles ethylene glycol in its properties, but is less toxic. Forms mono- and di-esters and ethers. Used as an anti-freeze and in the preparation of perfumes and flavouring extracts.

Propylene oxide. A colourless liquid; d^{20}_{20} 0·8313,

$$CH_3CH \cdot CH_2$$
$$\diagdown O \diagup$$

b.p. 34°. Soluble in water to 33% by weight; miscible with alcohol and benzene. Manufactured by heating propylene chlorohydrin with solid sodium hydroxide or quicklime. It reacts with water in the presence of sulphuric acid to give propylene glycol, and with alcohols and phenols to give ethers. It resembles ethylene oxide in properties, but is somewhat less reactive. Used in chemical syntheses and as a solvent for nitrocellulose.

Propyliodone, $C_{10}H_{11}I_2NO_3$. A white crystalline powder, insoluble in water, soluble in alcohol, m.p. 189°. Prepared by treating pyridine with thionyl chloride, hydrolysing, iodinating, treat-

ing with chloroacetic acid, and esterifying with propyl alcohol. It is a contrast medium, used in bronchography.

Propyne, allylene, $CH_3 \cdot C \equiv CH$. B.p. $-23 \cdot 3°/760$ mm. It is prepared by the action of alcoholic potassium hydroxide on 1,2-dibromopropane, or by the reaction of dimethyl sulphate on sodium acetylide in liquid ammonia. The chemical properties of propyne resemble closely those of acetylene.

Prostaglandins. A group of related compounds, occurring in mammalian tissues and secretions, which cause contraction of smooth muscle and

lowering of arterial blood pressure. They are oxygenated, unsaturated C_{20} acids containing a cyclopentane ring, derived biogenetically from corresponding acyclic unsaturated fatty acids, e.g. prostaglandin E_2 from arachidonic acid.

Prosthetic group. The non-protein group of a conjugated protein. See Enzymes.

Protactinium, Pa. At.no. 91. The most important isotope, ^{231}Pa, has a half-life of 34,300 years, d 15·37, estimated m.p. below 1600°. It has a tetragonal structure, $a = 3 \cdot 925, c = 3 \cdot 238$ Å. Protactinium occurs naturally in uranium ores but is most conveniently obtained by the irradiation of ^{230}Th with neutrons; its separation is very difficult, but has been effected by solvent extraction, ion exchange, and volatility procedures. The metal has been obtained by reduction of the tetrafluoride with barium at 1400°. It is hard, shiny, and malleable, but tarnishes slowly in air. All protactinium compounds are exceedingly hazardous to health.

Protactinium compounds. *Protactinium oxides*, $PaO_{2 \cdot 0 - 2 \cdot 5}$ are known, the colour varying from black to white. *Protactinium tetrafluoride*, PaF_4, is obtained by the action of a mixture of hydrogen fluoride and hydrogen on PaO_2 at 600°; a higher volatile fluoride is also known. *Protactinium chlorides*, $PaCl_5$ and $PaCl_4$, white and greenish-yellow respectively, are known. Both sublime at fairly low temperatures. A complex fluoride, K_2PaF_7, is prepared by dissolving $PaO_{2.5}$ in hydrofluoric acid and adding potassium fluoride.

Protalbic acid. See Protective colloid.

Protamines. These can be regarded as the simplest of the proteins or as large peptides. They are found associated with nucleic acid in the sperm of certain fish, typical protamines being spermine from the salmon and clupeine from the herring. They are bases, with arginine as the only basic amino-acid, and with two molecules of this to each neutral amino-acid molecule. Their molecular weights are probably under 10,000.

Protective colloid. Hydrophilic colloids, such as gelatin, which are themselves unaffected by small concentrations of electrolytes owing to hydration, are able, when added in very small quantities to hydrophobic sols, to protect the latter from the coagulating influence of electrolytes. They are therefore termed protective colloids.

All the hydrophilic colloids possess some degree of protective action and gelatin, starch, and casein are used commercially for this purpose. Interesting examples are protalbic and lysalbic acids, albumin decomposition products which are such powerful protective colloids that their presence enables hydrophobic sols of metals to be evaporated to dryness and the residual solid redispersed by mere addition of water. Silica gel, although strongly hydrated, has no protective action. See also Colloids, Hydrophilic, Hydrophobic, 'Salting out', Gold number.

Proteins. The proteins are the chief nitrogenous constituents of plants and animals; they are essential constituents of every living cell. They contain about 50% by weight of carbon, about 25% of oxygen, about 15% of nitrogen, about 7% of hydrogen, and some sulphur. They are mostly soluble in water, forming colloidal solutions. Many proteins have been obtained crystalline. They are optically active. They are precipitated by salts of the heavy metals, by the alkaloidal reagents, and by compounds containing large anions such as phosphotungstic acid and tannic acid. They are also precipitated by alcohol and by strong solutions of salts. On hydrolysis they break down to a mixture of about twenty amino-acids (*q.v.*). They give certain colour reactions which are caused by the presence of specific amino-acids in the molecule. With strong nitric acid a yellow colour is given, which turns orange on the addition of ammonia (Xanthoproteic reaction). A red colour is given by the addition of a mercuric salt and a nitrite (Millon's reaction). A purple colour is given by the addition of formaldehyde, mercuric sulphate, and sulphuric acid. Proteins also give the biuret reaction, a violet colour being given by

copper sulphate in the presence of sodium hydroxide.

The proteins can be classified as follows:

Simple proteins:

Protamines. Strongly basic, soluble proteins present in the nuclear material of fish.

Histones. Resembling the protamines, but less basic. Found in the nuclear material of all animals.

Albumins. Soluble proteins which are coagulated by heat. Found in all living tissues.

Globulins. Resembling the albumins in being coagulated by heat, but insoluble in water. Also found in all living tissues.

Glutelins. Insoluble in water and alcohol, soluble in acids and alkalis. Found in the seeds of cereals.

Prolamines. Also found in the seeds of cereals but differing from the glutelins in being soluble in 70% alcohol.

Scleroproteins. Insoluble proteins obtained from the skeletal and connective tissues of animals, hair, horn, etc.

Conjugated proteins:

Phosphoproteins. Contain phosphoric acid as part of the protein molecule.

Chromoproteins. Compounds of proteins with haem or some similar substance, and acting as respiratory pigments.

Glucoproteins. Compounds of proteins with carbohydrate groups, giving very viscous solutions.

Nucleoproteins. Compounds of proteins with nucleic acid, found in all nuclear material.

Derived proteins, protein breakdown products:

Metaproteins. Insoluble substances formed by the action of acids and alkalis on proteins at moderate temperatures.

Proteoses. Soluble substances, simpler than the metaproteins, formed by the action of enzymes on proteins.

Peptones. Substances of low molecular weight that can diffuse through parchment membranes. Soluble in water and all concentrations of salt solutions.

Peptides. Definitely characterized compounds containing a small number of aminoacids.

Proteins consist essentially of large numbers of amino-acids joined by the peptide link —CO—NH— into chains

where R' and R'' are amino-acid residues. They may consist of one or more chains; thus insulin consists of two chains joined through two disulphide groups. Proteins are synthesized in nature on ribosomes (*q.v.*) from available amino-acids. (See Nucleic acids.)

Modern methods of amino-acid and peptide analysis, largely ultimately depending on paper chromatography, have enabled the complete amino-acid sequence of a number of proteins to be worked out. The grosser structure can be determined by X-ray diffraction procedures. Proteins have molecular weights ranging from about 6,000,000 to 5,000 (though the dividing line between a protein and a peptide is ill defined).

In fibrous proteins the polypeptide chain is in the form of a regular helix, called the α-helix. Chains may be cross linked through hydrogen bonds; there may also be linkages to adjacent chains through amino-acid residues, particularly cysteine. Globular proteins consist of chains folded round themselves.

Proteoses, Albumoses. Degradation products of proteins, less complex than the metaproteins and derived from proteins by enzyme action. They are soluble in water, dilute acids and alkalis, and dilute salt solutions. They are precipitated by half-saturation with ammonium sulphate.

Prothrombin. See Thrombin.

Protocatechuic acid, 3,4-dihydroxybenzoic acid, $C_7H_6O_4$. Crystallizes in needles with one molecule of water, m.p. 199°. Soluble in alcohol, moderately soluble in water. It occurs in the free state in the onion and other plants; is a constituent of one group of tannins, and is a product of the alkaline decomposition of resins.

Proton. The proton, which is identical with the nucleus of an ordinary hydrogen atom, is one of the units from which all forms of matter are built up. It is an atomic unit of mass, and carries one unit of positive charge equivalent to the negative charge on the electron. The proton is 1840 times as heavy as an electron.

Protoporphyrin. See Porphyrins.

Proust, Joseph Louis (1754-1826). A French chemist, Proust was professor in Madrid from 1789 to 1809. In 1799 he announced the law of constant proportions. He isolated mannitol and urea. The notion of constant and reciprocal proportions became obvious about the period between 1780 and 1795, and several men, including Richter, Kirwan, Higgins, and Fischer, helped to establish it.

Prout, William (1785-1850). Born at Horton, Gloucestershire, Prout graduated in medicine at Edinburgh in 1811. For a time he was physician

and lecturer in chemistry at London. He investigated various chemical problems, and found that the acid contents of the stomach contain hydrochloric acid which could be separated by distillation. He regarded hydrogen as the protyl or *prima materia* of the ancients.

Proximate analysis of coal. The utility of a coal, from an industrial point of view, may be assessed by subjecting it to a series of arbitrary tests under conditions specified in the B.S.I. publication on the 'Sampling and Analysis of Coal and Coke', No. 735, 1944. Figures for the following are determined: (a) moisture content, (b) volatile matter, (c) ash, (d) fixed carbon. Besides these, values of the calorific value, sulphur content and agglutinating value are usually required.

Prussian blue. To chemists this term refers to the intensely blue compounds resulting from the mixture of solutions of ferrous salts with ferricyanides or ferric salts with ferrocyanides. The structures are derived from ferric ferricyanide or Berlin green, $Fe^{III}[Fe^{III}(CN)_6]$. Reduction of half the iron atoms gives the soluble prussian blues, e.g. $K[Fe^{II}[Fe^{III}(CN)_6]]$, also known as Turnbull's blue. These are not truly soluble but form colloidal solutions. Reduction of all the iron atoms gives ferrous ferrocyanide $K_2[Fe^{II}[Fe^{II}(CN)_6]]$. Alkali-free prussian blues, e.g. insoluble prussian blue, $Fe^{III}[Fe^{III}[Fe^{II}(CN)_6]]$ are formed by the action of excess of ferric ions on a ferrocyanide.

In the pigment industry these compounds are called Iron blues or Cyanide blues, and Prussian blue, Chinese blue, Milori blue, Bronze blue, and Gas blue are all varieties with slightly different shades made by using different oxidizing agents and under different conditions.

Prussiates. An old name for cyanides.

Prussic acid. An old name for hydrogen cyanide.

Pseudohalogens. Compounds which show a marked resemblance to the free halogen elements in their reactions and properties. Cyanogen $(CN)_2$, thiocyanogen $(SCN)_2$, selenocyanogen $(SeCN)_2$, and azidocarbondisulphide $(SCSN_3)_2$ are the principal pseudohalogens. The pseudohalogens X_2 form X^-, XO^-, and XO_3^- ions. The AgX compounds are insoluble in water.

Pseudoionone. See Citral.

Pseudomorphic. Having the same crystal form.

Psicose. See Allulose.

Psychotomimetic drugs. Drugs which produce changes in thought, perception and mood without seriously disturbing the autonomic nervous system. Examples are mescaline, lysergic acid diethylamide (LSD-25), psilocybin, and the active constituents of marihuana, notably tetrahydrocannabinol.

Pterins. Derivatives of pteridine, of interest in

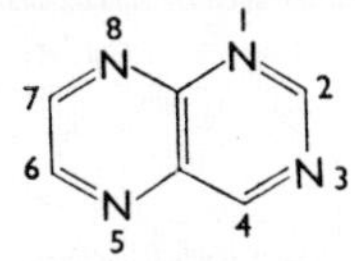

that they include the butterfly pigments leuco-pterin and xanthopterin and the vitamin folic acid.

Pteroylglutamic acid. See Folic acid.

Ptomaines. The word 'ptomaines' has fallen into disuse. It was applied to basic substances obtained from putrefying tissues, such as cadaverine, putrescine, choline, and muscarine. The so-called 'ptomaine poisoning', which was used with reference to almost any poisoning by bad food, is not in general caused by the ptomaines, many of which are not poisonous, but by bacterial toxins.

Pug mill. A mill used in the mixing of clay 'slip' or similar materials. It consists of an open trough containing a number of stout paddles slightly inclined to the horizontal and rotating slowly. Vertical forms of pug mill are sometimes used in other industries, e.g. in the manufacture of putty from linseed oil and whiting. The action of this type of mill is really one of kneading.

Pulegone, $C_{10}H_{16}O$. An optically active mono-cyclic ketone, the (+)-form alone of which is known; it occurs in oil derived from the *Labiatae*, and more especially from pennyroyal oils (from *Mentha pulegium* and *Hedeoma pulegioides*). It is an oil with a camphor-like smell, and can be purified by means of its crystalline compound with sodium bisulphite. Its constants are: b.p. 221°-222°, d_4^{15} 0·9346, n_D 1·4894, $[\alpha]_D$ +21°. By the action of hydrochloric acid on a mixture of pulegone and amyl nitrite, bisnitrosopulegone is formed of m.p. 81·5°. It forms (−)-menthol on reduction with sodium and alcohol. With hydrochloric acid it forms a monohydrochloride of m.p. 24°-25°. It forms a semicarbazone of m.p. 172°.

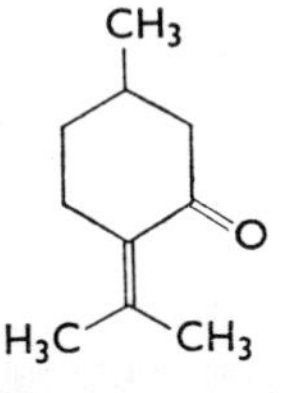

Pump. A device, usually but not invariably mechanical, for moving a fluid against a pressure. Pumps for handling liquids are normally of the *centrifugal* or *positive displacement* types (*q.v.*) though devices such as *acid eggs, air-lift pumps* and *ejectors* (*q.v.*) are occasionally used. Equipment for pumping gases may be subdivided into *fans, compressors* and *vacuum pumps* (*q.v.*) according to whether the gas is pumped against a low pressure, a high one, or from a space at below atmospheric pressure.

Purdie, Thomas (1843-1916). Born at Biggar, Purdie was educated at Edinburgh Academy, where his interests lay in classics and literature. After a period devoted to commerce in the Argentine, he took up the study of chemistry, first under Frankland in London, and then under Wislicenus at Würzburg. In 1884 he was appointed professor of chemistry at St. Andrews. He was elected F.R.S. in 1895. Although he laboured in a wide field of research, Purdie's name will be best remembered for the part he took in the development of research upon optical activity.

Purine, $C_5H_4N_4$. A crystalline solid, m.p. 216°-217°, readily soluble in water. It can be prepared

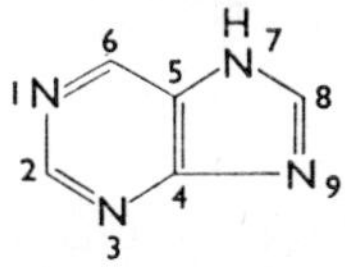

from uric acid, but is not obtained naturally, and is not physiologically important, although many of its derivatives are. It is the parent compound of a group of compounds of animal and vegetable origin, collectively called purines. The group includes adenine and guanine, which are constituents of the nucleic acid portion of nucleoproteins, their breakdown products, hypoxanthine, xanthine, and uric acid, and the drugs caffeine, theobromine, and theophylline.

Purple of Cassius. See Gold, colloidal.

Putrescine, Tetramethylenediamine,

$$H_2N \cdot [CH_2]_4 \cdot NH_2,$$

m.p. 27°-28°, b.p. 158°-159°, soluble in water and alcohol. Putrescine is one of the ptomaines, and is found, associated with cadaverine, in putrefying tissues, being formed by bacterial action on the amino-acid arginine. It is found in the urine in some cases of the congenital disease cystinuria. It is also present in ergot.

Putty powder. See Tin oxides.

PVC. See Polyvinyl chloride.

Pyknometer. An instrument for measuring the density of a solid or a liquid by determining the weight of a known volume. The specific gravity bottle with a drilled stopper is the simplest form.

Pyocyanin, $C_{13}H_{10}N_2O$. A blue pigment,

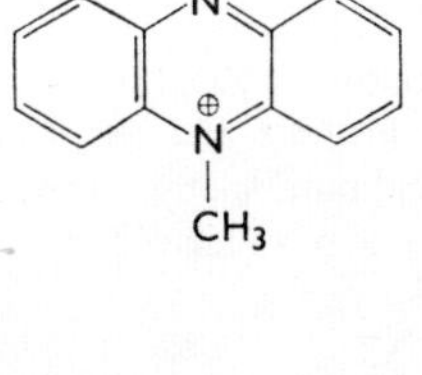

produced by *Bacillus pyocyaneus*, which acts as an oxygen carrier. It crystallizes in needles, m.p. 133°, soluble in hot water.

Pyranose. A term introduced by Haworth for the stable ring form of the sugars which contains the 5-carbon and oxygen ring skeleton. Glucose is structurally a 1,5-glucopyranose with a primary alcohol group CH_2OH as a side chain. Such pyranose derivatives are stable and crystalline in contradistinction to the furanose sugars (*q.v.*).

Pyrazole, $C_3H_4N_2$. A colourless crystalline

substance (I) m.p. 70°. Obtained by passing acetylene into cold ethereal solutions of diazomethane. It is a weak base. Partial reduction gives pyrazoline (II) and complete reduction leads to pyrazolidine (III). Pyrazole is an aromatic compound, undergoing electrophilic substitution with the usual reagents in the 4-position.

Pyrazolidine. See Pyrazole.

Pyrazoline. See Pyrazole.

Pyrazolone dyes. These dyestuffs, closely associated with those of the azo-series, contain the characteristic group:

R=alkyl or carboxy groups.
R', R''=aryl groups.

The most important method of preparation consists in condensing directly pyrazolones and diazonium salts. A large number of pyrazolones can readily be prepared from acetoacetic ester and phenylhydrazines (Fast Light Yellow G, etc.).

Pyrethrins. Constituents of pyrethrum. Pyrethrin I is the ester of pyrethrolone and chrysan-

Pyrethrin I

themum monocarboxylic acid, and pyrethrin II that of pyrethrolone and chrysanthemum dicarboxylic acid monomethyl ester. In pyrethrin II the CH_3^* group is replaced by acetate.

Pyrethrolone. The ketonic alcohol, esters of the *dextro-cis-* form of which, with chrysanthemum carboxylic acids, are the pyrethrins.

Pyrethrum. The mixture of substances known as pyrethrum, obtained by grinding or extracting the dried flowers of *Chrysanthemum cinerariaefolium*, is a powerful but non-persistent contact insecticide with rapid 'knockdown' effect. Being non-toxic to mammals it is used in the home and in the food industry, usually in conjunction with a synergist such as piperonyl butoxide (*q.v.*).

The individual constituents of pyrethrum are the pyrethrins and cinerins (*q.v.*), esters of chrysanthemum carboxylic acids. The flower heads contain up to 3% of the active compounds. Pyrethrum was first introduced into Europe from the Far East in the 1820s.

Pyrex. A trade name for a heat-resisting borosilicate glass containing a high percentage of silica, with boron trioxide and smaller quantities of alkalis and alumina. Pyrex has high mechanical strength, resists attack by strong acids and alkalis, and withstands sudden changes of temperature without breakage; it softens at a higher temperature than ordinary soda glasses.

Pyridine, C_5H_5N. Colourless refractive hygroscopic liquid, b.p. 115·3°, d^{25} 0·978. Strong characteristic smell. Burns with a smoky flame. Miscible in all proportions with water and organic solvents. Strong base, turns litmus blue, forms stable salts with mineral acids and quaternary compounds with alkyl halides, e.g. pyridine methiodide, $C_5H_5N \cdot CH_3I$. Forms a characteristic picrate and complexes with most metal salts. Reduced to piperidine, $C_5H_{11}N$, by sodium and alcohol. Very poisonous.

Commercially, pyridine is obtained from coal tar and coal gas; it is also possible to manufacture it from acetylene and ammonia. It is used as a solvent, particularly in the plastics industry, in the manufacture of nicotinic acid, various drugs and rubber chemicals. A related compound, 2-vinylpyridine, is used in the manufacture of a styrene-butadiene-vinylpyridine copolymer.

Pyridinium. The ion formed by co-ordination of pyridine to a proton. The reaction between pyridine and hydrogen chloride yields pyridinium chloride.

Pyridoxal phosphate. The coenzyme, or more

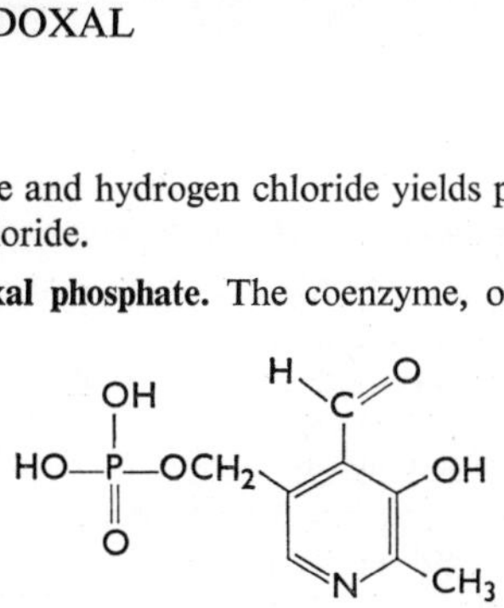

correctly the prosthetic group, of transaminations, i.e. the interconversions of amino-acids and their corresponding α-keto-acids, catalysed by transaminases (now 'aminotransferases' in systematic nomenclature). The mechanism of action appears to involve formation of a Schiff's base from reaction of the amino and keto groups. Pyridoxal phosphate also plays an important role in the decarboxylation of amino-acids to 'biogenic amines' (*q.v.*).

Pyridoxine, Vitamin-B$_6$ $C_8H_{11}NO_3$. Colourless

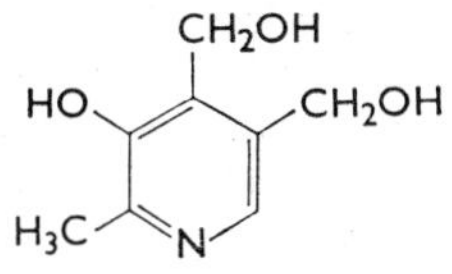

needles, m.p. 160°. Pyridoxine is needed by rats to cure dermatitis developed on a vitamin B-free diet, supplemented by thiamine and riboflavin. Its absence from the diet is also associated with anaemia. It is needed also by certain bacteria. It is present in rice husks, maize, wheat germ, yeast, and other sources of vitamin B and has been synthesized.

The related compounds pyridoxamine and pyridoxal, in which the CH_2OH group in the 4-position is replaced by CH_2NH_2 and CHO respectively, also possess vitamin B$_6$ activity and for certain bacteria are much more active than pyridoxine.

Pyrimidine, $C_4H_4N_2$. A crystalline compound with a penetrating smell, m.p. 20°-22°, b.p. 123·5°-124°. Soluble in water, giving a neutral solution. It can be prepared from barbituric acid via trichloropyrimidine.

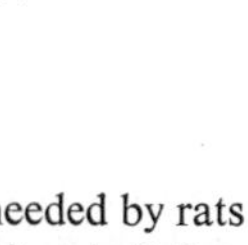

It is the parent substance of a group of compounds which includes cytosine, thymine, and uracil, which are constituents of nucleic acids and barbituric acid and its derivatives, which are important medicinally.

Pyrite, Pyrites, FeS_2. A common mineral crystallizing in the cubic system in cubes, octahedra, and pentagonal dodecahedra. Hardness 6, sp.gr. 5·1, colour brass-yellow with metallic lustre. Extensively mined and used in the production of sulphuric acid.

Pyro acids. Acids, sometimes hypothetical, which contain condensed oxyanions with two hetero atoms. The bridging atom is oxygen, e.g. the pyrosulphate ion is $[O_3S-O-SO_3]^{2-}$.

Pyrochlore. A complex calcium niobate, ideally $NaCaNb_2O_5F$ but usually of variable composition, containing 45-70% Nb_2O_5, rare earths, sodium oxide and a little Ta_2O_5. Occurs in small amounts in carbonatite rocks, from which it can be concentrated by physical methods. An important potential source of niobium, large reserves being available.

Pyrogallol, $C_6H_6O_3$. White lustrous needles, m.p. 132°, b.p. 210°, with partial decomposition. Readily soluble in water, alcohol, and ether. Alkaline solutions rapidly absorb oxygen from the air and become dark brown in colour.

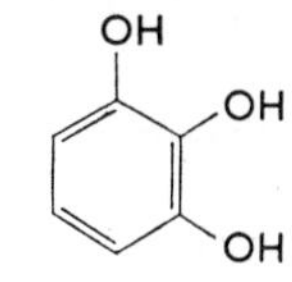

It is prepared by digesting gallic acid with water at 200°.

Extensively used as a photographic developer, and in gas analysis as an absorbent for oxygen.

Pyrogens. Thermostable polysaccharides produced by bacteria. Gram-positive bacteria produce exotoxins, while Gram-negative bacteria retain endotoxins on or near their cell surfaces. They produce a rise in temperature when injected, which is thought to be caused by central nervous system stimulation. As they stimulate the natural defences of the body they can be used in the treatment of allergies and in the stimulation of tissue repair. Usually, however, the problem is to produce drugs for injection which are pyrogen free. Drugs are tested for pyrogens by being injected into rabbits, whose rise in temperture is measured.

Pyroligneous acid. The crude brown liquor obtained by the distillation of wood. Its acid properties are due chiefly to the acetic acid it contains. Methyl alcohol and acetone are also present, together with small amounts of other substances. It was sometimes used as a source of acetic acid, methyl alcohol, and acetone.

Pyrolusite, MnO_2. One of the most important ores of manganese. Iron-grey in colour it usually occurs massive or in fibrous or powdery forms. Hardness from 2 to 6, sp.gr. 4·4-5·0.

Pyrometric cone equivalent (PCE). A term used in the ceramic industry indicating a measure of the melting-point or fusion-point of the refractory. A test pyramid of the refractory is made and placed in a furnace by the side of a series of standard cones called Seger or Pyrometric cones. A preliminary trial will determine the range of standard cones to be used. The furnace is now slowly heated until the tip of the test cone bends over to the level of the base. The number on the Seger cone which compares with the test cone in the degree to which the tip bent over is referred to as the Pyrometric Cone Equivalent of the refractory.

Pyromucic acid. See Furoic acid.

Pyrones. Compounds containing the ring systems

γ-   α-

Many occur in nature, for example as part of the anthocyans.

Pyrophoric alloy. An alloy of cerium (with lanthanum, neodymium, yttrium, and samarium) containing 30% iron which, when scratched with iron, produces sparks, and is used in pocket lighters. The cerium is obtained as a by-product in the production of thorium salts from monazite sand.

Pyrophoric metals. Many metals when produced in a porous condition by reduction at low temperatures are in a state of considerable activity and are often spontaneously inflammable. Thus pyrophoric iron can be obtained by reduction of ferrous oxalate and many others by distillation of amalgams at low pressures.

On heating pyrophoric metals, the activity decreases as the increased kinetic energy allows the atoms to flow together to the macro lattice structure and thus reduces the surface energy.

Pyrophyllite. A white aluminosilicate corresponding to the formula $Al_2(Si_4O_{10})(OH)_2$, though substitution is so common that the composition is very variable. The crystal structure is similar to that of talc. Usually occurs in radiating groups of rhombic crystals. Sp.gr. 2·7-2·9.

It is much less common than talc but is quarried in the U.S.A., Korea, China, and Newfoundland. Its uses are similar to those of talc.

Pyrosols. Cloudy solutions generally regarded as colloidal are formed in the electrolysis of fused salts, the free metal being the dispersed material. Pyrosols are easily obtained by dissolving the metal directly in the fused salt, e.g. by dissolving zinc in fused zinc chloride. Coloured glasses are sometimes cooled pyrosols. See Colloids.

Pyrosulphuric acid, $H_2S_2O_7$. Free pyrosulphuric acid is found in fuming sulphuric acid. Many salts, pyrosulphates, are formed which contain the $S_2O_7^{2-}$ ion. See Pyro acids.

Pyrosulphurous acid, $H_2S_2O_5$. Free pyrosulphurous acid is not known but pyrosulphites are prepared by treating alkali sulphites with sulphur dioxide.

Pyrotartaric acid, Methylsuccinic acid, $C_5H_8O_4$. (±)-Pyrotartaric acid is a colourless, crystalline solid, m.p. 115°. Very soluble in water; insoluble in cold chloroform. Prepared by the dry distillation of tartaric acid or by reduction of itaconic or citraconic acids. Forms an anhydride when heated to 200°. The active acids are obtained by fractional crystallization of the strychnine (±)-pyrotartrate. They melt at 115°, $[\alpha]_D^{23}$ ±9.89°.

$$CH_3CHCOOH$$
$$|$$
$$CH_2COOH$$

Pyrotechnics. The name given to a variety of combustible mixtures, including illuminating, incendiary, priming, and smoke-producing compositions. They contain an oxidant, such as nitrate or chlorate, and combustible substances such as charcoal, sulphur, antimony sulphide, etc. Metallic powders are incorporated to give illuminating effects and metallic salts provide coloured effects. In incendiary compositions a highly exothermic reaction occurs giving rise to intense heat, as in thermite. Smoke-producing compositions may contain phosphorus or hexachloroethane.

Pyroxenes. The pyroxenes constitute an important class of silicate minerals, structurally related to the amphiboles. Typical members of the group are enstatite, $MgSiO_3$, and diopside, $CaMg(SiO_3)_2$. The characteristic of the crystal structures of the pyroxenes is the presence of chains of formulae $(SiO_3)_n^{2n-}$ formed by linking SiO_4 tetrahedra corner to corner.

Pyroxylin. A nitrated cellulose, which can be obtained by treating defatted cotton wool with a mixture of nitric and sulphuric acids. A mixture of nitrates of a polysaccharide containing about two hundred glucopyranose units is obtained; it contains roughly two nitrate groups per sugar molecule.

It is used for the preparation of collodions, which are used for the protection of cuts.

Pyrrhotite, Magnetic pyrites, FeS to Fe_6S_7. This mineral occurs in hexagonal or pseudo-hexagonal plates. Hardness 4, sp.gr. 4·6. A yellowish mineral with a metallic lustre.

Pyrroaetioporphyrin. See Porphyrins.

Pyrrocoline ring system. See Indolizine ring system.

Pyrrole, C_4H_5N. A colourless oil, b.p. 130°, d_4^{20} 0·9691, n_D^{20} 1·5085, which on contact with air turns brown and eventually resinifies. It is found in coal tar and bone oil and may be prepared by heating ammonium mucate, or from butyne-1,4-diol and ammonia in the presence of an alumina catalyst. The pyrrole molecule is aromatic in character. It is not basic and the imino-hydrogen atom can be replaced by potassium. Many pyrrole derivatives occur naturally, for example proline, indican, haem, and chlorophyll.

Pyrrolidine, Tetrahydropyrrole, C_4H_9N. An almost colourless, ammonia-like liquid, b.p. 88°-89°, which fumes in air. A strong base, it disolves in water and organic solvents. It occurs naturally in tobacco leaves, but is made industrially by hydrogenation of pyrrole.

Pyrroporphyrin. See Porphyrins.

Pyruvic acid, $CH_3COCOOH$. A colourless liquid with an odour resembling that of acetic acid, m.p. 13°, b.p. 65°/10 mm. Soluble in water, alcohol, and ether. It is an intermediate in the breakdown of sugars to alcohol by yeast. Prepared by distilling tartaric acid with potassium hydrogen sulphate. Tends to polymerize to a solid (m.p. 92°). Oxidized to oxalic acid or acetic acid. Reduced to (±)-lactic acid. Forms a characteristic 2,4-dinitrophenylhydrazone (m.p. 218°). Detected by the violet-blue colour produced when a solution is made alkaline with ammonia and sodium nitroprusside added.

Pyruvic alcohol. See Acetol.

Q

Quadrupole moments. The coupling of the nuclear quadrupole with the asymmetric electron fields in compounds. Measurement of quadrupole moments gives information on the electronic distribution over the atoms of a molecule or ion.

Quadruple point. The unique conditions of temperature and pressure at which four phases of a two-component system are in equilibrium.

Qualitative analysis. Analysis for the identification of constituents.

Quantitative analysis. Analysis for the estimation of constituents.

Quantum. According to the quantum hypothesis, the energy associated with light must be regarded as occurring in discrete units, which have a definite value for light of a given frequency. The energy can only be transferred in these discrete parcels, or units, not continuously like a stream of fluid. For light of frequency v, the unit of energy, *the quantum*, is equal to hv, where h is Planck's constant, equal to $6.6256 \times$

10^{-27} erg per second. Clearly the magnitude of the quantum varies with the frequency (i.e. inversely with the wavelength) of the light, e.g. for red light it is about 2.5×10^{-12} erg, and for ultra-violet light about 5×10^{-12} erg. When the quantum has particle properties it is known as a photon.

Quantum efficiency. The quantum efficiency of a process is the number of molecules actually decomposed for each quantum of radiation absorbed.

Quantum hypothesis. In 1901 Planck abandoned the classical method of treating the problem of radiation. He assumed that the energy in certain vibrating systems could not be transferred continuously, but only in integral multiples of an energy unit E, the *quantum*, equal in magnitude to the frequency of vibration v multiplied by a constant h, known as Planck's constant, which has the same value for all such systems, viz. 6.6256×10^{-27} erg per sec. The concept of the quantum led to most important advances in all branches of science concerned with the energy of atomic or molecular systems, for they conform in detail to this principle. Thus, the transference to electronic, vibrational, and rotational energy in atoms or molecules occurs only in integral multiples of quanta, the magnitude of the quantum being determined in each case by the frequency of the radiation associated with such energy transitions. See Line spectrum and Band spectrum.

Quantum number. The planetary electrons in an atom (or the atoms in a molecule) are possessed of energy by reason of their rotation, vibration, or spin. It is a postulate of the quantum theory that the energy possessed by such a particle can only have certain definite values. Each such value for a particular form of energy (e.g. rotational) is a multiple—which is always a small whole number, or sometimes one-half—of a unit of energy, the quantum, which is characteristic of the particular form of energy under consideration. The multiple which defines the energy of the particle is called a quantum number.

Quartering. See Coning and quartering.

Quartz, SiO_2. One of the commonest of minerals and the chief constituent of sandstone rocks and sand. It exists in a low- and high-temperature forms, designated α- and β-quartz respectively, the transition temperature being 575°. Both forms crystallize in the hexagonal system, the high-temperature form having higher symmetry. The cell constants are:

α-quartz: $a = 4.903$ Å. $c = 5.393$ Å.
β-quartz: $a = 4.989$ Å. $c = 5.446$ Å.

The crystals of low-temperature quartz are optically active and crystallize in enantiomorphous pairs.

Quartz is used extensively for optical work. It is more transparent to ultraviolet radiation than is glass. Rock crystal is colourless and glassy; amethyst has a violet colour and becomes yellow on heating. The brown and yellow varieties are called cairngorm. On heating to a high temperature quartz is converted into one of the two other forms of silica, cristobalite and tridymite, with an increase in volume of 16%.

Quartz is insoluble in all acids except hydrofluoric acid. It has a refractive index of 1·544 to 1·553, m.p. about 1600°-1700° and vaporizes appreciably around 1770°. See Silica, Tridymite, Cristobalite.

Quassia. The wood of *Aeschrion excelsa*, a tree growing in Jamaica. It contains an intensely bitter principle known as 'quassin,' and is used as a bitter tonic in the form of an infusion, a tincture and an extract. Quassia is free from tannin, consequently it can be prescribed with compounds of iron without forming an ink.

Quebrachitol, $C_7H_{14}O_6$. The methyl ether of L-inositol (*q.v.*). It is found in quebracho bark and rubber latex. It crystallizes in needles, m.p. 247°, $[\alpha]_D$ −80°.

Quercitol, $C_6H_{12}O_5$. There are four inactive and six optically active forms possible for this molecule.

D-Quercitol, protoquercitol, occurs in acorns and the leaves of the palm *Chamoerops humilis*. It crystallizes in prisms, m.p. 235°-237°, $[\alpha]_D^{15} + 24·37°$ in water; L-quercitol, riboquercitol, which is not the optical antipode, has m.p. 180°-181°, $[\alpha]_D − 49·5°$.

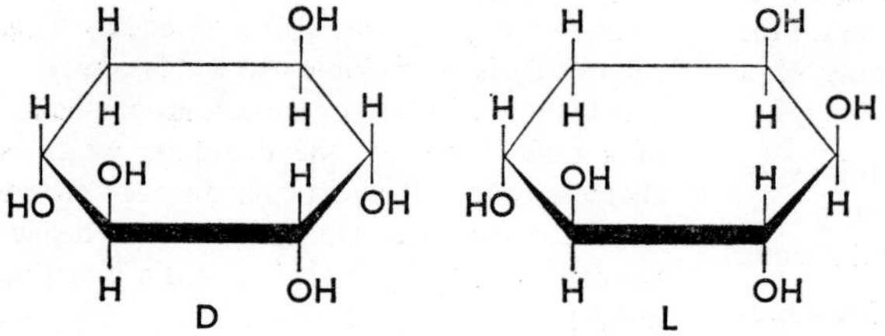

by acids to rhamnose and quercitin (3′, 4′, 5,7-tetrahydroxyflavanol). It is prepared commercially from oak bark, and is still used as a natural dyestuff (lemon flavin).

Quicklime. See Calcium oxide.

Quicksilver. An old name for mercury.

Quinaldine, $C_{10}H_9N$. Colourless oily liquid, b.p. 246°-247°. Odour resembling quinoline.

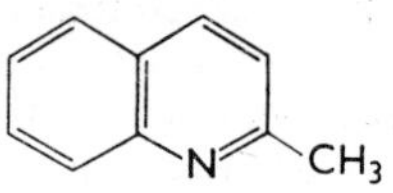

Volatile in steam. Sparingly soluble in water, miscible in all proportions with alcohol, ether, and benzene. Basic, forms stable salts and quarternary compounds.

It is prepared by heating together aniline, acetaldehyde, and zinc chloride.

It is used for the preparation of photosensitizing dyes. It also condenses with phthalic anhydride to give a coloured product which, after sulphonation, is the dyestuff quinoline yellow.

Quinapyramine, Antrycide, $C_{17}H_{22}N_6$. 2,6′-

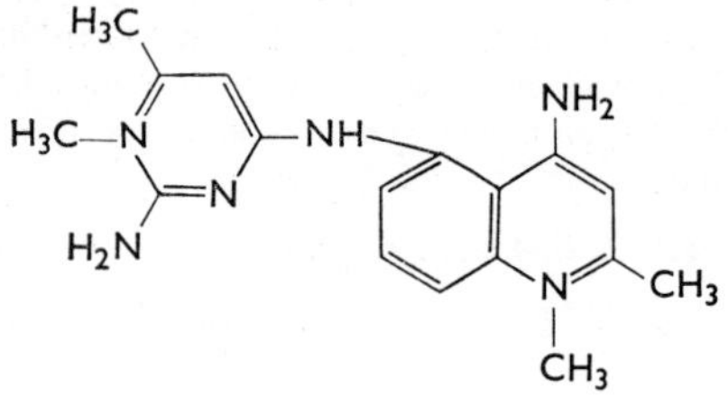

dimethyl-6,4′-pyrimidyl-amino-4,2′-diamino-quinoline. This is given by injection either

Quercitrin, $C_{21}H_{20}O_{11}$. A glycoside widely

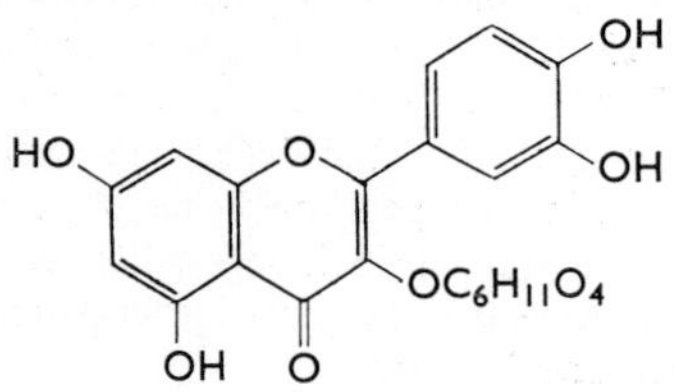

distributed in plants. It crystallizes in pale yellow needles or platelets, m.p. 182°. It is hydrolysed

as its chloride or its adduct with dimethyl sulphate in the treatment of trypanosomiasis in animals. The dimethyl sulphate is soluble in water and rapidly absorbed; the chloride is insoluble and acts as a slow release form.

Quinhydrone, $C_{12}H_{10}O_4$. A molecular compound stable in the solid state. X-ray studies show that it consists of alternate quinone and hydroquinone molecules linked together by hydrogen-bonds. It is prepared by mixing alcoholic solutions of quinone and hydroquinone and crystallizes in reddish-brown needles with a green lustre, m.p. 171°. It is very sparingly soluble in cold water, and is split into its constituents by boiling water. It was used in the quinhydrone electrode. Other related compounds of quinone with phenols have been prepared and these are collectively called quinhydrones; phenoquinone, for example, has a hydroquinone molecule attached to both oxygen atoms of quinone.

Quinhydrone electrode. This is a means of determining the pH of a solution. Quinhydrone is added to a solution and the redox potential, hydroquinone ⇌ quinone, established at a platinum electrode dipped in the solution is measured. The method is simple and accurate, but little used now.

Quinic acid, $C_7H_{12}O_6$. The carboxylic acid of

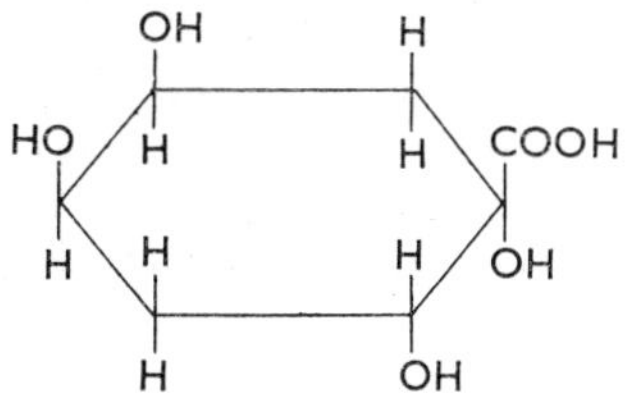

a tetrahydroxycyclohexane (see Inositol). It is found in cinchona bark, coffee beans, bilberries, etc., often conjugated with caffeic acid. It has m.p. 162°.

Quinidine, $C_{20}H_{24}N_2O_2$, $2H_2O$. A dextrorotatory stereoisomer of quinine. It occurs in cinchona bark and is obtained as a by-product in quinine manufacture. It has similar medicinal properties to quinine, but has a depressant action on the heart. It is chiefly used for the control of auricular fibrillation.

Quinine, $C_{20}H_{24}N_2O_2$, $3H_2O$. A white microcrystalline powder, m.p. 57° (177° when anhydrous). Almost insoluble in water, soluble in one part of alcohol; $[\alpha]_D^{15}$ (anhyd.) $-169°$ in alcohol. Quinine is the principal alkaloid of cinchona bark from which it is obtained by mixing with lime and extraction with alcohol

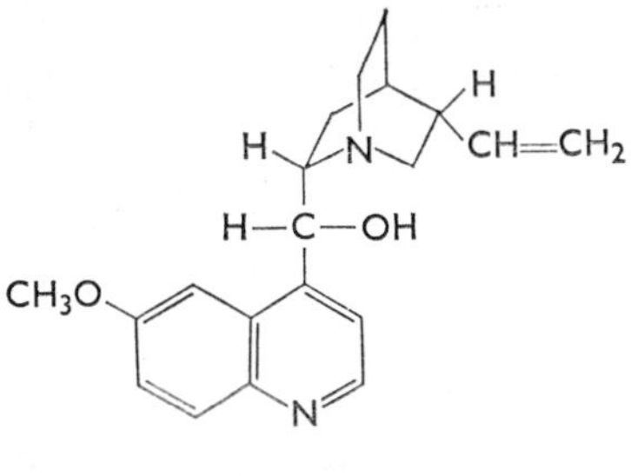

or by boiling the bark with acid and precipitation with ammonia. It is then purified via its

sulphate. It has been synthesized from 7-hydroxyisoquinoline. Quinine is one of the most important drugs known and with its salts is used in very large quantities for the treatment of malaria. It acts by destroying the malarial parasite. It is a general protoplasmic poison; it retards enzyme action and diminishes metabolism. It is an antipyretic and is a remedy for colds and influenza.

Quinizarin, $C_{14}H_8O_4$. Crystallizes in yellowish-red leaflets, m.p. 198°. It is very sparingly

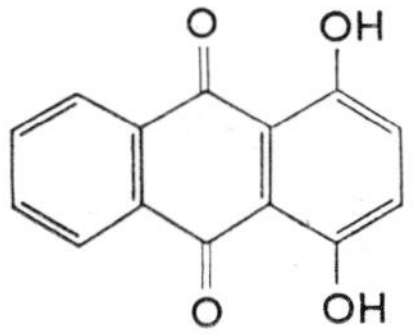

soluble in water, soluble in benzene and ether. In caustic alkalis it dissolves to an intense blue-violet solution.

It is prepared by condensing p-chlorophenol with phthalic anhydride in sulphuric acid solution in the presence of boric acid. The chlorine atom is replaced by hydroxyl during the condensation. It can also be prepared by oxidation of anthraquinone or 1-hydroxyanthraquinone by means of sulphuric acid in the presence of mercuric sulphate and boric acid.

Quinizarin is used for the preparation of acid wool colours. One or both hydroxyl groups are replaced in a condensation with one or two molecules of toluidine, and the resulting product is sulphonated. Alizarin Cyanine Green (Acid Green 25) is an example of such a dye.

Quinol. Another name for hydroquinone.

Quinoline, C_9H_7N. Colourless oily refractive liquid, b.p. 238°. Very hygroscopic, disagreeable odour. Sparingly soluble in water, miscible in all proportions with alcohol, ether, and benzene. Volatile in steam. Oxidized by alkaline permanganate to quinolinic acid (pyridine-2,3-dicarboxylic acid). Reduced by tin and hydrochloric acid to the tetrahydro-compound. Basic, gives stable salts with mineral acids, and quaternary ammonium compounds with alkyl halides, characteristic dichromate, m.p. 164°-167°.

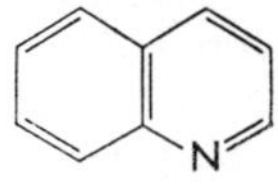

Occurs in the high-boiling fraction of coal tar. Most conveniently prepared by Skraup's reaction by heating a mixture of aniline, glycerol, sulphuric acid, and nitrobenzene.

It has a limited use in the manufacture of cyanine dyestuffs for photosensitizers.

Quinone. Another name for benzoquinone.

Quinones. Diketones formally derived by replacing the $\diagup\!\!\!>CH_2$ groups in a dihydro-aromatic system by $\diagup\!\!\!>C\!=\!O$. They are highly coloured substances many of which occur in nature, e.g. vitamin K. They are prepared by oxidation of phenols. They give addition compounds with many types of organic compounds, especially quinols. They are readily reduced to dihydric phenols, have characteristic redox potentials, and are used as dehydrogenating agents.

R

Racah parameters. The parameters, B and C, which are used to express quantitatively the interelectronic repulsion between various energy levels of an atom. The ratio between B in a complex and B in the free atom or ion is a measure of the covalency of bonds in the complex. See Nephelauxetic effect.

Racemate, Racemic compound. An equimolecular compound or mixture of the dextro- and laevoratatory optically active forms of a given compound.

Racemic acid. See Tartaric acids.

Racemization. The process in which an optically active stereoisomer is converted into a racemate. Epimerization ($q.v.$) is a special case of racemization. Heat and the action of acids or bases can encourage racemization.

Radical. Until recently this term was used for a group of atoms which is the invariable constituent of a number of compounds, and passes unchanged through a series of chemical reactions. Each radical has a characteristic valency, and can often be replaced by other radicals or by elements of equivalent valency. Now the term is often restricted to mean radicals in the free state (see Free radicals) which are unsaturated, and have one or more free valencies.

Radioactive decay series. The series of isotopes into which a radioactive nucleus is successively transformed.

Radioactivity. Shortly after the discovery of X-rays by Röntgen, Becquerel (1896) found that uranium salts had a pronounced effect on a photographic plate even when they were separated by thin sheets of metal. This property was called radioactivity. Three main types of radiation are concerned, α-, β-, and γ-rays, which arise from the spontaneous disintegration (i.e. splitting up) of the nucleus of the radioactive element. The emission of an α particle corresponds to a decrease in mass of the nucleus by four units; β particle emission corresponds to an increase in atomic number of the nucleus by one unit. The emission of γ-rays corresponds to loss in energy by the nucleus; they are often accompanied by X-rays.

There are other less common types of radioactive decay. Positron emission results in a decrease by one unit in the atomic number; K capture involves the incorporation of one of the extranuclear electrons into the nucleus, the atomic number is again decreased by one unit.

All elements of atomic number greater than 83 exhibit radioactive decay; potassium, rubidium, iridium and a few other light elements emit β particles. The heavy elements decay through various isotopes until a stable nucleus is reached. Known half-lives range from 10^{-7} seconds to 10^9 years.

The rate of radioactive transformations cannot be altered by changing the conditions which are available to us in the laboratory. The process is a spontaneous one.

Radioactive elements may often be prepared artificially by bombarding the atoms of ordinary stable elements with, e.g. the rapidly moving nuclei of helium atoms. See Radioactivity, artificial.

Radioactivity, artificial. When an element undergoes a nuclear reaction, e.g. as a result of bombardment with α-particles, protons, deuterons, or neutrons, the resulting atoms may be stable or metastable. In the latter case, they will be radioactive, and the phenomenon is known as artificial or induced radioactivity. Rutherford showed in 1919 that many elements underwent instantaneous disintegration when bombarded with α-particles

$$\text{e.g. } {}^{14}N + {}^{4}He \rightarrow {}^{17}O + {}^{1}H$$

and in 1934 Joliot-Curie and Joliot found that aluminium exposed to α-rays from polonium became radioactive, emitting positrons (or positive electrons) and decaying with a half-life period of 195 seconds. This is due to the formation of an active isotope of phosphorus which may be separated by chemical means. The reaction between the aluminium nuclei and the α-particles is expressed by the equation

$$\textstyle{}^{27}_{13}Al + {}^{4}_{2}He \rightarrow {}^{30}_{15}P + {}^{1}_{0}n$$

(the symbol ${}^{1}_{0}n$ represents a neutron which is emitted in the process). The new phosphorus atoms disintegrate into atoms of a silicon isotope and positive electrons: ${}^{30}_{15}P \rightarrow {}^{30}_{14}Si + {}^{0}_{1}e$; this process produces the observed artificial radioactivity. In this process, only a fraction of the α-particles causing disintegration actually give rise to active phosphorus, the majority following an (α, p) reaction giving ${}^{30}_{14}Si$ directly. The emission of positive electrons or other charged particles in such processes is detected experimentally by the ionization which they produce in gases; in counters this effect is used to count the number of particles emitted and hence to determine the rate of decay of the activity.

Normally, artificial radioactivity is only induced by bombardment with particles of appreciable mass, viz. α-particles, protons, deuterons, or neutrons, but γ-rays of very high energy are capable of disintegrating atoms with the ejection of a neutron from each nucleus and the formation of an isotope of the original element, which emits β-rays. Neutrons possess no electric charge and can penetrate the heaviest atoms without being subject to strong electrostatic forces. For this reason neutrons are particularly effective in producing artificial activity. The best sources of neutrons are chain-reacting piles and the cyclotron, and by their use several hundred radioactive isotopes have been prepared with half-life periods ranging from seconds to many years.

Radiocarbon dating. Carbon in living things contains a uniform amount of the radioactive ^{14}C nucleus; radiocarbon being produced constantly by the action of cosmic radiation. Once the host dies, exchange with atmospheric ^{14}C ceases, and, from the amount of ^{14}C present, the age of the sample may be deduced. The half-life of ^{14}C is 5570 years and the method is only useful for materials up to 30,000 years old.

Radium, Ra. At.no. 88, At.wt. 226·05. A radioactive element, the most stable isotope of which, ^{226}Ra, has a half-life of 1622 years. Its salts were first isolated in 1898 by Pierre and Marie Curie by fractional crystallization of barium halides obtained from the uranium mineral pitchblende. Metallic radium is obtained by electrolysis using a mercury cathode, followed by removal of the mercury by distillation. It is a white metal (m.p. 700°) which tarnishes in the air and decomposes water. Radium isotopes occur in the natural decay series of the heaviest elements and radium itself decays further to give radon and ultimately lead. As a result of radioactive decay radium and its salts, if in quantities of a few milligrams, appear luminous in the dark. They cause discoloration of glass and bring about decomposition of water, as well as other chemical changes (radiochemical action). Radium is used in medicine as a source of γ-rays and has been used in the production of self-luminous paints.

Radium compounds. These are very similar to the corresponding barium derivatives although they are generally less soluble. Radium halides, RaF_2, $RaCl_2$, and $RaBr_2$ are known. The carbonate, fluoroberyllate, and iodate are insoluble in water. See Bagnall, 'The Chemistry of the Rare Radioelements,' Butterworths, London, 1957.

Radon, Rn. At.no. 86. The three naturally occurring isotopes are ^{219}Rn, ^{220}Rn, and ^{222}Rn, all members of various radioactive decay series; m.p. $-71°$, b.p. $-61°$. Radon is a member of the noble gas group and forms fluorides, although these have not been fully characterized. Quite soluble in water. Used in radiation therapy.

Raffinate. The refined product obtained from a solvent refining process.

Raffinose, $C_{18}H_{32}O_{16}$. The best known trisaccharide, it is composed of galactose, glucose, and fructose. It forms large monoclinic prisms as the pentahydrate, m.p. 118°, $[\alpha]_D +104°$. It is often found in considerable quantities in the sugar beet, but the best source is cottonseed meal, which contains 8%. It has no reducing power.

Raman, Sir Chandrasekhara Venkata (1888-). Director of the Indian Institute of Science, Bangalore, Raman was formerly professor of physics at the University of Calcutta. His classic researches upon oscillation, diffraction, etc., gained for him the Nobel Prize in Physics and election to the Royal Society. He was knighted in 1929.

Raman effect. This effect, predicted by Smekal in 1923 on the basis of the quantum theory, was observed by Raman in 1928. When light of frequency v_0 is scattered by the molecules of a solid, liquid, or gaseous substance, which have vibrational frequencies v_i, the scattered light when analysed spectroscopically shows lines of frequency v, given by

$$v = v_0 \pm v_i.$$

The spectrum thus obtained, corresponding with the vibrational (or rotational) changes in the molecule, is called the Raman spectrum. The number of modes of vibration of a molecule depends upon the number of atoms, The selection rules for Raman activity are different from those for infra-red activity and hence a study of Raman spectra is often complementary to a study of infra-red spectra in obtaining information about structure.

Rammelsberg, Karl Friedrich (1813-1899). Born at Berlin, Rammelsberg was trained as an apothecary. In 1834, however, he matriculated at the University, where he took up the study of pure science. After holding several junior teaching appointments and directing a private laboratory, he became, in 1874, professor of inorganic chemistry in the University of Berlin and, in 1883, Director of the newly founded second Chemical Institute of the University.

A brilliant crystallographer, his inorganic researches were mainly on the halogen compounds, the phosphates, and the cyanides. See Chem. Soc. Mem. Lect., 1900.

Ramsay, Sir William (1852-1916). Born in Glasgow, Ramsay studied at the Universities of Glasgow, Heidelberg, and Tübingen before accepting a junior teaching post at Glasgow University. He was appointed professor of chemistry at University College, Bristol, in 1880, and at University College, London, in 1887. Created K.C.B. in 1902, he was awarded the Nobel Prize for chemistry two years later. A brilliant chemist, he discovered the group of elements known as the rare gases.

Ramsay-Shields constant. The constant, k, in the Ramsay and Shields equation connecting molecular surface energy of a liquid and the temperature

$$\gamma \left[\frac{M}{D} \right]^{2/3} = k(T_c - T - 6),$$

where γ is the surface tension of the liquid, M its molecular weight, D its density, T_c, is the critical temperature, and T is the temperature at which the measurement is made. For a number of liquids the value of k is approximately 2·12, and such liquids are believed to be unassociated.

Ramsbottom carbon test. See Carbon value.

Raney nickel. A special form of nickel prepared by treating an aluminium-nickel alloy with caustic soda solution. The nickel is left in a spongy mass which is pyrophoric when dry. This form of nickel is a most powerful catalyst, especially for hydrogenations.

Raoult, François Marie (1830-1901). Born at Fournes in the Départment de Nord, Raoult found it necessary for financial reasons to curtail his studies at Paris, and for a number of years he filled various junior teaching posts. In 1863 he was awarded his Doctorate in Science from the University of Paris, and in 1870 became professor of chemistry at the University of Grenoble. His name is best known in connexion with work on solutions and the determination of molecular weights of dissolved substances. See Mem. Lect., *J. Chem. Soc.*, 1902, 969.

Raoult's law. Solutions have a lower vapour pressure than that of the pure solvent. Raoult's law, formulated in 1883, states that the vapour pressure of a solution is proportional to the molar fraction of the solvent present in the solution. Since the lowering of vapour pressure causes an elevation of b.p. and a depression of f.p., the law implies that the elevation of boiling-point or depression of freezing-point of a solu-

tion is proportional to the weight of the dissolved substance in a given weight of the solvent, and inversely proportional to the molecular weight of the substance.

Raoult's law assumes that the solvent does not enter into chemical union with the dissolved substance, but this is rarely true, and deviations from the law are so common that it is best regarded as the hypothetical limiting law for ideal solutions (*q.v.*) to which actual solutions approximate. Deviations are particularly great with strong electrolytes and high polymers.

Rare earths. Strictly the oxides of certain metals belonging to the third group of the Periodic table. The term is less correctly applied to the elements themselves. The elements are lanthanum, La; cerium, Ce; praseodymium, Pr; neodymium, Nd; promethium, Pm; samarium, Sm; europium, Eu; gadolinium, Gd; terbium, Tb; dysprosium, Dy; holmium, Ho; erbium Er; thulium, Tm; ytterbium, Yb; lutetium, Lu. Their general physical properties and chemical compounds are very similar, and are summarized under this and the next heading, but properties and compounds confined to only one element of the series are to be found under the heading of that element.

The most important rare earth minerals are allanite, gadolinite, monazite, and samarskite—mainly mixed silicates or phosphates—but rare-earth elements occur in traces in very many minerals. The most abundant rare earth elements are cerium, neodymium, and lanthanum. The separation of the rare earth elements, after solution and concentration of the metals as oxalates, is carried out on the macroscale by utilization of the 'anomalous valencies' of the rare-earths Ce, Pr, Sm, Eu, Tb, Yb, followed by separation of the elements by chromatography or ion-exchange. Prior to the development of these techniques, separations were effected by the laborious method of fractional crystallization.

The metals have been prepared by reduction of the metal halides with calcium or magnesium, or by electrolysis of fused metal salts. The metals generally have either cubic or hexagonal close-packed structures. They tarnish fairly rapidly in air, oxygen, and nitrogen and are soluble in dilute acids.

The rare-earth elements have electronic configurations $4f^n$, $5s^2$, $5p^6$, $5d^1$, $6s^2$ (n varying from 0 to 14). The stable oxidation state is $+3$, corresponding to the group oxidation state. However, $+2$ and $+4$ oxidation states (the 'anomolous valencies'), strongly reducing and oxidizing respectively, are known for many of the elements. Since most rare-earth ions contain unpaired electrons their compounds are generally paramagnetic; the salts have been used to obtain very low temperatures.

Rare earth compounds. The compounds are very similar throughout the series of elements, differences being confined to the occasional presence of oxidation states of $+2$ and $+4$ in addition to the normal stable state of $+3$ and to slight variations in solubility. For their small variations the elements are divided into three groups. La—Sm, the cerium elements, which have insoluble sulphates; Eu, Gd, and Tb, the terbium elements, having moderately soluble double sulphates; Dy—Lu, the ytterbium elements having very soluble double sulphates.

Oxides, M_2O_3, are prepared by heating the nitrates or oxalates; for elements having a higher oxidation state extra oxygen is taken up on heating in oxygen. *Hydroxides*, $M(OH)_3$ are precipitated from hot solutions of rare-earth salts; basic salts are obtained from cold solutions. *Carbides*, MC_2, are prepared by reducing the oxides with carbon in an electric furnace. *Nitrides*, MN, are obtained by direct combination of nitrogen and the metal at high temperatures. *Fluorides*, MF_3, are insoluble in water. *Chlorides*, MCl_3, may be obtained anhydrous or with 6 molecules of water. The hydrated chlorides, bromides and iodides are extremely hygroscopic. *Sulphates*, $M_2(SO_4)_3$ are prepared by dissolving the oxides or hydroxides in sulphuric acid and crystallize with 12, 8, or 4 molecules of water. *Iodates*, $M(IO_3)_3$, are insoluble in water, as are oxalates. *Nitrates*, $M(NO_3)_3$, crystallize with 6 or 5 molecules of water; on heating, they give oxynitrates. *Phosphates*, MPO_4, and *carbonates*, $M_2(CO_3)_3$ are precipitated from solutions. *Hydrides*, MH_{3-x} are formed by absorption of hydrogen by the metal at 300°. Rare-earth metal complexes are formed mainly by chelating donors such as tartaric and citric acids. These derivatives are used in rare-earth separation procedures.

Rare gases. The six gases, helium, neon, argon, krypton, xenon, and radon, the first five of which occur in small amounts in the atmosphere, are known as rare gases, or alternatively as inert or noble gases. All are monatomic. Krypton, xenon and radon form chemical compounds.

Raschig rings. See Packings.

Rasorite. See Kernite.

Rast's method. A method for the determination of molecular weight which depends upon the lowering of the f.p. of a solvent (usually camphor) by a known quantity of solute of unknown molecular weight. It is accurate only to $\pm 10\%$ but can determine the value of n for E_n where E is the empirical formula weight.

Rationality of indices, law of. See Rationality of intercepts, law of.

Rationality of intercepts, law of. The intercepts of the faces of a crystal upon the axes of the crystal bear a simple ratio to each other. This is sometimes referred to as the law of rationality of indices.

Ratio of specific heats. This is the ratio between the specific heat of a gas at constant pressure (c_p), and that at constant volume (c_v), i.e. c_p/c_v. This ratio is characteristic of the number of atoms in each molecule of the gas; monatomic gases have the value $1\cdot67$; diatomic $1\cdot40$; and triatomic $1\cdot33$ approximately.

Rauwolfia. The dried roots of *Rauwolfia serpentina*, a shrub growing in India. The principal constituents are a complex mixture of alkaloids, including serpentine, reserpine and rauwolfinine. The drug is used in the treatment of hypertension, as it has hypotensive and sedative actions.

Rây, Sir Prafulla Chandrâ (1861-1944). Rây was born at Raruli-Katipara, Bengal. He studied at Presidency College, Calcutta, and at the University of Edinburgh, returning to Presidency College in 1889 as professor of chemistry. In 1916 he became Palit professor of chemistry in the University College of Science and Technology, Calcutta. He showed a practical interest in developing Indian chemical industry by founding the Bengal Chemical and Pharmaceutical Works, of which he was a director, and published numerous original papers, dealing chiefly with the nitrates, and a 'History of Hindu Chemistry.' He was first President of the Indian Chemical Society (1924-26). See *J. Chem. Soc.*, 1946, 216.

Rayleigh, John William Strutt, 3rd Baron Rayleigh (1842-1919). Strutt was born in Essex and educated at Trinity College, Cambridge. He was appointed professor of physics, Cavendish Laboratory, Cambridge (1879), professor of natural philosophy, Royal Institution (1887), and Chancellor of the University of Cambridge (1908). A research worker on many physical problems, his accurate determinations of the density of nitrogen led to the search for the inert gases and the discovery of argon. He was elected F.R.S. in 1873, and was one of the original holders of the O.M., instituted at the Coronation of Edward VII. In 1904 he received the Nobel Prize for Physics. See *Proc. Roy. Soc.*, Vol. 98, 1920-1921.

Raymond mill. See Ring-roller mills.

Reaction velocity. The rate at which a chemical reaction takes place, as measured either by the rate of disappearance of the reactant molecules or by the rate at which the product is formed. See Mass action, law of.

Reactive dyestuffs. An outstanding group of dyes mainly used for cellulosic fibres. Those first introduced include Procions (I.C.I.), Cibacrons (Ciba) and Remazols (F.H.).

The two former types are chloro-s-triazinyl dyes which are applied from a dyebath containing dyestuff plus salt to give better exhaustion. Alkali is then added to the dyebath to increase exhaustion and to promote the reaction between dye and fibre. The dyeings are then given a thorough washing-off and soaping to remove any loosely-fixed dyestuff which is simultaneously formed. Shades of high wet fastness are obtained due to the formation of covalent linkages with the cellulose by means of a substitution reaction with the halogen(s) in the dye.

A somewhat similar procedure is used for applying Remazol dyes and the resulting shades have high fastness properties. In this case, however, an addition reaction takes place through the double bond of the vinyl sulphone of the dye.

The major ranges also consist of:

Levafix and Levafix E dyes (Bayer)

The former contain two or more reactive groups based on the alkyl esters of mineral acids. These enable one molecule of the dye to form several bonds with the hydroxy groups in cellulose, giving stable ether linkages. The newer ranges of Levafix E dyes is more reactive than the standard Levafix dyes, and the reactive group is represented by 2,3-dichlorquinoxalin-6-carbonamide.

Primazin dyes (Badische)

These possess the acrylamide residue as the main basis of the reactive group and, like the Remazol dyes, they react with the hydroxyl groups of cellulose in the presence of alkali by an addition reaction. There is also a range of Primazin P dyes, intended for use in textile printing.

Drimarene dyes (Sandoz) and Reactone dyes (Geigy)

Both ranges were introduced in 1960 and are trichloropyrimidyl dyes derived from tetrachloropyrimidine. They have lower substantivity than the reactive dyes derived from cyanuric chloride, i.e. Procion M, Procion H and Cibacron dyes, but resemble them in forming covalent linkages with cellulose through a substitution reaction.

Among other reactive dyes recently introduced are the Solidazols (Hoechst) based on 1,4-dichloro-2,3-quinoxaline, and the Cavalite (Du Pont) range. These dyes are mostly of the Rema-

zol type but some members resemble Primazin P dyes. The Basazol dyes (Badische) incorporate a new principle in reactive dye formation and are recommended for use in printing. The dyestuff reacts with a colourless product (bonding agent) i.e. Fixing Agent P, which contains a reactive group. As a result the Basazol dye becomes a reactive dye which reacts immediately with the fibre. The prints are fixed by a short steaming or hot air treatment and they possess good wet fastness due to the high degree of bonding between dye and fibre.

All the above types of reactive dyes are intended for dyeing and printing of cellulosic fibres and are the most widely used dyes for textile printing. Some are also useful in dyeing silk and the polyamide fibres but a range of reactive disperse dyes has been introduced for dyeing Nylon. These (Procinyl) dyes contain a reactive group which under suitable conditions can react with the amine and amide groups in Nylon producing bright shades of high wet fastness.

For wool dyeing the reactive dyes are not yet established on a large scale, although they are finding use in special circumstances, e.g. for producing certain very bright or deep shades of high fastness. Many dyes in the existing ranges of Procion, Cibacron and Reactone dyes can be applied successfully to wool, but as with Nylon, new ranges have also been marketed, e.g. Cibacrolan, Remalan and Remazolan dyes.

Another interesting development is the introduction (by I.C.I.) of the Procilan range for dyeing wool and polyamide fibres. They are reactive premetallized dyes which give shades of high fastness to light and to wet treatments. The chromophore is a 1:2 metal complex and the dyes have high substantivity for the fibres. They can also combine covalently with it—hence the high wet fastness.

See Jordinson and Lockwood, *J. Soc. Dyers Colourists*, **78**, 122 (1962); **80**, 202 (1964).

Realgar. The mineral form of arsenic sulphide, As_4S_4. It occurs widely distributed, and was formerly used as an orange-red pigment. It may be prepared artificially by distilling a mixture of sulphur and excess of arsenic.

Reboiler. See Rectification.

Reciprocal proportions, law of. This is a special case of the law of equivalent proportions (*q.v.*), and states that 'the weights of two or more substances which separately react chemically with identical weights of another substance are also the weights which react with each other, or are simple multiples of them,' e.g. 23 g of sodium react with 35·5 g chlorine to give sodium chloride; 23 g sodium react with 1 g of hydrogen to yield sodium hydride; 35·5 g of chlorine react with 1 g of hydrogen to yield hydrogen chloride. The law is not of completely general application owing to the existence of variable oxidation states and non-stoicheio-metric compounds.

Reclaim rubber. A material made by 'devulcan-izing' scrap or waste vulcanized rubber. The processes used involve heating the ground scrap or waste with acid, alkali, or oils. Reclaim is used as a compounding ingredient for rubber, as it acts as a softener, does not adversely affect the properties of the vulcanizate, and is generally cheaper than raw rubber.

Recoil atom. When an atomic nucleus disinte-grates the fragments receive equal momentum. In the case of a heavy nucleus emitting a light fragment, the heavy remnant will recoil with a comparatively low velocity. This residue is termed a recoil atom. The recoil atom has a sufficiently high energy to rupture bonds which it may form with other atoms. The resulting group may not recombine (Szilard-Chalmers effect) and it may thus be possible to separate chemically the atoms which have undergone radioactive disintegration. The 'hot atom' may recombine with its original partner or may combine with another group to form a new chemical compound.

Recrystallization. The process of repeated crystallization, carried out with the object of removing some particular impurity by leaving it in the solution from which recrystallization occurs, or of obtaining more satisfactory crystals of a substance which is already pure.

Recrystallization temperature. When metals or alloys are cold worked, the deformed crystals are in a state of higher energy. Annealing or heating of the material provides the activation energy for diffusion, resulting in the nucleation and growth of new low-energy crystals at the expense of the higher energy deformed crystals. The minimum temperature at which this occurs for any metal or alloy is known as its recrystal-lization temperature.

Rectification. This particular method of separat-ing a mixture into its components by fractional distillation is of such importance that the terms rectification and fractional distillation are frequently used synonymously, despite the fact that two other methods are covered by the latter term. The process of rectification may be illus-trated most readily by reference to the separa-tion of a binary mixture into its components.

If a liquid mixture is brought into contact with a vapour containing less than the equilib-rium amount of the *lighter* (i.e. more volatile) component, an exchange of material between phases will occur, some of the more volatile material entering the vapour and a correspond-ing quantity of the less volatile material enter-ing the liquid phase. If the two phases are made to flow counter-current to each other over an extended path the lighter material will accumu-late in the vapour phase and the *heavier* in the liquid phase. The longer the path the purer the two phases will become.

A *rectifying* or *fractionating column* consists of a long vertical cylinder containing either a series of *plates*, or a *packing* material having a large specific surface, both these arrangements ensuring good liquid-vapour contacting over the length of the unit. At the top of the column there is a *condenser* and at the bottom a vaporiz-ing unit called a *reboiler*. The reboiler produces a stream of vapour which passes up the column to the condenser, where it is completely con-densed and some of it is returned to the column as *reflux*. Due to the phenomenon of exchange between phases the liquid and vapour at the top consist almost entirely of the light compo-nent, and the material at the bottom of the heavy component.

Rectifying columns may be operated either batchwise or continuously. In the former case the vaporizer unit is a vessel (*kettle*) into which the charge of material to be fractionated is put. As distillation proceeds the various components distil off in order of volatility, more or less sharp separations being achieved. In continuous operation the mixture is fed to the column at some point determined by its composition. Some of the liquid stream from the condenser is taken off continuously as *overhead product* (i.e. the light component), while the *bottoms product*, consisting of the heavy component, is drawn off via the reboiler. In the case of mixtures of more than two components, those of intermediate volatility accumulate at various points in the column from where they may be withdrawn.

The separating power of a rectifying column is dependent on the length of path over which vapour-liquid contacting can occur and the *reflux ratio* employed. The latter is the ratio of the quantity of liquid returned to the column as reflux to the quantity taken off as overhead product.

Rectification is of the greatest industrial importance; in particular, it is the principal separation process employed in the petroleum industry.

See also Packed column, Plate column.

Rectified spirits. A solution of ethyl alcohol in water which contains 90% v/v ethyl alcohol; $d_{15 \cdot 5}^{15 \cdot 5}$ 0·832-0·835, n_D^{20} 1·3645-1·3647. It is 57·80° over-proof. Made by dilution of 95% ethyl alcohol with water.

Rectifying column. See Rectification.

501

Red lead. See Lead oxides.

Redler conveyor. A machine for the conveying of particulate solids in which the material is dragged along a closed conduit by means of flights attached to a chain.

Red ochre. See Ochre.

Redonda phosphate. A naturally occurring aluminium phosphate, $AlPO_4$, containing 35-40% of phosphorus pentoxide, which occurs in the West Indies. It has been used in the manufacture of phosphorus in the electric arc furnace.

Redox. An abbreviation for oxidation-reduction, e.g. redox potential = oxidation-reduction potential (*q.v.*).

Redox catalyst. A combination of a free radical catalyst with a reducing ion or salt to increase the rate of free radical production. Its use allows polymerizations to be completed at either lower temperatures or at faster rates. Many synthetic rubbers are produced by this method (e.g. SBR).

Reduced mass. For any system of particles m and M in harmonic motion about one another the reduced mass, μ, must be used in calculations $\mu = mM/(m+M)$.

Reduction. Originally reduction was regarded as a process in which hydrogen was added to a compound, or oxygen was abstracted from it. Now the term has a broader meaning, and includes processes in which the proportion of electronegative or acidic constituent of a compound is decreased, e.g. in the conversion of $HgCl_2$ to Hg_2Cl_2, or the charge on an ion is algebraically decreased, e.g. Sn^{4+} to Sn^{2+}, $Fe(CN)_6^{3-}$ to $Fe(CN)_6^{4-}$. Such processes may be carried out chemically, the reagents used being known as reducing agents, or electrolytically at a cathode (electrolytic reduction).

Reductone, Glucic acid, 1,2-Dihydroxyacrolein, $C_3H_4O_3$. A solid, m.p. 140°, (decomp.), soluble in polar solvents, and prepared by the action of alkalis on

$$CH{=}C{-}CHO$$
$$\;\;\;\;|\;\;\;\;\;\;|$$
$$\;\;\;OH\;\;OH$$

hexoses or on dihydroxyacetone. It is a reducing agent, and a weak acid forming metallic salts. The redox potential is increased by replacing a hydroxyl group by an amino group. With diazomethane, methylreductone, m.p. 67°, is formed.

Reductones. Enediols stabilized by conjugation to a carbonyl or similar group.

Refining. The removal of impurities from metals or alloys in metallurgy. This may be accomplished by several methods: furnace oxidation, electrolysis, chemical separation, distillation, zone refining, etc.

Reflux. Liquid resulting from a partial condensation of vapour which is returned to the top of a fractionating column and allowed to flow down the column counter-current to the vapour rising up the column.

Reflux ratio. See Rectification.

Reformatski reaction. Aldehydes and ketones react with α-bromo- fatty acid esters in the presence of zinc powder to give β-hydroxyesters. α-Chloroesters will react if copper powder is used in conjunction with the zinc. The aldehyde or ketone is heated with the ester in solution in dry ether or benzene-ether; when the reaction is over the mixture is treated with cold dilute sulphuric acid and the organic layer separated, dried and distilled.

Reforming. The process in which straight run gasolines and naphthas are subjected to high temperatures and pressures to convert them to materials of high octane value. When a catalyst is used the process is known as catalytic reforming, without a catalyst as thermal reforming.

Refractive index, specific. See Specific refractivity.

Refractory materials. A general term for materials which are not damaged by heating them to 1500° in a clean (oxidizing) atmosphere. *Acid refractory materials* include fireclays, flint clays, china clays (kaolins), silica, flint, chalcedony, ganister, and titanium oxide. *Neutral refractory materials* include graphite, charcoal, coke, chromite, and various carbides. *Basic refractory materials* include lime, magnesia, various materials composed chiefly of alumina (bauxite, diaspore, laterite, gibbsite, etc.), dolomite, and most of the rarer refractory oxides, particularly zirconia.

To be satisfactory when in use, a refractory material must not only be undamaged by heating it to or maintaining it at a high temperature; it must also resist the abrasive action of flue-dust, the contents of the charge of the furnace, the corrosion of slag, hot gases, flames, etc., and movement of the various parts of the structure.

Regnault, Henri Victor (1810-1878). Born at Aix-la-Chapelle, Regnault worked for a number of years in a drapery establishment in Paris. In 1829 he entered the École Polytechnique and in 1832 the École des Mines. After studying under Liebig, he was appointed professor of chemistry at Lyons and, in 1840, received a similar appointment at the École Polytechnique, Paris. In 1854 he became Director of the Porcelain Manufactory, Sèvres. Apart from his organic researches, Regnault was noted for the accuracy with which he measured specific heats and heats of fusion and vaporization.

Regnault's method for determining the density

of gaseous substances. This method consists in weighing a known volume of a gas under definite conditions of temperature and pressure. The gas is usually accommodated in a large glass globe (2 to 50 litres) which is first weighed empty (evacuated) and then full of the gas at a known pressure and temperature.

Regular system. See Cubic system.

Reichert-Meissl value. The Reichert-Meissl value of a fat is the number of millilitres of 0·1-M potassium hydroxide required to neutralize the fatty acids volatile in steam in 5 grams of fat.

Reid vapour pressure. The vapour pressure of petroleum products measured in the Reid apparatus, which consists of an air chamber of specified dimensions fitted with a pressure gauge. The apparatus is kept at a temperature of 100°F. and shaken periodically until a constant reading is given on the gauge.

Reinecke's salt, Ammonium tetrathiocyanatodiamminechromate (III), $NH_4[Cr(NH_3)_2(SCN)_4]$.

College. In 1876 he went to Johns Hopkins University, where he established the *American Chemical Journal*, later incorporated with the *Journal of the American Chemical Society*. In 1901 Remsen was appointed President of the Johns Hopkins University. Most of his research work was upon oxidation of carboxylic acid derivatives. See *J. Chem. Soc.*, 1927, 3182.

Renin. An unidentified material, present in saline extracts of kidney, which is regarded as an enzyme mediating the vasoconstrictor action of the extracts. See Angiotensins.

Rennin. The milk-clotting enzyme of the membrane lining the stomach of young animals. It has been obtained crystalline with mol. wt. of about 40,000, and acts by hydrolysing peptide links. Under the name of rennet it is manufactured from calf stomachs, and is used in cheese making and for making rennet casein, junkets, etc.

Reserpine, $C_{33}H_{40}N_2O_9$. An alkaloid prepared by synthesis or from the roots of species of

Crystallizes in rose-coloured plates, moderately soluble in warm water. Prepared by adding ammonium dichromate to fused ammonium thiocyanate and extracting the cold mass with cold water. The insoluble residue is crystallized from water at 50°. Decomposes in water above this temperature. Forms sparingly soluble compounds with some organic bases. Used for the isolation of proline, histidine, creatinine, and other organic bases.

Relaxin. A polypeptide hormone secreted during pregnancy, which has the effect of relaxing the pelvic ligaments and facilitating parturition.

Remsen, Ira (1846-1927). Remsen was born in New York City. His early education was received in the Free Academy, now the College of the City of New York. For a time he studied medicine at Columbia University, but, in 1867, he proceeded to Germany to study chemistry under Volhard, and later Fittig. Returning to America in 1872, Remsen was appointed professor of physics and chemistry at Williams

Rauwolfia. It is a white or light brown powder, soluble in chloroform, less soluble in methanol, and insoluble in water; m.p. 270°.

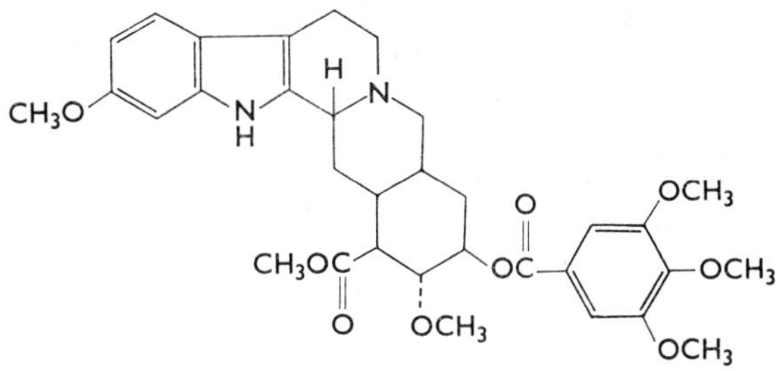

It is a depressant of the central nervous system, causing sedation and lowering of the blood pressure. It is used in treating hypertension, and also for its tranquillizing effect.

Reserve acidity and alkalinity. A buffer solution is sometimes referred to as a solution with reserve acidity or alkalinity.

Resin. A material characterized by high molecular weight, usually by variation in the weights of the molecules which comprise it and by its gummy or tacky consistency at certain temperatures. Natural resins occur in fossil form (congo copal and bitumen) as vegetable products (rosin) and are derived from insects (shellac). Synthetic resins may be formed by processes of addition and condensation polymerization.

Resolution. The name for the separation of a racemate into its two enantiomorphic forms (i.e. (+) and (−) forms).

Resonance. In the optical sense the term

'resonance' refers to the absorption by a system of radiation which it is capable of emitting. Mercury vapour, for example, when suitably excited in an electrical discharge, will emit light of wavelength λ 2536 Å. This same light is very readily absorbed by mercury vapour, and the energy so absorbed may be utilized in producing photochemical reactions. This process is analogous to acoustic resonance.

The term resonance has also been applied in connexion with the theory of valency. The general idea of resonance in this sense is that if the valency electrons in a molecule are capable of several alternative arrangements which differ by only a small amount in energy, then the actual arrangement will be a hybrid of these various alternatives. See Mesomerism.

Resorcin brown (Acid Orange 24). This primary disazo-dyestuff is the sodium salt of xylidineazo-sulphanilicazoresorcin. It is a brown powder, soluble in water and sulphuric acid, forming a brown solution. It dyes wool brown in an acid bath, but is more widely used in dyeing leather.

Resorcinol, $C_6H_6O_2$. Large colourless needles (from benzene), m.p. 110°, b.p. 276·5°. Very readily soluble in cold water. An aqueous solution gives a dark violet coloration with ferric chloride, reduces Fehling's solution and ammoniacal silver nitrate, and with bromine water gives a voluminous precipitate of tribromoresorcinol.

It can be obtained by caustic potash fusion of many resins. Prepared by fusion of m-benzenedisulphonic acid with caustic soda, also obtained to some extent in the caustic soda fusion of o- and p-benzenedisulphonic acids.

It is extensively used in the preparation of colouring matters. Combines with diazonium salts to form oxyazo-colouring matters. Gives rise to fluorescein dyes on fusion with phthalic anhydride.

Respiratory pigments. A group of pigments, of which haemoglobin is the most important member, which act as oxygen carriers in living organisms. They can be subdivided into the respiratory carriers, which carry oxygen from the respiratory organs to the tissues, and the respiratory catalysts, such as cytochrome, which are concerned with the respiratory activity of the cells. Other respiratory pigments are haemocyanin, haemerythrin, actiniohaematin, helicorubin, and chlorocruorin.

Retene, $C_{18}H_{18}$. Forms faintly yellow plate-like crystals, m.p. 101°, b.p. 390°. Soluble in benzene, insoluble in water. It occurs in the high boiling tar-oils from resinous pine wood and is the chief constituent of certain fossil resins of *coniferae*. It is produced when abietic acid is dehydrogenated.

Retinine, Vitamin-A aldehyde, $C_{20}H_{28}O$. Orange crystals, m.p. 61°-64°. Isolated from retinas, obtained by oxidation of vitamin A and β-carotene, and by various syntheses. Retinene generally refers to the all-*trans* isomer which has essentially the same bioactivity as the corresponding vitamin-A alcohol. Retinene is the intermediate in the conversion in mammals of β-carotene to vitamin A by oxidative cleavage of its central double bond.

Reverberatory furnaces. There are numerous types, but the characteristics are a shallow hearth of large area and a low arched roof from which the heat contained in the hot products of combustion is reflected or 'reverberated' down on to the charge.

Reversible process. A reversible change (process) is one which can be caused to proceed in either direction at will by an infinitesimally small alteration in one of the conditions controlling the equilibrium (pressure, temperature, concentration). Thus, if a minute alteration in pressure shifts the position of equilibrium, restoration of the pressure to its original value also restores the position of equilibrium exactly to its original position. An irreversible change is one in which a slight alteration in the conditions results in a complete and sometimes catastrophic change in the equilibrium, which cannot be brought back to its original position by the restoration of the conditions to their original values. A reversible change corresponds to a change in a body from a position of stable equilibrium; an irreversible change corresponds to a movement from a position of unstable equilibrium. A typical example of a reversible reaction is the dissociation of calcium carbonate in a closed vessel:

$$CaCO_3 \rightleftharpoons CaO + CO_2.$$

At a given temperature there is a given pressure of carbon dioxide in equilibrium with lime and undissociated calcium carbonate. A slight increase in the pressure (e.g. induced by pushing a piston into the vessel) causes a small amount of the carbon dioxide to react with some lime. If the pressure is now restored to its original value, the calcium carbonate is at once dissociated so that the conditions in the vessel are identical once more with those obtaining before the application of the pressure.

Reynolds, James Emerson (1844-1920). Born at Booterstown, Co. Dublin, Reynolds became keeper of the minerals at the National Museum, Dublin in 1867 and professor of chemistry at the Royal College of Surgeons in the same city in 1870. From 1875 to 1903 he occupied the chair of chemistry at Trinity College, then going to London to continue his researches in the Davy-Faraday Laboratory. Reynolds was President of the Society of Chemical Industry (1891) and the Chemical Society (1901-3), and a Vice-President of the Royal Society (1901-2). He wrote many papers on silicon compounds and discovered thiourea.

rH. The logarithm of the reciprocal of the partial pressure of hydrogen in equilibrium with a system, thus

$$rH = \log \frac{1}{P}.$$

It has a significance in redox reactions analogous to that of pH in neutralization reactions.

L-Rhamnose, $C_6H_{12}O_5$. A constituent of many glycosides, which is widely distributed in plants, particularly in combination with flavanol derivatives and in saponins. It crystallizes with a molecule of water, m.p. 94°; anhydrous, m.p. 122°. As a methylpentose it has the formula

It shows the usual carbohydrate reactions and most resembles mannose in behaviour; it exists in α and β forms which exhibit mutarotation.

Rhenium, Re. At.no. 75, At.wt. 186·31. A metallic element, m.p. 3167°, b.p. unknown, d 20·99, close-packed hexagonal structure, $a=2·7609$, $c=4·4583$ Å. It occurs in gadolinite, columbite, and other minerals. A convenient source is molybdenite which contains several parts per million of rhenium; it is also isolated as a by-product in the metallurgy of copper. Rhenium compounds are easily reduced to the metal by hydrogen. Metallic rhenium is attacked by oxygen, chlorine, and sulphur. Acids do not attack it but oxidizing agents such as nitric acid do. The finely divided metal is much more reactive and is a very efficient catalyst for the oxidation of alcohols. Rhenium compounds show all oxidation states from -1 to $+7$, they are superficially similar to manganese compounds but the higher states are much more stable with rhenium. Rhenium is used in protective coatings for metals; rhenium compounds are used as catalysts.

Rhenium chlorides. *Rhenium hexachloride,* $ReCl_6$, is prepared by action of chlorine on very reactive rhenium at 600°.

Rhenium pentachloride, $ReCl_5$, results from the action of chlorine on the metal at 700°.

Rhenium tetrachloride, $ReCl_4$, is prepared by chlorination of rhenium dioxide with thionyl chloride. It is a black solid and is the parent halide of many complexes M_2ReCl_6.

Rhenium trichloride, $ReCl_3$, has been reported to result from the action of a deficiency of halogen on the metal. It is the parent compound of many complexes containing metal-metal bonds.

Rhenium fluorides. Many rhenium fluorides are known. *Rhenium heptafluoride,* ReF_7, yellow, and *rhenium hexafluoride,* ReF_6, result from the action of fluorine upon the metal. ReF_6 is a pale yellow crystalline solid, m.p. 18·8°, b.p. 47·6°. It forms complexes with the alkali halides.

Rhenium pentafluoride, ReF_5, results from the reduction of ReF_6 with tungsten carbonyl. It is a yellow-green solid, m.p. 48°, b.p. 240°. On heating it disproportionates and gives *rhenium tetrafluoride,* ReF_4, a pale blue solid. Both fluorides give complexes with alkali metal fluorides.

The reduction of ReF_6 with tungsten carbonyl also yields $ReOF_4$, a blue solid, m.p. 108°. $ReOF_4$ reacts with Pyrex glass to give $ReOF_3$, black. Fluorination of ReO_2 with fluorine gives ReO_2F_2, pale yellow, m.p. $\sim 92°$, and $ReOF_5$, colourless, m.p. 34·5°, b.p. 55°. ReO_3F results from the action of HF on ReO_3Cl.

Rhenium oxides and oxy-acids. *Rhenium heptoxide,* Re_2O_7. A yellow or white substance, m.p. 304°, b.p. 350°, resulting when any rhenium compound is ignited in oxygen. With water it gives perrhenic acid, $HReO_4$. The perrhenates are very stable colourless salts having similar solubilities to the permanganates. By fusing rhenium heptoxide with alkalis mesoperrhenates, M_3ReO_5, are obtained.

Rhenium trioxide, ReO_3. Prepared by burning the metal in a slight deficiency of oxygen or by heating the heptoxide with rhenium to 200°. It may be any colour from blue to yellow. Green rhenates (VI), M_2ReO_4, are known in solution but they disproportionate on removal of water.

Rhenium pentoxide is unknown. Rhenates (V), $MReO_3$, are obtained as yellow salts by fusing a perchlorate with rhenium dioxide and alkali in the absence of air. They are very unstable and undergo ready disproportionation.

Rhenium dioxide, ReO_2. A black powder made by reducing the higher oxides with hydrogen. Rhenates (IV), M_2ReO_3, are prepared as brown solids by fusing the dioxide with alkalis in the absence of air.

Rhenium sesquioxide, Re_2O_3. A black hydrate may be obtained by treating a solution of tripositive rhenium with alkali. It is extremely easily oxidized and always contains a slight excess of oxygen.

Rheopexy. The gelation of some thixotropic (*q.v.*) sols may be accelerated by gentle mechanical treatment. This phenomenon was termed rheopexy by Freundlich. An example is given by a gypsum-water paste which, if left to itself, solidifies in about 10 minutes, but when gently rotated between the palms of the hands or tapped softly, sets in a few seconds. Vanadium pentoxide sol exhibits the same behaviour.

Rhodallin. See Allylthiourea.

Rhodamines. Dyestuffs which may be regarded as fluorescein derivatives in which the hydroxyl groups are replaced by amino- or substituted amino-groups. Rhodamines are manufactured by condensing phthalic anhydride with substituted aminophenols. Rhodamine-B (Basic Violet 10) and rhodamine-S (Basic Red 11) are salts (e.g. the chlorides) of the bases obtained by substituting $N(C_2H_5)_2$ and $N(CH_3)_2$, respectively, for each of the hydroxyl-groups in fluorescein. Rhodamines dye silk and wool a bluish-red colour; they are less suitable for dyeing cotton, although esters of rhodamine salts may be used as cotton dyes.

Rhodinal. See Citronellal.

Rhodinol. See Citronellol.

Rhodium, Rh. At.no. 45, At.wt. 102·905. Rhodium is a hard, white metal having the face-centred cubic structure, $a = 3·8034$ Å.; m.p. 1960°, b.p. 3700°, d 12·42. It is not attacked by any acid; even aqua regia has no action; and on heating in air it is only superficially attacked unless very finely divided, when it slowly forms the sesquioxide. Chlorine attacks it above 250°, but it is most easily brought into solution as the sulphate, by fusion with $KHSO_4$. In its compounds rhodium shows oxidation states of 0, 1, 2, 3, 4, 5 and 6. It is one of the rarer platinum metals, but is used in electrical contacts and in contact surfaces where wear resistance is important. Electroplated rhodium is used for decorative purposes and in optical instruments. Rhodium compounds are used as catalysts.

Rhodium alums. By crystallizing solutions containing $Rh_2(SO_4)_3$ and sulphates of mono-

positive cations a series of yellow alums may be obtained. The least soluble, and therefore most easily prepared, is the caesium alum, Cs_2SO_4, $Rh_2(SO_4)_3$, $24H_2O$.

Rhodiumammines. A large number of stable ammino compounds of tripositive rhodium are known. They are mostly white or yellow, and closely resemble the cobaltammines, but are even more stable. The principal types are the hexammine series, $[Rh(NH_3)_6]X_3$, the aquopentammine series, $[Rh(NH_3)_5(H_2O)]X_3$, and the acidopentammine series, $[Rh(NH_3)_5X]X_2$, where X represents a univalent acidic radical. The corresponding compounds in which NH_3 is replaced by organic amines are also known.

Rhodium carbonyls. Carbonyls $Rh_2(CO)_8$, $[Rh(CO)_3]_4$ and $Rh_6(CO)_{16}$ result from the action of a pressure of carbon monoxide on rhodium trichloride in the presence of a reducing agent. A hydride $HRh(CO)_4$ and halides, e.g. $[Rh(CO)_2Cl]_2$, are also known.

Rhodium chloride. Only one simple chloride exists, $RhCl_3$. The anhydrous substance is formed by direct union of the elements at about 300°, or by dehydrating the hydrated salt in a current of chlorine at about 400°. It is a red powder, insoluble in water or acids, and at bright red heat it decomposes into its elements. Although the anhydrous chloride is insoluble, solutions containing $RhCl_3$ can be prepared by the usual wet methods, and when these are evaporated a soluble hydrated form is obtained. This is an amorphous deliquescent substance whose composition does not correspond with that of any definite hydrate. It gradually loses water when heated, finally yielding the insoluble anhydrous salt.

Rhodium fluorides. *Rhodium trifluoride*, RhF_3, is a red crystalline substance formed by direct union of the elements at 500°. It is insoluble and very resistant to acids. Fluororhodates (III), M_3RhF_6, are obtained by fusing rhodinitrites, $M_3Rh(NO_2)_6$, with potassium bifluoride.

Rhodium tetrafluoride, RhF_4, is prepared as a purple-red solid by the action of bromine trifluoride on rhodium trichloride. Fluororhodates (IV), M_2RhF_6, are prepared by high temperature fluorination or by the action of bromine trifluoride on mixtures of rhodium and alkali metal chlorides.

Rhodium hexafluoride, RhF_6, is a black solid prepared by the action of fluorine on the metal. It is volatile and gives a red-brown vapour.

Rhodium halides, complex. Several series of tripositive complex halides are known. Ions $[RhX_6]^{3-}$, $[RhX_5(H_2O)]^{2-}$, $[RhX_5]^{2-}$, $[RhX_7]^{4-}$ $[Rh_2X_9]^{3-}$ are particularly common. Most of the complexes have a characteristic rose-red colour. Caesium hexachlororhodate (IV), Cs_2RhCl_6, has been obtained by oxidizing a rhodium (III) solution in hydrochloric acid with chlorine.

Rhodium iodide. *Rhodium tri-iodide*, RhI_3, is a dark red powder, insoluble in water, precipitated from solutions of rhodium compounds by addition of hydriodic acid.

Rhodium oxides. *Rhodium sesquioxide*, Rh_2O_3, is a grey solid, obtained by heating the metal in oxygen to 600°. Hydrated forms are known. Addition of excess alkali to the chlororhodate (III), Na_3RhCl_6, gives a black mass, whilst with a deficiency of alkali yellow $Rh(OH)_3 \cdot H_2O$ is precipitated. No pure oxide higher than Rh_2O_3 is formed. $RhO_2 1\text{-}2\ H_2O$ is formed by the action of chlorine or by electrolytic oxidation of a solution of $Ru(OH)_3$ in excess alkali. This hydrated oxide loses oxygen on removing water. Rhodium volatilizes in air as the dioxide.

Rhodium sulphate, $Rh_2(SO_4)_3$. The anhydrous salt is obtained as a brick-red powder by evaporating to complete dryness a solution of the hydrated sesquioxide in sulphuric acid. It is not very soluble in water, and the solution is hydrolysed on dilution. By precipitation from solution with alcohol, $Rh_2(SO_4)_3$, $15H_2O$ is obtained as yellow crystals. A number of other hydrates are known. The lower hydrates ($4H_2O$ or less) are red and are sulphato complexes.

Rhodium sulphides. Indefinite precipitates are formed by the action of hydrogen sulphide upon solutions of rhodium salts. A number of sulphides, Rh_9S_8, Rh_3S_4, Rh_2S_3 and Rh_2S_5, are formed by direct reaction between the elements. They are all grey-black, inert, insoluble, crystalline substances.

Rhodoporphyrin. See Porphyrins.

Rhodopsin, Visual purple. A major photosensitive pigment of the eye, composed of the

Neoretinene-b

protein opsin and neoretinene-b (11-*cis*-retinene). In the visual process, the latter is isomerized to all-*trans*-retinene (vitamin-A aldehyde) and dissociates from the opsin (bleaching of rhodopsin). Reconversion of retinene to neoretinene-b may then occur with regeneration of rhodopsin.

Rhombic system. See Orthorhombic system.

Rhombohedral system. One of the seven crystal systems, comprising crystals referable to a rhombohedral unit cell and therefore referred to three equal axes (of length *a*) equally inclined to one another at an angle (not 90°). Examples of rhombohedral crystals include: calcite, $NaNO_3$, and arsenic. A rhombohedral unit cell can always be expressed in terms of a trigonal cell and crystal planes and faces are generally referred to the trigonal system. See Crystal structure and Crystal symmetry.

Rhubarb. The dried rhizome of *Rheum palmatum*, cultivated in China and Tibet. Rhubarb is a valuable stomachic and aperient; it also possesses astringent properties. The powdered drug is administered along with powdered ginger and magnesium carbonate as compound rhubarb powder, also known as Gregory powder, for digestive disorders, particularly in children. Its chief constituents are anthraquinone derivatives.

Ribbon mixers. In these machines the mixing element consists of a spiral ribbon attached to a horizontal shaft which revolves in a trough. The exact form of the mixer depends on the duty involved, such factors as the number of spirals, ribbon width and pitch, and the clearance between ribbon and trough being variable from one machine to another. Applications range from the mixing of powders to the homogenizing of moderately thick pastes. They are sometimes known as trough mixers.

Riboflavin, $C_{17}H_{20}N_4O_6$. Crystallizes in orange

needles, m.p. 271°, with decomposition. Soluble in water. $[\alpha]_D -9\cdot80°$.

Riboflavin is that part of the original vitamin B_2 complex which stimulates the growth of rats. It acts as the prosthetic group of Warburg's yellow respiratory enzyme, cytoflavin, which is a component of many dehydrogenase systems. It occurs widely distributed in nature, particularly in yeast, liver, milk, and white of egg. It is prepared commercially by fermentation using the mould *Eremothecium ashbyii*.

D-**Ribose,** $C_5H_{10}O_5$. M.p. 87°, $[\alpha]_D -23°$ (in 4% solution). It is chiefly of interest as being the sugar of ribonucleic acid; it is therefore present in all plant and animal cells. It has the furanose structure shown.

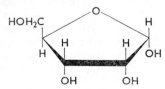

Ribosomes. Small, spherical, granular cell constituents, forming major components of the endoplasmic reticulum. Each ribosome has a molecular weight of about 2·5 million, and there may be several thousand in one cell, making up as much as a quarter of its mass. Ribosomes are the site of protein synthesis, each one forming one polypeptide chain at a time. They consist principally of protein (55%), ribonucleic acid (40%) and organic bases including spermine, cadaverine and putrescine. Ribosomal ribonucleic acids are of high molecular weight (0·5-1 million). Ribosomes also associate with 'messenger RNA' (also known as 'template RNA') molecules, which vary greatly in size. Messenger RNA is responsible for conveying genetic information to the site of protein synthesis in the ribosomes.

Ribulose, Erythro - 2 - ketopentose, Adonose,

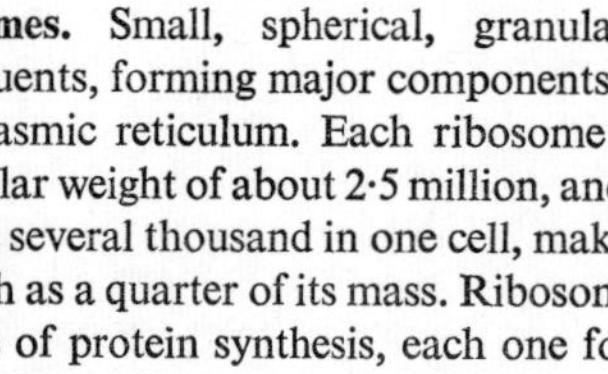

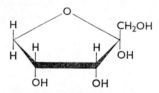

$C_5H_{10}O_5$. Ribulose-1,5-diphosphate is a key intermediate in the photosynthetic fixation of atmospheric carbon dioxide. It is formed from the 5-monophosphate by the action of ATP and a kinase. The combined action of carbon dioxide, light, water and enzyme on the diphosphate results in the formation of two molecules of 3-phosphoglyceric acid. This may be in part reconverted to ribulose diphosphate, and in part transformed to give acetyl-coenzyme A.

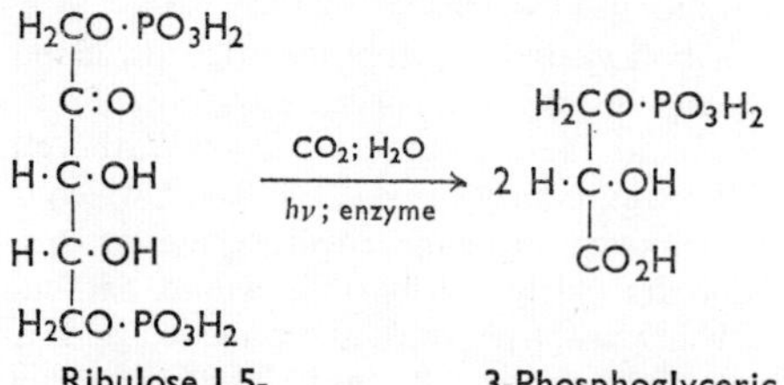

$$H_2CO \cdot PO_3H_2$$
$$|$$
$$C:O$$
$$|$$
$$H \cdot C \cdot OH \qquad \xrightarrow[hv \,;\, enzyme]{CO_2 \,;\, H_2O} \qquad 2 \; H \cdot C \cdot OH$$
$$|$$
$$H \cdot C \cdot OH \qquad\qquad\qquad\qquad CO_2H$$
$$|$$
$$H_2CO \cdot PO_3H_2$$

$$H_2CO \cdot PO_3H_2$$
$$|$$
$$H \cdot C \cdot OH$$

Ribulose 1,5-   3-Phosphoglyceric
disphosphate   acid

Richards, Theodore William (1868-1928). Born in Germantown, Pennsylvania, Richards began his education at Haverford College before proceeding to Harvard. Later he studied under V. Meyer and Nernst (Göttingen) and Ostwald (Leipzig). In 1901 he was appointed professor at Harvard, where in 1912 he became Erving professor of chemistry. Richards and his pupils determined the atomic weights of twenty five elements. In addition he made many investigations in thermochemistry. He received the Davy medal (1910), the Faraday medal (1911), the Willard Gibbs medal (1912), and the Nobel Prize in Chemistry (1915). See Chem. Soc. Mem. Lect., 1930, 1937.

Richter, Hieronymus Theodor (1824-1898). Born at Dresden, Richter became a metallurgical chemist, and later Director at the Freiberg School of Mines. An authority on blowpipe analysis, he observed the spectral lines of indium and, with Reich, isolated the metal.

Ricin. A protein, belonging to the albumin class, found in seeds of the castor-bean. It is poisonous, causing agglutination of the red blood corpuscles.

Ricinoleic acid, $C_{18}H_{34}O_3$. This is *cis*-12-hydroxy-9-octadecanoic acid. It is an oil,

$$\overset{\displaystyle OH}{\underset{\displaystyle |}{}}$$
$$CH_3 \cdot [CH_2]_5 \cdot CH \cdot CH_2 \cdot CH:CH \cdot [CH_2]_7 \cdot COOH$$

m.p. 4°-5°, b.p. 226°-228°/10 mm, $[\alpha]_D^{22} + 5 \cdot 05°$. It comprises about 85% of the acids of castor oil.

The name ricinoleic acid is used in commerce for the mixture of fatty acids obtained by hydrolysing castor oil, and its salts are called ricinoleates.

Rideal-Walter test. A method for determining the germicidal power of a disinfectant. Similar quantities of a strain of *B. typhosus* are submitted to the action of varying concentrations of phenol and of the disinfectant to be tested. The dilution of the disinfectant which sterilizes the suspension in a given time is divided by the dilution of phenol which sterilizes it in the same time, and the result expressed as a phenol coefficient. Full details of the procedure are laid down in the British Standards Specification, No. 541, 1934.

Riffled table. See Tabling.

Ringer's solution. A physiological saline solution isotonic with the serum of frog's blood and used for perfusion and tissue culture experiments.

Ring-roller mills. The characteristic feature of these machines, which are used for fine crushing, is that size reduction takes place between balls or rollers and one or more grinding rings. The grinding surfaces rotate relative to each other and material entering the mill is fed to them by centrifugal action. There are three basic types:

(a) The *Babcock and Wilcox pulverizers*. The simplest of these contains a ring of balls set between concave horizontal upper and lower rings, one stationary and the other rotating; pressure between the grinding surfaces is maintained by spring loading. Other machines of this type have two or three rings of balls separated by grinding rings set one above the other.

(b) The *Raymond mills* have heavy horizontal rollers hanging from a yoke attached to a vertical drive shaft. Rotation of this shaft causes the rollers to press outwards against a grinding surface formed by the inner side of a horizontal ring.

(c) In the *Raymond bowl mill* material is ground between heavy rollers and the vertical side of a horizontal ring; the *Lopulco* mill is similar except that the rollers run on a horizontal ring. In both cases it is the ring which is rotated and in both cases pressure on the grinding rollers is by spring loading. These two mills have the advantage over the previous types that since the grinding surfaces are not actually in contact, there is no wear on them when the mill is being run light or empty.

All the above machines are fitted with internal air classifiers which remove the fine material and return the oversize to the mill. They find a wide range of application, from the production of pulverized coal for feeding to boilers to the grinding of cornstarch.

Ring-roller mills are known by various other names, including centrifugal grinders, centrifugal attrition mills and ring-roll mills.

Rinmann's green, $ZnCo_2O_4$. A spinel formed when cobalt nitrate solution is placed on zinc oxide and the mixture heated to redness. The green colour forms a delicate test for zinc.

RNA. See Nucleic Acids.

Roasting. Defined in metallurgy as heating with excess of air and thus an oxidation process. It should not be confused with calcining which is simply a decomposition process as in the preparation of lime from limestone. If a sulphide is roasted to a sulphate the operation is often referred to as a sulphatizing roast. A chloridizing roast means treatment, generally with sodium chloride, producing the chloride.

Robertson, Sir Robert (1869-1949). Born at Cupar, Robertson was educated at Madras College and the University, St. Andrews. He was appointed chemist, Royal Gunpowder Factory (1892), Director of Explosive Research, Woolwich (1907), and was Government chemist from 1921 till 1936. His researches were chiefly upon explosives and absorption spectra in the infra-red. He was elected F.R.S. in 1917 and knighted in 1918. See *J. Chem. Soc.*, 1950, 434.

Robinson, Sir Robert (1886-   ). A graduate of Manchester University, Robinson was appointed professor of organic chemistry, Sydney (1912) and Liverpool (1915), Director of Research, British Dyestuffs Corporation, Ltd. (1920), professor of chemistry, St. Andrews (1921), professor of organic chemistry, Manchester (1922), University College, London (1928), and Waynflete professor of chemistry, Oxford (1930). Longstaff medallist and Davy medallist, his researches in organic chemistry cover a wide field, including studies on the alkaloids and phenanthrene derivatives. He was President of the Chemical Society, 1939-1941, and was elected President of the Royal Society in 1945. He was knighted in 1939, and awarded the Nobel Prize for chemistry for 1947.

Robison, Robert (1883-1941). Born at Newark-on-Trent, Robison was educated at Nottingham and Leipzig. In 1909 he became lecturer and demonstrator in chemistry at University College, Galway, and in the following year returned to Nottingham in a similar capacity. In 1913 he went as assistant biochemist to the Lister Institute, where he became head of the Department of Biochemistry in 1931 and professor of biochemistry in the University of London. He was elected a Fellow of the Royal Society in 1930 and in 1931 was Herter Lecturer at New York University. He published a monograph on phosphoric esters in metabolism and numerous papers. See *J. Chem. Soc.*, 1942, 67.

Rochelle salt. See Sodium potassium tartrate.

Rock crystal. See Quartz.

Rock salt. Naturally occurring sodium chloride. Extensive deposits occur in various parts of the world often associated with salts of potassium, magnesium and calcium. Hardness $2\frac{1}{2}$. See Sodium chloride.

Rockwell hardness. See Hardness.

Rod mill. See Ball mill.

Roller mill. This machine, used for fine grinding, consists of a pair of horizontal rolls rotating at different speeds in opposite directions, between which the material is fed. Size reduction is brought about by a combination of compression and attrition. The roller mill is employed for flour milling and the grinding of paint pigments.

Roman cement. A hydraulic cement made by calcining a natural mixture of clay and calcium carbonate which contains these substances in suitable proportions. It was erroneously supposed to be identical with the cement used by the ancient Romans. It may be regarded as a crude Portland cement.

Röntgen, Wilhelm Konrad von (1845-1923). Born at Lennep, Röntgen was educated in

Holland and Zürich. Later he studied at Würzburg and Strasburg. He was appointed professor of mathematics at Hohenheim (1875), Strasburg (1876), Physical Institute, Giessen (1879), and Würzburg (1885). It was at Würzburg that he noted the production of Röntgen rays or X-rays, when cathode rays are brought to a focus and allowed to impinge on a plate of a dense metal such as platinum. He was awarded the Rumford Medal of the Royal Society in 1896 and the Nobel Prize for Physics in 1901.

Röntgen rays. X-rays were discovered by Röntgen in 1895, and are often termed Röntgen rays in his honour.

Roozeboom, Hendrik Willem Bakhuis (1854-1907). Roozeboom was born at Alkmar and worked for several years in a butter factory before he accepted, in 1878, an invitation to become assistant to Jacob Maarten van Bemmelen, professor of chemistry at Leiden. Here he pursued his studies in chemistry and graduated in 1884. In 1896 he succeeded van't Hoff as professor of general chemistry in the University of Amsterdam. He introduced into chemistry the 'Phase Rule,' previously deduced by Willard Gibbs.

Roscoe, Sir Henry Enfield (1833-1915). Born in London, Roscoe studied chemistry under Graham and Williamson in London and under Bunsen in Heidelberg. In 1857 he succeeded Frankland as professor of chemistry at Owens College, Manchester. He was elected F.R.S. in 1863 and knighted in 1884. In 1885 Roscoe was elected a member of Parliament and served on many educational and scientific committees and commissions. He was sworn a member of the Privy Council in 1909. Roscoe isolated the element vanadium in 1869. See 'Life of Henry Enfield Roscoe,' by Thorpe (1916).

Rose's metal. See Lead alloys.

Rosin. Rosin or colophony is the residue left after removing the volatile oils from crude oil of turpentine by steam distillation. It is composed mainly of abietic acid. It is a very brittle solid that breaks with a glassy fracture.

Rosin ester. Rosin (colophony) is esterified, usually with glycerin, to give a product known as rosin-ester or ester-gum, of acid value usually 5 to 10. Improved rosin esters are obtained by incorporating special phenolic resins during the esterification process. Rosin-ester resins are used in the manufacture of paints, varnishes, and enamels.

Rotameter. This instrument is extensively used for measuring the flow of liquids and gases in pipes. It consists of a vertical glass tube, tapered slightly from top to bottom, which is installed in the pipeline in such a way that the fluid flows

upwards through it. Inside the tube is a metal or ceramic float, frequently shaped rather like a child's spinning top, whose diameter is just less than that of the narrow part of the tube. In operation the float takes up that position in the tube where the drag caused by the fluid passing through the annular clearance is just sufficient to keep it suspended there; the flow may then be read directly from a calibration on the tube.

A single rotameter can cover a wide flow range, (about 10 to 1) and this may be increased by the use of interchangeable floats. Unlike the orifice meter its accuracy is relatively insensitive to the presence of pipe fittings, such as bends and valves.

Rotary driers. These are used for the large-scale continuous drying of granular solids, and consist of a long cylinder, slightly inclined to the horizontal, which is slowly rotated. Wet material is fed in at the upper end and slowly works its way through under the action of gravity, to emerge dry at the other. Rotary driers may be divided into two types:

(a) Directly heated units. In these hot air or combustion gases are passed through the drier in either the same or the opposite direction to the flow of material, and come into direct contact with it. In order to achieve high drying rates *flights* are fitted to the inside, which lift the material and shower it through the gas stream. In another type of design an inner shell with a louvre construction carries the solid, and enables gas to pass through it.

(b) Indirectly heated units. Here the heat is transferred from hot gases through the shell or from steam pipes situated within it. In this type, too, flights or agitation are used.

Directly heated driers are usually simpler and cheaper than indirectly heated units and are used where contact between the material being dried and the hot gases can be tolerated. Because of the large gas volumes and consequent high velocities loss of fine material by entrainment may be appreciable. Indirectly heated driers do not suffer from this disadvantage, and can even employ special atmospheres if necessary.

Rotary drum filters. These have a horizontal drum with a perforated cylindrical surface covered by a filter medium, and rotate slowly with the lower portion immersed in the trough of slurry to be filtered. The inside of the drum is divided up into a number of sectors, and by means of a special rotary valve situated at the end of the drum any sector may be subjected either to vacuum or positive pressure. As a sector of the drum becomes immersed it is connected to the vacuum, which causes a cake to form, and as it emerges from the liquid this cake is washed by sprays and then sucked dry. At the discharge point the cake is loosened by the application of internal pressure and removed by a knife or in some other way. The proportions of the cycle allotted to the various operations may be altered by adjustment of the rotary valve.

There are a number of modifications of this basic form of the filter; most of them are concerned with the method of slurry feed and cake discharge.

Rotary drum filters operate continuously, have a high capacity for their size and are well adapted to the handling of free filtering materials. They are, however, limited to a maximum filtration pressure somewhat less than atmospheric and cannot be used with hot liquids or with slurries that are difficult to filter.

Rotary vacuum disc filter. The filtering elements in this machine consist of a series of discs mounted on a stout hollow horizontal shaft, the whole assembly slowly rotating with its lower half immersed in the slurry to be filtered. Each disc is divided up into a number of sectors, a sector consisting of a plate with both surfaces ribbed or serrated over which a bag of the filter medium is loosely fitted. All the sectors in any one row are connected to the same filtrate manifold running inside the central shaft.

Operation of this filter is broadly the same as that of the rotary drum type. As each sector enters the slurry it is connected by means of a special rotary valve to a vacuum, which causes a cake to form on either side, and this is afterwards sucked dry by continued application of vacuum after the cake has left the slurry. Wash is then applied if required. At the discharge point the bags are inflated by air pressure, and the loosened cake is taken off by scrapers or some other means.

Rotary vacuum disc filters are the cheapest of all continuous filters, and provide a large filtration area within a limited floor space. Their main disadvantage is that they cannot provide effective washing of the cake.

Rotational bands. See Rotational spectrum.

Rotational spectrum. When energy is absorbed by a molecule it may increase the rotational energy of the molecue as a whole (see Band spectrum). Conversely, the transition from a state of higher to one of lower rotational energy corresponds with the loss of energy, which may be emitted in the form of light, corresponding in frequency, v, with the energy liberated, E, by the relationship $E = hv$ (see Quantum hypothesis). The lines in a molecular spectrum due to such rotational transitions give rise to characteristic bands known as rotational bands, and taken together make up the rotational

spectrum of the molecule. Rotational transitions are associated with much less energy than electronic or vibrational transitions, and hence the frequency of the emitted light is small, and the bands occur in the far infra-red.

Rotatory power, specific. The specific rotatory power of a pure liquid is given by the expression

$$[\alpha]_D^t = \frac{\alpha}{ld}.$$

$[\alpha]_D^t$ is the specific rotatory power at a temperature t and for the sodium D line, and α is the rotation of the plane of polarization produced by a column of liquid of length l (decimeters) and density d. For solutions the expression becomes

$$[\alpha]_D^t = \frac{100\alpha}{lc}$$

where c is the concentration of solute in grams per ml. The molecular rotation is defined by

$$[M]_D^t = \frac{M[\alpha]}{100}$$

where M is the molecular weight.

Rotenone, $C_{23}H_{22}O_6$. White crystals, m.p. 163°,

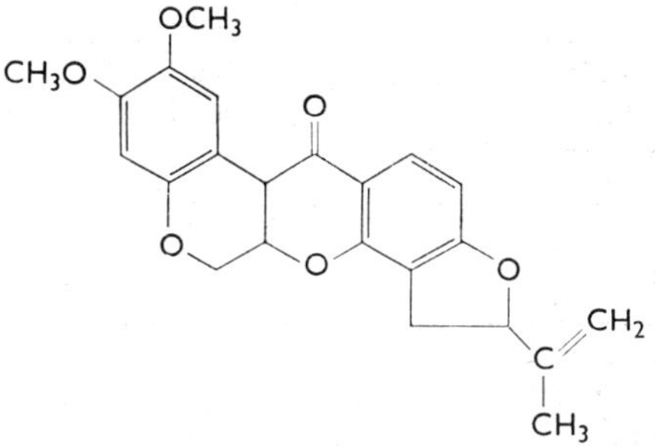

insoluble in water, soluble in organic solvents. Readily oxidized in presence of air and light to dehydrorotenone. It occurs with other related compounds in *Derris* and *Lonchocarpus*, from which it is obtained by extraction with chloroorganic solvents. It is a strong but slowly acting insecticide, harmless to most mammals, but very toxic to swine.

Rottenstone. A light earthy looking mass, resulting from the decay of siliceous limestones from which the lime has been removed by leaching. It is very variable in composition but usually contains 80-85% silica. It is used as a polishing agent for metals, glass, etc.

Rouge. A finely divided form of ferric oxide, Fe_2O_3, generally prepared by heating ferrous sulphate, and used for polishing purposes and in cosmetics on account of its smooth texture and freedom from gritty particles. Moderate heating of the sulphate gives a fine scarlet rouge used for polishing jewellery and glass; a coarser form ('crocus'), suitable for polishing metals, is obtained by stronger heating.

Royal jelly. The sole nutrient of queen bee larvae, and probably of the adult queen, comprising a mixture of proteins (31%), lipids (15%), carbohydrates (15%) and minor growth factors. The free fatty acid fraction is a mixture of C_{10} acids, the main component being 10-hydroxy-*trans*-dec-2-enoic acid. Royal jelly also contains 24-methylenecholesterol.

R, S convention. A scheme which is becoming widely used in place of the D, L system to denote configuration about an asymmetric centre in a molecule. The system is based on a set of rules (sequence rule and conversion rule) by which a priority sequence is assigned to substituents around an asymmetric centre. See R. S. Cahn, C. K. Ingold and V. Prelog, *Experientia*, **12**, (1956), 81.

Rubber. A natural or synthetic polymer of very high molecular weight, which exhibits elasticity at normal temperatures. Although occurring in many plants, natural rubber is obtained from the tree *Hevea Braziliensis* as a latex which exudes when grooves are cut into the bark. The 'tapped' latex is collected in cups and either preserved as a latex by the addition of ammonia and other alkalis or coagulated by the addition of formic or acetic acid, washed and dried in air (crepe rubber) or in wood smoke (smoked rubber). These are then the raw materials for the rubber industry. The natural latex contains up to 36% rubber, whereas the composition of the dried plantation rubber is 92-94% rubber hydrocarbon, the remainder being small quantities of water, resin (approx. 3%), proteins and ash. The resin fraction contains an important natural antioxidant which helps to preserve the natural rubber against oxidation. The rubber hydrocarbon has the structure of the *cis* form of polyisoprene (*q.v.*).

The elasticity and tensile strength of rubber is increased by chemical reactions known as vulcanization (*q.v.*). This gives rise to a small degree of cross-linking between adjacent polymer molecules which prevents the chains from slipping over each other. Vulcanization is usually essential before rubbers can be used commercially. In this state they are then capable of being extended or deformed 300-600% and yet recover when the applied stress is removed. They also become fairly resistant to moderate changes in temperature. The tensile strength as well as other mechanical properties such as abrasion and tear resistance can be considerably increased by incorporating a 'reinforcing filler' such as carbon black in the rubber (see Compounding).

To convert rubber from the raw state into its final vulcanized shape requires a number of processes such as mastication and compounding, and techniques which include moulding, extrusion or calendering to give the final shape or form which is then given permanence by vulcanization.

The physical properties of rubbers are dependent upon an amorphous or non-crystalline structure and the presence of very weak interchain forces. Upon stressing a piece of rubber, individual chains are able to stretch and uncoil and may become aligned so that crystallization can occur. This will lead to a considerable increase in tensile strength in the stressed state, termed a high gum tensile strength as seen with natural, butyl, neoprene and polyurethane polymers. Some rubbers however are unable to crystallize under stress and require reinforcement to increase their tensile strengths, e.g. SBR, nitrile and silicone rubbers.

An amorphous polymer requires an irregular chain structure to prevent crystallization occurring in the unstressed state. This is obtained by introducing bulky groups and arranging that any polar groups which may interact do not occur regularly along the chain and are thus prevented from establishing strong inter-chain forces. This principle can clearly be seen in the choice of co-monomers of intermediates during the preparation of synthetic rubbers.

Rubber conversion products. See Chlorinated rubber, Halogenated rubbers, Rubber hydrochloride, Rubber oxidation products.

Rubber hydrochloride. Rubber reacts with hydrogen chloride to give a compound with the empirical formula $C_{10}H_{18}Cl_2$. For the industrial manufacture a solution of rubber, generally in chloroform or benzene, is treated with dry hydrogen chloride below 10°. Rubber hydrochloride is soluble in chlorinated hydrocarbons and aromatic hydrocarbons, swells in esters, and is insoluble in alcohols, petrol, ether, acetone, and water. Films of rubber hydrochloride are used as wrapping materials and for rainproof clothing (Pliofilm).

Rubber oxidation products. The action of various oxidizing agents on rubber produces resinous substances containing varying proportions of oxygen according to the conditions of the reaction. The oxidation products can be used for lacquers, paints, varnishes, and adhesives. See Rubbone.

Rubber (synthetic). Tremendous developments in synthetic rubber production took place due to natural rubber scarcity during war-time conditions from 1942 onwards. The first major general-purpose rubber was a styrene-butadiene copolymer (*q.v.*) (designated GR-S or SBR) whose production showed extremely rapid growth from about 2,000 tons in 1942 to 700,000 tons in 1945. Other special-purpose rubbers such as neoprene, butyl, and nitrile were developed about this time. More recently, with the introduction of new catalyst systems such as the Zeigler-Natta type and those using lithium, the structural form of natural rubber has been accurately reproduced using dienes such as butadiene and isoprene. In particular, polymers of the latter are practically indistinguishable from natural rubber. Also arising from the use of Ziegler-Natta catalysts are the ethylene-propylene copolymer rubbers (*q.v.*) which, because of the absence of unsaturation, are resistant to ageing by ozone and also have a high abrasion resistance. Other elastomers based on vinyl polymers which have some particular speciality, such as resistance to ozone, oxidation or high temperatures, are those derived from the polyacrylates, those from polyethylene by chemical modification (e.g. Hypalon) and some copolymers of vinylidene fluoride with chlorotrifluoroethylene (Kel-F) or with hexafluoropropene (Viton). These latter two can be used up to about 230° and 290° respectively.

There are also rubbers which are basically condensation or non-vinyl type polymers (those mentioned above are all vinyl addition polymers). Such are silicone, polyurethane, and organic polysulphide (Thiokol) rubbers. These have for cost and other reasons only achieved the status of speciality rubbers. It is also possible by a correct choice of constituent intermediates (e.g. diols and dicarboxylic acids) to make rubbery polyesters and by chemical modifications to make Nylon-type polymers into rubbers. These have not yet achieved commercial importance.

Rubbone. A trade name for rubber oxidation products made by oxidizing rubber in the presence of catalysts such as cobalt linoleate. The Rubbones are viscous liquids which can be vulcanized with sulphur or sulphur monochloride. They are used in electrical insulation, in baking varnishes, and in the manufacture of asbestos boards and tapes.

Rubeanic acid, Dithio-oxamide. An orange-red solid, m.p. 41°. It is soluble in alcohol and slightly soluble in water. Prepared by adding a concentrated solution of potassium cyanide to an ammoniacal solution of copper sulphate until the blue colour is just discharged and then passing hydrogen sulphide into the cooled liquor. The rubeanic acid is precipitated and is recrystallized from alcohol.

$$S{=}C{-}NH_2$$
$$S{=}C{-}NH_2$$

It gives a black precipitate with solutions of copper salts and is used to detect small traces of copper in solution.

Ruberythric acid, $C_{25}H_{26}O_{13}$. The principal glycoside of madder, 1,2-dihydroxyanthraquinone primeveroside, the sugar being joined at position 2. It has m.p. 257°. Three other similar primeverosides are galiosin (1,2,4-trihydroxyanthraquinone-3-carboxylic acid), rubiadin (2,4-dihydroxy-3-methylanthraquinone) and munjistin (2,4-dihydroxyanthraquinone-3-carboxylic acid). See Anthraquinone glycosides.

Rubidium, Rb. At.no. 37, At.wt. 85·48, m.p. 38·5°, b.p. 696°, *d* 1·53. Rubidium salts occur in traces in saline deposits and are often associated with the lithium mineral lepidolite. Metallic rubidium is obtained by electrolytic reduction of rubidium salts or by decomposition of such salts as rubidium azide. It is a silvery-white metal, crystallizing with a body-centred cubic structure, $a{=}5{\cdot}62$ Å. Rubidium and its salts are radioactive because of the presence of the radioisotope [87]Rb.

Rubidium reacts immediately with oxygen, hydrogen, and water. It is an alkali metal. It is used in photoelectric cells.

Rubidium compounds. Rubidium forms a single series of compounds in which it is unipositive.

Ruby. A variety of aluminium oxide. Artificial rubies are made by fusing together alumina, potassium carbonate, and calcium fluoride, with traces of potassium chromate to give the red colour. They may also be made by fusing alumina with a trace of chromic oxide. Ruby crystals may be used as lasers. See also Corundum.

Rumford, Benjamin Thompson, Count (1753-1814). Born at Woburn, Mass., Rumford was during his lifetime storekeeper, soldier, and administrator, yet always enthusiastic over scientific research. In 1779 he was elected F.R.S., and in 1791 created a Count of the Holy Roman Empire. He chose the title of Rumford from the home town of his wife. In 1799, with Sir Joseph Banks, he was the means of bringing into existence the Royal Institution. He was the founder of the Rumford Medals of the Royal Society and the American Academy of Arts and Sciences, and of the Rumford Professorship at Harvard.

Running point. A term used in laboratory distillation tests; it signifies that the distillate must be measured at that specified temperature when the distillation has not been interrupted.

Russell, Sir John (1872-1965). Born in Gloucestershire, Russell's schooling stopped at the age of 14, but he ultimately went to Owens

College, Manchester, and graduated in chemistry. He became a lecturer at Wye Agricultural College in 1901 and moved to Rothamsted in 1907, where he was director of the Agricultural Research Station from 1912 to 1943. He was an expert not only in agricultural chemistry, but in applying many scientific methods to agriculture. See *Chemistry in Britain*, **2**, 97 (1966).

Russell-Saunders coupling. A system of arriving at the different energy levels associated with unfilled shells, in which electron spins are assumed to couple only with electron spins, and orbital momenta to couple only with orbital momenta. Used to describe the ions of the first row of the transition elements. The heavier elements require the use of jj-coupling in which spin-orbital interaction is assumed.

Rusting. The rusting of iron and steel takes place in a moist atmosphere when ferrous ions go into solution in the condensed film of moisture. These ions are oxidized by atmospheric oxygen to the ferric state and are precipitated as a loose, flaky layer of hydrated ferric oxide. Rusting is accelerated by impurities in the atmosphere such as sulphates in towns and chlorides in coastal districts. It is prevented by plating or painting or alloying the steel with 12-18% chromium which causes the formation of a protective chromium oxide layer on the surface. Rusting is negligible in hot, dry areas as the critical humidity is too low.

Ruthenates. Several ruthenates are known with the metal in varying oxidation states. Ruthenates (VII), containing the green or orange RuO_4^- ion, result by fusing ruthenium compounds with alkali in the presence of an oxidizing agent. Species with co-ordinated hydroxyl ions are formed in aqueous solution. Reduction gives the orange ruthenate (VI), RuO_4^{2-} ion.

Ruthenium, Ru. At.no. 44, At.wt. 101·7. Ruthenium is one of the platinum metals, and ruthenium compounds have found use as catalysts. It occurs to the extent of a few per cent. in native osmiridium. It is a hard white metal, rather brittle, and has the close-packed hexagonal structure ($a=2·7038$, $c=4·2816$ Å), m.p. 2250°, b.p. 4110°, d 12·45.

Acids have very little action on the metal, even *aqua regia* attacks it only very slowly, but it is readily dissolved by hypochlorite solutions with the formation of RuO_4, and oxidizing alkaline fusions convert it to ruthenates (VII) and (VI). In air it is superficially oxidized to RuO_2 at red heat, and at very high temperatures RuO_4 is formed. In its compounds it may exhibit oxidation states from 0 to 8.

Rutheniumammines. A number of stable ammino-compounds derived from tripositive

Ru are known. Many of these resemble the corresponding compounds of tripositive Rh, Ir, and Co, e.g. $[Ru(NH_3)_6]Cl_3$, $[Ru(NH_3)_5Cl]Cl_2$.

Some ammines of dipositive Ru are of interest in containing co-ordinated SO_2.

Ruthenium bromides. *Ruthenium tribromide*, $RuBr_3$, is obtained as brown, rather impure, crystals by the action of hydrobromic acid on ruthenium trihydroxide. It gives complexes in acid solution.

Complex tetrapositive bromides are known; they are stable and similar in their properties to the complex chlorides.

Ruthenium carbonyls. Carbonyls of formulae $Ru(CO)_5$, and $Ru_3(CO)_{12}$ are formed by the action of a pressure of carbon monoxide upon a ruthenium salt in the presence of a reducing agent. They undergo the normal reactions of carbonyls.

Ruthenium chlorides. *Ruthenium trichloride*, $RuCl_3$, is prepared by the action of chlorine on ruthenium. It is a black compound which forms a trihydrate.

Ruthenium tetrachloride, $RuCl_4$, is known only as the pentahydrate which forms large red crystals when Ru^{III} is oxidized with chlorine. It is hydrolysed to the hydroxy-chloride $Ru(OH)Cl_3$.

Ruthenium chlorides, complex. Chlororuthenates (IV) are complex salts of the type $M^I_2RuCl_6$. They are much more stable than $RuCl_4$, and are isomorphous with the chloroplatinates (IV). Chlororuthenates (III) are complex chlorides derived from $RuCl_3$. $HRuCl_4, 2H_2O$ exists in two isomeric forms, red and green. Salts derived from it, and from the hypothetical H_2RuCl_5, are known.

Ruthenium fluorides. *Ruthenium hexafluoride*, RuF_6, is a dark brown compound which results from the action of fluorine upon the metal.

Ruthenium pentafluoride, RuF_5, is also formed in this reaction; it is a green solid, m.p. 86·5°. Reduction of the pentafluoride with iodine in iodine pentafluoride gives *ruthenium tetrafluoride*, RuF_4, a yellow solid; reduction with iodine at 150° gives the dark brown *ruthenium trifluoride*, RuF_3. This compound is insoluble in water. The action of bromine and bromine trifluoride on the metal in the presence of glass gives *ruthenium oxytetrafluoride*, $RuOF_4$. This is nearly colourless, m.p. 115°.

Ruthenium fluorides, complex. *Hexafluororuthenates (V)*, $MRuF_6$. Obtained by fluorination of a mixture of ruthenium metal and the equivalent quantity of alkali halide with bromine trifluoride. They are cream coloured solids, rapidly hydrolysed by moist air.

Hexafluororuthenates (*IV*), M_2RuF_6. Hexafluororuthenates (V) oxidize cold water and hexafluororuthenates (IV) remain. On cooling in ice, pale yellow crystals of alkali hexafluororuthenates (IV) separate. They are hydrolysed by boiling water.

Hexafluororuthenates (*III*), M_3RuF_6. Stable hexafluororuthenates (III) are obtained by fusing ruthenium tri-iodide with potassium bifluoride.

Ruthenium hydroxide, $Ru(OH)_3$. This is obtained as a brown precipitate by treating solutions of tripositive ruthenium compounds with caustic alkalis. It cannot be washed free from alkali and is very readily oxidized.

Ruthenium iodide. RuI_3. Prepared from the tetroxide and hydriodic acid. It is a black, insoluble substance.

Ruthenium nitrosyls. Ruthenium forms extensive series of nitrosyl complexes, most of which contain the RuNO group, e.g. $K_2RuNOCl_5$, $K_2Ru(NO)(CN)_5$, $RuNOCl_3$. The nitrosyls are very stable and persist through many reaction sequences.

Ruthenium oxides. RuO_2 is a blue-black crystalline substance, which is obtained by the decomposition of RuO_4, or by its reduction with H_2O_2, or by heating $(NH_4)_2RuCl_6$ in air at about 600°. It is not attacked by acids and at temperatures above 1000° it decomposes, forming the metal and RuO_4.

Ruthenium volatilises in air as a gaseous trioxide in the range 800-1500°.

RuO_4 may be obtained by passing chlorine through a hot (80°-90°) acid solution of any ruthenium compound, when it distils readily and condenses to a mass of golden yellow crystals, m.p. 25·5°, sp.gr. 3·29. At temperatures above about 107° it decomposes violently, forming RuO_2, but at very high temperatures it is stable, and is formed from RuO_2 and oxygen. It has a smell somewhat resembling that of ozone; it is exceedingly poisonous. When dissolved in alkalis it is reduced to Ru (VI) or Ru (VII) with liberation of oxygen.

Ruthenium salts. Apart from the chlorides, scarcely any simple salts of ruthenium are known except in solution. Their tendency is either to be hydrolysed or to form complex salts. A sulphate, $Ru^{IV}(SO_4)_2$, is obtained by oxidation of RuS_2, and a sulphite, $Ru_2^{III}(SO_3)_3$, and a few basic acetates have been described.

Ruthenium sulphides. RuS_2 is a black precipitate. RuS_3 and RuS_6 have been reported.

Rutherford, Daniel. Was an independent discoverer of nitrogen in 1772. He was a professor of botany in Edinburgh.

Rutherford, Ernest, Baron Rutherford of Nelson (1871-1937). Born in Nelson, New Zealand, Rutherford studied at the Universities of New Zealand, Cambridge, and Giessen. He was appointed professor of physics, McGill University, Montreal (1898), Manchester (1907), and Cavendish professor of experimental physics, Cambridge (1919). His brilliant researches elucidated the problems of radioactivity, atomic structure, and the electrical nature of matter. He was elected F.R.S. (1903), and awarded the Rumford Medal (1905), the Copley Medal (1922), and the Nobel Prize for Chemistry in 1908. He was knighted in 1914, and created O.M. in 1925 and Baron in 1931.

Rutile, TiO_2. The crystals are tetragonal, $a=4·58$, $c=2·98$ Å. Hardness 6½, sp.gr. 4·3. Reddish-brown colour, with a metallic adamantine lustre, strong refraction, strongly birefringent. The crystals are often twinned, sometimes repeatedly twinned. It is common in many rocks, but commercial sources are dykes and pegmatites and beach sands and alluvials. It is an important source of titanium and its compounds, and is used in ceramics and for coating electric welding rods.

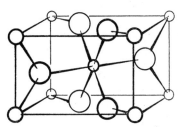

The Crystal Structure of Rutile
The larger circles represent oxygen, the smaller titanium

In the crystal structure of rutile each Ti ion is surrounded by six O ions and each O ion by three Ti ions (compare the fluorite structure, where the corresponding co-ordination numbers are eight and four). A considerable number of dioxides and difluorides crystallize with the rutile structure, e.g. PbO_2, SnO_2, MnF_2, ZnF_2, MgF_2, etc.

Rutin, $C_{27}H_{30}O_{16}·3H_2O$. The 3-rhamnoglucoside of 5,7,3′,4′-tetrahydroxyflavanol. It can be extracted in crystalline form from buckwheat, and is insoluble in water, almost insoluble in ethyl alcohol, soluble in methyl and isopropyl alcohols and alkalis. It has vitamin P activity and is used in the treatment of hypertension associated with capillary fragility.

Ruzicka, Leopold (1887-   ). Born in Vukovar, Yugoslavia. Except for three years at the University of Utrecht, he has spent most of his working life at the Technische Hochschule in Zürich, working on terpenes and particularly on carbon compounds with very large rings. He shared the Nobel Prize for chemistry with Butenandt in 1939.

Rydberg's constant. The wave-number of any line in a spectrum can be expressed as the difference of two terms which are of the form $\frac{R}{x^2}$, i.e.

$$\nu = \frac{R}{x_1^2} - \frac{R}{x_2^2},$$

where x_1 and x_2 are small whole numbers, and R is a constant which appears with only small variations in the terms of all such formulae. R is known as Rydberg's constant, and has the value 109,678. Compare Balmer series.

S

Sabatier, Paul (1854-1941). Educated at the École Normale, Sabatier was appointed professor of chemistry at the University of Nîmes (1878), Bordeaux (1880), and Toulouse (1882). In 1899 he discovered with Senderens the process for the catalytic hydrogenation of oils. He was awarded the Nobel Prize for chemistry in 1912 and the Davy Medal of the Royal Society in 1915.

Sabinene, $C_{10}H_{16}$. A dicyclic monoterpene, the (+)-form of which is found in oil of savin and many other essential oils. The (−)- and racemic forms occur occasionally in nature. It has not been prepared synthetically. No crystalline derivatives are known and the physical constants vary with the origin of the specimen, but average values are: b.p. 163°-165°, d^{20} 0·842, n_D^{20} 1·465, $[\alpha]_D$ +80·2°. When shaken with dilute sulphuric acid it is easily converted into terpinen-4-ol and 1,4-terpin.

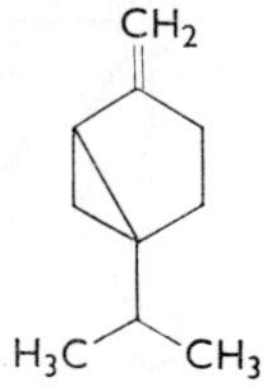

Sabinol, $C_{10}H_{16}O$. (+)-Sabinol is found both free and as the acetate in oil of savin and also in the oil from *Juniperis phoenicea*. It forms an oil which can be purified by means of its crystalline hydrogen phthalate and then has b.p. 208°, d^{15} 0·9518, n_D^{18} 1·4895, $[\alpha]_D$ +7·56°. It forms a crystalline hydrogen phthalate of m.p. 101°-102° and a nitrobenzoate of m.p. 76°. It can be reduced by hydrogen with a platinum or palladium catalyst at ordinary temperatures to form (−)-dihydrosabinol which is identical with (−)-thujyl alcohol.

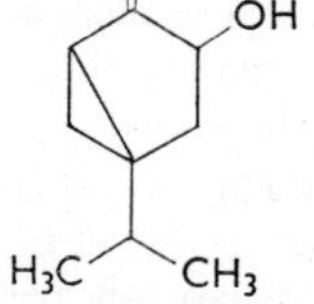

Saccharates. Normally the salts of saccharic acid, but the term is also used in the sugar industry for the alkali and alkaline earth compounds of sucrose: strictly these should be called sucrates.

Saccharic acid. The saccharic acids have the formula $COOH \cdot [CHOH]_4 \cdot COOH$, and are produced by the oxidation of the corresponding aldoses with nitric acid. Ten possible isomeric forms are known.

By saccharic acid is usually meant D-glucosaccharic acid, obtained by the oxidation of glucose or starch. This exists in water solution in equilibrium with its two γ lactones, both of which can be obtained crystalline, though the acid itself does not crystallize readily. The calcium and potassium hydrogen salts are sparingly soluble in water.

Saccharimetry. The estimation of sugars by means of a polarimeter. Polarimeters graduated to read the concentration of sugar directly are called saccharimeters.

Saccharin, $C_7H_5NO_3S$. White prisms or leaflets, m.p. 224° (decomp.), slightly soluble in cold water, more soluble hot, soluble in alkalis, alcohol, and acetone. It is made by the oxidation of toluene-*o*-sulphonamide with alkaline permanganate. Saccharin has about 550 times the sweetening power of sucrose, and is used extensively as a sweetening agent, usually in the form of the sodium salt, 'soluble saccharin.'

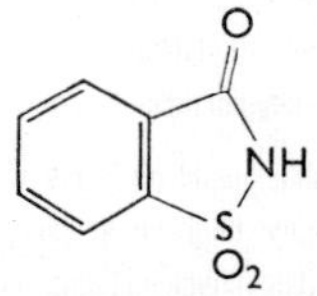

Safranine (Basic Red 2). A dyestuff having the formula

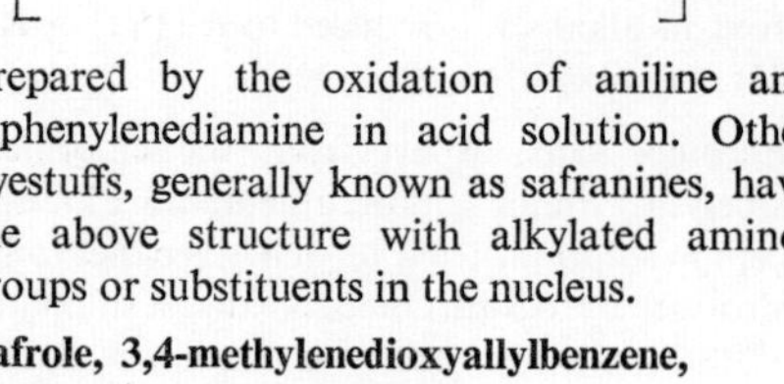

Prepared by the oxidation of aniline and *p*-phenylenediamine in acid solution. Other dyestuffs, generally known as safranines, have the above structure with alkylated aminogroups or substituents in the nucleus.

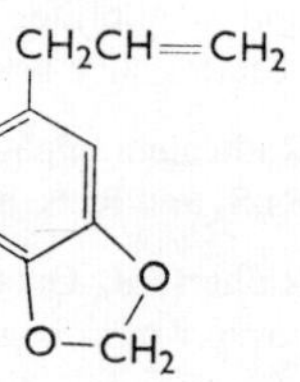

Safrole, 3,4-methylenedioxyallylbenzene, $C_{10}H_{10}O_2$. A colourless liquid, b.p. 231·5°-232°, d_4^{20} 1·100, n_D^{20} 1·5383, freezing at 11·2° to monoclinic prisms, insoluble in water, soluble in alcohol and ether. It is obtained from oil of camphor, and is the chief constituent of oil of sassafras and other essential oils. It is used medicinally as a counter-irritant and parasiticide.

Sainte-Claire Deville, Étienne Henri (1818-1881). Sainte-Claire Deville was born at St. Thomas, in the West Indies. After teaching at Besançon from 1845 to 1851 he went to Paris to become professor of chemistry at the École Normale and the Sorbonne. He made important contributions to the technical side of chemistry, including the manufacture of aluminium on a comparatively large scale, but is chiefly remembered as the originator of the theory of dissociation.

Sakurai, Joji (1858-1939). Sakurai was educated at Tokio and London, returning to Tokio in 1882 as professor of chemistry in the Imperial University. This position he retained until 1919. His original researches are overshadowed by his work as a teacher, in which capacity he assisted to a considerable degree in the progress of science in Japan. An honorary fellow of numerous chemical societies throughout the world, he was President of the Japanese Chemical Society on repeated occasions, was President of the National Research Council in 1925, and of the Imperial Academy in 1926.

Sal ammoniac. See Ammonium chloride.

Salicin, $C_{13}H_{18}O_7$. The β-D-glucoside of o-hydroxybenzyl alcohol,

$$C_6H_{11}O_5 \cdot O \cdot C_6H_4 \cdot CH_2OH.$$

Colourless, bitter crystals, m.p. 201°. $[\alpha]_D^{20}$ $-65\cdot2°$, soluble in water and alcohol, insoluble in chloroform. It occurs in the leaves, bark, and twigs of species of willow and poplar. On oxidation with dilute nitric acid it is converted into helicin, the glucoside of salicylaldehyde, which has been made the starting point of further syntheses. When salicin is shaken with benzoyl chloride populin is formed. Salicin is an antipyretic and analgesic, and is given in the treatment of rheumatism.

Salicyl alcohol, Saligenin, $C_7H_8O_2$. White crystalline plates, m.p. 87°. Readily soluble in water, alcohol, and ether. Gives a blue colour with ferric chloride.

It is obtained by the reduction of salicylaldehyde or by hydrolysis of the glucoside salicin.

Salicylaldehyde, $C_7H_6O_2$. Oily liquid of aromatic odour, b.p. 196°, d^{15} 1·172. Fairly soluble in water, miscible in all proportions with alcohol and ether. An aqueous solution gives a violet coloration with ferric chloride.

It is prepared by the action of chloroform and caustic potash on phenol, by the oxidation of the glucoside salicin, or by reduction of salicylic acid. It is easily reduced to salicyl alcohol or oxidized to salicylic acid.

Salicylamide, $C_7H_7NO_2$. A white crystalline powder, soluble in hot water and in alcohol, insoluble in cold water, m.p. 140°. It has antipyretic, analgesic, and antirheumatic properties.

Salicylic acid, $C_7H_6O_3$. Colourless needles from hot water, m.p. 159°. Very soluble in alcohol, ether and hot water, less so in cold water. At 200° it decomposes to phenol and carbon dioxide.

Occurs naturally as its methyl ester, oil of wintergreen, from which it can be obtained by hydrolysis with alcoholic potash. It is manufactured by heating sodium phenate with carbon dioxide under pressure and acidifying the sodium salicylate formed. The production of various pharmaceuticals, principally aspirin, accounts for the bulk of salicylic acid consumption, but it is also used in the manufacture of dyes.

Saligenin. See Salicyl alcohol.

Salmine. A protein, belonging to the protamine class, found in the sperm and testicles of the salmon. It closely resembles clupeine and on hydrolysis gives about 90% of the amino-acid arginine.

Salol, Phenyl salicylate, $C_{13}H_{10}O_3$. Colourless

acicular crystals or white powder, insoluble in water, soluble in alcohol and ether; m.p. 42°-43·5°. It is prepared by heating sodium salicylate and sodium phenoxide in the presence of phosphorus oxychloride. It is hydrolysed in the small intestine giving salicylic acid and phenol.

It is used as an enteric coating for pills, and as a paint for throat ailments. Its use as an intestinal antiseptic is doubtful as doses large enough to be effective may produce toxic effects due to liberation of phenol.

Salt. A term used commonly to denote sodium chloride. More generally a salt is the substance produced by interaction of equivalent quantities of acid and base. To consider aquo-acids; if replacement is complete the salt is said to be normal (e.g. Na_2SO_4), and if only partial an acid salt is formed (e.g. $NaHSO_4$). In general, only the salts of strong acids with strong bases are stable in solution. If either or both constituents are weak, hydrolysis occurs to a more or less marked extent, and the solution becomes acidic or basic.

Salt bath. A bath containing a molten mixture of low melting-point salts, used in the heat treatment of steels and non-ferrous alloys. The advantage over furnaces is that there is no atmospheric attack and temperature control is better. The container may vary in size from a refractory crucible to large refractory lined tanks which are generally heated by internal electrical resistance. A sodium carbonate-potassium carbonate eutectic mixture is commonly used for higher temperatures, while nitrates are used for lower temperatures.

Salt bridge. In many electrochemical cells, electrical conductivity may be achieved whilst keeping the two solutions in the cell apart by means of a porous plug. The resistance of the solution in this case is very high. In practice the liquid-junction potential may be greatly reduced by means of a salt bridge, which consists of a tube containing a saturated solution of a salt (usually potassium chloride) in an organic gel, e.g. agar. The ends of the salt bridge dip into the two half cells and the current is carried by the K^+ and Cl^- ions which have approximately the same ionic velocities.

Salting out. Hydrophilic colloids such as gelatin or soaps can be salted out or coagulated by the addition of a high concentration of electrolyte. This must not be confused with the coagulation of hydrophobic sols by small quantities of electrolyte.

The salting out action of the electrolyte depends on its dehydrating action on the hydrophilic colloid, and it can easily be demonstrated that a dehydrated hydrophilic colloid is as sensitive to electrolytes and other coagulating influences as a hydrophobic sol. See Colloids, Hydrophilic, Hydrophobic, Coagulation, Lyotropic series.

In addition, an alternative significance of the term salting out, which applies to non-colloidal solutions, is the reduction in solubility of a non-electrolyte by the addition of a strong electrolyte. Thus if sodium chloride is added to a solution of sucrose in water the solubility of the sucrose is less than in the absence of sodium chloride and some of the sucrose is thus salted out.

Sal volatile. Aromatic spirit of ammonia consisting of an alcoholic solution of ammonia and ammonium carbonate flavoured with the oils of lemon and nutmeg. It is used as a first-aid stimulant in cases of fainting and is frequently added to dyspepsia medicines for its stimulating and antacid properties.

Samarium, Sm. At.no. 62, At.wt. 150·43,

d 7·536, m.p. 1072°, b.p. 1900°. Metallic samarium is rhombohedral to 917° ($a = 8.996$ Å, $\alpha = 23°\ 13'$). It is a typical member of the rare-earth series ($q.v.$).

Samarium compounds. Samarium forms two series of salts. The tripositive salts are pale yellow in colour and are typical rare-earth compounds ($q.v.$). Dipositive samarium salts are obtained by reduction of the tripositive salts. Reduction of $SmCl_3$ by hydrogen at 600°-700° gives $SmCl_2$ and the bromide, iodide, and sulphate of dipositive samarium are also known. Dipositive samarium salts decompose water with liberation of hydrogen; the solid salts are red-brown in colour.

Sampling. The process of obtaining a small quantity of material, e.g. for analysis, such that it shall be truly representative of a much larger quantity. Specific methods of sampling are used for different materials, and details of these may be found in the appropriate B.S.I. publications.

If samples of material are withdrawn manually the process is known as *hand sampling*. It is less reliable than *mechanical sampling*, where representative portions are withdrawn automatically from a stream of the material by a *sampler*. Sometimes the size of a sample may be too large for convenient handling and it is necessary to reduce the quantity by taking a sample of the sample. This is referred to as *secondary sampling*.

See also Coning and quartering.

Sand. Natural sand is an accumulation of mineral matter, largely silica, resulting from the disintegration of rocks.

Sand filter. In this type of filter the separation of solid from liquid is effected by passage through a comparatively deep bed of graded layers of sand, the finest being at the top of the bed resting on progressively coarser layers. These filters are used to handle large quantities of liquid from which it is desired to remove a small proportion of solids and find their widest application in water treatment plant. For handling very large quantities of water, as in town water supply, it is normal practice to use open beds which may be of almost any required size. In industrial practice where space is a primary consideration the filter beds are contained in water-tight vessels and the liquid forced through under pressure; in such filters the bed may be cleared of deposited solids by back-flushing.

Other materials, such as graded coke, are often employed in the construction of filters of this type for special purposes.

Sandmeyer, Traugott (1854-1922). Born at Wettingen in Aargau, Sandmeyer entered the employment of a maker of scientific apparatus at Zürich and afterwards started business on his own. In 1882 he became assistant to V. Meyer and later to Hantzsch. In 1888 he joined the firm of J. R. Geigy, Basle, manufacturers of dyestuffs. In 1899 Sandmeyer synthesized indigo and introduced into organic chemistry the important reaction which bears his name.

Sandmeyer's reaction. The replacement of a diazonium group by a halogen or pseudo-halogen atom or group. It allows the conversion of an aromatic primary amine into the corresponding halogen compound. The amine is diazotized, and the diazonium salt solution is treated with cuprous halide, etc., causing the evolution of nitrogen and isolation of the halobenzene. Chloride, bromide and cyanide react easily; potassium iodide is sufficient for preparation of the iodo-compound. Aromatic fluorides are prepared after isolation and decomposition of the diazonium fluoroborate salt.

$$RN_2^{\oplus}X^{\ominus} \xrightarrow{HBF_4} RN_2^{\oplus}BF_4^{\ominus} \xrightarrow{Heat} RF + BF_3 + N_2$$

See also Gatterman reaction.

Sandwich compounds. A trivial name, originally applied to the bis-cyclopentadienyl metal compounds like ferrocene but since used variously to cover all the compounds where a metal atom is disposed between two hydrocarbon residues such as cyclopentadienyl, benzene, cyclohexadienyl, cyclobutadiene, tropylium, etc. Those compounds having only one such ring are correspondingly called half-sandwich compounds, e.g. cyclopentadienyl-manganese tricarbonyl, $C_5H_5Mn(CO)_3$. See Organometallic compounds, Metallocenes, Ferrocene.

Santene, C_9H_{14}. The only terpene-like natural hydrocarbon containing nine carbon atoms. It is found in East Indian sandalwood oil and also in Siberian, German, and Swedish pine-needle oils. It has a rather unpleasant smell, resinifies easily, and is difficult to obtain pure. Its constants are: b.p. 140°-141°/770 mm, d^{20} 0·863, n_D^{20} 1·46658. α-Santene nitrosochloride forms blue needles of m.p. 109°-110° which change on exposure into a colourless β-form.

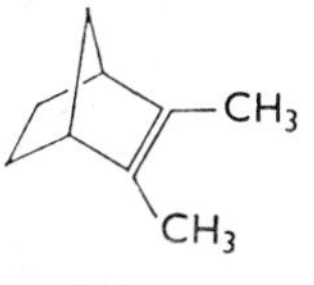

Santenone, π-Norcamphor, $C_9H_{14}O$. A saturated dicyclic ketone related to santene. (−)-Santenone is found in East Indian sandalwood oil. The optically inactive form is prepared by the oxidation of santene with chromic acid mixture. It is a crystalline solid of

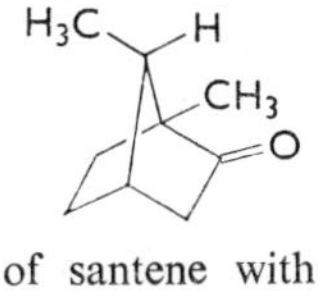

camphor-like smell. (−)-Santenone has m.p. 58°-61°, b.p. 193°-195°, $[\alpha]_D$ −4·40° (in alcoholic solution). For the inactive form m.p. 55°-57°, b.p. 197°, d^{20} 0·966, n_D^{20} 1·4690. The semicarbazone of the (−)-form has m.p. 222°-224° and that of the (±)-form 228°-229°.

Santonin, $C_{15}H_{18}O_3$. Colourless crystals, m.p.

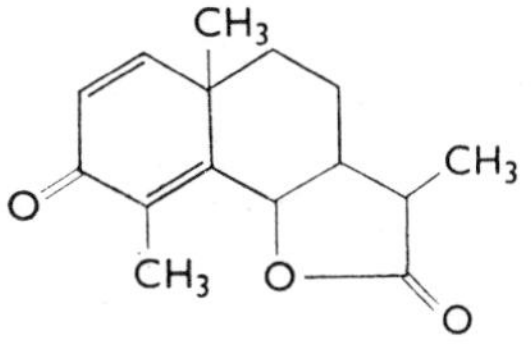

173°, insoluble in water, soluble in 50 parts of alcohol. It is obtained from the dried unexpanded flower heads of *Artemisia cina*.

Saponification. The alkaline hydrolysis of an ester to an alcohol and the alkali-metal salt of a carboxylic acid (a soap).

Saponification value. The saponification value of a fat is the number of milligrams of potassium hydroxide neutralized during saponification of one gram of the fat. It is a measure of the mean molecular weight of the fatty acids in the fat molecule. Fats such as lard give values about 195, whereas butter and other fats with a high proportion of the lower fatty acids have values about 225 to 230.

Saponins. Glycosides characterized by forming colloidal aqueous solutions which foam on shaking. Even in high dilution they effect hydrolysis of the red blood cells. The saponins themselves are hardly known in the pure state but their aglucones, termed sapogenins, have been characterized. They are divided into two groups, the one including the triterpenes hederagenin and oleanolic acid which are dehydrogenated to mixtures of naphthalene and picene homologues. The other group is closely related to the cardiac aglucones and sterols, it includes sarsasapogenin and smilagenin.

They are found in a great variety of plants and are strong fish poisons. On hydrolysis they yield a variety of sugars, frequently several molecules to each aglucone. Glucose, galactose, arabinose are the more common; pentoses, methylpentoses, and glucuronic acid are also obtained.

Sapphire. The blue form of corundum, now prepared artificially by fusing alumina. See Aluminium oxide.

Sarcosine, N-Methylglycine, $C_3H_7NO_2$, $CH_3 \cdot NH \cdot CH_2 \cdot CO_2H$. Colourless crystals, m.p. 212°-213° (decomp.). It is obtained on hydrolysing creatine with alkalis.

Satin-white. This important pigment is used as a base for the cheaper kinds of pulp colours for paper and for the surfacing of paper, as it produces on calendering a fine, glossy, white surface. Satin-white could be a calcium sulphoaluminate, but is probably a mixture of calcium sulphate and aluminium hydroxide. It is prepared by double decomposition of alum or aluminium sulphate with milk of lime.

Saturated compound. This is a substance in which the atoms are linked by single bonds, and which has no double or triple bonds. Thus ethane is a saturated hydrocarbon. However the term 'saturated' is often applied to compounds containing double or triple bonds which do not easily undergo addition reactions. Thus acetic acid is termed a saturated carboxylic acid and acetonitrile a saturated nitrile, whereas a Schiff's base (*q.v.*) is considered to be unsaturated.

SBR. See Styrene-butadiene rubber.

Scandium, Sc. At.no. 21, At.wt. 44·96, m.p. 1539°, b.p. 2727°, d 2·992. A rare element of Group III of the periodic table. Metallic scandium has been prepared by electrolysis of $ScCl_3$ in a eutectic melt of KCl and LiCl at 700°-800°. It is dimorphic; α-scandium is cubic-close-packed, $a=4\cdot532$ Å, $d=3\cdot20$; β-scandium is hexagonal-close-packed ($a=3\cdot3080$ Å, $c=5\cdot2653$ Å). Scandium occurs naturally as the major constituent of thortveitite, and most rare-earth minerals contain traces of scandium. After concentration scandium is separated as the thiocyanate, which may be extracted into ether. There are so far no technical uses for the metal or its compounds.

Scandium compounds. *Scandium oxide,* Sc_2O_3, is a white powder which is formed by heating the hydroxide, the oxalate, or the nitrate of the element. The *hydroxide,* $Sc(OH)_3$, is precipitated from solutions of scandium salts by the addition of ammonia or sodium hydroxide solution, and is not soluble in excess of the precipitant. *Scandium fluoride,* ScF_3, is precipitated by the addition of hydrofluoric acid to a solution of a scandium salt. It is soluble in excess of alkali fluoride solution to give solutions of hexafluoroscandates. *Scandium chloride* is known as the anhydrous salt and as the hexahydrate and is soluble in water, the solution being appreciably hydrolysed. *Scandium sulphate,* $Sc_2(SO_4)_3$, crystallizes with 0, 2, 4, and 5 molecules of H_2O. Unlike the rare-earth sulphates its solubility in water does not diminish with increase of temperature. *Scandium carbonate,* $Sc_2(CO_3)_3$, 12 H_2O is formed as a white bulky precipitate by adding sodium carbonate solution to a scandium salt. *Basic scandium carbonate,* $Sc(OH)CO_3 \cdot H_2O$, is formed as a white bulky precipitate by adding sodium carbonate solution to a scandium salt. The *oxalate* is only slightly soluble in water, and resembles the rare-earth oxalates. The *nitrate,* $Sc(NO_3)_3$, 4H_2O, forms colourless prismatic crystals.

Scandium is tripositive in all its compounds. It has very similar properties to the rare-earth elements.

Schäffer's acid, $C_{10}H_8O_4S$. Obtained by

sulphonating β-naphthol with a small amount of sulphuric acid at a higher temperature than is used for the preparation of crocein acid.

A valuable dyestuff intermediate; with nitrous acid, gives 1-nitroso-2-naphthol-7-sulphonic acid, the iron salt of which is the pigment Naphtol green.

Schardinger enzyme. See Xanthine oxidase.

Scheele, Carl Wilhelm. Scheele was born in 1742 at Stralsund, and at the age of fourteen was apprenticed to an apothecary in Gothenburg. He afterwards became an assistant to apothecaries or pharmacists in Malmö, Stockholm, Uppsala, and Köping. He discovered oxygen before the year 1773, but his discovery was not published until a few years after; he was the first to give an account of chlorine, manganese, and baryta, and he independently discovered ammonia gas and hydrochloric acid. He discovered molybdic, tungstic, arsenic, lactic, gallic, oxalic, citric, tartaric, malic, and uric acids, and was the first to isolate glycerin and milk-sugar. He died in 1786.

Scheele's green. A bright green colouring matter formerly used as a pigment. It is considered to be copper hydrogen arsenite but the exact composition varies with the method of production. It differs from Emerald green in not containing any copper acetate.

Scheelite. A heavy mineral composed of calcium tungstate, $CaWO_4$; sp.gr. 5·9-6·1, hardness, 4·5-5·0. Tungstic acid can be obtained from scheelite by boiling the mineral with hydrochloric acid.

Schiff, Hugo Josef (1834-1915). Born at Frankfurt-am-Main, Schiff was educated at Göttingen. Having to migrate to Switzerland on account of too liberal ideas, he taught for a time at Berne, and later at Pisa and Florence. In 1877 he was appointed professor of general chemistry at Turin and in 1879 at Florence. His researches covered a wide field, including investigations on the metal-ammonium compounds, the cinnamic series, glucosides, aldehydes, and their derivatives. See *J. Chem. Soc.*, 1916, 424.

Schiff's bases. *N*-Arylimides, $Ar \cdot N = CR_2$, prepared by reaction of aromatic amines with aliphatic or aromatic aldehydes and ketones. They are crystalline, weakly basic compounds which give hydrochlorides in non-aqueous solvents. With dilute aqueous acids the parent amine and carbonyl compounds are regenerated. Reduction with sodium and alcohol gives a secondary base. Secondary bases can also be obtained from the reactions with Grignard reagents and with alkyl halides.

Schiff's reagent. This is a solution of rosaniline in water decolorized with sulphurous acid. Aliphatic aldehydes and aldose sugars give a magenta colour with this reagent; with aromatic aldehydes and aliphatic ketones the colour develops more slowly; aromatic ketones do not react.

Schlippe's salt. An old name for antimony pentasulphide.

Schomaker-Stevenson equation. The equation $r_{A-B} = r_A + r_B - 0.09/(x_A - x_B)$ relating the bond length r_{A-B} to the individual radii r_A and r_B of the two atoms concerned and the electronegativities x_A and x_B of the two atoms concerned in the bond. This relation is only empirical and is not very accurate.

Schönbein, Christian Friedrich (1799-1868). Born at Metzingen, Swabia, Schönbein studied at Tübingen and Erlangen. After holding several junior teaching posts he was appointed professor of chemistry and physics at Basle in 1835. He carried out researches on ozone (which he discovered), hydrogen peroxide, and gun-cotton.

Schönite, K_2SO_4, $MgSO_4$, $6H_2O$. A mineral obtained from the Stassfurt salt deposits and used in the preparation of potassium sulphate. A series of schönites, analogous to the alums, is formed containing dipositive ions such as Zn^{2+}, Co^{2+}, Ni^{2+}, Fe^{2+}, Cu^{2+}, Mn^{2+}, V^{2+} in place of magnesium.

Schoop metallizing process. A method of coating a surface with a metal. The coating metal is sprayed on from a special type of atomizer.

Schotten-Baumann reaction. See Benzoyl chloride.

Schottky defect. In a solid it is possible that some of the atoms or ions may be displaced either to an interstitial lattice position (Frenkel defect) or to the surface of the solid itself. If a crystal is composed of ions of approximately the same dimensions, then movement to an interstitial position leads to electrostatic repulsions which are diminished by the further displacement of the migrating ion to the crystal surface. The vacancies caused in the lattice by this type of displacement are known as Schottky defects.

Schradan, Octamethylpyrophosphoramide, $C_8H_{24}N_4O_3P_2$. An insecticide with systemic properties.

$$(CH_3)_2N \underset{(CH_3)_2N}{\overset{O}{\underset{}{\diagdown}} \overset{\|}{P} - O - \overset{\|}{P} \overset{N(CH_3)_2}{\underset{N(CH_3)_2}{\diagup}}}$$

It is manufactured from tetramethylphosphorodiamidochloride, $[(CH_3)_2N]_2P(O)Cl$, by reaction with ethyl tetramethylphosphorodiamidate, $[(CH_3)_2N]_2P(O)OC_2H_5$, or with a tertiary amine such as pyridine, or merely with an alkali metal hydroxide. When pure it is a colourless, viscous liquid, b.p. 118°-122°/0·3 mm, miscible with water and most organic solvents, but not with paraffins. The crude material is a brown oil. It is not highly toxic to insects when used as a contact insecticide, but is readily absorbed by the roots and leaves of plants and translocated in the sap, so that the plant becomes toxic to species feeding on it. Pests controlled include aphids and red spider mite. Schradan has been officially approved for use on brassicas, main crop cucumbers, field beans, hops, mangold, sugar beet, and strawberries. Periods of up to 6 weeks should elapse between the last spraying and harvest.

Schroedinger wave equation. The fundamental equation of wave mechanics which relates energy to field. The equation which gives the most probable positions of any particle, when it is behaving in a wave form, in terms of the field.

Schweinfürter green. See Emerald green.

Schweizer's reagent. The dark blue liquid obtained by adding sodium hydroxide to copper sulphate solution, filtering off the precipitated copper hydroxide and redissolving it in concentrated ammonium hydroxide. The reagent is a solvent for cellulose, the cellulose being reprecipitated when the reagent is acidified. This is the basis of the cuprammonium process for the manufacture of artificial silk.

Scintillation counting. The detection and quantitative estimation of radioactivity by the scintillations produced when the ejected particles strike a screen of a material such as zinc sulphide. See Counters.

Scleroproteins, Albuminoids. A class of proteins obtained from the skeletal and connective tissues of animals and their outer covering and its appendages, and characterized by their insolubility in most reagents. Typical albuminoids are collagen from connective tissue, elastin from elastic tissue, and keratin from hair, nails, and feathers.

Scombrine. A protein belonging to the protamine class, found in the testicles of the mackerel.

Scopolamine. See Hyoscine.

Scott, Alexander (1853-1947). Born at Selkirk, Scott was educated at Cambridge and Edinburgh. After teaching at Durham School he returned to Cambridge in 1891 as Jacksonian Professor. In 1896 he became superintendent of the Davy-Faraday Research Laboratory of the Royal Institution, London, where he remained until 1911. From 1919 to 1938 he was Director of Scientific Research at the British Museum, where his work established beyond doubt the value of science to archaeology. Scott was President of the Chemical Society in 1915-17. See *J. Chem. Soc.*, 1950, 762.

Scraper conveyor. See Flight conveyor.

Screening. Separation of material containing particles of various sizes into fractions containing particles whose sizes lie within a certain range, by the use of sieves.

Screens. In all screening equipment the separation is effected by passing the feed through a wire cloth, or grid composed of metal bars, perforated plate, or other suitable arrangement such that the undersize passes through, and the oversize is retained on the screening surface. Industrial screens are normally shaken or vibrated mechanically or electrically.

Screw compressor. A type of rotary compressor having two parallel rotors revolving in opposite directions within a casing. Each rotor has a deep screw thread on it and the threads, which are in the opposite sense, intermesh. Gas entering at one end is compressed and squeezed along at the same time. These machines are capable of handling fairly large quantities of gas and produce a compression ratio of about 4 to 1.

Screw conveyor. A common and versatile solids conveyor consisting of a helix rotating inside a fixed case. In addition to conveying, these machines may be used to carry out mixing, cooling, heating or drying at the same time.

Screw feeder. A screw conveyor used to feed material to a process or vessel.

Screw pumps. The single rotor screw pump is basically similar in construction and action to a screw conveyor, while the two rotor machine is similar to a screw compressor. Screw pumps can work against high pressures and are also suitable for handling viscous liquids. One well-known design, the *Mono pump*, has a rubber-lined stator and is able to handle abrasive suspensions.

Scrubbers. These remove impurity from a gas by washing it with a liquid; the impurity may either be another gas or particles of suspended solid or liquid. In both cases the object is to ensure intimate contact between the two phases, and scrubbing equipment is therefore generally similar to gas absorption equipment.

Scymnol, $C_{27}H_{43}O_5$. Crystallizes in anhydrous

cubes from ethyl acetate, m.p. 187°, and with $2H_2O$ from aqueous acetone, m.p. 115°, $[\alpha]_D$ +38·2° in alcohol. It is a polyalcohol, related to the sterols and is found in the form of its sulphuric ester in shark's bile.

Seaborg, Glenn Theodore (1912-   ). Born in Michigan, Seaborg studied at the University of California. In 1940 he discovered the element plutonium, and four more transuranium elements were discovered by his team of workers. He became professor of chemistry at Berkeley in 1945 and is now Chairman of the U.S. Atomic Energy Commission. He shared the Nobel Prize for chemistry in 1951 with the physicist, E. M. McMillan, the discoverer of neptunium.

Sebacic acid, $C_{10}H_{18}O_4$, $HOOC\cdot[CH_2]_8\cdot COOH$. Crystallizes in colourless leaflets, m.p 134·5°. Sparingly soluble in water; soluble in alcohol. Manufactured by heating castor oil with alkalis or by distillation of oleic acid. Forms an anhydride, m.p. 78°-79°. The esters of sebacic acid are used as plasticizers, especially for vinyl resins.

Secondary radiation. A secondary radiation is defined as a radiation produced by the absorption of some other, generally more energetic, radiation. Thus, when X-rays strike a body it emits other X-rays, which are termed secondary rays, or secondary radiations, characteristic of the atom which acts as the emitter. This phenomenon is also observed with electrons and is then termed secondary emission.

Secretin. A gastro-intestinal hormone discovered by Bayliss and Starling (1905) who coined the word hormone to describe its action. Secretin is produced by the duodenal mucosa upon the appearance there of acidic food pulp from the stomach. The hormone, which consists of a number of polypeptides, stimulates the pancreas to secrete pancreatic juice and bicarbonate.

Sedimentation. Gravitational settling of solid particles suspended in a liquid so that the original suspension is divided into a reasonably clear effluent and a sludge with an increased solid content.

As the particles of a suspension obey Stokes's law (q.v.) their rate of sedimentation through a liquid of known viscosity gives a measure of their size. Although colloidal particles do not settle appreciably under the influence of gravity, they can be made to do so in a high-speed centrifuge.

A further consequence of the sedimentation theory is that the particles of a disperse system arrange themselves under the influence of gravity so that the disperse atmosphere is most dense at the bottom of the containing vessel. This was verified by Perrin.

Sedimentation potential. When the particles of a suspension are allowed to settle under the influence of gravity, the motion of the disperse phase through the dispersion medium gives rise to a measurable potential difference which is termed the sedimentation potential.

Seed crystals. Crystals which are added to a supersaturated solution to facilitate the crystallization of the whole.

Seger cones. A form of pyroscope invented by H. Seger and consisting of small tetrahedral pyramids 6 cm high and 1 cm base. They are placed vertically on a slab of stiff clay or other suitable material and are pressed into it just sufficiently to prevent them from falling. On being heated, the cones bend over and the tip eventually touches the slab; this is the critical point for each cone, and if the conditions of heating are constant it corresponds to a definite temperature for each cone. It is better, however, to quote the number of the cone and not the corresponding temperature. Seger's original series was modified by Simonis and Hacht who increased the number of different cones to 64, corresponding to temperatures between 600° and 2000° with an average difference of 20° between each pair. The cones are composed of feldspar, china clay, quartz, iron oxide, marble, and boric oxide, or some of these materials with the exception of No. 42 which is composed of pure alumina.

Seger cones are used for determining the refractoriness of clays, glazes, refractory materials, etc., and for indicating the temperature in kilns, ovens, etc.

Segregation. The tendency for solid particles, either dry or in suspension in a liquid, to arrange themselves in different layers according to size.

Seignette salt. Sodium potassium tartrate.

Selachyl alcohol, $C_{21}H_{42}O_3$. An oil, b.p.

$$CH_3 \cdot [CH_2]_7 \cdot CH : CH \cdot [CH_2]_8 \cdot O \cdot CH_2 \cdot \underset{\underset{OH}{|}}{CH} \cdot CH_2OH$$

242°/5 mm. A constituent of the liver oils of elasmobranch fishes.

Selenates. Salts of selenic acid. They may be prepared from selenic acid, or by the electrolytic oxidation of the corresponding selenites. The selenates closely resemble sulphates, but may be reduced to selenites by concentrated hydrochloric acid. With the exception of the calcium, strontium, barium, and mercurous salts the normal selenates are readily soluble in water. Double salts such as K_2SeO_4, $MgSeO_4$, $6H_2O$, and alums of the normal crystalline form such as M_2SeO_4, $Al_2(SeO_4)_3$, $24H_2O$ are readily produced, and many selenates are isomorphous with the corresponding sulphates. In general, the water of crystallization in selenates is less tenaciously held than in the corresponding sulphates. The selenates are less toxic than the selenites.

Selenic acid, H_2SeO_4. Selenic acid crystallizes in hexagonal prisms, isomorphous with sulphuric acid, d_4^{15} 2·951, m.p. 57-58°, b.p. 172°/85 mm. It is prepared by oxidizing aqueous selenious acid with chlorine, bromine, or potassium permanganate or in best yield with a mixture of barium chlorate and sulphuric acid. There is a mono- and a tetrahydrate. Aqueous solutions must not be heated above 210° and the final stages of concentration must be carried out under reduced pressure. Selenic acid resembles sulphuric acid in many of its properties. It is similar in strength, an oxidizing agent which attacks many organic compounds with charring, and is a dibasic acid yielding the well-defined selenates, very often isomorphous with the sulphates. In contrast to sulphuric acid, selenic acid dissolves iron only slowly, whilst gold is easily dissolved by the hot acid to give auric selenate and selenium dioxide.

Selenides. Formally derivatives of hydrogen selenide, H_2Se, but many selenides in fact contain ratios of elements which cannot be explained on this formulation. They may be prepared by the direct union of the elements, by the action of hydrogen selenide on the element or on an aqueous solution of the metallic salt, or by the reduction of an oxy-salt such as a selenite with carbon or hydrogen.

In general the properties of the selenides run parallel with those of the corresponding sulphides, but they are less stable, more easily oxidized, and more rapidly attacked by water to yield the hydride.

Selenious acid, H_2SeO_3. Colourless crystals d_4^{15} 3·00, which are deliquescent in moist air, but lose some of their moisture in dry air to yield SeO_2. The acid is formed by the action of water on selenium dioxide. The acid is much more stable than sulphurous acid, and can be separated as a crystalline solid by evaporating its aqueous solution to crystallization. Oxidation to selenic acid, H_2SeO_4, is only effected by powerful reagents, but reduction to elementary selenium is easily brought about. Selenious acid is a weak acid, but neutralizes hydroxides and carbonates with the production of selenites.

Selenite. A variety of gypsum, which occurs frequently as colourless, transparent crystals in London clay, Oxford clay, and some shales. In massive form it is used for the same purposes as gypsum.

Selenites. Salts of selenious acid, H_2SeO_3. Prepared by use of the acid in aqueous solution, or in the anhydrous condition by heating the metal oxides with selenium dioxide. In the presence of excess of selenious acid, acid selenites $MHSeO_3$ have been obtained. Owing to the feeble acidity of selenious acid, the selenites are alkaline in solution. They are readily reduced with the liberation of selenium, and have a strong tendency to yield complex salts. The alkali selenites are irritant poisons.

Selenium, Se. At.no. 34, At.wt. 78·96. Occurs in small amounts widespread in nature in sulphide ores, in the free state in volcanic deposits, and in selenides such as clausthalite, PbSe, and crookesite, $(CuTlAg)_2Se$. It was discovered in 1817 by Berzelius in a deposit from some sulphuric acid chambers, and is still prepared from such industrial residues by dissolution, followed by precipitation with sulphur dioxide.

There seem to be three main allotropes of selenium. Amorphous selenium exists as a black vitreous form resulting from the cooling of the liquid; a red form is deposited from selenites by sulphur dioxide. Monoclinic or red selenium may be extracted from the red amorphous form with carbon disulphide; there are two forms. On heating, all these forms are converted to grey, metallic selenium, d 4·82, m.p. 220·2°, b.p. 688°. It has a hexagonal structure, a=4·34, c=4·95 Å, with the selenium atoms arranged in spiral chains. It is insoluble in carbon disulphide.

This variety is a conductor of electricity, and the conductivity is greater in the light than in the dark. This property finds application in photo-electric cells and xerography.

Selenium combines directly with many elements, e.g. oxygen, hydrogen, and chlorine. Molten selenium is miscible with most metals, and readily yields metallic selenides, and poly-selenides, e.g. Na_2Se, Na_2Se_2, Na_2Se_3. The element is used industrially for decolorizing and tinting glass.

Selenium bromides, *Selenium monobromide*, Se_2Br_2. A deep-red liquid, with an unpleasant odour, d_4^{15} 3·604, b.p. 227° (decomp.). Prepared by the action of selenium tetrabromide, or bromine, on selenium.

Selenium dibromide, $SeBr_2$. The only stable molecule in the vapour phase of the system Se/Br is the dibromide, $SeBr_2$.

Selenium tetrabromide, $SeBr_4$. A reddish-brown crystalline powder, prepared by the action of excess of bromine on selenium or selenium monobromide. It is hydrolysed by water, and yields the hexabromoselenates (IV) with alkali bromides.

Selenium chlorides. *Selenium monochloride*, Se_2Cl_2. A clear, reddish-brown liquid, b.p. 130° (decomp.), m.p. −85°, d_4^{25} 2·77. Prepared by the action of chlorine on heated selenium, or by saturating with chlorine a suspension of selenium in carbon tetrachloride, in which the monochloride is soluble. It is slowly decomposed by water, and is a good chlorinating agent.

Selenium dichloride, $SeCl_2$. Selenium dichloride does not exist in the solid or liquid state but the vapour from Se_2Cl_2 and $SeCl_4$ is almost entirely selenium dichloride. The molecule is very stable in the vapour phase.

Selenium tetrachloride, $SeCl_4$, forms yellowish-white, deliquescent cubes, m.p. 305°, sublimes 196°. It has been prepared by the action of chlorine on selenium or selenium monochloride, or by distilling selenates with sulphuric acid and sodium chloride, and may be purified by distillation in an atmosphere of chlorine. Hexachloroselenates (IV), M_2SeCl_6, are obtained from solutions of $SeCl_4$ in concentrated hydrochloric acid.

Selenium compounds. In general chemical behaviour, selenium occupies a position intermediate between sulphur and tellurium, which it can replace in most of their compounds. It is tetrapositive in most of its stable compounds, but forms a large series of organic derivatives, such as $Se(CH_3)_2$ in which it has a valency of two. Most soluble or volatile compounds of selenium are extremely poisonous, the symptons generally resembling those of arsenical poisoning, and they have been used as bactericides, fungicides, and herbicides. Certain selenites are satisfactory pigments, e.g. those of barium and lead, while others are employed in photographic toning processes.

Selenium fluorides. *Selenium hexafluoride*, SeF_6; m.p. $-34.6°$, sublimes at $-46.6°$. Prepared by the action of fluorine on selenium at $78°$. It is a stable gas, which does not attack glass.

Selenium tetrafluoride, SeF_4; m.p. $9.5°$, b.p. $106°$. Prepared by the action of fluorine on a surface of sublimed selenium. Selenium tetrafluoride does not attack glass when free from HF, but is hydrolysed by water. Selenium tetrafluoride is a good solvent and has been used in the preparation of complex fluorides.

Selenium hydride. See Hydrogen selenide.

Selenium nitride, Se_4N_4. Prepared by the action of liquid ammonia on selenium tetrabromide in the presence of carbon disulphide. It is a brick-red amorphous powder, insoluble in water, alcohol, and ether, and slightly soluble in carbon disulphide, benzene and glacial acetic acid. When dry, it detonates violently, and is more sensitive than mercury fulminate.

Selenium oxides. *Selenium dioxide*, SeO_2, forms hygroscopic, colourless, lustrous, needle-shaped crystals, which sublime readily, and have d_4^{15} 3.954, m.p. *ca.* $340°$. It is prepared by burning the element in a stream of air or oxygen or in the wet way by oxidation with nitric acid. Molten selenium dioxide is orange-yellow, and the vapour is yellowish-green. Selenious acid H_2SeO_3 is formed by treatment with water.

Selenium dioxide finds wide application as an oxidizing agent in organic chemistry where it is used to oxidize α-hydrogen atoms to ketonic groups.

Selenium trioxide, SeO_3. It is prepared, mixed with the dioxide, by the action of a high-frequency discharge on a mixture of selenium and oxygen at a pressure of 15-20 mm. The mixture of oxides is white and hygroscopic, and yields selenious and selenic acids on treatment with water.

Selenium sulphoxide, $SeSO_3$. Formed by dissolving amorphous selenium in molten sulphur trioxide. It is a green liquid, which solidifies to a green solid, which easily passes to a yellow modification. The compound decomposes on gentle heating.

Selenocyanates. The salts of selenocyanic acid, which are usually prepared from potassium selenocyanate. Potassium selenocyanate, KSeCN, is formed by fusing together potassium cyanide and selenium. The selenocyanates are fairly stable compounds, and with the exception of the copper, lead, mercury, and silver salts, are soluble in cold water.

Selenocyanic acid, HSeCN or HNCSe. Prepared by the action of hydrogen sulphide on lead selenocyanate. It is stable only in neutral or alkaline solution.

Selenocyanogen, $(SeCN)_2$. A pseudohalogen, formed by the action of oxidizing agents on selenocyanates. Selenocyanogen is a fairly stable yellow powder which turns red on standing.

Selenosulphuric acid, H_2SeSO_3. The free acid does not exist, but the salts, analogous to the thiosulphates, are obtained when precipitated selenium is dissolved in aqueous solutions of alkali sulphites. The selenosulphates, e.g. K_2SeSO_3, are very unstable, and their solutions undergo decomposition, even on dilution with water, with the liberation of selenium.

Selinene, $C_{15}H_{24}$. A sesquiterpene, found in celery oil and oil from certain eucalyptus,

which can be isolated by means of its crystalline dihydrochloride.

Semenov, Nikolaj Nikalajevitz (1896-   ). Born in Saratov, Semenov studied physics at the University of Petrograd. In 1924 he became director for chemical physics at the physico-chemical institute, Leningrad, and in 1944 head of the department of chemical kinetics at the University of Moscow. He shared the Nobel Prize in chemistry for 1956 for his work on the mechanism of chemical reactions.

Semet-Solvay coke oven [horizontal flues]. The regenerators in this type of oven run parallel to the length of the battery. The air for combustion enters through a blower into the waste-heat flue and then into the regenerators, up the 'riser' into the top No. 1 flue. Its temperature here is about $800°$, and it meets the gas from the burners (3 on one side and 2 on the other). It then passes down the six side flues meeting and burning the gas from these five burners. The waste gases pass into the sole flue under the oven, and then through the regenerators and out ultimately to the chimney stack. Reversal of the air flow takes place every 15-20 minutes.

Semibituminous carbonaceous coals. These are the non-caking, short-flame coals containing about 90 to 93% carbon, 4 to 4.5% hydrogen, and 3 to 4.5% oxygen. They have a 'volatile matter' content of about 15 to 20% and a calorific value of about 15,600 Btu/lb. In this range are the important steam-raising coals.

Semicarbazide, CH_5N_3O, $NH_2 \cdot CO \cdot NH \cdot NH_2$. A colourless crystalline substance, m.p. 96°. Soluble in water and alcohol. Prepared by the electrolytic reduction of nitrourea in 20% sulphuric acid at 10°. The liquor is concentrated and semicarbazide sulphate crystallizes out. Forms crystalline salts with acids. Reacts with aldehydes and ketones to give semicarbazones. Used for the isolation and identification of aldehydes and ketones.

Semicarbazones. Organic compounds containing the group $> C:N \cdot NH \cdot CONH_2$. They are formed by treating a solution of an aldehyde or ketone in alcohol, dilute acetic acid, or pyridine with a concentrated solution of semicarbazide hydrochloride. Except when pyridine is used as solvent, it is usual to add solid potassium acetate to remove the free hydrochloric acid formed. The semicarbazones are crystalline substances, sparingly soluble in water, alcohol, and acetic acid. They have definite melting-points and are used to isolate and identify aldehydes and ketones.

Semiconductor. The band theory of metals postulates that electrons delocalized throughout the whole lattice are situated in energy levels which lie very close to one another, and substances which have partially filled energy bands are conductors. When the bands are almost full, however, the properties of the substances become very dependent on any slight amounts of impurity which may be present. Many solids (e.g. oxides, sulphides, germanium, tellurium), having low electrical conductivities which increase with rise in temperature, are called semiconductors. Their conductivity is due to lattice imperfections or impurities, the mobile species being electrons, ions or vacant lattice sites in the different substances.

In cuprous oxide, the lattice consists of Cu^+ and O^{2-} ions and in a compound of precise stoicheiometric composition, Cu_2O, there are no available conduction bands. Usually, however, there is a slight deficiency of copper, with some cupric ions replacing the cuprous ions in the lattice. There are then lattice holes due to the missing copper ions and conduction takes place by electron transfer from a Cu^+ ion to a Cu^{+2} species. Semiconductors where the process of defect formation involves oxidation are called p-type or defect semiconductors. Conversely, in zinc oxide where there is a slight excess of zinc atoms, a reduction process occurs and the semiconductor is of the excess or n-type.

Semiconductors are used in transistors, thermistors, photo-voltaic cells and solid reactifiers.

Semi-direct ammonia recovery process. This is the most common method of regaining the ammonia in coal gas as ammonium sulphate. The raw gas is first passed through the primary coolers, exhausters, tar extractors, reheaters and then to the sulphuric acid saturators where the ammonia in the gas combines with the acid to form sulphate of ammonia.

The ammoniacal liquor obtained from the coolers is treated in stills with steam and milk of lime and the liberated ammonia is introduced into the gas stream before the saturators.

The sulphate crystals are continuously ejected by means of a steam-compressed air ejector on to a draining table from which they are periodically removed into a centrifuge, neutralized with virgin liquor, 'whizzed' dry, further neutralized, and dried.

Modern lead-lined saturators have bottom discharge feeding directly into the centrifugal driers.

Semi-permeable membrane. A membrane which is permeable to some substances, e.g. water, and not to others, e.g. salt, ions, sugar molecules, is said to be semi-permeable. Those commonly used are composed of parchment, pig's-bladder, cellophane, or copper cyanoferrate(II) $Cu_2[Fe(CN)_6]$.

Semi-polar bond. Another name for a co-ordinate bond (*q.v.*).

Semi-steel. The term applied to cast iron to which has been added steel scrap. The name is misleading as the product is still cast iron since the carbon content usually varies between 2·5 and 3·2%.

Senarmontite. See Antimony trioxide.

Senderens, Jean Baptiste (1856-1937). Born at Barbachen in the Hautes-Pyrénées, Senderens became one of the foremost workers in the field of catalysis. In 1899 he discovered, with Sabatier, the process for the catalytic hydrogenation of oils.

Senega. The dried root of *Polygala senega*, a plant indigenous to North America. It contains two saponins, senegin and polygallic acid. It causes secretion of mucus in the bronchioles, and is used, in conjunction with other expectorants, in the treatment of chronic bronchitis.

Senna. Senna leaves are the dried leaflets of *Cassia acutifolia* and *Cassia angustifolia* from plants grown in Egypt and India respectively. Senna pods are the dried fruits of these plants. Both leaves and pods are used as purgatives. They contain various glycosides such as sennosides A and B, and a derivative of aloe-emodin.

Sensitization. Although the addition of a very small amount of a hydrophilic sol (such as gelatin) is able to protect a hydrophobic colloid (e.g. gold or arsenic sulphide) from the coagulating influence of electrolytes, the addition of still smaller amounts of the hydrophilic colloid either coagulates the hydrophobic sol or makes it more sensitive to the action of electrolytes. This phenomenon is known as sensitization and is thought to be due, in many cases, to the action of the hydrophilic colloid as a colloidal electrolyte. See Colloids, Hydrophilic, Hydrophobic, Coagulation, Protective colloid.

Sensitizing dyes. See Spectral sensitizers, Cyanine dyes, Merocyanine dyes.

Sephadex. A trade name for an insoluble hydrophilic substance prepared by cross-linking dextran, and used in the separation method of gel filtration (*q.v.*).

Sepiolite. See Meerschaum.

Sequestering agent. A term applied chiefly to a class of compounds which are very effective in forming complexes with metallic salts, thus preventing them reacting as simple cations. One of the most effective is ethylenediaminetetraacetic acid (EDTA) which forms complexes with most di- and tripositive metals. Gluconic acid and other hydroxy acids are also used for this purpose. Sequestering agents (sometimes called 'complexones') are used in many fields: e.g. for preventing the deleterious catalytic effects of traces of iron, copper, etc., and in many analytical procedures.

Sequoyitol, $C_7H_{14}O_6$. Methyl ether of *i*-inositol (*q.v.*), isomeric with bornesitol, extracted from the dry heartwood of redwood, *Sequoyia sempervirens*. Has m.p. 234° and a sweet taste.

Series, spectroscopic. A spectroscopic series is a group of lines the frequencies of which are related to each other in a simple manner and may be expressed by a simple formula (e.g. the Balmer series).

Serine, α-Amino-β-hydroxypropionic acid, $C_3H_7NO_3$. $CH_2OH \cdot CHNH_2 \cdot CO_2H$. Crystallizes in large prisms, m.p. 228°, with decomposition. Soluble in water. The naturally occurring substance is laevorotatory in water, $[\alpha]_D^{20}$ −6·83°, and dextrorotatory in acid, $[\alpha]_D^{25}$ +14·45° in molar hydrochloric acid. It is one of the amino-acids present in small quantities among the hydrolysis products of proteins.

Serotonin, 5-hydroxytryptamine, enteramine. A 'tissue hormone' with strong vasoconstrictor action, widely distributed in animals and plants.

It is derived from tryptophan by hydroxylation followed by decarboxylation; m.p. 214°. It

occurs in blood platelets, migrating into the serum during clotting. It is also present in intestinal mucosa, where it induces peristalsis. Serotonin is also found in the central nervous system but its function is not established.

Serpentine, $Mg_6Si_4O_{10}(OH)_8$, is hydrous magnesium silicate and is formed by the alteration of rocks rich in magnesium. It is usually green to black in colour, with a greasy lustre and soapy feel; sp.gr. 2·5-2·6, hardness 3-4. It is used for cutting into ornamental shapes. A fibrous variety is chrysotile. See Asbestos.

Sesamin, asarinin, $C_{20}H_{18}O_6$. The substance

responsible for the synergistic activity of sesame oil, m.p. 122·5°. It is not an insecticide in itself, but enhances the activity of pyrethrum. It has been superseded by other more efficient synergists.

Sesquioxide. An oxide in which there are three atoms of oxygen to two of the other element (e.g. Fe_2O_3). The prefix sesqui- is now little used, and the compound Fe_2O_3 is called ferric oxide or iron (III) oxide.

Sessile dislocation. See Dislocation.

Sextol. A trade name for methylcyclohexanol.

Sextone. A trade name for cyclohexanone; similarly Sextone B is a trade name for methylcyclohexanone.

Shelf drier. See Tray drier.

Shellac. A resinous secretion of the insect *Tachardia lacca* which breeds on the twigs of certain Indian trees. It was originally used as the source of a dyestuff, but is now almost entirely used for its content of resinous matter. Shellac has a softening point of 65°-75°. It is soluble in alcohol, except for about 4% of wax which is insoluble in cold alcohol. Shellac yields aleuritic acid, $C_{13}H_{26}O_4$, m.p. 101·5°, on extraction with alkali. It is used for the preparation of French polish, as a resin binder for mica-based insulating materials and in sealing waxes.

Shell-and-tube construction. In this type of construction, which is employed for the vast majority of heat exchangers, condensers, reboilers, etc., heat is transferred between a fluid flowing inside tubes to another surrounding them. It owes its widespread use, among other factors, to the fact that it is possible to incorporate a large heat transfer area within a comparatively small volume.

A typical shell-and-tube unit consists of a cylindrical vessel, the *shell*, closed at either end by flat *tube plates*; running between these is a *bundle* of tubes, the ends of which are expanded into holes in the tube plates to form fluid-tight joints. At either end the tubes open into a dish-shaped cover which is bolted to the shell; these covers serve as headers for distributing fluid to the tubes and/or chambers for the tubes to discharge into.

Fluid is admitted to the tubes through an inlet in one of the end covers, and depending on how many times it passes through them is discharged through an exit in the same or the opposite end cover; if the fluid makes more than one *pass* the covers are, of course, compartmented. On the shell side the arrangements for the admission and discharge of fluid depend on the duty being performed, whether heat exchange, vaporization or condensation.

In those cases where the fluid on the shell side does not undergo a change of state, it is usual to fit transverse *baffles*. These are plates extending about two-thirds of the way across the shell (with holes cut in them for the tubes) which are arranged along it so that the fluid follows a zig-zag path across the tube bundle. By preserving a good velocity across the tubes they ensure high rates of heat transfer. Sometimes longitudinal baffles are used.

Sheppard, Samuel Edward (1882-1948). A Londoner by birth, Sheppard was educated at University College, studying later at Marburg, Paris, and Cambridge. After two years' private practice as a photographic research chemist he joined the Eastman Kodak Co. in 1912, becoming assistant director of research in 1923. He wrote numerous books and papers on the chemistry of photography, and for his achievements in this field was awarded the Nichols Medal for 1930.

Sherardizing. Vapour galvanizing. The coating of articles of iron and other metals by heating them with zinc dust in a closed vessel at a temperature somewhat below the melting-point of zinc, 419°.

Shikimic acid, $C_7H_{10}O_5$. M.p. 190°, $[\alpha]_D^{28} - 184°$.

A 3, 4, 5 - trihydroxycyclohex - 1 - enecarboxylic acid found in the fruit of *Illicium anisatum* (*I. religiosum*). It is an intermediate in one pathway for the biogenesis of aromatic compounds in micro-organisms and plants. Important compounds arising by the shikimic acid route include *p*-aminobenzoic acid, phenylalanine, tyrosine, tryptophan and *p*-hydroxybenzoic acid. The role of shikimic acid was elucidated with the aid of mutant strains of *Escherischia coli*, *Neurospora crassa*, and other organisms.

The probable initial step in the pathway is the condensation of erythrose-4-phosphate with pyruvate, yielding dehydroquinic acid, which by elimination of the elements of water affords dehydroshikimic acid; reduction of the 3-keto group to hydroxyl gives shikimic acid. See Chorismic acid, Prephenic acid.

Short-tube vertical evaporator. This type, also known as the calandria evaporator, has been in use for many years, yet still finds application in the chemical and process industries. A typical unit consists of a vertical cylindrical vessel, height about twice diameter, whose lower half or third is occupied by a bundle of vertical tubes forming the calandria or heating element. These tubes, 1-3 in. in diameter and up to 8 ft. long, are set between two horizontal tube plates occupying the whole diameter of the vessel. Steam circulates round the outside of the tubes, while the liquid level is maintained somewhat below the tops of the tubes. Movement of the liquid is entirely by natural circulation, and in order to promote this one or more large-diameter downcomers run between the top and bottom of the calandria.

The upper part of the evaporator body is to allow disengagement of liquid and vapour and, usually, an entrainment separator is fitted at the vapour exit.

These evaporators are relatively inexpensive, and perform well provided there is adequate liquid circulation; this implies maintenance of a fairly high temperature difference across the tubes and use with low-viscosity liquids.

Sialic acid. A generic name for the naturally-occurring acylated derivatives of neuraminic acid (*q.v.*), e.g. acetylneuraminic acid, which is a characteristic constituent of gangliosides (*q.v.*) and of the 'bifidus factors'—oligosaccharides of human milk.

Side reaction. Few substances react in only one way. Generally a number of reactions occur simultaneously, one of which is predominant. This is termed the main reaction. The other reactions are termed side reactions.

Siderite. See Chalybite.

Sidgwick, Nevil Vincent (1873-1952). Born at Oxford, Sidgwick studied there and at Tübingen, later returning to Oxford as Fellow and Tutor of Lincoln College and professor of chemistry in the University. His chief work dealt with the organic chemistry of nitrogen, the electronic theory of valency, structural chemistry, wave mechanics and resonance. See *Proc. Chem. Soc.*, 1958, 310.

Siemens, William (Karl Wilhelm) (1823-1883). Born at Lenthe in Hanover, Siemens was educated at Magdeburg Polytechnic and Göttingen University. Inventor and engineer, he made his home in England and in 1859 was naturalized. His main researches were directed towards the applications of heat and electricity. In 1863 he introduced the open hearth or regenerative furnace which found use in the production of steel. He was elected F.R.S. in 1862 and, later, knighted. See 'Life of Siemens' (Pole).

Siemens process. A method of manufacturing steel from pig iron in an open-type furnace, sometimes called the open-hearth process. The charge of pig iron is put into the hearth of the furnace which is heated by hot gases and scrap steel is added. When the charge is melted, oxidation of carbon and silicon is effected by addition of haematite ore and final recarburization by ferromanganese. For pigs containing phosphorus a basic lining is employed as in the basic Bessemer process.

This method is more costly than the Bessemer process but gives a steel of more uniform composition, uses up waste scrap, and is capable of control between very narrow limits.

Sienna. Natural earth containing hydrated ferric oxide. The best-known deposits are in Italy. Siennas differ from ochres (*q.v.*) in that they are translucent rather than opaque. They are used as stains and coloured fillers for wood and other materials. Burnt sienna is obtained by calcining raw sienna and is a valuable pigment, orange brown to red in colour. See British Standard 312.

Sieve plate, sieve tray. This vapour-liquid contacting device, widely used in distillation and absorption columns, consists of a plate perforated by a large number of closely spaced holes $\frac{1}{8}$ to $\frac{1}{2}$ in. in diameter. Vapour passing up through the holes is broken up into streams of bubbles which rise through the liquid on the plate. Like the bubble-cap plate it is equipped with inlet and outlet weirs, and liquid passes from one plate to the next through downcomers. The sieve plate has become popular because it enjoys most of the advantages of the bubble-cap plate, but is considerably cheaper.

See Plate column.

Siglure, $C_{12}H_{20}O_2$. Trade name of a synthetic pheromone (*q.v.*) used to trap the Mediterranean

fruit fly (*Ceratitis capitata*).

Sigma (σ) bonds. Covalent bonds containing two electrons formed by overlap of orbitals from two atoms such that there is one volume of overlap directly between the two nuclei.

Silanes. See Silicon hydrides.

Silica, SiO_2. Silica, or silicon dioxide, is one of the most important constituents of the earth's crust. It is known in the amorphous form, and in a number of crystalline forms, the most important of which are the naturally occurring quartz, tridymite, and cristobalite. The stability ranges of these forms are as follows: α-quartz to 575°, β-quartz to 870°, tridymite to 1470°, cristobalite melts at 1710°. Naturally occurring silica is frequently discoloured. Yellow sand, for example, consists of silica discoloured by ferric oxide. A purple variety of quartz is known as amethyst. Common flint is amorphous silica, which has become discoloured by iron oxide.

Silica bricks. A term used exclusively for refractory bricks made of crushed silica rock, preferably ganister, and a very small proportion of lime or clay; the latter acts as a bond. The bricks are burned at about 1400° and are in great demand for the construction of many kinds of furnaces. They are highly refractory (Seger cone 34-35), very resistant to abrasion, and fairly resistant to slags and other corrosive agents.

Silica gel. An amorphous form of hydrated silica produced by the precipitation, flocculation, or coagulation of a silica sol or the decomposition of some silicates. When freshly prepared the silica appears to be in a gelatinous state and, on standing, it will set and form a jelly. After being heated it cannot easily be converted into a sol and so is termed an irreversible gel. Under favourable conditions it may contain 330 molecules of water to one of silica. When containing 90% of water it is solid enough to be cut easily, but with less than 75% of water it is friable and can be ground to powder.

Dehydrated silica gel is used commercially as an absorbent in the recovery of solvents, also for drying air, dehydrating gases, refining mineral oils, for filtration and as a support for various catalysts. Such a gel is in the form of hard granules, chemically and physically almost inert but highly hygroscopic. After use it can be regenerated by heat. In the laboratory it is uesd in the preparation of chromatographic columns.

Cobalt compounds are often incorporated in the gel. When the gel has absorbed a fair amount of moisture it will turn pink but will revert to blue on heating.

Silicates. A very extensive group of substances, many of which are minerals, which are to be regarded as derivatives of the acid-forming silicon dioxide. Natural silicates form a major constituent of most rocks. They range in composition from comparatively simple minerals, such as zircon, $ZrSiO_4$, which contain discrete silicate anions in their structure, to far more complex structures in which the silicate anion is an extended two- or three-dimensional structure in which oxygen atoms form bridges between the silicon atoms. All silicates are based on the SiO_4^{4-} tetrahderon with partial or complete sharing of oxygen atoms. Aluminium may replace silicon in this anion and the cations are in the holes in the lattice. See Feldspar, Mica, Zeolites.

The alkali silicates are soluble in water and are used industrially. See Sodium silicates.

Silica, vitreous. Silica may be fused in the oxyhydrogen blowpipe, and the amorphous vitreous product formed on cooling is known as vitreous silica, or quartz glass. It is transparent to ultraviolet light down to about 2000 Å, and is used in optical work on this account. The coefficient of cubical expansion has the remarkably low value of 5×10^{-7}, and for this reason apparatus constructed of vitrous silica may be subjected to irregular heating or to sudden changes of temperature without risk of fracture. A translucent variety of silica ware is known as Vitreosil.

Silicic acids. If a dilute sodium silicate solution is added slowly to an excess of dilute hydrochloric acid and the resulting clear solution dialysed, a colloidal solution of hydrated silica is obtained which is readily coagulated to a gel (see Colloids). There is no evidence for the existence of discrete hydrates, the whole range of compositions consisting merely of silica and water. Thus none of the silicic acids can be isolated as such. However, volatile esters, such as $Si(OMe)_4$, b.p. 121°, are well known.

Silicides. Binary compounds of the metallic elements with silicon (e.g. magnesium silicide,

Mg_2Si). Such compounds are related structurally to the carbides, and form a mixture of silicon hydrides and hydrogen when they are decomposed by aqueous solutions of acids.

Silicofluorides. The salts of hydrofluorosilicic acids, H_2SiF_6 and $HSiF_5$. The hexafluorosilicates may be prepared by neutralization of solutions of the acid with a base, or by the action of silicon tetrafluoride on the fluoride of the metal. The salts of sodium, potassium and barium are very sparingly soluble in water and are precipitated by adding a solution of the free acid to a solution of the metal salt. Pentafluorosilicates are precipitated by large cations. Silicofluorides are used in the electrodeposition of metals, as insecticides, and in the fluoridation of water.

Silico-mesoxalic acid, $H_4Si_3O_6$ and **Silicooxalic acid,** $H_2Si_2O_4$. Polymers formed by the controlled hydrolysis of Si_3Cl_8 and Si_2Cl_6 respectively. Both are reducing agents with no acidic properties. A similar substance, silicoformic anhydride, $H_2Si_2O_3$, is formed by hydrolysis of silicochloroform.

Silicon, Si. At.no. 14, At.wt. 28·09. It does not occur native but is of widespread occurrence in the form of its oxide, one form of which is quartz, and of numerous silicate rocks. The element is manufactured commercially by reduction of sand, which is impure silica, SiO_2, by means of coke. A mixture of crushed coke and sand is heated in the electric furnace. It forms a hard grey crystalline product, which is used in the manufacture of alloys. Silicon may be prepared in the laboratory by heating together silica and magnesium powder. Silicon crystallizes in the cubic system, $a = 5·42$ Å, with the diamond structure. The commercial material usually contains from 70 to 97·5% of Si.

Silicon has m.p. 1414°, b.p. 2350°, d 2·42. Silicon is oxidized when strongly heated in air or oxygen. It burns when heated in chlorine or in fluorine, forming the tetrahalide. When fused with alkali it forms a silicate and liberates hydrogen. It is insoluble in water, but is attacked by steam at a red heat.

Silicon is, after oxygen, the most abundant element of the earth's crust. It is used extensively as a semiconductor.

Silicon bromide. *Silicon tetrabromide*, $SiBr_4$. A colourless liquid (m.p. 5·2°, b.p. 154·6°, $d_4^{18·6}$ 2·789) prepared by the action of bromine vapour on silicon at a red heat. It fumes in moist air, and is rapidly hydrolysed by water with formation of hydrated silica and hydrobromic acid.

Silicon (or **Silicium**) **bronze.** Silicon is a powerful deoxidant and very small amounts increase the strength and ductility of the bronze to which it is added. Only traces are found in the solid alloys whose tin content is from 4 to 5%. These bronzes have a high electrical conductivity and are largely employed for telegraph and telephone wires.

Silicon carbide, SiC. A hard refractory material made by heating carbon with silicon or silica to 2000° in an electric furnace. It has a macro lattice and does not break up into its elements below 2200°. It is used for refractory bricks, crucibles, retorts, abrasive wheels, and refractory cement.

Silicon chlorides. *Silicon tetrachloride,* $SiCl_4$. A colourless liquid, m.p. $-70.4°$, b.p. $57.5°$, formed by heating finely powdered silicon or ferrosilicon in a current of chlorine, and purifying the product by fractionation with an efficient column. The liquid fumes strongly when exposed to moist air, owing to hydrolysis. With liquid water a gelatinous precipitate of hydrated silica is formed. Silicon tetrachloride reacts with oxygen at a red heat, forming the oxychloride Si_2OCl_6.

Passage of silicon tetrachloride over silicon at 1250° gives a mixture of chlorides containing 2, 3, 4, 5, 6, 12 and 16 silicon atoms. Some of these are cyclic.

Silicon tetrachloride is the most important raw material for the manufacture of silicones and other organo-silicon compounds. It is also used for preparing silica gel and very pure silicon.

Disilicon hexachloride, Si_2Cl_6. A colourless fuming liquid, b.p. 145°, which is formed, together with the *octachloride,* Si_3Cl_8, b.p. 210°-215°, and the *tetrachloride,* by the action of chlorine on heated silicon.

Silicon chloroform, $SiHCl_3$. A colourless liquid, b.p. 31·8°, d 1·3438, which is formed, together with the tetrachloride, by passing hydrogen chloride over powdered silicon heated to about 350°. It is separated from the tetrachloride by fractional distillation. It is much more reactive than chloroform, being rapidly hydrolysed by water. It is also inflammable and will form a violently explosive mixture with oxygen or air.

Silicone rubber. Obtained from the very high molecular weight condensation polymer polydimethylsiloxane, which may contain about 5% diphenylsiloxane units. The chain is extremely flexible with very weak interchain forces and as the polymer shows no tendency to crystallize on stretching, the tensile strength is very low and requires the reinforcing action of fine silica

$$\left[\begin{array}{c} CH_3 \\ | \\ Si-O \\ | \\ CH_3 \end{array} \right]_n$$

powder. Vulcanization is carried out by heating with an organic peroxide which removes hydrogen atoms from methyl groups on different chains, enabling the carbon atoms to form cross-links. The very wide range of temperature ($-90°$ to 250°) over which the rubber maintains its properties is the most attractive feature. It is also inert to weak or dilute acids or alkalis, paraffinic oils, and oxidizing agents and is resistant to ageing (*q.v.*).

Silicones. Polymerized organosilicon compounds containing silicon-oxygen-silicon linkages. The parent halides are prepared by the reaction of a silicon halide with a metal alkyl, by the action of a Grignard reagent on a silicon halide, by the action of an aryl or alkyl halide with a Cu—Si or Ag—Si alloy, by passing alkyl and silicon halide vapours over zinc or aluminium at 300°-500°, or by the direct interaction of silicon tetrachloride and ethylene. The first two methods are used in the laboratory; silicones are prepared industrially by the other three methods. Controlled hydrolysis of mixtures with various ratios of alkyl group to halogen gives the required degree of polymerization; concentrated sulphuric acid is also used to break down high polymers. Silicones are used as greases, hydraulic fluids, sealing compounds, varnishes, enamels, resins, and synthetic rubbers. Liquid silicones are colourless, odourless, and inert; are immiscible with water; have high flash points, and are scarcely volatile. Silicone greases and elastomers retain their properties over a range of temperatures from $-40°$ to 200°. Silicone resins are used for electrical insulation and as binders for some glass fibre laminates.

Silicon ester. See Ethyl silicate.

Silicon fluorides. *Silicon tetrafluoride,* SiF_4. A colourless gas, which fumes in air; m.p. $-90.2°$, sublimes at $-95.1°$. It is formed by heating a mixture of sand, calcium fluoride, and concentrated sulphuric acid, or in the pure form by the action of fluorosulphonic acid on silica. The gas is decomposed by water, with formation of a deposit of silica and a solution of hydrofluorosilicic acid. Silicon tetrafluoride forms many addition compounds and many derivatives in which other functional groups have been substituted in place of fluorine.

Higher silicon fluorides, e.g. Si_2F_8 are known. A lower fluoride (SiF_2) is formed by the action of silicon on silicon tetrafluoride at 1200°. It is very reactive and adds across double bonds to form Si—C—C—Si groups.

Silicon hydrides. A group of compounds, sometimes referred to as silanes, formed by the action of 20% hydrochloric acid on magnesium silicide, which is prepared by heating silicon with magnesium in the absence of air. More satisfactory methods of preparation are the action of ammonium bromide on magnesium silicide in liquid ammonia, or the reduction of silicon chlorides with lithium aluminium hydride. These hydrides form a homologous series, from which the following are well known: SiH_4 (b.p. $-111\cdot9°$), Si_2H_6 (b.p. $-14\cdot5°$), Si_3H_8 (b.p. $52\cdot9°$). Normal and *iso* Si_4H_{10} and higher hydrides to Si_8H_{18} are also known. Structurally these hydrides are similar to the saturated paraffins of the general formula C_nH_{2n+2}, but they are much more reactive. They inflame in oxygen at room temperature, or somewhat above it, according to the mixture composition. They are hydrolysed by alkalis with liberation of hydrogen and the formation of a silicate, and are decomposed at a red heat into silicon and hydrogen. Silicon forms a solid hydride of the empirical formula SiH_2, and a second solid hydride which approximates to SiH, but these are polymers, and in no sense analogous to ethylene and acetylene.

Silicon iodide, *Silicon tetraiodide*, SiI_4. A colourless crystalline solid, m.p. $123\cdot8°$, b.p. $290°$, which is formed by heating silicon to a red heat in the vapour of iodine. It is rapidly decomposed by water.

Silicon iodoform, $SiHI_3$. A colourless refractive liquid, m.p. $8°$, b.p. *circa* $185°$, d_4^{20} $3\cdot314$, which is formed by the action of a mixture of hydrogen iodide and iodine on heated silicon. It is decomposed both by air and by water.

Silicon nitrides. The nitride Si_3N_4 is prepared by heating finely divided silicon in a current of nitrogen at $1450°$. It is a grey-white solid, which is chemically rather inert. It is not decomposed by water vapour at $800°$, and is resistant to dilute acids. It forms ammonia and a silicate on fusion with an alkali. Many compounds containing Si—N bonds are known, particularly where the silicon is joined to organic groupings.

Silicon oxides. *Silicon monoxide*, SiO. Alleged to be a distinct chemical entity formed by reducing SiO_2 with carbon in an electric furnace. The brown powder which results is used commercially under the name Monox as a pigment and as an abrasive. It definitely exists in the vapour phase.

Silicon dioxide. See Silica.

Silicon oxychlorides. Several oxychlorides of silicon have been described, the simplest being the compound Si_2OCl_6, a liquid which boils at $137°$ and is formed by passing a mixture of air and silicon tetrachloride through a red-hot tube. The simple oxychloride $SiOCl_2$, which would correspond to phosgene, $COCl_2$, is unknown.

Silicon sulphide, SiS_2. A white solid, forming silky needle-shaped crystals which can be sublimed. It is prepared by heating silicon strongly in sulphur vapour, or by passing carbon disulphide vapour over a heated mixture of silica and carbon. It is decomposed rapidly by water with formation of hydrogen sulphide and silica. Thiosilicates, e.g. Na_2SiS_3, are formed when silicon sulphide is fused with alkali sulphides. The fusion of silicon sulphide with silicon gives *silicon monosulphide*, SiS.

Silliman, Benjamin (1779-1864). Silliman was born at Trumbull, Connecticut, and educated at Yale College as a lawyer. In 1804, however, he was appointed professor of chemistry and natural history, and retained this position until his retirement as professor emeritus in 1853. He was the first to produce hydrofluoric acid in America and to discover bromine in American brines, but his investigations are overshadowed by his reputation as a teacher and as founder of the *American Journal of Science and Arts*.

Sillimanite. An anhydrous aluminium silicate, $Al_2[SiO_4]O$, trimorphous with kyanite and andalusite. The crystals are orthorhombic, sp.gr. $3\cdot2$-$3\cdot3$. When heated it is converted into mullite and silica at $1550°$-$1650°$. Much commercial sillimanite is calcined kyanite, and is an indefinite mixture of kyanite, sillimanite and mullite. It is used chiefly as a refractory.

Siloxene, Si_2H_2O. A highly polymerized solid substance of the above empirical formula, which is formed by treating calcium silicide, Ca_2Si, with an alcoholic solution of hydrochloric acid, It is spontaneously inflammable in air and has strong reducing properties. It has been shown to be pseudomorphic with the calcium silicide from which it is produced, and is a flaky substance with high adsorptive power. Its oxidation in air or in suspension in an oxidizing liquid is accompanied by a pronounced chemiluminescence.

Silver, Ag. At.no. 47, At.wt. $107\cdot880$; m.p. $961°$, b.p. $2193°$, d^{20} $10\cdot492$. Silver occurs native, in Norway, Peru, and Idaho, occasionally nearly pure but more often together with gold and copper. The important silver ores are argentite or silver glance, Ag_2S; chlorargyrite or horn-silver, AgCl; pyrargyrite or ruby-silver, Ag_3SbS_3; silver-copper glance $(Cu,Ag)_2S$. The principal sources of silver are the Ontario cobalt mines (North America), Mexico, and Broken Hill (N.S. Wales).

Silver is removed from lead alloys by processes involving extraction of the silver into zinc— the Pattinson process. In the wet extraction processes, the silver ore is roasted alone or with common salt, when the sulphate or the chloride respectively is produced. These may be extracted with water or sodium thiosulphate. In the cyanide process, the finely ground ore is treated with 0·7% sodium cyanide solution, when soluble sodium argentocyanide, $NaAg(CN)_2$, is formed. From the various extracts the silver is precipitated as the sulphide by sodium sulphide and the silver sulphide reduced to silver by caustic soda and aluminium or zinc.

Silver is refined by an electrolytic process in which silver nitrate is the electrolyte, pure silver sheet the cathode, and the crude block silver the anode. The silver is deposited, copper dissolves, and any gold forms an anode slime.

Silver is a pure white, malleable, ductile metal, which can be beaten into leaves only 0·00025 mm thick. The metal crystallizes in the cubic system, having the cubic close-packed structure, $a = 4·0856$ Å. Crystals are obtained by fusion or by electrolysis of an acid silver nitrate solution. The metal dissolves in cold dilute nitric acid, and hot concentrated sulphuric acid but is unattacked even by fused alkalis.

Silver mirrors are formed by depositing silver on glass. The usual procedure is to reduce an ammoniacal solution of silver nitrate with tartaric acid or Rochelle salt.

Silver is used extensively in electrical work, jewellery, and as a coinage metal. Silver compounds are used in photography and as catalysts for many processes.

Silver bromide, AgBr. Obtained as a pale yellow precipitate by the addition of a bromide to a silver nitrate solution. It melts at 420° to an orange-red liquid. The solubility in water is about 6×10^{-7} mole/litre at 25°. It crystallizes in the cubic system with the sodium chloride structure. It is somewhat more soluble in concentrated hydrobromic acid, and partially soluble in ammonium hydroxide, and is soluble in sodium thiosulphate and cyanide solutions.

Silver carbonate, Ag_2CO_3. Prepared by precipitation from a solution of silver nitrate. It is a white solid, becoming yellow on exposure to light. It decomposes to silver oxide above 100°.

Silver chloride, AgCl. Readily obtained as a curdy white precipitate by the addition of hydrochloric acid or a chloride to silver nitrate solution. It melts at 456° to a dark-yellow liquid, which solidifies to a soft white mass. It is appreciably volatile at 360°. Like the bromide it crystallizes in the cubic system with the sodium chloride structure. Silver chloride is insoluble in water (solubility about $1·6 \times 10^{-5}$ mole/litre at 25°), somewhat more soluble in concentrated hydrochloric acid, and readily soluble in ammonium hydroxide, sodium thiosulphate,

and alkali cyanide solutions. Combines directly with ammonia to give the compounds AgCl, $3NH_3$; $2AgCl$, $3NH_3$; AgCl, NH_3. It is used in photography.

Silver fluoride, AgF. Prepared by slow evaporation of a solution of silver oxide in hydrofluoric acid, or by heating silver fluoroborate. The anhydrous salt is yellow and hydrates with 2 and 4 molecules of water are known. Silver fluoride is used as a fluorinating agent. It is very soluble in water. *Silver difluoride*, AgF_2, is a black or dark brown substance, m.p. 690°, formed by the action of fluorine on molecular silver. It is extremely reactive and is a very strong oxidizing agent. A complex fluoride, $KAgF_4$, may be obtained by the action of fluorine on a mixture of KCl and AgCl at high temperatures.

Silver fluoroborate, $AgBF_4$. Prepared by the action of bromine trifluoride on silver borate or by passing boron trifluoride through a solution or suspension of silver (I) fluoride in acetonitrile, nitromethane, sulphur dioxide or toluene. The solvent is removed to leave the solid material. It is a white solid, very soluble in water and ether, moderately soluble in benzene.

Silver halide grains. These are the individual silver halide crystals in a photographic emulsion. The considerable variation in properties of photographic emulsions results from the conditions of precipitation of the grains, and from the treatment of the precipitated grains, and from the absorption of addenda to only a part of the grain surface. Such criteria as emulsion speed, spectral sensitivity, development activity, fog level and stability are grossly affected by the adsorption of chemicals, often in monomolecular layers, to the grain surface.

Silver iodide, AgI. Produced as a light yellow precipitate, m.p. 556°, by the addition of an iodide to silver nitrate solution. Occurs naturally as iodoargyrite, in hexagonal crystals. It is trimorphic; the high temperature α-form is cubic and changes at 146° to the hexagonal β-form; below 137° the β-form is metastable with respect to the cubic form. Solubility in water is about 1×10^{-8} mole/litre at 25°. Silver iodide is readily soluble in potassium iodide solutions, from which the compounds AgI, KI, and AgI, 2KI may be obtained by crystallization. The solutions contain complex ions such as $(AgI_4)^{3-}$. It combines with ammonia to give the compounds 2AgI, NH_3, and AgI, NH_3.

Silver nitrate, $AgNO_3$. The most important compound of silver, obtained by dissolving the metal in dilute nitric acid, and crystallizing. The salt is dimorphous, crystallizing in the hexagonal and orthorhombic systems. No hydrates are known. On strong heating, silver nitrate decomposes into silver, dinitrogen tetroxide, and oxygen. It has m.p. 212°.

Silver nucleinate. Mild silver proteinate, silver vitellin, contains 19-23% silver as a colloidal solution, and is prepared by the action of a suitable protein, such as denatured serum albumin, on moist silver oxide. It has antibacterial properties and is used for the treatment of conjunctivitis and tonsilitis. Although containing a higher percentage of silver than strong silver proteinate, it is weaker in its antibacterial properties and less irritating.

Silver oxides. *Argentous oxide*, Ag_2O, is obtained as a brown amorphous precipitate by the addition of barium oxide to a silver nitrate solution. The dried material still contains 1-2% water, and retains 0·13% at 100°. The oxide begins to decompose at 160° with the formation of silver and oxygen. The oxide is soluble in ammonia, when the compound $[Ag(NH_3)_2]OH$ is formed.
  Argentic oxide. AgO, is a black diamagnetic substance formed by the action of ozone on Ag_2O or by the action of a persulphate solution on a solution of silver nitrate.

Silver perchlorate, $AgClO_4$. Prepared by the action of perchloric acid on silver carbonate. Silver perchlorate is extremely soluble in water and ether, and also soluble in benzene and toluene.

Silver proteinate. Strong silver proteinate, trade name Protargol, contains about 8% of silver combined with protein and a little alkali. It is antibacterial with an action similar to that of silver nucleinate, and is used for the same purposes, but is rather more irritant to the tissues.

Silver salt. The commercial name for sodium anthraquinone-β-sulphonate. See Anthraquinone sulphonic acids.

Silver salts, complex. Silver forms a number of complex salts in which the silver may be contained in either the cation or the anion. The cations are of the type $[AgR_2]^+$, where R is a monoamine or ammonia; obtained by the action of amines on silver salts.
  The salts containing silver in the anion are more complex. Solutions of silver sodium thiosulphate deposit crystals of complexes $Na_3[Ag(S_2O_3)_2]2H_2O$ & $Na_5[Ag(S_2O_3)_3]2H_2O$. Complex silver cyanides and thiocyanates contain the ions $[Ag(CN)_2]^-$, $[Ag(CN)_3]^{2-}$, and $[Ag(NCS)_2]^-$. Complex silver halides contain AgX_2^- ions.

Silver sulphate, Ag_2SO_4. Obtained by dissolving silver in concentrated sulphuric acid or by the addition of a sulphate to silver nitrate. It is only sparingly soluble in water (solubility 0·77 g in 100 g water at 0°). On strong heating the salt decomposes completely into silver, sulphur dioxide, and oxygen.

Silver sulphide, Ag_2S. Obtained as a black precipitate by the action of hydrogen sulphide on a solution of any silver salt. It is very insoluble in water and is an extremely stable substance.

Silver vitellin. See Silver nucleinate.

Silyl compounds. Compounds containing a Si—H bond. There are many silyl derivatives, formally analogous to aliphatic carbon compounds.

Simazine, 2-chloro-4,6-bis(ethylamino)-s-triazine, $C_7H_{12}ClN_5$. A pre-emergence herbicide

with no activity against insects or fungi. It is non-toxic. Simazine is prepared from cyanuric chloride and ethylamine, and forms white crystals, m.p. 225°. It is insoluble in water.

Simonsen, Sir John Lionel (1884-1957). Of Danish extraction, Simonsen was a graduate of Manchester University. He held the post of professor of Chemistry successively at the Presidency College, Madras (1910), the Forest Research Institute at Dehra Dun, India (1919), the Indian Institute of Science at Bangalore (1925), and the University College of North Wales (1930). In 1942 he became the first director of Colonial Products Research in London. Simonsen worked almost entirely on terpene chemistry, and his book 'The Terpenes' is the standard work on the subject. See *Proc. Chem. Soc.*, 1958, 61.

Sinapin, $C_{16}H_{25}NO_6$. Occurs as a glycoside in black mustard seed and the *Cruciferae*. Hydrolysed to sinapic acid and choline.

Single bond. A bond between two atoms with two electrons occupying the bonding orbital and no further electronic interaction between the atoms. Generally a σ bond, e.g. as in the C—H bonds in CH_4, but can be essentially a π bond, as in $Ni(PF_3)_4$.

Singlet state. See Spin multiplicity.

Sinigrin, $C_9H_{16}KO_9S_2$. The best known of the mustard glycosides; it is hydrolysed to allyl isothiocyanate, glucose and potassium hydrogen sulphate by the enzyme termed myrosin, which accompanies it in mustard seed.

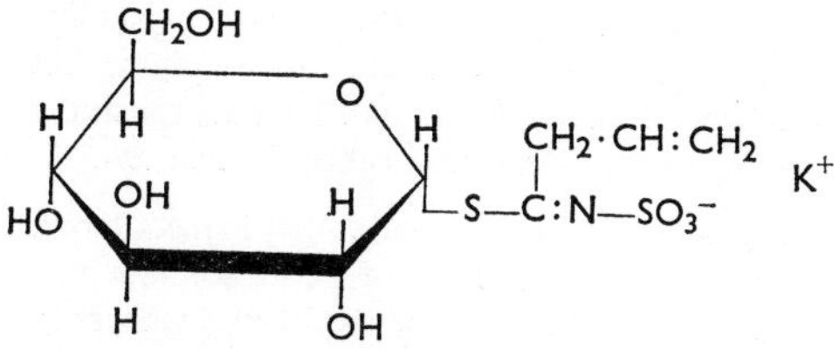

Its recognition as the active principle of black mustard seed dates from 1730. The myrosin and the glycoside are contained in separate cells and do not interact until brought together. Sinigrin has m.p. 126°, $[\alpha]_D -18°$.

Sintering. When two particles of a powder are heated together in close contact at a high temperature the atoms in the surface layers become sufficiently mobile to enlarge the contact area and to diffuse into one or other of the different lattices present. This process of bonding by atomic diffusion is known as sintering and is now much used in powder metallurgy and other branches of industry for the production of solid structures from powders without the use of operations such as fusion, casting, or machining. When sintering an artefact made from a single metal the temperature used is below the melting point of the metal. For a mixture of metals or other substances the sintering temperature is below the melting point of the major ingredient. The extent of bonding that takes place during sintering is dependent upon the time and temperature of the operation, the process being continued until the required physical properties in the product are obtained. Pressure applied during the heating operation is usually not necessary, but is an advantage where maximum density and strength are required. Processes of sintering are particularly suitable for the preparation of products of extremely high melting point, for example carbon products, or for high polymers, such as polytetrafluoroethylene, whose fusion is accompanied by partial decomposition.

β-Sitosterol, 24α-ethylcholesterol, $C_{29}H_{50}O$. A widely distributed phytosterol, m.p. 137°,

$[\alpha]_D -37°$, usually accompanied by congeneric sterols, from which it is separable with difficulty. Pure β-sitosterol may be made by partial hydrogenation of stigmasterol. β-Sitosterol glucoside, m.p. 250°, is also a common plant constituent and has been described under many different names.

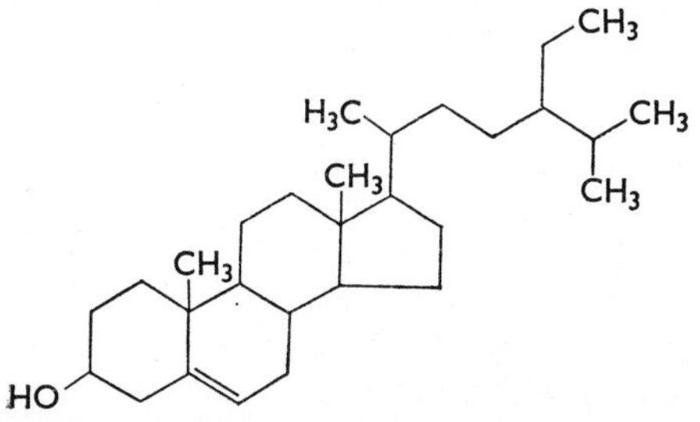

Size reduction equipment. For descriptions of some of the more important machines and methods of operation see Ball mill, Buhrstone mill, Colloid mills, Conical crusher, Crushing rolls, Disc grinder, Edge-runner mill, Gyratory crusher, Hammer mill, Jaw crusher, Ring-roller mills, Roller mill, Squirrel cage disintegrator, Symons disc crusher, Closed circuit grinding, Wet grinding.

Sizing. Unsized paper is a porous mat of cellulose fibres which absorbs ink rapidly and cannot be written on (e.g. blotting paper). In order to fit paper for its normal uses, the pores must be to some extent filled up and it has to be given some degree of water-repellency. This can be done either in the beaters by the addition of rosin and alum or a colloidal mixture, such as starch and water-glass, when the process is termed engine sizing, or by spraying the surface of the ready-made paper with glue or the like when it is known as surface sizing. See Paper.

Skatole, 3-Methylindole, C_9H_9N. Crystallizes in laminae, m.p. 95°, b.p. 265°-266°. It is the

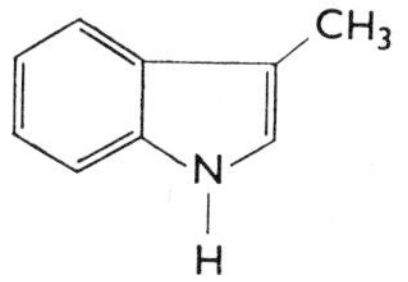

chief volatile constituent of the faeces, being formed by the action of the intestinal bacteria on tryptophan. It occurs also in coal tar and in beetroot.

Skip hoist. A machine for elevating solid materials, e.g. to the top of a silo. It consists of a large bucket or skip attached to wire ropes which raise and lower it, the skip running on guide rails. It differs from the bucket elevator in that its operation is batchwise rather than continuous.

Skraup's reaction. See Anthranol.

Slack wax. The product which is obtained from the chilling and filtering processes in the manufacture of paraffin wax; it is afterwards sweated to remove the oil and lower-melting waxes.

Slag. A liquid solution of oxides produced in the smelting and refining of metals. The primary function of slag in smelting is to take into solution the gangue of the ore and separate it from the liquid metal. To achieve this fluxes are added which reduce the melting point of the oxide mixture. Common fluxes are alumina, limestone or burnt lime, silica and iron oxide. In addition to removing gangue, the slag can also exert a refining function in smelting processes— an example of this is the desulphurization of iron in the blast furnace. In smelting, slag composition depends on the metal being smelted; thus in iron smelting it is basically a CaO—MgO— Al_2O_3—SiO_2 slag, while in copper smelting it is essentially FeO—SiO_2 slag. In lead smelting the slag is often used to collect the zinc in the ore charge and the slag composition is CaO— FeO—SiO —ZnO. The zinc is recovered from the slag in a slag fuming process.

Slags are also produced in metal refining processes where oxidation is used to separate the impurities. The most common examples of these processes are steel making, copper and lead refining. The aim in refining is to control the slag composition to effect the removal of impurities and this process invariably means that some of the parent metal is oxidized and passes into the slag. In steelmaking the aim is to remove carbon, sulphur and phosphorus and this requires a slag high in calcium oxide, i.e. a basic slag. The constituents of a basic steel making slag are FeO—CaO—MgO—SiO_2—P_2O_5— Al_2O_3—CaS.

Slags are often sold for use in other industries. Thus blast furnace slag can be used for manufacturing cement, as road metal, as slag wool and attempts are now being made to produce a ceramic material called 'slagceram'. The slag from the basic steelmaking process sometimes contains sufficient phosphorus pentoxide to make it suitable as an agricultural fertilizer and it is sold as 'basic slag'; the high lime content of these slags is also useful.

Slaked lime. See Calcium hydroxide.

Slip planes. Planes of weakness in crystals. When metals are plastically deformed, blocks of atoms slide over each other along such slip planes, thus allowing each individual crystal to change shape.

Slurry. A liquid containing an appreciable quantity of suspended solid.

Smalt. A potassium cobalt silicate glass ground to a powder under water; it contains 56-70% of silica, 12-22% of potassium oxide, and 6-16% of cobalt oxide, and is prepared by fusing specially prepared crude cobalt oxide ('zaffre') with silica and potassium carbonate. The presence of impurities considerably affects the colour of the product. Smalt is used in ceramics for tinting glazes and enamels.

At one time the word smalt was used to

describe the vitrified pigments used for painting on glass and was not necessarily limited to blue.

Smekal cracks. The canals or pores which, on Smekal's theory of the structures of crystalline solids, exist between small, structurally perfect lattice blocks in the crystal. They are much the same as the defects now called dislocations.

Smelting. The term is used widely in metallurgy, and denotes the melting of an ore accompanied by a chemical change, so that the substances in the liquid form are different from those originally started with.

Smith, Alexander (1865-1922). A native of Edinburgh, Smith was educated at the Universities of Edinburgh and Munich. He went to the United States in 1890, and in 1894 joined the staff of the University of Chicago, becoming professor of chemistry and Director of the Laboratories of General and Physical Chemistry in 1903. In 1911 he was appointed head of the department of chemistry at Columbia University, retiring in 1921. Smith wrote many papers, chiefly on amorphous sulphur and on the accurate determination of vapour pressures, and several textbooks which revolutionized the teaching of chemistry in America. He was president of the American Chemical Society in 1911.

Smith, Edgar Fahs (1854-1928). Born at York, Pennsylvania, he studied at Pennsylvania College and subsequently at Göttingen. In 1888 he became professor of analytical chemistry at the University of Pennsylvania, in 1898 he was appointed vice-provost, and in 1910 provost of the University. His most important researches were on electrochemical methods, with particular reference to electro-analysis, but his work also embraced organic, general inorganic, analytical, and historical chemistry. In 1926 he was awarded the Priestley Medal of the American Chemical Society, of which he was president in 1895 and 1921-1922.

Smith, John Lawrence (1818-1883). Born near Charleston, South Carolina, Smith studied at the University of Virginia, at the South Carolina Medical College, and in Paris. From 1847 to 1850 he explored the mineral resources of Turkey, revealing deposits of emery, chrome ores, and coal. After short periods as professor of chemistry at the Universities of Louisiana, Virginia, and Louisville, he carried out researches in his private laboratory. He wrote many papers, chiefly on the analysis of minerals and meteorites, and was a founder member of the American Chemical Society, of which he was president in 1877.

Smithsonite. See Calamine.

Smokeless fuel. As its name implies, it is a fuel which, when burnt in an open domestic fireplace or boiler, does not give rise to smoke. The fuel obtained from the low-temperature carbonization of coal is a smokeless fuel since the constituents which give rise to smoke have already been distilled off, but sufficient volatile matter (about 7 to 10%) has been left to allow the fuel to be easily ignitable and to burn freely.

All smokeless fuels should be compact, strong, and have a low ash content.

Smoke point. A quantity used as a measure of the tendency of a lamp oil to emit smoke when burning. The height of flame, burning in a standard lamp, at which smoke is first emitted is measured.

Soaps. Sodium and potassium salts of the fatty acids, particularly stearic, palmitic, and oleic acids. Animal and vegetable oils and fats, from which soaps are prepared, consist essentially of the glyceryl esters of these acids. In soap manufacture the oil or fat is heated with dilute sodium hydroxide (less frequently potassium hydroxide) solution in large vats. When hydrolysis is complete the soap is 'salted out', or precipitated from solution by addition of common salt. The excess of alkali, containing glycerol from the oil or fat, is run off, and the soap washed by boiling with water. The soap is then treated, as required, with perfumes, etc., and made into tablets. In the Twitchell process hydrolysis of the fat to free fatty acid and glycerol is effected by boiling with water in the presence of a compound of oleic acid with an aromatic sulphonic acid; the soap is obtained by neutralization of the fatty acid with alkali. 'Soft soaps' are potassium soaps containing the glycerol formed during hydrolysis of the fat.

Soapstone. A massive impure variety of talc.

Soda-asbestos. A mixture of caustic soda and asbestos used as an absorbent for carbon dioxide.

Soda ash. See Sodium carbonate.

Soda-lime. A granular material, prepared by slaking quicklime with caustic soda solution and heating the product until dry. It is a convenient absorbent for gaseous carbon dioxide, and is also used in testing for ammonium salts in qualitative analysis. These, when ground in a mortar with soda-lime, liberate free ammonia.

Sodamide. See Sodium amide.

Soddy, Frederick (1877-1956). Born at Eastbourne, Soddy studied at the University College of Wales (Aberystwyth) and Oxford. He was appointed professor of chemistry at Glasgow (1904), Aberdeen (1914), and Oxford (1919).

Soddy's work on radioactivity elucidated the problem of radioactive disintegration and led to the discovery of the isotopes. He was the author of numerous books on radioactivity and economics. Elected F.R.S. in 1910, Soddy was awarded the Nobel Prize for chemistry in 1921. See *Nature*, 1956, **178**, 893 and 1957, **180**, 1085.

Sodium, Na. At.no. 11. At.wt. 22·991, m.p. 97·5°, b.p. 880°, d 0·97. Sodium is a soft silver-white metal with a body-centred cubic lattice, $a=4·30$ Å; the vapour is violet in colour. Metallic sodium reacts rapidly with oxygen, the halogens, and water; it dissolves in liquid ammonia and certain ethers to give blue solutions having strong reducing properties. Sodium gives amalgams with mercury, these being used in the production of caustic soda and as reducing agents; alloys with potassium are liquid at room temperatures and have been used in heat-extractors.

Sodium is a member of the alkali metal family, and in its chemical compounds is unipositive, generally as ions.

Sodium is manufactured by the electrolysis of sodium chloride, with sufficient calcium chloride and alkali fluorides added to ensure that the mixture is liquid at the operating temperature of 600°. Chlorine is produced at the same time and the cell is specially designed to keep the two products apart.

The major use of sodium is in the production of the anti-knock additives lead tetraethyl and lead tetramethyl. It is also used in the manufacture of sodium cyanide, sodium peroxide and titanium.

Sodium acetate. Prepared by dissolving sodium carbonate in acetic acid and crystallizing the solution. The trihydrate, $NaC_2H_3O_2$, $3H_2O$, thus obtained, forms colourless monoclinic crystals, m.p. 75°, readily soluble in water; the water of crystallization is lost at 100°.

Sodium amide, $NaNH_2$. A white powder prepared by the action of ammonia on metallic sodium. It gives ammonia with water.

Sodium ammonium hydrogen phosphate. See Microcosmic salt.

Sodium antimonyl tartrate, $NaSbOC_4H_4O_6$. More soluble than the corresponding potassium compound, it is preferred to the latter for intravenous use, as it is considered to be less irritant. Its medicinal properties are identical with those of the potassium salt.

Sodium arsenates. Prepared by the interaction of arsenic pentoxide and sodium hydroxide or by electrolytic or chemical oxidation of sodium arsenite solution. The normal salt, Na_3AsO_4, and two acid salts, Na_2HAsO_4 and NaH_2AsO_4, are known. On heating the acid salts, sodium meta-arsenate, $NaAsO_3$, and sodium pyro-arsenate, $Na_4As_2O_7$, respectively are formed.

Sodium arsenites. Obtained by dissolving arsenious oxide in sodium hydroxide or sodium carbonate. An orthoarsenite, Na_3AsO_3, and a metarsenite, $NaAsO_2$, are known. Solutions of sodium arsenite are used in the determination of iodine.

Sodium azide, NaN_3. The sodium salt of hydrazoic acid.

Sodium benzoate, C_6H_5COONa. A white crystalline powder, soluble in 2 parts of water and 90 parts of alcohol. It has antiseptic properties, and is an expectorant. Its chief use is as a corrosion inhibitor. Medicinally it is used as a urinary antiseptic and for gout and rheumatism. It is excreted as hippuric acid.

Sodium bicarbonate, $NaHCO_3$. Prepared by passing carbon dioxide into a solution of sodium carbonate. On heating it decomposes into the normal carbonate. Sodium bicarbonate (9·65 g in 100 g water at 20°) is very much less soluble than potassium bicarbonate. Its main use is as an ingredient of baking powders, but it is also used pharmaceutically, in the manufacture of other chemicals, and in fire extinguishers.

Sodium bifluoride, Sodium hydrogen fluoride, $NaHF_2$. Prepared by dissolving sodium fluoride in aqueous or anhydrous hydrofluoric acid. The salt decomposes at 270° into sodium fluoride and hydrogen fluoride. It contains the bifluoride HF_2^-, ion.

Sodium bisulphates. Formed by the action of sulphuric acid on sodium sulphate. The following salts are definitely known: $2Na_2SO_4,9H_2SO_4$; $Na_2SO_4 \cdot 2H_2SO_4$; $NaHSO_4$; but there may be others present in the system. On heating, sodium bisulphate, $NaHSO_4$, gives sodium pyrosulphate, $Na_2S_2O_7$.

Sodium borate, $Na_2B_4O_7$. See Borax.

Sodium borohydride, $NaBH_4$. A white solid prepared by the reaction between sodium hydride or sodium methoxide and diborane. It is very stable and dissolves in water, the solution being stable under alkaline conditions. It is widely used as an organic reducing agent, reducing ketones and acids to alcohols; with boron trifluoride it liberates diborane.

Sodium bromate, $NaBrO_3$. M.p. 381°, d 3·254. Prepared by the electrolysis of aqueous sodium bromide, or by the action of bromine on hot caustic soda.

Sodium bromate is cubic, isomorphous with sodium chlorate. The solubility in water is 27·5 g in 100 g H_2O at 0°; supersaturated solutions are readily prepared.

Sodium bromide, NaBr, has m.p. 757°, b.p. 1393°, d 3·215. It is formed by the action of aqueous hydrobromic acid on sodium hydroxide or carbonate or, together with sodium bromate, by the action of bromine on hot caustic soda solution. The crystals have the NaCl structure, $a = 5·94$ Å. Solubility, 79·5 g in 100 g water at 0°; a hydrate, $NaBr \cdot 2H_2O$, is known. Sodium bromide is soluble in liquid ammonia; a solvate, $NaBr \cdot 5NH_3$, is known. The salt is also soluble in hydrazine, methyl and ethyl alcohols, acetone, pyridine, aniline, and formic and acetic acids.

Sodium carbonate, Na_2CO_3. Mainly manufactured by the ammonia-soda or Solvay process. Ammonia is dissolved in purified brine and the resulting solution treated with carbon dioxide. The ammonium bicarbonate formed reacts with the sodium chloride to precipitate sodium bicarbonate, leaving ammonium chloride in solution. The sodium bicarbonate is filtered off and heated to 175°, when carbon dioxide is evolved and anhydrous sodium carbonate formed. The carbon dioxide is recycled. The ammonia is also recovered by treating the ammonium chloride solution with milk of lime, so that the only end-product apart from the carbonate is a calcium chloride solution. This may be discharged as waste or the calcium chloride recovered. Some sodium carbonate is obtained from certain natural brines and deposits, while in some instances it may be economic to produce it from electrolytic caustic soda and carbon dioxide.

Sodium carbonate has m.p. 851° and solubility at 0° 7·1 g in 100 g water. Hydrates are known with 1, 1½, 3, 7 and 10 molecules of water. The anhydrous material is known commercially as soda ash, washing soda is the decahydrate.

Sodium carbonate is of the greatest commercial importance and is extensively used in the glass, soap, chemical and paper industries. World production is about 15 million tons per annum.

Sodium chaulmoograte and **Sodium hydnocarpate.** The sodium salts of the fatty acids from chaulmoogra and hydnocarpus oils. Aqueous solutions of these salts are administered for leprosy by intramuscular and intravenous injection.

Sodium chlorate, $NaClO_3$. Formed either by the action of chlorine on hot aqueous caustic soda, or by the electrolysis of sodium chloride solution. The latter method is used industrially; brine made slightly acid with hydrochloric acid being electrolysed at 40° in a cell so designed that the anode and cathode products come into contact and react with each other. Sodium chlorate crystallizes in the cubic system. The solubility is 79·5 g in 100 g water at 0°; it is also soluble in liquid ammonia, hydrazine, methylamine, ethylamine, and in water-alcohol mixtures. Its main use is in the pulp industry, where it is used to generate chlorine dioxide for bleaching. It is also used in the manufacture of other chlorates and perchlorates and as a herbicide.

Sodium chloride, NaCl; m.p. 801°, b.p. 1439°, d_0^4 2·168. Sodium chloride, or common salt, occurs naturally as rock salt, distributed extensively over the earth's surface, and to the extent of 3% in sea water. Commercially, salt is normally obtained as brine from underground deposits by pumping water into them and removing a saturated solution at a different point. The brine produced contains various impurities, principally calcium, iron and magnesium, which are removed by precipitation with sodium carbonate and caustic soda. The purified solution may then be used as such, e.g. for the production of caustic soda or sodium carbonate, or evaporated to yield salt crystals. Appreciable quantities of rock salt are obtained by mining, while in certain parts of the world salt is produced from sea water by solar evaporation. Pure sodium chloride is obtained on a laboratory scale by saturating a strong solution of brine with hydrogen chloride gas when the pure salt is precipitated. Magnesium chloride, a very common impurity, is removed by precipitating the sodium chloride with ether.

Sodium chloride is used for the removal of ice and snow, as a preservative, and in the manufacture of other chemicals.

Sodium chloride crystallizes in the cubic system, $a = 5·628$ Å. The structure of sodium chloride is illustrated in the accompanying figure. Many AX compounds possess this

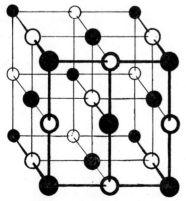

Sodium chloride structure

structure, including most of the alkali halides (except CsCl, CsBr, and CsI) and the alkaline earth oxides and sulphides. At about 1400° it decomposes into sodium and chlorine, the heat of dissociation being 128 kcal/mole. Only one hydrate, NaCl·2H₂O, is known. Sodium chloride is also soluble in liquid ammonia, a compound NaCl, 5NH₃ being the stable solid phase between −76·6° and −9·5°.

Sodium citrate, $C_6H_5O_7Na_3,2H_2O$. White granular crystals, very soluble in water. It is deliquescent in moist air, and efflorescent in warm dry air. It can also be obtained with $5\frac{1}{2}$ molecules of water of crystallization. It is used medicinally as an anticoagulant for blood and to prevent the formation of large curds in the stomach of infants. It is also used to raise the alkalinity of the blood in acidosis.

Sodium cyanide, NaCN. M.p. 563·7°, b.p. 1500°. The industrial salt usually contains as impurities carbonate, sulphide, chloride, and cyanate, and is most readily purified by recrystallization from liquid ammonia. Aqueous solutions are alkaline in reaction, and slowly evolve hydrocyanic acid. Sodium cyanide is extracted from the by-products of gas manufacture but is more usually prepared by reacting methane and ammonia to HCN followed by neutralization with NaOH.

Sodium dithionite. See Sodium hydrosulphite.

Sodium ethoxide, Sodium ethylate, CH_3CH_2ONa. A white amorphous solid. Soluble in alcohol; insoluble in benzene. Prepared by dissolving metallic sodium in ethyl alcohol and distilling off the excess alcohol. Decomposed by water to alcohol and sodium hydroxide. Reacts with alkyl halides to give ethers, and also with certain esters as in the Claisen reaction. Used in organic syntheses.

Sodium fluoride, NaF. M.p. 902°, b.p. 1705°, solubility at 25° 4·13 g in 100 g water. It is decomposed by sulphuric acid with evolution of hydrogen fluoride; the salt itself will add on one or more molecules of HF to form sodium bifluoride.

Sodium fluoroacetate. See Fluoroacetates.

Sodium formate, $HCO_2Na·H_2O$. Colourless monoclinic deliquescent crystals, which, on heating, melt in their water of crystallization and then solidify in an anhydrous mass. It is soluble in 2 parts of water, and has m.p. (anhydrous) 253°.

Sodium hydnocarpate. See Sodium chaulmoograte.

Sodium hydride, NaH. Sodium hydride is most readily prepared by passing a current of pure dry hydrogen over sodium at about 350°. It is a white crystalline substance, with the same lattice structure as sodium chloride. On heating to above 300° dissociation becomes apparent; at 400° the dissociation pressure is 355 mm. Electrolysis of the hydride in a fused mixture with lithium and potassium chlorides leads to the evolution of hydrogen at the anode.

Sodium hydride inflames spontaneously with oxygen at 230°, and with the halogens at ordinary temperatures. Reacts with water with the formation of caustic soda and the evolution of hydrogen; with liquid ammonia to give sodamide and hydrogen; and with acetylene at 100° to give an acetylide, $CH{\equiv}CNa$, and hydrogen. Sodium hydride reacts with alcohols to form sodium alkoxides; it is also very useful in organic reductions and condensations. It is used in the metallurgical industries as a descaling agent.

Sodium hydrosulphide, NaSH. The anhydrous salt is most readily prepared by saturating a solution of sodium in alcohol with dry hydrogen sulphide. The precipitate is washed with ether and dried at 110° in an atmosphere of hydrogen. From aqueous solutions the hydrates NaSH, $1·5H_2O$; NaSH, $2H_2O$; NaSH, $3H_2O$, have been isolated. On strongly heating *in vacuo* the anhydrous salt decomposes into the monosulphide and hydrogen sulphide. The aqueous solutions are only slightly hydrolysed (0·15% at 25° for 0·1M).

Sodium hydrosulphite, $Na_2S_2O_4$. Also known as sodium dithionite or sodium hyposulphite. It is prepared by the reduction of sodium bisulphite solutions with zinc, or by the action of sulphur dioxide on sodium amalgam. A crystalline precipitate of the dihydrate is obtained. The anhydrous salt is obtained on heating to 65°. Sodium hydrosulphite is very readily oxidized, especially in the presence of moisture and in solution. At 80° the products are sodium thiosulphate and bisulphite. It is used widely as a reducing agent in the dyeing industry and as an oxygen absorbent.

Sodium hydroxide, caustic soda, NaOH, has m.p. 318·4°, b.p. 1390°, d 2·130. It is soluble in water, alcohol and ether.

Caustic soda is now mainly manufactured by the electrolysis of sodium chloride. There are two basic types of cell.

The mercury cell, mainly used in Europe, consists of a long trough inclined at a slight angle to the horizontal. Over the bottom of this flows a shallow stream of mercury which forms the cathode, and above it flows a stream of purified brine in which the graphite blocks forming the anode are suspended. The cell operates at about 4·5 V and 60°-70°. Chlorine is liberated at the anode, collects under the trough cover and is taken off for purification and use; sodium is liberated at the mercury cathode where it forms an amalgam. After its passage through the trough the mercury is made to flow along a second trough where it meets a stream of water. Here caustic soda and hydrogen are formed.

In the diaphragm cell, widely used in the U.S.A., the anode takes the form of a number of vertical graphite plates. Intermeshed with these are a series of hollow leaves made of steel mesh, so that each pair of graphite plates is separated by a steel leaf which forms the cathode. The cathode leaves are covered by a mat of asbestos fibres which serves to keep the anode and cathode products separate. The flow of brine is from the anode to the cathode side of the mat. The cell operates at about 4 V and 90°.

Mercury cells produce a high purity caustic soda solution which merely requires concentration by evaporation. Diaphragm cells only achieve a 50% conversion to caustic soda, and the resulting solution therefore contains much sodium chloride. Much of the latter crystallizes out during subsequent concentration, but the final product may contain appreciable quantities of this impurity.

Caustic soda is also manufactured from sodium carbonate. A solution of the latter is reacted with slaked lime or milk of lime at 85°; the resulting calcium carbonate precipitate is removed and the solution concentrated.

Sodium hydroxide is a white, translucent, hygroscopic solid. Hydrates containing 7, 5, 4 (two forms α and β), $3\frac{1}{2}$, 2 and 1 molecules of water of crystallization are known. At high temperatures (about 1300°) the compound decomposes into its elements, and reduction with hydrogen can be detected at 800°. At 450° sodium reacts with the hydroxide to give sodium monoxide; the fused salt reacts with potassium, an equilibrium $K + NaOH \rightleftharpoons Na + KOH$ being established.

Sodium hydroxide dissolves in water, with the evolution of heat, producing a strongly alkaline solution. The solution, and sodium hydroxide itself, readily absorb acidic oxides such as CO_2 and SO_2.

Caustic soda is a chemical of the greatest industrial importance. Large quantities are required for the manufacture of other chemicals, while much is also used by the rayon, pulp and paper, aluminium, petroleum, textile, soap, and detergent industries. World production in 1964 was probably about 15 million tons.

Sodium hypochlorite, NaOCl. Formed, together with the chloride, by the reaction between chlorine and cold dilute caustic soda (see Hypochlorous acid). Hydrates with 5, $2\frac{1}{2}$, and 1 molecules of water are known. The aqueous solution possesses marked bleaching properties, and, in the form of a dilute aqueous solution, it is used as an antiseptic.

Sodium hyposulphite. See Sodium hydrosulphite.

Sodium iodate, $NaIO_3$. Formed by the action of iodic acid on sodium hydroxide or by oxidizing iodine with sodium chlorate. In addition to the anhydrous salt, hydrates with 5 and 1 molecules of water are known. Two acid iodates are known: $NaIO_3 \cdot 2HIO_3$ and $2NaIO_3 \cdot I_2O_5$.

Sodium iodide, NaI, has m.p. 660°, b.p. 1300°, d_4^{25} 3·665. Pure sodium iodide is obtained by neutralizing hydriodic acid with sodium carbonate, evaporation and crystallization. To obtain the anhydrous salt, evaporation to dryness in an inert atmosphere has been recommended. The anhydrous salt crystallizes in the cubic system. Two hydrates NaI, $5H_2O$ and NaI, $2H_2O$, are known, the latter crystallizing in monoclinic prisms. A number of stable compounds with sulphur dioxide are known (NaI with 1, 2, 3, and 4 molecules of SO_2). With liquid ammonia the compounds NaI, $6NH_3$ and NaI, $4 \cdot 5NH_3$ are formed. Sodium iodide is soluble in liquid ammonia, hydrazine, liquid sulphur dioxide and alcohols.

Sodium lactate, $C_3H_5O_3Na$. The sodium salt of lactic acid. It is obtained as a yellowish viscous liquid, completely miscible with water. It is used as a glycerin alternative particularly in calico printing; it has greater hygroscopic power than glycerin. It is also used in the finishing of various textiles and as a plasticizer for casein.

Sodium metabisulphite. See Sodium pyrosulphite.

Sodium morrhuate. A mixture of the sodium salts of the purified unsaturated fatty acids from cod-liver oil. A 5% aqueous solution is injected into varicose veins to promote sclerosis. Sodium morrhuate solutions are also injected subcutaneously in the treatment of tuberculosis and leprosy.

Sodium nitrate, $NaNO_3$. M.p. 310°. Known industrially as Chile saltpetre. The salt crystallizes in the rhombohedral system, and is isomorphous with calcite. No hydrate is known. The solubility in water is 73·4 g in 100 g at 0°; the salt is also soluble in liquid ammonia, hydrazine, and acetone.

Sodium nitrite, $NaNO_2$. M.p. 271°. For preparation see Nitrous acid. The anhydrous salt crystallizes in the orthorhombic system. Decomposes to oxides of nitrogen and sodium oxide and nitrate at 320°. On oxidation sodium

nitrate is formed. Solubility is 41·6 g in 100 g solution at 0°; a hydrate, $NaNO_2 \cdot \frac{1}{2}H_2O$ is known. Sodium nitrite is used in the dyestuffs industry and as a corrosion inhibitor.

Sodium oxalate, $C_2O_4Na_2$. Colourless needles, soluble in water up to 4%. Sodium hydrogen oxalate, C_2O_4HNa, crystallizes in monoclinic crystals with one molecule of water and is less soluble than sodium oxalate.

Sodium oxides. *Sodium monoxide,* Na_2O, is formed by the direct reaction between sodium and a deficiency of oxygen, the excess sodium being distilled off *in vacuo,* by the reduction of the peroxide with carbon, silver or sodium, or by heating sodium azide with sodium nitrate. It forms white or slightly yellow cubic crystals. It reacts directly with hydrogen at 180°, forming sodium hydroxide and hydride. With liquid ammonia it gives sodium amide and sodium hydroxide. It reacts exceedingly violently with water with the formation of caustic soda.

Sodium peroxide, Na_2O_2. Formed by the direct combination of sodium with oxygen in excess. It is a white, crystalline solid, which becomes yellow when hot. Sodium peroxide is a strong oxidizing agent, reacting directly with iodine vapour to give sodium iodate and iodide, together with ozone; in the presence of moisture the periodate, $Na_2H_3IO_6$, is formed. It reacts with carbon at about 300° with the production of carbonate and sodium metal. It reacts with excess water with the formation of sodium hydroxide and hydrogen peroxide, the latter decomposing rapidly in alkaline solution; from a cold solution at 0°, crystals of Na_2O_2, $8H_2O$, the octahydrate separate. Sodium peroxide contains a proportion of the paramagnetic *sodium superoxide,* NaO_2.

Sodium perchlorate, $NaClO_4$. M.p. 482°. Formed by the electrolysis of sodium chloride solutions, or by heating sodium chlorate (see Perchloric acid). Sodium perchlorate crystallizes in an orthorhombic form, stable at low temperatures, and in a cubic form, stable at high temperatures, with a transition temperature of 301·5°; both forms are hygroscopic. A hydrate, $NaClO_4$, H_2O, is known; solubility of $NaClO_4$ is 67·5 g in 100 g water.

Sodium periodates. *Disodium paraperiodate,* $Na_2H_3IO_6$. Formed by passing chlorine through a boiling solution of iodine and sodium hydroxide. The solubility is 0·104 g in 100 g H_2O at 0°.

Trisodium paraperiodate, $Na_3H_2IO_6$. Formed by passing chlorine through a solution of sodium iodate and caustic soda.

Sodium periodate, Na_5IO_6. Formed by oxidation of sodium iodide with sodium nitrate in the presence of sodium hydroxide at 700°.

Sodium metaperiodate, $NaIO_4$. Obtained by treating a paraperiodate with water and nitric acid. A trihydrate, $NaIO_4 \cdot 3H_2O$ is also known.

Sodium phosphates. The system $Na_2O—P_2O_5—H_2O$ is exceedingly complex. The orthophosphates are salts of the tribasic acid H_3PO_4. The normal sodium phosphate of commerce is disodium orthophosphate, Na_2HPO_4, and is manufactured by reacting phosphoric acid with slightly more than the theoretical quantity of sodium carbonate. From this the mono- and trisodium salts may be made by treatment with phosphoric acid and caustic soda respectively. By heating the disodium salt at 250° disodium dihydrogen pyrophosphate, $Na_2H_2P_2O_7$, is formed, while at higher temperatures tetrasodium pyrophosphate, $Na_4P_2O_7$, is produced. By heating monosodium orthophosphate at 760° and quenching quickly sodium hexametaphosphate is obtained. Sodium tripolyphosphate, the most important of the sodium phosphates, is made by the thermal dehydration of a mixture containing mono- and disodium orthophosphate in the molar ratio 1 to 2.

The various phosphates find a wide variety of uses, but by far the most important is in detergents. They are also used in water conditioning, food manufacture and medicine. See Hexametaphosphates.

Sodium potassium tartrate, Rochelle salt, $C_4H_4O_6NaK$, $4H_2O$. Colourless rhombic prisms, very soluble in water. It is a saline aperient and is used in the production of silver mirrors. The crystals have piezo-electric properties.

Sodium pyrosulphite, Sodium metabisulphite, $Na_2S_2O_5$. Prepared by saturating a 30% caustic soda solution with sulphur dioxide at 100°; on slow cooling crystals of anhydrous sodium pyrosulphite separate. From a study of the system $Na_2S_2O_5–H_2O$, hydrates, $Na_2S_2O_5, 7H_2O$ and $Na_2S_2O_5, 6H_2O$, have been shown to exist.

Sodium salicylate, o-$C_6H_4(OH)COONa$. A white crystalline powder, very soluble in water. It is a useful drug in the treatment of gouty and rheumatic ailments as it increases the elimination of uric acid. It also has antipyretic properties.

Sodium silicates. Numerous silicates of sodium are known. Sodium silicates prepared from aqueous solutions are salts of orthosilicic acid, H_4SiO_4. By fusing together a mixture of sodium carbonate and sand (silica) at 1300° in a furnace, a range of products in which the molar ratio Na_2O to SiO_2 varies from 2:1 to 1:4 may be obtained, depending on the proportion of reactants used. Na_2SiO_3 (1:1) is sodium metasilicate. Those silicates with the Na_2O to SiO_2 ratio in the range 1·6 to 4 are known as colloidal silicates or water-glasses, because these clear, glass-like compounds are soluble in water.

Because of the wide Na_2O to SiO_2 ratio possible, a whole range of properties may be achieved, and the sodium silicates are of great commercial importance. The greatest single use is in the manufacture of silica gel, obtained by treating sodium silicate solutions with a mineral acid. Other important applications are as adhesives, sizes, metal-cleaning compounds and in the manufacture of detergents.

Sodium stannate, Na_2SnO_3, $3H_2O$. Prepared by fusing tin oxide with caustic soda. It is used as a mordant.

Sodium sulphate, Na_2SO_4. M.p. 884°, b.p. 1429°. At ordinary temperatures sodium sulphate crystallizes in the orthorhombic system, but at about 250° there is a transition to the hexagonal system. From a study of the system $Na_2SO_4–H_2O$ the decahydrate and a metastable heptahydrate have been shown to be the only hydrates. $Na_2SO_4, 10H_2O$, the decahydrate, crystallizes in the monoclinic system. Sodium sulphate is only sparingly soluble in methyl, ethyl, and isopropyl alcohols. Sodium sulphate forms many double sulphates with transition metal sulphates.

Sodium sulphate is manufactured by heating together sodium chloride and strong sulphuric acid in a furnace at about 800°. The resulting material is dissolved in water, contaminating iron and aluminium precipitated, and the sodium sulphate crystallized. In another process, mainly used in Europe, sodium chloride is reacted with a gaseous mixture of sulphur dioxide, air and water vapour. In both cases hydrogen chloride is obtained as the other product. Much sodium sulphate is recovered from spent viscose rayon spin-bath liquor, while various industrial processes, such as the caustic fusion method for phenol production and the manufacture of sodium dichromate, yield the material as a by-product. In the U.S.A. the recovery of sodium sulphate from natural brines is of great importance.

Sodium sulphate is a material of very great commercial importance. About two-thirds of production is used in the manufacture of wood pulp, but it is also employed in the manufacture of glass, detergents and various chemicals. It is is also well known as a mild saline aperient (Glauber's salt).

Sodium sulphides, *Sodium sulphide*, Na_2S, is generally prepared by the reduction of sodium sulphate with carbon monoxide or hydrogen.

Hydrates with $4\frac{1}{2}$, 5 ,and $9H_2O$ are known, and, although aqueous solutions are hydrolysed, the anhydrous salt may be obtained by rigorous dehydration using phosphorus pentoxide. The aqueous solutions are readily oxidized to sodium thiosulphate.

Sodium polysulphides are readily obtained by reaction between sulphur and sodium in liquid ammonia; in addition to the monosulphide the di-, tetra-, and penta-sulphides can be isolated. Aqueous solutions of the polysulphides are unstable, sulphur being deposited; but many hydrates have been isolated from water-alcohol solutions.

Sodium sulphite, Na_2SO_3. The anhydrous salt is stable in air to about $100°$; at red heat it decomposes into sodium sulphate and sulphide. Only one hydrate, $Na_2SO_3, 7H_2O$, is known; it crystallizes in the monoclinic system. Aqueous solutions of the salt are unstable in the presence of oxygen, the sulphite being oxidized to sulphate. Sodium sulphite is used for removing chlorine from substances which have been bleached and in the paper industry to dissolve lignin.

The acid salt, $NaHSO_3$, is known only in solution.

Sodium tetraphenylborate, $NaB(C_6H_5)_4$. Used in the estimation of potassium by direct precipitation of the insoluble salt $KB(C_6H_5)_4$. Ammonium salts also give precipitates with this salt.

Sodium thiosulphate, $Na_2S_2O_3$. The anhydrous salt can be obtained by dehydration of a hydrate at less than $105°$, but it rapidly takes up moisture from the atmosphere. Hydrates of $Na_2S_2O_3$ with 7, 6, 5, 4, 2, $1\frac{3}{5}$, 1, and $\frac{1}{2}$ molecules of water are known.

Sodium thiosulphate is manufactured by treating a solution containing sodium carbonate and sodium sulphide (obtained as a by-product in the manufacture of the latter) with sulphur dioxide. Another method is to boil sodium sulphite with sulphur. Sodium thiosulphate is also formed as a by-product in the production of certain sulphur dyes, and is recovered.

The salt is extensively used in photography, under the name 'hypo', because of the ability of its solutions to dissolve silver halides. It is also employed in tanning, the preparation of mordants, the manufacture of other chemicals, and as a fermentation preventative in dyeing.

Softeners. Compounds added to the rubber mix to soften the mix, to facilitate mixing, and to improve the dispersion of compounding ingredients. The more important types are: fatty acids and soaps, aliphatic and aromatic hydrocarbons (mineral oils), asphalts and bitumens, coal-tar and pitch, wood-tars, synthetic and natural resins, vegetable oils and factices.

Sol. A colloidal solution. The term is used particularly for colloidal dispersions of inorganic solids in liquids (generally water), e.g. sulphur sol, gold sol.

Solacet dyes (I.C.I.). A somewhat limited range of water soluble dyestuffs which were introduced for dyeing acetate rayon. An early example is the bluish-red dye,

which is the sulphuric ester of a monoazo disperse dye.

Unlike Ionamines which suffer decomposition in the dyebath, the Solacet dyes are unchanged on standing. They are applied in a similar manner to direct dyes on cellulosic fibres, i.e. from an aqueous dyebath with the addition of salt to exhaust the bath. On some types of acetate rayon goods they enable improved penetration and levelness to be obtained compared with those resulting from dispersed dyes. Solacet dyes also have good affinity for Nylon.

Solapsone, $C_{30}H_{28}N_2Na_4O_{14}S_5$. A white powder, containing a variable amount of water of crystallization, soluble in water, insoluble in

organic solvents. It is bacteriostatic, acting by blocking essential metabolic processes. It is used in the treatment of leprosy, being given orally or by injection, and causes a marked subsidence of the lesions.

Solarization. The effect whereby exposure beyond a limited value produces diminishing silver density after development. This reversal effect was first observed in photography of the sun. The effect can be harnessed to provide direct-positive emulsions. The proposed

18*

mechanism for solarization is a recombination of the latent image silver with bromine produced by the heavy exposure. At low exposure levels solarization does not occur because the gelatin surrounding the grains acts as an adequate halogen acceptor, and even at high exposure levels halogen acceptors such as acetone semicarbazone can prevent solarization.

Solder. Solders are fusible alloys used for bonding metal parts. Hard solder or brazing metal is a low-melting brass with a m.p. of over 800°. Soft solders are normally lead-tin eutectic alloys. Electrician's solder contains about 50% tin and 50% lead, giving a low m.p. of around 200°. Plumber's solder is rich in lead, giving a wide range of solidification from 300° down to 180°. This results in a 'mushy' range which permits the making of wiped joints.

Soldering. Causing a melted metal to adhere to the surface of another metallic substance by a process of diffusion brought about by chemical solution.

Solid foams. It often happens that during a chemical decomposition in a liquid system, gas is evolved and a solid formed. From the physical conditions of its formation, this solid is composed of a porous network enclosing gas and possesses, therefore, a high specific surface. Examples of this type of colloid are charcoal and meerschaum.

Many plastics can be made in a highly expanded form, with either 'open' or 'closed' gas cells. Expanded polystyrene has the true structure of a solidified foam with thin-walled polyhedral cells. Other solid foams, e.g. bread and 'foamed slag' simply contain trapped spherical gas bubbles.

Solid solution. A solid solution is formed between two or more elements when they share a common lattice in their alloys. The composition may vary over very wide limits and normal valency laws do not hold. A substitutional solid solution is formed (e.g. nickel-copper alloys) when atoms of the solute replace atoms of the solvent in its lattice. An interstitial solid solution (e.g. carbon in iron) is formed when a small atom such as carbon enters the interstices of the solvent lattice.

Solid structures. The chemistry of solid compounds is complicated because the arrangement of the various atoms depends partly on the chemical attractions between the atoms and partly on the relative sizes of the atoms; the latter has an important bearing on the close-packing of solids.

Solidus. See Liquidus.

Solubility. The maximum quantity of one phase dissolved by another under given conditions. In the case of solutions of solids or liquids in liquids the solubility is expressed as the weight which can be dissolved by a given volume or a given weight of the liquid at a given temperature. For solubility of gases, see Henry's law.

Solubility curve. A curve expressing the variation with temperature of the amount of one substance which will dissolve in another. The commonest form is a curve showing the solubility of a salt in water at a series of temperatures. Solubility curves may, however, be constructed for other systems (e.g. liquid-liquid or solid-solid systems).

Solubility product. The processes occurring in a saturated solution of an electrolyte in contact with some undissolved electrolyte may be expressed by the equation

$$AB_{Solid} \rightleftharpoons AB_{Dissolved} \rightleftharpoons A^+ + B^-.$$

By the Law of Mass Action, at equilibrium,

$$\frac{[A^+][B^-]}{[AB]_{Dissolved}} = K.$$

The concentration of undissociated electrolyte is, however, constant, for it is in equilibrium with the undissolved solid, which has a constant active mass, hence

$$[A^+][B^-] = K_1,$$

another constant, called the solubility product of the electrolyte. Hence, if by the addition of some A^+ or B^- ions to the solution, K_1 is momentarily exceeded, precipitation of the salt occurs to restore the equilibrium.

Solute. See Solvent.

Solution. A liquid or solid may be dispersed through a liquid either by being in suspension, or by being dissolved in it, in the form of a solution. The qualitative characteristics of a solution are perfect homogeneity, and the absence of any tendency for the dissolved substance to settle out again. Unfortunately from the point of view of these criteria, a suspension of extremely minute particles (colloidal suspension) of a pure chemical compound behaves in a similar manner. A solution is better defined as a homogeneous mixture of substances which is separable into its components by altering the state of one of them (freezing or boiling out one component), and whose properties vary continuously with the proportions of the components between certain limits. Solutions are not confined to liquids and solids; solutions of gas in liquids, and of gases, liquids, and solids in solids are also formed. The amount of a substance dissolved in a given amount of another substance is described as the concentration of the solution, and may be expressed in grams per litre, gram equivalents per litre, or as a molar fraction (*q.v.*).

A solution containing only a small proportion of the dissolved substance is called dilute; one containing a high proportion is said to be concentrated. There is a limit to the solubility of most substances, and a solution containing the limiting amount of the dissolved substance is said to be saturated with respect to the substance, and is termed a saturated solution. Such solutions are prepared, e.g. by shaking the liquid with excess of the powdered solid until no more is taken up by the solution.

The maximum concentration attainable under such conditions is termed the solubility of the substance at the specific temperature used in the experiment, since solubility generally increases with rising temperature. Solubility is usually expressed in grams per 100 g of solvent, or grams per 100 g of solution. Sometimes, for practical convenience, it may be expressed in grams per 100 ml of solvent or solution.

Solvation. See Hydration (of ions).

Solvay, Ernest (1839-1922). Born at Rebecq in Brabant, Solvay devised the Solvay Process for the preparation of sodium carbonate through the interaction of sodium chloride, ammonia, and carbon dioxide. With his brother Alfred he erected works at Couillet near Brussels where they manufactured their product. See 'History of British Chemical Industries' (Miall), p. 13.

Solvay process. See Sodium carbonate.

Solvent. It is usual to speak of the substance, which, like water in the majority of cases, forms the bulk of a solution, as the *solvent*. The substance which is dissolved in the solvent is termed the *solute*. The terms are purely arbitrary, and cannot be given a more precise definition except in special cases. For example, when a chemical reaction occurs between certain constituents of a solution, the inert medium used to disperse the reactants is almost invariably termed the inert solvent.

Solvent refining. The term describes processes in which solvents are used to remove undesirable constituents, e.g. de-aromatization of lamp kerosine, dewaxing of lubricating oils, and de-asphalting of petroleum residues.

Solvolysis. This occurs when a compound reacts with a solvent. In the case of water the special term hydrolysis is used, e.g. the reaction of a salt with water giving the free acid and base.

$$BA + H_2O \rightarrow HA + BOH$$

Sorbic acid, $C_6H_8O_2$,

$$CH_3 \cdot CH:CH \cdot CH:CH \cdot COOH.$$

Crystallizes in white needles, m.p. 134·5°, b.p. 228° (decomp.); solubility in water 0·16 g in 100 g at 20°, more soluble hot; soluble in alkalis, alcohol, ether. Sorbic acid can be obtained from mountain ash berries, but is prepared by condensing crotonaldehyde and keten. It is a selective growth inhibitor for yeasts, moulds, and certain bacteria, and is used as a food preservative. Its esters can be used in the preparation of quick-drying oils.

Sorbite. The structure produced by tempering martensite at temperatures of 550°-650°. It is best described as the structure in which the carbide is just visible as small dots in a ferrite matrix when examined at a magnification of ×500. Steels with a sorbitic structure show a high degree of toughness.

D-**Sorbitol,** $C_6H_{14}O_6$. The alcohol correspond-

$$CH_2OH \cdot \overset{\text{HO}}{\underset{\text{H}}{C}} \cdot \overset{\text{H}}{\underset{\text{OH}}{C}} \cdot \overset{\text{OH}}{\underset{\text{H}}{C}} \cdot \overset{\text{OH}}{\underset{\text{H}}{C}} \cdot CH_2OH$$

ing to glucose. It is present in mountain ash berries and is characteristic of the fruits of the *Rosaceae*. It crystallizes in slender needles, m.p. 97°, $[\alpha]_D$ −1·9°.

Sorbitol is manufactured by the reduction of glucose in aqueous solution using hydrogen at 140°-200° and 100-125 atm. with a nickel catalyst. It is used in the manufacture of ascorbic acid (vitamin C), various surface active agents, foodstuffs, pharmaceuticals, cosmetics, dentifrices, adhesives, polyurethane foams, etc.

Sorbose, $C_6H_{12}O_6$. A ketose sugar having the formula

L-Sorbose, which forms colourless rhombic crystals, soluble in water, m.p. 160°, $[\alpha]_D$ −42°, is obtained by the fermentation of sorbitol with certain *Acetobacter*. It is an intermediate in the manufacture of ascorbic acid.

Sorel's cement. A basic magnesium chloride made by adding two parts of ignited magnesia to a concentrated solution of one part of magnesium chloride. On stirring, the whole sets to a solid mass.

Sørensen, Søreh Peter Lauritz (1868-1939). Born in the Danish island of Zeeland, Sørensen was educated at the University of Copenhagen. After holding various junior positions he was appointed Director of the Chemical Section of the Carlsberg Laboratory in succession to

Kjeldahl. Referred to as 'the father of pH,' his main investigations were biochemical, particularly on amino-acids, proteins, and enzymes.

Sorption. J. W. McBain proposed the term sorption to refer to any type of retention of a material at a surface, especially when the mechanism is not specified. *Ad*sorption is then restricted to the physical process which leads to mono- or multi-layers on the surface, *chemi*-sorption to the corresponding chemical process, and *ab*sorption to the solution of the sorbed material within the solid. There is no clear-cut distinction between these categories.

Soxhlet. Equipment for the continuous extraction of a solid by a solvent. The material to be extracted is usually placed in a porous paper thimble, and continually condensing solvent allowed to percolate through it, and return to the boiling vessel, either continuously or intermittently. Such extraction procedures are frequently encountered in the first stages of isolating natural products from raw materials.

Space group. A term applied to the whole array of symmetry-elements in a crystal framework or lattice. The total number of possible space groups is 230. The atoms in any crystal must be arranged so that they fit into one of these groups. The framework composing a space group is termed a *space lattice*.

Space lattice. A term applied to the array of points in any crystalline structure for which the pattern repeats. By joining these points the crystal can be divided into a series of parallel *unit cells*, each of which contains a complete unit of pattern. The atoms composing the crystal occupy the points in the lattice so that a space lattice affords a convenient means of representing the atomic structure of a crystalline substance. The position of the points relative to each other is found by means of X-ray analysis of the crystal.

Spalling. The general term applied to the breaking up of a refractory with ultimate mechanical failure. Spalling was primarily meant to be the resulting effect of sudden temperature changes on the refractory since the various crystalline forms of some of the constituents have different thermal coefficients of expansion. Insufficient care in heating would result in cracks on the surface of the brick.

Spalling is likely to occur: (1) when there is a high temperature gradient through the brick, especially when the brick contains substances of high coefficients of expansion such as magnesite; (2) when bricks are laid badly, consequent stresses being set up; (3) when there is reaction between the furnace gas or material in the furnace with the constituents of the refractory.

Spark spectrum. See Arc spectrum

Sparteine, $C_{15}H_{26}N_2$. An alkaloid obtained from

broom and yellow lupin seeds. It is a colourless liquid, volatile in steam. Sparingly soluble in water, soluble in alcohol. Dextrorotatory. It resinifies in air. It resembles coniine in its action, but is less poisonous.

Spear pyrites. See Marcasite.

Specific conductance. See Conductivity.

Specific dynamic action. The taking of food has a stimulating effect on the general oxidative processes in the body. It increases the rate of metabolism more than can be accounted for by the calorific value of the food. This phenomenon is called the specific dynamic action of foods. It is more marked with proteins, which increase metabolism by 30% more than would be expected, than with fats and carbohydrates (4-6%), and most marked with the amino-acids glycine, alanine, and phenylalanine. The reason for this is not known.

Specific refractivity. A quantity (r) defined by

$$r = \frac{n^2-1}{n^2+2} \cdot \frac{1}{d}$$

where n is the refractive index of a substance and d its density. The molecular refractivity is equal to the specific refractivity multiplied by the molecular weight.

Specific rotatory power. See Rotatory power, specific.

Spectral sensitization. The process, discovered by Vogel in 1873, by which the natural sensitivity of a photographic silver halide emulsion is extended to light of longer wavelengths, by means of sensitizing dyes. Crystals of silver chloride, bromide and iodide are intrinsically sensitive to ultra-violet and blue light. Spectral sensitizers are adsorbed on to the silver halide crystal surface, and often efficient sensitization can be achieved by partial surface coverage by a monomolecular layer of dye. The physical state of the dye (state of aggregation, surface coverage) may profoundly influence the dye absorption spectrum and hence the type of spectral sensitization obtained.

Using appropriate sensitizers, orthochromatic and infrared sensitive emulsions are produced. For colour photography, tri-pack materials incorporate three sensitive layers sensitized to red, green and blue light.

Spectral sensitizers. Dyes which extend the sensitivity of silver halide emulsions to light of wavelengths beyond the region of natural sensitivity of silver halide. Essential properties for sensitizers include intense light absorption in the appropriate region, powerful adsorption to the grain surface and the ability to transfer the absorbed energy to the conduction band of the crystal. Structurally, the majority of effective dyes are cyanines and merocyanines. Strong sensitizers have planar molecules, although many planar dyes of these classes do not sensitize. One of the earliest effective dyes was erythrosin, not a cyanine, whose spectral sensitivity to green light (orthochromatic) was observed by Eder in 1883.

Spectrochemical series. Ligands arranged in the order of their capacity for causing splittings of d orbitals. The series is $I^- < Br^- < Cl^- < F^- <$ $OH^- < H_2O <$ pyridine $< NH_3 <$ ethylenediamine $< NO_2^- < CN^-$. The degree of splitting of the d orbitals causes changes in magnetism and changes in the spectroscopic peaks originating from d-d transitions.

Specular iron. A variety of haematite.

Speculum metal. An alloy of 66% copper and 34% tin. It is silver-white in colour, extremely hard and brittle, and capable of taking a high polish. It is used in making mirrors, diffraction gratings, etc.

Speiss. A crude cobalt arsenide obtained from the smelting of arsenic-containing ores of nickel, copper and lead.

Spence metal. Used for making medallions, busts, etc. Made by melting iron sulphide with sulphur so as to give a product melting at about 160°.

Sphene, $CaSiTiO_5$. Occurs as dark coloured monoclinic crystals. The independent SiO_4 groups are linked by Ti atoms within octahedral groups of six O atoms, and Ca atoms between groups of seven O atoms. The cleavage is prismatic. It occurs widely as an accessory mineral in granites, syenites, and certain metamorphic rocks.

Spheroidal graphite cast iron (S.G. iron). See Cast iron.

Sphingomyelins. Phosphatides with the structure

$$O \cdot C_{18}H_{33}(OH)NH \cdot R$$
$$O = P-OH$$
$$O \cdot CH_2 \cdot CH_2 \cdot \overset{+}{N} \diagdown \begin{matrix} CH_3 \\ CH_3 \\ CH_3 \end{matrix}$$
$$OH^-$$

where R is a fatty acid radical, usually lignoceric acid, though others are found. Lignoceryl sphingomyelin crystallizes in white tablets or needles in star-like formation, m.p. 196°-198°.

It forms an opalescent solution with water, is insoluble in cold alcohol, acetone, and ether, and soluble in hot alcohol, chloroform, and benzene; $[\alpha]_D^{25} +8·20°$ in a 1:1 mixture of chloroform and methyl alcohol. Sphingomyelins occur abundantly in the brain and to a lesser extent in other animal tissues. They are always found in association with the cerebrosides, which they resemble in many properties, and consequently are not easily separated from them. On hydrolysis they split up into the bases choline and sphingosine, phosphoric acid, and a fatty acid.

Sphingosine, $C_{18}H_{37}NO_2$. A base, forming part

$$CH_3 \cdot [CH_2]_{12} \cdot CH : CH \cdot CH \cdot CH \cdot CH_2OH$$
$$\underset{OH}{|} \quad \underset{NH_2}{|}$$

of the molecules of sphingomyelins and the cerebrosides, from which it splits off on hydrolysis. It crystallizes in needles from ether.

Spiegeleisen. A low grade ferro-manganese containing 5-6% carbon and about 20% manganese. It is used for deoxidation and recarburization in the production of steel.

Spindle oil. The term originally described a stable low viscosity oil used to lubricate textile spindles, but now includes any low viscosity mineral lubricating oil.

Spinel. A term applied to a group of double oxides with the general formula $R^{2+}R_2^{3+}O_4$, the dipositive metal being usually Mg, Fe^{2+}, Zn, or Mn^{2+}, and the tripositive metal Al, Fe^{3+}, Mn^{3+}, or Cr^{3+}. The crystals are cubic, commonly octahedra or dodecahedra. They are double oxides having eight molecules in the unit cell with $a = 8·10$ Å in $MgAl_2O_4$, and $a = 8.40$ Å in Fe_3O_4. The oxygen atoms are in close packing. Each dipositive ion is in tetrahedral co-ordination and each tripositive ion is in octahedral co-ordination. In inverse spinels each dipositive ion is in octahedral co-ordination.

The mineral known as spinel is $MgAl_2O_4$ with hardness 8, sp.gr. 3·5-3·6, m.p. 2135°, refractive index 1·72.

Spin multiplicity, $2S+1$. S is the total spin quantum number of the electronic state. For n unpaired electrons $S = n/2$. When the spin multiplicity is 1 it is called a singlet state; when it is 3 it is called a triplet state, and so on.

Spin quantum number. See Electronic configuration.

Spinthariscope. An instrument devised by Crookes for detecting and counting α-particles by visual observation of a fluorescent screen. Its modern counterpart is the scintillation counter for recording β-particles.

Spirans, spiro-compounds. Bicyclic compounds

with one, and only one, atom common to both rings. An example is spiro[4,5]decane.

The atom common to both rings is called the spiro-atom; this may also be nitrogen, phosphorus, etc.

Spirit of salt. An old name for hydrochloric acid.

Spitzkasten. This type of classifier consists of a series of pyramidal tanks, each succeeding one being bigger and deeper than the last. The pulp, or suspension of solid matter in liquid, which it is desired to classify, is fed into the smallest tank and flows through the system, passing from the top of one tank to the top of the next. Owing to the continuous increase in size of these containers the velocity of the liquid decreases as it passes through the system so that the largest solid particles settle out in the first tank, where the velocity is highest, the smallest in the last tank, where it is lowest, and the intermediate sizes in the intervening tanks. A clear effluent overflows from the top of the final container and the settled solids are discharged from the bottoms of the tanks.

Spodumene, $LiAl(SiO_3)_2$. A monoclinic pyroxene with four molecules in the unit cell. The lithium and aluminium atoms are both surrounded by six oxygen atoms with average distances of Li-O = 2·26 Å and Al-O = 2·07 Å. It is an important source of lithium and its compounds, and has uses in the glass and ceramic industries. The largest deposits are in the pegmatites of the Black Hills, S. Dakota, where enormous crystals, up to 47 ft. long have been found.

Spray drying. This is a method of obtaining a solid in the form of a dry powder by evaporation from liquid droplets containing the substance either in solution or suspension.

A *spray drier* consists of a large diameter cylindrical vessel, usually vertical, into which the solution or slurry is introduced through atomizers as a fine spray. Hot air or combustion gases are fed into the chamber continuously, and because of the very high surface to volume ratio of the droplets, extremely rapid drying of the material occurs. Some separation of the cooled gases and dried product takes place in the vessel itself, the rest is carried out in external separators such as cyclones. The atomizers are an extremely important part of a spray drier, and may take the form of high-pressure nozzles or spinning discs, both of which produce a fine film which subsequently disintegrates.

Spray drying is used for heat-sensitive materials such as food products, and for materials that for other reasons are difficult to dry. It has the advantage that the product is obtained in a form that is easily handled and readily redispersed in a liquid: this is particularly useful with materials such as detergents. Its principal disadvantage is its high cost, due to the fact that all the liquid is removed by the expensive process of evaporation.

Spray ponds. A method of cooling water by atmospheric evaporation. The water to be cooled is sprayed through fine nozzles and collected in open ponds. The method is suitable for small-scale operations only.

Spray tower. The simplest form of scrubber. The gas to be purified passes up the tower and is met by a stream of liquid introduced by a series of sprays. The space inside the tower is empty, no packing being employed.

Spreading pressure. See Surface pressure.

Squalene, $C_{30}H_{50}$. An acyclic triterpene originally found in the livers of elasmobranch fish,

and shown to be of wide occurrence and significance as the natural precursor of cholesterol and of other sterols and triterpenoids. It is the major hydrocarbon of human skin surface lipid, forming about 10% of total lipid. Natural squalene is the all-*trans*-isomer of 2,6,10,15,19,23-hexamethyltetracosa-2,6,10,14, 18,22-hexaene and is a colourless oil, b.p. 261°/9 mm, m.p. − 5·50, d_4^{20} 0·8078, n_D^{20} 1·4516. Hydrogenation affords the saturated hydrocarbon, squalane, $C_{30}H_{62}$, b.p. 224°-226°/3 mm, n_D^{20} 1·4534, d_{20}^{20} 0·8107. Squalene, and especially the more stable squalane, are valuable non-toxic vehicles for cosmetics, and for promoting absorption of drugs applied to the skin.

Squill. The bulb of *Urginea maritima*, a plant indigenous to the Mediterranean countries. It contains a number of glycosides which have an action on the heart similar to that of digitalis. It is used chiefly for its expectorant properties and is an ingredient of many cough mixtures.

Scillaren A is made up of glucose, rhamnose, and scillaridin, $C_{24}H_{30}O_3$, which has one more carbon atom in its skeleton than the other cardiac aglucones. The compound of rhamnose and aglucone is termed proscillaridin A.

Squirrel cage disintegrator, Cage mill. A type of machine particularly useful for the disintegration of fibrous or friable materials. It consists of two or more 'discs,' with rods mounted round the circumference to form a 'cage,' arranged concentrically and rotating in opposite directions. The feed enters at the centre of the system, is thrown outwards by centrifugal force, and is disintegrated by impact with the bars of the cage. The product passes out of the mill through screens in the bottom of the casing.

Stability constant. When a complex is formed in solution between a metal ion and a ligand the equilibrium may be expressed by a constant which is related to the free energy change for the process:

$$M + A \rightleftharpoons MA; \quad K_1 = \frac{[MA]}{[M][A]}$$

K_1 is the stability constant, the terms in the brackets representing activities. Charges have been dropped for the sake of clarity and

$$-\Delta G = RT \ln K_1$$

Step-wise equilibria may also be expressed in this way, e.g.

$$M + A \rightleftharpoons MA; \quad K_1 = \frac{[MA]}{[M][A]}$$

$$MA + A \rightleftharpoons MA_2; \quad K_2 = \frac{[MA_2]}{[MA][A]}$$

$$MA_{(n-1)} + A \rightleftharpoons MA_n; \quad K_n = \frac{[MA_n]}{[MA_{(n-1)}][A]}$$

$K_1, K_2 \ldots K_n$ being called the step-wise stability constants. Overall stability constants, designated β, may be evaluated by multiplication of the individual stability constants, e.g.

$$M + 2A \rightleftharpoons MA_2; \quad \beta_2 = \frac{[MA_2]}{[M][A]^2} = K_1 K_2$$

Stabilizer. A distillation unit in which undesirable low-boiling liquids or gases are removed from a mixture by fractionating under pressure by means of which a sharp cut may be obtained. In particular it is applied to the working up of petroleum products in which connexion a series of stabilizers is frequently employed to remove several sharp fractions. The individual units are then frequently known as debutanizers, depropanizers, etc., according to the overhead product obtained.

Stachydrine, N-Methylprolinemethylbetaine, $C_7H_{13}NO_2$. Crystallizes with one molecule of water, m.p. (anhydrous) 235°, with decomposition. Decomposes in air, soluble in water and alcohol. A base obtained from the tubers of *Stachys tuberifera*, the leaves of the orange tree and other plant sources. It has also been obtained by methylating proline.

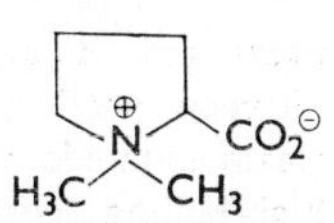

Stachyose, $C_{24}H_{42}O_2$. A tetrasaccharide found in ash manna and elsewhere. It has the raffinose structure with an extra galactose unit added. It tastes quite sweet, has m.p. 167°, $[\alpha]_D^{25} + 123°$.

Stahl, George Ernest. Born at Ansbach in 1660. In 1687 he became physician to the Duke of Weimar. He wrote on chemistry, and employed the hypothetical phlogiston to explain combustion and many other chemical operations. He died in 1734. See Thomson's 'History,' Vol. I, p. 250.

Stalagmometer. An apparatus for comparing the surface tensions or interfacial tensions of liquids by comparing the masses of drops formed at a given orifice.

Standard electrode or half cell. An electrode which produces a standard e.m.f. Electrode potentials are normally related to the hydrogen electrode (*q.v.*) but in practice reference is made to the calomel electrode.

Stanley, Wendell Meredith (1904-). Stanley was born in Indiana, educated at the University of Illinois, and worked largely at the Rockefeller Institute for Medical Research. He was the first to show that a virus, tobacco mosaic virus, could be obtained crystalline, and for this he shared the Nobel Prize for chemistry in 1946.

Stannane, Tin hydride, SnH_4. A colourless, poisonous gas, m.p. $-150°$, b.p. $-52°$, prepared by reaction of stannic chloride with lithium aluminium hydride. It is rather unstable, decomposing immediately at 150°, and acts as a reducing agent.

Stannates. See Tin hydroxides.

Stannic compounds, Stannous compounds. Tin (IV) and tin (II) compounds respectively.

Starch $(C_6H_{10}O_5)_x$. The carbohydrate which is being continuously formed and broken down in the living cell and which also serves as a reserve material. It is, like cellulose, made up of a long chain of glucopyranose units joined together through oxygen by α-glucosidic bonds. It yields glucose alone on complete hydrolysis, maltose when broken down by enzymes, and dextrin under other conditions.

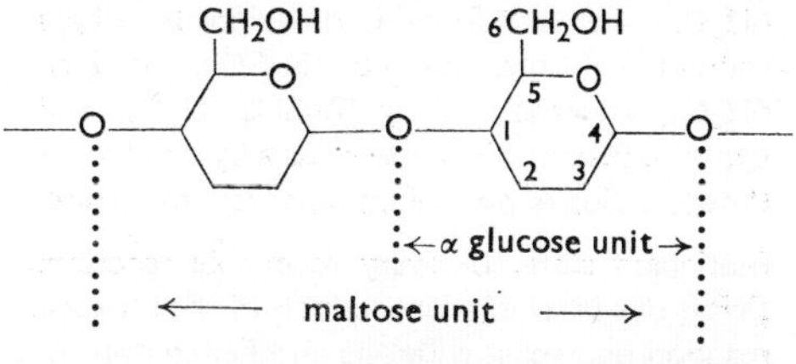

Starch consists of amylose, which is water-soluble and retrogrades on concentration forming an insoluble precipitate, and amylopectin, a mucilaginous substance with the characteristic paste-forming properties. Amylose is composed of long straight chains containing 200-1000 glucose units linked by α-1,4-glycoside links; amylopectin consists of comparatively short chains (about 20 glucose units) cross-linked by α-1,6-glycoside links. Both amylose and amylopectin have been synthesized from glucose-1-phosphate by the action of the enzyme phosphorylase.

Starch is insoluble in cold water, but in hot water the granules gelatinize to form an opalescent dispersion. It is made from corn, wheat, potatoes, rice, and other cereals by various physical processes such as steeping, milling, and sedimentation. It is used as an adhesive, for sizing paper and cloth, as an inert diluent in foods and drugs, and for many other purposes.

Starch can now be split into amylose and amylopectin by a commercial process based on selective solubilities. Amylose is used for making edible films, and amylopectin for textile sizing and finishing, and as a thickener in foods.

Stas, Jean Servais. Born at Louvain in 1813 he graduated as a doctor of medicine, after which he became a student of Dumas in Paris and worked on glucosides and other organic compounds. In association with Dumas he redetermined the atomic weight of carbon with greater accuracy than had previously been achieved. He left Paris in 1840 to become professor of chemistry in the École Royale Militaire in Brussels. He became Vice-President of the Council of Public Health and took part in much other public work; he received many scientific and other honours, and died in December, 1891. His great work was the very accurate determination, between 1843 and 1876, of the atomic weights of oxygen, silver, nitrogen, sulphur, chlorine, bromine, iodine, potassium, lithium, lead, and carbon. See *Chem. Soc. Memorial Lectures*, 1893-1900.

Stassfurt deposits. Deposits of various salts found at Stassfurt, Saxony. The salts are found in beds under alluvial deposits, and are mined for the production of potassium salts. The chief source of the latter is carnallite, KCl, $MgCl_2$, $6H_2O$. Other salts found in the deposits include sodium chloride, kainite (K_2SO_4, $MgSO_4$, $6H_2O$), kieserite (chiefly $MgSO_4$, H_2O), and gypsum. Bromine is prepared as a by-product of the extraction of potassium salts from carnallite.

Stationary state. In every reversible reaction, that is one in which the products of the forward reaction may react with one another to re-form the original reactants, a condition is reached when the rate of the forward reaction is exactly equal to that of the backward reaction. Thus, in the reaction $A + B \rightarrow C + D$, the forward reaction proceeds very rapidly at first, because A and B are present in large concentrations compared with C and D (see Mass action, Law of). After some time the concentration of C and D has had time to grow larger, and the backward reaction proceeds more quickly: $C + D \rightarrow A + B$. Eventually, the rates of the forward and backward reactions become equal, so that superficially no further reaction is occurring, for the concentrations of A, B, C, and D remain constant. This equilibrium state is often referred to as a stationary state. See also Photostationary state.

Stationary states of electrons. The stable electronic arrangements in atoms or molecules. Transitions between stationary states give rise to absorptions in the ultra-violet, visible or near infrared regions of the electromagnetic spectrum.

Staudinger, Hermann (1887-1965). Born in Worms, Staudinger studied at several German universities. He became professor of chemistry at the Technische Hochschule, Zürich in 1912 and at Freiburg in 1926. He was awarded the Nobel Prize in 1953 for his work with polymers and received many other awards. See *Nature*, 1965, **208**, 626.

Steam distillation. Distillation in a current of steam with the object of distilling away and so removing some particular constituent from a mixture, or of avoiding too high a temperature during distillation. The operation of steam distillation, as normally carried out, consists of distilling a mixture of two immiscible liquids (e.g. of aniline and water) in a current of steam. The ratio of the weights of the two substances distilling will be $\dfrac{m_1 p_1}{m_2 p_2}$, where m_1 and m_2 are the molecular weights of the two substances and p_1 and p_2 are their respective vapour pressures at the distillation temperature. In the steam distillation of organic substances from their mixtures with water, the relatively high molecular weight of the organic substance often results in its presence in considerable amount in the distillate, in spite of the fact that its vapour pressure at the distillation temperature may be relatively small.

Steam-refined asphaltic bitumens. Asphaltic bitumens produced by straight distillation with steam and under vacuum and which contain the high-boiling components of the asphaltic residue in an unchanged state.

Stearic acid, n-Octadecanoic acid, $C_{18}H_{36}O_2$; $CH_3 \cdot [CH_2]_{16} \cdot COOH$. Crystallizes in leaflets, m.p. 69·6°, b.p. 376°, with decomposition.

Soluble in ether and hot alcohol, insoluble in water. Stearic acid is one of the most common fatty acids, and occurs as glycerides in most animal and vegetable fats, particularly in the harder fats with high melting-points. A solid mixture of stearic and palmitic acids, 'stearine,' is used for making candles. The soaps are the sodium and potassium salts of stearic and palmitic acids.

Steatite. A compact variety of talc (*q.v.*). Sp.gr. 2·6-2·7, hardness 1-2. Specific heat at 100°, 0·2-0·3. Thermal conductivity 0·23-0·28 kg-cal./hr./sq.dm./°C/dm.thickness. Used formerly for the tips of gas-burners, now for electrical insulators, steatitic porcelain, steatite ware, sparking plugs. The chief sources of supply are India, Sardinia, and the U.S.A.

Steel. The name given to alloys of iron and carbon containing from 0·05 to 1·5% carbon. Harmful impurities include sulphur and phosphorus normally specified as 0·045% maximum. All steels contain about 0·5% manganese to combine with the sulphur as MnS and so prevent the formation of the embrittling FeS. The strength and hardness of steels increase with increasing carbon while the toughness and ductility fall. Thus mild steel, 0·1-0·2% carbon, which is tough is used for sheets, plates, girders and beams. Medium carbon steels, 0·3-0·4% carbon, are used where a compromise between toughness and strength is desired, e.g. high-duty components. High carbon steels, 0·6% carbon and over, are used as tool steels, since hardness is their main property. Mild steels are used in the normalized (i.e. air cooled) condition; medium carbon steels may be used in the normalized condition or may be quenched to give increased strength; high carbon steels are always quench hardened. Only mild steels can be welded without special precautions.

Alloy steels are steels containing deliberate additions of alloying elements over and above the amounts which are residual from the steel-making process. Small quantities, 1 or 2% of nickel, chromium, manganese and silicon are commonly added for improved quench hardening. Such steels may be quenched in oil in place of water, with less danger of cracking; 1-3% of nickel gives improved toughness especially at low temperatures. Carbide formers such as chromium (up to 18%), tungsten (up to 18%) and molybdenum (up to 10%) are added to high carbon steels to give wear resistance due to the alloy carbides. High-speed steels for cutting tools are based on the composition, 0·7% C, 18% W, 4% Cr, 1% V; 1% W may be replaced by $\frac{5}{8}$% Mo. Chromium in low carbon steels forms a solid solution with iron and in this condition it forms a protective invisible passive oxide layer on the surface giving corrosion and scaling resistance: 3-25% Cr is used.

Austenitic steels are steels which retain the face-centred cubic structure right down to room temperature. (Normally the structure of steel changes to body-centred cubic at around 700° on cooling.) For this reason these steels cannot be hardened by quenching. There are two main groups:

1. For corrosion resistance; see Stainless steel (below).

2. For wear resistance (Hadfield steel). This steel contains 12% manganese and 1·2% carbon. The austenite is metastable and abrasion of the surface causes it to break down and form hard wear resistant martensite. It is used for crushing plant, mechanical digger bucket edges and railway crossings.

Stainless steel. The name given to a group of chromium or chromium-nickel steels showing an unusually high resistance to corrosion by the atmosphere and many chemical reagents. In order to achieve this resistance to corrosion at least 12% chromium is necessary. Stainless steels may be classified according to the metallographic structure of the steel as follows: (1) Ferric steels, (2) Martensitic steels, and (3) Austenitic steels.

(1) Ferritic steels are only slightly hardenable being mainly straight chromium steels with low carbon contents, e.g. <0·1% C, 12 to 14% Cr, and are used for indoor ornamental work, general aircraft fittings, and turbine blades. This group may also be known as Stainless Irons.

(2) The martensitic steels are capable of being hardened and tempered and have higher carbon contents and sometimes small percentages of nickel. Typical steels:

% C	% Cr	% Ni	Uses
0·2	12	—	Steam valves, piston rods.
0·3	12	—	Table cutlery, surgical instruments, tools.
0·4 to 2·0	12	—	Springs and rolling bearings under corrosive conditions.
0·1	18	2	Valves and fittings subjected to high temperature and high pressure steam.

(3) Austenitic stainless steels are based on the 18% Cr, 8% Ni, 0·1% max. carbon alloy. The nickel is an austenite stabilizer and the chromium provides the corrosion resistance; 1% titanium is present in 'welding quality' stainless to prevent weld decay (*q.v.*). Small quantities of strong carbide formers such as molybdenum,

titanium, vanadium and niobium are added to give good creep resistance by a precipitation hardening mechanism; 3% molybdenum is added for improved acid resistance.

A 'soft austenitic steel' containing 12% chromium and 12% nickel is less difficult to fabricate and is used for tableware and ornamental work.

Steel is produced by refining pig iron by (a) the Bessemer process or (b) by the open hearth process. Highly alloyed steels are made from selected materials and scrap using the electric arc furnace or the high-frequency induction furnace.

For specified composition of steels see British Standards 970 and 1449.

Stellite. An alloy of approximate composition 45-50% Co, 25-30% Cr, 15-20% W, 2·5% C. It is used as a cutting tool tipping material, but differs from many other non-ferrous cutting alloys which are sintered and cemented as it can be cast. It is capable of being welded, and may be applied as a coating to a softer material to resist abrasion.

Stercobilin. A pigment excreted in the faeces, identical in structure to one form of urobilin (*q.v.*).

Stereochemistry. The study of the spatial arrangements of atoms in molecules and complexes.

Stereoisomerism. See Isomerism and Conformation.

Stereospecific reactions. Reactions in which bonds are broken and made at a single asymmetric atom (usually, but not necessarily carbon), and which lead largely to a single stereoisomer, are said to be stereospecific. If the configuration is altered in the process, the reaction is said to involve *inversion of configuration*. If the configuration remains the same, the transformation occurs with *retention of configuration*.

Steric hindrance. A term intended to denote the influence exerted on a reacting group by the spatial arrangement of neighbouring atoms. It was originally used to explain the difficulty experienced in forming the esters of certain benzoic acids having groups substituted in both ortho positions, the substituting groups being pictured as blocking the approach to the carboxyl group by reason of their size. Many similar cases of the non-reactive nature of other di-ortho substituted benzene derivatives were explained in this way. It is now realized that the size of the substituting groups in these cases is much less important than the polar effects they produce in the molecule, which affect the

reactivity of neighbouring groups. On the other hand, the optical activity of the di-ortho substituted derivatives of diphenyl is probably due entirely to the size of the substituting groups, which obstruct the free rotation of the benzene rings about the single bond joining them and so produce an asymmetric molecule. This is a case of true steric hindrance.

Steroids. A generic term for substances having the nuclear carbon skeleton of the sterols, or a very similar structure. The natural steroids, which arise from the oxidative cyclization of squalene, include sterols, bile acids, sex hormones, adrenocortical hormones, cardiac-active glycosides, sapogenins, alkaloids, and insect hormones such as ecdysone. Many synthetic steroids are known, and some of these are important drugs. See 'Steroids', by L. F. Fieser and M. Fieser (Reinhold, 1959).

Sterols. The sterols are unsaturated alcohols, possessing the following ring structure, which is numbered as shown:

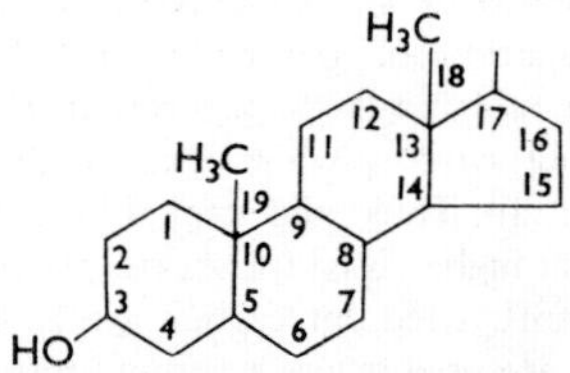

They contain one or more double bonds, one of them normally being between carbon atoms 5 and 6, and have an alkyl side chain attached in position 17. They are found in every animal and plant cell, with the exception of bacterial cells, partly in the free condition and partly esterified with the higher fatty acids. They can be isolated by hydrolysing the fat fraction with alcoholic alkali and extracting the unsaponifiable portion with ether or petroleum ether.

Stibine. See Antimony hydride.

Stibnite, Sb_2S_3. The only important antimony ore. It is found in China, Japan, Hungary, and elsewhere, and very fine crystals have been obtained from Japan. The crystals are orthorhombic. It commonly occurs in confused aggregates of acicular crystals. Hardness 2, sp.gr. 4·6. The crystals are transparent to infrared radiation; their colour is a steel-grey with a metallic lustre.

Stibophen, $C_{12}H_4Na_5O_{16}S_4Sb,7H_2O$, sodium

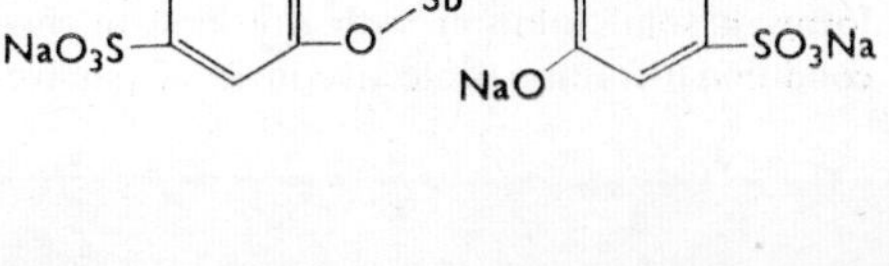

antimony bispyrocatechol-3,5-sodium disulphonate. A colourless crystalline powder, soluble in water, insoluble in alcohol and other organic solvents. The aqueous solution goes yellow and oxidizes in air. It is used in the treatment of bilharziasis and other diseases caused by protozoa.

Stieglitz, Julius Oscar (1867-1937). Born at Hoboken, New Jersey, Stieglitz was educated at Karlsruhe and Berlin. Joining the staff of Chicago University in 1892 as an unsalaried docent, he was appointed professor of organic chemistry in 1905, Director of the Chemical Laboratories in 1912, and Chairman of the Department of Chemistry in 1915, becoming professor emeritus in 1933. Author of a standard work on qualitative analysis, he wrote many papers on molecular rearrangements, catalysis, indicators, and the theory of colour production, stereoisomerism, and the application of the electronic theory to organic chemistry. He was also keenly interested in the relation of chemistry to medicine.

Stigmasterol, 24α-ethylcholesta-5,22-dien-3β-ol, $C_{29}H_{48}O$. Crystallizes with one molecule of

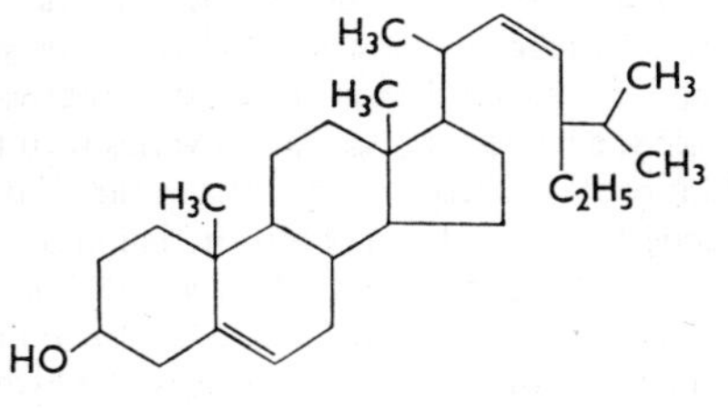

water from 95% alcohol, m.p. 170°, $[\alpha]_D - 51°$ in chloroform. Isolated in 1906 from *Physostigma venenosum* (Calabar bean), and readily obtained from a number of plant sources, notably soya beans, Because of its abundance as a phytosterol, it has served as a starting material for the synthesis of steroid hormones.

Stilbene, *trans-sym*-Diphenylethylene, $C_{14}H_{12}$.

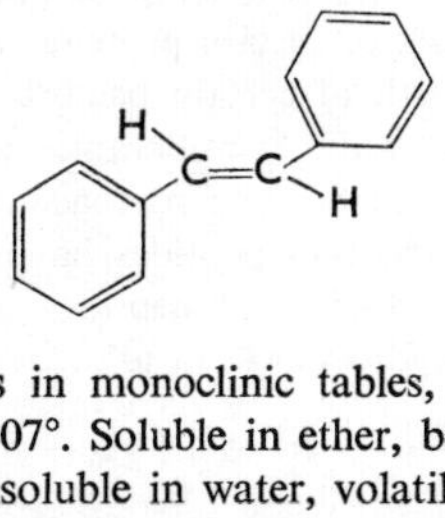

Crystallizes in monoclinic tables, m.p. 124°, b.p. 306°-307°. Soluble in ether, benzene, hot alcohol. Insoluble in water, volatile in steam. It can be prepared by the action of benzyl magnesium bromide on benzaldehyde, acidifying the product with sulphuric acid and distilling, and by many other methods. Derivatives of stilbene are important in the dye industry and some have oestrogenic activity (See Stil-

boestrol). Ultra-violet light converts stilbene into its *cis* isomer, isostilbene, a yellow oil.

Stilbite. A zeolite $(Na_2Ca)(Al_2Si_6)O_{16} \cdot 6H_2O$ used for softening hard water.

Stilboestrol, 4,4′-dihydroxy-αβ-diethylstilbene, $C_{18}H_{20}O_2$. White crystals, m.p. 168°-171°, very

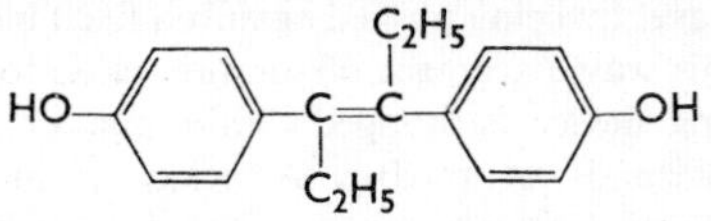

slightly soluble in water, readily soluble in alcohol and organic solvents. Prepared from deoxyanisoin by ethylation, conversion to the alcohol, dehydration, and demethylation. It is an oestrogenic substance which is highly active when administered orally. It is used for treating menopausal symptoms, for the suppression of lactation, and for palliative treatment of cancer of the prostate and breast.

Still. Any apparatus or plant in which distillation is carried out.

Stoicheiometric. A stoicheiometric compound is a compound in which the ratio of the number of atoms to each other, as determined from the atomic weights, is a ratio of small whole numbers. In nonstoicheiometric compounds this is not so, owing to there being defects in the crystal lattice, or to the replacement of atoms of one element by another.

Stokes's law. The rate of fall of particles through a liquid depends on the difference in density of the two phases, the viscosity of the liquid, the size of the particle and the gravity constant. These factors are related by Stokes's law,

$$v = \frac{2r^2(s-s')g}{9\eta}$$

where v is the velocity of sedimentation of the particle of radius r and density s; s' is the density of the liquid, and η its viscosity; g is the gravity constant. When this is applied to particles of colloidal dimensions the velocity v is found to be so small as to be more than counteracted by convection, etc., so that a colloidal sol can never separate out without aggregation of the particles. See also Colloids, Sedimentation.

Stop-end retorts. This type of retort for gas manufacture is D shaped (with the diameter as base). The dimensions are about 10 ft. long with an end section of about 21 in. × 15 in. The capacity is about ¾ cwt a charge with a throughput of about 15 tons/day.

They are set in arches containing 2-8 retorts, and are suitable for small works only.

Stopped flow spectrophotometric system. An instrument first developed by biochemists, which is used in the investigation of the rates of chemical reactions, the half-lives of which lie between 5×10^{-3} and 10 seconds. Two solutions contained in syringes are forced together tangentially in a Teflon (or Perspex) mixing chamber and the effluent flows into a third (stopping) syringe which is abruptly stopped in its travel by being pushed against a fixed block. In this way a segment of solution close to the mixing device is stopped within one or two milliseconds of mixing. A beam of monochromatic light passing through this portion of solution allows changes in optical density to be measured. After amplification of the signal, a trace of optical density as a function of time is relayed to an oscilloscope which may then be photographed.

Extensive use of this device is made in both inorganic and organic chemistry.

See 'Techniques in Organic Chemistry,' Vol. 8, part 2, ed. A. Weissberger, J. Wiley and Sons, New York, London, 1963; 'Fast Reactions in Solution,' by E. F. Caldin, Blackwell, Oxford, 1964.

Stop point. A term used in laboratory distillation tests. The percentage distillate obtained at a stop point is that amount obtained when the source of heat has been removed from the flask at the specified temperature and the apparatus allowed to drain for two minutes.

Storax. A semi-solid balsam obtained from the trunk of *Liquidamber orientalis*, a tree growing in Asia Minor. It contains upwards of 30% of balsamic acids, chiefly present as esters of cinnamic acid. Its principal use is as an ingredient of friar's balsam or compound tincture of benzoin.

Straight run. A term used to denote fractions produced from crude petroleum by distillation but not cracked or reformed.

Strain hardening. Another name for work hardening (*q.v.*).

Stramonium. The dried leaves and flowering tops and the seeds of *Datura stramonium* contain the alkaloid hyoscyamine to which this drug owes its medicinal properties. It is used chiefly for the relief of asthma, and for this purpose, in addition to being administered internally, the leaf is smoked in cigarettes or burnt in combination with powdered lobelia, tea leaves, and potassium nitrate, and the vapour arising is inhaled.

Strass. A dense glass used for making imitation gems and also for jewels to be cemented to vases and other ornamental ware. It is chiefly characterized by its high but variable refractive index.

Stream double refraction. Some colloidal sols such as aged vanadium pentoxide, whose dispersed particles are rod-shaped, are non-polarizing, as can be shown by placing the sol between crossed nicols, there being total extinction. When the liquid is stirred, however, or made to flow, polarization takes place, the stream lines being shown in a brightly illuminated image. This is due to the orientation of the rod-shaped molecules on stirring. See Anisotropic, Tactosols.

Streaming potential. A potential difference is set up if a liquid is forced through a diaphragm by pressure; this is the streaming potential. The streaming potential is most easily measured by forcing water through a capillary tube of the substance under examination and determining the potential difference between electrodes placed at each end of the tube. The streaming potential is the converse of the electro-osmotic flow.

Strengths of acids and bases. The strength of an aqueous acid is its ability to give hydroxonium ions (H_3O^+) and that of an aqueous base its ability to give hydroxyl ions or to accept protons. For Lewis acids and bases, acidic and basic character are measured by the tendency to react with standard bases and acids respectively. Since the degree of dissociation varies with the dilution, it is necessary to compare the relative strengths of acids or bases in solutions of equivalent concentrations. This can be done by measuring the concentrations of hydroxonium ion or of hydroxyl ion. Those acids like hydrochloric and nitric which are largely dissociated into their ions are strong acids; those like acetic and tartaric which are only slightly dissociated are weak acids. Potassium, sodium, and barium hydroxides which are largely dissociated are strong bases, whilst the slightly dissociated ammonium hydroxide is a weak base.

Streptogenin. The name was originally given to a peptide of unknown composition, present in tryptic digests of certain proteins, and needed for the growth of certain bacteria. It is now known that, while considerable specificity of structure is needed for streptogenin activity, a number of different peptides have this effect, including oxytocin and peptides obtained by the partial hydrolysis of insulin.

Streptomycin. $C_{21}H_{39}N_7O_{12}$. A complex organic base, produced by *Streptomyces griseus*. It is used in the form of its hydrochloride or sulphate, both white solids, usually containing 600 units per mg. It is active against both Gram-negative and Gram-positive bacteria. It is used chiefly, in combination with other drugs, in the treatment of tuberculosis, and to combat infections due to organisms not susceptible to other antibiotics. Disadvantages are that bacteria may become resistant to the

drug during treatment, and that it has some toxic action.

Streptomycin B (mannosidostreptomycin) has a mannose molecule attached to the methyl-glucosamine group, and is the first antibacterial product made, but is enzymatically converted to streptomycin later in the fermentation.

Dihydrostreptomycin, in which the CHO group in the middle ring is replaced by CH_2OH, is made by the catalytic reduction of streptomycin, and has similar antibacterial properties.

Stripping. The separation of the more volatile component(s) of a liquid mixture from the less volatile component(s) in such a way that the latter is obtained in a pure state, but the former not necessarily so. Stripping may be carried out either by a process of fractional distillation or by bringing the mixture into contact with an inert gas into which the light material will diffuse and be carried away. A *stripping column* or *stripper* is used in either case. This is similar to a rectifying column except that the feed is introduced at the top, instead of part way up, and no reflux is employed. If an inert gas is being used it is introduced at the bottom of the column and no reboiler is necessary.

Stripping is used for such purposes as the removal of benzole from the oil used to absorb it from coal gas and the removal of *light ends* from petroleum fractions. In both cases steam is used as the stripping agent. See Rectification.

Strontianite. This mineral is essentially stron-

tium carbonate, $SrCO_3$; white orthorhombic crystals, sp.gr. 3·7, hardness $3\frac{1}{2}$-4. It is used as a source of strontium compounds.

Strontium, Sr. At.no. 38, At.wt. 87·63; m.p. 771°, b.p. 1366°, d 2·50. Occurs in nature as the carbonate, strontianite, and as the sulphate, celestine. The metal is obtained by the reduction of the oxide with aluminium in an evacuated steel tube at 1000°. The metal may also be obtained by the electrolysis of fused strontium chloride, or, better, a mixture of strontium and potassium chlorides.

Strontium is a silvery-white metal, yellowish if impure. It crystallizes in the cubic system with the cubic close-packed structure, $a = 6·07$ Å. The metal reacts vigorously with water, and on warming with hydrogen, oxygen, nitrogen, or the halogens, with the formation of the corresponding hydride, oxide, etc. It dissolves readily in dilute acids with the evolution of hydrogen.

Strontium and strontium compounds are used in firework manufacture and in electronics.

Strontium carbonate, $SrCO_3$. Occurs naturally as strontianite. Prepared by the action of carbon dioxide on the oxide or hydroxide, or by passing the gas into a solution of a strontium salt, when the carbonate is precipitated. Strontium carbonate crystallizes in the rhombic system, changing over at 820° into a trigonal form. On strongly heating strontium carbonate is decomposed, with the formation of SrO.

Strontium chloride, $SrCl_2$. The anhydrous chloride is obtained directly from the elements, or by passing chlorine over the heated oxide, or hydrogen chloride over the heated oxide or carbonate. From aqueous solutions hexa-, di-, and monohydrates are obtained. It has m.p. 873°; solubility, 55·5 g of the hexahydrate in 100 g water at 25°.

Strontium halides, SrX_2. These are very similar to the calcium halides. Strontium fluoride, m.p. 1450°, b.p. 2489°, is almost insoluble in water. The bromide, m.p. 643°, and iodide, m.p. 402°, are extremely soluble in water and fairly soluble in alcohol.

Strontium hydroxide, $Sr(OH)_2$. Obtained as the octahydrate by crystallization of aqueous solutions of the oxide. This salt effloresces with the formation of $Sr(OH)_2$, H_2O, the monohydrate, and at 100° gives the anhydrous hydroxide.

Strontium hydroxide is fairly readily soluble in water, and the aqueous solutions are strongly basic.

Strontium nitrate, $Sr(NO_3)_2$. Prepared by the action of nitric acid on strontium carbonate. It crystallizes as a tetrahydrate but becomes anhydrous at 31·3°. Solubility at 20°, 70·8 g in 100 g water.

Strontium oxide, SrO. Formed by the ignition of the carbonate at high temperatures, or more readily by the ignition of the hydroxide or nitrate.

The oxide is soluble in water with the formation of the hydroxide. It has m.p. 2430°.

Strontium peroxide, SrO_2. Prepared from the monoxide and oxygen at a dull red heat under a pressure of 125 kg/cm². It is very similar in properties to barium peroxide. The hydrated peroxide is obtained by adding hydrogen peroxide to a cold saturated solution of strontium hydroxide. The crystalline precipitate has the formula $SrO_2, 8H_2O$. On gentle heating it loses water to give the anhydrous peroxide.

Strontium sulphate, $SrSO_4$. Occurs naturally as the mineral celestine. May be prepared by dissolving the oxide, hydroxide, or carbonate in sulphuric acid, or by the addition of a sulphate solution to a strontium salt solution, when the sulphate is precipitated. It is not so insoluble as barium sulphate; the solubility is about 1 g per litre.

Strophanthidin, $C_{23}H_{32}O_6$. A cardiac aglucone,

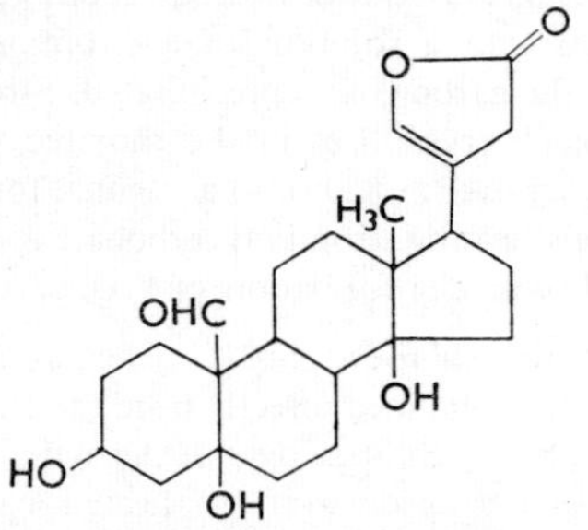

forming the non-carbohydrate portion of strophanthin and other strophanthus glucosides.

Strophanthus. The dried ripe seeds of *Strophanthus kombé* from which the natives of East Africa formerly prepared arrow poison. It contains a mixture of glycosides, and is used as a source of strophanthin-K, which is a standardized mixture of glycosides, equivalent in potency to 40% of that of ouabain. It has an action on the heart similar to that of digitalis, but is absorbed more rapidly; it strengthens the action of the heart and increases cardiac output.

Strutt, John William. See Rayleigh.

Strychnine, $C_{21}H_{22}N_2O_2$. Strychnine is the

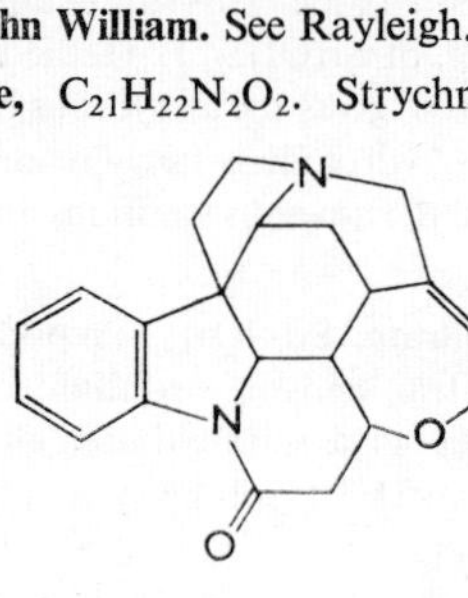

principal alkaloid of *Nux vomica* and other plants. Colourless prisms, m.p. 270°-280°, almost insoluble in water, soluble in chloroform. A solution in alcohol has $[\alpha]_D$ −105°. The hydrochloride is water soluble.

It stimulates all parts of the nervous system and in large doses produces convulsions. Due to its bitter taste it is used as a tonic, but is now largely abandoned as a therapeutic agent. It is used for killing vermin.

Styphnic acid, 2,4,6-Trinitroresorcinol, C_6H_3-N_3O_8. Yellow crystals, m.p. 178°, obtained

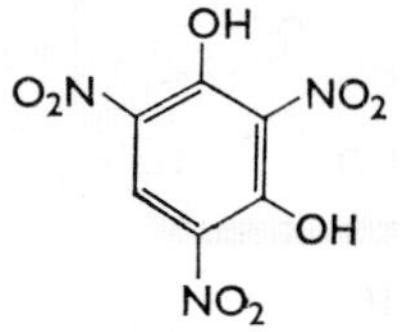

by nitrating resorcinol; sparingly soluble in water, soluble in alcohol and ether. Has properties similar to those of picric acid. Its salts are more violent explosives than the picrates, and lead styphnate (*q.v.*) is an initiator.

Styrene, C_8H_8. Colourless aromatic liquid,

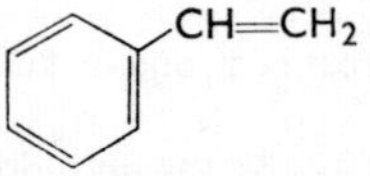

b.p. 146°, sp.gr. 0·925 at 0°. Insoluble in water, miscible in all proportions with alcohol and ether. Polymerizes on heating to a glassy resinous substance, metastyrene, which regenerates styrene on heating. Occurs in liquid storax. Most conveniently prepared by treating cinnamic acid with hydriodic acid and then heating the product with aqueous potash.

Styrene is manufactured by alkylating benzene with ethylene at 95° using aluminium chloride as catalyst; the resulting ethylbenzene is then purified and dehydrogenated in the presence of steam over a metal oxide catalyst at 600°. Styrene is used almost exclusively for the manufacture of polymers, of which the most important are polystyrene and styrene-butadiene rubber.

Styrene-butadiene rubber (SBR or GR-S). The most widely used general-purpose synthetic rubber. An emulsion copolymer containing 25% styrene and 75% butadiene, it is completely random containing both *cis*- and *trans*-1,4-butadiene sequences as well as some 1,2-sequences (see Polyisoprene). It does not crystallize on stretching, hence requires the presence of a reinforcing filler to attain high tensile strength. It is less resilient than natural rubber, being stiffer and having a greater heat build-up when used for tyres.

Sub-boric acid, $(OH)_2B\text{—}B(OH)_2$. Prepared by the hydrolysis of boron subchloride, B_2Cl_4, and $(Me_2N)_2B\text{—}B(NMe_2)_2$ which results from the action of sodium on $(Me_2N)_2BCl$. The free acid has been prepared by hydrolysis of an ester. Solutions of sub-boric acid are strong reducing agents. Used for the preparation of the diboron tetrahalides.

Suberic acid, $C_8H_{14}O_4$, $HOOC\cdot[CH_2]_6\cdot COOH$. Colourless needles, m.p. 140°. Sparingly soluble (0·16%) in water. It is obtained by the action of nitric acid on cork or castor oil, and by the electrolysis of the potassium salt of glutaric ester.

Suberin. The cork-like material occurring in the cell walls of higher plants. Commercial cork comes from the periderm of the cork oak. Suberin resembles cutin in being composed of a mixture of fatty acids and their soaps and esters.

Sublimation. Strictly the volatilization of a solid substance into the vapour state without passing through a liquid phase. In practice a substance may melt but the vapour may pass directly into the solid state on cooling; the process is then also called sublimation. These principles are utilized in the purification of suitable solid organic compounds as an alternative to crystallization or distillation.

Sublimation point. The temperature at which the vapour pressure above a solid is equal to the external pressure, e.g. the atmospheric pressure, is called the sublimation point, or sublimation temperature.

Submicron. A term proposed by Zsigmondy to describe particles invisible in the ordinary microscope but sufficiently large to appear in the field of the ultra-microscope. The size of a submicron thus lies between 10 mμ and 1μ. See Colloids, Micron, Ultramicroscope.

Substitution reactions. Reactions in which there is replacement of one atom or group in a molecule by another atom or group. An example from organic chemistry is the chlorination of benzene to give chlorobenzene in which one of the hydrogen atoms is substituted by a chlorine atom. Nucleophilic reactions are named as S_N1 (substitution, nucleophilic, monomolecular) and S_N2 (bimolecular) reactions and electrophilic reactions are designated S_E1 or S_E2.

Octahedral substitution reactions (e.g. those involving cobalt (III) complexes) may proceed by both S_N1 or S_N2 reactions. In the S_N1 case a slow dissociative mechanism (bond breaking) is thought to take place where there is extension of the metal-ligand bond to a critical distance with a lowering of co-ordination number. Reaction with the substituting ligand then yields the product. In S_N2 reactions direct participation of the incoming group causes the co-ordination number of the transition state intermediate to increase. Here bond making and bond breaking are equally important. Substitution reactions of square planar complex, e.g. those involving platinum (II) complexes, have also been shown to proceed via S_N1 and S_N2 reactions.

See 'Mechanisms of Inorganic Reactions,' by F. Basolo and R. G. Pearson, J. Wiley and Sons, New York, 1958; 'Structure and Mechanism in Organic Chemistry,' by C. K. Ingold, Cornell University Press, Ithaca, 1954.

Substrate. The substrate in an enzymic reaction is the substance on which the enzyme acts and which is activated by the enzyme.

Subtilin. A polypeptide, with antibiotic properties, produced by a strain of *B. subtilis*. It inhibits *in vitro* the growth of a number of pathogens, including *M. tuberculosis*, and is relatively non-toxic, but has been a failure clinically, probably due to its insolubility and failure to be absorbed.

Successive reactions, Law of. This law, discovered by Ostwald, states that a system never passes from a less stable condition into the most stable condition directly, but through conditions of intermediate stability.

Succinic acid. Crystallizes in colourless prisms, m.p. 185°, b.p. 235°. Soluble in hot water; moderately soluble in cold water and alcohol, sparingly soluble in ether. It occurs in amber, algae, lichens, sugar cane, beets, and other plants and is formed during the fermentation of sugar, tartrates, malates, and other substances by a variety of yeasts, moulds, and bacteria. Manufactured by the catalytic reduction of maleic acid or by heating ethylene dicyanide with acids or alkalis. Forms an anhydride when heated at 235°. Forms both acid and neutral salts and esters. Its salts are all soluble in water except the barium, calcium, silver, and basic iron (III) salts, which are sparingly soluble. The metals of the yttrium group of rare earths can be separated by crystallization of their succinates. Used in the manufacture of succinic anhydride.

Succinic anhydride. A white crystalline solid, m.p. 119·5°, b.p. 261°. Decomposed by water; soluble in chloroform; sparingly soluble in ether. Manufactured by heating succinic acid at 235°. Conveniently prepared by heating succinic acid with acetyl chloride; the anhydride crystallizes on cooling the liquor. Reacts with water to give succinic acid. Alcohols combine to give mono-alkyl succinates. Forms a mono-amide with ammonia in solution and this, on heating, changes to succinimide. Combines with primary amines in a similar manner. Reduced to butyrolactone by sodium amalgam. Used in the manufacture of certain dyestuffs.

Succinimide, $C_4H_5NO_2$. Crystallizes in colourless plates, m.p. 126°-127°, b.p. 287°-288° (decomp.). Soluble in acetone; sparingly soluble in water. Prepared by heating ammonium succinate. Decomposed by hot water to give ammonium succinate. Reacts as an acid and forms salts with metals; these replace the hydrogen atom of the $\rangle$NH group. Distillation with zinc dust gives pyrrole. Forms a chloroimide used for disinfecting water supplies.

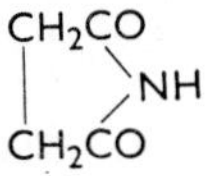

Succinyl sulphathiazole. White crystals, m.p. 192°-195°. Slightly soluble in water, soluble in

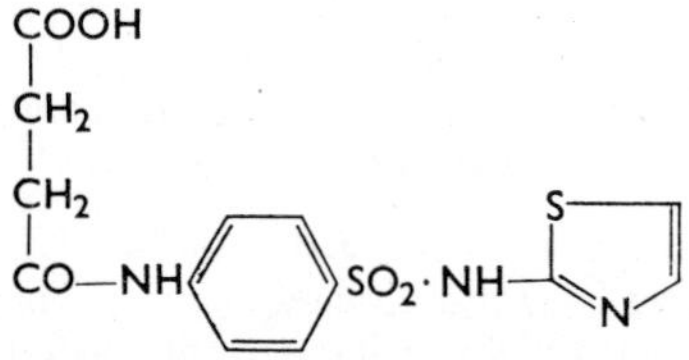

alkalis. It is one of the poorly absorbed sulphonamides and is used for the treatment of dysentery and other infections of the lower bowel. Its action is due to its being broken down and liberating sulphathiazole.

Sucrase. See Invertase.

Sucrose. $C_{12}H_{22}O_{11}$. Commercially known as

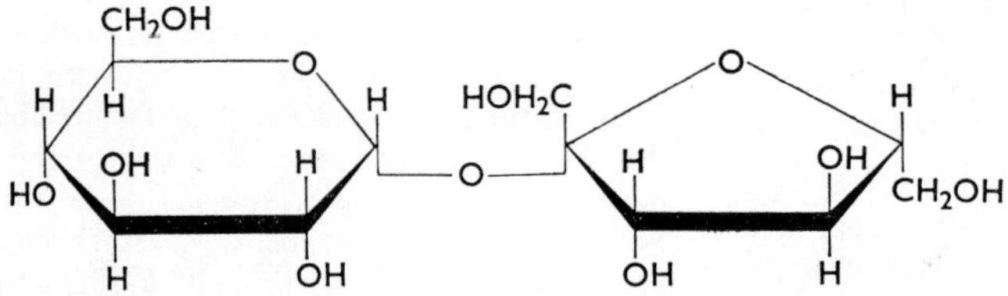

very soluble in water, stable towards alkali, and forms sucrates with the alkali and alkaline-earth metals. It contains 8 hydroxyl groups but gives rise to one series of derivatives only.

Sugar of lead. See Lead acetates.

Sugars. The sugars are carbohydrates, the majority of the natural sugars containing six or twelve carbon atoms in the molecule. They are crystalline, very soluble in water, and generally have a sweet taste. The sugar of commerce, called cane sugar or beet sugar according to its origin, is the disaccharide sucrose (q.v.).

Sugden, Samuel (1892-1950). Born at Leeds, Sugden studied at the Royal College of Science. In 1928 he was appointed reader in Physical Chemistry at Birkbeck College, London, and in 1932 became professor. He moved to University College as professor in 1937. His studies on molecular volumes and surface tension led to the introduction of the 'parachor.' See *J. Chem. Soc.*, 1952, 1987.

Sulphacetamide, *p*-**aminobenzenesulphonacetamide,** $C_8H_{10}N_2O_3S$ White crystals, m.p. 181°-183°, soluble in 150 parts of water and 15 parts of alcohol. Soluble sulphacetamide is the sodium salt and is soluble in 1·5 parts of water. It is

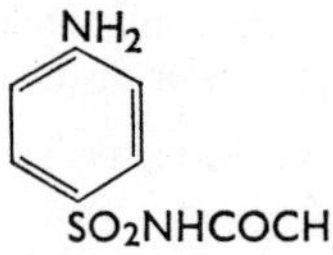

prepared by acetylating sulphanilamide and hydrolysing one acetyl group. Being more soluble than most of the sulphonamides it is used in treating urinary infections.

Glucopyranose   Fructofuranose

cane or beet sugar, it is 1-α-glucosido-2-β-fructofuranose. It has no reducing properties. It is readily hydrolysed by dilute acids to glucose and fructose and even more rapidly by invertase; the hydrolysed product which has a negative rotatory power is termed invert sugar. Sucrose has not been synthesized by purely chemical means, but has been prepared by the condensation of the potassium salt of D-glucose-1-phosphate by means of a bacterial phosphorylase. It crystallizes very readily in large monoclinic crystals, m.p. 170°-180°, $[\alpha]_D$ +66·5°, is

Sulphadiazine,2-(*p*-aminobenzenesulphonamido)-pyrimidine, $C_{10}H_{10}N_4O_2S$. A white

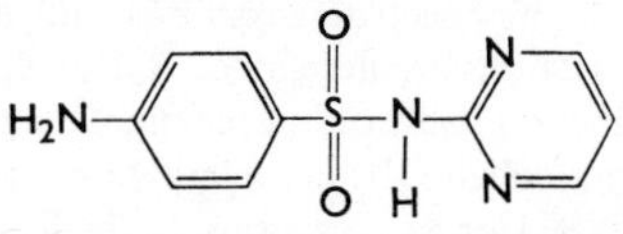

powder, which darkens on exposure to light, m.p. 255°-256°. Almost insoluble in water, sparingly soluble in alcohol. Prepared by condensing *p*-acetamidobenzenesulphonyl chloride with 2-aminopyrimidine and subsequent hydrolysis. Soluble sulphadiazine (soluble in 2 parts of water) is the sodium salt. Sulphadiazine is the least toxic of the more potent sulphonamides and in the U.S.A., where it was first introduced, is reckoned to be the most useful drug in the group. It is effective against streptococci, pneumococci, staphylococci, and other bacteria.

Sulphadimidine, 2-(p-aminobenzenesulphonamido)-4,6-dimethylpyrimidine, $C_{12}H_{14}N_4O_2S$.

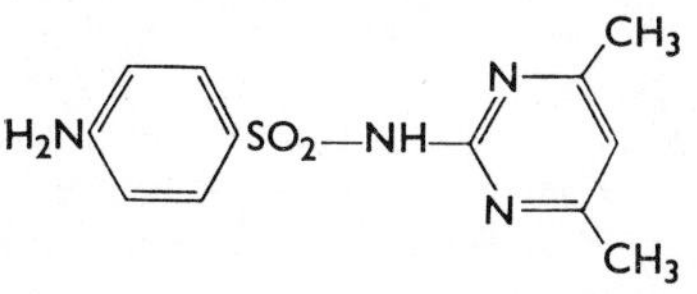

It has m.p. 198°. Solubility in water about 1 part in 3,000, sparingly soluble in alcohol. The sodium salt is very soluble in water. Sulphadimidine is rapidly absorbed but less rapidly excreted. Thus high blood concentrations can be obtained with moderate doses. It is effective against the same bacteria as sulphadiazine.

Sulphaguanidine, p-aminobenzenesulphonylguanidine, $C_7H_{10}N_4O_2S$. A white needle-like powder

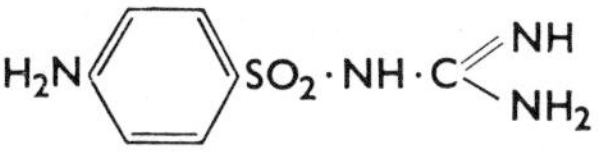

which darkens in air. Anhydrous; m.p. 189°-190°. Soluble in about 1,000 parts of cold water and 10 parts of boiling water. It is prepared by fusing dicyandiamide with sulphanilamide. It is used for treating intestinal bacterial infections.

Sulphamerazine 2-(p-aminobenzenesulphonamido)-4-methylpyrimidine, $C_{11}H_{12}N_4O_2S$. It

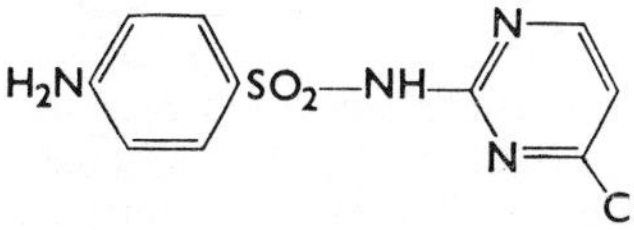

has m.p. 235°-236°. It is slightly soluble in water. As it is rapidly absorbed and slowly excreted, it is used to produce a high and persistent concentration in the blood. Its therapeutic properties resemble those of sulphanilimide.

Sulphamethoxypyridazine, $C_{11}H_{12}N_4O_3S$. 3-(4-Aminobenzene-sulphonamido)-6-methoxypyridazine. A white or yellowish white, crystalline

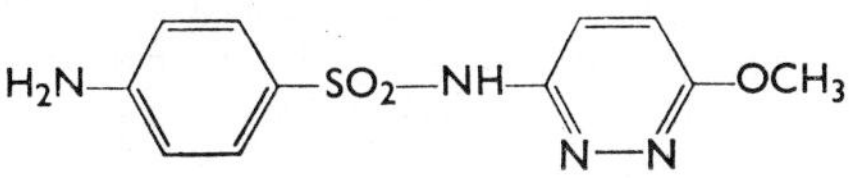

powder, m.p. 180°-183°. Very slightly soluble in water, sparingly soluble in alcohol and in acetone, freely soluble in dilute mineral acids and solutions of the alkali hydroxides. It is a

long-acting sulphonamide, a 0·5 g tablet producing effective blood levels for 12 hours.

Sulphamic acid, $H_3N^+ \cdot SO_3^-$. A colourless crystalline solid normally existing as a zwitterion; prepared by the reaction of sulphur dioxide with acetoxime, or, commercially, by the treatment of urea with fuming sulphuric acid. Sulphamic acid is very soluble in water and is a strong acid, forming a series of salts, the sulphamates. It is an excellent acidimetric primary standard. It is used in weed-killers, flame-proofing agents, and in electrolytes in metal deposition processes.

Sulphamide, and Sulphimide, $SO_2(NH_2)_2$ and $(SO_2NH)_n$. Colourless crystalline solids formed by the action of ammonia on a solution of sulphuryl chloride in benzene; free sulphimide exists only in the polymerized form. Both compounds are soluble in water, and are readily hydrolysed to sulphamic acid, $H_3N^+ \cdot SO_3^-$, and ammonia; the hydrogen atoms are in each case replaceable by metals to form salts.

Sulphan blue, $C_{27}H_{31}N_2NaO_6S_2$. The monosodium salt of anhydro-4,4′-bisdiethylaminotriphenylmethanol-2″,4-disulphonic acid. It is a violet powder, soluble in 20 parts of water, slightly soluble in alcohol, and is used as a colouring agent for medicinals, the colour being stable over a wide pH range.

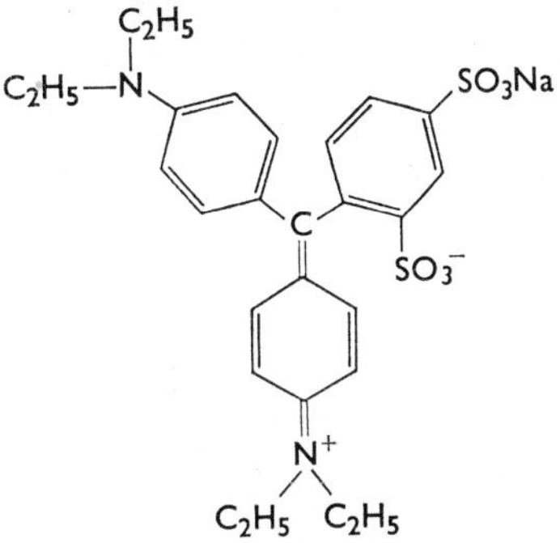

Sulphanilamide, p-aminobenzenesulphonamide, $C_6H_8N_2O_2S$. Colourless crystals, m.p. 164·5°-166·5°, soluble in 170 parts of water, sparingly

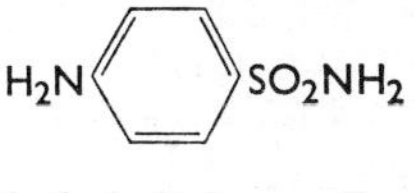

soluble in alcohol. It is usually prepared by treating p-acetamidobenzenesulphonyl chloride with ammonia, and hydrolysing the acetyl derivative to the base. Sulphanilamide was shown to be the portion of the protonsil molecule responsible for its bactericidal activity and has been widely used in medicine, particularly for the treatment of streptococcal infections, gonorrhoea, meningococcal meningitis, and urinary infections. Its chief disadvantage is that it is liable to cause unpleasant reactions, such as nausea, cyanosis, and skin rashes.

Sulphanilic acid, $C_6H_7NO_3S$. Colourless crystals obtainable in two forms: leaflets with $2H_2O$, needles with $1H_2O$, depending upon temperature of crystallization. Slightly soluble in water, readily in alkali solutions.

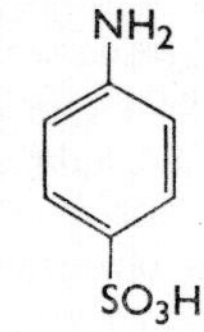

It is prepared by heating aniline sulphate for 8 hours at 190°. It readily diazotizes and is used as first component in a large variety of azo dyes.

Sulphapyridine, M. and B. 693, 2-(p-amino-benzenesulphonamido)pyridine, $C_{11}H_{11}N_3O_2S$.

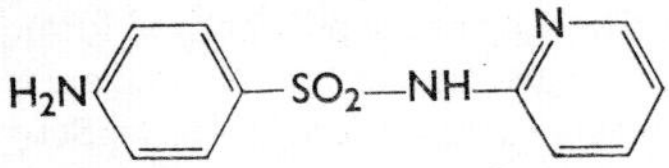

White crystals, which darken on exposure to air, m.p. 191°-193°. Sparingly soluble in water and alcohol. Prepared by condensing p-acetamido-benzenesulphonyl chloride with 2-aminopyridine and subsequent hydrolysis. Soluble sulphapyridine is the monohydrated sodium salt, soluble in 3 parts of water. When first introduced sulphapyridine was outstandingly successful in the treatment of pneumonia since, unlike sulphanilamide, it is effective against pneumococci. It has since been superseded by other sulphonamides.

Sulpharsphenamine, $C_{14}H_{16}As_2NNa_2O_8S_2$.

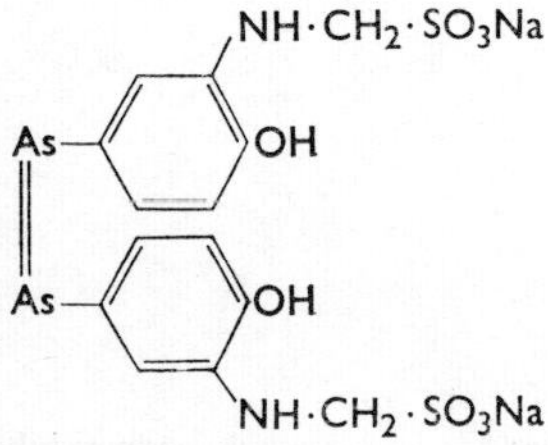

Prepared by treating 3,3′-diamino-4,4′-di-hydroxyarsenobenzene dihydrochloride with formaldehyde and sodium hydrogen sulphite. It is a yellow powder, soluble in water, insoluble in alcohol, m.p. 202°. It is a spirochaeticide, but has been largely replaced by penicillin for the treatment of venereal diseases.

Sulphatases. Enzymes which catalyse the hydrolysis of esters of sulphuric acid. One type, which splits the sulphuric esters of phenols, is widely distributed in animal and plant tissues. Another type, found in bacteria, splits the ethereal sulphates of aliphatic compounds.

Sulphates. Salts of sulphuric acid.

Sulphathiazole, 2-(p-aminobenzenesulphonamido)-thiazole, $C_9H_9N_3O_2S_2$. A white powder, m.p. 200°-203°, sparingly soluble in water and alcohol. Prepared by condensing p-acetamido-benzenesulphonyl chloride with 2-aminothia-zole with subsequent hydrolysis. Soluble sulphathiazole is the pentahydrated sodium salt, soluble in 3 parts of water, and is used for intravenous injection. Sulphathiazole has the typical actions of sulphonamides, being effective against β-haemolytic streptococci, pneumococci, gonococci, and staphylococci. It is readily absorbed by the oral route, and more rapidly excreted than sulphanilamide.

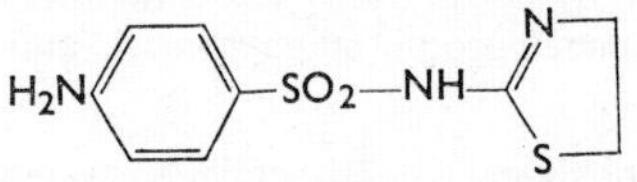

Sulphides. Compounds of other elements with sulphur. Most sulphides may be prepared by direct combination of the appropriate element with sulphur. Metallic sulphides are often extremely insoluble and are used in the separation of elements in qualitative analysis. Alkali metal sulphides are hydrolysed to hydrogen sulphide with water. Sulphides may be considered as salts of the weak acid, H_2S.

Sulphites. Salts of sulphurous acid.

Sulpholane, **tetrahydrothiophen-1,1-dioxide, tetramethylenesulphone,** $C_4H_8O_2S$. A viscous liquid, b.p. 285°, which readily solidifies to a colourless solid, m.p. 27·5°-28° when freed from water, with which it is miscible. It is partially miscible with octanes, olefins, and naphthenes and is used as a selective solvent for liquid-vapour extractions especially by gas-liquid chromatography. Used as a stationary phase the material is very suitable for the analysis of complex C_2—C_5 hydrocarbon mixtures. Most easily prepared by reduction of 2,5-dihydrothio-phene-1,1-dioxide, which is obtained from butadiene and sulphur dioxide.

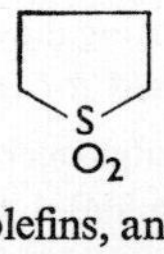

Sulphonal, $(CH_3)_2C(SO_2C_2H_5)_2$, and **Methyl-sulphonal,** $(CH_3)(C_2H_5)C(SO_2C_2H_5)_2$. Once used to a considerable extent as hypnotics but now superseded almost entirely by the barbituric acid derivatives. They are absorbed very slowly and excreted still more slowly, consequently repeated doses may have a cumulative action and produce symptoms of poisoning.

Sulphonamides. Compounds containing the grouping —$SO_2N\langle$. They are obtained by the action of ammonia and primary and secondary amines on sulphonyl halides. The term is also used for a group of drugs related to sulphanil-amide which contains the group

$$H_2N \diagdown \diagup SO_2NH—$$

The use of the sulphonamides dates from 1934 when the dye prontosil was shown to be an effective curative agent for certain infections caused by bacteria. Later it was found that sulphanilamide was the active portion of the prontosil molecule. Subsequently other and more effective derivatives of sulphanilamide have been introduced. Many of the more active sulphonamides have the structure

$$H_2N \diagdown \diagup SO_2NH—\overset{|}{C}{=}N—$$

They are prepared in general by condensing *p*-acetamidobenzenesulphonyl chloride with the appropriate amine and removing the acetyl group by hydrolysis.

The various sulphonamides differ in their specificity to various bacteria and in their ease of absorption and excretion. They are bacterio-static (inhibiting growth) and not bactericidal, acting by allowing the natural body mechanisms to destroy the bacteria.

The action of the sulphonamides is antagon-ized by *p*-aminobenzoic acid and it has been suggested that they act by blocking the position in an enzyme system that should be taken by *p*-aminobenzoic acid, known to be an essential growth factor for certain organisms.

Sulphonation. See Sulphonic acids.

Sulphones. Organic compounds containing an $\diagup$SO$_2$ group united directly to two carbon atoms. They are produced by oxidation of organic sulphides with nitric acid or potassium permanganate. They are colourless solids and are very stable.

Sulphonic acids (aromatic). Sulpho-compounds. These are a large group of organic compounds which contain the grouping —SO$_3$H.

The sulphonic acids are usually prepared by the action of sulphuric acid upon a compound. The concentration of the acid and the tempera-ture of reaction are varied according to the reactivity of the compound. Often oleum is used or even chlorosulphonic acid. Aminosulphonic acids such as sulphanilic and naphthionic acids are most conveniently prepared by heating the sulphate of the amine at 180°.

Prolonged sulphonation of benzene gives *m*-benzenedisulphonic acid. In the case of naphthalene, sulphonation gives α-substitution at low temperatures and β-substitution at higher temperatures.

The sulphonic acids are strongly acidic compounds, very soluble in water and readily give water-soluble metallic salts.

The most important reaction of the sulphonic acids is their conversion into phenols by fusion with caustic alkalis. When they are fused with potassium cyanide, nitriles are obtained, e.g. benzonitrile from benzenesulphonic acid.

Sulphonation is widely used for the solubiliz-ation of insoluble azo dyestuffs. Most of the acid wool colours are sulphonic acids.

Sulphonphthaleins. A group of dyes, many of which are used as indica-tors, made by heating *o*-sulphobenzoic anhydride with phenols or substituted phenols; they have the general formula shown, R being phenolic groups. See Phenol red.

Sulphonyl halides. Organic compounds which have the general formula shown, where R is an alkyl or aryl group and X is a halogen atom. A particularly important example is toluene-*p*-sulphonyl chloride (R=*p*-CH$_3$·C$_6$H$_4$, X=Cl). This is prepared by the action of chlorosulphonic acid on toluene, the *ortho* and *para* isomers being separated by centrifugation. Toluene-*p*-sulphonyl chloride is a white crystalline solid, m.p. 69°, which forms characteristic crystalline derivatives with many alcohols, phenols, sugars, and amines. The properties of sulphonyl halides thus resemble those of carboxylic acid chlorides. See Acetyl chloride, Toluene-*p*-sulphonyl chloride.

Sulphoxides. Organic compounds containing an $\diagup$SO group linked to two carbon atoms. They are obtained by the oxidation of organic sulphides with hydrogen peroxide. They are usually hygroscopic liquids and form addition compounds with acids. On oxidation, sulphones are produced. Dimethylsulphoxide (*q.v.*) is a useful solvent.

Sulphoxylic acid, H$_2$SO$_2$. An unknown acid of which only the cobaltous salt, CoSO$_2$, and esters are known. Cobalt (II) sulphoxylate is prepared by treating sodium hydrosulphite solution with cobalt acetate and ammonia. It is relatively unstable, being a strong reducing agent. Sulphoxylic esters can be made by decom-position of thiosulphurous esters with sodium ethoxide.

Sulphur, S. At.no. 16, At.wt. 32·066; m.p. of rhombic sulphur 112·8°, m.p. of monoclinic sulphur 119·06, b.p. 444·7°, *d* 1·957, mol.wt. of vapour at 1000° 64·14, mol.wt. at 500° 216. Native sulphur occurs in many parts of the world, especially in volcanic regions, and the world's supply comes mainly from southern U.S.A., where it is obtained from subterranean sources through bore holes with the help of superheated steam and an air lift for the molten sulphur. Considerable quantities of sulphur are nowadays obtained from hydrogen sulphide recovered from natural gas or petroleum fractions; this may be achieved by reacting it with sulphur dioxide over a catalyst, or by other means. Sulphur also occurs widely in the form of gypsum, $CaSO_4$, $2H_2O$, anhydrite, $CaSO_4$, and various pyritic ores, such as iron and copper pyrites, all of which are valuable sources of sulphur dioxide for the production of sulphuric acid.

Sulphur can exist in several allotropic forms and more especially as rhombic, monoclinic, and various forms of plastic sulphur. Rhombic, octahedral, or α-sulphur, the stable form under ordinary conditions, is a lemon-yellow, brittle solid of sp.gr. 2·03-2·06, insoluble in water and easily soluble in carbon disulphide. X-ray examination of rhombic sulphur shows that the structural units are discrete S_8 molecules with the form of a puckered ring. It burns in air when heated, forming sulphur dioxide and a small proportion of sulphur trioxide. It combines with various metals such as iron, copper, or zinc on heating. It is oxidized by nitric acid to sulphuric acid. At 94·5° it is converted into monoclinic sulphur.

Monoclinic, prismatic, or β-sulphur occurs in fine light yellow needles of sp.gr. 1·93. At ordinary temperatures it is slowly converted into rhombic sulphur without outward change of form. Plastic sulphur is obtained by pouring molten sulphur at 350° into cold water, and forms a tough plastic mass of sp.gr. 1·95. As thus prepared it is partially soluble in carbon disulphide. In its various compounds sulphur is di-, tetra-, or hexapositive.

Sulphur is largely used for the production of sulphuric acid, but it is also used in the manufacture of wood pulp, carbon disulphide, rubber and various dyes, insecticides, fungicides and other chemicals.

Sulphur bromide. *Sulphur monobromide*, S_2Br_2. This is the only bromide of sulphur that is known definitely. It dissolves sulphur, and bromides S_nBr_2 probably exist in solution.

Sulphur chlorides. Sulphur and chlorine combine in all proportions but the following compounds have fairly definite existence. All are prepared by adding chlorine to sulphur.

Sulphur monochloride, S_2Cl_2. A yellow liquid, m.p. $-80°$, b.p. 138°. Sulphur monochloride is decomposed by water to form sulphur dioxide, hydrochloric acid, and sulphur. It is used in the

rubber industry as a solvent for sulphur. Lower chlorides, S_nCl_2, are prepared by the reduction of S_2Cl_2 vapour with hydrogen or by dissolving sulphur in S_2Cl_2.

Sulphur dichloride, SCl_2. A garnet red liquid, m.p. $-80°$ to $-60°$, b.p. 59°. Possesses similar properties to sulphur monochloride.

Sulphur tetrachloride, SCl_4; m.p. $-30°$, is stable only as the solid; the liquid evolves chlorine.

Sulphur dyes. Complex substances containing sulphur; they are insoluble in water but soluble in a solution of sodium sulphide. From a bath of this latter solution they are applied to cotton, and are subsequently oxidized in air or treated with a metallic salt.

Sulphur blues are usually oxidized with sodium perborate or other similar oxidizing agent. Yellows and browns are often after-treated with metallic salts, e.g. dichromates, with or without copper sulphate. This results in a considerable improvement in the fastness to light, washing, and perspiration. The use of solubilized or water-soluble sulphur dyes is steadily increasing as these offer useful advantages when dyeing cotton in circulating machines.

Although they yield rather dull shades, sulphur dyestuffs fulfil a very useful purpose in cotton dyeing. They are much cheaper than vat dyes although not as fast, and they are far superior to the direct dyes in all-round fastness.

Sulphur fluorides. *Sulphur hexafluoride*, SF_6. Formed by the action of fluorine on sulphur, m.p. $-50·8°$, sublimes $-63·7°$. This gas is exceedingly inert. Small quantities of *sulphur decafluoride*, S_2F_{10}, are formed during the preparation of SF_6.

Sulphur tetrafluoride, SF_4. Prepared by heating together sulphur dichloride and sodium fluoride in acetonitrile, m.p. $-121°$, b.p. $-40·4°$. Sulphur tetrafluoride is much more reactive than the hexafluoride. It is used extensively as a fluorinating agent.

Disulphur difluoride. Prepared as a mixture of two isomers by the action of silver (I) fluoride on sulphur. The two isomers have the structures F—S—S—F and S—SF$_2$.

Sulphur fluoride derivatives. *Pentafluorosulphur compounds.* Many compounds containing the SF_5 group are known. *Pentafluorosulphur chloride* results from the action of ClF on sulphur. With hydrogen it gives disulphur decafluoride, S_2F_{10}, with oxygen SF_5OSF_5 and SF_5OOSF_5. The SF_5 and Cl groups add across the double bonds of olefins. See Roberts, *Quarterly Rev.*, 1961, **15**, 30.

Sulphuric acid, H_2SO_4, $SO_2(OH)_2$. A heavy,

viscous, colourless, odourless liquid, dangerous to handle. It has d_4^{18} 1·834, m.p. 10·4°, b.p. 340° with decomposition to sulphur trioxide and water. It is miscible in all proportions with water and forms an azeotrope, b.p. 339°, containing 98·3% H_2SO_4 by weight. Strong sulphuric acid is a powerful dehydrating agent, combining violently with water with contraction and the evolution of much heat: at 25° one g-mole H_2SO_4 diluted with a very large quantity of water evolves approximately 22 kcal. The hot concentrated acid behaves as an oxidizing agent and will react with carbon, phosphorus and sulphur, being itself reduced to sulphur dioxide. Sulphuric acid is a strong acid and is almost completely dissociated in dilute solution. Due to its low volatility it will displace most other inorganic and organic acids from their salts. Most metals are attacked by it, but strong sulphuric acid may be handled in cast iron and mild steel equipment, due to the formation of an insoluble sulphate film, and the dilute acid in lead for a similar reason.

Sulphuric acid is manufactured from sulphur dioxide. In the classical *lead chamber process* a mixture of sulphur dioxide, nitric oxide, air and steam is sprayed with water in a series of lead chambers. The nitric oxide acts as a carrier for oxygen in the oxidation of sulphur dioxide to sulphur trioxide, with the net result that sulphuric acid is formed. The latter contains 62-68% H_2SO_4, which concentration may be increased by further processing.

In the *contact process* a purified mixture of sulphur dioxide and air is passed into a reactor containing either a platinum or vanadium pentoxide catalyst, which causes a 95-99% conversion of the dioxide to the trioxide. The temperature in the first part of the reactor is 500°-600° and that in the second 400°-450°. The emerging gases are cooled to 100° and passed into a tower, where the sulphur trioxide is absorbed in 97% acid (lower concentrations cause the formation of a mist which is difficult to remove from the waste gases leaving the plant). It is possible by varying the degree of absorption and subsequent dilution to produce a range of strengths of oleum and sulphuric acid.

The sulphur dioxide used in these processes may be obtained by the combustion of sulphur pyrites or hydrogen sulphide (the last obtained from the purification of natural gas and petroleum fractions), or by the calcination of anhydrite with coke and clay. Sulphur dioxide made from elemental sulphur requires little purification, that from pyrites and anhydrite much, in order to prevent contamination of the catalyst and the final product.

Although lead chamber plants are still used they are becoming obsolete, and all modern plants employ the contact process. Of contact plants, those burning sulphur are the cheapest to construct and operate, those using anhydrite the most expensive. The latter are dependent for their economic viability on the cement produced at the same time. An advantage of pyrites and anhydrite plants, outside the U.S.A. at least, is that they are not so sensitive to political factors—the Korean war produced a serious sulphur shortage.

Sulphuric acid is a chemical of the greatest industrial importance, world production in 1964 being approximately 65 million tons H_2SO_4. It is used for such a wide range of manufacturing processes that its production has long been recognized as an indicator of the economic health of a country. About one-third is used for the manufacture of phosphate fertilizers, while large quantities are consumed in the production of ammonium sulphate, aluminium sulphate, explosives, inorganic pigments and other chemicals. It is also used in petroleum refining, for the pickling of iron and steel, and in the manufacture of rayon.

Sulphuric acid, fuming, Nordhausen sulphuric acid, Oleum, $H_2SO_4 \cdot xSO_3$. A solution of SO_3 in sulphuric acid obtained by the contact process (see Sulphuric acid). It is produced in various percentages of excess SO_3. The physical properties of these preparations indicate the existence of pyrosulphuric acid $H_2S_2O_7$ and other condensed acids. On heating fuming sulphuric acid, sulphur trioxide, SO_3, distils, which is the usual method of preparing this compound. Fuming sulphuric acid is largely used for the preparation of organic chemicals.

Sulphur nitride, S_4N_4 (also called nitrogen sulphide). An orange crystalline solid prepared by the action of dry ammonia on thionyl chloride, or on a solution of sulphur monochloride and chlorine in benzene. Sulphur nitride frequently explodes on percussion, but this effect may be due to traces of impurity. It reacts with chlorine to give a chloride, $S_4N_4Cl_4$, and with sulphur monochloride to give thiotrithiazyl chloride, S_4N_3Cl. It has m.p. 178°. S_4N_4 has a ring-shaped structure with alternating sulphur and nitrogen atoms. The ring is not flat but the nitrogen atoms are approximately in a plane.

Other sulphur nitrides, S_2N_2, and $(SN)_x$ are also known. For a review of properties of these compounds see *Quarterly Reviews*, 1956, **10**, 437.

Sulphurous acid, H_2SO_3. A colourless acid, a solution of which is obtained by dissolving sulphur dioxide in water. At 0° a crystalline hydrate, $SO_2 \cdot 7H_2O$, can be isolated but the pure acid is unknown. With bases, sulphites, M_2SO_3, are formed. The neutral sulphites, with the exception of the alkali sulphites, are usually but slightly soluble in water. They are easily decomposed by strong acids with liberation of SO_2. Sulphurous acid and its salts can be determined quantitatively under suitable conditions by titration with iodine solution, or by oxidation with bromine water to sulphuric acid and isolation as barium sulphate.

Sulphur oxides. *Disulphur monoxide.* Prepared by the action of a glow discharge on sulphur dioxide. The gaseous products are a mixture of SSO and SO_2.

Sulphur dioxide, SO_2, mol. wt. 64·06. A heavy colourless gas with the characteristic smell of burning sulphur. It is very poisonous. At 10° it liquefies at a pressure of 2·26 atm, m.p. $-75\cdot5°$, b.p. $-10°$. It is incombustible in the absence of a catalyst and is a powerful reducing agent when dissolved in water. At 0° one volume of water dissolves 79·8 vols. of SO_2 and at 20° 38·4 vols. On boiling the solution the whole of the gas is liberated. The solution probably contains both the free oxide and sulphurous acid, H_2SO_3. Sulphur dioxide is formed by the combustion of sulphur and of sulphur compounds such as iron and copper pyrites, and is usually produced industrially in this manner. As prepared in this way it always contains a small proportion of SO_3. In the laboratory it is usually prepared by the action of sulphuric acid on sodium bisulphite solution. It is recognized by its smell and by its property of reducing solutions of iodine and of alkali permanganate. Liquid sulphur dioxide is a good solvent.

Sulphur trioxide, Sulphuric anhydride, SO_3. This compound exists in at least three forms. The α-form, ice-like crystals, is formed when the liquid freezes at 16·8°. On condensing the highly dried vapours at $-80°$, the γ-form is deposited. Both these forms change, particularly under the influence of traces of moisture, to the very stable, asbestos-like, β-form. The liquid has b.p. 44·5°. All forms react violently with water to form sulphuric acid. It is a very powerful dehydrating agent. It is obtained by the oxidation of SO_2 with air or oxygen in presence of finely divided platinum or of vanadium compounds as catalysts and this reaction forms the first stage of the contact process of sulphuric acid manufacture. It is also formed as a distillate by heating sulphuric acid with phosphorus pentoxide and similarly by heating fuming sulphuric acid alone.

Sulphur sesquioxide, S_2O_3. Formed by dissolving sulphur in liquid sulphur dioxide. It is a blue-green solid, stable below 15°, but decomposing above this temperature.

Sulphur heptoxide, S_2O_7, and *Sulphur tetroxide,* SO_4, are poorly characterized liquids, m.p. about 0°, formed by passing sulphur trioxide or dioxide and oxygen through an electrical discharge.

Sulphur sensitization. A photographic term for the process of increasing the sensitivity of emulsions to light by the formation of silver sulphide specks on the surface of silver halide grains. The silver sulphide is produced as a result of interaction between sulphur compounds, for example thiosulphates, thioureas, thiocyanates present in trace amounts in gelatin, with silver halide, sometimes via intermediate complexes.

Sulphuryl chloride, SO_2Cl_2. A colourless liquid of b.p. 69° obtained on exposing a mixture of equal volumes of sulphur dioxide and chlorine to direct sunlight. The reaction is accelerated in presence of a little camphor. It is rapidly hydrolysed by water, forming sulphuric and hydrochloric acids. Sulphuryl chloride is used as a chlorinating agent for organic compounds. Sulphuryl fluoride and bromide are also known.

Sumner, James Batcheller (1887-1955). Distinguished as the first man to obtain an enzyme (urease) in crystalline state, Sumner was born in Massachusetts, educated at Harvard and became professor of biochemistry at Cornell in 1929. He shared the Nobel Prize for chemistry in 1946.

Sun-and-planet mixer. Two intermeshing blades rotating about vertical axes travel round the edge of the bowl containing the materials to be mixed. This relative motion may be achieved by having the blade axes fixed and the bowl rotating, or by keeping the bowl stationary and giving the blade axes a planetary motion round the edge of it. These machines are widely used for mixing viscous materials such as paints.

Superadditive developer mixtures. Certain photographic developing agents are known which used alone have relatively low activity. These same agents used in conjunction with a second developing agent give results superior to the sum of the results obtained from either agent used separately. This superadductive or synergistic effect is obtained from metol-hydroquinone mixtures (M.Q.-developers). More recently metol-hydroquinone mixtures have tended to be replaced by the more active 1 - phenylpyrazolid - 3 - one (Phenidone), hydroquinone mixtures (P.Q.-developers).

Other compounds useful as synergistic developers are 4-methyl- and 4,4-dimethyl-1-phenylpyrazolid-3-one and 1-*p*-hydroxyphenyl-pyrrolidine.

Supercooling. The phenomenon of cooling a

liquid to a temperature below that at which crystallization would normally occur, i.e. below its freezing-point, without the separation of solid. Pure water may often be cooled to several degrees below its freezing-point, especially if free from suspended dust particles, which act as crystallization nuclei. Supercooling is common with viscous liquids, and glass is to be regarded as an extreme example of the phenomenon for, in it, solidification has occurred without crystallization. The phenomenon of cooling a solution below the saturation temperature for the quantity of solute present is called supersaturation, and such a solution is said to be supersaturated.

Superfractionation. A term used in the petroleum industry for the production of materials with special boiling ranges by the use of fractionating columns of high efficiency.

Superoxides. Compounds containing O_2^-, e.g. potassium superoxide KO_2.

Superphosphates. Treatment of ordinary insoluble calcium phosphate, $Ca_3(PO_4)_2$, with concentrated sulphuric acid yields a product, calcium hydrogen phosphate, $Ca(H_2PO_4)_2$, which is soluble in water and is a very effective fertilizer. Commercially, one of the available forms of calcium phosphate is treated with sulphuric acid of carefully controlled concentration, preferably in a closed autoclave under pressure ('Oberphos' process). The dry product consists of the soluble calcium salt together with calcium sulphate and sulphates of other metals present as impurities in the raw material, and is known as 'superphosphate.' Care is taken in the manufacturing process to avoid a product containing excess phosphoric acid, or unattacked insoluble calcium phosphate, which results if too much or too little acid is used.

The grades of superphosphate most widely used have about 13·7% of phosphoric acid (30% tricalcium phosphate) and 16 to 17% of phosphoric acid. Higher grades are also manufactured.

Supersaturation. See Supercooling.

Supersensitization. The effect of increasing the efficiency of spectral sensitization by the introduction of a small proportion of a second dye or a colourless compound to an adsorbed sensitizer. The property is specific to a limited number of pairs of compounds. For example, pinacyanol is supersensitized by some styryl dyes. The phenomenon of supersensitization by J-band sensitization is probably associated with increased efficiency of energy transfer from the dye aggregate to the silver halide crystal.

Suramin, $C_{51}H_{34}N_6Na_6O_{23}S_6$. A white powder soluble in water, insoluble in alcohol.

It is effective against early stages of infections with trypanosomes, but as it does not penetrate

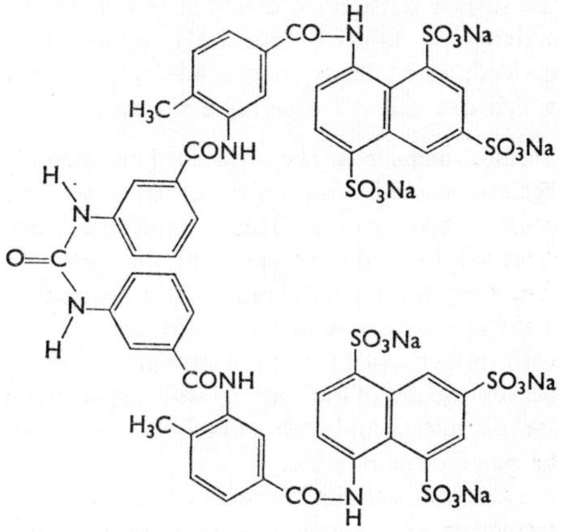

to the cerebrospinal fluid it is useless against later stages. It may produce toxic effects.

Surface active agents. Water, possessing powerful intermolecular attractive forces, has a high surface tension (72·8 dynes/cm at 20°). Many soluble substances (mainly organic) when dissolved in water, even in low concentration, cause its surface tension to be reduced considerably.

Thus a few hundredths of 1% of soap will cause a diminution of surface tension of between 40 and 50 dynes/cm. These surface active agents have weaker intermolecular attractive forces than the solvent, and therefore tend to concentrate in the surface at the expense of the water molecules. The accumulation of adsorbed surface active agent is related to the change in surface tension according to the Gibbs adsorption equation

$$\Gamma = \frac{-C\,d\gamma}{RT\,dc}$$

where Γ is the surface excess, c is the bulk concentration of the surface active agent and γ is the surface tension. Surface active agents, which include certain dyestuffs, wetting agents, detergents, antibiotics, bactericides, etc., may be electrically neutral, non-dissociating substances (non-ionic), or they may ionize to give surface active anions or cations with small oppositely charged counterions (usually metallic ions and halogen ions respectively).

Surface activity. A phenomenon which arises from the non-symmetrical distribution of attractive forces between molecules (and ions) residing within about 5–10 Å of any surface (i.e. within the surface layer). This results in their being attracted away from the surface towards the interior, and with liquids leads to the contraction of the surface to the smallest possible area. Work has therefore to be performed to cause the surface to expand, the amount, measured in ergs/cm^2, being numerically equal to the surface tension (in dynes/cm). The surface activity of solids, particularly when finely divided, often leads to gas adsorption, with which catalysis is frequently associated.

Surface compounds. The surfaces of many solids become coated with unimolecular layers of chemisorbed gases. These molecules are attached by ordinary chemical linkages and give to the solid its characteristic properties. Thus charcoal and many metals are covered with surface oxide films; the amount of oxygen per unit weight of the material will vary with the specific surface and so the compound appears to be non-stoicheiometric.

The first definite surface compound was recognized by Langmuir—a unimolecular film of chemisorbed oxygen on tungsten, which was stable to very high temperatures but reacted with further quantities of oxygen to form WO_3 which then distilled off. See Chemisorption, Active centres.

Surface energy. The surface energy of a system is defined as the work necessary to increase the surface by unit area against the force of surface tension.

Surface orientation. When films of organic materials spread on water, the molecules of the surface layers are usually orientated according to their structure. With large organic molecules there may, for example, be some group such as a sulphonate or carboxyl group which tends to confer solubility on the compound. Such groups are therefore hydrophilic and are attracted to the water so that the molecule turns round and is anchored, as it were, by the hydrophilic group which will penetrate below the water surface. On the other hand hydrocarbon chains are hydrophobic, and will tend to remove themselves as far as possible from the water. Thus a film of long-chain fatty acids on water will have the molecules orientated so that the hydrocarbon chains are all perpendicular to the surface with the acid groups dipping into the water.

Surface potential. The absolute electrical potential difference between two phases is not susceptible to determination, but the change in the apparent potential difference across an interface, as determined with a constant circuit arrangement, but first with a clean surface and then with the same surface carrying an adsorbed layer is measurable and is called the surface potential of the adsorbed layer. In some cases, e.g. monolayers of long-chain alcohols, esters, etc. on water, the surface potential can be related to the arrangement of molecular dipoles in the film.

Surface pressure. Thin films of spreading oils, e.g. oleic acid, lower the surface tension of the liquid (generally water) on which they are spread. Consequently, they exert a force of repulsion on floating particles. The force exerted by a spreading film per cm of boundary is numerically equal to the lowering of surface tension; it is called the surface pressure of the film by analogy (in two dimensions) with the pressure of a gas. The surface pressure exerted by a solid or liquid present in excess is termed its spreading pressure.

Surface tension. The molecules in the body of a liquid are equally attracted in all directions by the other molecules. Those at the surface, on the other hand, will have a residual inward attraction. This is associated with a *surface tension* which acts in a direction parallel to the boundary surface and tends to reduce that surface to a minimum. Work has to be done to increase the area of the surface against this force. This explains why an emulsified system always tends to be unstable and breaks down unless there is present some substance to lower the surface or interfacial tension. See Surface energy.

Surface viscosity. Unimolecular films on liquid surfaces may be either readily mobile (e.g. a 'gaseous' film) or slow to flow under the action of a two-dimensional stress (see Surface pressure). They therefore possess surface viscosity, the two-dimensional analogue of ordinary viscosity. It is defined and determined by analogous methods, e.g. by rate of flow along a surface canal or by a rotating disc viscometer. Some surface films show surface plasticity, i.e. they behave as solids until a critical shearing stress is applied.

Surgical spirit. Industrial methylated spirit further denatured by the addition of castor oil, methyl salicylate, and either ethyl phthalate or brucine.

Suspended transformation. It is often possible to maintain a system in a state which is far from the true equilibrium condition. Thus, in the absence of dust nuclei, or of mechanical shock, water may be heated far above its boiling-point without the occurrence of ebullition. Such a system is said to be metastable or in a state of suspended transformation. The phenomenon occurs frequently amongst allotropes, e.g. diamond is really metastable to graphite; white phosphorus to red phosphorus; and at low temperatures, white tin to grey tin.

Suspending agents. For many purposes the suspension of a small amount of material in a large volume of liquid is required. To prepare this the material to be suspended should be ground as finely as possible and given an electrical double layer by adsorption of an ionic detergent. A further method is to obstruct sedimentation by the use of a bulky hydrated precipitate which will hold up the solid to be suspended. Bentonite and related clays may be used for this purpose.

Suspensoids. Substances in the colloidal state can be divided into two classes, those which are coagulated by small concentrations of electrolytes and those which are stable. One school of colloid chemists called the former suspensoids and the latter emulsoids but the term appears to have gone out of use.

Suxamethonium chloride, $C_{14}H_{30}Cl_2N_2O_4$, $2H_2O$. A white crystalline powder, soluble in

$$\left[\begin{array}{l} CH_2 \cdot CO \cdot O \cdot CH_2 \cdot CH_2 \cdot N(CH_3)_3 \\ CH_2 \cdot CO \cdot O \cdot CH_2 \cdot CH_2 \cdot N(CH_3)_3 \end{array} \right] \begin{array}{l} 2+ \\ 2Cl^-, \\ 2H_2O \end{array}$$

one part water, less soluble in alcohol, m.p. 160°, prepared by treating dimethylaminoethanol with succinyl chloride and methylating the product.

Suxamethonium chloride is a short-acting relaxant of skeletal muscle; it affects transmission of the impulse at the nerve-muscle junction. It is used to relax muscle when manipulative operations are to be performed.

Svedberg, Theodor (1884-   ). Svedberg was born at Valbo, Sweden, and educated at Uppsala University, where he became docent in chemistry in 1907 and professor of physical chemistry in 1912. He has published numerous papers, dealing chiefly with colloid chemistry, and for his work in this field was awarded the Nobel Prize in Chemistry for 1926.

Swan, Sir Joseph Wilson (1828-1914). Born at Sunderland, Swan served his apprenticeship with a druggist and ultimately became partner in the business. The firm manufactured photographic materials and their production of dry plates was the result of Swan's researches. He also produced bromide paper and a commercial process for carbon printing. In 1860 he produced an electric carbon filament lamp and, in 1880, gave a demonstration in Newcastle of electric lighting. He was the first to make useful threads of artificial silk, exhibited at the Inventions Exhibition of 1885. He was knighted in 1904.

Sweating. The process of removing entrapped oil and low-melting waxes from the filter cake obtained in dewaxing processes. The wax is charged molten to a suitable sweating stove, such as the Alanmor or Henderson type, and allowed to solidify into cakes, the rate of cooling being adjusted so that a well developed crystalline structure is obtained. The tempera-

ture is then slowly raised and the oil and low-melting waxes allowed to drain off until the residue has the required melting point. The whole charge is then melted and withdrawn.

Sweetening. A process in the petroleum industry similar to Doctor treatment (q.v.).

Sweetland filter. This is a pressure leaf filter having transverse circular leaves mounted inside a horizontal cylindrical casing. The lower half of the casing may be dropped on hinges, so that when the cake is being removed it falls clear of the unit.

Swelling of colloids. When a piece of dry gelatin is exposed to moist air or placed in water, it swells greatly owing to hydration. This is an effect common to all hydrophilic colloids and thus to most natural organic matter, e.g. cellulose, wood, carbohydrates. The pressure produced by swelling is very high, and swelling thus takes place even when opposed by a pressure of many atmospheres.

The effect of electrolytes on swelling of gels is very marked, and is generally a minimum at the isoelectric point of the material. In general, sulphates, tartrates, etc., inhibit swelling while iodides and thiocyanates increase the effect. Thus gelatin disperses completely in potassium iodide solution even in the cold.

Swenson-Walker crystallizer. An open trough of U cross-section surrounded by a cooling water jacket and containing a slowly rotating helical agitator. The hot mother-liquor enters at one end and flows through the trough, the crystals which form being kept freely suspended in the liquid by the agitator, which also keeps the cooling surfaces clean. Control of the process may be obtained by manipulation of the cooling water to secure any desired temperature gradient. This type of crystallizer gives fairly uniformly sized crystals of good shape, but is limited to systems where adequate supersaturation can be achieved by cooling alone.

Switch oil. See Transformer oil.

Sydnones. Heterocyclic compounds for which satisfactory formulae using normal covalent bonds cannot be written. They have been termed 'mesoionic.' Sydnone itself can be represented as:

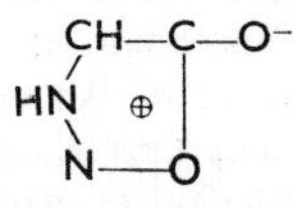

Sydnones are neutral, highly crystalline, stable compounds, soluble in most organic solvents. N-Arylsydnones typically are obtained by treating N-nitroso-N-aryl-glycines with acetic anhydride. The parent glycine is regenerated when the sydnone is heated with dilute alkali. Their formulation as aromatic systems is supported by a variety of physical properties.

Sylvan, α-methylfuran, C_5H_6O. A constituent of wood tar. It is a yellow liquid, b.p. 63°, which is soluble in water and many organic solvents.

Sylvestrene, $C_{10}H_{16}$. An optically active monocyclic terpene, the dihydrochloride of which is

obtained by the action of hydrogen chloride on various pine-needle oils, and on Finnish and Indian oils of turpentine. It has been found that sylvestrene is not present in these oils, but is formed by the isomerization of $Δ^3$- and $Δ^4$-carene. Sylvestrene is liberated from the dihydrochloride by treatment with aniline. Both (+)- and (−)-forms are known, as is also the racemic form, which is known as carvestrene. These hydrocarbons are inseparable mixtures of compounds of the two constitutional formulae given above. (+)-Sylvestrene is usually obtained from natural sources in the manner indicated above. (−)-Sylvestrene can be obtained from the terpene fraction of the oil from *Dacryodes hexandra* or from (−)-$Δ^3$-carene from *Kaempferia galanga*. Carvestrene can be obtained by various synthetic reactions from carvone. (+)-Sylvestrene has the following constants: b.p. 175°/751 mm, d^{18} 0·8479, n_D 1·4760, $[α]_D$ +83·18°. The various forms of sylvestrene are characterized by giving an intense blue coloration in acetic anhydride solution on addition of strong sulphuric acid. Sylvestrene gives a crystalline dihydrochloride of m.p. 72°–73°. Carvestrene dihydrochloride melts at 52°–53°.

Sylvite or **Sylvine**. Native potassium chloride. It has sp.gr. 1·99, hardness 2. It occurs at Stassfurt and in other saline deposits, and is an importance source of potassium salts.

Symmetry elements. The operators which give repetition and pattern in molecules and lattices. Symmetry elements comprise:

(1) Axes of symmetry. An axis about which rotation of the body through an angle of $2π/n$ (where n is an integer) gives an identical pattern; 2-fold, 3-fold, 4-fold, and 6-fold axes are known in crystals; 5-fold axes are known in molecules. In a lattice the rotation may be accompanied by a lateral movement parallel to the axis (screw axis).

(2) Planes of symmetry. Planes through which there is reflection to an identical point in the pattern. In a lattice there may be a lateral movement parallel to one or more axes (glide plane).

(3) Identity operator. Present in all lattices and molecules.

(4) Centre of symmetry. A point through which there is reflection to an identical point in the pattern.

Symons disc crusher. This device consists of two slightly concave plates one of which is stationary and the other revolving rapidly. The shaft of the rotating plate has keyed to it at the far end an eccentric bush which runs in a journal bearing, thus causing the plate to wobble as it rotates and to exert a crushing action on material fed in between the two plates. The Symons crusher takes feed of an intermediate size, such as the product from a jaw crusher or a gyratory crusher.

Synchrotron. A device for accelerating electrons and protons. The particles are kept in a circular orbit by means of a magnetic field and the acceleration is provided by a radio-frequency oscillator. Protons can be accelerated to energies of the order of a thousand million electron volts.

Syneresis. This term was given by Graham to the separation of liquid from a gel on standing. All gels show syneresis to a greater or less extent and the phenomenon is probably a continuation of the process of gelation, the gel material adhering at more and more places so that it shrinks and squeezes out a portion of the dispersion medium. Viscose gels synerize to a large extent and the phenomenon is commonly met in the cooking of foods. It is supposed to play an important part in gland secretion. See Colloids, Gel.

Synergist. A compound which, whilst formally inactive in a particular context, can give enhanced activity to another compound present in the system. For an example see Superadditive developer mixtures.

Syngenite. A native hydrated double sulphate of potassium and calcium, K_2SO_4, $CaSO_4$, H_2O, which forms colourless monoclinic crystals having a pseudo-orthorhombic habit; sp.gr. 2·6, hardness 2·5. Syngenite is decomposed by water with deposition of calcium sulphate. It commonly occurs in association with rock-salt, anhydrite, and gypsum.

Syntactic polymers. This is one of the stereoregular types of polymeric structures, in which the substituent groups lie alternately above and below the plane of the carbon chain. This type of structure is sometimes also referred to as a syndiotactic configuration.

Synthesis. In the chemical sense synthesis consists in building up complex molecules from smaller ones.

Synthesis gas. A mixture of hydrogen and carbon monoxide, used together with an olefin in the hydroformylation (oxo) synthesis.

Synthetic rubbers. These are synthetic materials which resemble natural rubber in some of their properties. The early synthetic rubbers (e.g. the German methyl rubber manufactured in the 1914 war) were attempts to reproduce the molecular constitution of rubber, but in recent work the reproduction of the properties of rubber is regarded as more important than the manufacture of a material with the molecular structure of the natural substance. The more important synthetic rubbers are polymers of butadiene (see Buna rubbers), vinyl halides, halogenated butadienes (see Neoprene), or mixed polymerizable materials, or are thioplasts (see Thioplasts, Thiokol). Many ester and other oxygen-containing polymers (see Plastics) also resemble rubber in some of their properties. The synthetic materials are more expensive than natural rubber, but many of them have the important advantage over rubber that they are oil-resistant. Also, their manufacture can be carried out in many countries from native materials, conferring independence of foreign sources of rubber.

Systemic insecticides. Compounds which, when applied to the leaves, stems and sometimes the roots of plants, are absorbed and translocated in the plant in the course of normal nutrition in concentrations safe for the plant but lethal to insects feeding on the plants. The most important systemic insecticides are certain organo-phosphorus compounds and these are thought to act as inhibitors of esterase activity in the organism. For examples of systemic insecticides in practical use, see Dimefox, Metasystox, Phosdrin, and Schradan.

Szent-Györgyi, Albert (1893-   ). Born in Budapest and educated there, Szent-Györgyi worked in a number of places, including Groningen and Cambridge, before returning to Hungary in 1932 as professor of medical chemistry at Szeged. He was given the Nobel Prize for medicine in 1937 for his work on the isolation and characterization of vitamin C. He has worked also on many other biochemical problems. Later he emigrated to the United States and worked at the Institute for Muscle Research at Woods Hole, Massachusetts. See *Ann. Rev. Biochem.*, **32**, 1, (1963).

Szilard-Chalmers effect. See Recoil atom.

T

2,4,5-T, 2,4,5-trichlorophenoxyacetic acid.

$C_8H_5Cl_3O_3$. Used as a selective herbicide. It is made from 2,4,5-trichlorophenol and sodium chloroacetate. It has m.p. 155°; soluble in alcohol. Its salts are water-soluble. Ester sprays and combined ester sprays with 2,4-D are available. 2,4,5-T products are of particular value in that they control many woody species, and eradicate perennial weeds such as nettles in pastures. 2,4,5-T is very active in low concentrations; beets, brassicas, lettuce, tomatoes, pears, and vines are particularly susceptible to drift damage. It is less phytotoxic than 2,4-D.

Tabling. This is a method of separating an ore into two fractions of different densities by the use of *riffled tables*. A riffled table consists of a flat deck, inclined at a slight angle to the horizontal, with a series of shallow parallel slats or *riffles* running diagonally across it. The material to be classified is fed continuously as a pulp to one of the inclined sides, and is caused to move across the table by a jerking motion imparted to the latter via a reciprocating mechanism. Wash water is fed to the top edge of the table and flows downwards across the riffles, tending to carry light material with it, but the heavy material remains behind the riffles to be discharged at the side. A series of launders arranged along the lower edge and side enables a number of fractions to be collected.

Tabling is suitable where there is only one valuable mineral and a considerable difference exists between the effective densities of the wanted and unwanted fractions. When several valuable minerals are present froth flotation (*q.v.*) is a better method of separation.

Tachydrite. See Calcium chloride.

Tactosols. Colloidal sols which contain non-spherical particles which are capable of orientating themselves are sometimes termed tactosols. Aged vanadium pentoxide sol separates into a concentrated tactosol with rod-shaped particles and a dilute isotropic atactosol. In a magnetic field, for example, the particles of such a sol arrange themselves along the lines of force. A tactosol is readily obtained by cooling a dilute boiling sol of benzopurpurin. See Colloids, Anisotropic, Stream double refraction.

Talc. A hydrous magnesium silicate mineral,

ideally $Mg_3Si_4O_{10}(OH)_2$. The crystals are mono-clinic, but it usually occurs as foliated or com-pact pale green or colourless masses. The struc-ture is similar to muscovite but the sheets of linked tetrahedra are composed of Si_4O_{10}, whereas in muscovite they are $AlSi_3O_{10}$. Mg fills all the six-co-ordinated positions. Talc has a perfect basal cleavage, giving somewhat flexible flakes with a pearly lustre and greasy feel. Sp.gr. 2·7-2·8, hardness 1, refractive index 1·54-1·60, high double refraction.

Steatite is a pure compact variety; soapstone is a massive impure form. Ground talc is mainly used as an extender and pigment in paint, as a constituent of whiteware bodies and electrical porcelain, as a filler and dusting agent in the manufacture of rubber, insecticides, and tar and asphalt roofing materials, and as a constituent of toilet powders.

Talose. See Hexose.

Tammann, Gustav (1861-1938). Tammann was born at Yamburg, Russia, and educated at the University of Tartu, Esthonia, where he became professor and director of the Physico-chemical Institute. In 1903 he went to Göttingen to take up the newly-established professorship of In-organic Chemistry, and in 1907 became Director of the Institute for Physical Chemistry. His chief work dealt with heterogeneous equilibria and states of aggregation, thermal analysis, metal-lography, the physical chemistry of glasses and silicates, and reactions between substances in the solid state.

Tannase. A number of moulds, e.g. *Asper-gillus niger*, contain an enzyme which splits tannins of the ester type, of which methylgallate is the simplest equivalent. The acid component must contain at least two phenolic hydroxyl groups.

Tannic acid, Gallotannic acid, Tannin.

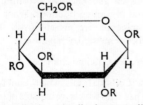

R = galloyl; m-digalloyl; m-trigalloyl.

A yellowish-white powder, with an astringent taste, soluble in water and alcohol; dextrorota-tory. It is obtained from oak-galls by fermenting them and extracting with ether. It gives precipi-tates with most metallic salts, with proteins, and with alkaloids. On hydrolysis it gives glucose and gallic acid.

Tanning development. During any photographic development process oxidized developer pro-ducts are formed and in some instances, e.g. from pyrogallol and catechol and its derivatives, the products react with the gelatin causing an increase in its melting point. The emulsion layer becomes differentially tanned in the areas of development, and the untanned gelatin can be removed by washing the developed film in warm water to give gelatin relief images useful in dye transfer print systems.

Tannins. A large class of amorphous substances present in plants. They have an astringent taste, give a blue or green colour with iron salts, and are precipitated from water solution by proteins and by alkaloids. They are condensation pro-ducts of various phenols, of which the most im-portant are pyrogallol and catechol. The struc-ture of tannic acid, the tannin from oak-galls, has been worked out; other tannins have similar types of structure. The tannins can be obtained by extracting the raw materials with water or other solvents and precipitating with lead acet-ate. It is their property of precipitating gelatin which is responsible for the uses of tannins in the treatment of hides to make leather. They are also used as mordants in the textile industry. See 'Chemistry of Vegetable Tannins', by E. Haslam, Academic Press, 1966.

Tantalic acids and Tantalates. These closely re-semble the corresponding niobium compounds. See Niobic acid.

Tantalite. The tantalum end of the tantalite-columbite isomorphous series of minerals (Fe, Mn) (Ta, Nb)$_2O_6$. It is the main ore of tan-talum and is found in alluvials in granite areas. See Columbite.

Tantalum, Ta. At.no. 73, At.wt. 180·88. A silver-white or greyish metallic element, sp.gr. 16·6, m.p. 2997°, b.p. ~ 5500°, sp.ht. 0·0346. The crystals are cubic, $a = 3·298$ Å, with the body-centred cubic structure.

The metal is notable for its hardness (30-40 Brinell; Mohs' scale 6-6·5), but can be drawn and worked in the cold. Tantalum always occurs in nature associated with niobium, the principal source being the mineral tantalite.

Tantalum is eventually recovered from its ore as the fluorotantalate, K_2TaF_7, from which the pure metal may be obtained by electrolysis at 750° using a fused mixture of K_2TaF_7, tantalum pentoxide, and an alkali halide; the product is heated in a high vacuum to remove adsorbed gases. Tantalum is oxidized on strong heating in air or oxygen, the powder or fine wire often burn-ing with incandescence. The powder also reacts with steam on heating. The metal is scarcely attacked by acids, except by a mixture of hydro-fluoric and nitric acids; it is also resistant to aqueous alkali solutions, but is attacked by fused alkalis. Tantalum reacts readily with fluorine and chlorine, and less easily with bromine, giving the pentahalides. Sulphur also combines readily.

Tantalum is used commercially in the fabrication of alloys where hardness and resistance to heat and to the action of acids are of importance; alloys with platinum, nickel, copper, and molybdenum have been used in this way. The tungsten and molybdenum alloys, of great hardness, can be used for cutting tools. The use of tantalum for electric lamp filaments has been superseded by the introduction of tungsten filaments, but tantalum is still used in wireless valves and X-ray tubes, and also in thermocouples. Tantalum has also been employed for the anodes of small electrolytic rectifiers. It is used for the fabrication of resistant containers for use in chemical manufacturing. In its compounds tantalum closely resembles niobium; it has oxidation states of five, four, three, two and one.

Tantalum bromides. The *pentabromide*, $TaBr_5$, is a pale yellow solid, m.p. 240°, b.p. 320°, closely resembling the pentachloride in its properties and methods of preparation. The *tribromide*, $TaBr_3$, has been described as a dark olive-green solid prepared by heating the pentabromide in hydrogen. Further reduction with hydrogen gives the *dibromide*, $TaBr_2$; the *tetrabromide*, $TaBr_4$, is also a product of the reduction of tantalum pentabromide with hydrogen.

Tantalum chlorides. The *pentachloride*, $TaCl_5$, is a pale yellow crystalline solid, m.p. 211°, b.p. 241°, prepared by passing chlorine over heated tantalum, or carbon tetrachloride vapour over heated tantalum pentoxide. It is very readily hydrolysed by water, and fumes slightly in moist air. It is readily soluble in carbon disulphide and acetone, reacting slowly with the latter solvent. A number of complex compounds of tantalum pentachloride with organic bases are known. On heating the pentachloride with aluminium and aluminium chloride, the lower chlorides $TaCl_2$, $TaCl_3$, and $TaCl_4$, which are green solids, are formed.

Tantalum fluorides. *Tantalum pentafluoride*, TaF_5. Colourless hygroscopic crystals, m.p. 95·1°, b.p. 229·2°, prepared by the action of fluorine on tantalum, or of hydrogen fluoride on the pentachloride. It is hydrolysed by water, but is somewhat less reactive than niobium pentafluoride. Double fluorides (e.g. $NaTaF_6$, K_2TaF_7, $(NH_4)_3TaF_8$), are readily formed.

Tantalum trifluoride, TaF_3, is obtained by the action of hydrogen fluoride on tantalum hydride.

Tantalum iodides. *Tantalum pentaiodide*, TaI_5, is a dark solid prepared by the action of aluminium iodide on tantalum pentoxide or by the reaction between tantalum and iodine under the influence of a high frequency current. It has m.p. 496°, b.p. 543°. The *tetraiodide*, TaI_4, is obtained by the interaction of iodine and excess tantalum.

Tantalum oxides. *Tantalum pentoxide*, Ta_2O_5, forms a refractory white powder, sp.gr. 7·5-7·7, generally prepared by igniting the hydrated oxide obtained on hydrolysis of some other tantalum compound; it is also formed on strong heating of tantalum in oxygen. The pentoxide is not reduced by heating in hydrogen (distinction from niobium pentoxide). It is attacked by fused alkalis, forming tantalates, and dissolves readily in hydrofluoric acid. A *dioxide*, TaO_2, is formed as a dark grey or brown powder on strong ignition of the pentoxide in absence of air.

Tantalum sulphide, TaS_2. A refractory grey or black powder prepared by heating tantalum with sulphur. It burns on heating in air, forming the pentoxide, and is slowly oxidized by boiling sulphuric or nitric acid. It also reacts with chlorine on heating, giving tantalum pentachloride. Other compounds in the tantalum-sulphur system are TaS_3 and TaS, but the elements and compounds are all intersoluble.

Tantiron. An iron-silicon alloy, containing 14 to 15% silicon and small quantities of carbon, manganese, phosphorus, and sulphur. It is resistant to nitric, sulphuric, and acetic acids at all concentrations and temperatures, but is very brittle.

Tar. Tar consists of the non-aqueous liquid condensate resulting from the destructive distillation of carbonaceous materials. It is subdivided according to the process from which it is derived, thus: (a) high-temperature tar from coke ovens; (b) low-temperature tar obtained by the low-temperature carbonization of coal; (c) high-temperature gasworks tar, from horizontal and vertical retorts; (d) oil tar from the carburetted water-gas process; (e) wood tar, or Stockholm tar, from the carbonization of wood.

Tar acids. These consist largely of phenols, and are obtained from tar by reaction with sodium carbonate to obtain the sodium phenolate and treatment of this compound with carbon dioxide to regain the phenol.

Taraxanthin, $C_{40}H_{56}O_4$. A carotenoid pigment, esters of which are present in dandelion petals, m.p. 185°. Dextrorotatory. Unlike violaxanthin, of which it is an isomer, it gives no blue colour with hydrochloric acid.

Tar oils. Heavy tar oils, consisting in the main of aromatic hydrocarbons, are applied to trees in the dormant season to kill eggs of certain insects. They are very phytotoxic.

Tartar emetic. See Potassium antimonyl tartrate.

Tartaric acids, $C_4H_6O_6$. Occur in two optically

$$HOOC-\underset{\underset{H}{|}}{\overset{\overset{OH}{|}}{C}}-\underset{\underset{OH}{|}}{\overset{\overset{H}{|}}{C}}-COOH$$

active and two inactive forms. (+)-Tartaric acid crystallizes in colourless prisms, m.p. 170°, $[\alpha]_D^{20}$ +11·98° (20% solution in water). Very soluble in water. It occurs in the grape and a few other fruits. Manufactured from argol and wine lees by precipitation as the calcium salt and decomposition of this with sulphuric acid. Potassium hydrogen tartrate is sparingly soluble in water. Many complex tartrates are known. Its chief use is in the manufacture of effervescent drinks.

(+)-Tartaric acid exists in three solid forms, the ordinary crystals, an amorphous form, and a glassy form. The crystals in plates cut perpendicular to an optic axis rotate to the left.

(−)-Tartaric acid is obtained from racemic acid by fractional crystallization of the cinchonine salt.

Racemic acid, (±)-tartaric acid, is a compound of the two active forms. It crystallizes below 73° with one molecule of water of crystallization, m.p. 205° (anhydrous). Less soluble in water than (+)-tartaric acid. Formed, together with mesotartaric acid, by boiling (+)-tartaric acid with 30% sodium hydroxide solution, or by oxidation of fumaric acid. Potassium hydrogen racemate is very insoluble.

Mesotartaric acid crystallizes in plates with one molecule of water of crystallization, m.p. 140° (anhydrous). Very soluble in water. Obtained from the mother-liquors in the preparation of racemic acid; or by oxidation of maleic acid. Potassium hydrogen mesotartrate is soluble in water.

Tartrazine (Acid Yellow 23), $C_{16}H_9N_4Na_3O_9S_2$.

The sodium salt of 4-*p*-sulphobenzeneazo-1-*p*-sulphophenyl-5-hydroxpyrazole-3-carboxylic acid. It is an orange-red powder, usually contains excess sodium chloride, and is soluble in water. It can be prepared by reacting phenylhydrazine sulphonic acid with dihydroxytartaric acid, but is more usually manufactured by condensing oxaloacetic ester with phenylhydrazine sulphonic acid and coupling with diazotized sulphanilic acid. It is one of the pyrazolone dyes (*q.v.*), is very fast to light, and dyes wool a pure yellow colour. It is a permitted colouring matter for foodstuffs and is used in lemonade powders (Food Yellow 4).

Tartronic acid, hydroxymalonic acid, $C_3H_4O_5$. Forms colourless crystals with one molecule of water of crystallization; this changes to the anhydrous

$$HO \cdot \underset{\diagdown}{\overset{\diagup}{CH}} \begin{array}{c} COOH \\ \\ COOH \end{array}$$

form at 60°, m.p. 160° (decomp.). Soluble in water and alcohol; the anhydrous acid is soluble in ether. It is prepared by heating dinitrotartaric acid in aqueous alcohol.

Taurine, Aminoethylsulphonic acid, $C_2H_7NO_3S$, $NH_2 \cdot CH_2 \cdot CH_2 \cdot SO_3H$. Crystallizes in columns, decomposing at 305°-310°. Soluble in water, insoluble in alcohol. In combination with cholic acid it forms one of the bile acids. It is formed in the liver from cysteine.

Taurocholic acid, Cholyltaurine, $C_{26}H_{45}NO_7S$. It occurs as its sodium salt in the bile. On hydrolysis it gives taurine and cholic acid. See Bile salts.

Tautomerism or dynamic isomerism. The interconversion of two isomers is called tautomerism and this is usually thought of as involving the migration of an atom or group as an ion. Thus *prototropy* frequently involves the interchange of a *proton* and a double-bond, e.g.

$$CH_3 \cdot \underset{\underset{O}{\|}}{C} \cdot CH_2 \cdot CO_2Et \leftrightharpoons CH_3 \cdot \underset{\underset{OH}{|}}{C} : CH \cdot CO_2Et$$

whereas *anionotropy* involves the interchange of an *anion* and a double-bond, e.g.

$$CH_3 \cdot CH : CH \cdot CH_2Br \rightleftharpoons CH_3 \cdot CHBrCH : CH_2.$$

Other tautomeric systems besides the *three-carbon* system exemplified are known.

Technetium, Tc. At.no. 43. ^{99}Tc (half-life 2×10^5 years) is prepared by neutron irradiation of ^{98}Mo. The element was formerly named masurium. The metal is obtained by hydrogen reduction of technetium compounds. It is a silvery metal with a hexagonal close-packed structure ($a=2\cdot735$, $c=4\cdot39$ Å) d 11·5, m.p. 2150°. The properties of technetium are similar to those of rhenium. Technetium compounds are corrosion inhibitors.

Technetium compounds. The chemistry of technetium is similar to that of rhenium and shows few similarities to that of manganese. Oxidation of technetium in air gives the yellow heptoxide, Tc_2O_7; a solution in water contains the pertechnetate ion TcO_4^-. Other oxides TcO_2 and

TcO_3 are also known. Chlorides $TcCl_4$, and $TcCl_6$ have been prepared. *Technetium hexafluoride*, TcF_6, is a golden-yellow solid, m.p. 33°, which results from the action of fluorine upon the metal. Fluorine upon TcO_2 gives *pertechnyl fluoride*, TcO_3F, a yellow solid, m.p. 18·3°.

Teeple, John Edgar (1874-1931). Teeple was born in Kempton, Illinois. He commenced an academic career but abandoned it in 1904 to become a consulting chemist in New York, where he opened his own office in 1908. His investigations were of a varied nature, frequently confidential in character, his best-known achievement being the successful development of the potash industry at Searles Lake, California. He was awarded the Perkin Medal in 1927.

Teepol. The trade name for an approx. 20% solution of the sodium salts of certain secondary alkyl sulphates, obtained as a by-product of the petroleum industry by sulphating the appropriate olefins. It is an anionic detergent and wetting agent, and is widely used for cleaning. It is an amber-coloured liquid, miscible with water, and tends to crystallize at temperatures below 15°.

Teflon. A trade name for polytetrafluoroethylene or PTFE, an extremely stable and inert plastic. Teflon is used extensively in the chemical and electrical industries.

Teichman's crystals. See Haemin.

Teichoic acids. Natural organic phosphate polymers, apparently unique to Gram-positive bacteria, in which they are constituents of the cell walls and cell contents. Teichoic acids, which are extractable with cold 10% trichloroacetic acid, comprise units of ribitol (or glycerol) linked by phosphate groups and bearing glucosyl or N-acetylglucosaminyl residues. D-Alanine is also present in an alkali-labile ester linkage with one hydroxyl group of each ribitol or glycerol unit. It is possible that teichoic acids play a part in the immunological specificity of bacteria.

Tellurates. Salts of telluric acid.

Telluric acid, H_6TeO_6. Prepared by the action of strong oxidizing agents on tellurium or tellurous acid. It separates from water as $H_6TeO_6 \cdot 4H_2O$, losing $4H_2O$ at 10°. On heating it yields allotelluric acid $(H_2TeO_4)_n$, where n is about 11. Telluric acid is a weak hexabasic acid and is easily reduced. Series of salts $MTeO(OH)_5$ and $M_2TeO_2(OH)_4$ are known.

Tellurides. See Hydrogen telluride.

Tellurites. The alkali tellurites are obtained by treating tellurium dioxide with aqueous alkalis, or by fusing it with an alkali carbonate. They are soluble in water, and the other tellurites may

be obtained from them by precipitation. Alkali tellurites in solution are oxidized to tellurates by halogens or hydrogen peroxide, and reduced to tellurium by such reagents as sulphur dioxide and hydrazine. They are derived from the acids H_2TeO_3, $H_2Te_2O_5$, and $H_2Te_4O_9$.

Tellurium, Te. At.no. 52, At.wt. 127·61, m.p. 452°, b.p. 1007°, d 6·2. Tellurium occurs in small quantities in Japanese red sulphur, in pyrites (Spain), and as tellurides such as hessite, Ag_2Te, and melonite, Ni_2Te_3. The dioxide TeO_2 occurs native as tellurite. Tellurium is extracted from the anode muds of copper refineries, which are roasted to form the dioxide, TeO_2, which is then smelted with carbon to yield the element. Amorphous tellurium, d 6·015, is a grey-black powder obtained by precipitation, and yields the ordinary crystalline variety, metallic tellurium, on heating. This form crystallizes in the hexagonal system $a=4·5559$, $c=5·9268$ Å, and is isomorphous with selenium. Both forms are poor conductors of heat or electricity. The element is used in small quantities for tinting glass red to violet, and in lead to confer toughness during cold working. In its chemical properties, it takes its natural place after sulphur and selenium in the periodic system, and differs from them in being more metallic and generally less reactive. It combines directly with halogens, oxygen, and many metals, and dissolves in nitric and sulphuric acids. Tellurium compounds are poisonous, and small amounts induce indisposition, accompanied by a most nauseating odour in the breath, perspiration, and faeces.

Tellurium bromides. *Tellurium dibromide*, $TeBr_2$. This is an unstable compound obtained by the action of powdered tellurium on the tetrabromide in ethereal solution. It has m.p. 210°, b.p. 339°.

Tellurium tetrabromide, $TeBr_4$, forms red needles, d 4·3, m.p. 380° (*circa*), b.p. 420° (*circa*). It is prepared by the action of an excess of bromine on tellurium. The vapour is largely dissociated into tellurium dibromide and bromine. It yields many addition compounds, and gives bromotellurates, e.g. K_2TeBr_6, with alkali-metal bromides.

Tellurium chlorides. *Tellurium dichloride*, $TeCl_2$. This is obtained as an unstable solid, m.p. 175°-209°, b.p. 324°, by refluxing the tetrachloride with tellurium.

Tellurium tetrachloride, $TeCl_4$. This is obtained as a colourless crystalline solid, m.p. 225°, b.p. 390°, by the prolonged action of chlorine on heated tellurium. It is readily hydrolysed by water, yields addition compounds with ammonia, e.g. $TeCl_4, 6NH_3$, and gives with the alkali-metal chlorides the chlorotellurates, e.g. K_2TeCl_6.

Tellurium compounds. Tellurium compounds are generally derived from the oxides TeO and TeO_2, and closely resemble the corresponding selenium compounds. The differences are generally due to the more metallic nature of the former element. Thus tellurium forms a definite tetraiodide, whereas selenium does not; tellurium forms basic salts derived from the amphoteric oxide TeO_2. Carbon ditelluride and carbonyl telluride are unknown. In its compounds with organic radicals, tellurium is uniformly bivalent, e.g. $Te(CH_3)_2$, but the compounds often yield addition products, e.g. $Te(CH_3)_2,HgI_2$.

Tellurium cyanide, $Te(CN)_2$. This is an unstable compound obtained when tellurium tetrabromide and silver cyanide are brought together in benzene solution.

Tellurium fluorides. *Tellurium tetrafluoride*, TeF_4, is a colourless, deliquescent solid prepared by the action of selenium tetrafluoride on tellurium dioxide; m.p. 130°. It is decomposed by water, forming tellurous acid, and gives crystalline salts of the general formula $MF \cdot TeF_4$ with alkali metal fluorides.

Tellurium hexafluoride, TeF_6, is a stable gas, m.p. $-35 \cdot 5°$, sublimes at $-39°$, obtained by the action of fluorine on tellurium at $-78°$.

Ditellurium decafluoride, Te_2F_{10}, is prepared, mixed with TeF_6, by the fluorination of tellurium or tellurium dioxide. It has m.p. $-33 \cdot 7°$, b.p. 59°. Oxyfluorides, $Te_3F_{14}O_2$ and $Te_6F_{26}O_5$, are also formed during the fluorination of tellurium dioxide.

Tellurium iodide, TeI_4. Forms black crystals, d_4^{15} 5·05, which dissociate above 100°. It is obtained by cautiously heating the powdered, well-mixed elements. Many addition compounds are known, including the iodotellurates, e.g. K_2TeI_6.

Tellurium nitride, TeN or Te_3N_4. This is obtained as a yellow, very explosive powder when liquid ammonia reacts with a tellurium tetrahalide.

Tellurium oxides. Three of these are known:

Tellurium monoxide, TeO. This oxide is formed by the decomposition of tellurium sulphoxide. It is a spongy black material which instantly reduces permanganate.

Tellurium dioxide, TeO_2. This oxide is known in two forms. Crystals of the tetragonal system, d 5·66, are obtained from the solution in nitric acid, whilst the molten oxide deposits rhombic needles, d 5·93. The oxide is formed by burning tellurium in air or oxygen, oxidizing tellurium with nitric acid, decomposing tellurites with acids, or by heating basic salts of tellurium. Unlike the sulphur and selenium analogues, it is

scarcely soluble in cold water (1 in 150,000). It is amphoteric; the aqueous solution contains tellurous acid, H_2TeO_3, whilst the oxide dissolves in hydrochloric acid to yield the tetrachloride. Aqueous solutions of the oxide in acids are readily reduced to tellurium. It has m.p. 452°.

Tellurium trioxide, TeO_3. A yellow solid, d 5·1, obtained by the careful decomposition of telluric acid at 360°. It is insoluble in water, and in cold hydrochloric acid and cold aqueous alkali. It is an oxidizing agent, being readily reduced to the dioxide. With hot concentrated alkalis the tellurates are formed. On prolonged heating it is converted to a grey form, d 6·21, which is very much less reactive than the yellow form.

Tellurium sulphides. A reddish brown precipitate is formed on passing hydrogen sulphide into an acidified tellurite solution. This and other solids which have been described as sulphides are very probably only mixtures of tellurium and sulphur.

Tellurium sulphoxide, $TeSO_3$. A cherry-red solid, formed by adding powdered tellurium to sulphur trioxide.

Tellurous acid. This has never been isolated. A flocculant white precipitate, TeO_2,nH_2O, is formed when potassium tellurite is treated with dilute nitric acid, but above 40° the precipitate is TeO_2. Salts are known, not only of H_2TeO_3, but also of condensed acids such as $H_2Te_2O_5$ and $H_2Te_6O_{13}$.

Temper brittleness. A serious fall in shock resistance occurring in certain alloy steels when tempered in the range 300°-600°. Steels containing manganese and chromium are particularly susceptible. Nitrogen and phosphorus impurities increase the susceptibility. The cause is due to a grain boundary segregation of these elements but no precipitate is formed. Molybdenum (less than $\frac{1}{2}\%$) prevents temper brittleness and is commonly present in nickel chromium steels for engineering components.

Tempering. The process of reheating a quenched steel to relieve internal stresses, reduce hardness and tensile strength, and restore ductility and resistance to impact loading. Tempering is carried out within the temperature range 200°-550° for plain carbon steels. For alloy steels the temperatures may be somewhat higher. The higher the tempering temperature the greater the loss in hardness.

Tenacity. That property which enables a substance to resist fracture under the action of tensile stress. It is expressed in tons per square inch of sectional area.

Tennant, Smithson. Born in 1761, and educated at Tadcaster and Beverley in Yorkshire. He studied chemistry under Black at Edinburgh, and visited Scheele in Sweden. In 1796 he proved that diamond is pure carbon; in 1804 he discovered osmium and iridium; and in 1813 became professor of chemistry at Cambridge. He died in 1815. See *Nature*, 1961, **192**, 1224.

Tennantite. See Tetrahedrite.

Terbium, Tb. At.no. 65, At.wt. 159·2, m.p. 1356°, b.p. 2800°, d 8·272. Terbium metal has the hexagonal close-packed structure ($a = 3·5990$, $c = 5·696$ Å). It is a typical rare-earth element (*q.v.*).

Terbium compounds. Tripositive terbium compounds are pale pink in colour and are typical rare-earth compounds (*q.v.*). Compounds in higher oxidation states are known. On heating Tb_2O_3 in air $TbO_{1·71-1·81}$ results. TbF_4 results from the action of fluorine on Tb (III) salts; complex tetrapositive fluorides are known.

Terebene. A mixture of terpene hydrocarbons obtained by the action of various acids on pinene, which contains *p*-cymene, camphene, and terpinolene.

It has b.p. 160°-190°, d 0·862-0·870. Soluble in alcohol, almost insoluble in water. It has a pleasant characteristic odour and is used medicinally as an inhalent, an expectorant, a deodorant, and a mild antiseptic.

Terephthalic acid, $C_8H_6O_4$. *p*-Benzenedicarboxylic acid. It crystallizes in colourless needles, m.p. 300° (sublimes), d 1·510; insoluble in water and most organic solvents, slightly soluble in hot alcohol, soluble in pyridine. It is manufactured by the oxidation of *p*-xylene and used in the production of Terylene.

Term symbols. The spectroscopic notation used to denote a particular electronic state.

Terpenes. In the strict sense terpenes are volatile, aromatic hydrocarbons of the empirical formula $C_{10}H_{16}$. In a wider sense the term includes sesquiterpenes, $C_{15}H_{24}$, diterpenes, $C_{20}H_{32}$, and higher polymers. In a still looser sense the term includes various oxygen-containing compounds derived from the terpene hydrocarbons, such as alcohols, ketones, and camphors. The terpenes are of great scientific and industrial importance, being characteristic products of many varieties of vegetable life and important constituents of most odorants, natural and synthetic, employed in perfumery. Many of them are also of medical importance, such as the constituents of many eucalyptus oils, menthol, and camphor. Practically without exception the terpene hydro-

carbons may be considered as polymers of isoprene, C_5H_8, and may be either open-chain compounds or may contain one or more C_6 and other rings. They are chemically unsaturated, very reactive and in many cases form characteristic compounds. Most of them have highly characteristic and usually pleasant odours. They are usually obtained from vegetable products by steam distillation. See 'The Chemistry of the Terpenes,' by A. R. Pinder, Chapman & Hall, 1960.

Terphenyl. *p*-Diphenylbenzene.

1,8-Terpin, $C_{10}H_{20}O_2$. A monocyclic dialcohol obtained together with α-terpineol and other substances by the action of dilute alkali on *trans*-dipentene dihydrochloride, by the cyclization of linalool, geraniol, and nerol, and by various other reactions. It forms *cis*- and *trans*-isomerides. *cis*-Terpin forms a hydrate which crystallizes from water in rhombic pyramids, melting at 116°-117° with a loss of water, forming *cis*-terpin, m.p. 104°-105°. *trans*-Terpin, which forms no hydrate, crystallizes in monoclinic prisms, m.p. 158°-159°.

Terpin hydrate has a similar physiological action to that of oil of turpentine, and is administered to relieve coughing in tuberculosis and chronic bronchitis.

Terpinenes. The three isomers, α-, β- and γ-terpinene, are monocyclic terpenes, $C_{10}H_{16}$, which all yield the same dihydrochloride of formula (1).

α-*Terpinene*, $C_{10}H_{16}$, formula (2). This is found in cardamom, marjoram, and coriander oils, from which it is separated as the nitrosite of m.p. 155°. It is also obtained as the main constituent of the product obtained by treating linalool and geraniol with concentrated formic acid, also by treating α-pinene with strong sulphuric acid or α-terpineol with oxalic acid. No method of complete purification is known, but the following constants have been recorded: b.p. 180°-182°, d_4^{15} 0·8484, $n_D^{15·6}$ 1·48133. It smells of lemons.

19*   575

β-Terpinene, $C_{10}H_{16}$, formula (3), is always present in α-terpinene but has not been obtained pure from natural sources. It has been prepared synthetically from sabinene. It has the following constants: b.p. 173°-174°, d^{22} 0·838, n_D^{22} 1·4754.

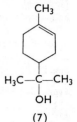

α-Terpineol, $C_{10}H_{18}O$, formula (7). An optically active alcohol. The (+)-form is found in petit-grain, neroli, and other oils, the (−)-form in camphor oils, and the racemic form in cajuput oil. α-Terpineol is widely used in the perfumery industry, and is most conveniently prepared by the dehydration of terpin. It can also be prepared directly by the action of sulphuric acid in acetic acid or alcoholic solution on turpentine oil. By all these technical processes a mixture of isomers is obtained from which α- and β-terpineols can be separated by fractional distillation. (+)-α-Terpineol gives the following constants: m.p. 37°, b.p. 104°/15 mm. d_4^{14} 0·9475, n_D^{18} 1·4832, $[\alpha]_D$ +100·5°. It yields a phenylurethane of m.p. 109·5°, the racemic form of which melts at 113°.

(3)   (4)

γ-Terpinene, $C_{10}H_{16}$, formula (4). A monocyclic terpene found in coriander, lemon, cumin, ajowan, and samphire oils. It also occurs, together with α-terpinene, in the mixture of hydrocarbons obtained by acting on terpin hydrate with weak sulphuric acid or by treatment of pinene with an alcoholic solution of sulphuric acid. Its constants are: b.p. 183°/760 mm, d^{15} 0·853, $n_D^{15·6}$ 1·4754. It forms a crystalline tetrabromide, m.p. 128°.

Terpinenols. The terpinenols, $C_{10}H_{18}O$, are monocyclic alcohols obtained from terpinenes by the addition of one molecule of water.

Terpinen-1-ol, $C_{10}H_{18}O$, formula (5). This alcohol occurs in the low-boiling fraction of commercial terpineol. It is an oil of b.p. 208°-210°, d^{18} 0·9265, n_D^{18} 1·4781.

(5)   (6)

Terpinen-4-ol, $C_{10}H_{18}O$, formula (6). An optically active alcohol, the (+)-form of which is found in Ceylon cardamom oil, marjoram oil, cypress oil, and nutmeg oil.

The racemic form is obtained by the action of dilute mineral acids or of formic acid on sabinene. Its smell resembles that of α-terpineol.

(+)-Terpinen-4-ol has the constants b.p. 209°-212°, d^{19} 0·9265, n_D^{19} 1·4785, $[\alpha]_D$ +25·2°. The constants of the racemic form are b.p. 212°-214°, d 0·929, n_D 1·4803.

Terpinen-4-ol yields a naphthylurethane of m.p. 104°-105°.

Terpineols, $C_{10}H_{18}O$. The terpineols are monocyclic terpene alcohols obtained by the dehydration of terpin. Theoretically four isomeric alcohols can thus be obtained, of which three are known, namely α-, β-, and γ-terpineols.

β-Terpineol, $C_{10}H_{18}O$, formula (8). This substance has not been found in nature. It is obtained from commercial terpineol as described under α-terpineol. It has the following constants: m.p. 32°-33°, b.p. 209°-210°/752 mm, d^{20} 0·919, n_D^{20} 1·4747, It yields a phenylurethane of m.p. 85°. It smells strongly of hyacinths.

(8)   (9)

γ-Terpineol, $C_{10}H_{18}O$, formula (9). It is doubtful whether this substance occurs in nature. It was originally prepared by the reduction of 1, 4, 8-tribromo-*p*-menthane. γ-Terpineol crystallizes from ether in thick prisms of m.p. 68°-70°, and forms a dibromide of m.p. 103°.

Terpinolene, $C_{10}H_{16}$. A monocyclic terpene, which is found as a constituent of terebene which is in turn obtained by the action of acids on pinene. It is also formed by the action of dilute acids on terpin, α-terpineol, and other similar compounds. It forms a crystalline tetrabromide of m.p. 116°. It is doubtful whether it has been obtained in a pure state. The following constants are recorded: b.p. 67°-68°/10 mm, d^{20} 0·854, n_D 1·484. Mineral acids convert it into its isomer terpinene.

Terramycin. A trade name for oxytetracycline.

Terylene. A trade name (I.C.I.) for the polymer formed by reacting the dimethyl ester of terephthalic acid with ethylene glycol. It has the structure

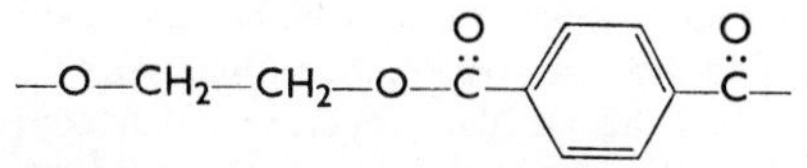

$$-O-CH_2-CH_2-O-\overset{O}{\overset{\cdot\cdot}{C}}-\underset{}{\bigcirc}-\overset{O}{\overset{\cdot\cdot}{C}}-$$

Terylene is a hard horny substance, which melts at about 265° and can be drawn into fibres of high tensile strength. Materials made from it have high strength both wet and dry and are resistant to abrasion and creasing. Dacron (Dupont) is another trade name.

Testosterone, **17β-hydroxyandrost-4-en-3-one,**

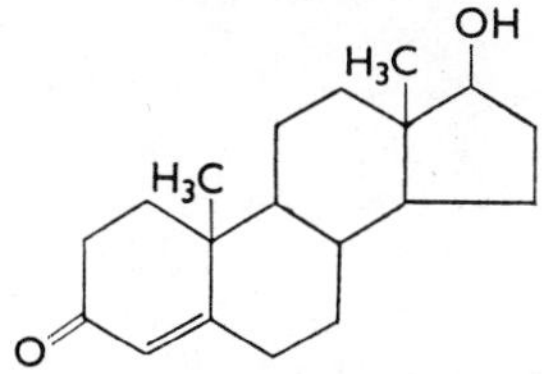

$C_{19}H_{28}O_2$. Crystallizes in needles from acetone, m.p. 154°, $[\alpha]_D$ +109° in alcohol. Testosterone is the androgenic hormone formed in the testes: it controls the development and maintenance of the male sex organs and secondary sex characteristics, and is used, together with synthetic analogues, in treating disorders due to impaired secretion of the natural hormone. Testosterone is obtained commercially from the corresponding 3β-hydroxy-Δ⁵-ene (dehydroepiandrosterone, androstenolone).

Test screens. For the purpose of securing a size analysis of a sample test screens are used. These usually consist of a nest of small circular screens fitting on top of each other with the coarsest at the top and the finest at the bottom. The sample is placed in the topmost screen and the whole assembly subjected to vibration for a standard time. The weight of the fractions remaining on the surface of each screen then gives the proportions of the sample lying between certain limits of size.

Different systems of screens are available including the Tyler, Institute of Mining and Metallurgy (I.M.M.), and British and U.S. Standard screens. In all these series the screen sizes are designated by numbers, the mesh numbers of consecutive screens having a fixed relation to the size of the aperture.

Tetracene, $C_2H_8N_{10}O$. 1-Guanyl-4-nitroso-aminoguanyltetracene. It is a colourless or pale

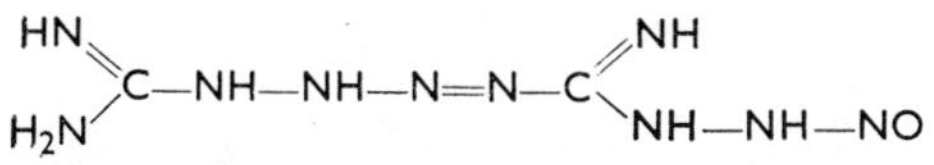

yellow solid formed by the action of nitrous acid on aminoguanidine. It is almost insoluble in water, alcohol, and ether. It is somewhat more sensitive to impact than mercury fulminate, and

is used as a constituent of some detonating compositions.

Tetrachloroethane. See Acetylene tetrachloride.

Tetrachloroethylene, Perchloroethylene, $CCl_2:CCl_2$. M.p. −22·4°, b.p. 121·2°, d_4^{20} 1·623, n_D^{20} 1·502. It is manufactured by reacting pentachloroethane, obtained from chlorine and trichloroethylene, with milk of lime; by the direct chlorination of light hydrocarbons (methane, ethane, propane) at 500°-650°; by the direct chlorination of ethylene. It is non-inflammable and is used very largely as a dry cleaning solvent; another use is for metal degreasing. It is used in doses of 1 ml as a vermifuge to expel hook worms. The vapour is poisonous but it is considered to be less toxic than carbon tetrachloride which is used for the same purpose.

Tetrachloromethane. See Carbon tetrachloride.

Tetrachlorophthalic **anhydride,** $C_8O_3Cl_4$. Crystallizes in prisms, m.p. 255°-257°. It is insoluble in cold water and sparingly soluble in ether. It sublimes on heating strongly. It is prepared by the direct chlorination of phthalic anhydride in 50-60% oleum in the presence of iodine, the temperature being raised from 50°-200° as the reaction proceeds.

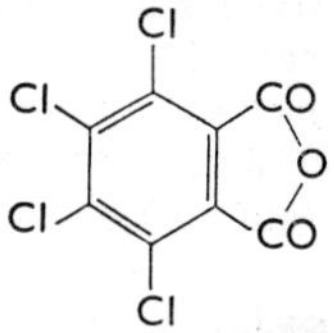

It is used instead of phthalic anhydride in the preparation of certain Eosin dyes (Phloxines, etc.) which are bluer and brighter than those from unchlorinated intermediates.

Tetracyanoethylene, TCNE. A sublimable white crystalline solid, smelling of hydrogen cyanide, m.p. 200°, which has high thermal and oxidative sta-

bility. Reacts with most compounds containing an active hydrogen and with dienes in typical Diels-Alder additions. It is probably the strongest π-acid known; it forms a series of coloured complexes with aromatic hydrocarbons and gives salts of the radical anion with many metals, e.g. $K \cdot TCNE$.

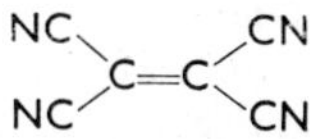

Tetracyclines. An important group of antibiotics isolated from *Streptomyces* spp., having structures based on a naphthacene skeleton. Tetracycline (trade names Achromycin, Tetracyn), the parent compound, has the structure:

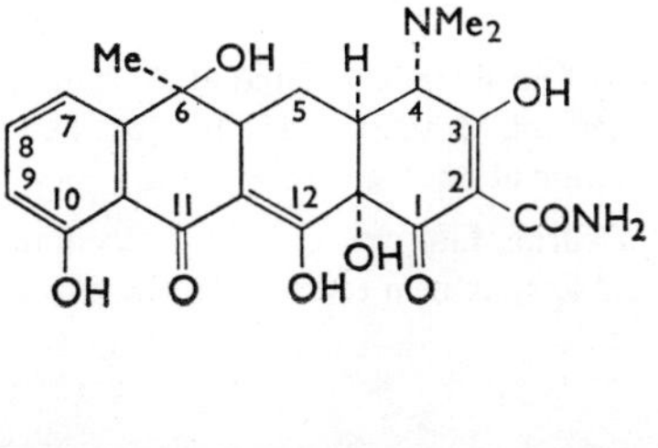

It crystallizes as the trihydrate; when anhydrous it has m.p. 170°-175° (decomp.), $[\alpha]_D^{25}$ $-239°$ (1% in methanol). The 7-chloro-derivative, the first of the group to be isolated (1948) is known as chlortetracycline or Aureomycin (trade name). The 5-hydroxy-derivative is oxytetracycline or Terramycin (trade name). More recently introduced tetracyclines are 6-demethyl-7-chlortetracycline (Ledermycin) and 5-hydroxy-6-deoxy-6-methylenetetracycline (Rondomycin).

Tetracyclines are broad-spectrum antibiotics, effective against Gram-positive and Gram-negative bacteria, also against Rickettsiae (typhus fever) and certain other organisms.

Tetraethyl pyrophosphate, TEPP, $C_8H_{20}O_7P_2$.

$$(C_2H_5O)_2\overset{\displaystyle O}{\overset{\displaystyle \|}{P}}-O-\overset{\displaystyle O}{\overset{\displaystyle \|}{P}}(OC_2H_5)_2$$

An insecticidal substance which is prepared by reaction of triethyl phosphate with phosphorus pentoxide or oxychloride. It is a colourless mobile hygroscopic liquid, b.p. 104°-110°/0·08 mm, 135°-138°/1 mm, d1·1847. It is miscible with water, alcohols, benzene, but not with kerosine and other paraffins. Acidic products of hydrolysis, which form within a few hours, are corrosive to metals. TEPP was originally produced as a substitute for nicotine, but it is useful only as a direct aphicide or acaricide because of its rapid decomposition by water. It is acutely toxic to mammals, and is readily absorbed through the skin and respiratory tract.

Tetrafluorohydrazine, N_2F_4. See Nitrogen fluorides.

Tetragonal system. A term used to describe crystals which have three crystallographic axes at right angles, two only of which are of equal length. The essential symmetry characteristic of the system is the four-fold axis (taken as the z axis), but further symmetry elements may be present up to a maximum of four two-fold axes and five planes of symmetry. Examples of compounds crystallizing in the tetragonal system are rutile, zircon, and calcium carbide. See also Crystal symmetry.

Tetrahedral co-ordination. Regular co-ordina-

$$\begin{array}{c} \text{L} \\ | \\ \text{M} \\ \diagup\,|\,\diagdown \\ \text{L}\quad\text{L}\quad\text{L} \end{array}$$

tion by four ligands situated at the corners of a tetrahedron. Methane, CH_4, has tetrahedral co-ordination about the carbon.

Tetrahedrite, fahl ore, Cu_3SbS_3. Crystallizes in the cubic system in tetrahedra, the edges often

bevelled by [211]. Hardness $3\frac{1}{2}$, sp.gr. 4·7. Steel-grey crystals with a metallic lustre. This is a common copper ore of variable composition, arsenic replacing part of the antimony, and iron, zinc, or other metals replacing part of the copper. When the antimony is entirely replaced by arsenic the mineral is called tennantite. It is widely distributed throughout the world, though found in greatest quantity in the western U.S.A.

Tetrahydrocannabinol. The active component of hashish (marihuana), the psychotomimetically active resin of the female flowering tops of *Cannabis sativa* L. The member of the active fraction present in most hemp plants is the Δ^1-3,4-*trans* isomer $C_{21}H_{29}O_2$ but the isomeric Δ^6-3,4-*trans* isomer (with the double bond between positions 1 and 6) also occurs naturally and is similar to the Δ^1 isomer in physiological potency.

Tetrahydrofuran, THF, C_4H_8O. It is a colourless liquid, b.p. 66°, m.p. $-108·5°$, n_D^{20} 1·4073, d^{20} 0·892, miscible with water in all proportions, also with esters, ketones, alcohols, ethers, aliphatic, aromatic and chlorinated hydrocarbons. It has found a wide use in industry as a solvent for resins, many plastics (especially of the PVC type) and elastomers; as an ether type solvent for chemical reactions it often produces increased reaction rates and yields. Prepared via furfural, furoic acid and furan by acid hydrolysis of the polysaccharides in oat husks.

Tetrahydrothiophen, THT, tetramethylene sulphide. Can be obtained by the catalytic reduction of thiophen or tetrahydrothiophen-1,1-dioxide (sulpholane). It is a colourless mobile liquid, with a penetrating odour, b.p. 118°-119°. It is insoluble in water, but miscible with most other solvents. The odour associated with town gas is mostly that of a few parts per billion of tetrahydrothiophen, which is deliberately added for detection.

Tetrakisazo-dyestuffs. See Azo-dyes and Direct cotton-dyes. Most of these dyestuffs are produced directly on the fibre by the diazotization and development of the material dyed with some substantive cotton dye containing two diazotizable amino-groups (Benzo brown G, etc.).

Tetralin, tetrahydronaphthalene, $C_{10}H_{12}$. A colourless liquid, b.p. 207°, d^{17} 0·9738; n_D^{17} 1·54529. It is obtained by the catalytic hydrogenation of naphthalene. Owing to the presence of one aromatic ring it can be nitrated and sulphonated. It is non-toxic and is very largely used as a solvent for fats, oils, and resins.

Tetramethylsilane, TMS, $(CH_3)_4Si$. Used as an internal reference standard for proton magnetic resonance spectroscopy. According to the widely accepted τ-scale TMS protons appear at 10·00 τ and most protons bonded to carbon then appear downfield (smaller τ-value) from TMS.

Tetranitromethane, $C(NO_2)_4$. A colourless liquid, m.p. 12·5°, b.p. 125·7°. Insoluble in water; miscible with alcohol and ether. It is made by nitration of acetic anhydride with anhydrous nitric acid. Decomposed by alcoholic solutions of potassium hydroxide to nitroform. Reacts with alcohols in the presence of alkali to give the nitrate of the alcohol. Gives a yellow colour with derivatives of cyclopropane and unsaturated compounds. Used as a test for unsaturation.

Tetrathionic acid. See Polythionic acids.

Tetrazo-dyes. See also Azo-dyes and Direct cotton dyes. These are the most important direct cotton colours, and are derived from diamines with the two amino-groups generally in different nuclei, but occasionally in the same nucleus. Among the diamines which produce direct cotton dyes certain regularities can be seen: (1) if the amino-groups are in different nuclei they must be para- to the point of juncture of the two nuclei or to the ends of the chain connecting the nuclei; (2) this chain must be unsaturated or contain an atom with residual affinity; (3) with derivatives of diphenyl, the ortho-position to the joining bond or chain must be free or part of a ring; (4) if the amino-groups are in the same nucleus, they must be para- or, in the case of naphthalene, 1,5 or para- to one another.

The actual preparation of a disazo-dyestuff from a diamine is brought about by treating the diamine with nitrous acid and converting into the tetrazo-salt. The difference between the formation of the azo-compound and the disazo-compound is that in the case of the latter two molecules of the amine or phenol (as second component) have to be employed. Typical examples are Congo red and Congo Corinth.

Tetrazolium salts. Quaternary salts derived from

Blue Tetrazolium

tetrazoles. They are colourless or yellow, crystalline solids, usually soluble in water and alcohols. Certain tetrazolium salts, e.g. 'blue tetrazolium' (3,3'-dianisolebis-[4,4'-(3,5-diphenyl)-tetrazolium chloride]) are much used in the detection of reducing substances, especially in chromatography and in histology. Their value depends on their very facile reduction to coloured formazans. Tetrazolium salts are also applied in colour photography.

Tetrose. A carbohydrate with four carbon atoms. There are four aldo-tetroses, the two stereoisomers of erythrose and threose, and two possible keto-tetroses.

Tetryl, trinitrophenylmethylnitramine,

$C_7H_5N_5O_8$. A pale yellow powder, m.p. about 129°, which decomposes rapidly above this temperature. It is insoluble in water, but soluble in alcohol and organic solvents. It is obtained by nitrating a solution of dimethylaniline in concentrated sulphuric acid. Tetryl is a very stable explosive, more powerful than TNT and picric acid, but more sensitive to shock, and is much used as a primer or booster. It is also known as C.E. (composition exploding).

Thallium, Tl. At.no. 81, At.wt. 204·39. Thallium occurs as a major constituent in a few minerals, such as crookesite, which is a selenide of thallium, copper, and silver. In small quantities it is widely distributed in minerals and rocks, and occurs in certain mineral waters, as well as in the vegetable kingdom. The element was discovered as the result of the spectroscopic examination of selenium residues from a sulphuric acid plant (Crookes, 1861). It is soft, and of metallic appearance, resembling lead closely. Its density is 11·85 at 20°. The element exists in two modifications, the first of which (α-form) is stable below 262°, and has the hexagonal close-packed structure, $a = 3·4564$, $c = 5·531$ Å, while the variety stable at higher temperature has the face-centred cubic structure $a = 4·84$ Å. The m.p. is 303·5° and the b.p. is 1457°. Commercial thallium usually contains small amounts of lead, tin, copper, and aluminium. The commercial source is the flue dust or chamber deposit from sulphuric acid plants in which thalliferous iron pyrites is utilized.

Thallium does not combine with hydrogen. The metal oxidizes slowly in air at room temperature. When it is heated in oxygen thallous oxide, Tl_2O, or thallic oxide, Tl_2O_3, are formed. The metal reacts directly with the halogens, sulphur, selenium, tellurium, phosphorus, arsenic and antimony. It dissolves slowly in hydrochloric, acid, more rapidly in sulphuric acid, and very readily in nitric acid. Thallium forms two main series of salts: the thallous salts, in which it is unipositive and the thallic salts, in which it is tripositive. Thallous salts show a close resemblance in solubility and general properties to silver (I) salts. The thallic salts resemble salts of aluminium. Thallium is used in the manufacture of special optical glass. Thallous salts are very poisonous.They find some use as fungicides.

Thallium bromides. *Thallous bromide*, TlBr, has m.p. 456°, b.p. 815°, solubility 0·048 g in 100 g water at 20°. It is very similar in properties to thallous chloride.

Thallic bromide, $TlBr_3$, is formed by the action of bromine on thallous bromide. It is very unstable, decomposing to $Tl[TlBr_4]$.

Thallium carbonate, Tl_2CO_3. M.p. 272°. Solubility 5·2 g in 100 g water at 18°. It is prepared by the action of carbon dioxide on thallous hydroxide; the solution has an alkaline reaction.

Thallium chlorides, *Thallous chloride*, TlCl. A white crystalline solid, m.p. 430°, b.p. 806°, which is precipitated on adding hydrochloric acid to a solution of a thallous salt. It is sparingly soluble in cold water (2·4 g per litre at 10°), but more soluble in hot water. Thallous chloride, bromide and iodide bear a close resemblance to the corresponding lead salts, both in appearance and in physical properties.

Thallic chloride, $TlCl_3, 4H_2O$. This hydrate is a colourless crystalline solid which is obtained by suspending thallous chloride in water, passing chlorine until solution is complete, evaporating below 60°, and crystallizing. It forms a monohydrate at 55°. The anhydrous salt is obtained by dehydration of the tetrahydrate at room temperature over sulphuric acid. It is very hygroscopic, and is decomposed with evolution of chlorine when it is heated to 100°. The anhydrous salt is soluble in alcohol and ether. It melts at 25°.

Thallium chromate, *Thallous chromate*, Tl_2CrO_4. A yellow crystalline powder, sparingly soluble in water, which is precipitated by adding potassium chromate solution to a solution containing a thallous salt.

Thallium fluorides. *Thallous fluoride*, TlF. A colourless solid, which is readily soluble in water, from which it crystallizes in regular octahedra, m.p. 327°, b.p. 655°. It may be prepared by dissolving thallous hydroxide in dilute hydrofluoric acid, evaporating and crystallizing the residue. It forms an acid fluoride TlF, HF, which is stable up to 100°.

Thallic fluoride, TlF_3. Prepared by passing fluorine over thallic oxide at 300°. It is a white solid, immediately hydrolysed by moist air; m.p. (in fluorine) 550°.

Thallium hydroxide. *Thallous hydroxide*, TlOH. A strongly basic substance, which may be prepared by decomposing thallous sulphate with barium hydroxide solution. It crystallizes from aqueous solutions in the form of yellow needles. It is readily soluble in water (352·7 g per litre of saturated aqueous solution at 20°) and in alcohol. The aqueous solution has a strongly alkaline reaction, and will precipitate the insoluble hydroxides of many metals. The aqueous solution absorbs carbon dioxide readily to form thallous carbonate.

Thallium iodides. *Thallous iodide*, TlI; m.p. 440°, b.p. 824°. Solubility 0·0079 g per 100 g water at 25°. Thallous iodide is dimorphic. It is yellow at room temperature, becomes red at 170°, and melts to a black liquid.

Thallic iodide, TlI_3, is prepared by the addition of potassium iodide to a thallic solution, but is probably thallous periodide. It readily loses iodine.

Thallium nitrates. *Thallous nitrate*, $TlNO_3$. Formed by dissolving thallium or thallous hydroxide or carbonate in nitric acid, and crystallizing. It is polymorphic, m.p. 205°. The nitrate decomposes when heated above 300°. Solubility in water 9·55 g in 100 g at 20°.

Thallic nitrate, $Tl(NO_3)_3 \cdot 3H_2O$, is formed in concentrated nitric acid. It is immediately hydrolysed by water.

Thallium oxides, *Thallous oxide*, Tl_2O. A black powder, formed by the oxidation of thallium in air at about 350°, or by heating thallous hydroxide to 100°. It reacts with acids to form thallous salts and also absorbs water very readily to yield thallous hydroxide.

Thallic oxide, Tl_2O_3. Thallic oxide is formed by ignition of thallium in air at a red heat, by dehydrating thallic hydroxide, or by heating thallous nitrate. The colour varies from black to brown, according to the mode of preparation, and the oxide may be obtained under certain conditions as a crystalline material. It is reduced to thallium by hydrogen or carbon monoxide at a red heat. It is insoluble in water or alkalis, but is attacked by hydrochloric acid with liberation of some chlorine, and by hot concentrated sulphuric acid with formation of thallous sulphate and oxygen. Thallic oxide is decomposed above 100° into thallous oxide and oxygen.

Thallium sulphates, *Thallous sulphate,* Tl_2SO_4. Prepared by dissolving thallium in hot concentrated sulphuric acid, or by neutralizing thallous hydroxide with dilute sulphuric acid and crystallizing. It crystallizes in rhombic prisms, which are isomorphous with potassium sulphate. Thallous sulphate forms many double sulphates, and with the sulphates of tripositive aluminium, chromium, iron, vanadium, gallium, and rhodium it yields well-defined alums. Its solubility in water at 20° is 4·87 g per 100 g of water.

Thallic sulphate, $Tl_2(SO_4)_3$. The existence of anhydrous thallic sulphate is doubtful. An acid sulphate, $Tl_2(SO_4)_3, H_2SO_4, 8H_2O$, crystallizes from a solution of thallic hydroxide in concentrated sulphuric acid. Basic sulphates have also been prepared. Solutions containing thallic sulphate are hydrolysed very readily by water with precipitation of thallic hydroxide

Thallium sulphides. *Thallous sulphide,* Tl_2S. A bluish-black crystalline solid which is precipitated by hydrogen sulphide from slightly acid solutions of thallous salts. It is insoluble in ammonium sulphide or alkalis, but dissolves readily in dilute mineral acids. The moist sulphide is rapidly oxidized on exposure to air; m.p. 433°. A polysulphide, Tl_2S_5, is formed as shining black crystals, m.p. 310°, by adding thallous chloride to an ammonium polysulphide solution.

Thallic sulphide, Tl_2S_3. A hard black solid, m.p. 260°, which is formed by fusing thallium with excess of sulphur, and removing excess of the latter by distillation. Solutions of thallic salts when treated with hydrogen sulphide do not yield thallic sulphide, but a mixture of thallous sulphide and sulphur.

Thebaine, $C_{19}H_{21}NO_3$. One of the alkaloids of

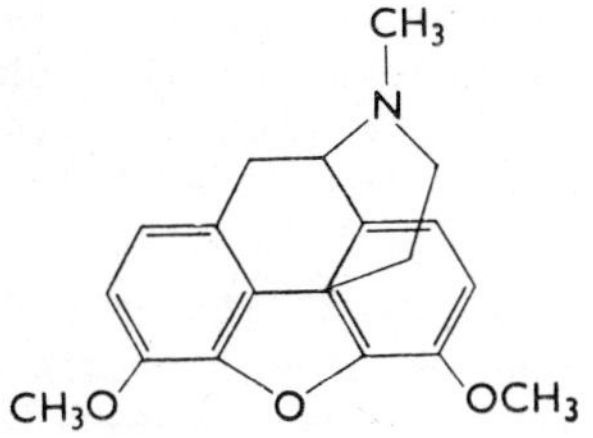

opium. It crystallizes in plates from aqueous alcohol, and prisms from anhydrous alcohol, m.p. 193°. Soluble in alcohol, insoluble in water. Laevorotatory. It is a violent tetanic poison.

Thénard, Louis Jacques. Born in 1777 and studied chemistry under Vauquelin and Berthollet. He became a professor at the Collège de

France and worked with Gay-Lussac on the preparation of potassium and sodium. He discovered hydrogen peroxide and hydrogen persulphide and investigated catalysis, fermentation, and many organic substances. He was ennobled by Charles X in 1824, and died in 1857.

Thénard's blue. A blue material produced on igniting aluminium oxide with cobalt nitrate, and consisting of cobalt aluminate, $CoAl_2O_4$. This compound is produced in the test for aluminium in blowpipe analysis, when aluminium oxide is moistened with a solution of cobalt nitrate and ignited on a charcoal block.

Theobromine, $C_7H_8N_4O_2$. 3,7-Dimethylxanthine, an alkaloid obtained from cacao seeds or

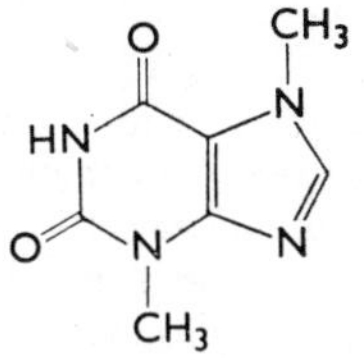

prepared synthetically. Constitutionally it is similar to caffeine, being an extremely weak base. It is sparingly soluble in water, in alcohol, and in ether, but forms soluble compounds with alkali hydroxides which, however, are decomposed by carbon dioxide. It is usually administered as the sodium compound combined with either sodium acetate or sodium salicylate, and is employed almost entirely as a diuretic. Physiologically theobromine resembles caffeine, but its effect on the central nervous system is less, while its action on the kidneys is more pronounced.

Theophylline, Theocine, $C_7H_8N_4O_2$. 1,3-Dimethylxanthine. Occurs to a small extent in

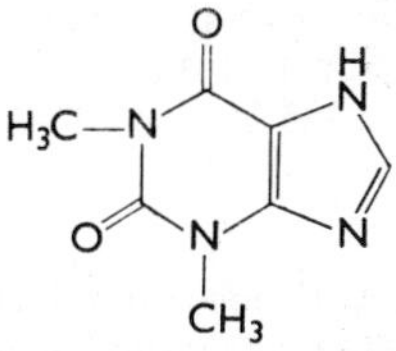

tea, but is chiefly prepared synthetically. Like caffeine and theobromine, it is a very weak base which forms water-soluble compounds with alkalis. It is a more effective diuretic than theobromine but is somewhat irritant to the stomach. It is usually administered in combination with sodium acetate or ethylenediamine.

Theoretical plate. A theoretical plate in a distillation or absorption column is one on which perfect liquid-vapour contacting occurs, so that the two streams leaving it are in equilibrium with each other. By definition it is 100% efficient. Although in practice plates of this efficiency are rarely encountered, the concept is a useful one because the degree of separation possible during fractional distillation is dependent on the number of theoretical plates available and the reflux ratio employed. An analogous situation holds in the case of gas absorption. The number of theoretical plates to which a column is equivalent under specified operating conditions is a measure of its efficiency under these conditions.

In the case of a plate column the performance of a real plate is related to the performance of a theoretical one by the *plate efficiency* (*q.v.*). In the case of a packed column the *height equivalent to a theoretical plate* (*HETP*) gives a measure of the contacting efficiency of the packing.

See Plate column, Packed column, Rectification.

Thermite. The name given to a mixture of powdered aluminium and a metallic oxide, generally ferric oxide. If thermite is ignited by a fuse such as a piece of magnesium ribbon it becomes incandescent, the chemical reaction proceeding very rapidly with great evolution of heat, the temperature rising to about 2,400°. The reaction gives aluminium oxide and metallic iron.

The reaction under the name of the thermite process finds extensive use in welding broken castings, etc. Thermite mixtures of varying compositions are used also in incendiary bombs.

Thermochemistry. Most chemical reactions occur with the absorption or evolution of heat. That branch of chemistry concerned with the heat changes accompanying reactions is called thermochemistry.

Thermodynamics, First law of. The first law of thermodynamics is the logical consequence of the law of the conservation of energy, and states that mechanical energy and heat energy are quantitatively interconvertible. The validity of the law was tested by Joule (1843-1880), who showed that

$$E = JQ,$$

where *E* is the work done in producing a quantity of heat *Q*, while *J* is a constant, known as Joule's Equivalent, and equal to $4 \cdot 18 \times 10^7$ ergs per calorie at 15°.

Thermodynamics, Second law of. This states that 'It is impossible for a self-acting machine, unaided by any external agency, to transfer heat from a body at a low to one at a higher temperature,' or alternatively, 'Heat cannot of itself pass from a colder to a warmer body.' This means that if heat is to be transferred from a colder to a warmer body, work must be done by some external agency.

Thermodynamics, Third law of. Einstein (1907) predicted that the specific heats of all substances would approach zero at the absolute zero of temperature, and shortly afterwards Planck (1912) concluded that the entropy of pure solids or liquids approached zero at the same temperature. The statement that 'the entropy of every pure crystalline substance is zero at absolute zero' is often called the third law of thermodynamics, and is a general statement which includes the Nernst heat theorem as a special case.

Thermonuclear reaction. See Atomic energy.

Thermoplastic resins. Resins which are composed of separate linear non-reactive macromolecules. On heating they become plastic due to the reduction of the intermolecular forces. In this state such materials can be made to flow under pressure. On cooling the original physical properties are regained. This cycle of changes can be repeated so long as no thermal degradation of the polymer takes place. For this reason most thermoplastics are fabricated by forcing the heated material under pressure into a mould or through a die and then chilling prior to removal. The important thermoplastic processing techniques include injection moulding, extrusion, and calendering. Many thermoplastics are also soluble in various organic solvents; the same intermolecular cohesive forces being overcome during the process of solution. Such organosols or dopes are widely used as impregnants and for film casting. The more important thermoplastics include polyvinyl chloride, Polythene, polystyrene, cellulose acetate. See Thermosetting resins for comparison.

Thermoprenes. Cyclized rubbers (cyclo-rubbers) made by treating rubber with acid compounds of the general formula $R \cdot SO_2 \cdot X$, where R is an organic radical or hydroxyl group and X is chlorine or another hydroxyl group, i.e. sulphuric, chlorosulphonic, or organic sulphonic acids. Most cyclo-rubbers are soluble in common rubber solvents, the solubility decreasing with hardness. They are used mainly for chemically resistant surface coatings, i.e. in the 'Vulcalock' process for lining tanks. Thermoprenes are also used for bonding rubber and plastics to wood, leather, ceramics, glass, metals, etc.

Thermosetting resins (also known as thermohardening or thermocurable resins). Resins which are composed of large molecules that, on heating, will undergo either further reaction with themselves, or with other smaller molecules (known as cross-linking agents), to give large three-dimensionally linked macromolecules, characterized by their general insolubility and infusible nature. In this state, the resins are described as being thermoset, full crosslinked, or completely cured. Thermosetting moulding materials for compression and transfer moulding are produced by compounding thermosetting resins and any necessary cross-linking agent and/or catalyst with substantial quantities of inert fillers. It should be noted that some liquid thermosetting resins, such as epoxides and unsaturated polyester resins used for laminating and casting, can be cured at ordinary temperatures, without the application of either heat or pressure. The following thermosetting resins are some of those in current use: phenol-formaldehyde resins, urea and melamine-formaldehyde resins, unsaturated polyester resins, epoxide resins, and silicone resins.

Thiacetazone, amithiozone $C_{10}H_{12}N_4OS$. A white powder, m.p. 225°, insoluble in water, sparingly soluble in alcohol, soluble in glycols.

can be assayed by a fluorimetric method after oxidation to thiochrome, or microbiologically using yeast or a *lactobacillus* species. Thiamine is concerned in carbohydrate metabolism (see Thiamine pyrophosphate). The minimum daily requirement is believed to be about 500 international units or 2 mg.

Thiamine pyrophosphate, (TPP). A coenzyme which is concerned in a number of important metabolic processes. Examples are the decarboxylation of α-oxoglutaric acid in the Krebs cycle, and the conversion of alanine, through pyruvic acid, to acetyl-coenzyme A. In these reactions thiamine pyrophosphate effects transfer of 'active aldehyde' groups, which become attached (as carbinol substituents) to the thiazole ring at position 2:

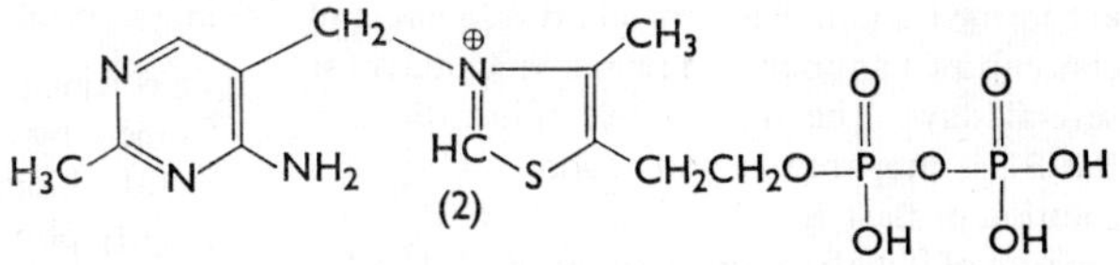

Prepared by treating *p*-acetamidobenzaldehyde with thiosemicarbazide, and recrystallizing the product.

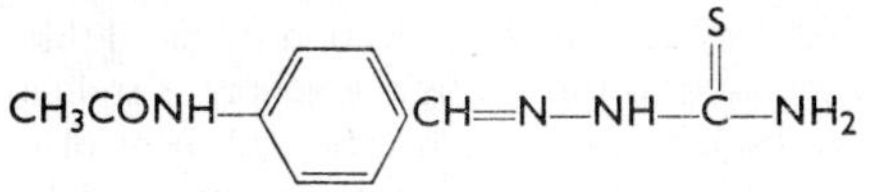

It is used in the treatment of tuberculosis; it is less active than streptomycin, and is useful for treating recent lesions of the lungs. Toxic side effects can occur.

Thiamine, Aneurine, Vitamin B$_1$. This is the anti-neuritic factor, the absence of which from the diet of man leads to the disease beri-beri, and from that of mammals and birds to polyneuritis, the most fundamental symptom of which is a general nervous atrophy. It is isolated as the chloride hydrochloride, $C_{12}H_{18}Cl_2N_4OS, H_2O$. It crystallizes in colourless needles from aqueous

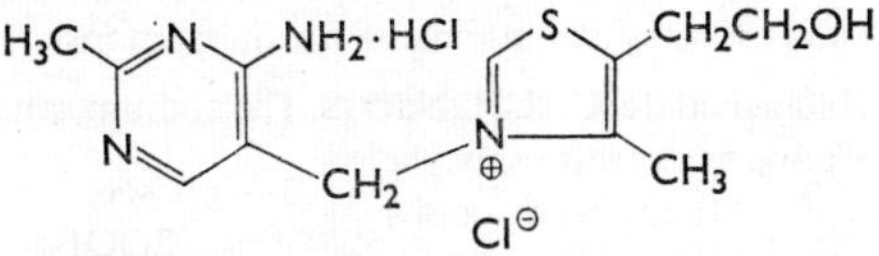

alcohol, m.p. 246°. It is soluble in water, sparingly soluble in alcohol, and insoluble in ether. It is destroyed by heating above 100° in water solution. The richest natural sources of the vitamin are yeast, eggs, and the germ of cereals. It is not present in polished rice and other highly purified cereal products. Thiamine preparations

The term co-carboxylase was formerly used to denote this coenzyme.

Thiazole ring. The ring is numbered as shown.

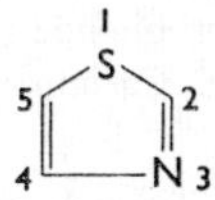

Thickening. A method of reducing the liquid content of a suspension by allowing the solids to settle out under the action of gravity and then withdrawing the supernatant liquid. Thickeners may be of the batch or continuous type, but the latter are by far the more common. See Continuous thickeners.

Thiele, Johannes (1865-1918). Professor in Munich and Strasburg, best known for his theory of partial valencies and the constitution of benzene, discussed in 1899 and subsequent years.

Thienyl ring. The ring system is numbered as shown.

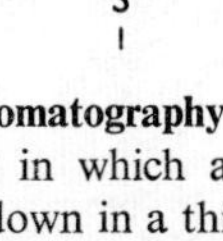

Thin layer chromatography. A process of chromatography in which a slurry of active material is laid down in a thin film on a plate, dried, and the chromatography subsequently carried out in one or more directions on the plate. See Chromatography.

Thioantimonates and **Thioantimonites**. See Antimony sulphides.

Thioarsenates and **Thioarsenites**. See Arsenic sulphides.

Thiocarbanilide, $C_{13}H_{12}N_2S$. Colourless flakes,

m.p. 151°. Easily soluble in alcohol. Prepared by boiling aniline with carbon disulphide. It is used commercially as a rubber accelerator.

Thiocarbonic acid, H_2CS_3. The parent acid of the thiocarbonates. Sodium thiocarbonate, Na_2CS_3, is formed by shaking carbon disulphide with a concentrated solution of sodium sulphide. Yellow solutions of ammonium thiocarbonate are formed on allowing carbon disulphide and concentrated ammonia to remain in contact for several days. The most stable thiocarbonate, $BaCS_3$, is prepared by the action of CS_2 on a solution of $Ba(HS)_2$. The free acid, H_2CS_3, or a mixture of it with perthiocarbonic acid, H_2CS_4, separates as a yellow-red oil on acidifying a thiocarbonate. Thiocarbonates are used in destroying the fungus *phylloxera*, which occurs on vines. The latter are sprayed with a solution of sodium thiocarbonate, which is slowly decomposed by atmospheric carbon dioxide with formation of carbon disulphide. Carbon disulphide is the actual fungicide.

Thiocarboxyamine, Thiazole purple,

$C_{21}H_{21}IN_2S_2$. A magenta trimethinecyanine dye, prepared from 2-methylbenzothiazole ethiodide and ethyl orthoformate in boiling pyridine. It is a powerful green and yellow sensitizer, and the corresponding dye prepared from the naphthothiazole salt is a red sensitizer, superior to pinacyanol. Analogous dyes with alkyl substituents in the *meso* position of the trimethine chain and with benzoselenazole rings are also strong spectral sensitizers, with a marked tendency to J-sensitization.

Thiochrome, $C_{12}H_{14}N_4OS$. The colouring matter

of yeast. It can be extracted from yeast, prepared by oxidizing thiamine, or synthesized. It

crystallizes in yellow prisms, m.p. 227°-228°, soluble in methyl alcohol, fairly soluble in water. It gives an intense blue fluorescence in neutral or alkaline solution.

6,8-Thioctic acid. See Lipoic acid.

Thiocyanates. The salts of thiocyanic acid, HSCN. The salts are prepared from cyanides by direct combination with sulphur. The thiocyanate ion can co-ordinate to metals through either the nitrogen or sulphur atoms. Thiocyanates can be used in the estimation of silver and of ferric iron. They are photographic sulphur sensitizers. See Sulphur sensitization.

Thiocyanic acid, HSCN. Prepared by the action of potassium bisulphate on potassium thiocyanate. It is a gas at room temperature but it polymerizes fairly readily. Two series of esters, the thiocyanic, RSCN, and the isothiocyanic or mustard oils, RNCS, are known.

Thiocyanogen, $(SCN)_2$. A pseudohalogen (*q.v.*) formed by the action of oxidizing agents on metal thiocyanates. Above 0° the solutions rapidly polymerize but below this temperature they are quite stable.

Thioglycollic acid, $HS \cdot CH_2 \cdot COOH$. When pure it is a colourless liquid with a faint odour; the odour of the impure material is penetrating and unpleasant; b.p. 123°/29 mm; d^{20} 1·325. Obtained by electrolytic reduction of the dithioglycollic acid formed by the action of sodium hydrosulphide on chloroacetic acid. It oxidizes readily in the air and is very reactive. It adds across double bonds of unsaturated compounds and has been used as a test for unsaturation. The hydrogen of the —SH group is replaceable by metals. It is an important constituent of the cold process for waving hair. It is also used as a test for iron, giving a purple colour with ammoniacal solutions of iron salts.

Thiokol. A thioplast (*q.v.*) made by interacting ethylene dichloride and sodium polysulphide. Thiokol and Thiokol-rubber mixtures can be vulcanized by heating with zinc oxide without addition of sulphur. The material is oil-resistant, but has poor mechanical strength.

Thiols. The systematic name for mercaptans.

Thiomersalate, $C_9H_9HgNaO_2S$. The sodium salt of ethyl mercurithiosalicylic acid. Made from ethyl mercuric chloride and thiosalicylic acid. It is a cream-coloured powder, very soluble in water, soluble in alcohol, and unstable to light. It is used for treating fungal infections of the skin, and for other sterilizing purposes, including the preservation of pharmaceutical products against microbial attack.

Thionic acids, $H_2S_xO_6$ ($x=2-6$). A mixture of the thionic acids is formed by the action of sulphur dioxide on thiosulphate solutions. The various thionic acids may be obtained pure by specific reactions; there is evidence that acids with more than six sulphur atoms are capable of existence.

Thionyl chloride, $SOCl_2$. A colourless liquid of m.p. $-99\cdot5°$, b.p. $75\cdot7°$ obtained by treating dry sulphur dioxide or sodium sulphite with phosphorus pentachloride, PCl_5. It is decomposed by water to form hydrochloric and sulphurous acids. Thionyl chloride is used in the replacement of hydroxyl groups by chlorine in organic chemistry and for dehydration of metal salt hydrates. Thionyl fluoride and bromide are also known.

Thiopentone sodium, $C_{11}H_{17}N_2O_2SNa$. The

monosodium salt of 5-ethyl-5-(1-methylbutyl)-2-thiobarbituric acid. It is a yellowish white powder, unstable in air, so is packed in an atmosphere of nitrogen. It is soluble in $1\cdot5$ parts of water. It is administered by intravenous injection to produce short duration general anaesthesia.

Thiophen, C_4H_4S. A colourless liquid with a faint odour resembling that of benzene, m.p. $-38\cdot3°$, b.p. $84°$; d^{20} $1\cdot0617$; n_D^{20} $1\cdot5246$. It occurs to the extent of about $0\cdot5\%$ in commercial benzene and can be prepared by heating sodium succinate with phosphorus pentasulphide. It is manufactured from butane and sulphur. It can be nitrated, sulphonated, and brominated, and gives rise to two series of monosubstituted derivatives (2 and 3) according to which of the hydrogen atoms is replaced. It gives a blue colour (indophenin) with isatin and sulphuric acid, and forms an insoluble compound with mercuric acetate. In derivatives the ring system shown is called the thienyl ring.

Thiophenol,   phenylthiol,   phenylmercaptan,

C_6H_5SH, is the sulphur analogue of phenol. It is a colourless, foul-smelling liquid, b.p. $168°$.

Thiophosgene, thiocarbonyl chloride, $SCCl_2$.

A red liquid, d $1\cdot508$, b.p. $73°$, which is insoluble in water but soluble in organic solvents.

Thioplasts. Synthetic, rubber-like materials prepared by interaction of dihalogenated aliphatic compounds and metallic polysulphides. They can be made in bulk form or as emulsions. Many thioplasts are oil-resistant. See Thiokol.

Thioselenic acid. See Selenosulphuric acid.

Thiosinamine. See Allylthiourea.

Thiostannic acid. See Tin sulphides.

Thiosulphuric acid, $H_2S_2O_3$. A dibasic acid, the salts of which are known as thiosulphates. Free thiosulphuric acid has not been isolated. Solutions of its salts are immediately decomposed by mineral acids with formation of SO_2 and a precipitate of free sulphur. They interact quantitatively with solutions of iodine to form sodium tetrathionate. This is one of the most important reactions used in volumetric analysis.

Thiouracil, $C_4H_4N_2OS$. A white powder, slightly soluble in water and alcohol, soluble in alkali. It is prepared by condensing sodium ethylformyl acetate with thiourea. Thiouracil decreases the activity of the thyroid gland by interfering with the iodination of tyrosine and so preventing thyroxine production.

Thiourea, CH_4N_2S.   Colourless crystals, m.p. $172°$, soluble in hot water and ethanol. It is decomposed on heating with water to give ammonium thiocyanate, but in many of its properties it resembles urea. It forms complexes with many metal salts. It is manufactured by the action of hydrogen sulphide on cyanamide. It is used as a photographic sensitizer. See Sulphur sensitization.

Thiram, TMTD, TMTDS, Tetramethylthiuram

disulphide. $C_6H_{12}N_2S_4$. A fungicidal substance prepared from sodium dimethyldithiocarbamate by reaction with iodine or hydrogen peroxide. The pure substance is a colourless crystalline solid, m.p. $155°-156°$, insoluble in water, sparingly soluble in alcohol, but soluble in benzene and chloroform. When crude it is yellow. Thiram may be applied to soil to prevent 'damping-off' of seedlings and may also be applied to foliage or seed. It is not phytotoxic and has low mammalian toxicity, but is reported to act as a mouse repellant. Feeding to hens causes egg production to be lowered.

Thiuram disulphides. See Thiram.

Thixotropy. This isothermal gel-sol transformation is brought about by vigorous shaking or other mechanical means, and appears to be essentially a packing phenomenon. Ferric hydroxide gels are thixotropic and on shaking form sols which rapidly set again when allowed to rest. Thixotropy is common with suspensions such as clay or oil paints, and emulsions. The term is due to Freundlich. See Gel, Rheopexy.

Thomas, Sidney Gilchrist (1850-1885). Born at Canonbury, London, Thomas served for a time as a police court clerk. Interested in chemistry, he took up the study at Birkbeck Institute. He solved the problem of the separation of phosphorus from iron by the introduction of the basic lining into the Bessemer Converter. See 'Memoirs and Letters of Sidney Gilchrist Thomas' (Burnie).

Thomsen, Hans Peter Jörgen Julius (1826-1909). Born at Copenhagen, Thomsen was educated at the Von Westens Institute and the Polytechnic. In 1853 he patented a method of obtaining soda from cryolite, and in 1858 planned the present large factory at Oeresund for working up the mineral for caustic soda and alumina. In 1866 he was appointed professor of chemistry and Director of the Chemical Laboratory at the University, Copenhagen. His main researches lie in the field of thermochemistry. In 1883, with Berthelot, he was awarded the Davy Medal of the Royal Society. See *Chem. Soc. Mem. Lect.*, 1910.

Thomson, Sir Joseph John (1856-1940). Born near Manchester, Thomson was educated at Owens College and at Trinity College, Cambridge. From 1884 till 1918 he was Cavendish professor of experimental physics at Cambridge. In 1918 he was appointed Master of Trinity College. His brilliant researches were chiefly in the field of electricity; he determined the masses and electrical charges of the electron and the proton, and the velocity of their flight. He was awarded the Nobel Prize for Physics in 1906, knighted in 1908, and created O.M. in 1912. See *Nature*, 1940, **146**, 351.

Thomson, Thomas (1773-1852). Thomson was born at Crieff, Perthshire, and educated at Edinburgh, where he delivered lectures on chemistry from 1801 to 1811. After an interval in London he became Regius Professor of Chemistry at Glasgow University, retaining the chair until 1841. It was in his 'System of Chemistry,' 1807, that the principles of Dalton's atomic theory were first published. In addition to this work he published several textbooks, a 'History of Chemistry,' 1830-1831, and numerous original papers.

Thomson, William. See Kelvin.

Thorium, Th. At.no. 90, At.wt. 232·12, m.p. 3050°, b.p. ~4400°, d 11·2. Thorium has two structures, α-thorium, stable below 1400°, face-centred cubic, $a = 5\cdot086$ Å, β-thorium, stable 1400°-1750°, body-centred cubic, $a = 4\cdot11$ Å. Thorium occurs naturally in a wide variety of minerals, the most important of which are thorite and thorogummite (thorium silicates), thorianite (thorium dioxide), and monazite (a mixed phosphate). After digestion with sulphuric acid, thorium is extracted from nitric acid solution with tributyl phosphate or other selective organic solvents (see *Chem. and Ind.* 1959, 235). Thorium metal has been prepared by reduction of the dioxide, tetrafluoride, or tetrachloride with calcium; it has also been obtained by electrolysis of a fused ThF_4—KCl—$NaCl$ mixture. The metal is extremely reactive, forming an oxide or nitride merely by heating in air; it is soluble in dilute acids but concentrated nitric acid renders the metal passive. Thorium dioxide was used in the production of incandescent gas mantles. By bombardment of thorium with slow neutrons the fissile isotope ^{233}U is obtained.

Thorium, compounds of. Thorium absorbs hydrogen when heated in the gas, the product being an interstitial compound rather than a definite hydride. In its compounds the element is tetrapositive. The oxide thoria, ThO_2, is a white powder, and is obtained by igniting any thorium salt in air. It is commonly coloured yellow or brown by traces of rare-earth oxides. Thorium hydroxide, $Th(OH)_4$, is precipitated by alkalis from solutions of thorium salts, and forms a white gelatinous precipitate, which yields the dioxide on ignition. Thorium tetrafluoride, ThF_4, is insoluble in water. Other thorium halides, $ThCl_4$, $ThBr_4$, ThI_4, are known and are appreciably volatile at elevated temperatures. They are hydrolysed in water to give the oxyhalides $ThOX_2$. Thorium fluoride forms an extensive series of double salts with alkali fluorides. Thorium sulphate is a white crystalline solid which may be isolated with 9, 8, 6, 5, 4, or 2 molecules of water of crystallization. All are soluble in water. Double sulphates such as Na_2SO_4, $Th(SO_4)_2$, $6H_2O$ are also known. Commercial thorium nitrate has the formula $Th(NO_3)_4$, $4H_2O$. Thorium acetylacetonate can be sublimed at 160° but the most volatile compound of thorium is the borohydride, $Th(BH_4)_4$, prepared by interaction of thorium fluoride and aluminium borohydride.

Thorpe, Sir Joselyn Field (1872-1940). Thorpe was educated at Worthing College, King's College (London), the Royal College of Science, and the University of Heidelberg. He was appointed lecturer in chemistry and biochemistry, Manchester (1908), Sorby Research Fellow of the Royal Society (1909), and professor of organic chemistry, Imperial College, London (1914). Author of many books and original papers, Thorpe was elected F.R.S. in 1908, and created C.B.E. in 1917. He was awarded the Longstaff Medal in 1921 and the Davy Medal in 1922. See *J. Chem. Soc.*, 1941, 444.

Thorpe, Sir Thomas Edward (1845-1925). Born at Harpurhey, near Manchester, Thorpe was educated at Manchester Diocesan School and Owens College. Later he worked under Roscoe, Bunsen (Heidelberg), and Kekulé (Bonn). He was appointed to the Chair of Chemistry, Andersonian College, Glasgow (1870), Leeds (1874), Royal College of Science, London (1885). In 1894 he became Director of the Government Laboratories, and in 1909 professor of general chemistry at the Imperial College of Science and Technology. Author of numerous books, he made a study of the elements vanadium and gold, and of the compounds of fluorine. He was elected F.R.S. in 1876, created C.B. in 1900, and knighted in 1909. See *J. Chem. Soc.*, 1926, 1031.

Three centre bonds. A normal covalent bond is envisaged as existing through overlap of electronic orbitals from two atoms. This concept has been extended to include overlaps from three or more atoms. Each such centre contains two electrons and the bonds occur in electron deficient compounds, e.g. the boron hydrides and platinum tetramethyl.

Threitols. See Erythritol.

Threo-. See Erythro-.

Threonine, α-Amino-β-hydroxy-*n*-butyric acid,

$$
\begin{array}{c}
COOH \\
| \\
CHNH_2 \\
| \\
CHOH \\
| \\
CH_3
\end{array}
$$

$C_4H_9NO_3$. An amino-acid, m.p. 251°-252°, $[\alpha]_D^{26} -28\cdot4°$, that occurs widely in proteins, and has been shown to be an essential component of foods.

Threose, $C_4H_8O_4$. A tetrose sugar. The D-form

$$
\begin{array}{c}
CHO \\
| \\
HOCH \\
| \\
HCOH \\
| \\
CH_2OH
\end{array}
$$

has been obtained crystalline, m.p. 126°-132°. It is very hygroscopic and soluble in water and alcohol. L-Threose has been obtained only in solution.

Thrombin. An enzyme which plays a part in the clotting of blood by converting the soluble protein fibrinogen to the insoluble fibrin. Thrombin is not normally present in the blood, but is formed from a precursor prothrombin by the joint action of an activator, thrombokinase, and ionized calcium.

Through retorts. Used in the manufacture of coal gas. They are U-shaped, 20-22 ft. long with end section 24 in. × 16 in. There are 8-10 retorts in each arch.

Short through retorts are 12-16 feet long, and are set in arches containing 6-8 retorts. They have a through-put of 10-50 tons a day.

Thudichum, John Lewis William (1829-1901). Born at Büdingen in Hesse, Thudichum studied medicine at Heidelberg and at Giessen, where he was inspired by Liebig to take an interest in chemistry. He moved to London and though practising medicine he lectured on pathological chemistry at St. Thomas Hospital and for many years carried out private research on the chemistry of the brain, being the first to isolate sphingomyelin, cephalin and many related compounds. See *Nature*, 1965, **207**, 814.

Thujane, $C_{10}H_{18}$, formula (1). A dicyclic hydrocarbon obtained by the catalytic hydrogenation of α- and β-thujene and sabinene, and by other reactions. (+)-Thujane only has been described, and is a colourless mobile oil with a faint smell, having the constants b.p. 157°/758 mm, d_4^{20} 0·8139, n_D^{20} 1·4376, $[\alpha]_D$ +62·03°. It forms no characteristic crystalline derivatives.

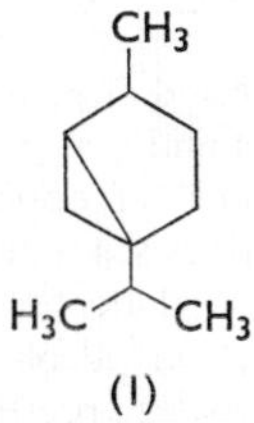

(1) 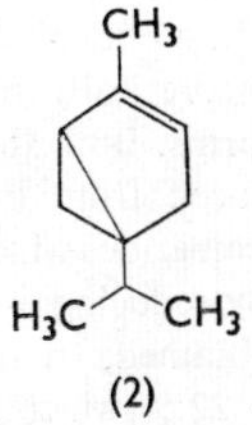   (2)

α-**Thujene,** $C_{10}H_{16}$, formula (2). A dicyclic monoterpene, the (+)-form of which is present in the oil from the gum-oleo-resin of *Boswellia serrata*. It is formed, together with β-thujene, by distilling thujyl alcohol methyl xanthate or trimethylthujylammonium hydroxide. α-Thujene is a mobile oil with a rather penetrating smell, and has the following constants: b.p. 151°, d_4^{20} 0·8301, n_D^{20} 1·45155, $[\alpha]_D$ +37·7°. The compound obtained synthetically from (+)-thujyl alcohol is laevorotatory.

β-**Thujene,** $C_{10}H_{16}$, formula (3 over). A dicyclic monoterpene obtained as described under α-thujene and also by the decomposition of the methyl xanthate of (−)-thujyl alcohol at 183° which results in the formation of (+)-β-thujene. It has the following constants: b.p. 147°/739 mm, d_4^{20} 0·8208, n_D^{20} 1·4471, $[\alpha]_D$ +110·8°.

(3)

(4)

Thujone, $C_{10}H_{16}O$, formula (4). This dicyclic ketone occurs in thuja, tansy, wormwood, and many other oils. It is a colourless oil the smell of which resembles that of menthol. α-Thujone has b.p. 74·5°/9 mm, d_4^{24} 0·9109, n_D^{25} 1·4490, $[\alpha]_D^{18}$ −19·9°. β-Thujone has b.p. 76°/10 mm, d_4^{25} 0·9135, n_D^{25} 1·4500, $[\alpha]_D^{18}$ +72·5°. Inversion of the optical activity from + to − occurs in distillation of the dextrorotatory form in steam. On oxidation with potassium permanganate thujone forms α-thujaketonic acid of m.p. 75°-76°. When thujone is dissolved in cold sulphuric acid it is converted into a mixture of stereoisomerides, isothujone of b.p. 231°-232°, d^{20} 0·927, n_D^{20} 1·4822.

Thujyl alcohol, $C_{10}H_{18}O$. A secondary dicyclic alcohol, also known as tanacetyl alcohol, found both free and combined with various acids in wormwood oil. It can also be prepared by reducing thujone with sodium in alcohol. Thujyl alcohol can exist theoretically in 8 optically active and 4 racemic forms. Both the natural alcohol and that produced from thujone are mixtures of optical isomerides which have been partially separated. By reducing α-thujone, a (+)-thujyl alcohol is obtained, m.p. 66°-67°, $[\alpha]_D$ (in alcohol) −22·5°, which gives a p-nitrobenzoate m.p. 101°. On oxidation this alcohol gives α-thujone. By catalytic hydrogenation of (±)-sabinol, (−)-neothujyl alcohol is obtained, m.p. 22°-23°, b.p. 96°/13 mm, n_D^{25} 1·4624, $[\alpha]_D$ (in alcohol) −8·8°, giving a p-nitrobenzoate, m.p. 90°. On oxidation this also gives α-thujone. Reduction of α-thujone with sodium in alcohol gives (±)-isothujyl alcohol, b.p. 103°/16 mm, n_D 1·4630, $[\alpha]_D$ +108·8°, giving a p-nitrobenzoate, m.p. 78°. On oxidation this gives (±)-β-thujone. These are the only isomers so far obtained in a pure state.

Thulium, Tm. At.no. 69. At.wt. 169·4, d 9·332, m.p. 1545°, b.p. 1727°. Thulium metal has a hexagonal close-packed lattice up to 1000°

(a=3·5372, c=5·5619 Å). It is a typical rare-earth element (q.v.).

Thulium compounds. Thulium forms a series of pale green tripositive compounds, in which it behaves as a typical rare-earth. TmI_3 reacts with thulium metal to give TmI_2, a strongly reducing compound.

Thymine,   5-methyl-2,6-dioxytetrahydropyrimidine, $C_5H_6N_2O_2$. Crystallizes in plates, which sublime when carefully heated, and when rapidly heated melt at 321°-325°. Sparingly soluble in cold water, readily soluble in hot. Sparingly soluble in alcohol. Thymine is a constituent of deoxyribose nucleic acid.

Thymol, 3-Hydroxy-p-cymene, $C_{10}H_{14}O$. Crystallizes in colourless plates, m.p. 51·5°, b.p. 233·5°. Soluble in 1000 parts of water, very soluble in alcohol and ether. It has the pungent odour of thyme. It is a constituent of oil of thyme and numerous other essential oils. It is manufactured from piperitone and used as a disinfectant. It is used to a small extent as a vermifuge, but its chief use is for the preparation of antiseptic lotions, mouth washes, and gargles, and also for oily sprays for the nose and throat.

Thymol blue, thymolsulphonphthalein. One of the sulphonphthalein group of indicators. It is used in 0·04% aqueous solution after neutralization with 4·3 ml of 0·05 M-sodium hydroxide per 0·1 g. It has two useful pH ranges, 1·2 (red) to 2·8 (yellow) and 8·0 (yellow) to 9·6 (blue).

Thymolphthalein, $C_{28}H_{30}O_4$. An indicator,

Colourless form

prepared from phthalic anhydride and thymol. It is used in 0·04% solution in alcohol and has a pH range of 9·3 (colourless) to 10·5 (blue).

Thyroglobulin. See Thyroxine.

Thyrotropin, Thyrotropic hormone. A glycoprotein hormone, mol. wt. about 10,000, secreted by the anterior lobe of the pituitary gland.

Its action is to stimulate the thyroid gland to produce thyroxine: the level of circulating thyroxine or tri-iodothyronine (*q.v.*) in turn controls the secretion of thyrotropin.

Thyroxine, $C_{15}H_{11}I_4NO_4$. Crystals, m.p. 231°-233°, with decomposition, insoluble in water

HO—⟨⟩—O—⟨⟩—CH₂·CH·COOH

$$HO \longleftarrow O \longleftarrow CH_2 \cdot CH \cdot COOH$$
$$NH_2$$

and solvents, soluble in alkalis. One of the longest known hormones, isolated in 1915 from the thyroid gland by Kendall. It is formed from protein-bound tyrosine and iodine (derived from the blood) and occurs as a protein-bound form, thyroglobulin. Natural thyroxine is the L-isomer; the D-isomer has very little activity. Racemization occurs during extraction of thyroxine from thyroid tissue by alkali.

Thyroxine or tri-iodothyronine (*q.v.*) are secreted by the thyroid into the blood, especially when the gland is stimulated by thyrotropin, and circulate in combination with a specific protein, thyroxine-binding globulin (TBG). The thyroid hormones are essential regulators of the basal metabolic rate. Deficiency of the hormones leads to goitre, myxoedema, and cretinism, while excessive secretion causes Graves' disease (exophthalmic goitre). In addition to its metabolic action, thyroxine affects growth, and its stimulation of the metamorphosis of tadpoles provides a possible bioassay. Thyroxine also acts as a metabolic stimulant on respiring cells *in vitro*: it 'uncouples' oxidative phosphorylation, i.e. increases oxygen consumption without generating more ATP. It is uncertain to what extent this effect is concerned in normal physiological metabolic regulation.

Tiemann, Johann Karl Ferdinand (1848-1899). Born at Rübeland in the Harz, Tiemann was apprenticed to a druggist but in 1869 went to Berlin to work under Hofmann. There he was appointed Privatdozent (1878) and ultimately Professor Extraordinary (1882). Apart from investigations on chemical analysis, his researches were mainly organic, on the nitriles, terpenes, and camphors. He carried out the synthetic preparation of vanillin. See *J. Chem. Soc.*, 1900, 600.

Tiglic Acid, *cis* - 1, 2 - dimethylacrylic acid, $C_5H_8O_2$. A colourless crystalline solid, m.p. 64°, b.p. 198·5°. Soluble in water and alcohol. Occurs

$$H_3C—CH$$
$$\|$$
$$H_3C—C—COOH$$

in Roman oil of cumin and in croton oil. Prepared by heating angelic acid either alone or in aqueous solution. Separated from angelic acid by means of its insoluble calcium salt.

Tilden, Sir William Augustus (1842-1926). Born in London, Tilden was apprenticed at the age of fifteen to a pharmacist. Stimulated by the lectures of Hofmann he turned his attention to chemistry, and in 1863 was appointed demonstrator at the Pharmaceutical Society, London. After a period as science master at Clifton College, Bristol, he was appointed professor of chemistry at Birmingham and in 1894 succeeded T. E. Thorpe as professor of chemistry at the Royal College of Science. He was elected F.R.S. in 1880 and knighted in 1909. Tilden was one of the early workers in terpene chemistry but made many valuable contributions to other branches of chemistry. See *J. Chem. Soc.*, 1927, 3190.

Tin, Sn. At.no. 50, At.wt. 118·70. A metal that has been known since prehistoric times. It exists in three allotropic modifications, the commonest of which forms tetragonal crystals; this—the ordinary tin—is a white lustrous metal with a sp.gr. of 7·28 to 7·31. The dimensions of the tetragonal unit cell are $a = 5·8194$, $c = 3·1753$ Å. It is harder than lead, malleable, and can be rolled into sheet or foil. At 200° it becomes brittle, and can be powdered; its sp.ht. at 18° is 0·0524, m.p. 232°, b.p. about 2270°. Ordinary tin is crystalline and when a bar of it is bent there is a creaking noise known as the 'cry' of tin.

Below 13·2° ordinary tin gradually changes into a grey powder, with a lower sp.gr. than ordinary tin. Grey tin is cubic with the diamond structure, $a = 6·46$ Å. At a temperature above 161° ordinary tin gradually changes into a rhombic variety.

The principal tin ore is cassiterite or tinstone, SnO_2, which is found in many parts of the world. This oxide is reduced by heating with charcoal or coal in a furnace; tin is also recovered from tinplate by an electrolytic process.

As the ore is generally found contaminated with compounds containing tungsten, the process involves several ore-dressing operations. Ores containing as little as 1-2% of metal are concentrated up to 50-70% before roasting. As tin is an expensive metal its recovery from waste tin-plate is practised. The chief method, due to Goldschmidt, consists in packing absolutely dry scrap in an iron cylinder and passing in dry chlorine under pressure. Only the tin is attacked, giving tin chloride. Tin is also recovered from scrap electrolytically.

The metal is used extensively for tinning (*q.v.*), and with various metals as alloys, the chief being bronze.

Tin alloys. Tin forms a component of many alloys, of which aluminium solder, anti-friction metal, Babbitt metal, bell-metal, Britannia metal, bronze, gun-metal, pewter, solder, and type-metal are the best known. Aluminium solder contains about 70% tin, 25% zinc, 3% aluminium, and a little copper, antimony, or phosphorus. Anti-friction metal contains about 75% tin, about 12·5% antimony, and about 12·5% of copper. Babbitt metal contains about 90% tin, about 7% antimony, and about 3% copper. Bell-metal contains about 20 to 24% of tin, the remainder being copper. Britannia metal contains about 90 to 95% tin, 4·5 to 9% antimony, and 0·5% copper. Bronze usually contains from about 5 to 10% of tin, the remainder being copper.

Gun-metal contains about 10% tin and 2% zinc, the remainder being copper. Pewter contains 3 to 4 parts of tin to 1 of lead; sometimes a little antimony is added. Type-metal contains about 72% lead, 18% antimony, 10% tin, and sometimes a little copper. See also Solder.

Tin bromides. *Stannous bromide*, $SnBr_2$, m.p. 215°, b.p. 619°, has very similar properties to stannous chloride.

Stannic bromide, $SnBr_4$, m.p. 33°, b.p. 203·3°, is prepared from the elements. It forms a tetrahydrate and complex bromides in acid solution.

Tin chlorides. *Stannous chloride*, $SnCl_2$, is a transparent solid with fatty lustre, m.p. 247°, b.p. about 603°. It has reducing properties, combines with ammonia, and forms hydrates with water. The dihydrate $SnCl_2, 2H_2O$ is known commercially as 'tin salt' and is made by dissolving tin in HCl; mono and tetrahydrates are also known. The salt is very soluble in water; it is used as a mordant, and has other industrial uses

Stannic chloride, $SnCl_4$, is a thin, colourless, fuming liquid, density 2·28 at 0°, m.p. $-36·2°$, b.p. 114·1°. It dissolves readily in alcohol, ether, and benzene. It dissolves sulphur, phosphorus, iodine, and bromine. Stannic chloride is normally hydrolysed by water but from acid solution a hydrate $SnCl_4 \cdot 5H_2O$ is formed. It is used as a mordant and has other industrial uses. Stannic chloride readily gives chlorostannates, M_2SnCl_6, from concentrated hydrochloric acid solution.

Tin fluorides. *Stannous fluoride*, SnF_2, is prepared by dissolving the metal or stannous hydroxide in hydrofluoric acid, m.p. 213°, b.p. 850°. Forms complexes $MSnF_3$ with alkali fluorides. Extensively used in toothpastes.

Stannic fluoride, SnF_4, is prepared by the action of hydrogen fluoride gas on stannic chloride. It sublimes at 705°. It is very hygroscopic, but is much more salt-like than the other stannic halides. Fluorostannates, M_2SnF_6, are readily prepared.

Tin hydroxides. Ill-defined stannic acids and stannic hydroxides have been described but are all hydrated tin(II) oxide. Stannates, e.g. $K_2SnO_3 \cdot 3H_2O$, are known but these contain $[Sn(OH)_6]^{2-}$ species. Hydrated tin (II) oxides are also known. In strongly alkaline solution stannites are present but the nature of the species is not known.

Tin iodides. *Stannous iodide*, SnI_2, m.p. 320°, b.p. 720°, is very similar to stannous chloride but less soluble in water. It can be precipitated from a stannous chloride solution with potassium iodide.

Stannic iodide, SnI_4, m.p. 144·5°, b.p. 346°, is prepared from the elements; it forms complex iodides.

Tin organic compounds. Stannic and stannous derivatives are known. The stannic derivatives include halides, oxides, and acids. They are prepared by the action of Grignard reagents on stannic halides. Derivatives such as Me_3SnBr are ionized in aqueous solution. Organic derivatives of tin are used as fungicides and in wood preservatives.

Tin oxides. *Stannous oxide* is a dark green or black solid; a red variety can be obtained, that quickly turns black on exposure to air. It can be prepared by precipitating the hydrated oxide from stannous solution and dehydrating at 100°.

Stannic oxide, SnO_2, exists in at least three forms. It occurs in tetragonal crystals as cassiterite or tinstone; when pure these are colourless and transparent, but they are often yellow, brown, or black, owing to the presence of impurities; m.p. about 1127°. Stannic oxide can also be obtained in hexagonal and rhombic crystals and in an amorphous state. It is insoluble in water and is used, under the name of putty powder, for polishing glass and metal.

Tin sulphides. *Stannic sulphide*, SnS_2, is a yellowish solid that may be formed by precipitating a solution of a stannic salt with H_2S. If thiostannic acid, H_2SnS_3, is heated it is converted into a golden-yellow solid variety of SnS_2. A crystalline variety of SnS_2, known as mosaic gold, is obtained by heating a mixture of tin filings, sulphur, and sal-ammoniac. It is used as a pigment.

Stannous sulphide, SnS, is prepared from its elements, m.p. 950°-1000°, b.p. 1090°. Above 265° it slowly changes into a mixture of stannic sulphide and tin.

Tincture of iodine. An alcoholic solution of iodine containing $2\frac{1}{2}\%$ iodine and $2\frac{1}{2}\%$ potassium iodide, which is used as an antiseptic.

Tinning. The coating of iron with tin, chiefly used for making 'tin' cans, etc. The sheet iron is first pickled and then passed into the tin bath, the surface of which is protected from oxidation by a flux of zinc chloride containing a little ammonium chloride. A former practice was to dip the plates in a tallow bath before putting them into the tinning vat. A cheap form of tinplate called 'terne plate' is coated from a lead-tin bath.

Tinstone. See Cassiterite.

Tiselius, Arne Wilhelm Kaurin (1902-   ). Born in Stockholm, Tiselius studied at Uppsala, where he was assistant to Svedberg. He was awarded the Nobel Prize for chemistry in 1948 for his work on electrophoresis and adsorption analysis, in particular concerning the nature of serum proteins.

Titanates. See Titanium dioxide.

Titanium, Ti. At.no. 22, At.wt. 47·90. This element, which was discovered in 1789, occurs widely in nature, the most important minerals being ilmenite, which is essentially ferrous titanate, $FeTiO_3$, and rutile, which is almost pure TiO_2. The metal is obtained by heating the tetrachloride with magnesium at 750°-900° in an atmosphere of helium, the magnesium and $MgCl_2$ being subsequently removed by leaching with cold dilute HCl. In another process sodium is used as the reducing agent. In the impure state titanium is obtained by the high temperature reduction of the oxide or by electrolysis (e.g. of fused potassium titanate). The metal crystallizes in the hexagonal system with the hexagonal close-packed structure, $a=2·95$, $c=4·72$ Å but assumes a cubic body-centred structure at 880°; d 4·43, m.p. 1668°, b.p. 3262°.

The metal is stable in air, but becomes coated with a protective layer of oxide. The massive metal burns in oxygen at about 600°. Oxidation of powdered material occurs at lower temperatures. It is attacked by the halogens above about 300°, by sulphur at about 700°, and by nitrogen above about 800°. The metal is dissolved by hot hydrochloric acid, forming the violet trichloride. It is only attacked by dilute sulphuric or nitric acids in the presence of fluoride ions; concentrated nitric acid renders the metal passive. Titanium metal is used as a light-weight corrosion-resistant material (see Titanium alloys); titanium compounds find extensive uses as catalysts.

Titanium alloys. Developed mainly for the aircraft industry where their light weight (sp.gr. 4·5), corrosion resistance and high strength makes them suitable for many applications, including the low-temperature stages of jet engines. Common alloy additions include aluminium, tin, manganese, chromium and iron.

Titanium carbide, TiC. A steel-grey crystalline solid, m.p. approx. 3200°, formed by heating a mixture of sugar charcoal and titanium dioxide in an electric furnace. It is unattacked by hydrochloric acid, or by water vapour at 700°. The carbide acts as a deoxidizing agent in steel. It is used in small proportions in sintered tungsten carbide tool tips.

Titanium chlorides, *Titanium dichloride*, $TiCl_2$. A black powder, which is formed together with the tetrachloride by heating titanium trichloride at 420°. The two halides are readily separated by distillation. The dichloride is decomposed at 600° into titanium and the tetrachloride. It is a strong reducing agent, and when dissolved in liquid hydrogen chloride will reduce titanium tetrachloride to the trichloride. It is instantly decomposed by water.

Titanium trichloride, $TiCl_3$. A violet-brown scaly solid, formed by reducing titanium tetrachloride with hydrogen at about 700°. The dichloride is always formed simultaneously. A deliquescent hydrated salt, $TiCl_3, 6H_2O$, is also known. It is violet in colour, and is best obtained by electrolytic reduction of a solution of the tetrachloride in hydrochloric acid. Solutions of the trichloride have strong reducing properties and are used in volumetric analysis. Mercury, silver, gold, copper, platinum, iridium, and palladium are precipitated by the trichloride from solutions of their salts.

Titanium tetrachloride, $TiCl_4$. A colourless, refractive liquid (d_4^0, 1·7604; b.p. 136·4°, m.p. −25°), formed by heating titanium dioxide or powdered rutile mixed with carbon in a stream of dry chlorine at 700°. Various alternative methods of preparation are known. The product is purified by fractional distillation. It may be freed from carbonyl chloride by heating in a current of dry air or carbon dioxide at 120°. Titanium tetrachloride fumes in moist air, and forms oxychlorides of titanium. It is used in the preparation of pure titanium and for making smoke screens. It is hydrolyzed completely by excess of water at 100°. This compound is technically important as an intermediate in the preparation of titanium compounds from minerals.

Titanium dioxide, TiO_2. The most important of all commercial white pigments. It occurs in nature in three crystalline forms, rutile (tetragonal), brookite (orthorhombic) and anatase (tetragonal). Rutile occurs in Virginia and Norway but is relatively unimportant as a source of titanium. By far the most important ore is ilmenite, which contains up to 45% by weight TiO_2, the rest being iron oxides; this is found in the U.S.A., India, Canada and other places.

Titanium dioxide is produced by digesting ilmenite with concentrated sulphuric acid, which converts the titanium and iron to sulphates.

These are leached from the dry reaction mass with water, the iron is reduced to the dipositive and the titanium to the tripositive state by scrap iron, and the ferrous sulphate crystallized out. The mother liquor is concentrated and hydrolyzed by steam to insoluble metatitanic acid, H_2TiO_3. After purification the solid is calcined at 900°-950° to yield the dioxide. This is further purified and the final product is anatase, one of the basic commercial forms. Rutile, the other, is obtained by seeding the liquor at the hydrolysis stage with rutile seed crystals and adding antimony trioxide or alumina to the precipitated solid prior to calcination.

When the natural rutile is used as a source of titanium dioxide the crude material is heated with carbon and chlorine to produce titanium tetrachloride. The latter is then, after purification, hydrolysed and heated to produce the dioxide.

Anatase forms a brown or black crystal, $d3·84$, m.p. 1560°, rutile a colourless crystal, d 4·26, m.p. 1640° with decomposition. Titanium dioxide is attacked by the halogens at high temperatures, and is not blackened by hydrogen sulphide at room temperature. On heating to 2000° it loses oxygen and the black oxide, Ti_2O_3, results. This oxide is extremely inert and is not attacked by any acid except sulphuric. By heating the dioxide with titanium *in vacuo* at 1600°, the monoxide, TiO, is formed.

Titanium dioxide is amphoteric and forms salts with strong acids. These are, however, readily hydrolysed. On fusion with alkali hydroxides or carbonates titanates are formed. Alkali metal titanates are not well established and are generally hydrates. Titanates such as $CaTiO_3$ and $BaTiO_3$ can be prepared by fusion of the appropriate oxides. These are mixed oxides and generally have close packing of oxygen atoms.

Titanium dioxide owes its wide commercial use as a pigment to the high refractive indices of its crystals, 2·7 for rutile and 2·55 for anatase. This gives it an extremely high covering power, weight for weight five to six times that of lithopone. The pigment is frequently extended by mixing it with anhydrous calcium sulphate. About two-thirds of the titanium dioxide made is used as a pigment; large quantities are also used for coating papers, and smaller quantities in the production of floor coverings, rubber, fabrics, leather and printing inks.

Titanium halides. In its halides titanium shows oxidation states of 4, 3, and 2. The tetrafluoride, TiF_4, is a white solid which sublimes at 284°. Complex fluorotitanates (IV), M_2TiF_6, are known. The tetrabromide, $TiBr_4$ (m.p. 38·2°, b.p. 230°), and the tetraiodide, TiI_4 (m.p. 150°,

b.p. 377·2°), show considerable covalent character. All the tetrahalides are prepared from the elements. The trifluoride, TiF_3, is a violet powder obtained by the action of hydrogen fluoride on the metal; complex fluorides, M_3TiF_6, are known. The tribromide and tri-iodide form violet hexahydrates similar to titanium (III) chloride. The difluoride and dibromide are unknown; the black di-iodide, TiI_2, is prepared by heating the tri-iodide *in vacuo* at 200°. See also Titanium chlorides.

Titanium hydride. Metallic titanium when heated at 400° in hydrogen will absorb considerable quantities of the gas. The formula of the product approximates to $TiH_{1·7}$, but the amount of hydrogen taken up depends upon the temperature and pressure and interstitial compounds (*q.v.*) are formed. Hydrogen is completely removed from titanium by heating in vacuum at 1000°.

Titanium nitride, TiN. Formed by reducing a titanium compound in nitrogen or when the complex between titanium tetrachloride and ammonia is heated to a high temperature. It has the sodium chloride lattice; if made below 1400° it has excess titanium and is blue-black, if made above 1600° it is golden-brown. It is soluble in boiling aqua-regia and yields ammonia on treatment with hot sodium hydroxide solution.

Titanium sulphates, $Ti_2(SO_4)_3$. The sulphate of tripositive titanium is obtained as a crystalline octahydrate by treating titanium trichloride with dilute sulphuric acid, and evaporating in vacuum at 60°. The anhydrous salt may also be obtained. Solutions of the sulphate have reducing properties similar to those of the trichloride. $Ti_2(SO_4)_3$ can enter into the composition of alums. The sulphate of tetrapositive titanium is also known. It is stable in the presence of excess of sulphuric acid, but is readily hydrolysed. Basic sulphates, e.g. titanyl sulphate $TiOSO_4·nH_2O$, are also known.

Titanocene dichloride, $C_{10}H_{10}Cl_2Ti$. A red

crystalline solid, m.p. 290°, sparingly soluble in organic solvents. Prepared from cyclopentadienyl sodium and titanium tetrachloride, it is of interest as a potential catalyst in Ziegler-type polymerization systems.

Titration. It is often necessary to determine the volume of a solution required to react quantitatively with a given volume of some other solution. This is conveniently achieved by the process known as titration, which consists in adding the one solution a small amount at a time from a graduated vessel provided with a tap to the other solution, until just sufficient has been added to complete the reaction, when the substances are present in equivalent amounts. This equivalence point (q.v.) may be evident by the cessation of a precipitation (e.g. in the reaction between solutions of silver nitrate and sodium chloride), or by a colour change (e.g. in the reaction between oxalic acid and potassium permanganate). Where no visible change occurs, a substance may be added which does not materially affect the reaction, but which provides a visible change at the end-point. Such indicators (q.v.) are nearly always employed.

Any reaction which proceeds to completion in aqueous solution may generally be made the basis of a titration. Those most often met with are concerned with the neutralization of acids with bases; with oxidation and reduction reactions (see Indicators, oxidation-reduction); and with reactions involving precipitation.

The determination of the equivalence-point is often made by electrical measurements. See Electrometric and Conductiometric titrations.

TNT. See Trinitrotoluene.

Toad venoms. The poisonous substances of the toad are secreted by the skin glands and have an action on the heart of animals similar to that of digitalis and related plant glycosides, but without the persistence of action associated with digitalis. They are conjugated compounds consisting of genins of a sterol-like structure combined as esters with suberylarginine. The free genins are also present. The best-known toad venom is bufotoxin.

Tocopherols. These are methylated derivatives of tocol, which has the formula shown:

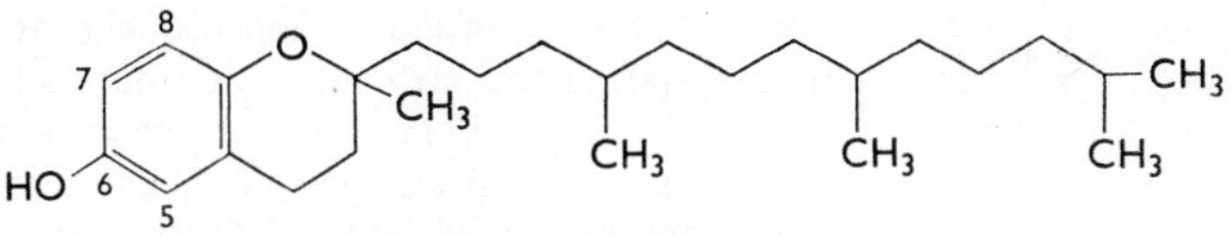

α-Tocopherol, which has the strongest vitamin E activity, is obtained from soya bean oil. It is used as the acetate, which is a pale yellow liquid, soluble in fat solvents, insoluble in water, m.p. about 25°, d_{25}^{25} 0·950-0·964.

Todd, Lord (Alexander Robertus) (1907-   ). Educated at Glasgow University, Todd worked under Sir Robert Robinson at Oxford (1931-1934), at Edinburgh (1934-1936), and at the Lister Institute (1936-1938) before becoming professor of chemistry at Manchester University (1938) and professor of organic chemistry at Cambridge (1944). Todd's researches have dealt with the chemistry of certain vitamins and drugs and with the synthesis of nucleosides, for which he was awarded the Nobel Prize for chemistry in 1957.

Tolan. The trivial name given to diphenylacetylene, $C_6H_5 \cdot C \equiv C \cdot C_6H_5$. Obtained as volatile colourless crystals, m.p. 61°, by mercuric oxide oxidation of benzil bis-hydrazone.

Tolbutamide, Rastinon, N-butyl-N′-toluene-4-sulphonylurea, $C_{12}H_{18}N_2O_3S$. A white crystal-

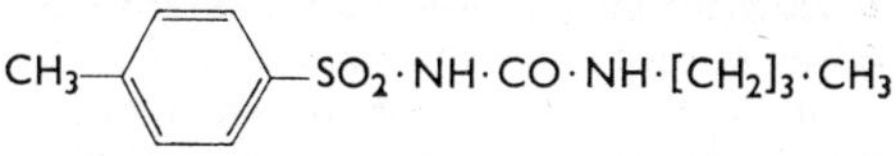

CH_3—⟨benzene ring⟩—$SO_2 \cdot NH \cdot CO \cdot NH \cdot [CH_2]_3 \cdot CH_3$

line powder, insoluble in water, soluble in 10 parts of 95% alcohol. It is a hypoglycaemic substance, taken orally in the treatment of diabetes.

Tolidine, $C_{14}H_{16}N_2$. The commonest isomer is

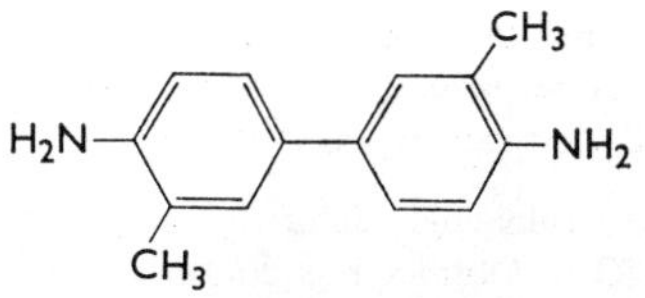

o-tolidine, 3,3′-dimethylbenzidine. Made by zinc reduction of o-nitrotoluene and subsequent

They are widely distributed in vegetable lipids, and in the body fat of animals, though animals cannot synthesize them. They have vitamin E activity and can protect unsaturated lipids against oxidation. Four are found naturally:

α-tocopherol, $C_{29}H_{50}O_2$, is 5,7,8-trimethyltocol,
β-tocopherol, $C_{28}H_{48}O_2$, is 5,8-dimethyltocol,
γ-tocepherol, $C_{28}H_{48}O_2$, is 7,8-dimethyltocol,
δ-tocepherol, $C_{27}H_{46}O_2$, is 8-methyltocol.

acid catalysed rearrangement of the intermediate o-hydrazotoluene. A light-sensitive white solid, m.p. 130°-131°, soluble in polar solvents. Used in dyes and as an extremely sensitive test for detecting gold (1 part in 10⁷).

Tollens reagent. An ammoniacal solution of silver oxide which is used as a test for aldehydes, which, unlike ketones, cause the deposition of a silver mirror.

Toluene, C_7H_8. Colourless refractive liquid with characteristic smell. Burns with a smoky flame; b.p. 111°, m.p. −95°, d_4^{20} 0·866. Very volatile in steam. Insoluble in water, miscible with most organic solvents.

It is obtained commercially as a by-product of the carbonization of coal, being recovered from coal tar by distillation, and from coal gas by absorption in oil followed by steam stripping and distillation. It is also produced from certain petroleum fractions rich in naphthenes by catalytic reforming in the presence of hydrogen (hydroforming); in this process dehydrogenation and dealkylation take place simultaneously and a mixture of aromatics is produced.

Chromic or nitric acids cause oxidation to benzoic acid; milder oxidation gives benzaldehyde and benzoic acid. The action of chlorine on boiling toluene gives mainly side chain substitution to benzyl chloride, benzal chloride, and benzotrichloride, all used for the preparation of benzaldehyde and benzoic acid. Cold chlorination in the presence of iron causes nuclear substitution to a mixture of o- and p-chlorotoluenes. Easily nitrated in the cold to mixture of o- and p-nitrotoluenes; more vigorous conditions produce ultimately 2,4,6-trinitrotoluene, which is widely used as an explosive (TNT). Sulphonates to a mixture of o- and p-isomers, the latter preponderating; the sulphonic acids are used for the preparation of saccharine and chloramine-T respectively. Toluene is used as a constituent of high-octane aviation and motor gasolines, as a solvent, and as a raw material in the manufacture of benzene, caprolactam, phenol, many dyestuffs and various other chemicals.

Toluene-p-sulphonyl chloride, tosyl chloride, $C_7H_7ClO_2S$. Obtained as colourless crystals, m.p. 71°, by the action of chlorosulphonic acid on toluene. Esters of toluenesulphonic acid are frequently called tosylates and their formation tosylation. Many tosylates are easily obtained crystalline, and the reaction is thus of considerable importance.

o-Toluidine, C_7H_9N. Colourless liquid, b.p. 198·1°, density at 20° 0·9986. Insoluble in water, miscible with organic solvents, volatile in steam, soluble in acid solutions. It is prepared by the reduction of o-nitrotoluene.

It is basic, forms a stable hydrochloride and sulphate, both moderately soluble in water. The sulphate is converted at 200° into o-toluidinesulphonic acid. Readily diazotizes and in this

form used as first component in many dyestuffs. Used for condensation with benzaldehyde in preparation of magenta.

p-Toluidine, C_7H_9N. Colourless leaflets, m.p. 45°, b.p. 200·4, d 1·058. Slightly soluble in water, readily soluble in alcohol, ether, and benzene. Volatile in steam.

It is basic and gives well-defined salts with mineral acids. Prepared by reduction of p-nitrotoluene with iron and hydrochloric acid. Easily sulphonated. It is used as a first component in azo dyes and in the manufacture of magenta.

Tone, Frank Jerome (1868-1944). Born at Bergen, N.Y., Tone graduated from Cornell University in 1891 as an electrical engineer. About four years later he accepted a position at the Acheson works, of which he became superintendent and then works manager, and in 1919 was elected to the Presidency of the Carborundum Co. He was largely responsible for the development of the synthetic abrasives and refractory industries in America, and for his work in this field was awarded the Perkin Medal for 1938.

Toning. Chemical toning is the process used in photography to alter the colour of the silver image by changing its chemical composition. Early methods involved the deposition of gold on the silver image, which can also be modified in tone by converting the silver to silver sulphide or selenide. Alternatively, coloured images can be formed by adsorption of dyes on to the silver or by converting the silver image to a dye image.

Toning can also be effected by a change in the physical condition of the silver which results if development, particularly physical development (q.v.), is carried out in the presence of certain heterocyclic thiols.

Topaz, $Al_2SiO_4(F,OH)_2$, is an aluminium fluorosilicate occurring in igneous rocks and pegmatites, often in association with tin ores. The crystals are orthorhombic with four molecules in a unit cell. The structure consists of linked octahedral groups around Al and tetrahedral groups around Si; four of the six atoms around each Al belong to SiO_4 groups, the remaining two are F atoms which may be partially replaced by OH. Sp.gr. 3·4-3·6. It is used in the manufacture of glasses and glazes and as a slag thinner in the steel industry. On ignition it yields a refractory material of the mullite class. Transparent crystals in various colours are used as gemstones.

Tor. A pressure unit used for vacuum systems. One tor is 1 mm Hg pressure.

Torpex. See Aluminized high explosives.

Tosyl. See Toluene-*p*-sulphonyl chloride.

Total pressure. The pressure exerted by a mixture of gases or vapours is usually referred to as the total pressure to distinguish it from the pressures exerted by the individual vapours or gases present, which are referred to as partial pressures. Thus, a mixture of oxygen at a partial pressure of 10 mm and nitrogen at a partial pressure of 35 mm has a total pressure of 45 mm. See Partial pressure.

Total reflux. A distillation column is said to be operating under total reflux when all the vapour leaving the column is condensed and returned to it. In this case no products are withdrawn from the system and the reflux ratio is infinity. Total reflux is frequently employed when starting up a column. See Rectification.

Toughness. The resistance offered to fracture by repeated bending or twisting. A common test for wire is to ascertain the number of times a short length can be bent to and fro through a certain fixed angle before breaking.

Tourmaline. A complex aluminium borosilicate

$$(Na,Ca)(Mg,Fe^{II},Al,Li)(Al,Fe^{III})(BO_3)_3(Si_6O_{18})(OH,F)_4$$

occurring as black or blue-black hexagonal crystals. Sp.gr. 2·98-3·2. Strongly pleochroic and piezo-electric. Occurs widely in granites, in pegmatites associated with granitic intrusions, and in various metamorphic rocks.

Town gas, Coal gas. Made by the thermal decomposition of coal, either in horizontal or vertical retorts, which are usually heated by producer gas, at a temperature up to 1250°. The chief by-products are coke, coal-tar (from which numerous important aromatic derivatives are obtained), and ammonium sulphate. After purification, a typical town gas has the composition:

Hydrogen	.	.	56·0%
Methane	.	.	22·8%
Carbon monoxide	.	.	10·9%
Nitrogen	.	.	6·0%
Other hydrocarbons	.	.	2·5%
Carbon dioxide	.	.	1·3%
Oxygen	.	.	0·5%

Such a gas has a calorific value of about 500 Btu/ft.^{3} (gross).

The gas is often enriched by the addition of water gas which increases the proportion of hydrogen and carbon monoxide.

Toxaphene. A chlorinated camphene insecticide of approximate formula $C_{10}H_{10}Cl_8$. It is a light yellow waxy solid, melting range 65°-90°, *d* 1·6, soluble in organic solvents, including refined kerosine. The technical product is prepared by chlorination of camphene and is a mixture of compounds. It has proved useful against many species including cutworms, boll weevil, aphids, thrips, bed bugs, body lice, and house flies; it also controls cockroaches and carpet beetles. Toxaphene is a general convulsant and its chronic toxicity to mammals is relatively high. It may be absorbed through the skin, but suitable animal dips and sprays have been used successfully. It is not phytotoxic.

Tracer. A substance added to a system to enable the experimenter to follow the course of a process without seriously altering the conditions. More particularly, the term is chiefly used for isotopic species added as tracers, especially radioactive isotopes or rare isotopes of the lighter elements (e.g. ^{18}O). The former are detected and determined with the aid of a Geiger counter, the latter with a mass spectrograph. As these detectors are very sensitive, only small proportions of tracer are needed. Furthermore, the isotopic tracers are practically indistinguishable in chemical and physical properties from the ordinary forms of the elements. Many physical, chemical and, particularly, biochemical studies have been greatly facilitated by the use of tracers in place of chemical analysis and some have been made possible for the first time (e.g. investigation of the self-diffusion of molecules in liquids and solids).

Tragacanth. See Gum tragacanth.

Transaminases. Enzymes catalysing the transfer of amino groups. A number are found in animal tissues, plants, and micro-organisms, most of which act on glutamic acid, but others transfer amino groups to and from glutamine, asparagine, and other amino acids. Glutamic acid is thus of great importance in the formation of amino acids from keto acids and ammonia.

Trans effect. In substitution in complexes the

proportions of *cis* and *trans* products depends markedly upon the other ligands present. Thus in square-planar platinum complexes the proportion of the two products A and B depends upon the relative *trans*-directing effects of L and L′. Ligands can be placed in a series of ability to direct trans substitution; some common ligands in order are $H_2O < NH_3 < Cl^- < CO$.

Transformer oil. A highly refined lubricating oil of low viscosity, practically colourless, resistant to oxidation, and not forming a sludge on standing. It is used for cooling and insulation in electrical installations, e.g. transformers and heavy duty switch gear.

Transition elements. The elements of the periodic table in which there is a partially filled d shell. Thus the elements from scandium to zinc, yttrium to cadmium, and lanthanum to mercury are classed as transition elements, the first named element in each series having no d electrons and the last ten d electrons. Transition elements are characterized by variable oxidation state, coloured ions, and a tendency to form complexes. Many of the elements and their salts are paramagnetic.

Transition interval. The visible colour change of an indicator is limited to a definite range of hydrogen-ion concentrations or of potential. The region between the limiting values, expressed in terms of pH or rH, is the transition interval, or region of change of the indicator, e.g. litmus changes from red to blue in the interval pH 5·0-8·0. See Hydrogen-ion concentration; Indicators, oxidation-reduction.

Transition point. This is the same as the transition temperature.

Transition state theory. Most *rate processes* (e.g. viscous flow of liquids, diffusion and electrolytic conduction in liquids and solids, chemical reactions) obey the Arrhenius equation (*q.v.*). It is therefore implied that they proceed by thermal activation. The activated state (or 'transition state') is a high-energy configuration through which the 'reactants' must pass before changing into 'products'.

H. Eyring and others developed a quantitative theory of the rates of many such processes on the assumption that the activated state has a characteristic enthalpy, entropy, and free energy; hence the concentration of activated molecules can be calculated by the principles of statistical mechanics. The activated complex may either return to its initial state or pass over into the 'final' state. The theory gives a very plausible treatment of rate processes of many kinds, but unfortunately it is often impossible to calculate *a priori* the thermodynamic properties of the transition state.

Transition temperature. Many allotropic or polymorphous substances have forms which are converted into each other at a definite temperature, which is known as the transition temperature, e.g. rhombic sulphur is transformed into monoclinic sulphur at 95·6°. Below this point, rhombic sulphur is the stable form, while the monoclinic variety is stable above it. Transition temperatures are influenced by the pressure exerted on the system.

Transmethylases. Enzymes that catalyse the transference of methyl groups in biological systems. The methyl groups are transferred from the amino-acid methionine, which is converted to homocysteine. This can be remethylated at the expense of choline or betaine.

Transmutation. The process of transforming one element into another is called transmutation, and has occupied the attention of scientists since the earliest times. The search for the Philosopher's Stone, a substance by means of which base metals like iron could be converted into gold, was one of the chief preoccupations of the alchemists, but it is only since 1919 that successful transmutation of any kind has been achieved. It was then found that when a proton is fired with a high velocity at an atom of lithium, the proton may be taken up by the lithium atom, which then splits up to yield two atoms of helium. ${}_{3}^{7}\mathrm{Li} + {}_{1}^{1}\mathrm{p} \rightarrow 2\ {}_{2}^{4}\mathrm{He}$. Numerous nuclear transformations have been induced by processes in which atoms have been bombarded with neutrons, protons, or deuterium atoms.

Until recently, the quantities of product obtained by transmutation were exceedingly small. During the development of atomic energy, however, the new elements neptunium and plutonium have been produced in quantity by neutron bombardment of uranium. Subsequently many isotopes have been obtained by transmutation and synthetic isotopes of elements such as Ac and Pa are more easily obtained than the naturally occuring species. Synthetic species of lighter elements, e.g. technetium and promethium are also prepared.

The transformations of the radioactive elements, whereby, e.g. uranium ultimately becomes lead, are not usually regarded as instances of transmutation because the processes are spontaneous, and cannot be controlled by the experimenter.

Transport number. The fraction of the total current carried by a particular ion during electrolysis is termed the transport number of that ion.

Traumatic acid, trans-2-dodecenedioic acid,

$$\mathrm{HO_2C[CH_2]_8}\overset{H}{\underset{}{}}C{=}C\overset{CO_2H}{\underset{H}{}}$$

$C_{12}H_{20}O_4$. M.p. 165-166°. It is a plant growth hormone, which is produced in damaged plant tissue, and on diffusing into adjacent intact tissue cells stimulates them to divide. Traumatic acid has been isolated from the pods of green beans.

Tray column. See Plate column.

Tray drier, shelf drier. This consists of a chamber containing a series of trays or shelves on which the material to be dried, usually a granular solid, is placed. Warm air, heated outside or inside the unit, is circulated through it. Operation is batchwise.

Tray efficiency. See Plate efficiency.

Trehalose, $C_{12}H_{22}O_{11}$, $2H_2O$. (α-D-Glucosido)-α-D-glucoside, is a non-reducing disaccharide, which forms the principal carbohydrate of insect

haemolymph. It comprises about 25% of trehala manna, the cocoons of a parasitic beetle. Trehalose also occurs in fungi, e.g. *Amanita muscaria*, generally replacing sucrose in plants lacking chlorophyll and starch. Trehalose forms rhombic prisms, m.p. 96·5°-97·5° (dihydrate).

Tremolite. An asbestos mineral, a member of the amphibole family, $Ca_2(Mg,Fe^{II})_5Si_8O_{22}(OH)_2$. It occurs chiefly in Lombardy and Piedmont, $d \sim 3\cdot0$, hardness 5-6, refractive index 1·636-1·608, birefringence 0·028. Used in the manufacture of acid-resisting filters.

Triacetin. See Acetins.

Triacetoneamine, 2,2,6,6-Tetramethyl-γ-piperidone, $C_9H_{17}NO$. Crystallizes in colourless

needles, m.p. 34·9°, b.p. 205°. Forms a crystalline monohydrate, m.p. 58°. Soluble in water, alcohol, and ether. Prepared by treating diacetoneamine with acetone, or by passing ammonia gas into acetone containing fused calcium chloride. It is weakly basic. Decomposed to phorone and ammonia. Reduced to tetramethyl-3-hydroxypiperidine. Used in the synthesis of benzamine hydrochloride.

Triamcinolone, $C_{21}H_{27}FO_6$. The free alcohol has

m.p. 269°-271°. The 21-acetate after drying off adducted solvent has m.p. 235°. The acetate has

the same action and uses as cortisone, but is more potent and without the sodium retention effect. Triamcinolone is used topically in the treatment of dermatoses as the 16,17-acetonide derivative.

Triangular diagram. A graphical representation of the phase-rule data for a system of three components.

Tribasic acid. An acid which has three replaceable hydrogen atoms, and therefore may yield three series of salts, is termed a tribasic acid, e.g. H_3PO_4, which yields salts of the types NaH_2PO_4, Na_2HPO_4, and Na_3PO_4.

Tribromoethyl alcohol, $CBr_3 \cdot CH_2OH$. Crystallizes in colourless needles or prisms; m.p. 80°, b.p. 92°-93°/10 mm. Sparingly soluble in water. Soluble in alcohol or benzene. Manufactured by the reduction of bromal with aluminium ethoxide. This substance dissolved in amylene hydrate and then diluted with water is injected into the rectum for the production of anaesthesia. It is non-irritant, and can be given safely to children. It has also been used with success in childbirth. It is easily decomposed with formation of free tribromoacetic acid and other decomposition products, and it is essential that it should be tested for free acid immediately before use.

Trichloroacetaldehyde. See Chloral.

Trichloroacetic acid. See Chloroacetic acids.

Trichloroethylene, $CHCl:CCl_2$. A colourless liquid with a chloroform-like odour, d_{20}^{20} 1·466, b.p. 87°, insoluble in water, miscible in all proportions with alcohol, ether and benzene. It is non-inflammable but toxic.

Trichloroethylene is manufactured by the dehydrochlorination of tetrachloroethane derived from the chlorination of acetylene. This is accomplished either by reacting the liquid with a lime slurry at 100° or by vapour-phase cracking over a barium chloride-carbon catalyst at 250°-300°.

Trichloroethylene is not attacked by dilute acids or alkalis, but when heated with sodium hydroxide under pressure it yields sodium glycollate. In the presence of light and oxygen dichloroacetyl chloride is formed, which can react with any moisture present to give small amounts of highly corrosive HCl. Numerous stabilizers have been patented.

Most of the trichloroethylene produced is used for metal degreasing, a field which it dominates. Other important uses are in the scouring of wool and as an extractive solvent, e.g. for olive and soya bean oils. Minor uses are as a heat transfer medium, analgesic and anaesthetic, insecticide and fumigant, paint remover and fire extinguisher.

Trichlorofluoromethane, Cl_3CF. A colourless liquid, b.p. 24°, which has been suggested as an internal standard with $\delta = 0$ for ^{19}F N.M.R. spectroscopy.

Trichloromethyl chloroformate, Diphosgene, Superpalite, $C_2O_2Cl_4$, $Cl \cdot CO \cdot OCCl_3$. An oily liquid; its vapour is extremely poisonous, having effects similar to phosgene when inhaled, d^{15} 1·653, b.p. 128°; 49°/50 mm. Manufactured by treating methyl alcohol with phosgene to form methyl chloroformate and then chlorinating this with chlorine under the influence of ultra-violet light. It is decomposed by water to give carbon dioxide and hydrogen chloride. When heated strongly it is converted to phosgene. It has been used as a lethal gas in shells; it is more persistent than phosgene owing to its higher boiling-point.

2,4,6-Trichlorophenol, $C_6H_3Cl_3O$. A colourless crystalline substance, m.p. 68°, soluble in water and most organic solvents and used medicinally as an antiseptic and disinfectant.

Triclinic system. A term used to describe crystals having three unequal crystallographic axes which intersect one another obliquely. Such crystals have no planes and no axes of symmetry. Copper sulphate pentahydrate and potassium dichromate are examples of substances which crystallize in this system. It is sometimes referred to as the anorthic system. See Crystal symmetry.

Tricresyl phosphate. See Phosphate esters.

Tridymite, SiO_2. A variety of silica rarely found in nature, but produced on heating quartz and other forms of silica to a high temperature. Hardness 7, m.p. 1670°. Tridymite is more readily attacked by hydrofluoric acid than

quartz, but less readily than cristobalite. It is a very desirable constituent of silica bricks as it has a lower coefficient of expansion and is less susceptible than cristobalite to sudden changes in temperature.

Tridymite is the stable form of silica between the temperatures 870° and 1470°. Below 870° quartz is the stable form; above 1470°, cristobalite. The changes from one form to another take place very slowly. As in the case of quartz and cristobalite, tridymite exists in two forms— the α- or low temperature form and β- the high temperature form, and α- changes into β-tridymite between 120° and 160°.

α-Tridymite is orthorhombic: $a = 9·88$, $b = 17·1$, $c = 16·3$ Å with 64 SiO_2 in the unit cell, sp.gr. 2·27. β-Tridymite is hexagonal, $a = 5·03$, $c = 8·22$ Å, with 4SiO_2, in the unit cell. As in all forms of silica, tetrahedral SiO_4 groups are linked by corners. The structure of α-tridymite has not been determined in detail but is probably a distorted form of the simpler β-tridymite structure (compare α- and β-quartz).

Triethanolamine. See Ethanolamines.

Triethoxymethane. See Orthoformic ester.

Triethylamine. See Ethylamines.

Trifluoperazine, $C_{21}H_{24}F_3N_3S$, 2HCl,

10-[3-(4-Methylpiperazin-1-yl)propyl]-2-trifluoromethylphenothiazine (trade name Stelazine). It is a pale cream crystalline powder, m.p. ~240°. Soluble at 20° in 2 parts of water, slightly soluble in alcohol. It is used medicinally as a major tranquilliser and antiemetic.

Triglyme, $C_8H_{18}O_4$. The dimethyl ether of tri-
$CH_3OCH_2CH_2OCH_2CH_2OCH_2CH_2OCH_3$.
ethylene glycol.

Trigol. The trivial name for triethylene glycol, $HO(CH_2)_2O(CH_2)_2O(CH_2)_2OH$, a colourless hygroscopic liquid, b.p. 285°, which is soluble in water and aromatic solvents.

Trigonal bipyramidal co-ordination. Co-ordination from five ligands as in phosphorus pentafluoride.

Trigonal system. A crystal system with a threefold axis as principal element of symmetry.

The unit cell has one axis parallel to the principal axis and three other axes at right angles. Many trigonal crystals are rhombohedral. Crystals with a six-fold axis as principal element are generally indexed on a trigonal unit cell.

Trigonelline, N-Methylnicotinic acid betaine,

$C_7H_7NO_2$. Crystallizes in prisms with one molecule of water, m.p. (anhydrous) 218° (decomp.). Soluble in water and alcohol. A base found in the seeds and fruits of many plants.

Trihydroxypropane. See Glycerol.

Tri-iodomethane. See Iodoform.

3,5,3′-Tri-iodothyronine, L-$C_{15}H_{12}I_3NO_4$. This appears to be the principal circulating thyroid hormone, present in blood plasma

and in the thyroid gland. It is about five times as active as thyroxine in preventing development of goitre in rats from which the thyroid has been removed.

Trilene. A trade name for trichloroethylene (*q.v.*) when used as an anaesthetic. It is given by inhalation for short operative precedures.

Trimethylamine. See Methylamines.

Trimethylamine oxide, C_3H_9NO. Crystallizes from water in colourless needles containing two molecules of water of crystallization, m.p. 255°-257° (hydrate); 96° (anhydrous). Soluble in water and methyl alcohol; sparingly soluble in ethyl alcohol. Occurs widely distributed in fish and animal tissues. Prepared by treating an aqueous solution of trimethylamine with hydrogen peroxide. Forms alkaline solutions in water and combines with acids to give crystalline salts. Decomposes when heated at 180° into trimethylamine and formaldehyde.

1,3,5-Trimethylbenzene. See Mesitylene.

Trimethylene. See Cyclopropane.

Trinitrobenzene, $C_6H_3N_3O_6$. A yellow crystalline

solid, m.p. 122°. Soluble in alcohol and benzene, insoluble in water. Best prepared by oxidizing trinitrotoluene to 2,4,6-trinitrobenzoic acid with sodium dichromate, and then boiling a suspension of the acid in water.

Its complexes with aromatic hydrocarbons have characteristic melting points and may be used for the identification and purification of the hydrocarbons.

Trinitrocresol, $C_7H_5N_3O_7$. Forms yellow crys-

tals, m.p. 107°. In its chemical and physical properties it closely resembles picric acid, e.g. it is acidic and forms explosive metallic salts. It is prepared by the direct nitration of *m*-cresol. It is now little used as a military explosive.

Trinitrotoluene, TNT, $C_7H_5N_3O_6$. Forms

pseudo-rhombic yellow crystals, m.p. 81°. Soluble in benzene and alcohol. It forms complexes with aromatic hydrocarbons and their derivatives such as amines. It condenses with nitrosodimethylaniline and dimethylaminobenzaldehyde.

It is prepared by the direct nitration of toluene with a mixture of nitric and sulphuric acids. TNT is a very stable, violent, and powerful high explosive, but less sensitive to shock and friction than picric acid. It is widely used as a filling for shells, bombs, etc., often mixed with ammonium nitrate and other high explosives. The lower grades of TNT may contain isomers which under hot storage conditions may give rise to exudation.

Triose. A carbohydrate with three carbon atoms. Three trioses are known, dihydroxyacetone and two stereoisomers of glyceric aldehyde.

Trioxymethylene. See Paraformaldehyde.

Triphenylene, 9,10-benzphenanthrene, $C_{18}H_{12}$.

Occurs in coal tar but may also be obtained from the spontaneous trimerization of benzyne. It forms long needles, m.p. 199°, and sublimes easily. Solutions exhibit blue fluorescence.

Triphenylmethane dyes. The hydrocarbon triphenylmethane is the basis of a large number of

$$HC{\Large\langle}\begin{matrix}C_6H_5\\C_6H_5\\C_6H_5\end{matrix} \qquad HOC{\Large\langle}\begin{matrix}C_6H_5\\C_6H_5\\C_6H_5\end{matrix}$$

Triphenylmethane   Triphenylcarbinol

important dyestuffs, which can all be considered as anhydro-derivatives of triphenylcarbinol. These dyestuffs are all derived from amino- and hydroxy-triphenylcarbinols in which the substituent groups are in the para-position to the methane carbon. The colours are nearly all extremely pure and bright shades, and have a high tinctorial power. The basic colours come on the market in the form of hydrochlorides, oxalates, and chlorozincates. They are generally crystalline solids, soluble in water, the solutions in dilute acids being more stable. By reduction they become colourless 'leuco'-compounds. The basic colours dye animal fibres and tannin-mordanted cotton direct from neutral solution, being used mainly for the latter fibre. In wool dyeing the acid of the dye salt is liberated and the dye goes on to the material as the base, or rather its salt with the complex amino-acids of the wool. The simpler basic dyes are very readily bleached by sunlight. They are also not fast to washing agents, particularly alkalis. Triphenylmethane colours, however, containing electronegative substituents are fast. Many sulphonated triphenylmethane colours, being of great beauty and brilliance of tone, are used as acid dyes for wool. They are, however, not very fast to light or to alkali, although this has been greatly improved, for example, in the Patent Blues. There are dyestuffs containing two basic groups (Malachite Green series), containing three basic groups (Rosaniline series) and containing hydroxyl groups (Rosolic acid series).

Triphenylmethyl. The anion, cation and radical have been prepared. The discovery of the radical, the first known free radical, was announced by Gomberg in 1900. It can be isolated only in the bimolecular form, hexaphenylethane, a colourless solid, m.p. 145°-147°. In solution an equilibrium is established between hexaphenylethane and the triphenylmethyl radical. The proportion of the radical increases with dilution

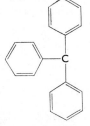

or rise in temperature: a 2% solution of the bimolecular form in benzene contains 1-3% triphenylmethyl at 5° and 27% at 80°. The equilibrium mixture is obtained by heating triphenylmethyl chloride with mercury, silver, or zinc in the complete absence of oxygen. The free radical is very reactive, combining with atmospheric oxygen to give a peroxide and with iodine to give triphenylmethyl iodide. It will also react with nitrogen dioxide, quinone, and alkenes. Solutions containing the radical are yellow, and exhibit paramagnetism due to the one unpaired electron.

If triphenylmethyl chloride in ether is treated with sodium, a yellow colour is produced due to the presence of the anionic species $Ph_3C^\ominus$. Alternatively, if triphenylmethyl chloride is treated with silver perchlorate in a solvent such a THF, the triphenylmethyl cation is obtained. More conveniently, triphenylmethyl salts, $Ph_3C^\oplus X^\ominus$, can be obtained as orange-red crystalline solids from the action of the appropriate strong acid on triphenylcarbinol in acetic or propionic anhydride solution. The perchlorate, fluoroborate, and hexafluorophosphate salts are most commonly used for hydride ion abstraction from organic compounds (e.g. cycloheptatriene gives tropylium salts). The salts are rather easily hydrolysed to triphenylcarbinol.

The radical and ions are exceptionally stable due to resonance: the free electron or charge is not localized on the methyl carbon atom but is distributed over the benzene rings.

Triphenylphosphine, $(C_6H_5)_3P$. A colourless crystalline solid, m.p. 81-82°, which sublimes easily. It is used widely as a stabilizing ligand for low oxidation states of many transition metal derivatives (many of the complexes are used as catalysts), and, via the appropriate phosphonium salt, for conversion to a phosphorane used in the Wittig alkene synthesis.

Triple bond. See Double bond.

Triple point. Three phases in a one component system can be in equilibrium only at a certain temperature and pressure, e.g. ice, water, and water vapour are in equilibrium at 4 mm pressure and 0·0075°. This is called the triple point.

Triplet. See Multiplet.

Triplet state. See Spin multiplicity.

Tripoli. A very fine grained soft silica usually resulting from the weathering of a siliceous limestone. Somewhat similar to rottenstone in physical properties and chiefly used as a mild abrasive.

Tripolite. A variety of diatomite (q.v.).

Triptycene, $C_{20}H_{14}$. The symmetrical hydrocarbon tribenzobicyclo-[2,2,2]-octatriene; it is a

colourless solid, m.p. 255°-256·5°, which is best obtained by a Diels-Alder reaction between benzyne and anthracene.

Trisazo dyestuffs. Nearly all of these dyes contain a diamine of the type of benzidine as one component, which makes them substantive to cotton. Many of them have the valuable property of dyeing well on mixed fabrics containing animal and vegetable fibres. One class is prepared from benzidine colours containing a secondary component with a diazotizable amino-group (e.g. Diamine Bronze G, Benzo Fast Blue B). Another method for the preparation of these dyestuffs consists in allowing a diazo-salt to react with one of the components of a benzidine dyestuff (e.g. Diamine Green G). If phenol is used in place of salicylic acid, Diamine Green B is obtained. Another example is Congo Brown G. See also Azo-dyes and Direct cotton dyes.

Triterpenes. Triterpenoid compounds are widely distributed in nature. They contain 30 carbon atoms and are derived from the hydrocarbons $C_{30}H_{50}$. They include squalene and tetracyclic compounds such as lanosterol.

Trithionic acid. See Polythionic acids.

Tritium, $^{3}_{1}H$. The heaviest isotope of hydrogen, occurring in a proportion of less than 1 in 10^{17} in natural hydrogen. It is β-active and is used as a radioactive tracer and in thermonuclear reactions. It may be prepared by the deuterium bombardment of various light atoms.

Tritolyl phosphate. Another name for tricresyl phosphate. See Phosphate esters.

Trityl. A name given to the triphenylmethyl group (*q.v.*). Triphenylmethyl chloride reacts with pyridine solutions of certain hydroxy compounds and sugar derivatives to form trityl ethers.

Trommel. A trommel consists essentially of a cylinder of perforated sheet metal or of wire screen; the axis of the cylinder is tilted and the whole revolves slowly. Material to be classified enters at the upper end of the trommel; undersize material escapes through the perforations in its surface; oversize material is discharged at the other end. By covering sections of the cylinder with screens of different mesh it is pos-

sible to separate out a series of size fractions. A disadvantage of this arrangement is that the finest screens, being nearest the feed entrance, are subjected to the heaviest wear, and are also liable to become blocked by large particles. The difficulty may be avoided by arranging the screens in the form of concentric cylinders, with the coarsest in the centre.

Trommel test. An empirical test for coke which gives an indication of the resistance of the sample to abrasion.

Trona. Naturally occurring sodium sesquicarbonate, Na_2CO_3, $NaHCO_3$, $2H_2O$, which is found in various localities and is formed by the spontaneous evaporation of soda lakes. This material is also known as urao.

Troostite. The term refers to very fine structures in heat-treated steels. Primary troostite is an obsolete term denoting nodular pearlite. Secondary troostite is a sub-microscopic dispersion of plate-like Fe_3C in ferrite, produced when martensite is tempered between 300° and 500°. This is the structure of spring steels. The term is also used for a variety of zinc silicate, Zn_2SiO_4.

Tropilidene, 1,3,5-cycloheptatriene, C_7H_8. Obtained as a degradation product of the alkaloids atropine and cocaine. For a more recent preparation see Norbornadiene. It is a liquid, b.p. 116°-118°, but yields solid salts of the tropylium cation by hydride abstraction, and tropolone by alkaline permanganate oxidation.

Tropine, $C_8H_{15}NO$. A basic secondary alcohol, which crystallizes in hygroscopic plates, m.p. 63°, b.p. 229°. Very soluble in water and alcohol. It is formed by hydrolysis of its esters, which are called tropeines, and are important medically. See Atropine, Homatropine, Hyoscine, Hyoscyamine.

Tropolones. Tropolones are 2-hydroxy-derivatives of cycloheptatrienone (tropone). The parent compound, *tropolone*, forms colourless needles, m.p. 49°-50°. Soluble in water and alcohols. Dissolves in aqueous sodium bicarbonate with evolution of carbon dioxide to give a yellow sodium salt. Reacts with cupric chloride to give a green copper derivative which is soluble in chloroform. It may be prepared from cyclohepta-1,2-dione by bromination followed by dehydrobromination. A number of tropolones occur naturally including colchicine (*q.v.*), stipitatic acid—a β-hydroxy-β-

carboxytropolone from *Penicillium stipitatum*—and the thujaplicins, which are isopropyltropolones present in the essential oils of the *Cupressaceae*.

Tropylium. The trivial name given to the cation $[(C_6H_7)^+]$ of 1,3,5-cycloheptatriene, obtained when a hydride ion is abstracted from 1,3,5-cycloheptatriene by, e.g., trityl salts. It is an aromatic system having 6 π electrons distributed equally over seven carbon atoms, and is an unusually stable carbonium ion. Alkaline hydrolysis produces tropone.

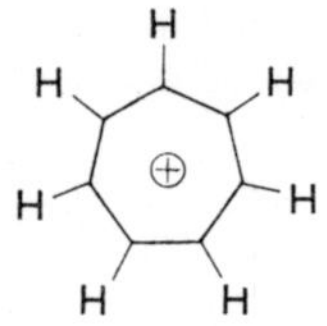

Trough mixers. See Ribbon mixers.

Trouton's rule. The molecular weight of a liquid (*M*) is related to the latent heat of evaporation (*l*) and the boiling-point of the liquid on the absolute scale (*T*) by the expression

$$\frac{Ml}{T} = \text{const.}$$

For most normal liquids the constant, which is known as *Trouton's constant*, has a numerical value close to 21. Associated liquids show marked deviations from this rule. The Trouton constant is the molar entropy of vaporization.

Troxidone, Trimethadione, $C_6H_9NO_3$. Colourless crystals, m.p. 46°, prepared by condensing

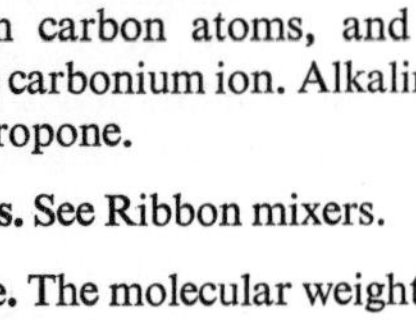

ethyl α-hydroxyisobutyrate with urea and methylating the product. It is soluble in water and alcohol. Troxidone prevents attacks of 'petit mal' epilepsy, being used to treat patients who suffer from lapses of consciousness, but is of no use in treating 'grand mal'.

Tryparsamide, tryparsone, $C_8H_{10}AsN_2NaO_4$.

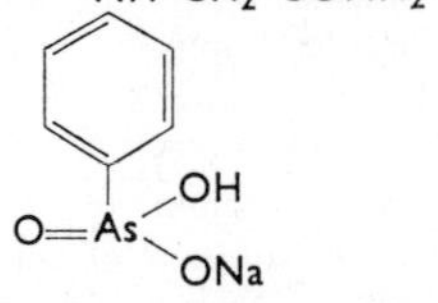

The sodium salt of N-phenylglycineamide-*p*-arsonate. Colourless crystals, soluble in water, almost insoluble in alcohol. Prepared from sodium-*p*-aminophenylarsonate and chloroacetamide. It is used in the treatment of sleeping sickness and neurosyphilis.

Trypsin. An important digestive enzyme, formed in the pancreas as its inactive precursor, trypsinogen. This proenzyme is activated in the intestine by enterokinase or, autocatalytically, by trypsin itself. In the process, the hexapeptide Val.Asp.Asp.Asp.Asp.Lys is split off. Both trypsin and trypsinogen have been obtained crystalline. Trypsin has a molecular weight of 24,000; it acts optimally at pH 7-9, and is specific for cleavage of peptide linkages adjacent to arginine or lysine residues. The reactive site of trypsin contains a serine residue. Trypsin also serves as the activator to convert chymotrypsinogen into chymotrypsins (*q.v.*), accompanying intestinal enzymes which also act at pH 7-9 but have different specificities.

Tryptophan, α-Amino-β-indolylpropionic acid,

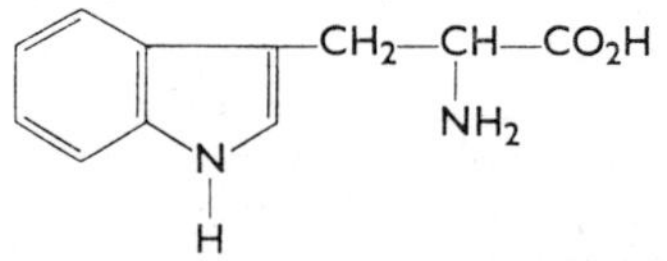

$C_{11}H_{12}N_2O_2$. Crystallizes in hexagonal and rhombic leaves, m.p. 289°. Slightly soluble in cold water, readily soluble in hot. The naturally occurring substance is laevorotatory, $[\alpha]_D - 33°$. Tryptophan is an essential amino-acid, its presence in the food of animals is necessary for proper growth. It is present in small quantities in the hydrolysis products of most proteins, although absent in certain vegetable proteins.

Tschugaeff-Zerewitinoff method. A method for determining the number of hydroxyl groups present in the molecule of an organic compound. A stock solution is prepared of methyl magnesium iodide in amyl ether or pyridine and an excess of it is allowed to react with a solution of the compound in question in a modified nitrometer apparatus. Reaction occurs according to the following equation:

$$R \cdot OH + CH_3MgI \rightarrow R \cdot OMgI + CH_4$$

and the amount of methane produced is measured. It is clear that substances containing, in addition to hydroxyl groups, groups that can react with the Grignard reagent with evolution of gas, such as primary amino-groups, are not suitable for this type of determination.

TTT curves (time, temperature, transformation) were formerly known as Bain's S curves. These curves illustrate the rate of isothermal decomposition of austenite, showing the nucleation and growth times for the more stable diffusion-controlled decomposition products such as pearlite and bainite. They are much used as a guide in the quench hardening of steels, since they indicate the rate of quenching which must be employed to prevent the diffusion of carbon and so allow the formation of martensite.

Tube mill. See Ball mill.

d-**Tubocurarine chloride**, $C_{38}H_{44}Cl_2N_2O_6, 5H_2O$.

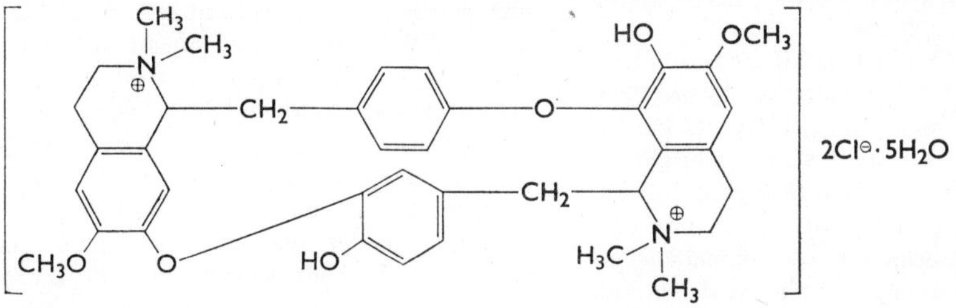

The chloride of an alkaloid found in the stems of *Chondrodendron tomentosum*. It is a white crystalline powder, sparingly soluble in water and alcohol; m.p. 275°.

As it prevents the transmission of the nerve impulse at the neuromuscular junction, it causes paralysis of skeletal muscle. It is used for relaxing muscles during operations.

Tumbler mixers. A class of mixers widely used for blending powders, consisting of a barrel which is slowly rotated, usually about a horizontal axis, the tumbling motion of the material inside producing a mixing action. The barrel may be any one of a number of shapes and have baffles inside. The cement mixer is a familiar example of a machine of this type.

Tung oil, China-wood oil. A rapidly drying oil obtained from the nuts of *Aleurites cordata* and *Aleurites fordii*, trees of the euphorbia order that are native in China and Japan and now cultivated in America and elsewhere. Tung oil is used on a considerable scale with natural resins in the preparation of oil varnishes; when it is heated with certain metallic oxides driers are formed which are known as tungates. The residue left after the extraction of the oil from the nuts and seeds contains about 5% of nitrogen, 2% of phosphorus, and 1% of potassium, and is useful as a fertilizer.

Tungstates. Tungstic acid forms several series of tungstates; the normal tungstates derived from the hypothetical acid H_2WO_4 are insoluble in water with the exception of those of the alkali metals. The insoluble tungstates can be obtained in a crystalline form by fusing together sodium tungstate and the metal chloride in an excess of sodium chloride and then leaching out the soluble chloride. Calcium, cadmium, and to a smaller extent magnesium and zinc tungstates prepared in this way are used in the preparation of fluorescent

screens for X-ray work and for coating bulbs of electric discharge lamps; each salt gives a characteristic fluorescence colour varying from green to blue, but the colours may be modified by the introduction of carefully regulated quantities of impurities. $Na_2WO_4, 2H_2O$, sodium tungstate, has been used as an impregnating material in the fireproofing of fabrics and as a mordant in dyeing. Solutions of sodium tungstate dissolve relatively large amounts of tungstic acid forming numerous complex tungstates of which the paratungstate is the best known; this salt, which comes into commerce under the name 'tungstate of soda,' crystallizes in transparent triclinic crystals having the composition $Na_{10}W_{12}O_{41} \cdot 28H_2O$. Simple tungstates contain tetrahedral WO_4^{2-} groups but on acidification these polymerize to form WO_6 units linked to one another by bridging oxygen atoms. Paratungstates contain $[W_{12}O_{46}]^{2-}$ ions and metatungstates $[W_{12}O_{40}]^{8-}$ ions. Heteropolytungstates, in which a hetero ion occupies a central position, are known.

Tungsten. W. At.no. 74, At.wt. 183·92. The element occurs in nature chiefly as wolframite, a tungstate of iron and manganese, and as scheelite, calcium tungstate; both minerals are generally associated with tin ores. Decomposition of the ores with concentrated hydrochloric acid affords a residue of tungstic acid which is purified by solution in ammonia and reprecipitation with hydrochloric or nitric acid. The purified tungstic acid is heated to redness to obtain tungsten trioxide which, on heating at 1100°-1200° in a current of hydrogen, is reduced to a heavy grey crystalline powder of the pure metal. Compact ductile tungsten cannot be prepared by melting this powder, but is readily obtained by compressing it into bars under high pressure and sintering these bars in an atmosphere of hydrogen by passing through them such a current as will heat them to a temperature just below the m.p. The sintered bars are then worked by swaging into rod at a bright red heat, and finally the rod is drawn into wire by passing it through dies at gradually decreasing temperatures.

Compact tungsten has a colour resembling that of platinum, but unlike platinum it acquires 'temper colours' on heating in air. It has m.p. 3370°, b.p. 5930°, d 19·2, sp. heat at 20° 0·0358, mean coefficient of expansion (0°-500°) $4·6 \times 10^{-6}$, and hardness (Mohs' scale) about 7. α-Tungsten has a body-centred cubic lattice, $a_0 = 3·1652$ Å.

Tungsten oxidizes in the air at a red heat forming the trioxide but is not attacked by nitrogen. The halogens combine directly with it, fluorine at room temperature, and iodine at a bright red heat. It combines readily with carbon, silicon, and boron at high temperatures forming very hard compounds which are used in making cutting tools. Sulphur and phosphorus are without action on tungsten at any temperature. Compact tungsten is not appreciably attacked by any single acid, nor by *aqua regia*, but dissolves violently in a mixture of hydrofluoric and nitric acids. Solutions of alkali hydroxides do not attack the metal but fused alkali hydroxides and carbonates dissolve it, the rate of dissolution being considerably increased by addition of oxidizing agents, such as chlorates or peroxides, to the mixture.

The chief uses of tungsten are in the manufacture of filaments for electric lamps, cutting tools for high-speed lathe work, electrical contacts, and special alloy steels.

Tungsten alloys. The most important alloys are the tungsten steels which contain up to 18% of tungsten; the tungsten forms carbides which give improved wear resistance and gives the matrix high temperature strength. This is the basis of high-speed tool steel. An alloy of tungsten with nickel and copper made by a powder metallurgical process has d 16·5 and is used for making radium containers, owing to its high screening power for radiation. Stellite, an extremely hard alloy of tungsten with chromium and cobalt, is used for high-speed cutting tools. Electric contacts for switch-gear are made from copper- and silver-tungsten alloys prepared by impregnating porous sintered tungsten shapes with silver or copper; these are not true alloys, but simply intimate mixtures of the constituents combining the high electrical conductivity of the silver or copper with the hardness and strength of the tungsten. See Stellite.

Tungsten blue. Partially reduced tungsten trioxide, obtained by gentle reduction of WO_3 or tungstates. The formation of a blue colour on treating a tungstate with stannous chloride and hydrochloric acid is a sensitive test for tungsten.

Tungsten bronzes. Highly coloured compounds of formula $M_n WO_3$, where M is a unipositive metal and $0 < n < 1$, prepared by reducing the appropriate tungstate with hydrogen. The com-

pounds are defect structures containing both W^{VI} and W^V atoms.

Tungsten carbides. Two carbides, W_2C and WC, are obtained by heating tungsten powder with carbon. W_2C melts at about 2750°, while WC is formed by a peritectic reaction at 2600°. The two compounds form a eutectic at 2525°, 4·5% carbon, and W_2C also forms a eutectic with tungsten at 2475°, 1·5% carbon. Both compounds are extremely hard and are used for making cutting tools and wire-drawing dies; for this purpose, the carbide is ground with 5-10% of nickel or cobalt powder, the mixture is compressed under hydraulic pressure into compacts of the desired shape and these are sintered in hydrogen at about 1350°. Various other metallic carbides, borides, silicides, or nitrides are frequently added to the mixture to improve the mechanical properties. A double carbide of titanium and tungsten, obtained by melting tungsten and titanium with nickel in a graphite crucible and then dissolving the nickel in aqua regia, is also used for making cutting tools.

Tungsten chlorides. Four chlorides are known, WCl_2, WCl_4, WCl_5, and WCl_6, as well as two oxychlorides, WO_2Cl_2 and $WOCl_4$. The hexachloride is formed as violet crystals, soluble in carbon disulphide, by heating tungsten in a current of oxygen-free chlorine. It melts at 275°, boils at 346°, and is only slowly decomposed by water. Reduction with hydrogen affords the lower chlorides and heating in air or oxygen the oxychlorides. The pentachloride melts at 248° and boils at 276°, the trichloride is infusible but decomposes into the di- and penta-chlorides at a red heat. Reduction of the hexachloride with aluminium and powdered quartz affords the dichloride; this is soluble in hydrochloric acid, and on saturating the solution with hydrogen chloride yellow needles of $H_2(W_6Cl_{14} \cdot 2H_2O)$ are obtained.

Tungsten fluorides. *Tungsten hexafluoride*, WF_6. A colourless, reactive gas obtained by the action of fluorine on the metal, m.p. 2·5°, b.p. 19·5°. It gives coloured solutions in many organic solvents and forms complexes, M_2WF_8, with alkali fluorides. Mixed chlorofluorides, WF_5Cl and WF_3Cl_3, are also known.

Tungsten oxyfluorides, WOF_4. White hygroscopic crystals, prepared from HF and $WOCl_4$. WOF_2 is formed by the action of HF on WO_2 at 500°.

Tungsten tetrafluoride, WF_4. The hexafluoride can be reduced at 110° with benzene to give the tetrafluoride.

Tungsten oxides, *Tungsten dioxide*, WO_2, is obtained as a brown powder by heating the trioxide at a dull red heat in a current of hydrogen. If the reduction is effected at 900° in a very slow current of moist hydrogen the oxide may be obtained in the form of bronze-coloured spangles, d 12·1, but it is difficult to obtain it free from the blue intermediate oxide, W_2O_5. In a current of chlorine at 500°-600°, WO_2 yields the oxychloride WO_2Cl_2, and when fused with alkali tungstates various highly coloured 'tungsten bronzes' are formed.

Tungsten trioxide, WO_3, occurs naturally as tungstite, and is the final product of the oxidation of tungsten or any of the other oxides in air. It is a bright canary-yellow powder, d 7·16, insoluble in acids but soluble in alkali hydroxides or carbonates. It is used in the ceramic industry for imparting a yellow colour to silicate glazes.

Tungstic acid. Tungsten trioxide has several hydrates but it is doubtful whether these are true acids. Tungstates (*q.v.*) are the salts of tungstic acids. Extensive polymerization occurs.

Tunnel drier. This consists of a long tunnel through which is passed a current of warm air, the material to be dried being slowly carried along the tunnel on trays, trolleys or a conveyor belt. The plant is used for the drying of solid objects, such as pieces of pottery ware, in large-scale production.

Turacin. A red pigment present in the feathers of the turaco, an African bird. It is a copper salt of uroporphyrin. See Porphyrins.

Turanose, $C_{12}H_{22}O_{11}$. The product, together with glucose, of the mild hydrolysis of melezitose. It is fructopyranose-6-α-glucoside. It has m.p. 157°, $[\alpha]_D$ +75·3°. It is of interest as being isomeric with sucrose, but differs in being a reducing sugar.

Turbidity-point. See Indicators, turbidity.

Turbidimetry. A method of quantitative analysis which involves the spectrophotometric estimation of absorption by a colloidal dispersion of a precipitate.

Turbine mixer, turbine agitator. A development of the paddle mixer, this machine has a number of flat, vertical, radial blades attached to a disc on the end of a vertical shaft. The assembly revolves at high speed, producing a centrifugal motion which results in efficient liquid circulation. This mixer is suitable for liquid-liquid mixing or suspending solids in liquids; unlike the propeller mixer it is effective in liquids of high viscosity.

Turkey red. A red lake formed from alizarin and aluminium hydroxide.

Turkey-red oil. This is a sulphonated castor oil, consisting chiefly of ricinoleosulphuric acid, ricinoleic acid, and anhydrides of ricinoleic acid. It is used in the preparation of the cotton fibre for

dyeing with Turkey red and as an anti-foaming agent.

Turnbull's blue. See Prussian blue.

Turpentine. Various types of turpentine are produced; all are light volatile essential oils obtained as exudates from coniferous trees. Turpentine is a mixture of cyclic terpene hydrocarbons, chiefly α-pinene; it begins to boil at over 150°, has d about 0·85-0·875, n_D^{20} 1·46-1·48. It is used as a thinner for paints and varnishes and as a solvent. See British Standard 244.

Turquoise. Essentially basic hydrated aluminium phosphate, $Al_2(OH)_3PO_4 \cdot H_2O$, containing small amounts of copper to which the sky-blue colour is due. Usually microcrystalline, but amorphous in appearance, waxy lustre, sp.gr. 2·6-2·8. It is used as a gemstone.

Tutton, Alfred Edwin Howard (1864-1938). Born at Stockport, Tutton studied at Owens College, the Royal College of Science, and at Oxford University. From 1895 till 1924 he served as H.M. Inspector of Schools (Technical Branch). Author of numerous books, Tutton made many original contributions to crystallography. He was elected F.R.S. in 1899 and was President of the Mineralogical Society from 1912 till 1915.

Tutton salts. The salts $M^I_2SO_4 \cdot M^{II}SO_4 \cdot 6H_2O$. M^I is an alkali metal and M^{II} is a dipositive transition metal.

Twaddell. See Hydrometer.

Twinning. A term used in crystallography to denote a set of crystals that have one or more planes or faces in common but whose main developments away from that plane are not those of a single crystal.

Two-component system. A system consisting of two components; such systems are most commonly met with in problems involving the distillation of two liquids.

Tyndall, John (1820-1893). Born in Co. Carlow, Ireland, Tyndall held posts in the Ordnance Survey and as a teacher before, in 1848, he took up the study of science at Marburg. He was appointed professor of natural philosophy (1854) and superintendent (1867) at the Royal Institution. He discovered the 'Tyndall effect'—the detection of colloidal particles by their ability to diffract light rays. He was elected F.R.S. in 1852.

Tyndall effect. When a beam of light is projected through a disperse system, the scattering of the light by the particles of the disperse phase makes its path visible. This is known as the Tyndall effect. Colloidal sols as well as coarse suspensions show the effect, and a common example is the illumination of dust particles by a ray of sunlight. The light thus produced by Tyndall scattering is polarized. The scattering effect is greatest for light of low wavelengths and so the Tyndall cone is usually bluish in colour. Even distilled water is not optically void when examined by ultra-violet light; this is not due to impurities but is ascribed to random molecular fluctuations in the local density of the liquid. See Colloids, Ultramicroscope.

Type-metal. See Tin alloys.

Tyramine, *p*-*β*-**Aminoethylphenol,** $C_8H_{11}NO$. Colourless crystals, m.p. 164°, soluble in 95 parts of water, 8 parts of boiling alcohol. A base found in ergot, and in putrefying animal tissues and certain cheeses where it is formed by bacterial action on tyrosine. It is usually made synthetically and has a weak and prolonged pressor action, resembling its derivative, adrenaline.

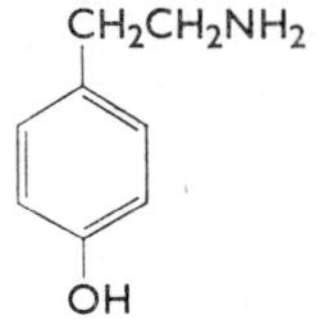

Tyrian purple, $C_{16}H_8Br_2N_2O_2$. A purple vat dye

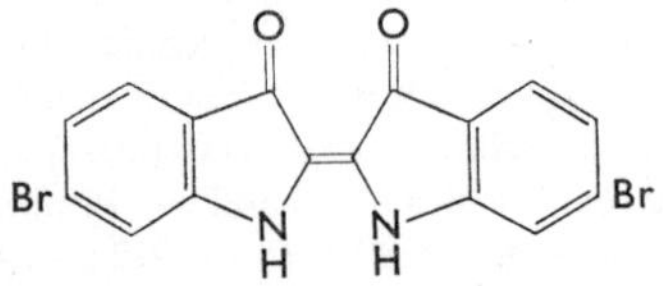

of great antiquity. Occurs in the shell fish *Murex brandaris* from which it was once extracted for making royal purple.

Tyrocidine. An antibiotic, which has been obtained crystalline in colourless needles from cultures of *B. brevis*. It is a mixture of two cyclic polypeptides, of which tyrocidine A has the structure:

L-Orn—L-Leu—D-Phe—L-Pro—L-Phe
| |
L-Val—L-Tyr—L-Glu—L-Asp—D-Phe

In tyrocidine B the L-phenylalanine is replaced by L-typtophan. Tyrocidine has a haemolytic effect and has been used only in the form of tyrothricin (*q.v.*).

Tyrosinase. An enzyme of the oxidase class; it is responsible for the darkening of the cut surface of many plants and vegetables. It converts tyrosine first into a red substance and then into black melanin. It may be prepared from potato peel-ings, bran, fungi, etc. Preparations free from laccase and peroxidase are obtained from the meal worm (*Tenbrio molitor*). It is most active between pH 6 and 8. Tyrosinase also oxidizes other monophenols, the initial product being *o*-quinones.

Tyrosine, *p*-**Hydroxyphenylalanine,** $C_9H_{11}NO_3$. Crystallizes in fine needles, m.p. 314°-318°. Slightly soluble in cold water, more soluble in hot. Insoluble in alcohol. The naturally occurring substance is laevorotatory, the specific rotation varying with the concentration. Tyrosine is the least soluble amino-acid obtained on the

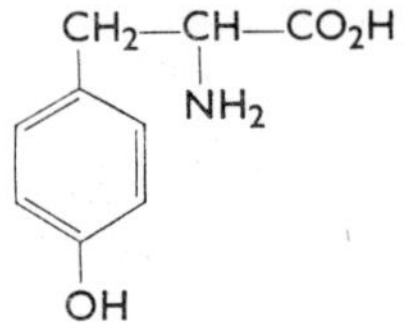

hydrolysis of proteins, and it is thus the easiest to prepare from protein hydrolysates.

Tyrothricin. A mixture of the antibiotic substances obtained by autolysis of cultures of *B. brevis*. It contains gramicidin and tyrocidine. It is used medicinally in the treatment of skin infections and infected ulcers, wounds, and burns. It has also been found effective in the treatment of streptococcal mastitis in cows.

U

Ubichromenol. A polyisoprenoid chromene

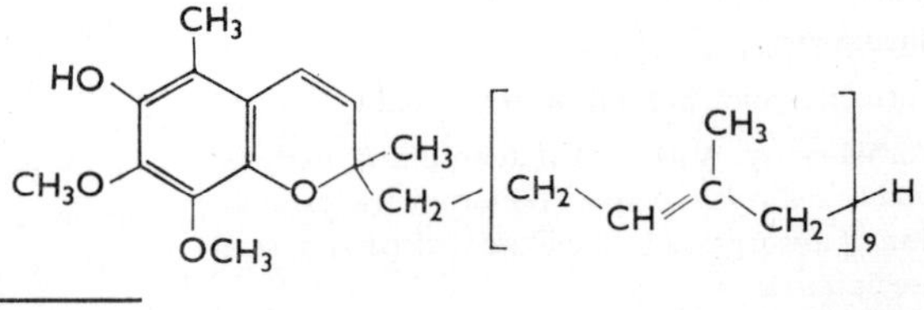

isolated from kidney. It is readily prepared by the pyridine-catalysed cyclization of ubiquinone, and the compound isolated from tissue may be an artifact.

Ubiquinones, Coenzymes Q. A family of

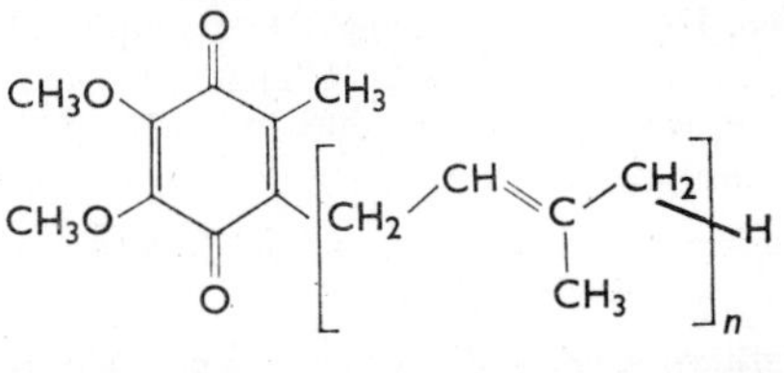

naturally occurring tetrasubstituted 1,4-benzoquinones, the members differing only in the length of the 3-polyisoprenoid chain. In the

606

typical ubiquinone of animal tissues there are 10 units (C_{50}: 'Q-10'); yeasts produce Q-6 and Q-7 and some bacteria produce Q-8. Their biological function is not clearly established but appears to be concerned with electron transport. See R. A. Morton, *Endeavour*, 1965, **24**, 81.

Ullman reaction. The synthesis of diaryls by the condensation of aromatic halides with themselves or other aromatic halides, with the concomitant removal of halogens by a metal, e.g. copper powder: thus bromobenzene gives diphenyl. The reaction may be extended to the preparation of diaryl ethers and diaryl thioethers by coupling a metal phenolate with an aryl halide.

Ultimate analysis. A determination of the percentage of every element in a compound without regard to its molecular structure.

Ultracentrifuge. In this device, introduced by Svedberg, colloidal sols are subjected to a force many times that of gravity, and sedimentation made to take place. By this means the molecular weights of sol particles may be determined and size distribution determined. The sedimentation of large organic molecules in aqueous solution and even that to heavy inorganic ions such as caesium can be accomplished by ultrafiltration.

Ultrafiltration. This is a method of filtration in which particles of colloidal dimensions are separated from molecular and ionic substances by drawing the sol liquid through a membrane, the capillaries of which are very small. Membranes of collodion supported on filter paper are often used for this purpose, and may be formed in different degrees of porosity so that particles of different maximum size are retained. The mechanism of ultrafiltration is not merely a sieve effect; the electrical conditions of the membrane and of the colloid are also important.

Ultramarine. One of the most beautiful blue pigments, occurring rarely as the mineral lapiz lazuli, but manufactured on a very large scale. Broadly it is a complex silicate of sodium and aluminium with the structural framework of a zeolite with S-atoms at the corners and centre of the unit cube. Part of the sulphur may be in the form of S_2 groups.

Two types of ultramarine are known in industry: those poor in silica, and those rich in silica, i.e. with an Al: Si ratio of 2:3. The colour becomes darker with increasing sulphur content. Lithium and thallium ultramarines are dark violet; calcium and zinc ultramarines are almost colourless. If Se replaces S the product is red, but if Te replaces S the product is yellow, sp.gr. 2·3-2·5, hardness 5-6. Common ultramarine is made by heating china clay, sulphur, soda, silica, rosin, and salt-cake in crucibles or muffles.

Ultramarine is the basis of lime-blue pigment, laundry blue, and other blue colours. It is decomposed on heating, so is useless as a ceramic colour. See British Standard 314.

Ultramicroscope. When a beam of light is brought to a focus in a colloidal sol and the Tyndall effect (*q.v.*) examined from above by means of a microscope, particles of colloidal dimensions are made visible by the light which they scatter. By this means the presence and motion of particles as small as 5-10 mμ may be investigated.

Although the actual particle is not visible in the ultramicroscope, but only the halo of scattered light, some idea of shape can be obtained, long or disc-shaped particles giving a peculiar twinkling effect.

Ultrasonics. Ultrasonic vibrations have frequencies of the order of 2×10^5 cycles per second; they may be set up by applying an alternating current to quartz, tourmaline, or Rochelle salt, or by the effect of oscillating magnetism on a rod of magnetic material immersed in a liquid. They can be used to bring about the liquefaction of gels, the depolymerization of macromolecules and to bleach solutions of coloured dyestuffs. With their help it is possible to make an emulsion of mercury and water, or to sterilize milk. They are also used in descaling metals, during soldering, and for crack detection.

Ultrasonic absorption has recently been used in the investigation of fast reactions in solution. If a system is at equilibrium and the equilibrium is disturbed in a very short time (of the order of 10^{-7} seconds) then it takes a finite time for the system to recover its equilibrium condition. This is called a relaxation process. When a system in solution is caused to relax using ultrasonics, the relaxation time of the equilibrium can be related to the attenuation of the sound wave. Relaxation times of 10^{-4} to 10^{-9} seconds have been measured using this method and the rates of formation of many mono-, di- and tripositive metal complexes with a range of anions have been determined.

See 'Techniques in Organic Chemistry,' Volume 8, part 2, ed. A. Weissberger, J. Wiley & Sons, New York, London, 1963.

Ultra-violet light. The radiation which occurs beyond the visible violet light in the spectrum, i.e. light of wavelength less than about 3600 Å, is termed ultra-violet light. Radiation of yet shorter wavelength is called X-rays. Ultra-violet light possesses much greater energy than visible radiation, and is generally much more effective in inducing photochemical reactions, but possesses much less penetrating power. Ordinary glass is opaque to light of wavelength less than about 3600 Å. Quartz is transparent down to

21

about 1800 Å, and is therefore used for making prisms and lenses in ultra-violet optical apparatus.

Umbellic acid, 2,4-dihydroxycinnamic acid,

$C_9H_8O_4$. A yellow powder, darkening at 240° and decomposing at 260°. Soluble in alcohol and hot water. It occurs in asafoetida as an ester with its anhydride, umbelliferone.

Umbelliferone, 7-hydroxycoumarin, $C_9H_6O_3$.

Crystallizes in needles, m.p. 223°-224°. Soluble in 100 parts of hot water; very soluble in alcohol. It occurs in many plants.

Umbellulone, $C_{10}H_{14}O$. An unsaturated dicyclic ketone found in the essential oil from the leaves of *Umbellularia californica*, with pungent mint-like smell. It is easily isolated by means of its compound with sodium sulphite, and has the characteristics b.p. 92·5°-93°/10 mm, d^{20} 0·950, n_D^{20} 1·48325, $[\alpha]_D$ −36·30°.

Umber. A natural ferric hydroxide often containing manganese dioxide. It is a brown powder much used as a pigment. Burnt umber is the calcined raw umber. See British Standard 312.

Uncertainty principle. See Heisenberg uncertainty principle.

Undecenoic acid, $CH_2:CH[CH_2]_8COOH$. A pale yellow liquid, freezing point 20°-24°, insoluble in water, miscible with alcohol. It is prepared by the vacuum distillation of castor oil; n_D^{25} 1·449. It is a fungicide used in treating tinea pedis and infections of the vulva and vagina.

Uniaxial. All crystals except those belonging to the cubic system exhibit double refraction. For light travelling along the principal axis of hexagonal, tetragonal, and rhombohedral crystals there is no double refraction, and crystals belonging to these systems are accordingly described as uniaxial. Orthorhombic, monoclinic, and triclinic crystals are termed biaxial.

Unimolecular films. Classic experiments of Rayleigh, Devaux, Langmuir, N. K. Adam and others showed how it is possible to prepare and study the properties of films of certain insoluble oils and fats (e.g. stearic acid) as unimolecular layers ('monolayers'), i.e. only one molecule thick, on the surface of water. In such films the hydrophilic or 'head' group is oriented towards the water while the hydrophobic group or 'tail' is oriented away from it. In some cases the molecules in the monolayer are close-packed, in others they are well separated, thus forming in different cases two-dimensional solids, liquids or gases.

Unimolecular reaction. A type of homogeneous gas reaction in which the molecular mechanism involves only single molecules of the reactant. Although many reactions are first order (see Order of reaction) true unimolecular reactions are rare; the thermal decomposition of certain alkyl halides is believed to be an example. The disintegrations of radioactive elements are true unimolecular nuclear reactions.

Unit cell. Since in a crystal there is a regular repetition of some arrangement of atoms in three dimensions, in order to describe the structure of the crystal it is in general sufficient to describe that characteristic portion of the structure which, if indefinitely repeated in the directions of the three crystallographic axes, reproduces the structure of the crystal. This portion of the structure is contained within a parallelopiped termed the unit cell, whose sides are parallel to the crystallographic axes. See Crystal structure.

Unsaturated compound. See Saturated compound.

Uracil, 2,6-dioxytetrahydropyrimidine, $C_4H_4N_2O_2$. A colourless crystalline powder,

turning brown at 280° and melting at 338°, with decomposition. Sparingly soluble in cold water, readily soluble in hot. Sparingly soluble in alcohol. Uracil is a constituent of ribose nucleic acid.

Uramil, $C_4H_5N_3O_3$. A colourless crystalline substance. Does not melt below 400°. Insoluble in cold water; soluble in hot water. Prepared by the reduction of violuric acid. Forms salts with acids.

Darkens on exposure to air. Forms murexide on boiling with ammonia. Oxidized by nitric acid to alloxan.

Uranates. The most common uranates are derived from the hypothetical acids H_2UO_4 and $H_2U_2O_7$, but polymeric uranates, containing oxygen bridges, are also known. They are all insoluble, even those of the alkali metals. The best known is sodium di- or pyro-uranate or uranium yellow, $Na_2U_2O_7$, $6H_2O$, which is made by precipitating a uranyl salt with sodium hydroxide and used in the manufacture of uranium glass.

Uraninite. The crystalline form of pitchblende.

Uranium, U. At.no. 92, At.wt. 238·07, m.p. 1132°, estimated b.p. 3900°. Uranium crystallizes in three forms, α-uranium, stable up to 665°, orthorhombic, $a=2·85$, $b=5·87$, $c=4·96$ Å, $d=18·9$; β-uranium, stable 665°-770°, tetragonal, $a=10·76$, $c=5·66$ Å, $d=18·11$; γ-uranium, stable 774°-1132°, body-centred cubic, $a=3·525$ Å, $d=18·06$. Uranium occurs naturally in many minerals but the most important commercial ores are pitchblende (uranium oxide, $UO_{2·2·25}$), autunite (hydrated calcium uranyl phosphate), and torbernite (hydrated copper uranyl phosphate). The most important deposits of uranium ores occur in Canada, in Northern Colorado, in the Congo, and in the Rand goldfields of South Africa. There are also large deposits in Soviet Kazakstan. Extraction of uranium is carried out in various ways; the first stage is generally by differential flotation followed by roasting and extraction of the uranium into concentrated sulphuric acid; alkaline leaching with sodium carbonate solution is an important alternative to the use of acid. Uranium is generally recovered from leach solutions by solvent extraction procedures. Full details of the various extraction procedures in use for uranium are given by Katz and Seaborg, 'The Chemistry of the Actinide Elements.' Metallic uranium has been prepared by reduction of the oxides or halides with calcium, lithium, or barium. It is an extremely reactive metal, reacting with oxygen even at room temperature. Uranium is of great importance on account of the existence of the fissile isotope [235]U, but it is also an important starting point in the production of the transuranic elements. In its compounds uranium shows oxidation states from two to six.

Uranium halides. For hexapositive uranium, in addition to the uranyl salts (q.v.), *uranium hexafluoride*, UF_6, and *uranium hexachloride*, UCl_6, are known. Uranium hexafluoride is obtained as pale yellow crystals by the action of fluorine or bromine trifluoride on uranium or uranium compounds. It sublimes at 56·5°, and has been used in the separation of uranium isotopes by gaseous diffusion. Uranium hexachloride has been prepared as a black, unstable compound by the disproportionation of uranium pentachloride. *Uranium pentafluoride*, UF_5, and *pentachloride*, UCl_5, have been obtained by interaction of UF_6 and UF_4 and by chlorination of UCl_4 respectively. Uranium (V) is unstable in

water but an ion UO_2^+ exists in acid solution. *Tetrapositive uranium halides*, UX_4, are readily prepared by reduction of the higher halides or by the action of a suitable halogenating agent—e.g. CCl_4, $C+Cl_2$, HF—on UO_2. Colours are generally green-black; these are the most stable halides of uranium. Uranium tetrafluoride is insoluble in water but the other halides are hydrolysed in solution. *Tripositive uranium halides*, UX_3, are known for fluorine, chlorine, and bromine. They are prepared by reduction of the tetrahalides with hydrogen and are reddish-brown in colour. Uranium trifluoride is insoluble; the other halides are oxidized in solution.

Uranium oxides. Uranium forms an extensive series of stoicheiometric and non-stoicheiometric oxides, the most important being UO, UO_2 (brown to black), U_3O_8 (greenish-black), UO_3 (yellow to orange), and $UO_4·2H_2O$ (yellow). The first four oxides may be prepared by varying the pressure and temperature of oxygen over uranium but uranium trioxide is best obtained by heating uranyl nitrate. Uranium peroxide, $UO_4·2H_2O$, is precipitated from a solution of a uranyl salt with hydrogen peroxide. Uranium trioxide is amphoteric and uranates are formed by addition of alkali to the solution of a uranyl salt.

Uranyl compounds. These are salts of hexapositive uranium and contain the grouping UO_2; most of them are greenish-yellow, very soluble substances. *Uranyl acetate*, $UO_2(CH_3COO)_2$, crystallizes with 0 and 2 molecules of water and is made by dissolving UO_3 in acetic acid. *Uranyl nitrate*, $UO_2(NO_3)_2$ crystallizes with 0, 2, 3, and 6 molecules of water and is soluble in ether. It is prepared by dissolving UO_3 in nitric acid. *Uranyl halides*, UO_2X_2, are formed by all the halogens. *Sodium zinc uranylacetate*,

$$NaZn(UO_2)_3(CH_3COO)_9·9H_2O$$

is used in the identification of sodium, since it is insoluble.

Urao. See Trona.

Urbain, Georges (1872-1938). Urbain was born and educated at Paris. After teaching at the École Alsacienne he became director of the research laboratory of the Compagnie générale d'Electricité in 1899. In 1905 he went to the École de Physique et de Chimie and in 1908 became professor of inorganic chemistry in the University of Paris. His work dealt chiefly with rare-earth and spectrum analysis.

Urea, Carbamide, CH_4N_2O. Crystallizes in colourless rhombic prisms, m.p. 132°, soluble in water and alcohol, insoluble in ether. It is a weak base, and forms salts with strong acids. Urea was first obtained synthetically by Wöhler in 1828 by evaporating a solution of ammonium cyanate. It can be made by the addition of water to cyanamide, by passing water into fused phenylcyanamide, and by numerous other methods. Commercially it is made by reacting carbon dioxide with ammonia at 200° and pressures up to 400 atm., the ammonium carbamate formed initially largely dehydrating to urea. There are a number of processes available but all employ the same basic route.

Urea occurs in human urine to the extent of about 2%, being the chief nitrogenous constituent and the end product of protein metabolism. It is present in the urine of all mammals and in small quantities in the blood of mammals and fish, being formed by the breakdown of arginine, which splits under the action of the enzyme arginase to ornithine and urea. Ornithine combines with ammonia and carbon dioxide to form citrulline, which takes up an extra molecule of ammonia to form arginine and complete the cycle.

Urea is largely used as a fertilizer, and as a non-protein feed supplement for sheep and cattle. The most important chemical use, which however accounts for only a small part of urea production, is in the manufacture of urea-formaldehyde resins. It is also used in the manufacture of adhesives, pharmaceuticals, dyes and various other materials.

Urea-formaldehyde resins. Urea may be condensed with formaldehyde to give a thermosetting clear resin. In industrial production the proportion of formaldehyde used in the condensation varies from the theoretical 2 molecular proportions (adhesive) to 1·5 molecular proportions (moulding materials). The condensation is usually carried out first under alkaline catalysis, while the cure is completed under acid catalysis. Urea-formaldehyde resins are compounded with fillers to modify their physical properties, usually with a view to increasing the form stability, and mechanical strength of the resins. Plastics based on urea resins fall in the general category of the amino-plastics.

Urease. The enzyme which catalyses the hydrolysis of urea to ammonia and carbon dioxide. It was the first enzyme to be obtained crystalline (by Sumner in 1926 from the jack bean). Another good source is the soya bean, and it is found in many plant tissues, but not in vertebrates. The crystalline enzyme is a water-soluble protein with mol.wt. of about 480,000.

Ureides. Compounds of urea with organic acids. They are closely related to many complex nitrogenous substances occurring in plants and animals. With monocarboxylic acids, mono-

ureides are formed by union of one acid molecule and diureides by union of two acid molecules with urea. Dicarboxylic acids and α-hydroxy-acids give cyclic ureides—examples of these are barbituric acid and hydantoin. They are crystalline colourless solids, sparingly soluble in water but soluble in alcohol. Decomposed by alkalis. They have acidic properties and form salts.

Urethane, ethyl carbamate, $NH_2 \cdot COOC_2H_5$. Colourless prisms, m.p. 49°-50°, b.p. 184°. Very soluble in water and alcohol. Prepared by the action of ammonia on ethyl chloroformate. It is a mild hypnotic which produces sleep without giving rise to unpleasant after-effects. It is also used for the treatment of leukaemia.

Urethanes. Esters of carbamic acid, $NH_2 \cdot COOH$. They are colourless crystalline solids, soluble in water, alcohol, and ether; they distil without decomposition. They are prepared by the action of ammonia on carbonic or chlorocarbonic esters, or by treating alcohols with urea nitrate or isocyanates. When heated with ammonia they form urea and an alcohol. Phenyl- and α-naphthylurethanes are used for characterizing alcohols and phenols.

Urey, Harold Clayton (1893-   ). Born in Indiana, Urey took a zoology degree at the University of Montana but later developed an interest in physical chemistry under G. N. Lewis at the University of California. He worked with Bohr in Copenhagan, at Johns Hopkins University, and became full professor at Columbia in 1934. He was awarded the Nobel Prize in chemistry in 1934 for his work on the separation of heavy hydrogen.

Uric acid, 2,6,8-trihydroxypurine, $C_5H_4N_4O_3$. Exists in two tautomeric forms:

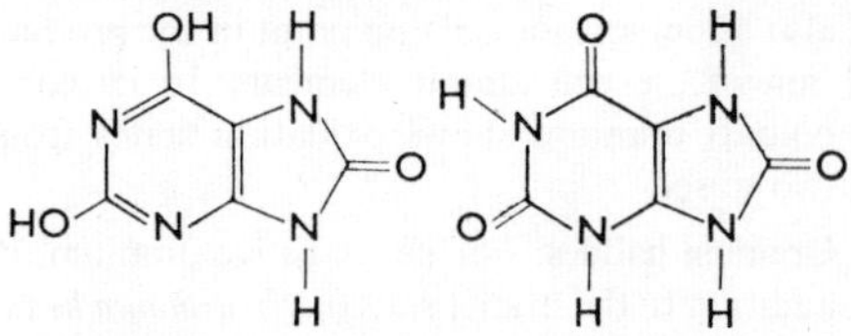

A colourless microcrystalline powder, odourless and tasteless, which decomposes on heating above 250°. Almost insoluble in water, insoluble in alcohol and ether, soluble in alkalis. It is dibasic and forms two series of salts. It occurs in small quantities in human urine, the average daily excretion being 0·6 g, being excreted as the end product of nucleic acid metabolism. In the excrement of birds and reptiles it is present as ammonium urate and is the chief nitrogenous substance. It is prepared commercially from guano by extracting with alkali and reprecipitating with acid. It can be synthesized by fusing glycine with urea, and by other processes.

Uricase. An enzyme present in the liver and kidney which oxidizes uric acid to allantoin and carbon dioxide.

Uridine. See Nucleosides.

Urobilin, $C_{33}H_{44}N_4O_8$. One of the yellow pigments of the urine. It is a reduction product of bilirubin, and has a similar structure with an opened porphyrin ring, but more than one type of urobilin exists, and the exact structures of these and the closely related stercobilin are in doubt.

Urocanic acid, β**-Imidazoleacrylic acid,**

$C_6H_6N_2O_2$. A substance found in the urine of dogs after feeding large quantities of histidine. It is also formed by bacterial action on histidine.

Urochrome. The chief yellow pigment of urine. It appears to be formed in the body from tryptophan, but its chemical constitution is unknown.

Uronic acids. Formed by oxidation of the primary alcohol groups of sugars, and named after the sugar from which they are formed, thus glucuronic acid from glucose. Only D-glucuronic, D-mannuronic, and D-galacturonic acids are important. Polyuronides are constituents of the gums and mucilages; alginic acid is a polymer of mannuronic acid and pectic acid of galacturonic acid.

Uroporphyrin. See Porphyrins.

V

Vaccenic acid, trans-11-octadecanoic acid, $C_{18}H_{34}O_2$, $CH_3 \cdot [CH_2]_5 \cdot CH : CH \cdot [CH_2]_9 \cdot CO_2H$.

A white solid, which is present in small quantities in animal fats and in milk. It is the only naturally occurring fatty acid with the *trans* configuration. It crystallizes in platelets, m.p. 43°-44°,

Vacuum crystallizer. In this type of crystallizer a warm saturated solution is introduced into a vessel under a vacuum corresponding to a b.p. of the solution which is lower than its actual temperature. As a result, vapour flashes off and cooling occurs through adiabatic evaporation. The advantage of this type of plant is that heat is removed without the use of a heat transfer surface, and that some concentration of the solution is produced at the same time. Like other cooling crystallizers, its use is limited to substances whose solubilities show an appreciable temperature dependence.

Vacuum pump. The function of a vacuum pump is to suck gas from a space where the pressure is much below atmospheric and discharge it to atmosphere. Mechanical pumps for this purpose are normally of the rotary positive displacement type and can give pressures down to 10^{-2} mmHg. Steam jet ejectors are widely used in the chemical industry, especially with distillation columns and evaporators, the vacuum produced being from 100 to 0·5 mmHg, depending on the number of stages. For very high vacua, such as are required in molecular distillation, diffusion pumps are employed. See Compressors, Ejector, Diffusion pump.

Valence isomerization. The isomerization of molecules which involve structural changes resulting only from relocation of single and double bonds is termed valence isomerization. If a dynamic equilibrium is established between the two isomers it is also referred to as valence

tautomerism, e.g. for the cyclo-octa-1,3,5-triene system.

Valency. A term sometimes used to denote what is now called oxidation state (*q.v.*). It was formerly used to designate combining power.

Valency electrons. See Valency, theory of.

Valency, theory of. The valency and chemical bonding of any atom are determined by the outermost or valency electrons of the atom. The elements in which the outer shells are full are relatively inert chemically and simple valency theory is based on the concept that elements tend to gain, lose, or share electrons in order to complete their outer electron shells. The elements having these filled shells are the noble gases and other elements try to approach the noble gas structures. The theory is made more complex by the electronic configuration of the transition metals where it is often impossible to reach a noble gas structure and it is found that relative stability is given by having the sub-shells (d or f) filled, half-filled, or empty.

The Electrovalent Bond is formed by electrostatic attraction between oppositely charged ions. Thus sodium, with one outer electron, loses this electron to achieve the noble gas neon structure, whilst chlorine, with seven outer electrons, gains one electron to achieve the argon structure.

$Na(1s^2, 2s^2, 2p^6, 3s^1) \rightarrow Na^+(1s^2, 2s^2, 2p^6) + e$
$Cl(1s^2, 2s^2, 2p^6, 3s^2, 3p^5) + e \rightarrow$
$\qquad\qquad\qquad\qquad Cl^-(1s^2, 2s^2, 2p^6, 3s^2, 3p^6)$

Crystalline sodium chloride consists of sodium and chloride ions.

Covalent Bonds are formed by the sharing of electrons. Thus the carbon atom, with four equivalent electrons shares with the electrons from four hydrogen atoms.

$$4H\times \;+\; \cdot\overset{\displaystyle\cdot}{\underset{\displaystyle\cdot}{C}}\cdot \;\longrightarrow\; H\overset{\bullet\times}{\underset{\bullet\times}{\times}}\overset{H}{C}\times H$$

The carbon atom has a share in eight electrons (neon structure) whilst each hydrogen atom has a share in two electrons (helium structure). This is a tremendous simplification of covalent bonding, since the actual electrons are present in molecular orbitals which occupy the whole space around the five atoms of the molecule.

Co-ordinate bonds are formed by the sharing of electrons, both electrons being donated by the same atom. Thus the hydrogen ion, H^+, has no outer electrons whilst ammonia has eight, six shared with hydrogen atoms and one lone-pair. This lone-pair is donated to the hydrogen ion and the ammonium ion is formed

$$H\overset{\bullet\times}{\underset{\bullet\times}{\times}}\overset{H}{N}\!\!: \;+\; H^+ \;\longrightarrow\; \left[H\overset{\bullet\times}{\underset{\bullet\times}{\times}}\overset{H}{N}\!\!:H\right]^+$$

The nitrogen retains its share in eight electrons (neon structure) and each hydrogen atom has a share in two electrons (helium structure). Each hydrogen atom is equivalent (see Hybridization).

Valentine, Basil. Said to have written about the year 1470, but the books bearing his name were probably written by Thölde about the year 1600. The best-known is the 'Triumphal Chariot of Antimony,' first published in 1604.

Valentinite. See Antimony trioxide.

Valeric acids, Valerianic acids, $C_5H_{10}O_2$. *n-Valeric acid*, $CH_3 \cdot CH_2 \cdot CH_2 \cdot CH_2 \cdot COOH$, is a colourless liquid with an unpleasant odour, d^{20} 0·9387, b.p. 186·4°. Moderately soluble in water; miscible with alcohol. Prepared from *n*-butyl iodide by the Grignard reaction or by oxidation of *n*-amyl alcohol.

Isovaleric acid is a colourless liquid with the

$$\begin{matrix} H_3C \\ \\ H_3C \end{matrix}\!\!\!\!>\!CHCH_2COOH$$

unpleasant odour of valerian, $d^{17\cdot6}$ 0·9332, b.p. 176·7°. Moderately soluble in water; miscible with alcohol. Occurs in the roots of valerian and angelica together with an optically active form of methylethylacetic acid. Prepared by oxidation of isoamyl alcohol. A mixture of acids similar to that obtained from valerian roots is prepared by oxidation of fusel oil.

Valine, α-**aminoisovaleric acid,** $C_5H_{11}NO_2$.

$$\begin{matrix} H_3C \\ \\ H_3C \end{matrix}\!\!\!\!>\!\underset{\underset{\displaystyle NH_2}{|}}{CH \cdot CH} \cdot COOH$$

Crystallizes in white shiny leaves, m.p. 315°. Soluble in water. The naturally occurring substance is dextrorotatory, $[\alpha]_D^{20}$ +6·42°. It is one of the amino-acids obtained on the hydrolysis of proteins.

Vallez filter. The Vallez leaf filter consists of a series of circular leaves mounted crosswise in a cylinder as in the Sweetland filter. In this type, however, they are carried on a slowly rotating central shaft which is hollow, and serves also as an effluent outlet. The slurry is fed in under pressure, the cake, when formed, being blown off inside the casing and removed by a screw conveyor, so that the drum need never be opened during normal operation.

VAMA. See Krilium.

Vanadic acids, Vanadates. The vanadic acids probably do not exist in the free state, either solid or in solution; the vanadates, however, form a well-defined and very large group of compounds. The simpler salts may be regarded as derived from the hypothetical ortho- meta-, and pyro-vanadic acids, H_3VO_4, HVO_3, and $H_4V_2O_7$, respectively. The metavanadates are the most stable; orthovanadates, which are of infrequent occurrence, are readily hydrolysed in solution, giving pyrovanadates. The vanadates are oxidizing agents. The alkali-metal salts are usually readily soluble in water; in other cases the solubility varies. *Sodium metavanadate*, $NaVO_3$, is manufactured by decomposing the commercial iron vanadate obtained in the working-up of vanadium ores with sodium carbonate or hydroxide; in solution it is decomposed by acids like other vanadates, giving hydrated vanadium pentoxide or its colloidal solution. *Sodium orthovanadate*, Na_3VO_4, $12H_2O$, is prepared by adding excess of caustic soda to a solution of the pyrovanadate, and crystallizing; it is isomorphous with $Na_3PO_4, 12H_2O$. *Sodium pyrovanadate*, $Na_4V_2O_7, 18H_2O$, is formed by fusing vanadium pentoxide with two molecular proportions of sodium carbonate, extracting with water, and crystallizing. Other alkali metal vanadates are prepared by similar methods, and vanadates of other metals are usually prepared by double decomposition, using the alkali metal or ammonium salts.

Vanadates contain VO_4 units which become bridged to form polymeric units. In acid solution a V_{10} unit is known.

Vanadium, V. At.no. 23, At.wt. 50·95. A hard grey or silver metallic element, forming crystals having a body-centred cubic structure, $a = 3 \cdot 01$ Å, d^{22} 5·96, m.p. 1710°, b.p. 3000°, hardness 7·5, sp.ht. 0·120. Vanadium is non-magnetic. It can be cold-rolled into wire, becoming harder in the process. Vanadium occurs naturally as patronite (V_2S_5 + free sulphur) (particularly in Peru), carnotite ($KUO_2VO_4 \cdot 1\frac{1}{2}H_2O$) (from which vanadium is obtained as a by-product in uranium and radium extraction), and vanadinite ($3Pb_3(VO_4)_2$, $PbCl_2$); smaller quantities are found in many other minerals. The methods of extraction vary in detail; generally the ore is roasted with sodium chloride or carbonate, and the product leached with water to remove the vanadium as soluble vanadates. Calcium and aluminium are precipitated with sodium carbonate, and ferrous sulphate added to precipitate the vanadium as iron vanadate. Alternatively the roasted ore is extracted with sulphuric acid and the vanadium precipitated as the pentoxide by adding an oxidizing agent (e.g. a hypochlorite). Pure vanadium metal is obtained by electrolysis of a fused vanadium salt or by reduction of a halide with, e.g., potassium. Pure vanadium retains its lustre in air, but burns incompletely to the pentoxide on heating in oxygen. It also burns in chlorine (giving vanadium tetrachloride), and reacts with nitrogen at a bright red heat to form a nitride. Vanadium is unattacked by cold hydrochloric acid; hot concentrated sulphuric acid is slowly reduced, an oxide of vanadium being formed. Nitric acid readily reacts, giving vanadic acid. Vanadates are also formed by the action of fused alkalis on the metal. In its compounds vanadium shows oxidation states ranging from -1 to $+5$. Aqueous solutions have the following colours: $+2$ violet, $+3$ green, $+4$ blue, $+5$ colourless. Metallic vanadium is chiefly used (as ferrovanadium) in the manufacture of special steels, in which the metal has an oxygen- and nitrogen-removing ('scavenging') action, and also effects a more homogeneous distribution of carbon in the steel. Other vanadium alloys are also used commercially. Vanadium compounds are efficient catalysts in oxidation reactions, and are used as such as in the contact process for sulphuric acid manufacture.

Vanadium bromides:—

Vanadium dibromide, VBr_2. Can be prepared as light reddish-brown crystals by reducing vanadium (III) bromide with hydrogen.

Vanadium tribromide, VBr_3, is a dark green or black deliquescent solid, prepared by the action of warm bromine on vanadium; it gives a green aqueous solution, which on concentration *in vacuo* gives a green crystalline hydrate, VBr_3, $6H_2O$.

Vanadium oxytribromide, $VOBr_3$, is a dark red, deliquescent, somewhat unstable liquid, prepared by passing bromine vapour over red-hot vanadium trioxide.

Vanadyl dibromide, $VOBr_2$, is a yellow powder obtained by heating the oxytribromide to 180° or by passing a mixture of bromine and sulphur bromide over heated vanadium pentoxide.

Vanadium oxymonobromide, $VOBr$, is a violet crystalline solid, insoluble in water, prepared by heating vanadyl dibromide *in vacuo*.

Vanadium carbides. The carbide, VC, forming silvery-white crystals, m.p. 2750°, sp.gr. 5·25-5·4, is prepared by heating vanadium pentoxide with sugar charcoal in an electric furnace. Other carbides, V_3C, V_3C_2, V_2C_2, V_2C_3 have been reported; some or all of these probably enter into the constitution of vanadium steels.

Vanadium chlorides:—

Vanadium tetrachloride, VCl_4, is a reddish-brown viscous liquid, b.p. 154°, prepared by heating the metal in chlorine and extracting the tetrachloride from the distillate with carbon tetrachloride. When kept dry it decomposes slowly into vanadium trichloride and chlorine; it is hydrolysed by water giving a blue solution of vanadyl dichloride.

Vanadium trichloride, VCl_3, is a peach-blossom coloured, very hygroscopic crystalline solid prepared by heating vanadium in hydrogen chloride, or by boiling the oxytrichloride with sulphur. A green hexahydrate, VCl_3, $6H_2O$, is prepared from the hydroxide, $V(OH)_3$, and hydrochloric acid. Liquid ammonia reacts with the anhydrous trichloride, giving the salt $[V(NH_3)_6]Cl_3$.

Vanadium dichloride, VCl_2, is a green solid formed on passing vanadium tetrachloride vapour, mixed with hydrogen, through a red-hot tube; with acids it gives a violet solution which has a powerful reducing action. This solution may also be prepared by electrolytic reduction of a solution of vanadium pentoxide in hydrochloric acid.

Vanadium oxytrichloride (vanadyl trichloride), $VOCl_3$, is the most readily prepared of all the vanadium halogen compounds. It is a light yellow mobile liquid, b.p. 127°, sp.gr. 1·84/15°, prepared by passing chlorine over heated vanadium pentoxide, preferably mixed with carbon, or by heating vanadium trichloride in oxygen. Vanadium oxytrichloride is readily hydrolysed by water.

Vanadyl dichloride, $VOCl_2$, forms green deliquescent crystals, prepared by partial hydrolysis of vanadium tetrachloride, or by reduction of the oxytrichloride with hydrogen. Complex salts are formed with hydrogen chloride and organic bases.

Vanadium oxymonochloride, $VOCl$, is a flaky

brown solid prepared by heating vanadium trichloride with carbon dioxide for several hours.

Vanadium fluorides:—

Vanadium pentafluoride, VF_5, is obtained by the action of fluorine on the metal or by heating the tetrafluoride in nitrogen at 600°. It is a white solid, m.p. 19·5°, b.p. (extrap.) 48·3°, rapidly hydrolysed by water. It is a good fluorinating agent and forms complexes, MVF_6, in bromine trifluoride.

Vanadium tetrafluoride, VF_4, is a deliquescent and readily hydrolysed brown powder, prepared by the action of hydrogen fluoride on the tetrachloride.

Vanadium trifluoride, VF_3, is prepared by a similar method from the trichloride; it forms a greenish-yellow powder; a green trihydrate, $VF_3,3H_2O$, is also known. The trifluoride is a strong reducing agent. It forms numerous double fluorides in which the vanadium (co-ordination number six) occurs in a complex ion.

Vanadium iodides:—

Vanadium tri-iodide, VI_3, is prepared as a black powder by the action of iodine *in vacuo* at 150°. It is oxidized in air at 130°. A green deliquescent hexahydrate, $VI_3 \cdot 6H_2O$, is made by electrolytic reduction of a solution of vanadium pentoxide in hydrogen iodide at 0°.

Vanadium di-iodide, VI_2, is prepared by heating the tri-iodide *in vacuo* at 400°. It is in the form of rose-coloured plates and is oxidized in air at 125°.

Vanadium nitride, VN. An inert greyish-brown powder, prepared by heating vanadium in nitrogen, or by igniting ammonium metavanadate and strongly heating the residue in dry ammonia gas. It is insoluble in hydrochloric and sulphuric acids but dissolves in nitric acid. It is hydrolysed by alkalis to ammonia.

Vanadium oxides. The principal oxide of vanadium is the *pentoxide* V_2O_5, which is obtained in the commercial treatment of vanadium minerals, and forms an important source of other vanadium compounds. It is prepared in a pure state by igniting ammonium vanadate or mercurous vanadate, the latter being precipitated on adding a solution of a mercurous salt to a neutral vanadate solution. Vanadium pentoxide normally occurs as a red, apparently amorphous, powder, melting at 658° to a dark red liquid which can be vaporized only in the electric furnace; a yellow amorphous form is also known, and the amorphous forms give a red crystalline form on fusion and cooling. The pentoxide is very sparingly soluble in water (*c.* 0·90 g/litre); it dissolves in acids and alkalis, forming vanadyl salts and vanadates, respectively. It is a powerful oxidizing agent, forming lower oxides in its oxidizing

reactions; acid solutions of the pentoxide are very readily reduced to blue solutions containing tetrapositive vanadium compounds. Hydrated vanadium pentoxides which have been regarded as vanadic acids, $V_2O_5 \cdot H_2O$ and $2V_2O_5 \cdot H_2O$, are formed on addition of acids to vanadate solutions. On shaking with water, these hydrated oxides readily form a red sol of vanadium pentoxide, in which the particles carry a high negative charge; on standing the colloidal particles form rod-shaped aggregates which confer peculiar properties (e.g. strong double refraction) on the sol. Vanadium pentoxide is used in the preparation of catalysts for the contact process for sulphuric acid manufacture, and for certain organic reactions.

Vanadium dioxide, VO_2, is a black, blue, or green crystalline powder, m.p. 1637°, sp.gr. 4·399; it is prepared by heating the greyish-white hydrated dioxide which is precipitated on adding an alkali to excess of vanadyl sulphate or vanadyl dichloride solution. The dioxide is oxidized to the pentoxide by heating in air or by treatment with nitric acid. With other acids it gives vanadyl salts, containing the grouping $[VO]^{2+}$; these are more conveniently prepared by treating a solution of vanadium pentoxide in the corresponding acid with sulphur dioxide. Hydrated vanadyl salts and their solutions are blue, the solutions turning green on exposure to air. Vanadium dioxide also dissolves in hot alkali solutions, giving salts known as hypovanadates or vanadites, $M_2V_4O_9$, yellow or brown salts unstable in solution. Other vanadates (IV), e.g. MVO_3, M_2VO_4 and M_3VO_5 (M is an alkaline earth metal) have been obtained by fusion of VO_2 with metal oxides.

A number of oxides intermediate in composition between vanadium pentoxide and dioxide (e.g. $VO_2 \cdot V_2O_5$), generally blue or green in colour, have been described.

Vanadium trioxide or *sesquioxide*, V_2O_3, is a black or greyish-black powder prepared by heating the pentoxide in hydrogen at 900°-1000°, or in carbon monoxide; m.p. 1965°, sp.gr. 4·87. It is readily oxidized to the pentoxide on warming in air, and forms blue VO_2 on exposure for long periods at ordinary temperatures. The trioxide readily combines with chlorine, giving vanadium oxytrichloride, $VOCl_3$. It is insoluble in alkalis and in most acids. Acid solutions containing salts derived from the trioxide are prepared by reducing solutions of the pentoxide with metallic magnesium; a greyish-green hydroxide, $V(OH)_3$, is precipitated from these solutions on addition of alkalis.

Vanadium sulphates:—

Vanadium (IV) *oxysulphates*, e.g. $(VO)_2(SO_4)_3$, have been obtained as red or yellow crystalline solids by boiling vanadium pentoxide with sulphuric acid.

Vanadyl sulphate, $VOSO_4$, exists in two forms, one soluble and one insoluble in water; hydrates with 0, 3 and $5H_2O$ are known. These are formed from solutions of vanadium (IV) in sulphuric acid. Vanadyl sulphate forms two series of blue soluble double sulphates, $2VOSO_4$, M_2SO_4, xH_2O and $VOSO_4$, M_2SO_4, xH_2O, with sulphates of alkali metals.

Vanadium (III) *sulphate*, $V_2(SO_4)_3$, is obtained in solution by reduction (electrolytically, or with magnesium) of sulphuric acid solutions of vanadium pentoxide; electrolytic reduction of vanadyl sulphate solution gives two green acid sulphates, which leave anhydrous $V_2(SO_4)_3$ as an insoluble yellow powder on gentle heating of the solution in an atmosphere of carbon dioxide. Vanadous sulphate forms alums, $V_2(SO_4)_3$, M_2SO_4, $24H_2O$, and a series of double salts with alkali-metal sulphates.

Vanadium (II) *sulphate*, VSO_4, $7H_2O$, is formed as reddish-violet crystals from the violet solution obtained by careful reduction (electrolytically or with sodium amalgam) of a sulphuric acid solution of vanadium pentoxide. It is isomorphous with $FeSO_4$, $7H_2O$, and gives double salts, VSO_4, M_2SO_4, $6H_2O$ of the schönite type.

Vanadium sulphides. These occur as black glistening scales, or black or brownish-black powders, which are readily oxidized to vanadium pentoxide and sulphur dioxide on heating in air. They dissolve in colourless and yellow ammonium sulphide solutions, forming purple, wine-red, or brownish solutions. They are only slowly attacked by acids, except nitric acid, which reacts readily.

Vanadium tetrasulphide, VS_4, is prepared by heating the trisulphide with excess sulphur and removing the excess with carbon disulphide. It is very probably a polysulphide; it occurs in nature as patronite.

Vanadium trisulphide, V_2S_3, sp.gr. 3·7-4·0, is the most stable sulphide of vanadium. It is prepared by passing carbon disulphide vapour for a long period over red-hot vanadium pentoxide, or by treating any chloride or oxychloride of vanadium with hydrogen sulphide at a red heat.

Vanadium monosulphide, VS, sp.gr. 4·2-4·4, is obtained in an impure state by the action of hydrogen sulphide on vanadium dioxide.

van de Graaff generator. An electrostatic machine for accelerating positive ions.

van der Waals. See Waals.

van der Waals adsorption. See Adsorption, physical.

van der Waals equation. Real gases do not obey the ideal gas laws to a high degree of accuracy.

The deviations can be attributed mainly to the fact that the gas molecules occupy an appreciable volume and to the attraction which the molecules exert on each other. These effects were taken into account by van der Waals (1873) in the equation

$$(p + a/v^2)(v - b) = RT$$

where a and b are constants characteristic of each gas. The term a/v^2 allows for the reduction of pressure from the ideal value owing to intermolecular attraction, and b, the 'co-volume,' allows for the volume occupied by the molecules; it is about four times the actual volume of the molecules.

van der Waals forces. The physical forces of attraction and repulsion that exist between molecules and which are responsible for the cohesion of liquids and of molecular crystals. The forces are so-called as their influence on the compressibility of gases is allowed for in the van der Waals equation. The forces arise partly from dipole-dipole, or dipole-induced-dipole interactions; but even non-polar molecules and atoms exert a certain attraction on one another —the so-called London forces. The van der Waals forces act only over relatively short distances, being proportional to the inverse of the seventh power of the intermolecular distance.

Vandyke brown. A slightly alkaline water extract of clean peat beds in selected areas. The liquor is well boiled and strained, concentrated by evaporation, and dried, usually with some dextrin added, to give the grade known as Vandyke crystals.

Cheaper brown pigments made from more earthy deposits or from German brown coal by washing and grinding are known as Cassel brown.

Vanillin, $C_8H_8O_3$. Fine white needles, m.p. 81°-82°, b.p. 285°, strong vanilla odour, characteristic taste. Slightly soluble in cold water, readily in hot water, alcohol, and ether. Aqueous solutions give a blue-violet coloration with ferric chloride. It occurs extensively in nature, and is the odoriferous principle of the vanilla pod; it can be obtained from the glucoside coniferin. Vanillin is made commercially from the ligno-sulphonic acid obtained as a by-product in the manufacture of wood pulp; this is subjected to alkaline degradation in the presence of air at 100 atm. and 225° and the sodium vanillate removed by solvent extraction. It is one of the most important flavouring and perfuming materials, and large quantities are used in the manufacture of foodstuffs and toilet goods.

van't Hoff, Jacobus Heinricus (1852-1911). Born at Rotterdam, van't Hoff began, in 1872, his first experimental investigations in the laboratory of Kekulé at Bonn. In 1874 he published his epoch-making theory of the tetrahedral carbon atom and ten years later his 'Études de Dynamique Chimique,' one of the classics of chemical science, which led, in 1886, to the enunciation of the osmotic theory of solutions. In 1896 he accepted election to the Academy of Berlin and appointment as honorary professor in the University. There he spent the remainder of his life studying the problems of solution and the conditions of formation and separation of the salts of the Stassfurt deposits. See *J. Chem. Soc.*, Mem. Lect., 1913, 1127.

van't Hoff reaction isochore. This is the name generally given to the important thermodynamic equation

$$\frac{d\ln K}{dT} = \frac{\Delta H}{RT^2}$$

where K is an equilibrium constant of a reversible reaction, ΔH the enthalpy of the reaction, T the absolute temperature and R the gas constant. By use of this equation heats of reaction can be calculated from equilibrium constants if the latter are determined for several temperatures. Conversely, if K is known only at one temperature, it can be calculated for other temperatures if ΔH is available, e.g. from calorimetric data. The equation is therefore of great value in thermochemistry.

van't Hoff reaction isotherm. The free energy ΔG of a reversible reaction such as
$$aA + bB = cC + dD$$
is given by an equation of the type

$$\Delta G = -RT\ln K + RT\ln\frac{[C]^c[D]^d}{[A]^a[B]^b}$$

where R is the gas constant, T the absolute temperature, K the equilibrium constant, $[A]$, $[B]$, etc. the activities of A, B, etc. under the conditions prevailing in the reaction. The above expression is generally called the van't Hoff reaction isotherm.

Vapour compression evaporator. Most of the heat absorbed during the evaporation of an aqueous solution appears as latent heat in the steam evolved. However, because the temperature of this steam is the same as or lower than that of the solution from which it came, it cannot be utilized in the same evaporator unit unless it is upgraded, i.e. its saturation pressure and temperature increased. This may be done by compressing the vapour mechanically or by mixing with it a quantity of high-pressure steam; in either case the resulting stream is passed back into the calandria (heating unit) of the evaporator. A vapour compression evaporator can achieve

about 1·7 lb. evaporation per pound of steam used, roughly the same as a double effect evaporator.

See also Evaporator, Multiple effect evaporator.

Vapour compression refrigeration. This is by far the most important method of achieving refrigeration on an industrial scale. In its simplest form the cycle consists of compressing a refrigerant vapour, condensing it, and then passing the high-pressure liquid through a reducing valve. The reduction in pressure causes some of the liquid to vaporize, and, because the process is adiabatic, a considerable lowering in temperature results. The cold liquid goes to an evaporator, where it is vaporized by heat exchange with the fluid to be cooled, and the vapour formed passes back into the compressor. A wide variety of condensable vapours have been used as refrigerants, but nowadays the principal ones are the chlorofluorocarbons (Freons and Arctons), ammonia and carbon dioxide.

Vapour density. The vapour density of a substance is the ratio between the weight of a given volume of its vapour and that of the same volume of hydrogen measured under the same conditions of temperature and pressure. The vapour density is not an integer but, within experimental accuracy, may be compared with a value based on whole number mass units.

Vapour pressure. Over every liquid (or solid) there is a certain pressure of its vapour. In a closed vessel after a sufficient time, equilibrium is set up, so that as many molecules leave the liquid surface to form vapour as return to it from the vapour phase to form liquid. The pressure of vapour above any liquid or solid at any temperature, when equilibrium obtains, is called the vapour pressure of the liquid or solid at that temperature.

Vaseline. A trade-name for soft paraffin. Yellow and white varieties are made and are semi-solid, partly translucent mixtures of hydrocarbons of the paraffin series ranging from $C_{15}H_{32}$ to $C_{20}H_{42}$. They are insoluble in water and acetone, but soluble in benzene, ether, and chloroform. Obtained from the high-boiling fractions of petroleum or shale oil. They are chemically very inert, and are used as bases for ointments and as dressings for wounds.

Vasopressin. A cyclic peptide hormone secreted

$$\begin{array}{l}(3)\\ \text{Phe.Tyr.CyS} \diagdown \qquad (8)\\ \text{Glu(NH}_2).\text{Asp(NH}_2).\text{CyS.Pro.Lys.(or Arg.)Gly(NH}_2)\end{array}$$

by the posterior lobe of the pituitary gland, and obtained commercially from beef pituitaries (arginine-vasopressin) or hog pituitaries (lysine-vasopressin). Vasopressin differs from oxytocin in the amino-acids at positions 3 and 8; the action of the two hormones is quite different. Injection of vasopressin leads to a prolonged rise in blood pressure. Physiologically it is extremely important as an antidiuretic; it promotes reabsorption of water by the kidney. Deficiency of vasopressin causes the disease *diabetes insipidus*, in which large volumes of extremely dilute urine are excreted.

Vat dyes. These are dyestuffs insoluble in water. However, their 'leuco' compounds (after reduction) are soluble in dilute alkali. In this condition they have a great affinity for the fibre, which after being impregnated with the reduced dye is exposed to the action of air to cause the reoxidation of the leuco-compound to the insoluble dyestuff. The vat dyes are among the fastest known, and in spite of the development of new classes of fast dyestuffs, they continue to be used where high standards of fastness are required.

There has been vast progress in many directions both on the chemical side in extending the range and on the application side. The development of pigment padding has necessitated the use of very fine dispersions of vat dyes with which the fabric is impregnated. The dye is then reduced with caustic soda and sodium hydrosulphite.

The introduction of special machines such as the Standfast Molten Metal Machine for continuous vat dyeing has led to the use of specific vat dyes suitable for this process. Essentially, dyeing takes place whilst the cloth is passed through a column of molten fusible alloy (m.p. 70°) at a temperature of approx. 100°. Similarly, a range of vat dyes has been introduced specially for the Thermosol process, by which these dyes are applied to Terylene in a process requiring a high temperature (200°-230°) to complete the penetration and fixation of the dye.

On the chemical side this range has been extended from the original indigoid and anthraquinone dyes to include derivatives of:
(a) Carbazole.

Thus the Hydron Blues are obtained by the

sulphurization of carbazolaminophenol and similar compounds. These, when dyed on cotton, yield shades similar to indigo but having higher fastness to light, washing and chlorine. They are applied from a caustic soda/hydrosulphite vat or from a caustic soda/hydrosulphite/sodium sulphide vat.

(b) Thioindigo and violet dyes in which half

C.I. Vat Red 41 (Durindone Red B)

the molecule is indigoid and the other half thioindigoid, e.g. Indanthren Printing Violet BBF (*q.v.*).

(c) Benzoquinone (*q.v.*). There is a small range

(yellow to brown) of vat dyes for dyeing wool, e.g. Helindon Yellow CG (C.I. Vat Yellow 5).

(d) Phthalocyanines (*q.v.*). To this class belongs Indanthren Brilliant Blue 4G (C.I. Vat Blue 29) which gives bright blue shades on cotton of very high fastness to light. It is a partly sulphonated cobalt phthalocyanine.

Vauquelin, Louis Nicolas. Born in 1763 he became assistant to an apothecary in Rouen. In 1780 he went to Paris, and entered the laboratory of Fourcroy. He became professor of chemistry at the Jardin des Plantes, and later professor of the Medical Faculty. He discovered chromium and beryllium. With Robequet he isolated asparagine. With de la Grange he discovered camphoric acid. He died in 1828.

Velocity of reaction. The velocity of a chemical reaction is the weight of the reactants transformed, or the weight of the reaction product produced, per unit of time. The velocity is generally expressed in gram molecules, or gram atoms, per second.

Venable, Francis Preston (1856-1934). Venable was born at Farmville, Virginia, and studied at the Universities of Virginia and Göttingen. From 1880 onwards he was professor of chemistry at the University of North Carolina, becoming president of the University in 1900, and retiring as professor emeritus in 1930. He wrote numerous papers, chiefly on zirconium, and was president of the American Chemical Society in 1905.

Venetian red. A native high grade ferric oxide of the haematite type, or more usually, a chemically prepared ferric oxide with some calcium sulphate made by the calcining of iron (II) sulphate in the presence of lime. See British Standard No. 272.

Verbenone, $C_{10}H_{14}O$. An unsaturated ketone found in Spanish verbena oil in association with citrals *-a* and *-b*. These latter are removed by condensation with cyanoacetic acid. Both (+)- and (−)-verbenones are produced by the auto-oxidation of (+)- and (−)-pinenes respectively. It is a colourless oil and smells both of camphor and peppermint. The (+)-form has constants m.p. 9·8°, b.p. 227°-228°, d_4^{20} 0·9976, n_D^{18} 1·49928, $[\alpha]_D +$ 249·6. The (−)-form has b.p. 253·5. d^{15} 0·982, n_D^{20} 1·4961, $[\alpha]_D −144°$. On oxidation verbenone forms pinonic acid.

Verdet's constant. A constant relating to the rotation of the plane of polarization of plane-polarized light in its passage through a transparent medium, when the medium is placed in a magnetic field. This phenomenon is known as magnetic rotation. The light beam must travel in the same direction as the magnetic lines of force. The angle of rotation of the plane of polarization (ω) is related to the length of medium traversed (l) and to the magnetic field strength (H) by the expression $\omega = \phi l H$, the constant ϕ being known as Verdet's constant. It is important to note that magnetic rotation is not connected with ordinary optical activity. It is an effect shown by all transparent substances, whether or not they have asymmetric structures.

Verdigris. The green compound to which copper or bronze is converted on exposure to the atmosphere. It is usually a basic copper carbonate, but near the sea will be a basic chloride, The term is also used for basic copper acetate, which is used as a pigment.

Vermiculite. A hydrated silicate mineral containing Mg^{2+}, Al^{3+}, Fe^{3+}. Crystallizes in the monoclinic system and resembles biotite in appearance. It has a chlorite-type structure with Si_4O_{10} sheets widely separated by molecular water. On heating at 800°-1100° it exfoliates with over a tenfold increase in bulk due to separation of the laminae owing to the rapid evolution of water of composition. Expanded vermiculite, because of its low apparent density, is used as a thermal insulator (as a loose fill or in concretes and plasters) and as a rooting medium and soil additive in horticulture.

Vermilion. The red variety of mercury sulphide which occurs naturally as cinnabar. It has been made for many centuries, notably in China. The red colour of Chinese lacquer painting, Chinese red ink, and the general redness of painted temples in China are due to it. It was used extensively for illuminating manuscripts, and this art of 'miniatura' was practised by the 'miniatori' or workers in 'minium' as vermilion was then called. Later red lead largely displaced vermilion and finally stole the name 'minium.'

Veronal. A trade name for barbitone.

Vetivazulene, 4, 8-Dimethyl-2-isopropylazulene, $C_{15}H_{18}$. Obtained by the dehydrogenation of vetivone. It forms violet needles, m.p. 32°-33°.

Vetivone, $C_{15}H_{22}O$. Two stereoisomeric ketones

have been isolated from oil of vetiver. The α-isomer has m.p. 51°-51·5°, $[\alpha]_D +225°$ (in alcohol) and gives a semicarbazone m.p. 222°-223°. The β-isomer has m.p. 44°-44·5°, $[\alpha]_D −24·1°$ (in alcohol) and gives a semicarbazone m.p. 229°. Both isomers on heating with selenium give vetivazulene.

Vibrating conveyor. This is a machine for conveying particulate solids. It consists of a trough which is vibrated by some means, e.g. mechanically or electrically. The vibration is designed to give the particles a forward and upward movement, so that they move along in a series of short hops. Vibrating conveyors are extremely versatile and are manufactured in a wide range of sizes.

Vibrating screens. Machines of this type consist of one or more slightly inclined screening surfaces mounted in a robust frame. To increase the capacity and prevent blinding the screening surfaces are caused to vibrate. This may be done by mounting the screen on powerful springs and causing it to bear down on a series of cams which rotate on bearing surfaces on the underside of the frame. An alternative method is to stretch the wire screen to a high tension and mount at some convenient point on the frame an electromagnet actuated by an alternating current. The magnet works against the springs on which the screen is mounted and in this way very rapid vibration can be secured and blinding greatly reduced.

Vibrational spectrum. Energy absorbed by a molecule may go to increase the vibrational energy of the constituent atoms relative to each other. Conversely, a transition from a state of higher to one of lower vibrational energy corresponds with the emission of energy, generally in the form of light, the frequency (v) of which is related to the energy E lost in the transition by the relationship $E = h\nu$. Vibrational transitions are usually associated simultaneously with rotational transitions, and give rise to bands in the infrared and near infrared, characteristic of the vibrational and rotational changes, and called the vibration-rotation bands. These bands constitute the spectrum of the same name.

Vic-. The prefix *vic-* (short for vicinal) in the name of an organic compound indicates that substituent atoms or groups are bonded to adjacent carbon atoms. Thus 1,2,3-trichlorobenzene can be called *vic*-trichlorobenzene.

Vicker's hardness. See Hardness.

Victor Meyer's method for determining vapour densities. This method consists in determining the volume occupied by a known weight of the vapour. A small quantity of the liquid under examination is weighed in a small stoppered bottle. The liquid is then rapidly vaporized in a suitable apparatus when it expels an equivalent volume of air, which is collected over water, and is measured.

Vinegar. A dilute solution of acetic acid prepared by the oxidation of alcoholic liquors by various species of *Acetobacter*—usually *Acetobacter aceti*. The amount of acetic acid is usually 4-10%, depending upon the material used and upon the process. In England vinegar is obtained from malt, the sugars of which are converted to alcohol by yeast. The alcoholic liquor is then treated with *Acetobacter*. On the Continent much vinegar is made from poor quality wine and is known as wine vinegar.

Vinyl, Ethenyl. The name given to the group $CH_2{=}CH-$.

Vinyl acetate, $CH_2{:}CHOOC{\cdot}CH_3$. A colourless liquid with an ethereal odour; its vapour is lachrymatory, d_4^{20} 0·932, b.p. 73°. Slightly soluble in water; miscible with alcohol and acetone. Manufactured by the vapour-phase reaction of acetylene and acetic acid in the presence of a zinc acetate catalyst at 200°. Purified vinyl acetate absorbs free oxygen, reacting to give acetaldehyde and the free acid. In the absence of catalysts, vinyl acetate shows little tendency to polymerize, but conversion to polyvinyl acetate is readily achieved in nitrogen under the influence of a peroxide catalyst.

Besides finding wide use in the manufacture of adhesives, paints, coatings, paper and textile finishes, moulding compounds, etc., polyvinyl acetate is of great importance as an intermediate in the manufacture of polyvinyl alcohol. The copolymers of vinyl acetate, particularly those with vinyl chloride, are also of commercial importance.

Vinyl alcohol, $CH_2{:}CHOH$. The enol form of acetaldehyde. It cannot be isolated in the pure state but vinyl esters and ethers are known and hydrolysis of these gives either acetaldehyde or a polymer of vinyl alcohol. The polyvinyl alcohols, as the polymers are called, are resinous substances and are of industrial importance.

Vinylation. A term used occasionally to describe the reaction between acetylene and certain classes of compounds such as alcohols, phenols, carboxylic acids and amines which contain active hydrogen atoms. Under the influence of catalysts, addition occurs across the triple bond to give vinyl compounds, e.g.

$$H{-}C{\equiv}C{-}H + HX \rightarrow CH_2{=}CHX$$

Vinyl chloride, monochloroethylene, $CH_2{:}CHCl$. A colourless gas, b.p. $-14°$, with a pleasant ethereal odour. It is manufactured by reacting acetylene with hydrogen chloride over a mercuric chloride catalyst at 150°-250°, by the pyrolysis of ethylene dichloride at 500° and 4 atm., or by the hydrolysis of dichloroethylene at 150° and 10 atm. using dilute caustic soda.

Vinyl chloride is used almost exclusively for the manufacture of polymers and copolymers. These are of the greatest commercial importance and are used for the manufacture of film and sheeting, cloth and paper coatings, cable coverings, floor tiles, tank linings, mouldings and extrusions and many other purposes.

Vinyl ether, C_4H_6O, $CH_2{:}CH{\cdot}O{\cdot}CH{:}CH_2$. A colourless inflammable liquid, with a characteristic ethereal odour, b.p. 28°-31°, d_{20}^{20} 0·774. Miscible with alcohol, diethyl ether, and chloroform. Prepared by the action of caustic potash on $\beta\beta'$-dichlorodiethyl ether. It is unstable, breaking down to formaldehyde and formic acid. The British Pharmacopoeia grade contains alcohol and 0·01% of phenyl-α-naphthylamine as a stabilizer, and is used as an anaesthetic, being about four times as potent as diethyl ether.

Vinylidene chloride. $CH_2{:}CCl_2$. This important monomer is manufactured as a colourless liquid, b.p. 31·7°, d^{20} 1·2129, n_D^{20} 1·4249, by the dehydrochlorination of trichloroethane. In the presence of light and air, it decomposes with the evolution of hydrogen chloride, phosgene, and formaldehyde, and deposition of some polyvinylidene chloride. Consequently it must be stored away from light and in the presence of dissolved inhibitors (such as phenols and amines). Under the influence of free radical and ionic polymerization catalysts, the monomer can be readily converted to give the industrially important vinylidene chloride polymers.

Vinylidene chloride polymers. An important group of polymers, originally developed in the U.S.A. (Saran polymers) and Germany (Diurit polymers), derived from the copolymerization of a major proportion of vinylidene chloride with vinyl chloride, acrylonitrile, acrylic esters, or maleic esters. They have been used as a basis for the production of many thermoplastic materials including drawn monofilaments for upholstery fabrics and industrial filter cloths, thin extruded oriented film for food packaging and rigid extruded pipe for handling mineral acids and alkalis. The homopolymer has not been utilized, because of its high softening point, degradation at working temperatures, and incompatibility with usual plasticizers.

Vinylogs. Compounds related by the introduction or removal of —CH=CH— units in a chain. Vinylogous functional groups have two parts of a functional group separated by a —CH=CH— unit.

Vinyl polymers and resins. A major class of polymeric materials that are important in the plastics, synthetic fibre, and surface coatings industries. Such materials are derived from the polymerization of compounds containing the vinyl group; i.e. from monomers of the general formula $CH_2:CH \cdot X$, where X represents a monovalent substituent group. Consequently the corresponding vinyl polymers can all be represented by the general structure,

$$+CH(X)—CH_2+_n$$

However, this structure must not be taken to indicate the absence of branched chains, as evidence shows that all vinyl polymers exhibit, to some extent, a branched chain structure. The important members of this class include polyvinyl chloride, polyvinyl acetate, polyvinyl alcohol, and polyvinyl acetals. The term 'vinyl' is sometimes used to refer to compositions based only on vinyl chloride polymers or copolymers. Although styrene can be considered as a vinyl monomer (i.e. vinyl benzene) it is normal prac-

1-Vinylpyrrolidone. A colourless liquid, m.p. 17°, b.p. 64°-66°/2 mm. Prepared from butyrolactone and ethanolamine by dehydration of the 1-hydroxyethylpyrrolidone first formed. Also obtained from pyrrolidone and acetylene. Polymerization gives a substance (PVP) used as a blood-plasma extender.

Violaxanthin, $C_{40}H_{56}O_4$. A carotenoid pigment, esters of which are present in viola and other blossoms. It has the normal carotenoid structure (see Carotene) with the ring shown and its mirror image.

Reddish-brown spears m.p. 200°, soluble in alcohol and ether; $[\alpha]_{Cd}^{20}$ +35° in chloroform.

Violuric acid, $C_4H_3N_3O_4$. A colourless crystalline substance. Soluble in water and alcohol.

Prepared by treating barbituric acid with a solution of sodium nitrite or by the action of hydroxylamine on alloxan. It dissolves in water to give a violet solution; forms salts with metals—these are intensely coloured. Reduced to uramil. Gives a blue colour with a solution of ferric chloride.

Viomycin, $C_{22}H_{36}N_{12}O_8$. A polypeptide antibiotic produced by strains of *Str. puniceus* and

tice to place polystyrene outside this classification. The vinyl polymers, along with the polystyrenes, polyethylenes, acrylics, and others, all derived from the polymerization of monomers containing the ethylenic link, are included in the wider group of polymers, the ethenoids.

other *Streptomyces*. It is used as the sulphate, which is a white or pale yellow powder, very soluble in water, insoluble in organic solvents. It has bacteriostatic activity against the tubercle bacillus, but has toxic side-effects and is used only in desperate cases.

Virginium. A name proposed for the element francium (*q.v.*).

Viridian, Guignet's green. Extremely permanent pigments which are variants of hydrated chromic oxide, $Cr_2O_3 \cdot 2H_2O$, sometimes containing potassium and chromium borates.

Virtanen, Artturi Ilmari (1895-   ). Virtanen has spent most of his life in his native town, Helsinki, where he became professor of biochemistry in 1931 at the Technical College and in 1939 at the University. He was awarded the Nobel Prize for chemistry in 1945 for his work in agricultural chemistry and in particular for his discovery of a way of making silage by acidifying the grass or other crop with mineral acids.

Visco-elasticity. Many plastics and other long-chain macro-molecular compounds show rheological properties intermediate between those of an elastic solid and a Newtonian liquid. In rubber-like plastics, the application of a stress immediately produces a large strain ('high elasticity') which is recoverable only if its duration is very short. If the stress is maintained, the material acquires a permanent strain. It is as though the chain molecules, at first simply extended, slowly flow past one another as in a very viscous liquid. This is visco-elasticity. The higher the temperature, the more marked the flow.

At the other extreme are materials which flow like liquids but show a tendency to recoil when the stress is removed. This has been called 'flow-elasticity' or 'elastico-viscosity.' Such liquids (e.g. molten nylon) can be spun to form threads.

Viscose. In the viscose process for the manufacture of artificial silk carbon disulphide is reacted with cellulose in alkaline solution to give cellulose xanthate. This is a viscous colloidal solution which when extruded into an acid solution regenerates cellulose as a yarn or in sheets.

Viscosity. All fluids show a resistance to flow, which is called viscosity. Mobile liquids like water have a low viscosity, while treacle, which flows with greater difficulty, has a high viscosity. Viscosity is compared in terms of the coefficient of viscosity.

Viscosity, coefficient of. This is the force required per unit area of fluid to maintain unit difference of velocity between two parallel planes in the fluid, one centimetre apart. The c.g.s. unit of viscosity is the poise.

Viscosity index. An empirical scale used to indicate the rate of change of viscosity of lubricating oils with temperature. A high viscosity index (V.I.) oil has a relatively low change of viscosity with change of temperature and vice versa.

Visual purple. See Rhodopsin.

Vitallium alloys. A series of cobalt-chromium-molybdenum alloys having good corrosion resistance, which are particularly useful in dilute acid environments. The presence of molybdenum is associated with their ability to withstand hot oils. Typical uses are in blades for turbines.

Vitamins. The vitamins are substances other than proteins, carbohydrates, fats, and mineral salts, that are essential constituents of the food of animals. In their absence the animal develops certain deficiency diseases or other abnormal conditions. Vitamins might also be defined as substances that play an essential part in animal metabolic processes, but which the animal cannot synthesize, although certain animals can synthesize certain vitamins and all animals needing vitamin D can manufacture it from ergosterol in the presence of ultra-violet light. The vitamins belong to no single class of chemical compounds and play various roles in the body. Thus vitamin C is an oxygen carrier, and several of the B vitamins act as co-enzymes. The conception of vitamins was formulated about 1912. It was then believed that certain diseases, scurvy, beri-beri, rickets, and pellagra, were caused by the lack of certain substances in the food, and it was also known that animals would not thrive on a diet of carefully purified substances containing adequate quantities of carbohydrates, proteins, fats and mineral salts. In 1915 it was shown that at least two factors were needed to supplement such an artificial diet, a fat-soluble factor and a water-soluble factor, later called vitamins A and B. Vitamin B has since been shown to be a mixture of a number of different substances. Vitamin C, or ascorbic acid, the antiscorbutic factor, vitamin D, the antirachitic factor, and others have since been discovered.

Vitamin A. Vitamin A is the original fat-soluble vitamin. Its absence from the diet leads to a loss in weight and failure of growth in young animals, to the eye diseases xerophthalmia and night blindness, and to a general susceptibility to infections. The most fundamental effect of its deficiency is a keratinization of epithelial tissues. Vitamin A is present in animal fats, butter, yolk of egg, and in particularly large quantities in fish-liver oils, especially halibut liver oil. It has been shown that carotene is converted into vitamin A in the liver, hence good sources of carotene, such as green vegetables, are good potential sources of vitamin A. Vitamin A is structurally related to carotene. It has the empirical formula $C_{20}H_{30}O$ and the structural formula

Two molecules of vitamin A are formed on hydrolysis of one molecule of β-carotene. Vitamin A crystallizes in pale yellow needles with m.p. 64°. It is optically inactive. It is soluble in organic solvents and insoluble in water. It is unstable in solution when heated in air, but comparatively stable without aeration. It is estimated spectrophotometrically in cyclohexane solution, having an absorption maximum at 327·5 mμ. The unit of vitamin-A activity is contained in 0·000344 mg of standard preparation. Vitamin A is manufactured by extraction from fish liver oils and by synthesis from β-ionone.

Vitamin B. The original vitamin B has been shown to consist of a number of different substances. It has been subdivided, purely arbitrarily, into vitamin B_1 or thiamine and the vitamin B_2 complex, which includes riboflavin, nicotinic acid, pyridoxine, pantothenic acid, biotin, p-aminobenzoic acid, inositol, folic acid, and other factors. Some of these substances have been shown to be necessary for the growth of certain micro-organisms, but have as yet not been proved to be necessary for mammalian nutrition.

Vitamin B_{12}, cyanocobalamine,

$$C_{63}H_{90}CoN_{14}O_{14}P.$$

Dark red crystals, sparingly soluble in water and alcohol, insoluble in chloroform and ether. Its structure was elucidated partly by chemical means, but mainly by X-ray crystallography.

Vitamin B_{12} is produced by the growth of certain micro-organisms, and occurs also in liver, being the extrinsic anti-pernicious anaemia factor the isolation of which was sought for many years. It is given in microgram doses in the treatment of pernicious anaemia, and is best given with hog's stomach, which contains the intrinsic anti-pernicious anaemia factor responsible for the absorption of vitamin B_{12} from the gut.

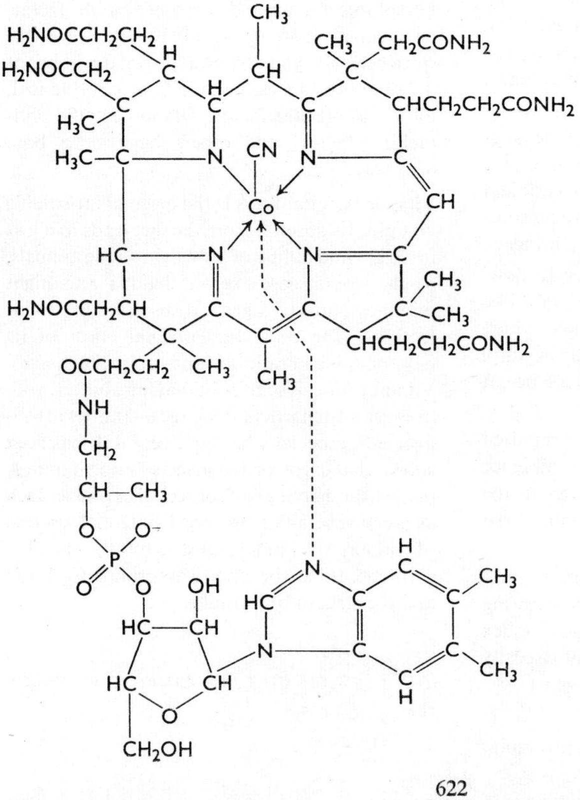

Vitamin C. See Ascorbic acid.

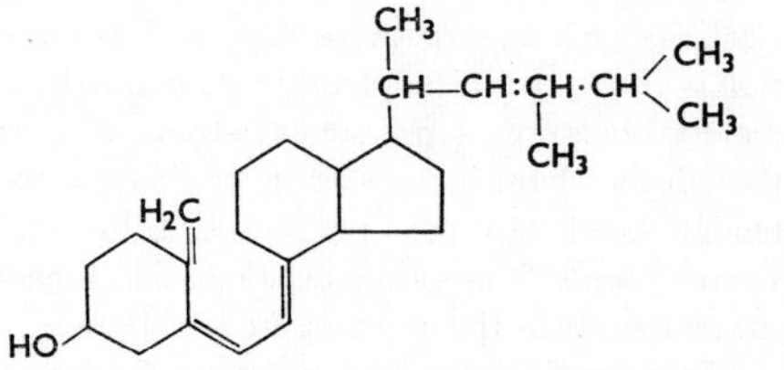

Vitamin D. The anti-rachitic vitamin. The absence of vitamin D in the food of young animals leads to the development of rickets unless the animal is exposed to sunlight or ultra-violet irradiation. It is soluble in fats and fat solvents, and is present in animal fats, milk, butter, and eggs. The richest sources of vitamin D are fish-liver oils, particularly those of the halibut and the cod. The first vitamin D to be discovered was a crude mixture called vitamin D_1. Irradiation of ergosterol with ultraviolet light gives calciferol or vitamin D_2, with the formula shown above. Irradiation of 7-dehydrocholesterol gives the natural vitamin D or vitamin D_3, which differs in structure only in the side chain, which is

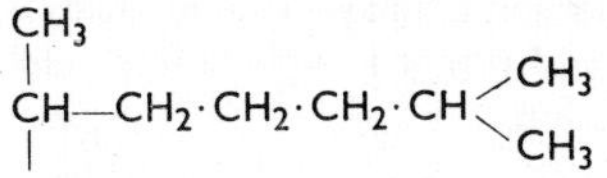

$$\begin{array}{c} CH_3 \\ | \\ CH-CH_2\cdot CH_2\cdot CH_2\cdot CH \diagdown{}^{CH_3}_{CH_3} \\ | \end{array}$$

Vitamin D_2 has m.p. 115°-117° and D_3 m.p. 82°-83°. Both vitamins, which have almost identical actions, are used for the prevention and cure of infantile rickets; they are essential for the normal development of teeth, and are used for treating osteomalacia and dental caries. They are necessary for the absorption of calcium and phosphorus from the gut. Vitamin D_2 is much less potent for chicks than vitamin D_3, which is therefore preferred as a nutritional factor for poultry.

Vitamin E. This vitamin is essential for fertility and reproduction. Deficiency leads to abortion in the female and loss of fertility in the male. It is fat-soluble, and the richest sources are seed embryos and green leaves. Vitamin E activity is possessed by several of the tocopherols (*q.v.*).

Vitamin K. An accessory factor needed by chickens, ducks, and geese, the absence of which is characterized by haemorrhages due to a failure of the blood to clot properly. The factor is associated in some way with prothrombin, and may be part of the prothrombin molecule. It is fat-soluble, and found in liver fats, vegetables, and to a lesser extent in cereals. It is stable to heat and light and destroyed by alkalis.

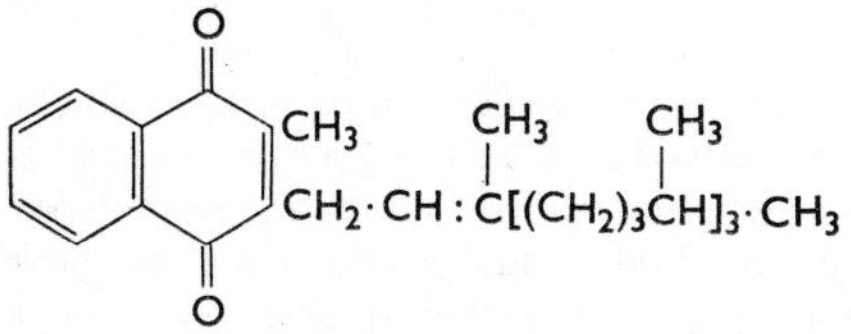

Vitamin K_1

Several substances having vitamin K activity have been isolated from natural sources. Vitamin K_1, from alfalfa oil, is 2-methyl-3-phytyl-1,4-naphthoquinone.

The term vitamin K_2 was applied to 2-methyl-3-difarnesyl-1,4-naphthoquinone, m.p. 54°, isolated from putrefied fish meal. It now includes a group of related natural compounds ('menaquinones'), differing in the number of isoprene units in the side chain and in their degree of unsaturation.

Other substituted 1,4-naphthoquinones including menaphthone (menadione, 'vitamin K_3') and the pigment phthiocol have vitamin K activity. Menaphthone (*q.v.*) is the best commercial source of the vitamin.

Vitamin P. Originally suggested for a substance present in lemon juice, which decreased capillary permeability, the name has become discredited, as many different substances possess this activity, and the effect is influenced by the personal physical characteristics of the patient and also by his environment.

Flavone derivatives have vitamin P-like activity, e.g. epicatechin, hesperidin, and rutin. Deficiency is shown by tiny red spots indicating haemorrhages in the skin. The vitamin has been used in cases of retinal haemorrhage.

Vitellin. The chief protein of yolk of egg. It is a phosphoprotein, containing about 1% of phosphorus. It can be obtained as a yellow granular powder, insoluble in water, neutral salts, and dilute acids.

Vitrain. A macroscopic constituent of coal which exists in thin horizontal bands up to 20 mm thick. It has a bright glassy appearance, and fractures either perpendicularly or conchoidally. It is usually free from all striations, thus differing from clarain which shows striations due to plant structure.

Vulcanite. See Ebonite.

Vulcanization. The process of converting weak, plastic, inelastic, and soluble raw rubber into a strong, elastic, non-plastic, and insoluble material. Vulcanization is essential for the successful exploitation of rubber. Prior to the work of Hancock and Goodyear (1839-1842) rubber products had become soft and sticky in the summer and hard and rigid in the winter. They found that heating an intimate mixture with about 2% sulphur rendered the material elastic and flexible over a much wider range of temperatures. Although many compounds have been found which vulcanize rubber, sulphur is still the most widely used vulcanizing agent. Accelerators (*q.v.*) and activators (*q.v.*) are also used to increase the rate of vulcanization; but to prevent any tendency to scorch (i.e. premature vulcanization whilst compounding and processing) a retarder is frequently added. Vulcanization is usually carried out by heating the rubber compound under pressure to 140° for a time which may vary between several seconds to over 1 hour, depending on the type of accelerator system used. Vulcanization in the cold can be achieved by the use of sulphur chloride. Highly specialized vulcanization agents are required for some synthetic rubbers such as Hypalon, silicone, ethylene-propylene co-polymers and certain grades of neoprene. See also Ebonite.

Vulcanized latex. The rubber particles in latex can be vulcanized without coagulation occurring by heating latex under pressure in an autoclave with finely divided sulphur or alkali polysulphides, or by treating latex at temperatures well below 100° with sulphur and an ultra-accelerator such as piperidine pentamethylenedithiocarbamate or sodium *iso*propylxanthate. Vulcanized latex can be used for almost all of the processes for which normal latex is used, and dries to a coherent film of vulcanized rubber with high tensile strength.

Vulcanizing agents. Materials which bring about vulcanization. The most important is sulphur, but selenium, tellurium or organic peroxides are used instead of sulphur for some applications. Some sulphur-containing accelerators, such as tetramethylthiuram disulphide, effect vulcanization in the absence of sulphur.

1877, he was appointed professor of physics in the University of Amsterdam. He built up a kinetic theory of the fluid state and, in 1873, introduced the van der Waals equation to give more accurately the relationship between pressure and volume of a gas. In 1910 he was awarded the Nobel Prize for physics.

Wackenroder's liquid. A solution, containing colloidal sulphur and polythionic acids, formed by passing hydrogen sulphide into sulphurous acid solution.

Wagner-Meerwein rearrangement. A rearrangement of the carbon skeleton of a compound occurring in the course of an addition reaction to an olefin, an olefin-forming elimination, or a substitution reaction. The rearrangement may involve a migration of an alkyl group or a change in ring structure, and it is frequently encountered in the chemistry of the bicyclic terpenes. The mechanism is essentially the same as that of the pinacol-pinacolone rearrangement (*q.v.*). An example of the change is:

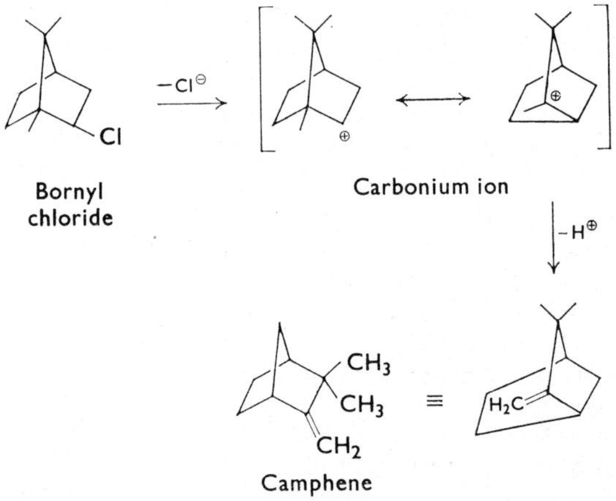

Bornyl
chloride

Carbonium ion

Camphene

W

Waage, Peter (1833-1900). Born at Flekkefjord in Southern Norway, Waage was educated at Bergen Grammar School and the University of Christiania. Like many others, he entered chemistry through the portals of medicine. After studying in Germany for some time he was appointed in 1862 professor of chemistry in the University of Christiania. He was associated with his brother-in-law, Guldberg, in the enunciation of the 'Law of Mass Action.' See *J. Chem. Soc.*, 1900, 591.

Waals, Johannes Diderik van der (1837-1923). Born and educated at Leyden, van der Waals taught physics in a number of schools before, in

This involves the formation of a carbonium ion which is best described as a hybrid of the two structures shown. This then rearranges by migration of a bond, and in so doing a more stable tertiary carbonium ion is produced from a secondary carbonium ion. Elimination of a proton yields camphene. See H. C. Brown, *Chemistry in Britain*, 1966, **2**, 199.

Walden, Paul (1863-1957). Born in Latvia, Walden was educated at Riga, where he became professor in 1894 and subsequently rector. He fled to Germany in 1919, becoming professor of physical chemistry at the University of Rostock. He retired officially in 1934, but continued working and in 1942 moved to Tübingen as guest professor. Famous for his discovery of the Walden inversion, he also worked extensively on the chemistry of non-aqueous solutions. See *Proc. Chem. Soc.*, 1960, 186.

Walden inversion. A phenomenon discovered in 1895 by Walden. When one of the atoms or groups attached to the asymmetric carbon atom in an optically active compound is replaced by a different atom, the product is sometimes a derivative of the optical isomer of the original compound. It is thus possible to pass from one isomer to the other without the formation and separation of a racemic compound. (+)-Malic acid, when treated with phosphorus pentachloride gives (−)-chlorosuccinic acid, which may be converted to (−)-malic acid by silver oxide or back to (+)-malic acid by potassium hydroxide. Similarly, (−)-malic acid is converted to (+)-chlorosuccinic acid which undergoes similar changes. A Walden inversion occurs at a tetrahedral carbon atom when the entry of the reagent and the departure of the leaving group are synchronous—the so-called bimolecular nucleophilic substitution mechanism. Since the reagent must approach from the side of the molecule opposite to that of the leaving group an *inversion* of optical configuration results:

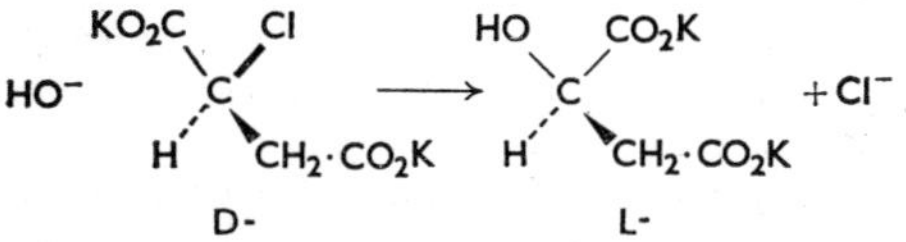

An alternative mechanism of substitution is unimolecular and involves ionization of the leaving group to give a carbonium ion (*q.v.*) which reacts rapidly with the reagent. The lifetime of this carbonium ion determines the stereochemical course of the reaction—*inversion* if it is short, *racemization* if it is long. In the examples quoted above the silver oxide reaction involves the formation of a carbonium ion, but the carboxyl group forms a weak bond with the developing centre of positive charge so that the approach of the reagent from this side is blocked and must occur from the side of the leaving group. The original optical configuration is thus *retained* because of neighbouring group participation in the reaction. See 'Structure and Mechanism in Organic Chemistry,' by Ingold.

Walker, Sir James (1863-1935). Born at Dundee, Walker attended the High School there. On leaving school he entered commerce, but in 1882, he proceeded to Edinburgh University to study science. Later he studied at Dundee, Munich, and Leipzig. In 1894 he was appointed professor of chemistry, University College, Dundee, and in 1908 he received a similar appointment at Edinburgh University. His research work was mainly upon electrosynthesis of dibasic organic acids, ionization constants, hydrolysis, and amphoteric electrolytes. He was elected F.R.S.

in 1900, awarded the Davy Medal in 1926, and knighted in 1921.

Walker, John (1781-1859). Born and educated at Stockton-on-Tees, Walker set up business as a chemist and druggist in his native town. In 1826 he invented the first friction match, known as the 'Friction light.' See 'The Centenary of the Friction Match' (Miller Christy).

Wallach, Otto (1847-1931). Born at Königsberg, Wallach studied at Göttingen and Berlin. In 1870 he went to Bonn as an assistant and, with the exception of a brief period in Berlin with the Aktien-Gesellschaft für Anilin-Fabrikation, remained there until 1889, becoming lecturer in 1873 and extraordinary professor in 1876. In 1889 he returned to Göttingen as ordinary professor of chemistry and Director of the Chemical Institute, and remained there until his retirement in 1915. His most important work dealt with the essential oils and the terpenes, and gained him the Nobel Prize for chemistry in 1910. See *J. Roy Inst. Chem.*, 1959, **83**, 359.

Wardlaw, William (1882-1958). Graduating in the University of Durham, Wardlaw became lecturer in chemistry at Birmingham University in 1918 and professor of physical chemistry at Birkbeck College, London in 1937. He worked chiefly on the chemistry of the transition elements and contributed appreciably to modern ideas in inorganic chemistry. He served as President both of the Chemical Society and the Royal Institute of Chemistry. See *Proc. Chem. Soc.*, 1961, 397.

Warfarin, 3-(α-Acetonylbenzyl)-4-hydroxycoumarin, $C_{19}H_{16}O_4$. An anti-coagulant rodenticide with the formula:

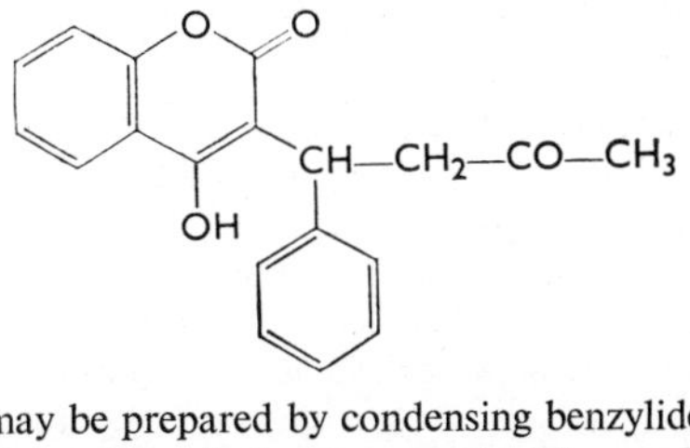

It may be prepared by condensing benzylidene acetone with 4-hydroxycoumarin. The product is a racemic mixture; it is a colourless, practically odourless and tasteless solid, m.p. 159°-161°, insoluble in water and benzene, soluble in alcohol, ether, and acetone and forming a water-soluble sodium salt. Warfarin baits need contain only 0·025% active principle, and rats are killed after ingesting about 5 doses; the bait can be left down and the risk of acute toxicity to man or domestic animals is not serious. In common with other coumarin derivatives, warfarin reduces the clotting power of blood and death is caused by haemorrhages initiated by any slight injury.

Warfarin is a vitamin K antagonist, and large oral doses of the vitamin can be given as an antidote.

The sodium derivative (trade name Marevan) is used therapeutically as an anticoagulant.

Wash oil. The oil used for recovering benzol from coal gas; it may be either a medium light creosote oil obtained from the distillation of tar or a mineral oil fraction such as gas oil.

Washing soda. Sodium carbonate decahydrate, $Na_2CO_3 \cdot 10H_2O$.

Washing tray thickener. This plant is used for the counter-current washing of soluble material from finely divided solids, and comprises a number of thickeners in series contained in the same unit. A vertical cylindrical vessel contains several shallow conical trays mounted one above the other, each equipped with a raking mechnism which drags settled solid to a central washing seal. Here it is mixed with supernatant liquid from the next washing stage before passing on to the tray below for thickening. Solids thus flow downwards through the thickener, liquid upwards, the washed solid leaving at the bottom and the pregnant liquor at the top. See also Continuous thickeners.

Waste heat boiler. A boiler which produces steam by utilizing the heat in the gases or liquid from a chemical process, e.g. a calcining operation.

Waste heat coke ovens. When no regenerators are used to preheat the air before combustion in the flues, the waste gases are drawn off beneath the oven into a main flue which conducts them to the boilers for steam raising purposes. The boilers are placed as near as possible to the battery, in order to conserve the sensible heat in the waste gases.

Water, H_2O. A colourless or faintly blue-green liquid (m.p. $0°$, b.p. $100°$, density at $0°$ $0\cdot99987$). The density of water is a maximum at $4°$, and the value at this temperature is defined as unit density. The latent heat of fusion of solid water (ice) to liquid water at $0°$ is $79\cdot74$ calories per g. The latent heat of vaporization of water to steam at $100°$ is $539\cdot1$ calories per g. In its chemical behaviour water behaves as a neutral oxide. It has only a slight conductivity due to dissociation into the ions H_3O^+ and OH^-. Molecules of water enter into the constitution of many crystalline salts (e.g. $CuSO_4$, $5H_2O$), in which they may be reversibly held. The outstanding chemical reactions of water are: (a) its reaction with certain metals (eg.. Na, Ca, Fe) with more or less ease, with liberation of hydrogen; (b) its reaction with oxides of non-metals (e.g. SO_3, P_2O_5) to form acids; (c) its reaction with the halides of non-metals to form hydrogen halides and an oxy-

acid; (d) its reaction with dissolved salts of weak acids or weak bases, forming solutions with an alkaline or acid reaction (hydrolysis); (e) its reaction with coke at high temperatures to form water gas $(C + H_2O = CO + H_2)$.

Water contains groups of molecules oriented with respect to one another. These groups are being continually formed and destroyed. The association of water molecules is explicable in terms of hydrogen bonding.

Water gas. See Blue water gas.

Water-glass. See Sodium silicates.

Wave mechanics. The electronic theory of matter is confronted by certain difficulties which have only been overcome by assumptions of a very arbitrary nature. To overcome these difficulties by a general theorem, de Broglie and Schrödinger independently devised systems of mechanics which are essentially mathematical, and may only be very approximately described in terms of physical pictures. According to de Broglie, every kind of particle is associated with a wave motion, phase waves or ϕ-waves, which is different from any of the radiations with which we are familiar. The interaction of these waves gives rise, however, to the familiar forms of radiation such as light. Wave-mechanics has led to a considerable clarification of many difficulties inherent in the older quantum theory and in the electronic theory of matter, but it is still necessary to use these conceptions because of their more concrete nature.

Wave-number. The number of waves which occupy 1 cm is the wave-number, e.g. the wavelength of violet light is 4000 Å $= 4 \times 10^{-5}$ cm; the wave-number is $\dfrac{1}{4 \times 10^{-5}} = 2\cdot5 \times 10^4$ cm^{-1}.

Wave-numbers are often loosely termed frequencies, and are denoted by the letter v.

Waxes. The scientific term wax is defined as a fatty acid ester of an alcohol other than glycerol. This excludes some substances normally called waxes, for example, Japan wax, and includes liquids such as sperm oil. The principal esters occurring in waxes are cetyl palmitate in spermaceti, ceryl palmitate in opium wax, ceryl cerotate in Chinese wax, and melissyl palmitate in bees' wax.

Weizmann, Chaim (1874-1952). Born in Russia and educated at Pinsk, Weizmann later studied at Berlin and Freiburg and was a lecturer at Geneva before coming to England in 1904 and working at Manchester University. Here he discovered a fermentation process for making acetone and butyl alcohol. In 1916 he became Director of the Admiralty Laboratories and in the second World War was Honorary Adviser to the Ministry of Supply. He was President of the

World Zionist Organization for many years and the first President of the State of Israel. See *J. Chem. Soc.*, 1953, 2840.

Weld decay. A term denoting the loss of corrosion resistance which occurs in austenitic chromium nickel steels after slow cooling through the range 900°-600°. It also occurs in the vicinity of welds. It is caused by the precipitation

Werner studied at Karlsruhe, Zürich and Paris, becoming professor at the Technische Hochschule in Zürich in 1895. He studied the stereochemistry of oximes, but his greatest contribution to chemistry was his co-ordination theory of valency (1893). He was awarded the Nobel Prize for chemistry in 1913.

Weston cell. One of the most widely used

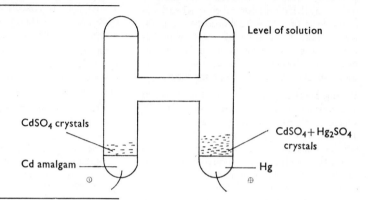

of chromium carbides from supersaturated solid solution, thus depleting the matrix in chromium. It occurs preferentially at grain boundaries. It may be prevented by the addition of 1% titanium, which is a stronger carbide former than chromium.

Weldon, Walter (1832-1885). Born at Loughborough, Weldon went to London in 1854 to try to earn a living. In 1860 he founded 'Weldon's Register of Facts and Occurrences in Literature, Science and Art.' With no chemical training, he experimented upon the process for chlorine production at St. Helens and his work greatly cheapened this valuable product. He took an active part in the formation of the Society of Chemical Industry, and was elected F.R.S. in 1882. See *J.S.C.I.*, 1885, 517, 577.

Weldon mud. This is a by-product of the Weldon process for manufacturing chlorine by the action of manganese dioxide on hydrochloric acid. The manganese chloride solution formed is precipitated with milk of lime to give Weldon mud, which contains calcium manganate (IV), and manganese (II) manganate (IV). It is used in gas purifiers (*q.v.*).

Welsbach, Auer von (1858-1929). Born and educated in Vienna, Welsbach later studied chemistry at Heidelberg. Investigations which he carried out in 1884 in the laboratories of Bunsen at Heidelberg on the oxides of the rare metals led to the introduction of the incandescent gas mantle, originally known in Germany as the 'Auerlicht.' See *Industr. Chemist*, 1958, 420.

Werner, Alfred (1866-1919). Born at Mulhouse,

standard cells in electrochemistry. The cathode consists of a 12·5% cadmium amalgam which is covered with crystals of $CdSO_4 \cdot 8/3H_2O$. The anode is made of a mercury layer covered by a mixture of mercury and mercurous sulphate. The electrolyte in the cell is a saturated solution of cadmium sulphate.

The cell e.m.f. at $t°$ is given by the expression

$$E = 1·01485 - 4·05 \times 10^{-5}(t-20) - 9·5 \times 10^{-7}(t-20)^2$$

absolute volts. Thus at 20°, $E = 1·01485$ V.

Wet-bulb temperature. The dynamic equilibrium temperature attained by a liquid surface when exposed to a stream of gas under adiabatic conditions. The rate of heat transfer to the liquid is then equal to the rate at which heat is taken up by evaporation. The importance of this temperature is that its value is dependent on the humidity of the gas, so that if both the wet bulb and the actual (dry bulb) temperature of the gas are known, the humidity may be calculated. The term almost invariably refers to the air-water system.

Wet-bulb thermometer. A thermometer for measuring wet-bulb temperatures in which the surface of the bulb is kept damp by means of a wick surrounding it, liquid being allowed to evaporate adiabatically into the gas stream.

Wet grinding. The grinding of a solid in the presence of a liquid. This prevents fine particles caking on the grinding surfaces, especially if a dispersing agent is added, and enables a finer product to be obtained. Compared with dry grinding the power consumption per ton of product is less and the plant capacity is greater, but the wear on the machine is greater and the method may not be convenient if a dry product is desired.

Wet process. Any chemical metallurgical process where an ore is leached or extracted by a solvent.

Wetted-wall absorber. This consists of a number of vertical tubes up which the gas to be absorbed is passed, the solvent being fed to the tubes in such a way that it falls down their inner surfaces in the form of a film. This absorber is useful where there is considerable heat evolution during the solution process, as in the case of hydrogen chloride and water, since cooling water may be circulated outside the tubes.

Wetting agents. Water, because of its powerful intermolecular attractive forces, does not readily spread over many surfaces (e.g. greasy solids). The addition of surface active agents (*q.v.*), which lower the surface tension, permits this to take place readily. These molecules (or ions) usually have an oil-attracting part (e.g. an alkyl chain, or an alkyl substituted aromatic nucleus) and a water-attracting part (e.g. a negatively charged carboxyl, sulphate, or sulphonate, a positively charged quaternary ammonium or pyridinium group, or a chain of etheric oxygen atoms as in a polyethylene oxide condensate).

Whirling or sling hygrometer. An instrument for measuring the quantity of water vapour in air consisting of a wet-bulb thermometer and a dry-bulb thermometer mounted next to each other in a frame, the assembly being whirled around manually. See Wet-bulb temperature, Wet-bulb thermometer.

White arsenic. Arsenic (III) oxide, As_2O_3.

Whiteheart iron. See Cast irons.

White iron. See Cast irons.

White lead. See Lead carbonate.

White-metal alloys. Alloys of tin, lead, and antimony are termed white-metal alloys. Tinner's solder is 50% Pb and 50% Sn, while plumber's solder contains $66\frac{2}{3}$% Pb.

Tin and antimony alloy in all proportions. Britannia metal, consisting of about 90% Sn and 10% Sb, is the chief commercial alloy. If the antimony does not exceed 10% it can be cold rolled, cast, stamped, or spun with ease.

Lead and antimony give alloys of the type-metal series. They give the sharp castings essential for good printing. Type-metals contain 80% Pb, 20% Sb, and sometimes a little bismuth. Fusible metal, used for boiler safety plugs, etc., contains 50% Bi, 25% Pb, and 25% Sn.

Antifriction alloys and bearing metals are also chiefly lead-tin-antimony alloys. Babbitt metal contains 88% Sn, 8% Sb, and 4% Cu; magnolia metal 80% Pb and 20% Sb, and Parson's white

bronze 68% Sn, 30% Zn, 1% Cu, and 1% Pb. These alloys are characterized by their plasticity and low coefficient of friction.

White oils. Oils used in medicinal and toilet preparations obtained by drastic refining of lubricating oil stocks.

White spirits. Refined distillates, used variously as paint thinners, solvents, dry cleaners, and 'lighter fuel.' Intermediate in boiling range between gasoline and kerosine, the actual range and composition depending on the particular use.

Whiting. A form of calcium carbonate made by grinding chalk and collecting the finer sediments from water. It is extensively used in the chemical and many other industries.

Whitmore, Frank Clifford (1887-1947). Whitmore was born at N. Attleboro, Massachusetts, and educated at Harvard. He taught at Williams College, the Rice Institute, the University of Minnesota, and North-Western University, where he was professor of organic chemistry from 1920 to 1924 and head of the department from 1925 to 1929. In 1929 he became dean of the School of Chemistry and Physics at Pennsylvania State College. His work on metallo-organic compounds and aliphatic chemistry gained him the Nichols Medal in 1937, and in 1938 he was president of the American Chemical Society.

Whytlaw-Gray, Robert (1877-1948). Whytlaw-Gray was educated at St. Paul's School and University College, London, where he worked under Ramsay on the redetermination of the atomic weight of nitrogen and became assistant professor in 1908. In 1914 he became a science master at Eton College and was professor of chemistry at Leeds University from 1923 to 1945. He specialized in the study of disperse systems in gases and in atomic weight determinations. See *Proc. Chem. Soc.*, 1959, 18.

Wieland, Heinrich Otto (1877-1957). Wieland was born at Pforzheim, Baden. After studying at Munich, Berlin, and Stuttgart he returned to Munich in 1909 as an extraordinary professor, and in 1917 was appointed ordinary professor of organic chemistry at the Technische Hochschule. In 1921 he went to Freiburg in a similar capacity and remained there until 1925, when he returned to Munich in succession to Willstätter. His researches dealt chiefly with organic nitrogen compounds, organic radicals, and oxidation-reduction processes, and his work on the bile acids, etc., gained him the Nobel Prize for chemistry for 1927. See *Proc. Chem. Soc.*, 1958, 210.

Williamson, Alexander William (1824-1904). Born at Wandsworth, Williamson was handicapped by delicate health, losing ultimately the sight of his right eye and much of the power of his left arm. After some months spent in the study of medicine at Heidelberg, he decided to take up chemistry and studied at Giessen and Paris. In 1849 he was appointed professor of analytical and practical chemistry at University College, London; in 1855 he was elected F.R.S. and succeeded Graham in the chair of chemistry. Williamson's most important work was in connexion with the theory of etherification. See 'Famous Chemists,' by Tilden (1921), 228.

Williamson's violet. A form of Prussian blue (*q.v.*).

Willstätter, Richard (1872-1942). Born at Karlsruhe, Willstätter studied at Munich, where he later became professor. He moved to Zürich in 1905 and returned to Munich in 1915. He worked on alkaloids, chlorophyll and other plant colouring matters, enzymes and plant physiology in general. He received the Nobel Prize for chemistry in 1915.

Wilson, Charles Thomson Rees (1869-1959). Born at Glencorse, Midlothian, Wilson was educated at Owens College, Manchester, and the University of Cambridge. He was Jacksonian professor of natural philosophy, Cambridge, from 1925 till 1934. Wilson was noted for his work on atmospheric electricity, particularly his detection of the paths of the alpha-particles. With Professor A. Compton he was awarded the Nobel Prize for Physics in 1927. See *Nature*, 1959, **184**, 1842.

Wilson chamber. When electrons or other ionizing particles pass through a gas, ions are produced which can act as centres for the condensation of water vapour. In the Wilson cloud chamber air saturated with water vapour is cooled by rapid expansion; droplets of water are then formed along the tracks of ionizing particles, and with suitable illumination the tracks can be observed visually or photographically.

Windaus, Adolf (1876-1959). Born in Berlin, Windaus studied at Freiburg and in his native city, where he worked for a time with Emil Fischer. In 1901 he returned to Freiburg to carry out research on cholesterol, the sterols, digitalis glucosides and similar cardiac poisons, colchicine, and imidazoles. In 1913 he was appointed professor of applied medical chemistry at Innsbruck, and in 1915 went to Göttingen. He was awarded the Nobel Prize for chemistry for 1928 for his work on the composition of the sterols. See *Proc. Chem. Soc.*, 1961, 131.

Winkler, Clemens Alexander (1838-1904). Winkler received his early training in chemistry at the School of Mines at his native town of Freiberg in Saxony. He rapidly established himself as an analyst and was appointed to the chair

of chemical technology and analytical chemistry at Freiberg. He discovered the element germanium and made pioneer researches on indium.

Wislicenus, Johannes Adolf (1835-1902). The son of a Lutheran pastor of liberal views, Wislicenus was born at Klein-Eichstädt, near Querfurt, but in 1853, owing to the modernist views of the father, the family had to find safety in America. Wislicenus obtained a post at Harvard University and also conducted an analytical laboratory in New York. In 1855, when the family returned to Europe, he resumed his studies at Halle where, in 1870, he became professor of chemistry at the Polytechnic. In 1872 Wislicenus went to Würzburg and in 1885 succeeded Kolbe at Leipzig. He was one of the leading organic chemists of his period. See *J. Chem. Soc.*, 1905, 508.

Witherite. The naturally occurring form of barium carbonate. It is white, with sp.gr. about 4·3 and hardness 3-5. Commercial deposits occur in Durham and Northumberland. It is used as a source of barium compounds, and in the brick and ceramic industries.

Witt, Otto Nikolaus (1853-1915). Born at St. Petersburg, Witt was educated at the Gymnasium and Polytechnic, Zürich. In 1873 he became an analytical chemist at the Vulken Iron Works and in 1874 entered a printing works at Hardt. After a period of further study at the Polytechnic, he came to England to enter the colour works of Williams, Thomas, and Dower. Leaving England in 1879, he worked with various industrial concerns until, in 1886, he decided to take up teaching. In 1891 he was appointed professor at Charlottenburg. His many researches were chiefly on colour and chemical constitution and on the synthesis of azo-dyes. See *J. Chem. Soc.*, 1916, 428.

Wittig reaction. The reaction between an alkylidene phosphorane, $\begin{smallmatrix} R \\ R' \end{smallmatrix}\!>\!C\!=\!PR''_3$ and an aldehyde or ketone, $\begin{smallmatrix} R° \\ R^× \end{smallmatrix}\!>\!C\!=\!O$ to produce an alkene, $\begin{smallmatrix} R \\ R' \end{smallmatrix}\!>\!C\!=\!C\!<\!\begin{smallmatrix} R° \\ R^× \end{smallmatrix}$ is usually referred to as the Wittig reaction. Although the position of the double bond in the alkene is known, the reaction is not completely stereospecific and can produce *cis-trans* mixtures.

Wöhler, Friedrich (1800-1882). Born at Eschersheim, near Frankfurt, Wöhler after qualifying in medicine took up the study of chemistry. From 1825 till 1831 he taught chemistry in the Technische Hochschule at Berlin. Afterwards he became professor at the Technical School at Cassel and in 1836 professor of chemistry at the

University of Göttingen. Wöhler, by his synthesis of urea, bridged the gulf between organic and inorganic chemistry. He was the first to investigate the properties of aluminium. See *J. Chem. Soc.*, 1883, 258.

Wolff bottle. A form of gas-absorption apparatus in which the gas is passed over the surface of the solvent. The liquid is contained in a series of stoneware or other suitable jars and flows right through the system, the concentration of the solution increasing from inlet to outlet. The gas flows in the reverse direction, through a second set of connexions above the surface of the liquid.

Wolfram. An old name for tungsten.

Wolframite. A mineral tungstate of iron and manganese, $(Fe,Mn)WO_4$. It is brownish-black, with a sub-metallic lustre, crystallizing in the monoclinic system, commonly in tabular forms; $d\,7\cdot0\text{-}7\cdot5$, hardness $5\text{-}5\frac{1}{2}$. It is the most important ore of tungsten, and occurs in quartz veins and pegmatite dykes in granite rocks, frequently associated with cassiterite.

Wollaston, William Hyde. Born about the year 1767, and educated at Cambridge. He practised as a physician at Bury St. Edmunds for some years, and afterwards in London. He learned how to purify platinum and make platinum vessels, discovered palladium and rhodium, discovered the dark lines in the solar spectrum, and invented the reflecting goniometer. For a time he was the secretary of the Royal Society. He died in 1829. See Thomson's 'History,' II, p. 247.

Wollastonite. A naturally occurring calcium metasilicate, $CaSiO_3$. There are two natural forms, triclinic or β, and the less common monoclinic or para form. On heating to 1200° these give the pseudo-hexagonal α form. The largest deposits are in New York State, but it also occurs in California, Finland and Russia. The main use is in the ceramic industry in wall tile mixtures and low-loss electrical ceramics.

Wood flour. Finely ground timber used in plastics, linoleum, and sheet metal work. For plastics the flour, which is segregated according to the type of timber, is graded according to particle size, 80 mesh being standard for phenolic moulding powder production and 120 mesh for amino moulding materials.

Wood naphtha, Wood spirit. See Methyl alcohol.

Wood's metal. See Bismuth alloys.

Woodward, Robert Burns (1917-   ). Graduating from the Massachusetts Institute of Technology in 1936, Woodward has worked since 1937 at Harvard, where since 1960 he has been Donner professor of science. He was awarded the Nobel Prize for chemistry for 1965 for his part in the synthesis of many organic substances including quinine, cortisone, strychnine, chlorophyll and oxytetracycline and for his work on determining, amongst other substances, the structure of the tetracyclines and the macrolide antibiotics.

Work function, Threshold potential. The potential which must be applied between a heated cathode and an anode in order to obtain electron emission (thermionic emission).

Work hardening. When a metal or alloy is plastically deformed at a temperature below its recrystallization temperature (i.e. normally at room temperature) its strength and hardness increase while its ductility and toughness decrease. This is a result of the mutual interference of dislocations moving on intersecting slip planes and also of grain boundary obstruction of dislocations. Work hardening is beneficial in many processes, such as the production of high-tensile wire by cold drawing, and spring strip by cold rolling. It can cause trouble in other processes such as deep drawing or pressing of metal sheet, where excessive hardening may necessitate an intermediate anneal to soften the sheet by recrystallization.

Wrought iron. A fairly pure iron with numerous slag inclusions. It was formerly much used by blacksmiths because of its ease of welding and malleability. Its resistance to rusting is superior to mild steel. The manufacturing process, which is now almost obsolete, consisted of melting pig iron in a small hearth furnace. The carbon and other impurities were oxidized out by the admission of air and the addition of scale. This loss of carbon causes the melting point to rise so that the iron gradually became solid at about 1400°-1500°. It was then removed from the furnace, hammered to remove the entrapped liquid slag, and rolled into billets, rods or strips.

Wulff-Bock crystallizer. This consists essentially of a slightly inclined, shallow, open trough which is supported on rollers and made to rock gently from side to side. Cooling by natural convection occurs while the liquid flows from one end of the trough to the other. Large crystals are produced but the capacity is relatively small owing to the low rate of cooling.

Wurtz, Charles Adolphe (1817-1884). Born at Strasburg, Wurts was educated at the Protestant Gymnasium there before taking up the study of medicine. Later he took up the study of chemistry and was, for many years, professor of chemistry at the École de Médicine and at the Sorbonne, Paris. He was editor of a 'Dictionnaire de Chemie Pure et Appliquée' and after 1868 one of the editors of the 'Annales de Chimie et de Physique.' Discoverer of methyl- and ethylamine, he gave his name to a method of synthesizing hydrocarbons. See Life by Gautier (1884).

Wurtzite. This form of zinc sulphide gives its name to an important crystal structure type. It crystallizes in the hexagonal system and the structure resembles that of zinc blende in that in both structures each Zn (S) atom is tetrahedrally co-ordinated by four S (Zn) atoms. For wurtzite $a=3\cdot82$, $c=6\cdot26$ Å. Examples of compounds crystallizing with this structure include ZnS, ZnO, BeO, AlN, CdSe. The structure is illustrated in the accompanying figure:

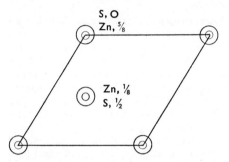

S, O
Zn, ⅝

Zn, ⅛
S, ½

Wurtz synthesis. Alkyl halides react with sodium in dry ethereal solution to give hydrocarbons. If equimolecular amounts of two different halides are used, then a mixture of three hydrocarbons of the types R—R, R—R′, and R′—R′, where R and R′ represent the original radicals, will be formed. The yields are often poor owing to subsidiary reactions taking place.

Wynne, William Palmer (1861-1950). Born at Stafford, Wynne was educated at the Royal College of Science, London. He was appointed professor of chemistry, School of Pharmacy (1902), and held the chair of chemistry, University of Sheffield, from 1904 till 1931. He will be remembered chiefly for his work with H. E. Armstrong on the determination of the orientation of naphthalene derivatives and the laws of substitution of these compounds. See *J. Chem. Soc.*, 1951, 1936.

X

Xanthates. These compounds are salts or esters of unstable acids of the type shown, where R may be either an alkyl or aryl group. The sodium salts are formed by treating an alcohol or some hydroxy compounds with carbon disulphide and sodium hydroxide or by treating a sodium alkoxide with carbon disulphide. The esters are formed by treating the sodium salts with alkyl halides. The free acids are very unstable; other metallic

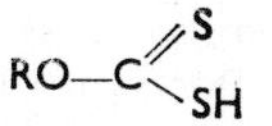

xanthates are formed by double decomposition with the sodium salts; the cuprous salts are yellow and gave rise to the name 'xanthate.' Cellulose xanthate is formed in the viscose process for making artificial silk. Other xanthates are used in flotation processes and for the detection of certain metals.

Xanthene ring system. The system

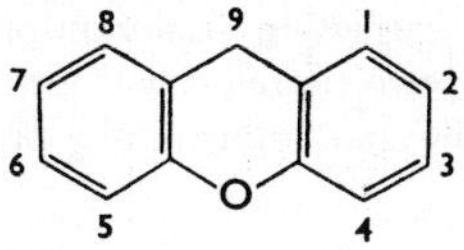

numbered as shown.

Xanthine, 2,6-Oxypurine, $C_5H_4N_4O_2$. A colourless crystalline powder with one molecule of

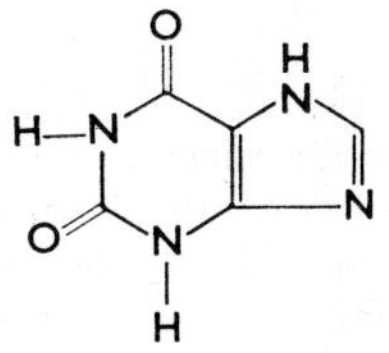

water of crystallization, which it loses at 125°-130°. Decomposes without melting. Sparingly soluble in water, insoluble in organic solvents. It is a breakdown product of nucleic acid metabolism, being formed from guanine by the action of the enzyme guanase and from hypoxanthine by oxidation. It is itself oxidized in the body to uric acid.

Xanthine oxidase. An enzyme of the oxido-reductase group, present in the liver and certain other organs, which is responsible for the oxidation of hypoxanthine and xanthine to uric acid. Xanthine oxidase has been obtained crystalline; it is a flavoprotein containing molybdenum, and has mol.wt. about 290,000. It shows very little substrate specificity, effecting oxidation of many purines and pterins, and it is identical with the 'Schardinger enzyme' of milk which oxidizes aldehydes to acids. Methylene blue will act as a hydrogen acceptor and will be decolorized if it is added with formaldehyde to milk containing the enzyme; boiled milk will not give this test.

Xanthommatine. See Ommochromes.

Xanthone, $C_{13}H_8O_2$. Forms colourless crystals,

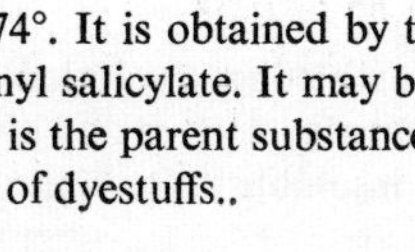

m.p. 173°-174°. It is obtained by the action of heat on phenyl salicylate. It may be reduced to xanthene. It is the parent substance of the xanthone group of dyestuffs..

Xanthophyll. A name originally given to a substance of formula $C_{40}H_{56}O_2$ found with carotene in grasses, green leaves, and other vegetable sources. This substance has been shown to be two isomers, lutein and zeaxanthin, which are oxidation products of α- and β-carotene respectively. The name has been extended to include all hydroxylated carotenoids. The xanthophylls are yellow pigments that can be separated from carotene by extracting a solution of the mixed pigments in petroleum ether with methyl alcohol, in which the xanthophylls are preferentially soluble.

Xanthopterin, $C_6H_5N_5O_2$. A yellow pigment

obtained from the wings of butterflies as an amorphous hygroscopic mass; m.p. over 410°. It is practically insoluble in water but soluble in acids and alkalis.

Xanthorhamnin, $C_{34}H_{42}O_{20}$. The glycoside of Persian berries and other *Rhamnus* species. It is hydrolysed to rhamnetin (quercetin-7-methyl ether) and a triose sugar (rhamninose) composed of galactose and rhamnose (2 mols.). It crystallizes in golden-yellow tiny needles.

Xanthosine, Xanthine riboside. Crystallizes in prisms. It does not melt, but darkens on heating.

Slightly soluble in cold water, easily soluble in hot, $[\alpha]_D^{30}$ $-51 \cdot 2°$ in alkaline solution. It is a nucleoside consisting of one molecule of xanthine, combined with one molecule of D-ribose. It is formed by deamination of guanosine.

Xanthydrol, $C_{13}H_{10}O_2$. Colourless needle-

shaped crystals, m.p. 121°-123°. It is prepared by reducing an alcoholic solution of xanthone with sodium amalgam. It reacts with urea to give a compound insoluble in alcohol, and is used as

a means of estimating urea in blood and urine; for this purpose the urea is precipitated as the dixanthydryl compound which is then oxidized by excess standard dichromate solution, and the excess dichromate determined by iodometric methods.

Xenon, Xe. At.no. 54, At.wt. 131·3, m.p. $-111 \cdot 9°$, b.p. $-108 \cdot 1°$, d (liquid) 3·06. One of the noble gases. Occurs in the atmosphere to the extent of $8 \times 10^{-6}\%$. Moderately soluble in water; forms hydrates, and clathrate compounds with quinols. Reacts with fluorine to form fluorides which can be converted into other derivatives.

Xenon compounds. Xenon reacts with fluorine under various conditions to give XeF_2, colourless crystals, m.p. 140°, linear structure; XeF_4, colourless crystals, m.p. $\sim$114°, square planar structure; and XeF_6, colourless crystals, yellow liquid, m.p. 46°. XeF_6 is hydrolysed by water to $XeOF_4$, colourless crystals, m.p. $\sim$ $-30°$, square pyramidal structure. Xenon fluorides react with Lewis acid fluorides to form adducts, e.g. $XeF_2 \cdot 2SbF_5$, $XeF_2 \cdot TaF_5$; XeF_6 forms adducts, e.g. $RbXeF_7$, with alkali metal fluorides.

Xenon fluorides are hydrolysed to Xe (VI) 'xenic acid'. Evaporation gives the very explosive XeO_3. The solutions are strong oxidizing agents. Oxidation of the solutions gives xenates (VIII), e.g. $Na_4XeO_6 \cdot 8H_2O$.

Xenylamine. A name for *p*-aminodiphenyl,

$C_{12}H_{11}N$. Substituted derivatives are called xenylamines.

Xerogel. A method of classification of gels divides these into xerogels which are relatively free from the dispersion medium and lyogels which are rich in it.

X-ray. Electromagnetic radiation of short-wave length (1 Å as compared with 5000 Å for visible light). X-rays are generated in various ways, including the bombarding of solids with electrons, when they are emitted as a result of electron transitions in the inner orbits of the atoms bombarded. Each element has a characteristic X-ray spectrum.

X-rays may be detected either by their power of blackening a photographic plate with a fluorescent screen, or with an ionisation counter. They have great penetrating power which increases with their frequency, and owing to this are used to photograph the interior of many solid objects, notably the human body.

X-rays find wide applications in X-ray photography and in crystallography. Prolonged exposure of the human body to the rays induces a dangerous form of dermatitis, and even sterility, but controlled exposures are applied to alleviate cancer.

X-ray diffraction. A powerful technique for the study of crystal structure, discovered by von Laue (1912) and developed for crystal analysis by W. H. and W. L. Bragg (1912-13). The atomic nuclei in a crystal lattice act as diffraction gratings; the rows of atoms have spacings of a few Ångstrom units, which are comparable with the wavelength of X-rays. Strong scattering of the rays by the crystal therefore occurs in certain directions, according to Bragg's equation (*q.v.*). Various techniques are available for applying X-ray diffraction to the study of single crystals, powders, fibres, etc., and by modern methods of computing it is possible to work out 3-dimensional electron-density maps of complicated molecules from the recorded X-ray patterns.

X-ray spectrometer. An apparatus used in the X-ray study of crystals in which a fine beam of monochromatic X-rays impinges at a measured angle on the face of a crystal mounted in its path, and in which the intensity of the X-rays diffracted in various directions by the crystal is measured with an ionization chamber mounted on an arm of the spectrometer table, or is recorded photographically.

X-ray tube. The apparatus employed for producing X-rays is termed an X-ray tube. It consists essentially of an aluminium electrode, the cathode, and an anode (always called the anti-cathode in X-ray work), the surface of which is arranged at 45° to the axis of the tube. Under the influence of a high potential, cathode rays emitted by the cathode strike the anti-cathode, which emits X-rays. These are directed out of the tube by the sloping anti-cathode.

Xylan. Occurs in association with cellulose in lignified cell walls, in the wood of deciduous trees, in the bran and straw of cereals, and in similar plant substances. Xylan from esparto grass has been obtained in a relatively pure state; it is made up of 18 or 19 xylopyranose units, connected by 1,4-β-linkages, with a terminal arabofuranose residue. It is strongly laevorotatory, $[\alpha]_D - 109°$ in 2·5% caustic soda solution.

Xylene, C_8H_{10}. As usually obtained xylene is a colourless refractive liquid of characteristic smell, burns with a smoky flame, and is a mixture of the three possible isomers, *o*-xylene, b.p. 144°, *m*-xylene b.p. 139·3°, and *p*-xylene b.p. 138°. It is insoluble in water, miscible with most organic solvents, very volatile in steam.

Oxidation with chromic acid or permanganate gives the corresponding dicarboxylic acids.

o m p

Commercially, xylene is obtained by recovery from coal tar and coal gas, or by the catalytic reforming of naphthenes in the presence of hydrogen (see Toluene). The material so-produced is suitable for use as a solvent or gasoline ingredient, these uses accounting for a large part of xylene consumption. If xylene is required as a chemical, raw material separation into the isomers is usually necessary, and although the *o*-compound can be readily removed by fractional distillation, the separation of the *m*- and *p*-isomers requires techniques such as fractional crystallization, solvent extraction or clathration. *o*-Xylene is used in the manufacture of phthalic anhydride, and the *m*- and *p*-isomers in the manufacture of isophthalic and terephthalic acid respectively.

Xylenols. The xylenols are hydroxydimethyl-benzenes of which six isomers are possible. The pure substances are low-melting solids having the general properties of phenols. Xylenol is the name given to a mixture of the isomers separated from the phenolic fraction of coal tar and used as a solvent. The chlorinated derivative known as *p*-chloro-*m*-xylenol is used as a disinfectant.

Xylidines, $C_8H_{11}N$, $C_6H_3(CH_3)_2NH_2$. The mixture of isomeric xylenes obtained from coal-tar is usually nitrated without separation of the isomers. Reduction of the nitroxylenes with iron and hydrochloric acid gives a mixture of five aminoxylenes or xylidines.

The mixture of xylidines has been used as a first component for azo-dyes. The chief constituent of the mixture is '*m*-xylidine' (4-amino-1,3-xylene). It can be separated by crystallization from glacial acetic acid. It is also used for the preparation of azo-dyes.

D-Xylose, $C_5H_{10}O_5$. The pentose sugar of straw, cotton-seed hulls, and various hemi-celluloses, and of some glycosides, including the primeverosides. The formula is

It crystallizes in needles, m.p. 153°, [α] +19°. It is not fermentable and behaves chemically as other sugars.

Y

Y alloy. See Aluminium alloys.

Ylides. Internal salts, the commonest having the negative charge on a carbon atom and the positive charge on nitrogen, phosphorus or sulphur. An example is the phosphorane

$$R_2C \overset{-}{\longrightarrow} \overset{+}{PPh_3} \leftrightarrow R_2C = PPh_3.$$

Yohimbine, $C_{21}H_{26}N_2O_3$. An alkaloid obtained

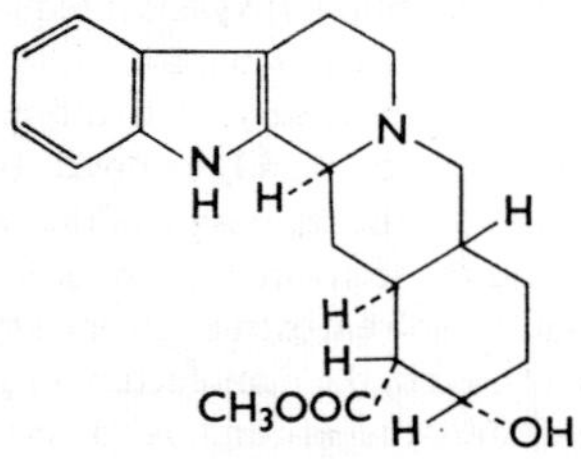

from the bark of the West African tree, *corynanthe yohimbe*, and from quebracho bark in the Argentine. It crystallizes in colourless needles, m.p. 235°. Soluble in alcohol, sparingly soluble in water, dextrorotatory.

Ytterbium, Yb. At.no. 70, At.wt. 173·04, d 6·997, m.p. 824°, b.p. 1427°. Below 798° the metal has a cubic close-packed structure (a = 5·481 Å) above 798° it has a body-centred cubic lattice (a = 4·44 Å). It is a typical rare-earth element (q.v.).

Ytterbium compounds. Ytterbium forms two series of salts. Those in which the metal is in the +3 state are colourless and are typical rare-earth compounds (q.v.). By reduction of normal ytterbium salts a moderately stable dipositive state is obtained.

Ytterbium (II), *Ytterbous chloride*, YbCl₂, is obtained by reducing YbCl₃ in hydrogen for some hours at 580°-640°; it forms colourless crystals which give a yellow solution in water and with acid liberate hydrogen. *Ytterbium* (II) *bromide* and *iodide* have been prepared similarly; these salts are black and yellow

respectively. *Ytterbium* (II) *sulphate*, YbSO₄, has been prepared by electrolytic reduction of ytterbium (III) sulphate.

Yttrium, Y. At.no. 39, At.wt. 88·92, d 4·478, m.p. 1509°, b.p. 2927°. Yttrium is the first element of the second transition series and is very similar in its properties to the rare-earth elements (q.v.). It is the major constituent of gadolinite, 4BeO·FeO·Y₂O₃·2SiO₂, where it occurs mixed with the rare-earth elements. Metallic yttrium resembles iron in appearance, it has the hexagonal close-packed structure below 1495° (a = 3·6451, c = 5·7305 Å) and is body-centred cubic above 1459° (a = 4·11 Å). At present it has no commercial uses.

Yttrium compounds. Yttrium forms a single series of colourless salts, the metal being in the +3 oxidation state. Yttrium compounds are very similar to the rare-earth compounds (q.v.).

Z

Zeaxanthin, $C_{40}H_{56}O_2$.

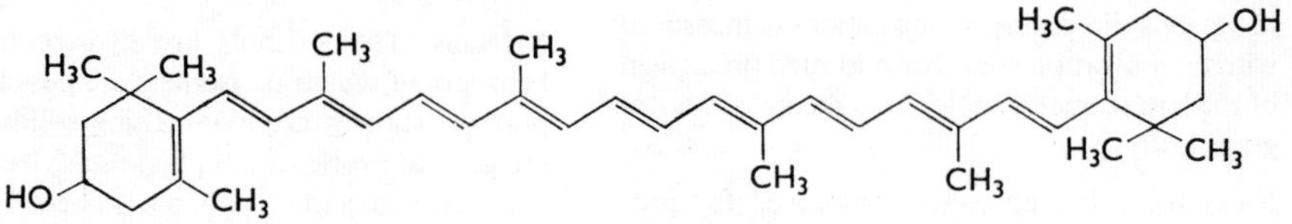

One of the xanthophyll pigments present in various leaves, seeds, and fruits, and in yolk of egg; m.p. 215°. It is often present in company with lutein, of which it is an isomer. It bears the same relation to β-carotene as lutein does to α-carotene. Xanthophyll.

Zein. A protein, belonging to the prolamine class, present in maize. It is an incomplete protein, containing no lysine or tryptophan. Zein is prepared commercially by extracting maize gluten with alcohol and precipitating with water. It is made into fibres and has also various uses in the plastics, paint, paper, printing, and other industries.

Zeolites. A large family of natural hydrous aluminium silicates containing Na and Ca and occasionally K, Ba, and Sr. Typical zeolites are analcite, NaAlSi₂O₆·H₂O and chabazite, CaAl₂Si₄O₁₂·6H₂O. Zeolites exhibit base exchange properties, Na and K atoms being readily replaced by Ca and Mg or vice versa. They contain loosely held water which is lost on gentle heating and regained on exposure to a moist atmosphere. Some zeolites on dehydration form robust network crystals permeated by regular narrow diffusion paths. They show marked molecular sieve effects, selectively occluding gases according to their relative molecular sizes. Artificial zeolites are made by fusing china clay, sand, and sodium carbonate, giving a product roughly corresponding to $Na_2Al_2Si_2O_8 \cdot 6H_2O$. They are chiefly used for water softening, but also as absorbents.

Zeta(ζ)-potential. Another name for electro-kinetic potential (*q.v.*).

Ziegler catalysts. Complex catalysts prepared by interaction between an organometallic deriva-tive and a transition metal derivative. A typical catalyst is the product of the interaction of titan-ium (IV) chloride and tri-n-butylaluminium. These catalysts polymerize olefins, particularly ethylene, to polyolefins.

Zimmermann reaction. A colour reaction used for the determination of ketonic steroids, especially urinary 17-ketosteroids. Treatment with *m*-dinitrobenzene in alcoholic alkali pro-duces a pigment having a transient violet colour, with an absorption maximum near 520mμ. Although other steroid ketones having adjacent methylene groups (especially 3-ketones) also react, under suitable conditions the reaction is almost specific for 17-ketones.

Zinc, Zn. At.no. 30, At.wt. 65·377, m.p. 419·5°, b.p. 907°, *d* 7·14. The principal source of zinc is the sulphide ZnS, known as zinc blende, or when coloured yellow or brown by iron, as 'black-jack,' and possessing a characteristic resinous lustre. It is found in England, in parts of Europe and America, in Rhodesia, Burma, and New South Wales. Other important minerals are calamine or smithsonite, $ZnCO_3$, willemite, Zn_2SiO_4, and franklinite, $Zn(FeO_2)_2$.

Zinc is extracted from its ores by roasting to give the oxide, followed by reduction at 1300° with carbon. Most ores are contaminated with lead, iron, and cadmium, but as their boiling-points are widely separated from each other, and from that of zinc, they can be separated by fractional distillation. Some 25% of zinc metal is produced by a hydrometallurgical process in-volving leaching followed by electrolytic depo-sition of the metal.

The pure metal is used as a coating for steel, e.g. galvanizing, and sherardizing. Alloyed, it is found in brasses, nickel-silver, etc.

Zinc crystallizes in hexagonal prisms with a bluish-white colour. The crystals have a de-formed hexagonal close-packed structure (des-cribed under cadmium), $a = 2·659$ $c = 4·935$ Å.

The vapour is monomeric. The metal is moder-ately hard and brittle.

Zinc burns readily on heating in air or oxygen. It combines directly with chlorine and sulphur. It decomposes steam at red heat, with the forma-tion of a crystalline oxide. The metal is readily tarnished in moist air, with the formation of basic carbonates.

Zinc dissolves in dilute acids, evolving hydro-gen (except with nitric acid) and producing zinc salts. It also dissolves readily in hot solutions of caustic potash or soda, with the evolution of hydrogen and formation of zincates, con-taining the anion $Zn(OH)_4^{2-}$.

Zinc alloys. The alloys commonly contain 4% aluminium and up to 3% copper. Their low m.p., 380°, and good fluidity makes them suitable for the pressure die casting of small components such as motor-car accessories and toys.

Zinc blende. This cubic form of zinc sulphide gives its name to an important crystal structure type. The Zn and S atoms occupy alternate posi-tions in the diamond structure so that each kind of atom is tetrahedrally co-ordinated by four atoms of the other sort. For ZnS, $a = 5·42$ Å. Among the many compounds crystallizing with this structure may be mentioned SiC, AlP, CuCl, CuBr, CuI, ZnSe, and GaSb.

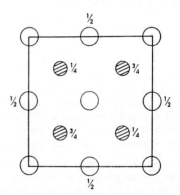

Zinc borates. Compounds of rather indefinite composition which may be prepared by treating a solution of borax with zinc sulphate. They are widely used for fireproofing textiles and in the ceramic and pharmaceutical industries.

Zinc carbonate, $ZnCO_3$. A basic carbonate is precipitated by the addition of an alkali car-bonate to a solution of a zinc salt. An alkali bicarbonate gives a white precipitate of zinc carbonate, $ZnCO_3$. On boiling with sodium carbonate solution, the carbonate and basic carbonates form zinc oxide.

The basic carbonate, which has the approximate composition $ZnCO_3, 2ZnO, 3H_2O$, is used medicinally for similar purposes to zinc oxide. See Calamine.

Zinc chloride, $ZnCl_2$. The anhydrous chloride is obtained, as a soft white mass, by passing hydrogen chloride over heated zinc or by distilling the metal with mercuric chloride. It is formed in solution by dissolving zinc or the oxide in hydrochloric acid. Hydrates with 4, 3, $2\frac{1}{2}$, $1\frac{1}{2}$, and 1 molecules of water are known; it is extremely difficult to remove the last traces of water from the hydrates. Anhydrous zinc chloride is very deliquescent, and is soluble in alcohol, ether, acetone, and pyridine.

Zinc chloride is used in wood preserving, as a flux, in filling cotton goods, in Leclanché batteries, mixed with zinc oxide and powdered glass as a dental stopping, and as a dehydrating agent in many organic reactions.

Zinc chromate. A yellow pigment made by preprecipitation from zinc sulphate with potassium chromate. The composition is uncertain and depends upon the conditions of precipitation and washing. Mixed with Prussian blue in various proportions the products are known as zinc greens, which are more stable and fast to light than pigments derived from lead chromates. A variety of zinc chromate is the zinc tetroxychromate used as a rust-inhibiting pigment. See British Standard No. 282.

Zinc dithionate. See Zinc hydrosulphite.

Zinc fluoride, ZnF_2. Zinc fluoride normally occurs as the tetrahydrate but the anhydrous salt may be obtained by heating the hydrate to 100°. It is only slightly soluble in water. Zinc fluoride is used as a catalyst and as a wood preservative. Zinc fluorosilicate, $ZnSiF_6 \cdot 6H_2O$, a water-soluble salt, is used in the plastics industry, as a wood preservative, and as a fungicide,

Zinc hydrosulphite, zinc dithionate. ZnS_2O_4. Made by treating an aqueous suspension of zinc dust with sulphur dioxide at about 40°. Solutions are used as bleaches and in the vat dyeing process.

Zinc hydroxide, $Zn(OH)_2$. Obtained as a white flocculent precipitate by the addition of caustic alkali to a zinc salt solution. It can be dried at 85°, but loses constitutional water at higher temperatures. A crystalline form is obtained by allowing zinc plate and iron turnings to stand in concentrated ammonia.

Zinc hydroxide is amphoteric. It is used as an absorbent in surgical dressing, in the preparation of Rinman's green, and as a rubber 'filler'.

Zinc lactate $(C_3H_5O_3)_2Zn, 3H_2O$. Colourless four-sided rhombic prisms, soluble up to $1\frac{1}{2}\%$ in cold water, more soluble in hot. It loses its water of crystallization at 100°. It crystallizes better than any other lactate.

Zinc oxide, ZnO. A soft white powder turning yellow when hot, obtained by burning zinc metal directly (the French process) or from the ore (the American process). It dissolves readily in acids, forming zinc salts, and in alkalis, producing zincates.

Zinc oxide is used as a reinforcing agent for rubber, as a vulcanizing agent, in ceramics, and medicinally for external application. It is an important pigment (Zinc white, Chinese white) in paints, not being blackened by hydrogen sulphide.

Zinc peroxide, ZnO_2. Made by treating a zinc chloride solution with sodium peroxide at 12°. It is a white, insoluble powder used as a disinfectant in pharmacy.

Zinc sulphate, $ZnSO_4$. Prepared by dissolving the metal, oxide, or carbonate in dilute sulphuric acid and crystallizing. Below 30° crystals of the heptahydrate, isomorphous with magnesium sulphate, $MgSO_4, 7H_2O$, and known as white vitriol, separate. Above 30°, $ZnSO_4, 6H_2O$ is deposited. On heating $ZnSO_4, 7H_2O$ to 100°, the monohydrate is formed; at 450° this loses water to give the anhydrous salt. At higher temperatures it is completely decomposed to the oxide. It is widely used in the textile industry and in arsenical sprays in agriculture.

Zinc sulphide, ZnS. Occurs naturally as blende, cubic, and more rarely as wurtzite in hexagonal crystals. For the crystal structures of zinc blende and wurtzite see under the respective headings. It may be prepared directly from the elements, and by precipitation of a zinc salt solution with ammonium sulphide. Impure zinc sulphides are phosphorescent, but very pure zinc sulphide is not. It is easily soluble in dilute acids. Zinc sulphide is used as a pigment and in luminescent coatings.

Zingiberene, $C_{15}H_{24}$. The main constituent of

ginger oil, b.p. 134°/14 mm, d^{20} 0·8684, n_D^{20} 1·4956, $[\alpha]_D$ −73·38°. It is always accompanied by a small quantity of bisabolene, from which it cannot be separated. Zingiberene forms a characteristic dihydrochloride, m.p. 169°-170°. By removal of hydrogen chloride this does not regenerate zingiberene but its isomer, isozingiberene.

Zircon, Zirconium silicate, ZrSiO₄. A common minor constituent of acid igneous rocks such as granite and syenite. Being very resistant to weathering it occurs in the heavy fraction of many sands and sedimentary deposits. It crystallizes in the tetragonal system, with high refractive index and brilliant lustre, sp.gr. 4·6-4·8, hardness 7·5. The colour varies widely from colourless and pale yellow to yellow and brown. Yellowish-red stones used as gems are known as hyacinth. Zircon is obtained from beach sands, mainly in Australia and used in the manufacture of zirconium refractories, as a foundry sand, in ceramics, and in the preparation of zirconium compounds and metal. Zircon contains small amounts of hafnium, normally 1-6%, and this has to be removed in the manufacture of reactor-grade zirconium.

Zirconium, Zr. At.no. 40, At.wt. 91·22. A whitish metal resembling cast-iron, crystallizing in broad, hexagonal plates, m.p. 1857°, b.p. 2900°, d 6·49. There are two forms of the metal, α-Zr stable at low temperatures and β-Zr stable above 862°. The former has the hexagonal close-packed structure $a=3·22$, $c=5·12$ Å, while the latter has the body-centred cubic structure $a=3·61$ Å (at 867°). Zirconium burns in oxygen at white heat; the flame has a temperature of 4930°, and is one of the hottest known. Hydrofluoric acid and *aqua regia* are the only acids that attack the metal. It can be made to alloy with iron. The metal is prepared by reducing zircon with carbon in an electric furnace, converting the carbide to chloride with anhydrous chlorine, purifying the zirconium chloride, and reducing it with molten magnesium at 850°-900°. Zirconium has a very low cross-section for neutron capture and is accordingly used for canning fuel elements in reactors.

Zirconium chlorides. *Zirconium tetrachloride,* ZrCl₄, is a white, crystalline solid that reacts vigorously with water; it sublimes at about 437° and may be prepared by the action of chlorine on a mixture of zircon or zirconium oxide and charcoal, or by the action of chlorine and carbon tetrachloride on the oxide at 800°.

Zirconium trichloride, ZrCl₃, is prepared by the reduction of the tetrachloride with aluminium powder. It forms brown crystals which are oxidized by air to ZrOCl₂. By heating the trichloride *in vacuo* a black *dichloride,* ZrCl₂, is formed. Both lower chlorides are strong reducing agents.

Zirconium halides. In its halides zirconium shows oxidation states of IV, III, and II. Zirconium tetrafluoride is formed by heating (NH₄)₂ZrF₆. It forms mono- and trihydrates in water; many complexes are known. The other tetrahalides are formed from the elements; sublimation points are: ZrBr₄, 357°; ZrI₄, 431°. Zirconium tribromide and tri-iodide are similar to the trichloride; the dibromide and di-iodide are also known.

Zirconium hydride, ZrH₂. A grey solid obtained by passing hydrogen over red-hot zirconium; it burns in air, forming the sesquioxide Zr₂O₃.

Zirconium nitrate, Zr(NO₃)₄,5H₂O. Obtained by evaporating a solution of zirconium hydroxide in nitric acid over phosphoric oxide and sodium hydroxide. A basic nitrate, ZrO(NO₃)₂,2H₂O, is known.

Zirconium oxide, zirconia, ZrO₂. Occurs as baddeleyite in Ceylon and Brazil in monoclinic crystals, m.p. 2960°, b.p. 4570°, d 5·4-5·7, hardness about 6. Hydrofluoric acid is the only acid that attacks zirconia, but alkalis give zirconates. Peroxyzirconates, e.g. K₄ZrO₈·6H₂O, are formed by the action of hydrogen peroxide. Zirconia will stand a very high temperature, and has a very low coefficient of expansion; it has been used in the manufacture of refractory crucibles.

Zone refining. A method of refining metals and certain inorganic and organic compounds depending on the difference in solubility of impurities in the liquid and solid states. A narrow molten zone is caused to move along a bar or column of the substance; those impurities which lower the melting point will tend to remain in solution and will be moved in the direction of zone travel. Solutes which raise the melting point will preferentially freeze out and will move in a direction opposite to that of zone travel. By successive traverses the substance can be obtained in a very pure state. This method is applied to the production of pure germanium and other metals required very pure but in small quantities. See 'Zone Refining' by N. L. Parr, R.I.C. Monograph No. 3, 1957.

Zsigmondy, Richard (1865-1929). Born at Vienna, Zsigmondy was educated at the Technische Hochschule there and at the Universities of Munich and Berlin. In 1897 he entered the employment of Schott of Jena, glass manufacturers, and in 1907 was appointed professor of physical chemistry and Director of the Institute, Göttingen. His researches were chiefly upon problems connected with glass and colloids. He invented the ultramicroscope, which paved the way for important advances in colloid chemistry. In 1925 he was awarded the Nobel Prize for chemistry. See *Nature*, 1929, **124**, 845.

Zwitterion. A zwitterion is an electrically neutral ion with both a positive and a negative charge. For example, the amino-acid glycine exists in solution at the isoelectric point as the zwitterion $^+H_3N \cdot CH_2 \cdot COO^-$.

Zymase. The discovery that cell-free non-living yeast juice can cause alcoholic fermentation was made by Buchner, and later studied by Harden. The yeast preparations ferment sugar slowly, but more quickly when inorganic phosphate is added. The enzyme responsible, termed zymase, has been proved to be a complex mixture of enzymes and co-enzymes, each of which is responsible for one stage on the series of reactions which first convert glucose into a more reactive form, combine this with phosphoric acid, split the molecule into two trioses, and rearrange these by stages to pyruvic acid.